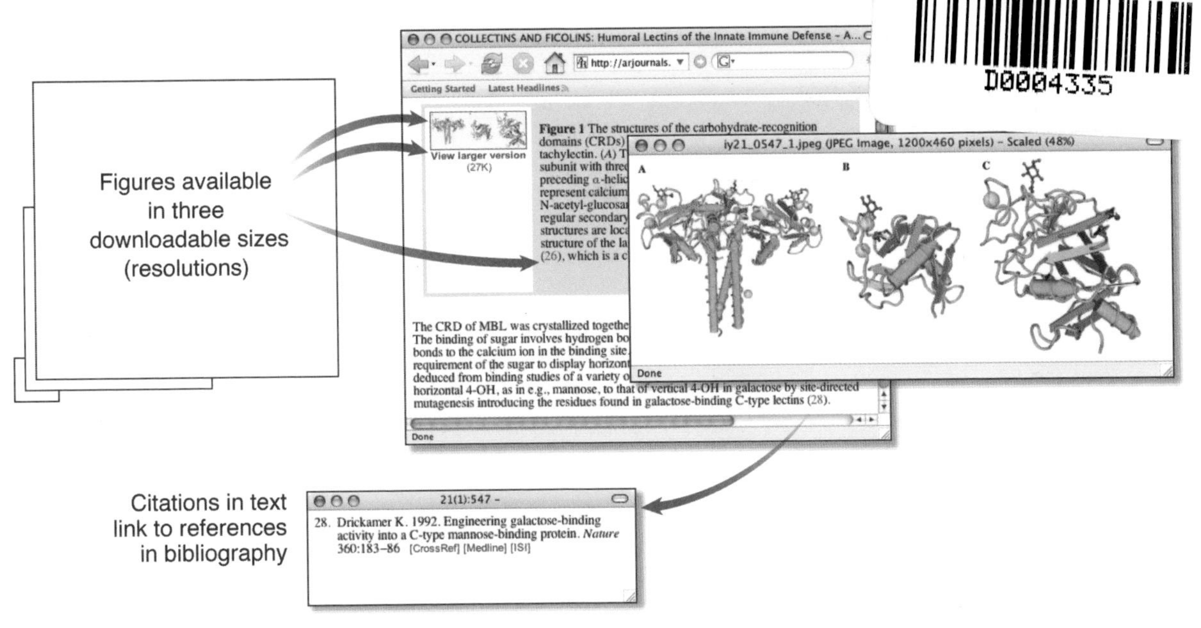

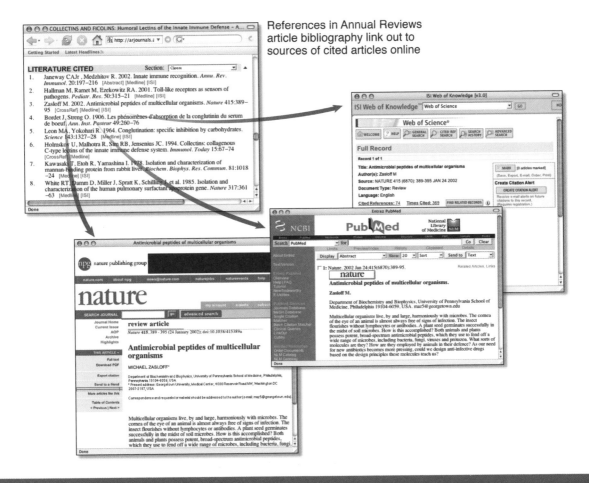

Figures available in three downloadable sizes (resolutions)
COLLECTINS AND FICOLINS: Humoral Lectins of the Innate Immune Defense - A...
Figure 1 The structures of the carbohydrate-recognition domains (CRDs)
View larger version (27K)
iy21_0547_1.jpeg (JPEG Image, 1200x460 pixels) - Scaled (48%)
The CRD of MBL was crystallized together
mutagenesis introducing the residues found in galactose-binding C-type lectins (28).
Citations in text link to references in bibliography
21(1):547 -
28. Drickamer K. 1992. Engineering galactose-binding activity into a C-type mannose-binding protein. Nature 360:183–86 [CrossRef] [Medline] [ISI]

References in Annual Reviews article bibliography link out to sources of cited articles online

LITERATURE CITED

1. Janeway CAJr, Medzhitov R. 2002. Innate immune recognition. *Annu. Rev. Immunol.* 20:197–216 [Abstract] [Medline] [ISI]
2. Hallman M, Ramet M, Ezekowitz RA. 2001. Toll-like receptors as sensors of pathogens. *Pediatr. Res.* 50:315–21 [Medline] [ISI]
3. Zasloff M. 2002. Antimicrobial peptides of multicellular organisms. *Nature* 415:389–95 [CrossRef] [Medline] [ISI]
4. Bordet J, Streng O. 1906. Les phénomènes d'absorption de la conglutinin du serum de boeuf. *Ann. Inst. Pasteur* 49:260–76
5. Leon MA, Yokohari R. 1964. Conglutination: specific inhibition by carbohydrates. *Science* 143:1327–28 [Medline] [ISI]
6. Holmskov U, Malhotra R, Sim RB, Jensenius JC. 1994. Collectins: collagenous C-type lectins of the innate immune defense system. *Immunol. Today* 15:67–74 [CrossRef] [Medline]
7. Kawasaki T, Etoh R, Yamashina I. 1978. Isolation and characterization of mannan-binding protein from rabbit liver. *Biochem. Biophys. Res. Commun.* 81:1018–24 [Medline] [ISI]
8. White RT, Damm D, Miller J, Spratt K, Schilling J, et al. 1985. Isolation and characterization of the human pulmonary surfactant apoprotein gene. *Nature* 317:361–63 [Medline] [ISI]

ISI Web of Knowledge — Web of Science — Full Record

Title: Antimicrobial peptides of multicellular organisms
Author(s): Zasloff M
Source: NATURE 415 (6870): 389-395 JAN 24 2002
Document Type: Review
Language: English
Cited References: 74 Times Cited: 369

Entrez PubMed

1: Nature. 2002 Jan 24;415(6870):389-95.

Antimicrobial peptides of multicellular organisms.

Zasloff M.

Department of Biochemistry and Biophysics, University of Pennsylvania School of Medicine, Philadelphia 19104-6059, USA. maz5@georgetown.edu

Multicellular organisms live, by and large, harmoniously with microbes. The cornea of the eye of an animal is almost always free of signs of infection. The insect flourishes without lymphocytes or antibodies. A plant seed germinates successfully in the midst of soil microbes. How is this accomplished? Both animals and plants possess potent, broad-spectrum antimicrobial peptides, which they use to fend off a wide range of microbes, including bacteria, fungi, viruses and protozoa. What sorts of molecules are they? How are they employed by animals in their defence? As our need for new antibiotics becomes more pressing, could we design anti-infective drugs based on the design principles these molecules teach us?

nature — review article

Nature 415, 389 - 395 (24 January 2002); doi:10.1038/415389a

Antimicrobial peptides of multicellular organisms

MICHAEL ZASLOFF*

Production Editor: Erin Wait
Managing Editor: Jennifer L. Jongsma
Bibliographic Quality Control: Mary A. Glass
Electronic Content Coordinator: Suzanne K. Moses
Illustration Editor: Douglas Beckner

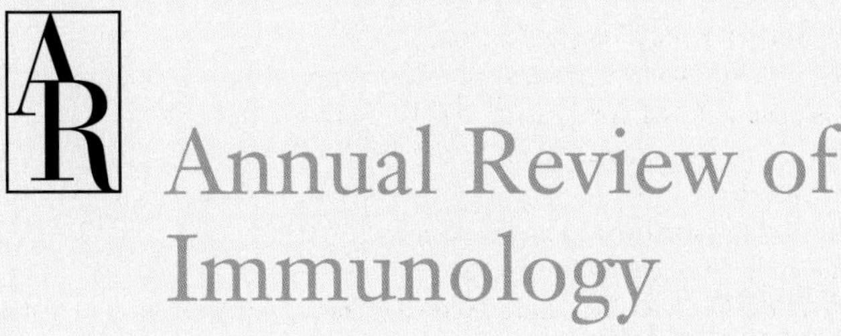

Annual Review of Immunology

Volume 28, 2010

William E. Paul, *Editor*
Bethesda, Maryland

Dan R. Littman, *Associate Editor*
New York University School of Medicine

Wayne M. Yokoyama, *Associate Editor*
Washington University School of Medicine

www.annualreviews.org • science@annualreviews.org • 650-493-4400

Annual Reviews
4139 El Camino Way • P.O. Box 10139 • Palo Alto, California 94303-0139

Annual Reviews
Palo Alto, California, USA

International Standard Serial Number: 0732-0582
International Standard Book Number: 978-0-8243-3028-6

TYPESET BY APTARA
PRINTED AND BOUND BY FRIESENS CORPORATION, ALTONA, MANITOBA, CANADA

Annual Review of Immunology

Volume 28, 2010

Contents

Indexes

Errata

An online log of corrections to *Annual Review of Immunology* articles may be found at http://immunol.annualreviews.org/errata.shtml

Annual Reviews is a nonprofit scientific publisher established to promote the advancement of the sciences. Beginning in 1932 with the *Annual Review of Biochemistry*, the Company has pursued as its principal function the publication of high-quality, reasonably priced *Annual Review* volumes. The volumes are organized by Editors and Editorial Committees who invite qualified authors to contribute critical articles reviewing significant developments within each major discipline. The Editor-in-Chief invites those interested in serving as future Editorial Committee members to communicate directly with him. Annual Reviews is administered by a Board of Directors, whose members serve without compensation.

Annual Reviews of

Analytical Chemistry
Anthropology
Astronomy and Astrophysics
Biochemistry
Biomedical Engineering
Biophysics
Cell and Developmental Biology
Chemical and Biomolecular Engineering
Clinical Psychology
Condensed Matter Physics
Earth and Planetary Sciences
Ecology, Evolution, and Systematics
Economics
Entomology
Environment and Resources
Financial Economics
Fluid Mechanics
Food Science and Technology
Genetics
Genomics and Human Genetics
Immunology
Law and Social Science
Marine Science
Materials Research
Medicine
Microbiology
Neuroscience
Nuclear and Particle Science
Nutrition
Pathology: Mechanisms of Disease
Pharmacology and Toxicology
Physical Chemistry
Physiology
Phytopathology
Plant Biology
Political Science
Psychology
Public Health
Resource Economics
Sociology

SPECIAL PUBLICATIONS
Excitement and Fascination of Science, Vols. 1, 2, 3, and 4

Max D. Cooper, MD

A Life of Adventure in Immunobiology

Max D. Cooper

Georgia Research Alliance Eminent Scholar, Professor of Pathology and Laboratory Medicine, Emory University School of Medicine, Atlanta, Georgia 30322; email: max.cooper@emory.edu

Annu. Rev. Immunol. 2010. 28:1–19

First published online as a Review in Advance on October 16, 2009

The *Annual Review of Immunology* is online at immunol.annualreviews.org

This article's doi:
10.1146/annurev-immunol-030409-101248

0732-0582/10/0423-0001$20.00

Key Words

T and B cell development, immunodeficiency diseases, lymphocytic malignancies, evolution of adaptive immunity, variable lymphocyte receptors

Abstract

This article outlines my early start in medicine, a late start in immunology research, and my efforts to integrate the two activities. I first describe some of the background information, excitement, and implications of the recognition of T and B cells as separate but functionally intertwined arms of the adaptive immune system. The article continues with a brief account of my colleagues' and my efforts to use the model of hematopoietic stem cell differentiation along T and B cell lines to gain a better understanding of immunodeficiency diseases and lymphoid malignancies. It concludes with the discovery of a more ancient adaptive immune system in which T-like and B-like cells in jawless vertebrates use variable lymphocyte receptors constructed with leucine-rich-repeat sequences to recognize antigens.

INTRODUCTION

One of the most remarkable things about a career in biomedical research is that one can start almost anywhere and end up in the most unforeseen places, being constantly amazed by what you are learning along the way. Little did I imagine while growing up in rural Mississippi that I would eventually pursue a research career in immunology. My childhood was rich in unfettered time, space to roam freely, woods and streams to explore, an uncontaminated view of starry night skies to ponder, and an abundance of books to read. The treasure of books and the thirst to read them were gifts of my father, a mathematician and educator who loved learning, and my mother, who was also a dedicated teacher. We lived on the campus of the 12-grade school where my father was the superintendent. During my early childhood in the mid-1930s, the recovery from the Great Depression was just beginning and was proceeding at a snail's pace in the agrarian South. The tranquility of life circumscribed by economics, social customs, and geography was abruptly altered in 1941 by U.S. entry into World War II. Older boys in the community were drafted into the military services, my mother began to work in an underground munitions plant, and, in 1945, my older brother joined the Marines at age 17, just before peace was declared.

As a high school senior obsessed with sports, hunting, and girls, I began to realize that reaching my stated goal of becoming a doctor would require a long time in school and a great zeal for study. I rationalized that the high cost of a medical education provided a face-saving escape, given the modest income of educators such as my parents. The tragic death of my wonderful and adventurous older brother in an automobile accident abruptly changed this equation for me. He had made me the beneficiary of his service insurance policy, and that took away the convenient financial excuse to jettison my plan for medical education. During the time of intense family grieving, my father took me aside to tell me that I now must do what my brother and I both would have done. Although my interests did not change overnight and my study habits failed to undergo any miraculous transformation, I began the well-prescribed course to become a doctor: premed, medical school, internship, and residency, which for me was in pediatrics. Although not the most industrious student, I managed to complete this course of training by age 26. More importantly, my fascination with the challenges of caring for patients and understanding the pathophysiology of their diseases grew at each step along this career path. It became more and more obvious that I had stumbled into an endless wonderland of challenging problems and career opportunities. Even more fortuitously, in 1959, while I was a resident at Tulane University in New Orleans, Rosalie Lazzara came to visit her brother, my friend and fellow trainee, Ralph. Luckily for me, my successful courtship of this lovely young lady led her to temporarily abort her teaching career. In the next eight years, we had four wonderful children, Melinda, Bo, Michael, and Christopher in London, San Francisco, Minneapolis, and Birmingham.

TURNING POINT IN ENGLAND

After finishing pediatrics residency training in New Orleans, Rosalie and I moved to London, where I worked at the Hospital for Sick Children, first as a house officer and then as a research assistant in neurophysiology. London was glorious, both for extending my training in pediatrics and for the opportunity to experience things that Rosalie and I had only read about. We feasted during that year on a cornucopia of theater, concerts, ballet, opera, museums, cathedrals, castles, and European travel. It was also a time, however, when I needed to make a decision about what to do next. Ralph Platou, my Tulane mentor in pediatrics, wrote to indicate that he felt I would do well in an academic career and to offer me a junior faculty position. Uncertain whether I could survive as an academic physician without specialty skills, I decided to seek fellowship training in allergy and immunology, having become interested in clinical immunology caring for children who were unusually susceptible to infections. Inherited immunodeficiency diseases were just beginning to be characterized at this time, notably congenital agammaglobulinemia in boys by Ogden Bruton, Charles Janeway (the elder), and Robert Good (later to be my scientific mentor) and the more severe lymphopenic form of agammaglobulinemia by Walter Hitzig and other Swiss physicians. In addition to the challenge of understanding inherited defects of immunity, I thought that allergy and immunology training could allow me to go into private practice or pursue an academic career.

William Deamer at the University of California in San Francisco accepted me as a trainee, but just before we were to leave London he wrote to ask that I stop by Frank Dixon's laboratory in Pittsburg to learn the immunofluorescence technique. Having no acquaintance with Dixon, no laboratory experience, and barely sufficient funds for the journey from London to San Francisco, I was unsettled about how to deal with this request from my new mentor. My London colleagues suggested that they could introduce me to Robert White, who had learned immunofluorescence from Albert Coons, the father of this technique. However, White was then on sabbatical in the United States. The solution to my dilemma was provided by an opportunity to visit with another English immunologist, E.J. Holborough, who used immunofluorescence to study the role of autoantibodies in autoimmune diseases. The highs and lows of that experience would set the course for my career.

Shortly after my arrival at his lab in Buckinghamshire, Holborough gently informed me that setting up an immunofluorescence assay involved a lengthy series of experimental steps, most of which were bewildering to me. Indicating that ongoing experiments in his laboratory would afford the opportunity to observe each of these steps, he inquired about the kind of fluorescent microscope I would be using. After I exposed my complete ignorance of fluorescence microscopy, his next question was about what I wished to use immunofluorescence to learn. Parroting a phrase from my future mentor's letter, I answered that the project was to determine the role of cell-mediated immunity in phlyctenular conjunctivitis. He indicated that immunofluorescence was then used to study humoral immunity and that, to his knowledge, cell-mediated immunity did not involve antibodies. Deeply embarrassed and uncomfortable in standing behind busy researchers performing laboratory procedures that I was ill prepared to understand, I retreated whenever possible to the small conference room to read a rather boring technical manual for bacterial identification by immunofluorescence. My salvation came with the discovery of Frank Macfarland Burnet's (1) book entitled *The Clonal Selection Theory of Acquired Immunity*, which was written with such clarity that one could understand basic principles without deep esoteric knowledge of immunology. Fascinated by Burnet's introduction to the intricacies of the immune system and shamed by the exposure of my ignorance in immunology, I vowed then that I would at least learn the difference between cellular and humoral immunity.

Leaving England by boat, we arrived in Hoboken, New Jersey, and drove first to Tampa, Florida, to visit Rosalie's family and then on to Jackson, Mississippi, to see my family. Crossing from Alabama into Mississippi early in the summer of 1961, we followed the highway patrol–escorted Greyhound buses carrying the Freedom Riders of the civil rights movement. The Freedom Riders were taken unceremoniously into the Jackson city jail, while we were welcomed a few blocks away into the home of my then retired parents, who joined us as we continued the drive across the country to San Francisco.

ALLERGY TRAINING IN SAN FRANCISCO

The year in the University of California at San Francisco proved pleasant and informative but, in many ways, frustrating. Clinical allergy as practiced then seemed a rather repetitive exercise that lacked a firm scientific base. There was little impetus to test the therapeutic tenets of desensitization by allergy shots and the avoidance of ill-defined allergens. The embarrassing fact that I had failed to master immunofluorescence technology was never exposed; apparently the study proposal had not been considered fundable—the only time I have ever been happy about the rejection of an NIH grant application! There was plenty of time to read more about immunology during this year of personal indecision, but textbooks on the subject were pretty dry, and I was not excited by reading about the calculation of antigen-antibody binding equilibrium curves. A highlight of that year was the opportunity to hear seminars by Linus Pauling, Gerald Edelman, and Burnet on their views of immunology. The most entertaining was Pauling's lecture, which was given without the aid of a single slide. He began by citing the principles of antigen-antibody binding that he had learned from Heidelberger and Landsteiner, before using his knowledge of protein structure to deduce that antibodies must be bivalent. With his arms stretched out to each side and using his hands to indicate antigen-binding sites, he concluded the lecture by saying, "If I couldn't figure a way for monovalent antibodies to work, I figured that God couldn't either"—not an exact quote, but pretty close.

My anxiety over not knowing what to do next was buffered by the ambiance of San Francisco; temporary rescue came with renewal of the offer of an instructor position from my mentor Ralph Platou.

BACK TO NEW ORLEANS

Returning to Tulane University, I began to conduct an allergy clinic together with Vincent Derbes, a scholarly internist/dermatologist, who had also specialized in allergy and immunology. In addition to my teaching activities, I initiated a few experiments, all of which were quite elementary given that I had virtually no laboratory skills and no grant funding. My first successful investigation was the demonstration of immunological tolerance in humans. Following Ray Owen's demonstration that lasting blood cell chimerism was conferred by an intrauterine exchange of hemopoietic cells between calf twins with different fathers, Billingham, Brent, and Medawar's experimental induction of tolerance in newborn mice led many investigators to examine the requirements for tolerance induction. Noting that newborns with erythroblastosis fetalis (Rh disease) sometimes received exchange transfusions of maternal A- or B-type blood instead of their own O-type blood, I was curious to know if these babies would mount an immune response to the foreign blood group antigens. The survival curve for the donor A or B erythrocytes proved to be perfectly normal in these recipients, and their selective delay in producing A or B isohemagglutinins provided another indication of tolerance induction (2). Tolerance to the blood group A and B antigens has since been demonstrated in blood group O newborns who received heart transplants from blood group A or B donors to correct their congenital heart malformations (3). Tolerance in this instance was shown to be associated with the deletion of reactive B cell clones, but this gets ahead of my story.

Realizing that I would need to learn how to conduct basic laboratory research to have any chance of making an original contribution, I applied for fellowship training with several famous immunologists: Burnet, Jonathan Uhr, Richard Smith, and Robert Good. All of them surprisingly agreed to accept me for training with various stipulations, such as the need to bring my salary. I felt my best chance for success was in Good's program because his research interests in immunodeficiency diseases and other immunological disorders were most congruent with my background in human developmental biology and my interest in disease pathogenesis. I thought this could help in my struggle to acquire laboratory skills and much needed knowledge in basic sciences. Good wanted me to wait for a year, however, because his lab then was full. Eager to get started and with help from my Tulane colleagues, I convinced him to let me join his laboratory immediately.

STARTING OVER AT 30 IN MINNEAPOLIS

On our arrival in Minneapolis, we checked into the Golden Gopher Motel, where I awakened in the middle of the night with a cold sweat in sheer terror. The cause of my fearful awakening was the realization that I must be utterly stupid or just plain crazy to risk everything for my family and me by starting over as a complete novice in a highly competitive research field. On the one hand, with my extensive medical training and breadth of clinical experience, I was pretty confident that I had something of value to offer in providing health care for children and that I could satisfactorily support my family in doing so. On the other hand, beginning with less knowledge and experience than the most junior laboratory technician, the odds were overwhelmingly against my success in the rapidly moving research field of immunology. But it was too late to turn back then, so early the next morning I headed to the laboratory eager to receive instructions about what I should begin to do. Good informed me that Maclyn McCarty had not given him instructions when he arrived for fellowship training at the Rockefeller University and suggested that I should work on the ideas that I had presented to argue my case for early admission to his laboratory. As I followed Good around his laboratory looking for a place where I could work, he assigned me about three feet of bench space in the already overcrowded domain of Ben Pollara, a senior postdoctoral fellow. My space was quickly translated into a drawer demarcated by a strip of tape with my name written on it.

Immunobiology was a burgeoning field of research when I joined Good's laboratory in 1963. Miller, Good, Jankovic, and their coworkers had recently discovered the importance of the thymus for lymphocyte development and immunological competence (4–6). Gowans had traced the circulation of lymphocytes and shown that they could become antibody-producing plasma cells (7). Porter and Edelman had elucidated the paired heavy and light chain composition of antibodies (8, 9). Immunologists were invigorated by the possibility of understanding the molecular basis of antibody diversity and clonal diversity. Good's laboratory then was teaming with a diverse, capable, and energetic group of individuals, whose research themes reflected his broad interests in immune system phylogeny, ontogeny, inherited and acquired immunodeficiencies, autoimmune diseases, lymphoid malignancies, the biological basis of antibody responses, the complement cascade, organ transplantation, and the effects of thymectomy in various animal models. Overwhelmed, I often retreated to the library as I tried to understand my new environment and fathom how I might best fit into it. In lieu of a better strategy, I embarked on a frenzy of experiments involving rabbits, chickens, mice, guinea pigs, and immunodeficient patients, all in different locations and most of which yielded inconclusive or unexciting results. Ray Peterson, another senior fellow, took me under his wing during this period. In collaboration with Ben Burmester at the U.S. Regional Poultry Laboratory in Michigan, Ray had shown that virus-induced lymphomas in chickens were prevented by removal of the bursa of Fabricius, whereas thymectomy had no effect (10). This was an interesting finding because all the mouse models of lymphomas could be prevented by thymectomy. Parenthetically, Jacques Miller was investigating the role of the thymus in lymphoma development when he discovered that neonatal thymectomy led to profound immunodeficiency. The virus-induced lymphomas in chickens appeared 5–9 months after virus inoculation of newly hatched chicks, and Ray invited me to join his study of the effects of bursectomy at different times. We found that removal of the bursa anytime before five months of age prevented lymphoma development, but how the bursa controlled tumor development was still unclear (11). Because the lymphomas were found in the spleen, liver, and heart, but not in the bursa, the possibility of hormonal control by the bursa was favored.

THE SETTING FOR DISCOVERY OF SEPARATE LYMPHOCYTE LINEAGES

Immunology was clearly in a fermentative period in the early 1960s, irrespective of one's portal of vision. The molecular biology revolution was in its infancy, but reductionist molecular biologists were beginning to be attracted to immunology because of the puzzle posed by the enormous diversity of antibodies, which was considered the key to understanding clonal diversity. A few developmental biologists were enticed to study lymphocytes as an interesting model of cell differentiation. Many immunologists with medical, veterinary, or related biomedical backgrounds were attracted to the field of immunology for disease-oriented reasons. Studies of the immune system were conducted primarily in whole animal models, as cell culture systems were not yet well developed. Theories abounded to interpret the phenomena of cellular and humoral immunity, tolerance, autoimmunity, and the newly discovered role of the thymus. There is little wonder that most basic scientists were loath to recognize immunology as a science and considered immunologists to be phenomenologists.

Nevertheless, there were many loosely connected pieces to the puzzle that I wish to describe here, some of which I have already mentioned. Before discovery of the effects of neonatal thymectomy on immune system development, Landsteiner & Chase (12, 13) had found that lymphocytes were essential for the transfer of contact allergy and delayed-type hypersensitivity, although debate continued about whether antibodies were involved in these examples of so-called cellular immunity. There were two contemporaneous theories about how the thymus influenced development of lymphocytes elsewhere in the body, neither of which was exclusive. One held that lymphocytes generated in the thymus were seeded to the peripheral lymphoid tissues, and the other favored hormonal control by the thymus. In studies unnoticed by most immunologists, Glick and colleagues (14) found that antibody production was profoundly impaired in chickens after the removal at hatching of the hindgut lymphoid organ called the bursa of Fabricius. Bursal development and antibody production can also be inhibited by testosterone treatment, and Noel Warner and colleagues found that some testosterone-treated chicks had cortical thymic atrophy and that skin allograft rejection was delayed in these birds and following surgical removed of the thymus at hatching as well. These investigators interpreted their composite results to suggest a tripartite model in which the thymus governed allograft rejection, the bursa controlled antibody production and delayed-type hypersensitivity, and the bone marrow controlled graft-versus-host reactivity (15). However, it was difficult to integrate this model with contemporaneous views of mammalian immune system development. Because neonatal removal of either the thymus or the appendix had similar inhibitory effects on the ability of rabbits to produce antibodies, Good was convinced these lymphoid organs exerted complementary effects on the immune system and suggested that the effects of thymectomy and bursectomy in newly hatched chicks should be reexamined. Ed Yunis and I undertook this challenge and could easily reproduce the inhibitory effects of bursectomy on antibody production, but we failed to find an effect of thymectomy on either antibody production or allograft rejection. After confirming these disappointing results, we abandoned this approach as a blind alley.

Observations in boys with the Wiskott-Aldrich syndrome (WAS) of thrombocytopenia, eczema, and recurrent ear infections later led me to revisit the chicken model. In some patients with this X-linked disorder, herpes simplex virus lesions around the mouth spread relentlessly with a fatal outcome. The inability of these boys to contain their viral infections contrasted with the effective control of virus infections in boys with X-linked agammaglobulinemia, whose cell-mediated immunity appeared to be intact. In reviewing hospital records and tissue samples of our WAS patients, I found a progressive depletion of lymphocyte stores and obtained evidence for an attendant deficit in cellular immunity that could explain their profound susceptibility to virus infections (16). However, their lymphoid tissues were loaded with plasma cells, and immunoglobulin levels were elevated. These paradoxical findings were difficult to reconcile with the prevailing view of a single lymphocyte lineage, but they could be explained if the plasma cell precursors did not belong to the thymus-dependent lineage of lymphocytes.

THE PIVOTAL EXPERIMENTS

The avian immune system seemed the most promising animal model for examining the possibility of an alternative lymphocyte lineage, although a new experimental design would obviously be required. We knew that neonatal thymectomy impaired immune responsiveness more in mice than in rabbits, which are more immunologically mature at birth. This observation suggested that strain-dependent differences in immunological maturity of chickens might explain the differences that we and our Australian colleagues had observed in the effects of thymectomy at the time of hatching. This interpretation implied that earlier removal of the thymus or bursa was needed to clarify their respective roles in immune system development, but I could not think of a way to selectively inhibit or ablate these organs before hatching. It occurred to me that if lymphocytes generated during embryonic life could be destroyed after hatching, then thymus or bursa removal would yield a clearer view of their respective roles. Whole body irradiation, although a rather drastic solution, seemed the most feasible way to achieve the necessary depletion of lymphocytes. After determining a near lethal dose of irradiation for newly hatched chicks, I removed the thymus, bursa, both, or neither before irradiating them. The plan was to compare the immunological status of the different experimental groups after they recovered from the effects of surgery and irradiation. During the course of this experiment, I began to doubt the validity of this plan, especially when some of the thymectomized birds became anemic and died. I learned later that Good had also questioned when I was going to stop fooling around with sick chickens and do something more productive. Fortunately, he spared informing me of this assessment, as I was already pretty discouraged. Ray Peterson advised me that all experiments look awful during the course of their execution, and it is important to persist with one's original experimental plan. This proved to be excellent advice.

The first results obtained in these experiments indicated a complete absence of 19S and 7S immunoglobulins, as IgM and IgG were then called, in every bursectomized and irradiated bird. The other results were equally clear (17, 18). None of the bursectomized and irradiated birds had germinal centers, plasma cells, or the ability to make antibodies in response to immunization, even though they had normal thymus development and an abundance of lymphocytes elsewhere in the body. Conversely, the thymectomized and irradiated chickens were grossly deficient in lymphocytes, yet retained the ability to produce germinal centers, plasma cells, and circulating immunoglobulins. Follow-up studies indicated that the thymus was essential for development of the lymphocytes that mediate allograft rejection, delayed-type hypersensitivity, and graft-versus-host reactions. Irradiated animals that were both thymectomized and bursectomized had combined cellular and humoral immune deficits, yet retained the ability to clear antigens from the bloodstream. Interestingly, none of the thymectomized and irradiated birds could mount the severe inflammatory responses that are normally observed in experimental animals after injection of complete Freund's adjuvant. These results revealed an unmistakably clear view of two lymphocyte lineages, one thymus-dependent and the other bursa-dependent. My excitement over these results evoked a flood of adrenalin over a week of very little sleep and several telephone calls to discuss the new findings and their implications with Bob Good, who was then attending meetings in Chicago.

IMPLICATIONS OF THE T AND B MODEL

Our model of the development of separate lymphocyte lineages provided a reliable operational map of these two differentiation pathways. In this 1965 model, the thymus-dependent system of lymphocytes was responsible for cellular immunity but was also physically and functionally integrated with the immunoglobulin-producing lineage of bursa-dependent cells in peripheral tissues. The precursors of both types of lymphocytes were thought to derive from bone marrow stem cells, whose multilineage hematopoietic differentiation potential had been demonstrated in mice by the Till and McCullough group (19) and whose lymphocyte differentiation capability had been shown by Ford & Micklem (20). The hematopoietic stem cell origin of both the thymus-dependent and bursa-dependent lymphocytes was later elucidated in chickens by Moore & Owen (21).

The new view of separate lymphocyte differentiation pathways brought fresh insight into basic and clinical issues that we and others sought to understand. This model radically changed our perspective of lymphocyte differentiation defects in patients with primary or secondary immunodeficiency diseases. Peterson and Good had written an article in which they proposed points of arrest in a thymus-dependent pathway of lymphocyte differentiation that might account for the clinical and pathological findings in various immunodeficient patients. I joined them as a coauthor when it became evident the article needed to be revised in accordance with the two separate lymphocyte lineages (22). For example, the absence of germinal centers, plasma cells, and antibodies in patients with Bruton's X-linked agammaglobulinemia, who had a normal thymus and intact cell-mediated immunity, could be explained by an arrest in differentiation of the immunoglobulin-producing lineage of lymphocytes. On the other hand, the lymphopenic form of Swiss-type agammaglobulinemia reflected defective differentiation of both lymphocyte lineages, as seen in birds after bursectomy and thymectomy combined with irradiation, and this combined immunodeficiency could theoretically be explained by defective differentiation of a common lymphoid progenitor. Finding an example of pure thymus system deficiency in humans that coincided with the immunological consequences of neonatal thymectomy in mice and thymectomy and irradiation in chickens was more problematic. The closest clinical parallel then was a description of hereditary thymic hypoplasia and lymphopenia in siblings who had an abundance of plasma cells and serum immunoglobulins (23). A more compelling correlate was subsequently provided by Angelo DiGeorge's description of patients with congenital absence of the thymus, who had an abundance of plasma cells and normal immunoglobulin levels (24).

Clinicians were generally accepting of our view of the separate T and B cell lineages, probably because the model incorporated observations in patients with primary immunodeficiency diseases and because of its potential usefulness for understanding the pathogenesis of lymphoid malignances. The morphological similarities between the bursa-dependent germinal centers and the bursa-dependent nodular lymphomas versus the thymus-dependent lymphomas in mice clearly suggested lymphocyte lineage-specific modes of lymphomagenesis. This insight provided a new way to view the pathogenesis of human malignancies of the thymus and its dependent lineage of lymphocytes compared with malignancies of the germinal center/plasma cell lineage of immunoglobulin-producing cells, to wit the follicular lymphomas and multiple myelomas.

Basic scientists initially were skeptical of the separate T and B lineage concept, perhaps because they distrusted extrapolative interpretations of data obtained in whole animal models and the fanciful theories of immunobiologists. Comparative immunology was not in vogue then, and most immunologists were loath to accept principles established by studies in animals other than their favorite mammalian species. Nevertheless, this view of compartmentalized lymphocyte differentiation immediately raised questions of a fundamental nature. How do the thymus-dependent lymphocytes collaborate with the bursa-dependent lineage of lymphocytes to facilitate antibody production? What do the thymus-derived lymphocytes use to recognize antigens given that they do not make immunoglobulins? What is the bursa equivalent in mammals?

Despite the importance of these questions, none of them would be easily answered. Our early efforts to demonstrate cooperation between T and B cells, as the two lymphocyte types were dubbed (25), were foiled by lack of sufficiently inbred chickens for transplantation studies. However, the basic principle of T and B cell cooperation was soon established in inbred mice by the classical studies of Claman and coworkers (26), Mitchell & Miller (27), and Mitchison (28). Much, of course, has since been learned about the incredible complexity of the interactions between different cell types during immune defense and in autoimmune diseases.

There were many twists and turns in the quest to determine how T cells recognize antigens. Along the way, we and others established beyond a reasonable doubt that only B cells can make immunoglobulins. The numerous examples of T cell binding of unprocessed antigens were attributable to their coating with IgM antibodies made by B lineage cells (29). Zinkernagel & Doherty (30) discovered the MHC restriction of cytotoxic T cell recognition, and a definitive solution to the nature of the antigen recognition receptors for T cells came much later with identification of T cell receptor genes (31, 32).

We needed to identify a mammalian bursa-equivalent site in which B cells were generated in order to validate the compartmentalized lymphocyte differentiation model. We also needed this information to be able to examine the earliest stages of B cell differentiation in mammals. The search for where precursor cells begin their B lineage differentiation in mammals occupied me and my colleagues for the next decade, during which time I moved to the University of Alabama at Birmingham (1967) and was often asked at annual FASEB meetings, "Where is the bursa-equivalent this year, Max?" However, during this time we used the avian model to learn about immunoglobulin isotype switching by B cells, the vulnerability of immature B cells to IgM ligation, and the lymphoid follicle–associated epithelial M cells that provide a transcytotic channel for sampling intestinal antigens (33). I describe some of these efforts next.

IMMUNOGLOBULIN ISOTYPE SWITCHING BY B CELLS

A variety of observations suggested an orderly developmental sequence in production of the different immunoglobulin isotypes. Our studies in chickens indicated that IgM was expressed first, then IgG before IgA. Moreover, the progression of this sequence could be aborted by removing the bursa at different developmental stages (34–36). Bursectomy on embryonic day 16 prevented production of all Ig isotypes, bursectomy on embryonic day 19 allowed IgM production and prevented IgG and IgA production, and bursectomy after hatching on day 21 resulted in isolated IgA deficiency. Paul Kincade and I thought these results might be explained either by a single lineage of B cells that could switch from IgM to the production of the other Ig isotypes or by the serial intrabursal development of B cells committed to production of a single Ig isotype. A way to determine which of the two possibilities was correct was to selectively inhibit the IgM B cells. The use of antibodies against the μ heavy chains for this purpose was suggested by the prior demonstration of selective antibody-mediated inhibition of immunoglobulin allotypes in rabbits (37). Paul spent the summer of 1970 purifying goat antibodies with specificity for chicken μ heavy chains, and with these we obtained results that favored the isotype switch hypothesis (38, 39). The initiation of anti-μ treatment during embryonic life inhibited production of all three Ig isotypes and led to permanent agammaglobulinemia when combined with bursectomy after hatching. The suppression instead was limited to IgM production when the anti-μ treatment was begun following bursectomy at hatching. Although the mechanism of inhibition was not obvious, we noticed that anti-μ antibodies induced lymphocyte death and diminished cellularity in the bursa. These results indicated that chicken B cells, all of which express IgM initially, can switch to the production of other Ig isotypes.

We found that anti-μ treatment of newborn mice could also inhibit B cell development and production of all immunoglobulin isotypes (39). However, IgM receptor ligation effectively inhibited B cell development only when the anti-μ treatment was initiated immediately after birth. Paradoxically, B cell stimulation was observed when anti-μ treatment was delayed even for a week. These findings implied that mature B cells are relatively insensitive to inhibition by IgM ligation, and subsequent in vitro studies demonstrated that immature B cells are exceptionally sensitive to receptor cross-linkage (40). This implied that tolerance might also result from antigen-mediated ligation of the immunoglobulin receptors on immature B cells, a concept that was validated in experiments by Nossal & Pike (41) and more thoroughly elucidated in Goodnow's (42) mouse transgenic models. These early studies of immunoglobulin isotype switching by B cells preceded discovery of the immunoglobulin genes by several years (43), but other investigators had then suggested that Ig variable and constant regions could be encoded separately (44). We used the evidence then available to propose a switch model in which formation of a DNA loop in the heavy chain coding region could allow the sequential pairing of a V region with different constant region gene segments (45), but others would elucidate the genetic basis for isotype switching (46).

SEARCH FOR THE MAMMALIAN BURSA-EQUIVALENT

Our search for the mammalian bursa-equivalent was focused initially on lymphoepithelial tissues along the digestive tract. We thought the extensive proliferation needed for the generation of a clonally diverse population of B lymphocytes would be reflected by a follicular lymphoid structure. The tonsils were my first candidates for the bursa-equivalent, but their removal in newborn rabbits had no effect on antibody production. Intestinal Peyer's patches and the appendix were more promising candidates in view of their morphologic similarity with the avian bursa. Both of these gut-associated lymphoid tissues contained an abundance of lymphoid follicles in close apposition with the overlying intestinal epithelial cells. Moreover, Sutherland (47) had shown that neonatal appendectomy impaired antibody responses in rabbits. Rabbits have only eight Peyer's patches, but it was not feasible to remove all of them at birth; the terminal patch overlaps the ileo-caecal junction, thereby necessitating intestinal dissection and reanastomosis. Dan Perry and I decided on the strategy of neonatal appendectomy followed later by Peyer's patch removal in combination with whole body irradiation to destroy preexisting lymphocytes. He performed this difficult surgery on more than 90 rabbits, only six of which survived the surgery and irradiation. After their recovery, we found these rabbits had immunological deficits comparable to those we observed in older chickens subjected to bursectomy and irradiation. The impaired antibody responsiveness contrasted with their normal ability to reject skin allografts (48). Dan continued his studies along these lines at the University of Minnesota. I also continued with this line of investigation with my new colleagues after I moved to the University of Alabama in Birmingham. Both of us obtained results that were consistent with the idea that B cells are generated in these intestinal lymphoid tissues but that fell short of proving this hypothesis (49).

The most stringent test of the hypothesis that intestinal lymphoid tissues represent the bursa-equivalent was to determine whether removal of the intestines early in fetal development would prevent B cell development. This experiment was performed in lambs with the fetal physiology group of Geoffrey Dawes in Oxford during my sabbatical with Av

Mitchison's group at University College London in 1973–1974. For these experiments, Bill Gathings and I made antibodies to sheep Ig and used these to show that B cells appeared at around 65 to 70 days of fetal life. The intestines therefore were removed at 60 days from one fetal twin before its replacement in the uterus, while the other twin was examined to confirm the absence of B cells. Two weeks later, we found that B cell development proceeded normally in intestine-less fetuses. Meanwhile in London, John Owen, Martin Raff, and I performed experiments to test the alternative hypothesis that B cells were produced in hematopoietic tissues. John had devised an organ culture system that could be used to determine whether or not B cells were produced in the hematopoietic fetal liver. When mouse fetal liver was placed in culture before the appearance of B cells, we found that B cells were indeed generated (50). Concurrent experiments by other investigators indicated the derivation of Ig-bearing B cells from resident Ig-negative cells in mouse bone marrow (51, 52). In a complementary study, we demonstrated that B cells were also generated ex vivo in fetal long bones (53). These observations established that mammalian hematopoietic tissues are sites in which B cells are generated.

The development of B cells in fetal liver cultures could be aborted by ligation of their cell surface IgM. Lymphocytes surviving this treatment contained intracellular immunoglobulin determinants, although IgM could not be detected on their cell surface (54). This distinguishing feature of pre-B cells allowed us to show in subsequent experiments that large pre-B cells undergo proliferation before giving rise to small resting pre-B cells that in turn differentiate to become B cells, the immaturity of which makes them exquisitely vulnerable to receptor cross-linkage (55). The elucidation of this sequence of events provided a useful model of early B cell differentiation and the means to demonstrate B cell generation in hematopoietic tissues of other mammalian species, including humans and rabbits (56–58). We originally thought pre-B cells made both heavy and light chains, but studies of pre-B cell hybridomas convincingly showed that they only produce μ heavy chains (59). The sequential rearrangement of heavy and light chain genes was later shown to underlie this sequence of events (60).

INTEGRATING PATIENT CARE AND LABORATORY RESEARCH

Throughout my academic career, until very recently, my efforts were divided between patient care and laboratory research. Fortunately, a highly talented group of individuals with diverse skills joined me in research and clinical activities devoted primarily to immune system disorders, including immunodeficiency diseases and lymphoid malignancies. After our model of normal B cell development was refined through studies in mice and humans (61), we began to use this information as a guideline to identify the stages at which B cell differentiation was aborted in patients who had recurrent infections because of an inability to make antibodies normally (62). Boys with X-linked agammaglobulinemia were shown to have pre-B cells in their bone marrow but very few B cells, findings indicative of an early arrest in B lineage differentiation (63, 64). Patients with common variable immunodeficiency, then known as late-onset or acquired agammaglobulinemia, instead were found to have many B cells, although they failed to undergo plasma cell differentiation (62, 63). Patients who only made IgM B cells and their antibody products obviously had an isotype switch defect (65). The more frequently occurring isolated IgA deficiency featured an arrest in the terminal differentiation of IgA1 and IgA2 B cells (66). Many of the primary immunodeficiency diseases that we and others sought to understand at cellular and clinical levels have now been attributed to specific gene defects. Of the more than 100 different types of primary immunodeficiency diseases that have now been identified, some are correctible by hematopoietic stem cell transplantation and, in a few instances, by gene therapy (67). The analysis of patients continues to be very informative regarding the roles of different immune system components and their integrated host defense functions in providing protection against potential pathogens.

Our approach to the study of lymphoid malignancies in humans drew heavily on the analysis of animal models. Through serial studies of the lymphoid leucosis virus-infected chicks, we found that histological changes could be seen in the bursa very soon after virus inoculation after hatching (68). Among the thousands of normal lymphoid follicles in the bursa, we could find rare follicles within the first month that were larger than normal and filled with lymphoblastoid cells that stained brightly with a pyronin dye for RNA. These changes suggested that preneoplastic transformation begins in an oligoclonal fashion very early in B lineage differentiation within the bursa. The slow growth of the transformed follicles coupled with the ability to prevent lymphoid tumor development elsewhere either by surgical bursectomy anytime before five months of age or by natural bursal involution caused by the endogenous androgens produced during sexual maturation suggested that other transformational events were required for tumor evolution. Others would elucidate the cumulative mutational events that occur in this RNA virus-initiated transformational process (69). We were also influenced by John Cairns's analysis of cancer mutations in which he deduced that an initial transformational event in stem cells in the intestinal crypts is essential to allow accumulation of the multiple mutational events needed for the evolution of intestinal carcinomas (70); he argued that mutations arising in the daughter cells would be inconsequential in that these committed epithelial cells would soon undergo suicidal death on migration to the tip of the intestinal villus.

With these principles in mind, we began to analyze lymphoid malignancies in patients together with our hematology-oncology colleagues. We found that acute lymphocytic leukemias of childhood represent pro-B or pre-B cell tumors (71, 72). Their hematopoietic stem cell origin was inferred by the development of pre-B cell leukemia in an individual with chronic myelogenous leukemia; the clonal stem cell origin of both tumors was indicated by the Philadelphia chromosomal translocation, which could also be found in normal white blood cells (73). For the study of malignancies representing later stages in B lineage differentiation, such as IgM-bearing follicular lymphomas and IgA-producing plasma cell myelomas, Hiromi Kubagawa made monoclonal anti-idiotype antibodies with specificity for each study patient's tumor cells. When these were used to determine the extent of clonal involvement, we found pre- and postisotype switch members of the neoplastic clones that did not manifest malignant growth behavior (74–76). While much has since been learned about the progression of mutational events that lead to the evolution of B cell malignancies, it is still unclear whether eliminating the earliest clonal progenitors is necessary to cure these tumors.

Although our studies were devoted primarily to B cells, we maintained an interest in T cell biology. For many years Chen-lo Chen and I worked with others to learn more about T and B cell differentiation in chickens. With Craig Thompson, we began to define the chicken *TCR* genes in comparison with the *TCR* genes that had been elucidated in mammals. Chickens were found to have TCR γ, δ/α, and β loci and to use the same rules that mammalian T cells employ for TCR diversification by somatic recombination and insertion of nontemplated sequences at the V(D)J junctions (77–79). However, chickens have fewer and less diverse V and J gene segments, which allowed us to make monoclonal antibodies against the Vβ1 and Vβ2 TCR subclasses. We also made antibodies against other discriminating differentiation antigens of $\alpha\beta$ and $\gamma\delta$ T cells. These reagents were used in combination with the analysis of the excision circles created by V(D)J recombination to show that $\gamma\delta$ and $\alpha\beta$ T cells were sequentially generated exclusively within the thymus and to elucidate their patterns of migration to the peripheral lymphoid tissues (80–83). Mouse $\gamma\delta$ T cells and, to a lesser extent, $\alpha\beta$ T cells were then thought to be produced within extrathymic sites as well as in the thymus. We found that frogs whose thymus was removed as early as the fifth day of embryogenesis did not develop T cells later in life (84). The same is true for congenitally athymic humans, in keeping with the currently accepted view that the thymus is essential for T cell development. We found that recent thymic emigrants could be identified in the peripheral lymphoid tissues of chickens by their retention of TCR V(D)J excision circles and expression of a thymocyte differentiation antigen (85, 86). The development of a convenient method for identifying TCR excision circles in recent thymic emigrants in humans has proven useful for evaluating thymus function in patients with HIV-AIDS and primary immunodeficiencies (87, 88).

AN ANCIENT ALTERNATIVE ADAPTIVE IMMUNE SYSTEM

Late in my career, several intriguing observations led Jan Klein and me to begin a search for the roots of the adaptive immune system in lampreys. My colleagues and I had identified an IgA receptor in humans that led us to seek a mouse *FcαR* ortholog, but mice proved not to have this gene (89). Instead, Hiromi Kubagawa found a related Ig gene superfamily, members of which encode proteins that we named the paired Ig-like receptors, PIR-A and PIR-B, because of their activating or inhibitory potential (90). Glynn Dennis found related genes in chickens with two Ig domain coding regions, one of which resembles those of the *pir* genes and the other of which is more like *FcγR* Ig domains (91). Randall Davis and others identified a family of *Fc receptor-like* genes expressed primarily by B cells that encode transmembrane proteins with activating and inhibitory motifs in their cytoplasmic tails (92). We were curious about the evolution of these Ig gene families. A lamprey ortholog of the PU.1/Spi-B transcription factor known to be important for mammalian lymphocyte differentiation was then identified in the laboratory of Jan Klein, who had a long-standing interest in evolution (93). During a visit with Jan, we decided to begin a transcriptome analysis of lamprey lymphocyte-like cells to look for recognizable components of an adaptive immune system in these basal vertebrates.

We found orthologs of many genes used by mammalian lymphocytes, but to my disappointment we could find none of the *TCR*, *BCR*, or *MHC* genes that might explain antigen-specific responses noted much earlier in the jawless vertebrates (94, 95). Jan then closed his Max Planck laboratory in Tübingen, and Zeev Pancer joined me to continue the transcriptome analysis of the lymphocyte-like cells in lampreys. After failing again to find orthologs of any of the key elements of our adaptive immune system, we decided to challenge lampreys with a cocktail of antigens and mitogens and then generate a selective cDNA library from their responding blood cells. Still we identified none of the Ig-like genes that we hoped to find. Instead, we found many leucine-rich-repeat (LRR) sequences, and a summer student, Jill Ceitlin, undertook the project of sequencing these while we continued the search. When each of the LRR cDNAs proved to have a different sequence, we realized this could reflect another way of constructing diverse anticipatory receptors for antigens. This proved to be the seminal clue we needed to elucidate an alternative adaptive immune system in the jawless vertebrates.

Instead of the immunoglobulin-based receptors that all vertebrates with jaws use for antigen recognition, the surviving jawless vertebrates, lamprey and hagfish, use variable lymphocyte receptors (VLR) that are composed of LRR segments (96). Two germ line genes for the VLRs, *VLRA* and *VLRB*, are incomplete in that they encode only the leader sequence, the invariant stalk region, and small portions of the amino-terminal and carboxyl-terminal LRR sequences (96–98). Each germ line *VLR* gene is flanked by hundreds of donor LRR-coding sequences, however, and these can be used as templates to add the missing LRR sequences needed to complete the gene (98–100). During lymphocyte differentiation, the donor LRR sequences are randomly selected and anchored by short stretches of nucleotide sequence homology to the recipient *VLR* sequence while being copied to extend the coding sequence. This assembly process proceeds in stepwise fashion to completion of the *VLR* genes, each of which is assured of having a different sequence due to the great variety of donor LRR sequences and their random piecewise usage during gene assembly. The *VLR* assembly process is limited to only one allele (96, 100, 101) and appears to involve the participation of activation-induced cytidine deaminase orthologs called CDA1 and CDA2 (98, 101). This complex recombinatorial process is used to generate clonally diverse lymphocytes with a virtually unlimited repertoire of anticipatory receptors in the jawless vertebrates.

During the course of this phylogenetic exploration, my colleagues and I moved to Emory University (2008), and another surprise came with the discovery that both the *VLRA* and *VLRB* genes are assembled in monoallelic fashion by separate populations of lymphocytes that resemble T and B cells in jawed vertebrates (101). Both the VLRA and VLRB lymphocytes respond to immunization by undergoing lymphoblastoid transformation and proliferation, but only the VLRB lymphocytes bind native antigens and respond to this stimulus by undergoing differentiation into plasma cells that secrete antigen-specific VLR antibodies (99, 101). The VLRA lymphocytes instead respond preferentially to stimulation with the classical T cell mitogen, phytohemagglutinin, and do not secrete their membrane-based VLRA proteins (101). A limited gene profile analysis indicates that the two types of lamprey lymphocytes express many of the genes used by our T and B lineage cells. For example, the VLRA cells express orthologs for some of the key transcription factors, chemokine receptors, and the Notch1 cell fate–determining element that lymphocyte progenitors in jawed vertebrates use for homing to the thymus and commitment to the T cell lineage. VLRA cells also express the IL-17 proinflammatory cytokine and the receptor for IL-8. Conversely, the VLRB cells preferentially express Toll-like receptors, downstream signaling components used by B cells, the IL-8 proinflammatory chemokine, and the receptor for IL-17. These patterns of gene expression suggest that the VLRA and VLRB cells may work together in coordinating immune responses.

A system designed by Brantley Herrin for generating monoclonal VLRB antibodies has facilitated their structural and functional characterization (102, 103). The lamprey antibodies are composed of ten uniform chains that are joined at their base to form five pairs of long flexible arms ending with hand-shaped LRR regions that bind antigens. The multivalency, the flexibility of the arms, and the relatively large antigen-binding pocket all contribute to the avid antigen-binding ability of the VLRB antibodies. These structural features, coupled with their remarkable stability and the ease with which the VLR antibodies can be engineered, may make them very useful reagents for biomedical purposes, a possibility that my colleagues and others are exploring.

These two very different types of anticipatory receptors of comparable diversity may have arisen through convergent evolution following the divergence of jawless and jawed vertebrate lineages some 500 or 400 mya. Although different genes were co-opted for making the two types of receptors and different mechanisms are employed for their somatic diversification, the same basic strategy of clonal expression of anticipatory receptors by separate lineages of functionally intertwined lymphocytes is evident in the two vertebrate lineages. The evolutionary pressure leading to these alternative modes for generating clonally diverse lymphocytes with proinflammatory potential could have been imposed by infectious agents. The ability to mount a specific immune response to any potential pathogen and to be protected from reinfection by antibodies and an expanded population of primed effector cells could have significant survival value. At the same time, the ability to generate antigen receptors of virtually unlimited diversity on lymphocytes with proinflammatory function would inevitably create the hazard of autoimmunity. An important safeguard against autoimmunity in jawed vertebrates is provided by the TCR receptor repertoire selection in the thymus to avoid self-reactivity and by the T cell–mediated regulation of the B cell responses to antigens. The remarkably similar construction of these analogous adaptive immune systems suggests that jawless and jawed vertebrates have employed the same basic strategy to avoid autoimmunity.

This glimpse of an alternative adaptive immune system that in many ways resembles our adaptive immune system offers fresh insight into the evolution of adaptive immunity. It also raises a flood of intriguing questions. Where is the thymus-equivalent in jawless vertebrates? How do the VLRA cells see antigens? Are antigens processed and presented by MHC analogs and are VLRA cells selected for survival during development on the basis of self-reactivity? How do the VLRA and VLRB lymphocytes work together and with other types of cells to provide protective immunity? The search for answers to these and other questions promises to be an exciting venture. At the same time, it is humbling to realize that 150 years after Darwin published *Origin of the Species* we still have so much more to learn about how and why our complex immune system evolved.

CONCLUSION

In writing this personalized account of a joyful career in medicine and immunology, I am reminded of the many missed opportunities to follow the next most important question through misjudgment or lack of the necessary research skills. When difficulties arose over the years, I often recalled the pep talk of my early mentor, Bob Good: "What we know compared with what we don't know is like a crumb in the corner of this room. As long as you start with a reasonable hypothesis and do the experiment right, you're bound to find something new!" This is likely still true, and I cannot imagine a field of research that is more exciting or one that offers better opportunity to explore the balance of life on our planet. Perhaps this view explains why I am hooked for life with immunobiology.

DISCLOSURE STATEMENT

The author is not aware of any affiliations, memberships, funding, or financial holdings that might be perceived as affecting the objectivity of this review.

ACKNOWLEDGMENTS

I greatly appreciate the guidance, support, help, and friendship of my invaluable mentors, colleagues, and students in this biomedical scientific journey, and the research support by the National Institutes of Health, Howard Hughes Medical Institute, and Georgia Research Alliance. Finally, I wish to express my immense gratitude for the unequivocal love and support of my wife Rosalie and our family, who made everything possible.

LITERATURE CITED

1. Burnet FM. 1959. *The Clonal Selection Theory of Acquired Immunity*. Nashville, TN: Vanderbilt Univ. Press
2. Cooper MD, Lusher J. 1964. Immunologic tolerance of ABO incompatible erythrocytes in human neonates. *J. Pediatr.* 65:831–38
3. West LJ. 2004. Crossing the ABO barrier in infant heart transplantation at the Hospital for Sick Children. *Clin. Transpl.* 18:243–52
4. Miller JFAP. 1961. The immunological function of the thymus. *Lancet* 2:748–49
5. Good RA, Dalmasso AP, Martinez C, Archer OK, Pierce JC, et al. 1962. The role of the thymus in development of immunologic capacity in rabbits and mice. *J. Exp. Med.* 116:773–76

6. Jankovic BD, Waksman BH, Arnason BG. 1962. Role of the thymus in immune reactions in rats. *J. Exp. Med.* 116:159–76
7. Gowans JL, Knight EJ. 1964. The route of recirculation of lymphocytes in the rat. *Proc. R. Soc. London Ser. B Biol. Sci.* 159:257–82
8. Porter RR. 1959. The hydrolysis of rabbit γ-globulin and antibodies with crystalline papain. *Biochem. J.* 73:119–27
9. Edleman GM. 1959. Dissociation of γ-globulin. *J. Am. Chem. Soc.* 81:3155–56
10. Peterson RDA, Burmester BR, Fredrickson TN, Purchase HG, Good RA. 1964. Effect of bursectomy and thymectomy on the development of visceral lymphomatosis in the chicken. *J. Natl. Cancer Inst.* 32:1343–54
11. Peterson RDA, Purchase MG, Burmester BR, Cooper MD, Good RA. 1966. Relationships among visceral lymphomatosis, bursa of Fabricius, and bursa-dependent lymphoid tissue of the chicken. *J. Natl. Cancer Inst.* 36:585–98
12. Landsteiner K, Chase MW. 1942. Experiments on transfer of cutaneous sensitivity to simple compounds. *Proc. Soc. Exp. Biol. Med.* 49:688–90
13. Chase MW. 1945. The cellular transfer of cutaneous hypersensitivity to tuberculin. *Proc. Soc. Exp. Biol. Med.* 59:134–35
14. Glick B, Chang TS, Jaap RG. 1956. The bursa of Fabricius and antibody production. *Poult. Sci.* 35:224–25
15. Warner NL, Szenberg A, Burnet FM. 1962. The immunological role of different lymphoid organs in the chicken. I. Dissociation of immunological responsiveness. *Aust. J. Exp. Biol. Med. Sci.* 40:373–87
16. Cooper MD, Chase HP, Lowman JT, Krivit W, Good RA. 1968. Wiskott-Aldrich Syndrome. An immunologic deficiency disease involving the afferent limb of immunity. *Am. J. Med.* 44:499–513
17. Cooper MD, Peterson RDA, Good RA. 1965. Delineation of the thymic and bursal lymphoid systems in the chicken. *Nature* 205:143–46
18. Cooper MD, Peterson RDA, South MA, Good RA. 1966. The functions of the thymus system and the bursa system in the chicken. *J. Exp. Med.* 23:75–102
19. Becker AJ, McCulloch EA, Till JE. 1963. Cytological demonstration of the clonal nature of spleen colonies derived from transplanted mouse marrow cells. *Nature* 197:452–54
20. Ford CE, Micklem HS. 1963. The thymus and lymph nodes in radiation chimaeras. *Lancet* 281:359–62
21. Moore MAS, Owen JJT. 1967. Stem cell migration in developing myeloid and lymphoid systems. *Lancet* 290:658–59
22. Peterson RDA, Cooper MD, Good RA. 1965. The pathogenesis of immunologic deficiency diseases. *Am. J. Med.* 38:579–604
23. Nezelof C, Jammet ML, Lertholary P, Labrune B, Lamy ML. 1964. L'hypoplasie héréditaire du thymus: sa place et sa responsabilité dans une observation d'aplasie lymphocytaire normoplasmocytaire et normoglobulinémique du nourrison. *Arch. Franc. Pediatr.* 21:897
24. Cooper MD, Peterson RDA, Good RA. 1965. A new concept of the cellular basis of immunity. (Discussion). *J. Pediatr.* 67:907–908
25. Roitt IM, Greaves MF, Torrigiani G, Brostoff J, Playfair JHL. 1969. Cellular basis of immunological responses. *Lancet* 294:367–71
26. Clamen HN, Chaperon EA, Triplett RF. 1966. Thymus-marrow cell combinations. Synergism in antibody production. *Proc. Soc. Exp. Biol. Med.* 122:1167–71
27. Mitchell GF, Miller JFAP. 1968. Cell to cell interaction in the immune response. II. The source of homolysin-forming cells in irradiated mice given bone marrow and thymus or thoracic duct lymphocytes. *J. Exp. Med.* 128:126–35
28. Mitchison NA. 1971. The carrier effect in the secondary response to hapten-protein conjugates. II. Cellular cooperation. *Eur. J. Immunol.* 1:18–27
29. Webb CS, Cooper MD. 1973. T cells can bind antigen via cytophilic IgM antibody made by B cells. *J. Immunol.* 111:275–77
30. Zinkernagel RM, Doherty PC. 1973. Cytotoxic thymus-derived lymphocytes in cerebrospinal fluid of mice with lymphocytic choriomeningitis. *J. Exp. Med.* 138:1266–69
31. Yanagi Y, Yoshikai Y, Leggett SP, Clark J, Aleksander I, Mak TW. 1984. A human T cell specific cDNA clone encodes a protein having extensive homology to immunoglobulin chains. *Nature* 308:145–49

32. Hedrick SM, Cohen DI, Nielsen EA, Davis MM. 1984. Isolation of cDNA clones encoding T cell-specific membrane-associated proteins. *Nature* 308:149–53
33. Bockman DE, Cooper MD. 1973. Pinocytosis by epithelium associated with lymphoid follicles in the bursa of Fabricius, appendix, and Peyer's patches. *Am. J. Anat.* 136:455–78
34. Cooper MD, Cain WA, Van Alten PJ, Good RA. 1969. Development and function of the immunoglobulin system. I. Effect of bursectomy at different stages of development on germinal centers, plasma cells, immunoglobulins and antibody production. *Int. Arch. Allergy Appl. Immunol.* 35:242–52
35. Kincade PW, Cooper MD. 1971. Development and distribution of immunoglobulin-containing cells in the chicken. An immunofluorescent analysis using purified antibodies to μ, γ and light chains. *J. Immunol.* 106:371–82
36. Kincade PW, Cooper MD. 1973. Immunoglobulin A. Site and sequence of expression in developing chicks. *Science* 179:398–400
37. Dray S. 1962. Effect of maternal isoantibodies on the quantitative expression of two allelic genes controlling γ-globulin allotypic specificities. *Nature* 195:677–80
38. Kincade PW, Lawton AR, Bockman DE, Cooper MD. 1970. Suppression of immunoglobulin G synthesis as a result of antibody-mediated suppression of immunoglobulin M synthesis in chickens. *Proc. Natl. Acad. Sci. USA* 67:1819–925
39. Lawton AR, Asofsky R, Hylton MB, Cooper MD. 1972. Suppression of immunoglobulin class synthesis in mice. I. Effects of treatment with antibody to μ chain. *J. Exp. Med.* 135:277–97
40. Raff MC, Owen JJT, Cooper MD, Lawton AR III, Megson M, Gathings WE. 1975. Differences in susceptibility of mature and immature mouse B lymphocytes to anti-immunoglobulin induced immunoglobulin suppression in vitro: possible implications for B cell tolerance to self. *J. Exp. Med.* 142:1052–64
41. Nossal JV, Pike BL. 1975. Evidence for the clonal abortion theory of B lymphocyte tolerance. *J. Exp. Med.* 141:904–17
42. Goodnow CC. 1996. Balancing immunity and tolerance: deleting and tuning lymphocyte repertoires. *Proc. Natl. Acad. Sci. USA* 93:2264–71
43. Tonegawa S. 1983. Somatic generation of antibody diversity. *Nature* 302:571–81
44. Dryer WJ, Bennett JC. 1965. The molecular basis of antibody formation: a paradox. *Proc. Natl. Acad. Sci. USA* 54:864–69
45. Cooper MD, Lawton AR. 1974. The development of the immune system. *Sci. Am.* 231:58–72
46. Honjo T, Kinoshita K, Muramatsu M. 2002. Molecular mechanism of class switch recombination: linkage with somatic hypermutation. *Annu. Rev. Immunol.* 20:165–96
47. Sutherland DER, Archer OK, Good RA. 1964. Role of the appendix in development of immunological capacity. *Proc. Soc. Exp. Biol. Med.* 115:673–76
48. Cooper MD, Perey DY, McKneally MF, Gabrielsen AE, Sutherland DER, Good RA. 1966. A mammalian equivalent of the avian bursa of Fabricius. *Lancet* 287:1388–91
49. Cooper MD, Lawton AR. 1972. The mammalian "bursa-equivalent": Does lymphoid differentiation along plasma cell lines begin in the gut-associated lymphoepithelial tissues (GALT) of mammals? In *Contemporary Topics in Immunobiology*, ed. MG Hanna, pp. 49–68. New York: Plenum
50. Owen JJT, Cooper MD, Raff MC. 1974. In vitro generation of B lymphocytes in mouse fetal liver, a mammalian 'bursa equivalent.' *Nature* 249:361–63
51. Osmond DG, Nossal GJV. 1974. Differentiation of lymphocytes in mouse bone marrow. II. Kinetics of maturation and renewal of antiglobulin-binding cells studied by double labeling. *Cell. Immunol.* 13:132–45
52. Ryser JE, Vassalli P. 1974. Mouse bone marrow lymphocytes and their differentiation. *J. Immunol.* 113:719–28
53. Owen JJT, Raff MC, Cooper MD. 1975. Studies on the generation of B lymphocytes in the mouse embryo. *Eur. J. Immunol.* 5:468–73
54. Raff MC, Megson M, Owen JJT, Cooper MD. 1976. Early production of intracellular IgM by B lymphocyte precursors in mouse. *Nature* 259:224–26
55. Owen JJT, Wright DE, Habu S, Raff MC, Cooper MD. 1977. Studies on the generation of B lymphocytes in fetal liver and bone marrow. *J. Immunol.* 118:2067–72

56. Gathings WE, Lawton AR, Cooper MD. 1977. Immunofluorescent studies of the development of pre-B cells, B lymphocytes and immunoglobulin isotype diversity in humans. *Eur. J. Immunol.* 7:804–10
57. Burrows PD, Kearney JF, Lawton AR, Cooper MD. 1978. Pre-B cells: bone marrow persistence in anti-μ suppressed mice, conversion to B lymphocytes, and recovery following destruction by cyclophosphamide. *J. Immunol.* 120:1526–31
58. Hayward AR, Simons MA, Lawton AR, Mage RG, Cooper MD. 1978. Pre-B and B cells in rabbits: ontogeny and allelic exclusion of kappa light chain genes. *J. Exp. Med.* 148:1367–77
59. Burrows PD, LeJeune M, Kearney JF. 1979. Evidence that murine pre-B cells synthesize μ heavy chains but no light chains. *Nature.* 280:838–41
60. Willerford DM, Swat W, Alt FW. 1996. Developmental regulation of V(D)J recombination and lymphocyte differentiation. *Curr. Opin. Genet. Dev.* 6:603–9
61. Abney ER, Cooper MD, Kearney JF, Lawton AR, Parkhouse RME. 1978. Sequential expression of immunoglobulin on developing mouse B lymphocytes: a systematic survey that suggests a model for the generation of immunoglobulin isotype diversity. *J. Immunol.* 120:2041–49
62. Cooper MD, Lawton AR. 1972. Circulating B-cells in patients with immunodeficiency. *Am. J. Pathol.* 69:513–27
63. Cooper MD, Lawton AR, Bockman DE. 1971. Agammaglobulinemia with B lymphocyte: a specific defect of plasma cell differentiation. *Lancet* 298:791–95
64. Vogler LB, Pearl ER, Gathings WE, Lawton AR, Cooper MD. 1976. B-lymphocyte precursors in the bone marrow of patients with immunoglobulin deficiency diseases. *Lancet* 308:376
65. Levitt D, Haber P, Rich K, Cooper MD. 1983. Hyper IgM immunodeficiency: a primary dysfunction of B lymphocyte isotype switching. *J. Clin. Investig.* 72:1650–57
66. Conley ME, Cooper MD. 1981. Immature phenotype of IgA cells in IgA deficient patients. *N. Engl. J. Med.* 305:495–97
67. Ochs HD, Smith CIE, Puck J. 2007. *Primary Immunodeficiency Diseases: A Molecular and Genetic Approach*. New York: Oxford Univ. Press
68. Cooper MD, Payne LN, Dent PB, Burmester BR, Good RA. 1968. Pathogenesis of avian lymphoid leukosis. I. Histogenesis. *J. Natl. Cancer Inst.* 41:373–90
69. Thompson CB, Challoner PB, Neiman PE. 1986. Normal and neoplastic B cell development in the bursa of fabricius. *Curr. Top. Microbiol. Immunol.* 132:209–14
70. Cairns J. 1975. Mutation selection and the natural history of cancer. *Nature* 255:197–200
71. Vogler LB, Crist WM, Bockman DE, Pearl ER, Lawton AR, Cooper MD. 1978. Pre-B cell leukemia: a new phenotype of childhood lymphoblastic leukemia. *N. Engl. J. Med.* 298:872–78
72. Vogler LB, Crist WM, Sarrif AM, Pullen DJ, Bartolucci AA, et al. 1981. An analysis of clinical and laboratory features of acute lymphocytic leukemias with emphasis on 35 children with pre-B leukemia. *Blood* 58:135–40
73. Volger LB, Crist WM, Vinson PC, Sarrif A, Brattain MG, Coleman MS. 1979. Philadelphia chromosome pre-B leukemia presenting as blast crisis of chronic myelogenous leukemia. *Blood* 54:1164–70
74. Kubagawa H, Vogler LB, Capra JD, Conrad ME, Lawton AR, Cooper MD. 1979. Studies on the clonal origin of multiple myeloma: use of individually specific (idiotype) antibodies to trace the oncogenic event to its earliest point of expression in B-cell differentiation. *J. Exp. Med.* 150:792–807
75. Mayumi M, Kubagawa H, Omura GA, Gathings WE, Kearney JF, Cooper MD. 1982. Studies on the clonal origin of human B cell leukemia using monoclonal anti-idiotype antibodies. *J. Immunol.* 129:904–10
76. Bertoli LF, Kubagawa H, Borzillo GV, Burrows PD, Schreeder MT, et al. 1988. Bone marrow origin of a B cell lymphoma. *Blood* 72:94–101
77. Cooper MD, Chen CH, Bucy RP, Thompson CB. 1991. Avian T cell ontogeny. *Adv. Immunol.* 50:87–117
78. Göbel TWF, Chen CH, Lahti J, Kubota T, Kuo C, et al. 1994. Identification of, T cell receptor alpha (TCRa) genes in the chicken. *Proc. Natl. Acad. Sci. USA* 91:1094–98
79. Kubota T, Wang J-Y, Gobel TWF, Hockett R, Cooper MD, Chen CH. 1999. Characterization of an avian (*Gallus gallus domesticus*) TCR α/δ gene locus. *J. Immunol.* 163:3858–66
80. Coltey M, Bucy RP, Chen CH, Cihak J, Lösch U, et al. 1989. Analysis of the first two waves of thymus homing stem cells and their T cell progeny in chick-quail chimeras. *J. Exp. Med.* 170:543–57

81. Bucy RP, Chen CH, Cooper MD. 1990. Ontogeny of T cell receptors in the chicken thymus. *J. Immunol.* 144:1161–68
82. Dunon D, Courtois D, Vainio O, Six A, Chen CH, et al. 1997. Ontogeny of the immune system: γ/δ and α/β T cells migrate from thymus to the periphery in alternating waves. *J. Exp. Med.* 186:977–88
83. Bucy RP, Chen CH, Cihak J, Lösch U, Cooper MD. 1988. Avian T cells expressing $\gamma\delta$ receptors localize in the splenic sinusoids and the intestinal epithelium. *J. Immunol.* 141:2200–5
84. Horton JD, Horton TL, Dzialo R, Gravenor I, Minter R, et al. 1998. T-cell and natural killer cell development in thymectomized Xenopus. *Immunol. Rev.* 166:245–58
85. Kong F-K, Chen CH, Cooper MD. 1998. Thymic function can be accurately monitored by the level of recent T cell emigrants in the circulation. *Immunity* 8:97–104
86. Kong F-K, Chen CH, Six A, Hockett RD, Cooper MD. 1999. T cell receptor gene deletion circles identify recent thymic emigrants in the peripheral T cell pool. *Proc. Natl. Acad. Sci. USA* 96:1536–40
87. Douek DC, McFarland RD, Keiser PH, Gage EA, Massey JM, et al. 1998. Changes in thymic function with age and during the treatment of HIV infection. *Nature* 396:690–95
88. Patel DD, Gooding ME, Parrott RE, Curtis KM, Haynes BF, Buckley RH. 2000. Thymic function after hematopoietic stem-cell transplantation for the treatment of severe combined immunodeficiency. *N. Engl. J. Med.* 342:1325–32
89. Monteiro RC, Kubagawa H, Cooper MD. 1990. Cellular distribution, regulation and biochemical nature of an Fcα receptor in humans. *J. Exp. Med.* 171:597–613
90. Kubagawa H, Burrows PD, Cooper MD. 1997. A novel pair of immunoglobulin-like receptors expressed by B cells and myeloid cells. *Proc. Natl. Acad. Sci. USA* 94:5261–66
91. Dennis G Jr, Kubagawa H, Cooper MD. 2000. Paired Ig-like receptor homologs in birds and mammals share a common ancestor with mammalian Fc receptors. *Proc. Natl. Acad. Sci. USA* 97:13245–50
92. Davis RS, Wang Y-H, Kubagawa H, Cooper MD. 2001. Identification of a family of Fc receptor homologs with preferential B cell expression. *Proc. Natl. Acad. Sci. USA* 98:9772–77
93. Shintani S, Terzic J, Sato A, Saraga-Babic M, O'hUigin C, et al. 2000. Do lampreys have lymphocytes? The Spi evidence. *Proc. Natl. Acad. Sci. USA* 97:7417–22
94. Mayer WE, Uinuk-ool T, Tichy H, Gartland LA, Klein J, Cooper MD. 2002. Isolation and characterization of lymphocyte-like cells from a lamprey. *Proc. Natl. Acad. Sci. USA* 99:14350–55
95. Uinuk-ool T, Sato A, Dongak R, Mayer WE, Cooper MD, Klein J. 2002. Lamprey lymphocyte-like cells express homologs of genes involved in immunologically relevant activities of mammalian lymphocytes. *Proc. Natl. Acad. Sci. USA* 99:14356–61
96. Pancer Z, Amemiya CT, Ehrhardt GRA, Ceitlin J, Gartland GL, Cooper MD. 2004. Somatic diversification of variable lymphocyte receptors in the agnathan sea lamprey. *Nature* 430:174–80
97. Pancer Z, Kasahara M, Saha NR, Kasamatsu J, Amemiya CT, Cooper MD. 2005. Variable lymphocyte receptors in hagfish. *Proc. Natl. Acad. Sci. USA* 102:9224–29
98. Rogozin IB, Iyer LM, Liang L, Glazko GV, Liston VG, et al. 2007. Evolution and diversification of lamprey antigen receptors: evidence for involvement of an AID-APOBEC family cytosine deaminase. *Nat. Immunol.* 8:647–56
99. Alder MN, Rogozin IB, Iyer LM, Glazko GV, Cooper MD, Pancer Z. 2005. Diversity and function of adaptive immune receptors in a jawless vertebrate. *Science* 310:1970–73
100. Nagawa F, Kishishita N, Shimizu K, Hirose S, Miyoshi M, Nezu J, et al. 2007. Antigen-receptor genes of the agnathan lamprey are assembled by a process involving copy choice. *Nat. Immunol.* 8:206–13
101. Guo P, Hirano M, Herrin BR, Li J, Yu C, et al. 2009. Dual nature of the adaptive immune system in lampreys. *Nature* 459:796–802
102. Herrin BR, Alder MN, Roux RH, Sina C, Ehrhardt GRA, et al. 2008. Structure and specificity of lamprey monoclonal antibodies. *Proc. Natl. Acad. Sci. USA* 105:2040–45
103. Han BW, Herrin BR, Cooper MD, Wilson IA. 2008. Antigen recognition by variable lymphocyte receptors. *Science* 321:1834–37

B Cell Signaling and Fate Decision

Tomohiro Kurosaki,[1,2] Hisaaki Shinohara,[2] and Yoshihiro Baba[1,2]

[1]Laboratory of Lymphocyte Differentiation, WPI Immunology Frontier Research Center, Osaka University, Osaka 565-0871, Japan

[2]Laboratory for Lymphocyte Differentiation, RIKEN Research Center for Allergy and Immunology, Yokohama, Kanagawa 230-0045, Japan; email: kurosaki@rcai.riken.jp

Annu. Rev. Immunol. 2010. 28:21–55

First published online as a Review in Advance on August 25, 2009

The *Annual Review of Immunology* is online at immunol.annualreviews.org

This article's doi:
10.1146/annurev.immunol.021908.132541

0732-0582/10/0423-0021$20.00

Key Words

B cell antigen receptor, calcium/NF-κB signaling pathway, microRNAs, B cell development, immune response, germinal center

Abstract

Antigen receptors on the surface of B lymphocytes trigger adaptive immune responses after encountering their cognate antigens but also control a series of antigen-independent checkpoints during B cell development. These physiological processes are regulated by the expression and function of cell surface receptors, intracellular signaling molecules, and transcription factors. The function of these proteins can be altered by a dynamic array of post-translational modifications, using two interconnected mechanisms. These modifications can directly induce an altered conformational state in the protein target of the modification itself. In addition, they can create new binding sites for other protein partners, thereby contributing to where and when such multiple protein assemblies are activated within cells. As a new type of post-transcriptional regulator, microRNAs have emerged to influence the development and function of B cells by affecting the expression of target mRNAs.

BCR: B cell receptor

miRNA: microRNA

GC: germinal center

INTRODUCTION

B lineage cells are the central mediators of humoral immunity. Plasma cells (PCs) are the terminal effector cells of the lineage, and they can neutralize pathogens by secreting pathogen-specific antibodies. PCs arise as a consequence of a highly regulated differentiation process that is initiated when B lymphocytes encounter antigens through their B cell receptors (BCRs) (1). However, it is clear that BCRs can also signal independently of antigen, a process termed tonic signaling, thereby regulating the antigen-independent phase of B cell development (2, 3).

For these antigen-dependent and -independent signals to be correctly interpreted, the expression of the BCR, other cell surface receptors, and intracellular molecules must be regulated correctly, depending on the developmental and activation stage of the B cells (4). In addition to the complex transcriptional programs already known to regulate the expression of genes involved in B cell signaling, microRNAs (miRNAs) have emerged as a new type of post-transcriptional regulator of gene expression.

At a given developmental and activation stage of the B cells, in response to extracellular microenvironmental cues, intracellular molecules must be integrated into a signaling complex dictated by temporal and spatial demands. Over the past few years, investigators have better appreciated the requirements for the proper localization of signaling molecules at a given time. Changing the localization and activation status of these molecules is frequently mediated by reversible covalent modifications. These post-translational modifications (5) include phosphorylation, methylation, acetylation, ubiquitylation, and sumoylation. In this review, we summarize the major advances in our understanding of the mechanisms by which transcriptional, post-transcriptional, and post-translational modifications interact spatiotemporally and how B cells integrate these interactions to make the correct cell fate decisions during development and humoral immune responses.

miRNA-MEDIATED POST-TRANSCRIPTIONAL REGULATION

miRNAs, which investigators initially discovered from a curiosity in nematodes, have recently been recognized as important mediators of post-transcriptional gene regulation in higher metazoans, including mammals. In this section, we discuss the cellular function of miRNAs, focusing specifically on the role of miR-150 and miR-155 in regulating B cell development and immune responses.

At present, biochemical and genetic studies have provided a basic understanding of the biogenesis of miRNAs (6–9). The processes involved appear to be tightly regulated, depending on the developmental and activation stages of B cells. For instance, as discussed below, miR-150 is expressed selectively in mature B cells but not in pro-/pre-B cells (10). In the case of miR-155, its expression increases after BCR, LPS, or CpG stimulation, probably contributing to the fact that it exerts its function in germinal center (GC) responses (11, 12). Such differential expression of miRNAs is likely to be regulated at various points in their biogenesis, including the transcriptional and post-transcriptional levels; however, the molecular mechanisms underlying these regulations remain unclear.

The usual result of miRNA-mediated gene regulation is a reduction in the amount of target protein that is synthesized. Some, but not all, of the mechanisms by which miRNA achieves this outcome have been clarified. In most cases, miRNAs repress target gene expression by inhibiting translation, so that the mRNA levels remain constant while the encoded protein's level declines. Less frequently, miRNAs repress target gene expression by triggering the degradation of target mRNAs, using the same mechanisms as siRNA and shRNA to silence gene expression. Compared with other gene-regulatory mechanisms (such as chromatin modification and transcriptional controls occurring in the nucleus), miRNA-mediated gene regulation typically occurs during the step directly before protein synthesis and thus is highly suited for fine-tuning gene expression. Moreover, at the molecular level, one species of miRNA can regulate the expression of multiple genes simultaneously, thereby more broadly impacting biological processes. For instance, miR-181a controls the T cell receptor (TCR) signaling threshold and strength in part by simultaneously dampening the expression of multiple phosphatases, such as SHP2 and PTPN22, which are negative regulators of the TCR signaling cascade (13).

The function in B cell differentiation of two types of miRNA, miR-150 and -155, has been well elucidated. As mentioned above, miR-150 expression cannot be detected in pro-/pre-B cells, but it increases in mature B cells. Xiao and colleagues (10) recently demonstrated the importance of miR-150 in B cell formation and humoral immune responses using gain- and loss-of-function mouse models. *miR-150* knockout mice have increased numbers of B-1 cells and augmented T-dependent (TD) immune responses. In terms of miRNA target validation, bioinformatics analyses suggested that c-Myb could be a miR-150 target in this system. To test this possibility directly, Xiao and colleagues generated mice that ectopically express miR-150, in which the expression level of miR-150 in pro-/pre-B cell stages was comparable with that in mature B cells. B cell development in these miR-150 transgenic mice was blocked at the pro- to pre-B cell transition. This phenotype is similar to that previously seen in *c-Myb*-deficient mice, indicating that the enforced expression of miR-150 probably suppressed c-Myb in pro-/pre-B cells. Furthermore, in vitro analysis using a reporter assay showed that miR-150 directly inhibits c-Myb expression by binding to the 3′ untranslated region of the *c-Myb* mRNA.

miR-155 is overexpressed in certain human B cell lymphomas, including diffuse large B cell lymphoma, Hodgkin's lymphoma, and Burkitt lymphoma (14), suggesting that it might participate in B cell growth. Mice carrying mutated *miR-155* are less responsive to immunization. Indeed, two groups elegantly demonstrated that miR-155 regulates the formation and response of GC B cells (11, 12). The transcription factor PU.1 has been validated as one of the crucial targets of miR-155-mediated inhibition (11), and thus its level is downregulated in wild-type B cells. Accordingly, some phenotypes observed in *miR-155* knockout mice, such as fewer IgG1-bearing B cells, are recapitulated when PU.1 is ectopically overexpressed in a wild-type background. The activation-induced cytidine deaminase (AID) has been demonstrated recently to be another miR-155 target (15, 16), and mutation of the AID miR-155 target site resulted in increased AID expression, thereby causing enhanced class switching and defective affinity maturation (15). As the mutated AID did not change the frequency or overall pattern of Ig variable region gene mutations in GC B cells, a certain narrow range of AID expression is probably required for the in vivo positive selection of high-affinity B cells, and this optimal level is apparently titrated by miR-155 and possibly other miRNAs.

POST-TRANSLATIONAL MODIFICATIONS

The cellular response to changing environmental conditions is mediated frequently by the reversible covalent modifications of preexisting molecules, a process termed post-translational modification. One mechanism by which post-translational modifications can alter a protein's function is by directly inducing a new conformational state. A classic example is the phosphorylation of the activation loop of protein kinases (**Figure 1*a***). Protein kinases have a common "on" state, in which they are phosphorylated on one or two serine, threonine, or tyrosine residues of a key segment known as the activation loop. Activation-loop phosphorylation stabilizes the assembly of an enzymatic site that catalyzes the Mg^{2+}-dependent transfer of the γ-phosphoryl group of the ATP to the substrate protein (17). Such conventional allosteric regulation alone, however, cannot adequately explain why distinct signaling complexes are formed and how the activation status of these complexes is spatiotemporally regulated. Therefore, the notion that post-translational modifications create binding sites for specific protein-interaction domains, which in turn contribute to the formation of signaling complexes, has strong appeal. A single modification cannot guarantee specificity; therefore, a combination of various post-translational modifications (including phosphorylation, methylation, acetylation, ubiquitylation, and sumoylation) is thought to be required for the selective assembly of proteins into signaling complexes and for their subsequent activation and cellular location (**Figure 1**). In the following section, we discuss the common mechanisms by which post-translational modifications regulate protein-protein interactions and subsequent signaling processes.

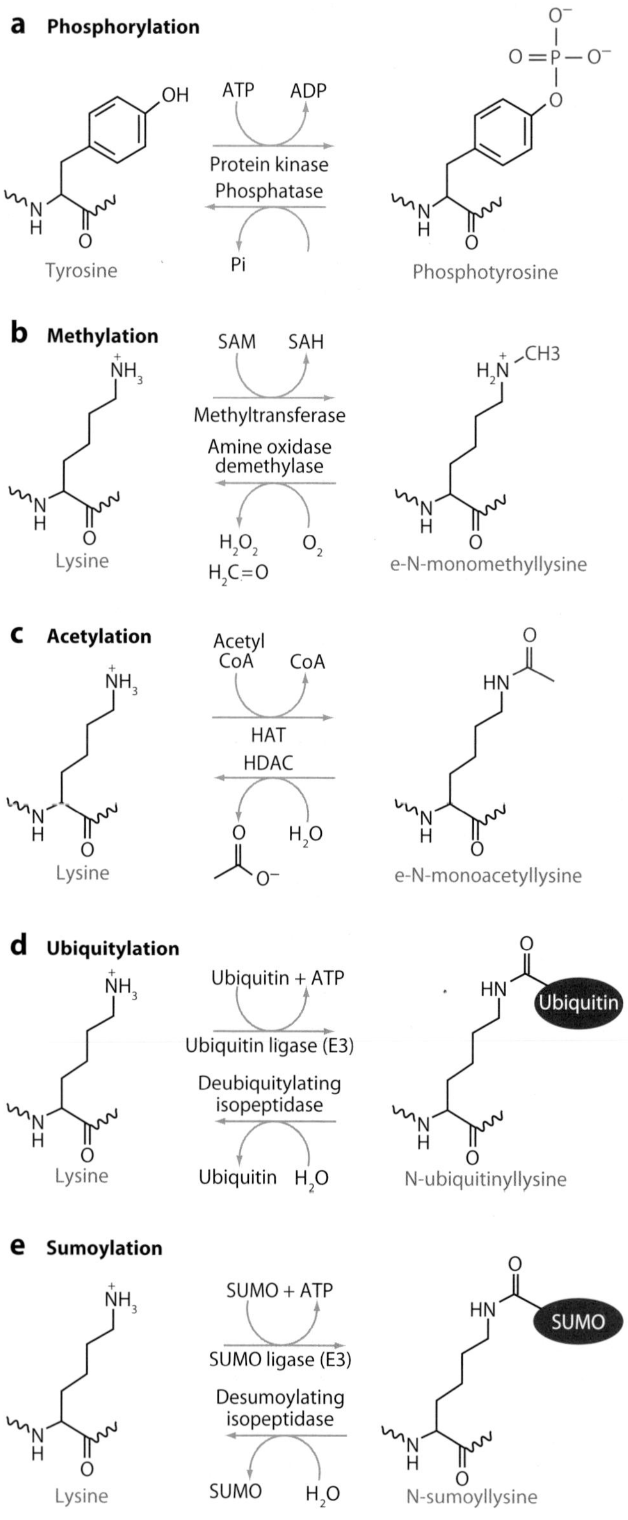

Protein Phosphorylation

Protein tyrosine kinases (PTKs) can activate intracellular pathways through the inducible recruitment of proteins with SH2 domains. SH2 domains typically bind to pTyr-containing peptide motifs of five to eight residues in a manner that depends on ligand phosphorylation and the identity of the flanking amino acids (5). The biological importance of this type of association is typically exemplified by the interaction between the two SH2 domains of Syk and the doubly phosphorylated (dp) immunoreceptor tyrosine-based activation motifs (ITAMs) of Igα/Igβ (18). With the assumption that Syk has a structural organization similar to the T cell PTK, Zap-70, recent crystallographic analysis has provided significant insight

Figure 1

Examples of post-translational modification reactions. Various amino acid side chains can be modified by, for instance, (*a*) phosphorylation, (*b*) methylation, (*c*) acetylation, (*d*) ubiquitylation, and (*e*) sumoylation. The enzymes that are involved in the addition and removal of these post-translational modifications are shown on the reaction arrows. Adapted by permission from Macmillan Publishers Ltd., *Nature Reviews Molecular Cell Biology*, 7:474, **Figure 1**, copyright 2006.

into how Syk maintains the autoinhibited state and how this state is broken down by the binding of dp-ITAMs to the tandem SH2 domains of Syk (19). Two tyrosine residues (Tyr342 and Tyr346) in the SH2-kinase linker region of Syk are involved in aromatic-aromatic interactions that connect this linker to the kinase domain, thereby helping to keep the Syk kinase in the inactive state. Binding of the SH2 domains of Syk to dp-ITAMs disrupts the aromatic-aromatic interactions, removing this inhibitory constraint and subsequently activating Syk kinase activity by facilitating phosphorylation on Tyr519 in the activation loop (20). Another means to disrupt the suppressive aromatic-aromatic interactions is mediated by phosphorylation on Tyr342 and Tyr346. In fact, Tyr342 and Tyr346 are phosphorylated following BCR stimulation, and this phosphorylation plays a positive role for BCR signaling (18). Assuming that this post-translational modification is maintained even after disengagement of the dp-ITAMs and Syk, it could keep Syk activated persistently. Therefore, the phosphorylation status of Tyr342/Tyr346 could potentially impact how strongly Syk activity is maintained and for how long during and after BCR signaling. These structural and functional studies clearly demonstrate that the dp-ITAMs overcome the inherent promiscuity of Syk SH2 domains, making the recruitment of Syk to the BCR complex highly specific. In addition, this binding releases Syk from its autoinhibited state, thereby facilitating the activation of its kinase domain and probably restricting the location of the activated form of Syk to the vicinity of the BCR.

Ser/Thr phosphorylation is more prevalent than Tyr phosphorylation, and there is a correspondingly larger array of domains that selectively bind to pSer/pThr sites. Many of these associations can be discerned for pSer/pThr-binding proteins, such as the ubiquitously expressed 14-3-3 proteins (21). These proteins form noncovalent homo- and heterodimers, which can consequently bind to two pSer/pThr-containing peptides that have an appropriate consensus sequence. As a result, 14-3-3 proteins can regulate the conformation and catalytic activity of the associated phosphorylated enzymes and can control their interactions and localizations.

Protein Methylation and Acetylation

Peptide motifs that contain Lys residues can be methylated or acetylated (**Figure 1*b*,*c***), which can lead to their recognition by chromodomains (CDs) or bromodomains, respectively (5). These modifications are not restricted to nuclear proteins such as histones; for instance, a recent study showed that the type I interferon receptor on the cell surface undergoes acetylation mediated by the coactivator p300/CBP (CREB-binding protein), which possesses histone acetyltransferase activity, and that this post-translational modification is crucial for subsequent antiviral gene expression (22). Nevertheless, acetylation and methylation are particularly prominent features of the flexible N- and C-terminal tails of histones and are important for coupling histones to changes in chromatin organization and the epigenetic control of gene expression. The methylation of histone 3 at Lys9 (H3K9) serves as the prototype for the regulation of histone function. Di- or trimethylation of H3K9 creates a binding site for CD-containing proteins of the heterochromatin protein 1 family, and this binding is speculated to lead to gene repression via changes in higher-order chromatin structure (23).

Indeed, histone methylation/acetylation may control *Ig* gene locus accessibility to $V_H(D)J_H$ recombination. In early developing bone marrow B cells, D to J_H rearrangement precedes V_H to DJ_H joining. Prior to D to J_H recombination, histone H3 acetylation is abundant within a 120-Kb region that encompasses the D gene segments and extends to the $C\mu$ exons. Then the hyperacetylated domain spreads into the distal V_H gene region in an interleukin (IL)-7-dependent manner accompanied by V_H to DJ_H recombination (24, 25). However, acetylation alone appears to be insufficient to allow recombination factors access to the DNA template. H3K9 methylation correlates inversely with the efficiency of $V_H(D)J_H$ recombination (24). Recombinase access requires the removal of this repressive methylation mark, a process regulated by the transcription factor Pax5 (26). The repressive role of methyl H3K9 in $V_H(D)J_H$ recombination has been supported further by the observation that *TCRβ* mini-locus recombination is inhibited when the DNA substrate is tethered to the histone H3K9 methyltransferase G9a (27).

DUB: deubiquitylating enzyme

Protein Ubiquitylation and Sumoylation

Many proteins are modified by ubiquitin (Ub) or the Ub-like protein SUMO (**Figure 1*d*,*e***). Ubiquitylation occurs through a three-step process involving Ub-activating (E1), Ub-conjugating (E2), and Ub-ligating (E3) enzymes (28, 29). The pathway of sumoylation is mechanically analogous to ubiquitylation; however, SUMO conjugation requires a set of enzymes that is distinct from that acting on Ub (30). Ub is a 76-residue protein that is most often linked to the Lys side chains on target proteins. The types of Ub modifications are diverse. In the simplest form, a single Ub molecule is attached, which is defined as monoubiquitylation. Because Ub itself contains several Lys residues, Ub molecules can form different types of chains on the target proteins in an iterative process called polyubiquitylation. All seven Lys residues in Ub can potentially be involved in chain formation in vivo, but Ub chains linked via Lys48 or Lys63 are the best characterized. Lys48-linked poly-Ub chains clearly represent a signal for the degradation of the modified substrate by the proteasome. However, other types of Ub conjugates (e.g., those that are Lys63-linked) are involved in the regulation of different processes, such as the facilitation of signaling and intracellular trafficking by the formation of macromolecular complexes. Ub is essentially a transferable interaction domain, which, following its attachment to target proteins, is recognized by proteins that contain specialized interaction modules (Ub-binding domains). So far, at least 11 families of Ub-binding domains have been identified (31). They are structurally different but generally bind with relatively low affinity to the same hydrophobic patch on Ub, centered on Ile44. Many Ub-binding proteins possess several Ub-binding domains and can therefore be coupled to distinct Ub signals simultaneously. This feature seems ideally suited for the rapid assembly and disassembly of multiple proteins through Ub-based protein-interaction networks.

Ubiquitylation is now known to be a reversible reaction in which the Ub chains are deconjugated by deubiquitylating enzymes (DUBs) (32). Similar to the E3 Ub ligases, DUBs have a certain degree of substrate specificity, which appears to be created in at least three ways. First, DUBs often contain protein-interaction domains, which enable them to bind specific target proteins. Second, some DUBs have a preference for specific Ub branches, such as Lys48- or Lys63-linked chains. Third, the mode of expression and the subcellular localization of DUBs could contribute to their in vivo functions, although this aspect has not been studied extensively.

This paradigm apparently also holds for sumoylation. For example, SUMO-binding proteins contain a SUMO-interacting motif, which forms a β strand that binds in a parallel or antiparallel orientation to the β2 strand of SUMO (33, 34). A sumoylated Lys residue therefore recruits a different set of effectors than if the same residue was ubiquitylated. For instance, the sumoylation of proliferating cell nuclear antigen (PCNA), a polymerase processivity factor that forms a sliding clamp around DNA, at Lys164 promotes high-fidelity replication by recruiting a helicase (Srs2) that contains a SUMO-interacting motif to replication forks, thereby preventing inappropriate recombinational repair. By contrast, in the case of DNA repair, DNA damage promotes the monoubiquitylation of PCNA at the same Lys residue (Lys164), recruiting preferentially damage-tolerant polymerase η and mediating post-replicative lesion bypasses (35, 36).

B CELL RECEPTOR SIGNALING PATHWAYS

The earliest biochemical events of the BCR signal have been well characterized. However, these previous analyses have two main weaknesses. First, because they required a relatively large number of B cells, experiments usually have been conducted using antigen stimulation. As discussed below in more detail, in addition to ligand-induced signaling, ligand-independent signaling also plays a critical role. For instance, the cell surface expression of the pre-BCR, per se, has been thought to be sufficient for inducing biological outcomes. Because of the difficulty of analyzing such cell surface expression-dependent signaling, our understanding of the biochemical nature of ligand-independent signaling has been limited, and models for this type of signaling are often speculative extrapolations from studies of ligand-induced events. Second, because biochemical analyses rely on the examination of populations of cells, these studies cannot provide quantitative data at the single-cell level or on the dynamic localization of membrane receptors and signaling molecules. Thus, to overcome this second limitation, investigators have employed a new technology using supported planar lipid bilayers, which are thought to mimic the recognition of membrane-tethered antigens on the surface of an antigen-presenting cell. This approach is combined with advanced imaging techniques such as total internal reflection fluorescence and Förster resonance energy transfer (FRET), providing insight into novel aspects of the spatio-temporal dynamics of receptor signaling. Therefore, the following section discusses new ideas generated by such imaging studies and the progress made in understanding signaling events through biochemical and genetic studies.

Early B Cell Receptor Signaling Events

The ligand-binding subunit of the BCR complex consists of the transmembrane form of Ig, composed of two identical heavy chains (IgH) and two identical light chains (IgL) in covalent association. BCR signal transduction capability is provided by a noncovalently associated heterodimer of Igα/Igβ. BCR oligomerization induced by multivalent antigen binding was thought to be sufficient to initiate the signaling event (18, 37). The question then arose about what structural changes, particularly in the cytoplasmic domains of Igα and Igβ, take place after BCR oligomerization. Pierce and colleagues (38) addressed this question by monitoring FRET between individual BCR subunits. After binding of multivalent antigen, the cytoplasmic domains of the BCR components also cluster. Then the Igα and Igβ cytoplasmic domains are separated by a considerable distance, transitioning from a closed to an open conformation. The open conformation is dependent on ITAM phosphorylation, most likely by the action of Lyn, one of the Src family PTKs. Supporting Lyn's involvement in the transition to this open conformation, the BCR selectively and transiently associates with Lyn after antigen engagement, followed by induction of the open conformation (39). Thus, imaging analysis using the FRET methodology supports the model previously proposed based on biochemical and genetic analyses; namely, the phosphorylation of ITAMs located in the cytoplasmic domains of Igα and Igβ, mediated by Lyn, leads to an open conformation, thereby recruiting other signaling molecules, including Syk.

IgH: immunoglobulin heavy chain

Although B cells do respond to soluble antigen in vitro, some proportion of the antigens encountered in vivo are in a membrane-associated form. For instance, in the interaction between follicular dendritic cells (FDCs) and B cells, FDCs hold large amounts of intact antigens on their surfaces by virtue of antigen binding to the FDC Fc and complement receptors. In this physiologically relevant context, B cells will recognize cognate antigens in a cell-cell contact-dependent manner. Batista and colleagues (40) have analyzed the molecular events that follow this type of recognition by using TIRF microscopy and

IP_3: inositol-1,4,5-trisphosphate

SOCE: store-operated Ca^{2+} entry

planar lipid bilayers containing ICAM-1 and antigens.

During the early stages of membrane-bound antigen recognition, B cells spread out over the antigen-bearing membranes and then contract, collecting bound antigen in a central aggregate. This response is concomitant with the formation of the immunological synapse, which is similar to that originally described for T cells (41, 42). This structure is characterized by the central accumulation of BCR and antigen, termed the central supramolecular activation cluster (c-SMAC), surrounded by a ring of adhesion molecules (peripheral SMAC, or p-SMAC). Intracellular signaling molecules such as Syk, phospholipase Cγ2 (PLCγ2), and Vav1 are colocalized with the initial BCR-containing microclusters (43). After maximal spreading (approximately 3 min), these BCR clusters started to translocate to form c-SMACs. However, unlike the BCR, clusters including Syk (referred to here as microsignalosomes) did not move to the c-SMACs and appeared to dissociate from the BCR clusters. Similarly, after the recognition of membrane-bound antigens, CD19 was transiently recruited into the BCR clusters. This recruitment is functionally important for amplifying BCR signaling because CD19-deficient B cells exhibited a decrease in early signaling events, including calcium mobilization and tyrosine phosphorylation (44). These observations suggest that the microsignalosomes (probably including CD19, Syk, PLCγ2, PI3K, and Vav) are a critical site for the initiation of BCR signaling. At a later time point (15 min after stimulation), the microsignalosomes dissociate from the BCR clusters that reside in the c-SMACs, suggesting that the Igα/Igβ signaling components of the BCR inside the c-SMACs might be dephosphorylated. Given the evidence that the nonphosphorylated form of the Igα is preferentially endocytosed (45), the non-tyrosine-phosphorylated BCR in the c-SMACs may no longer be involved in signaling, but instead would be internalized for subsequent antigen presentation on the B cell surface.

Effector Systems

During BCR signaling, PLCγ2 and PI3K are crucial lipid metabolizing effector enzymes that generate key second messengers, which in turn activate IκB kinase (IKK) and extracellular signal-related kinase (ERK). In the following section, we discuss how the activation status of these important enzymes is regulated and how these activities are translated into biological outcomes.

PLCγ2/calcium/NFAT pathway. Activation of PLCγ2 by Syk, Btk, and BLNK results in production of the second messenger, inositol-1,4,5-trisphosphate (IP_3), and diacylglycerol (DAG) (see Reference 46 for a detailed discussion of PLCγ2 activation mechanisms). BCR stimulation induces a dramatic increase in the intracellular Ca^{2+} concentration, which is derived from two main sources: Ca^{2+} release from the intracellular Ca^{2+} stores, mainly from the endoplasmic reticulum (ER), and Ca^{2+} entry from the extracellular space. The binding of IP_3, a product of PLCγ2 activity, to IP_3 receptors in the membrane of the ER results in a rapid and transient release of Ca^{2+} from the ER Ca^{2+} stores into the cytosol (47). The subsequent reduction of Ca^{2+} within the ER lumen triggers a sustained influx of extracellular Ca^{2+} across the plasma membrane. More than 20 years ago, Putney (48) proposed the so-called store-operated Ca^{2+} entry (SOCE) model, which postulated that the Ca^{2+} influx across the plasma membrane results from emptying of the ER Ca^{2+} stores (49). The recent identification of two molecular players, STIM1 (49, 50) and Orai1 (51, 52), and analysis of their knockout cells have identified the SOCE mechanism as the predominant effector in immune cells, including B cells (**Figure 2**).

STIM1, a type I ER membrane protein, was originally identified as a molecule on stromal cells that support bone marrow B cell differentiation (53). STIM1 has turned out to be the ER Ca^{2+} sensor and SOCE activator, but not a channel by itself, as demonstrated by

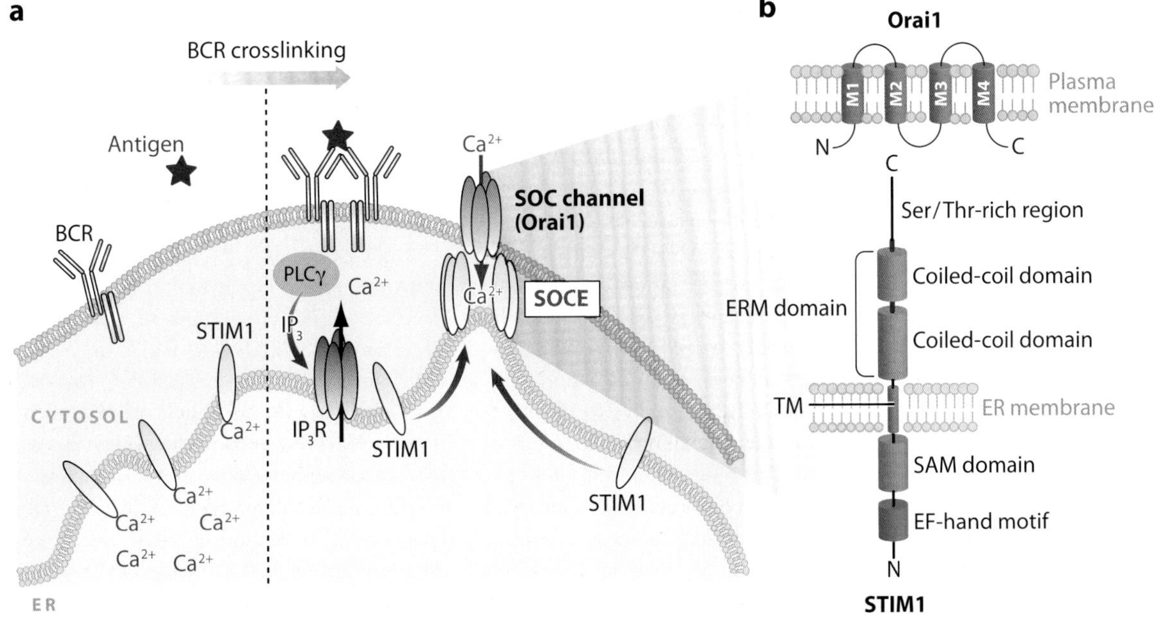

Figure 2

Functional coupling between STIM1 and Orai1 in BCR-mediated store-operated Ca^{2+} entry (SOCE) activation. (*a*) BCR stimulation causes PLCγ/IP_3/ IP_3R-mediated Ca^{2+} release and store depletion followed by the relocation of STIM1 into puncta. The decrease in luminal ER Ca^{2+} results in the dissociation of Ca^{2+} from the EF-hand motif, which induces STIM1 aggregation and redistribution in the ER in close proximity with the plasma membrane. Here STIM1 functionally associates with the Orai1 channel in the plasma membrane, leading to SOCE. (*b*) A schematic representation of the functional domain of STIM1 and Orai1 proteins. The STIM1 protein contains an EF-hand motif (Ca^{2+}-binding site), a sterile α motif (SAM) domain, a transmembrane (TM) domain, coiled-coil domains, an ERM domain, and a Ser/Thr-rich region. The Orai1 protein contains four TM domains (M1–M4).

knockdown experiments in fibroblasts, T cells (49), and endothelial cells (50) and by knockout studies in mast cells (54), T cells (55), and platelets (56). STIM1 also functions in SOCE activation in B cells, as shown by analysis of gene-targeted DT40 B cells (57) and primary B cells (Y. Baba & T. Kurosaki, unpublished results). STIM1 contains several conserved domains, including the EF-hand motif, sterile α motif (SAM), and coiled-coil domains. In resting B cells, STIM1 looks to move dynamically in a tubulovesicular way on the ER, along with microtubules (57). This behavior is mediated through the coiled-coil domain and Ser/Thr-rich C-terminal region, which are located in the cytosolic side. After BCR-induced store depletion, Ca^{2+} dissociates from the EF-hand motif located in the ER lumen, which may result in a conformational change in STIM1 to form a homomultimer. STIM1 is then rapidly redistributed into discrete puncta that are located underneath the plasma membrane and associate with store-operated Ca^{2+} channel components both physically and functionally (57–59). The SAM, coiled-coil domains, and Ser/Thr-rich domains are essential for the store-depletion-induced cluster formation of STIM1 and subsequent SOCE activation (57).

STIM2, a related homolog of STIM1, is also located in the ER membrane, but its precise role remains unclear. Consistent with a slight reduction of SOCE in STIM2 knockdown fibroblasts (49), SOCE is also moderately inhibited in *STIM2*-deficient DT40 B cells (Y. Baba & T. Kurosaki, unpublished results). Although possessing similar conserved domains, functional differences between STIM1 and STIM2 have been proposed. Unlike STIM1, STIM2 plays a more dominant role in regulating basal cytosolic and ER Ca^{2+} concentrations; STIM2 can induce SOCE following a smaller reduction in ER Ca^{2+} content than STIM1 (60). Thus, STIM2 appears to be more sensitive to Ca^{2+} store depletion than does STIM1.

The molecular identification of the store-operated Ca^{2+} channel has been advanced by an analysis of T cells derived from severe combined immunodeficiency syndrome patients deficient in SOCE. A linkage analysis and RNAi-based screening identified *Orai1* (also known as *CRACM1*) as the gene mutated in these patients (51, 52). The coexpression of Orai1 and STIM1 apparently results in synergic effects on SOCE (61, 62). A direct physical association between STIM1 and Orai1 has been proposed but is still controversial; however, these two molecules clearly colocalize after Ca^{2+} store depletion. Thus Orai1 is currently the best candidate for the store-operated Ca^{2+} channel or a subcomponent of this channel, which is a target of STIM1. The Orai family consists of Orai1, Orai2, and Orai3 (58, 59). In chicken DT40 B cells, Orai1 and Orai2 have a redundant role for STIM1-mediated SOCE (Y. Baba & T. Kurosaki, unpublished results). One study of Orai1-deficient mice demonstrated that SOCE was abolished in mast cells but not in T cells (63), whereas another report showed that Orai1-deficient T cells have severe defects in SOCE, similar to the human severe combined immunodeficiency case mentioned above (64). Recent reports suggest that the store operated Ca^{2+} channels are composed of the Orai family and the C-type transient receptor potential family, and that STIM1 is not a component of the channels but is essential for their activation (65, 66).

In most cells (including B cells), calmodulin is a cytosolic Ca^{2+}-binding protein that functions as a calcium sensor by binding Ca^{2+} with its two EF hands. Calmodulin bound with Ca^{2+} activates several molecules, and one important target is calcineurin phosphatase, which is a heterodimer composed of a catalytic subunit (Aα, Aβ, and Aγ) and a regulatory subunit (B1 and B2). Nuclear factor of activated T cells (NFAT) is a well-studied calcium-dependent transcription factor downstream of calcineurin (67). NFAT is a cytosolic protein and requires a continuous increase in Ca^{2+} to remain in the nucleus, wherein it activates transcription of target genes. B cells express three NFAT family members, NFATc1 (alternatively named NFAT2 or NFATc), NFATc2 (NFAT1 or NFATp), and NFATc3 (NFAT4 or NFATx) (68), which are components of the BCR signaling cascade. Although mice deficient in each NFAT member have been reported (69–71), these reports have not addressed the B cell–intrinsic phenotype caused by NFAT inactivation. As demonstrated by the B cell–specific ablation of the regulatory B1 subunit of calcineurin (CnB1) (72), this phosphatase is not essential for the development of mature B2 B cells, although it is required for B1 B cell development. However, B cell–specific CnB1-deficient mice have reduced PC differentiation, which in turn leads to decreased antigen-specific antibody responses to TD antigens. Because interferon regulatory factor 4 (IRF4), a critical transcription factor for the differentiation of B cells into PCs (73, 74), cannot be induced properly after in vivo as well as in vitro antigen stimulation in these knockout B cells, IRF4 induction is regulated by the calcineurin-NFAT pathway, possibly explaining the phenotype of B cell–specific CnB1-deficient mice. Indeed, the IRF4 promoter has several NFAT consensus binding sites.

PI3K pathway. CD19 is a B cell–specific cell surface molecule expressed from the pro-B cell stage to the plasmablast stage (75). On BCR ligation, the cytoplasmic tail of CD19 can be phosphorylated on multiple tyrosines by Lyn, providing binding sites for the SH2 domains of the p85 subunit of PI3K, Vav, and Lyn (76–78). As discussed above, the importance of CD19, particularly after the recognition of membrane-bound antigens, can be accounted for by its association with Lyn and its role in further amplifying Lyn activity in the context of BCR signaling. Indeed, the SH2-dependent association of Lyn with tyrosine-phosphorylated CD19 was reported to release the autoinhibition of Lyn, thereby enhancing its enzymatic activity (77).

Although CD19's involvement in the BCR-induced activation of PI3K is clear, this mechanism does not fully account for the activation of PI3K. Investigators have reported that the cytoplasmic adaptor molecule BCAP (B cell adaptor for PI3K), which possesses binding sites for the SH2 domains of the p85 subunit (YxxM motifs), is tyrosine phosphorylated and is required to target PI3K to the plasma membrane in DT40 B cells (79, 80). Recently, $CD19^{-/-}BCAP^{-/-}$ primary immature B cells were found to have almost complete abrogation of BCR-mediated PI3K activation, supporting overlapping functions for BCAP and CD19 in this activation (81). Furthermore, the YxxM motifs in BCAP and CD19 are critical for the development of immature B cells, as well as for PI3K activation (81).

Three developmental defects in $CD19^{-/-}$ mice are prominent: the loss of peritoneal B1 lineage cells, spleen marginal zone (MZ) B cells, and spleen $CD1d^{hi}CD5^{+}$ B cells. Although investigators have not addressed directly the requirement of PI3K activation in the development of $CD1d^{hi}CD5^{+}$ cells, the development of B1 and MZ B cells clearly requires PI3K activation (82, 83). P13K p110δ, the predominant isoform activated downstream of the BCR, is also required for B1 and MZ B cell development (84). Moreover, the defective development of MZ B cells in $CD19^{-/-}$ mice is restored in $CD19^{-/-}PTEN^{-/-}$ mice (85). PTEN and SHIP hydrolyze PIP_3 (a product of PI3K action) to $PI(4,5)P_2$ and $PI(3,4)P_2$, respectively. The $CD1d^{hi}CD5^{+}$ B cells appear to be the B cell subset that is responsible for evoking IL-10 production, which in turn can alleviate autoimmune diseases in experimental autoimmune encephalomyelitis, collagen-induced arthritis, and inflammatory bowel disease (86). Thus, in addition to a positive role in inducing humoral TD immune responses, CD19 exerts a negative role, namely suppressing TD inflammatory responses by participating in the development of the $CD1d^{hi}CD5^{+}$ subset.

PTEN is thought to be constitutively active, although various mechanisms have been reported to regulate its activity. In contrast, SHIP is activated specifically by the coligation of FcγRII and the BCR and, to a lesser extent, by BCR ligation alone. Analysis of B cell–specific *PTEN*-deficient mice has revealed that optimal PI3K activity is required for two aspects of B cell biology during TD immune responses (87). First, hyper-PI3K activation inhibits class switch recombination. Second, this activation also enhances antibody-secreting cell (ASC) formation. Therefore, mice lacking B cell–specific *PTEN* generated large numbers of IgM-ASCs but failed to produce IgG1 ASCs in TD immune responses.

IKK/NF-κB pathway. Recent elucidation of the connecting mechanism between BCR and IKK has inspired the notion that covalent modifications (phosphorylation and ubiquitylation) take place coordinately and affect the localization and activation status of signaling molecules, thereby changing their transcriptional activities (**Figure 3**). As many excellent reviews describe the role of NF-κB transcription factor components (p105, p100, RelA, RelB, and c-Rel) (88–90), we focus here on how IKK activity is fine-tuned in the context of BCR signaling.

NF-κB transcription factors are retained in the cytoplasm by binding to the inhibitor IκB. Stimulation of antigen receptors, including the BCR, activates the IKK complex consisting of IKKα, IKKβ, and IKKγ (alternatively named NEMO), thereby phosphorylating IκB and subsequently inducing its degradation (91). In B cells, protein kinase Cβ (PKCβ) is activated by DAG and Ca^{2+}, both of which are generated by PLCγ2 activation. Ablation of PKCβ leads to the defective activation of the canonical NF-κB pathway, which in turn results in defects in B cell activation and maturation (92). In the signaling pathway between PKCβ and IKK activation, the formation of

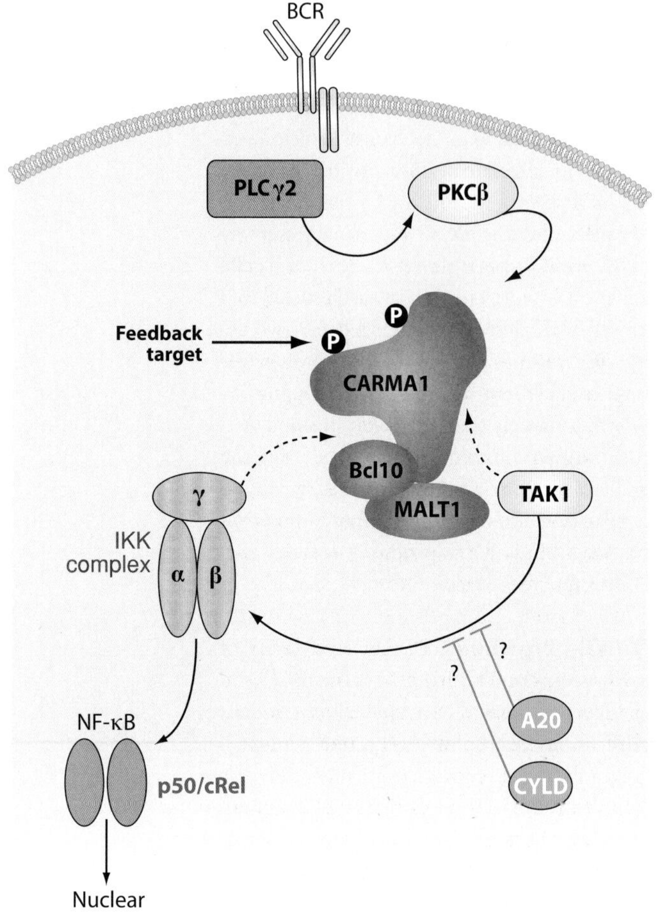

Figure 3

A model for BCR-mediated IKK activation. Stimulation of BCR leads to the activation of phospholipase Cγ2 (PLCγ2) through the proximal protein tyrosine kinases and the subsequent activation of protein kinase Cβ (PKCβ). Activated PKCβ phosphorylates CARMA1 (S668), directly or indirectly, which results in recruitment of TAK1 to the phosphorylated CARMA1. Meanwhile, the IKK complex is recruited, probably through the Bcl10/MALT1 complex, to the phosphorylated CARMA1. These interactions (CARMA1-IKK and CARMA1-TAK1) allow access of two key protein kinases, TAK1 and IKK, leading to the activation of the IKK complex. IKKβ also facilitates the formation of the CARMA1/Bcl10/MALT1 complex by phosphorylating S578 of CARMA1 (feedback target), thereby optimizing the strength and duration of the NF-κB signal. The CYLD and A20 deubiquitinases negatively regulate the signals that lead to IKK and NF-κB activation, but their exact targets are unknown.

a macromolecular NF-κB signaling complex is required. This complex is composed of adaptor molecules: CARMA1, Bcl10, and MALT1 (93). Both *MALT1* and *Bcl10* are targets of chromosomal rearrangements associated with the formation of MALT lymphomas, and oncogenic *CARMA1* mutations have been found recently in human diffuse large B cell lymphoma (83, 94–100). The fine-tuned regulation of the NF-κB signaling pathway imposed by CARMA1/Bcl10/MALT1 is crucial to maintain normal B cell proliferation/survival and differentiation.

PKCβ phosphorylates CARMA1 on Ser668, which is essential for subsequent CARMA1/Bcl10/MALT1 association, as well as IKK activation (101, 102). In addition to this critical phosphorylation site on CARMA1, Ser/Thr phosphorylation of CARMA1/Bcl10 on other sites may contribute to the formation of a positive and negative feedback regulation of IKK activation (102–104), thereby fine-tuning the NF-κB pathway. As a positive feedback, the activated IKKβ phosphorylates CARMA1 on Ser578, which in turn facilitates or stabilizes its association with Bcl10/MALT1, thereby enhancing IKK activation. As a negative feedback, the activated IKKβ also phosphorylates Bcl10, thereby inducing its degradation and the disengagement of Bcl10 and MALT1. Thus, the timing of these IKKβ-mediated phosphorylation events and the lag time between phosphorylation and degradation are key determinants in fine-tuning NF-κB activity.

MALT1 is a caspase-like protein related to the so-called paracaspases found in metazoans and *Dictyostelium* (98). The importance of its proteolytic function has been appreciated in T cells. Rebeaud et al. (105) demonstrated that the proteolytic activity of MALT1 is required for optimal TCR-mediated NF-κB activation. Recently, the importance of the MALT1 proteolytic activity toward its substrate, A20, has been suggested (106). A20 inhibits NF-κB signaling by deubiquitinating its substrates (K63-linked chains) on target molecules including TNF receptor–associated factor (TRAF)2, TRAF6, RIP1, and IKKγ (32, 107). This K63-linked ubiquitination has been thought to play a positive role in canonical NF-κB activation. By cleaving and inactivating A20, MALT1 contributes to IKK activation. A similar mechanism is likely utilized by B cells, making clarifying how and when paracaspase activity is regulated during BCR activation important.

The dynamic balance between K63-linked ubiquitylation and deubiquitylation thus plays a crucial role in BCR-mediated IKK activation. The CARMA1/Bcl10/MALT1 complex is also associated with the ubiquitylating enzymes UBC13 (Ub-conjugating enzyme 13), UEV1A (Ub-conjugating enzyme E2 variant 1A), and TRAF6 (Ub E3 ligase), possibly triggering the recruitment of IKK and TAK1 and inducing K63-linked ubiquitylation of IKKγ and TAK1 (108–111). Counteracting this ubiquitylation is a DUB, cylindromatosis (turban tumor syndrome) (CYLD), which plays an important role in regulating NF-κB activity (112–116). Indeed, CYLD deficiency in B cells results in the constitutive activation of the canonical NF-κB pathway, leading to an enlarged B cell compartment (117, 118). The B cell targets of CYLD are unknown, but based on T cell data, it seems reasonable to propose that the K63 ubiquitylation of IKKγ and TAK1, both of which are critical for IKK activation in the BCR signaling context, is a likely candidate.

Because the Ser residues in the activation loop of IKKα and IKKβ are not in the context of a PKCβ consensus phosphorylation site, it has been thought that PKCβ mediates phosphorylation of IKK indirectly through an intermediate kinase, which then directly phosphorylates the Ser residues on IKKα/IKKβ. TAK1, a member of the MAP3K family, corresponds to this IKK kinase (111). Indeed, *TAK1*-deficiency in DT40 B cells resulted in the complete abrogation of BCR-mediated IKK activation (101). Moreover, immunoprecipitated TAK1 can phosphorylate activation-loop Ser residues of IKKβ in vitro. Studies with *TAK1* conditional knockout mice using CD19Cre to delete the gene in B cells have shown that TAK1 is dispensable for NF-κB activation induced by BCR engagement (119). However, these conflicting results between primary and transformed B cells may be due to incomplete deletion of *TAK1* in the conditional knockout mice. Indeed, in another study using a different B cell–specific Cre (mb1-Cre), BCR-mediated IKK activation was markedly reduced (H. Shinohara & T. Kurosaki, unpublished results).

ERK pathway. Similar to other cell types, B cells activate Ras following BCR stimulation. The introduction of a dominant-negative Ras inhibits BCR-mediated ERK activation in DT40 B cells, as well as in primary B cells, demonstrating that Ras functions as an upstream regulator for subsequent ERK activation (4, 120). Investigators have assumed for some time that Sos, a nucleotide exchange factor for Ras, participates in BCR-mediated Ras activation (18). However, data emerging from several laboratories indicate that RasGRP3, another Ras exchange factor, plays a more important role than Sos in coupling the BCR to Ras activation (121–123). Ras activation occurred normally even in *Sos1/Sos2* double-deficient DT40 B cells, whereas this activation was inhibited, although not completely, in *RasGRP3*-deficient DT40 B cells. The necessity of RasGRP3 in Ras activation appears to explain the previous findings that PLCγ2 was required for BCR-mediated Ras activation (124). Because the C1 domain of RasGRP3 binds to DAG (a product of PLCγ2 action), PLCγ2 may participate in the recruitment of RasGRP3 in a DAG-C1-dependent manner. Indeed, RasGRP3 with a C1 domain deletion does not move to the plasma membrane and thus fails to activate Ras in BCR signaling. Moreover, wild-type RasGRP3 cannot move to the plasma membrane in *PLCγ2*-deficient DT40 B cells (121). In addition to RasGRP3's recruitment to the membrane, the phosphorylation of Thr133 on RasGRP3 is also important for its full activation (125, 126). This is mediated by activated PKCβ, thereby leading to the increased enzymatic activity of RasGRP3. Thus, a new model has been proposed in which DAG generated by PLCγ2 facilitates the recruitment of both PKCβ and RasGRP3 to the plasma membrane, where PKCβ phosphorylates Thr133 on RasGRP3, which is crucial for RasGRP3's full activation. Once activated, this GTP-bound Ras binds directly to Raf-1, the MAP3K in the ERK pathway. Activated Raf-1 and B-Raf phosphorylate and activate MEK1/MEK2, which both in turn phosphorylate ERK1/ERK2. Phosphorylated ERKs form dimers, a step required for nuclear translocation and the subsequent phosphorylation of transcriptional regulatory proteins, including Fos, Jun, and Ets family members (127).

Antigen Presentation

In addition to the above-mentioned signaling events, the recognition of antigen by BCR induces the rapid internalization of engaged receptors, which is required for the effective presentation of antigen-derived peptides to major histocompatibility complex (MHC) class II–restricted T cells (128–130). The signaling and internalization processes are interconnected. For instance, assuming that signaling takes place predominantly on the plasma membrane, internalization would eventually negatively regulate signaling because crosslinked BCRs are ultimately degraded following their uptake. For example, BCR signaling was augmented and prolonged in mice that carry Igβ_{AA}, a mutant form of Igβ lacking phosphorylation and internalization motifs (37). Conversely, endocystosis might also play a positive role in receptor-mediated cellular activation. Indeed, some receptors such as the epidermal growth factor receptor continue to signal in endosomes (131), amplifying their impact after internalization and before degradation. Signaling cross talk also should be considered. The innate immune receptors, Toll-like receptor (TLR)7 and TLR9, are predominantly expressed in endosomes but not on the plasma membrane. In this setting, B cells can recognize DNA- or RNA-containing antigens through their cell surface BCRs, which in turn deliver the DNA/RNA ligands to TLR9/7-containing compartments (132, 133). In this scenario, the BCR functions as a transfer vehicle for inducing TLR9/7 signaling. Thus, BCR internalization can affect several distinct signaling outcomes.

With regard to antigen presentation, successful antigen processing in B lymphocytes relies on the following directional membrane trafficking events: (*a*) antigen internalization through BCR and targeting into multivesicular late endosomes (alternatively named MHC class II–containing endosomes), presumably through early endosomes; (*b*) MHC class II complexes, proteases, and H2-DM convergence toward this incoming pool of antigen-BCR complexes; and (*c*) the export of MHC class II–peptide complexes to the cell surface (**Figure 4**) (129). The initial internalization of antigen-bound BCRs requires clathrin, but not Igβ ubiquitylation (134), but further trafficking to late endosomes requires Igβ ubiquitinylation, which appears to be mediated by the E3 ligase Itch (135).

In addition to antigen capture, the generated BCR signal has been thought to be necessary to bring resting B cells into an activated state for efficient antigen presentation. The requirement of Syk in antigen presentation may be due to its participation in the enhancement of the above-mentioned directional membrane trafficking events through the reorganization of the actin cytoskeleton (136). In the transition of immature dendritic cells (DCs) to their mature professional state, two mechanisms have been well recognized. First, upon maturation, intracellular cystatin C, an inhibitor of cathepsin S, is decreased, thereby enhancing cathepsin S proteolytic activity, which in turn facilitates the degradation of the invariant chain and subsequent peptide loading into class II molecules. Second, before maturation, MHC class II accumulates in lysosomes, where it is constitutively degraded, whereas the cell surface expression of MHC class II is upregulated upon maturation (137). Similar mechanisms are likely to operate in B cells. Indeed, a few hours after BCR engagement, cathepsin S activity is increased. With regard to the second mechanism, the importance of membrane-associated ring finger (MARCH)-1 has been highlighted recently. Knockout of *MARCH-1*, an E3 polyubiquitin ligase, resulted in constitutive high expression of MHC class II on B cells (138). More importantly, expression of MARCH-1 is downregulated upon BCR crosslinking, which may be involved in terminating constitutive MHC class II degradation in vivo as well (M. Hoshino,

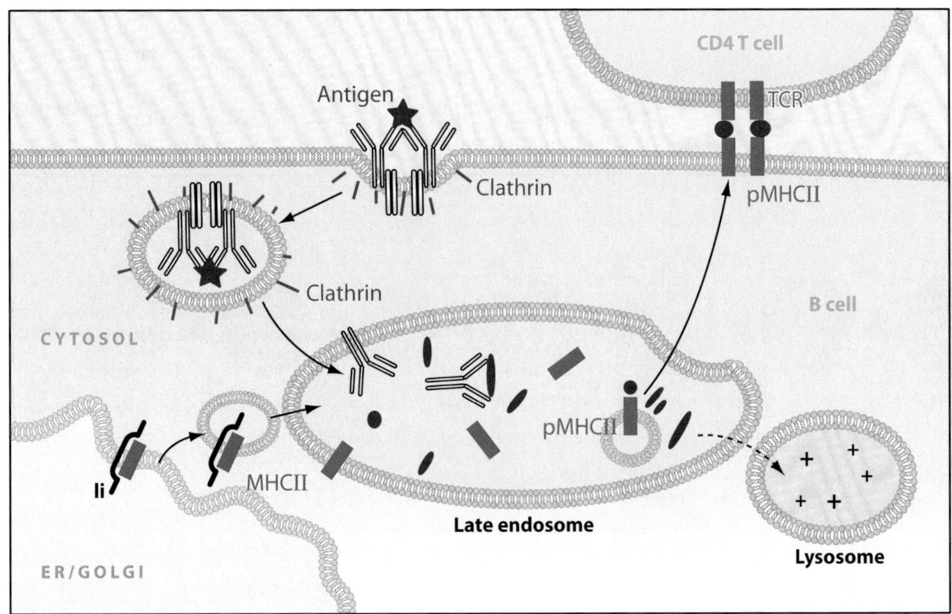

Figure 4

Antigen presentation by B cells. B cells can capture soluble or membrane-bound antigen through their BCRs. Whether the BCR-antigen complex traffics through early endosomes before its arrival at late endosomes is not clear and might depend on the type of B lymphocyte. MHC class II molecules associate with their chaperone molecule invariant chain (li) in the ER. In the antigen-processing late-endosomal compartment, the antigen and li are proteolyzed. The cysteine protease CatS is specifically required for a late step of li cleavage and allows for peptide exchange by H2-DM. By removing the cytosolic tail of li, this proteolytic event liberates the li motif for endosomal retention and permits mature peptide complexes (pMHC) to be exported to the cell surface for interaction with cognate T cells. TCR, T cell receptor.

Y. Aiba, T. Kurosaki & S. Ishido, unpublished data).

B CELL DEVELOPMENT

Important insights concerning the requirement of receptor and signaling components in B cell development have been obtained using conventional knockout mice. However, this approach has at least two potential problems. First, if early B cell development were arrested by the simple gene knockout mice, the function of these genes in later phases of development cannot be addressed using these mice. Second, if B cell outcomes are dictated by combined effects of both B cell–intrinsic and –extrinsic factors, this approach cannot be used to dissect these two factors. These problems are now closer to resolution through spatiotemporal gene deletion.

Pre-Pro-B to Pro-B Cell Stages

Pre-pro-B cells have low expression of the recombination activating genes (*Rag1* and *Rag2*). Their *IgH* and *IgL* genes are in the germline, unrearranged configuration, so no Ig is produced in these cells (**Figure 5*a***) (139). Pro-B cells are distinguished from earlier precursors because $V_H(D)J_H$ recombination is initiated at this stage. Pro-B cells also differ from pre-pro-B cells in that they are the first B lineage cells to express Igα, Igβ, and cell surface calnexin (pro-BCR) (4). Ig gene recombination begins with diversity (*D*) to joining (J_H) segment rearrangements. After formation of DJ_H rearrangements, V_H genes become accessible to the $V_H(D)J_H$ recombinase, and complete heavy-chain transcription units are assembled. The switch from DJ_H to $V_H(D)J_H$ recombination in pro-B cells is probably

a

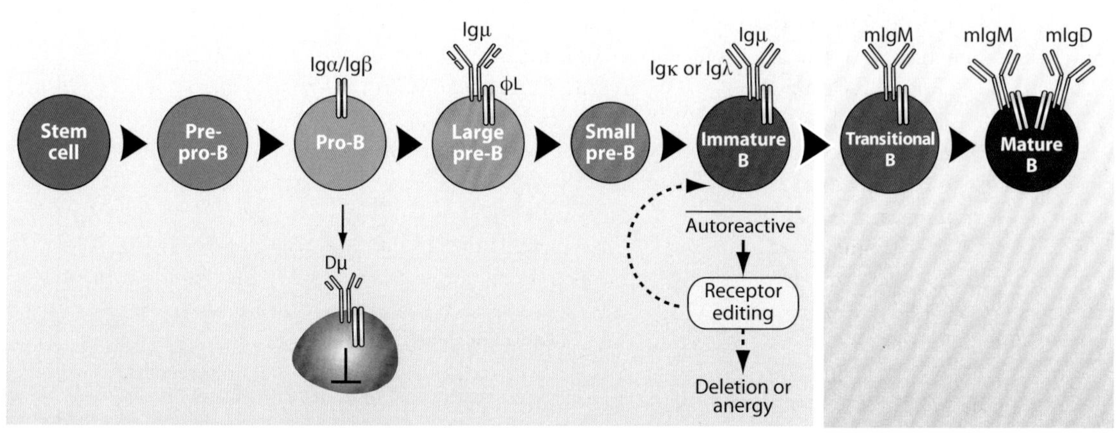

RAG:	-	Low	+	-	+	Low	-	-
IgH:	GL	GL	DJ_H	V_HDJ_H	-	-	-	-
IgL:	GL	GL	GL	GL	V_LJ_L	V_LJ_L?	-	-

b

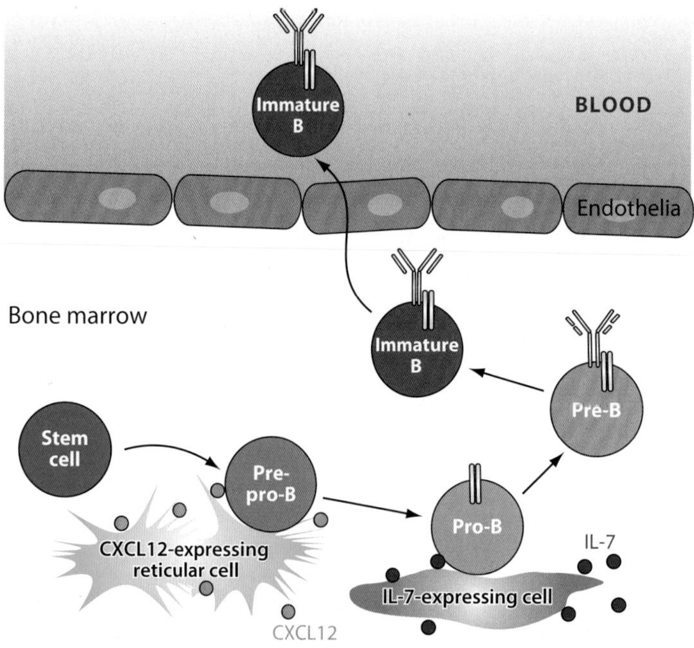

regulated at the level of V_H gene accessibility and appears to require the cytokine IL-7, the transcription factors Pax5 and YY1, and high levels of Rag1/Rag2 (13, 140–143). The requirement for IL-7 in $V_H(D)J_H$ recombination fits well with recent observations that pro-B cells are in contact with IL-7-expressing stromal cells in bone marrow microenvironments. In bone marrow, several types of stromal cells (at least three types: osteoblasts, CXCL12^{hi} reticular cells, and IL-7-expressing cells) have been proposed to function as specific cellular niches for promoting early B cell development in a stepwise manner (**Figure 5*b***) (144). Most pre-pro-B cells are in contact with CXCL12^{hi} reticular cells, whereas pro-B cells move away from CXCL12^{hi} reticular cells and instead associate with IL-7-expressing stromal cells.

V_H gene accessibility is dependent on transcriptional regulatory elements, including the IgH chain enhancer, and is associated with the onset of transcription of germline V_H gene segments. Indeed, it has been proposed that transcription per se renders the V_H gene segments accessible to the recombinase (145). Both sense and antisense germline V_H transcripts may impact the accessibility of these segments. Recent data have shown that antisense transcripts are generated in the vicinity of nonrearranged V_H gene segments and that they are found in pro-B cell populations that are actively undergoing V_H to DJ_H joining (146). A second possibility is that *cis* regulatory elements in *IgH* promoters and enhancers recruit factors that remodel chromatin domains and make V_H genes accessible for recombination independently of transcription. For instance, YY1, a zinc finger protein, binds to the intronic enhancer ($iE\mu$) of the *IgH* locus, where it is essential for distal V_H to DJ_H recombination (147). Finally, histone modifications by acetylation and demethylation, as discussed above, contribute to V_H gene accessibility in an IL-7- and Pax5-dependent manner, respectively (148).

Although the chromatin state of the *IgH* locus is a main determinant of Rag-mediated recombination, another mechanism is the transcriptional regulation of the components of the recombination machinery. In fact, regulation of the *Rag* genes by Foxp1 has been demonstrated recently (149). Forkhead (Fox) transcription factors are proteins that share a winged-helix DNA-binding domain and regulate diverse biological processes. Foxp1 regulates the B cell–specific expression of *Rag1* and *Rag2* in pro-B cells by binding directly to sequences in the *Erag* enhancer, located near the 5′ end of the *Rag2* gene. This *Erag* enhancer is known to be a critical sequence for the lineage-specific expression of *Rag* genes in B cells, but not in T cells.

Pre-B Cell Stage

The expression of μHC results in the assembly of the pre-BCR and marks the transition to the pre-B cell stage. The pre-BCR is composed of the transmembrane form of μHC (mIgμ), the surrogate light chains (λ5 and VpreB), Igα, and Igβ. Its expression on the cell surface, which occurs after the cell has made a successful $V_H(D)J_H$ rearrangement, is a key checkpoint regulator in B cell development (**Figure 5*a***). The primary functions of the pre-BCR are to trigger clonal expansion, heavy-chain allelic exclusion, and further differentiation (150).

Whether pre-BCR crosslinking by an unknown ligand or by simple surface expression

Figure 5

(*a*) B cell differentiation scheme and (*b*) a model of the movement of early B cells as they develop in the bone marrow. (*a*) Developmental stages of B lymphopoiesis, RAG expression, and rearrangements on both heavy (*IgH*) and light (*IgL*) chain loci. (GL: *IgH* or *IgL* loci in the germline configuration.) (*b*) Pre-pro-B cells move toward CXCL12^{hi} reticular cells and associate with them, whereas pro-B cells move away and instead adjoin IL-7-expressing cells. Subsequently, pre-B cells leave the IL-7-expressing cells. B cells expressing IgM exit the bone marrow and enter the blood to reach the spleen, where they mature into peripheral mature B cells that coexpress IgD. Not illustrated here is the extensive proliferation that occurs at the large pro-B and pre-B cell stages.

is sufficient to trigger these biological consequences is still debated. However, receptor self-aggregation likely is required for signaling and subsequent cellular responses because pre-B cell development cannot occur in the absence of ITAMs in the cytoplasmic domains of Igα and Igβ (151). With regard to the self-aggregation property of the pre-BCR, Ohnishi & Melchers (152) provided an intriguing model in which the unique non-Ig-like regions at the N terminus of λ5 and the C terminus of VpreB mediate constitutive pre-BCR aggregation on the cell surface via their homotypic ionic interactions, which in turn are critical for inducing signaling and internalization. This model has been verified by recent crystallographic and electron microscopic analysis, revealing the existence of pre-BCR dimers, consisting of two pre-BCR monomers connected by a flexible hinge between the tips of the variable domains (153). As predicted by the previous report (152), this hinge region has turned out to be formed by the unique non-Ig-like regions of λ5 and VpreB (153). Functional data also support this concept. Surrogate light-chain expression strongly enhances the autonomous ability of mIgμ to induce calcium flux irrespective of additional receptor crosslinking (154).

The pre-BCR transmits a signal to induce several rounds of cell division and eliminate the dependence of developing B cells on IL-7. Because of its analogy to BCR signaling, Src family and Syk family PTKs had been considered critical for transmitting the pre-BCR signal for cell expansion. Indeed, three Src kinases (Lyn, Fyn, and Blk) contribute to pre-B cell expansion in a redundant fashion (155). Because pre BCR-mediated NF-κB activation was abolished in *Lyn/Fyn/Blk* triple knockout pro-B cells, this pathway has been proposed to be critical for pre-BCR-mediated expansion; however, direct evidence for the involvement of the NF-κB signaling pathway in pre-B cell expansion is still lacking. In contrast, the mechanisms by which Syk family kinases participate in pre-BCR-mediated expansion are becoming clearer. Downstream of Syk and Zap-70, ERK1 and ERK2 are activated through Ras in a pre-BCR signaling context and are required for pre-BCR-mediated cell expansion through the activation of the transcription factors Elk1 and CREB (156). In line with this model, mice expressing a constitutively activated Ras mutant transgene on a *Rag*-null background bypass the pre-BCR checkpoint; conversely, mice expressing a transgenic dominant-negative Ras, H-RasN17, show a developmental arrest at the pro- to pre-B cell stage (120, 157). Moreover, mice overexpressing a dominant-negative form of CREB lacking the ERK phosphorylation site (Ser119 to Ala mutation) in a B cell–specific manner have the same developmental block as mice lacking *ERK1* and *ERK2* (158).

Ig HC allelic exclusion, the process by which successful rearrangement of one *IgH* allele inhibits further rearrangement of the other allele, remains an enigmatic aspect of pre-BCR signaling. Because of allelic exclusion, rearrangement of the endogenous *IgH* genes is normally inhibited in wild-type mice carrying a prerearranged μH chain transgene. However, $Syk^{-/-} Zap70^{-/-}$ double mutants cannot allelically exclude the endogenous *IgH* genes in the presence of a μH chain transgene (159). Downstream of Syk and Zap-70, the above-mentioned Ras-ERK pathway appears not to be involved in this process because deletion of both *ERK1* and *ERK2* does not break allelic exclusion (T. Yasuda & T. Kurosaki, unpublished data). In contrast, PLCγ is critical; $PLC\gamma 1^{+/-}\ PLC\gamma 2^{-/-}$ mice on an *IgH* chain transgenic background fail to induce allelic exclusion (160). The mechanism for the involvement of PLCγ in allelic exclusion is not understood, but it is possible that protein kinase D (PKD), which is downstream of PLCγ, can function to connect the cytoplasmic and nuclear events required for allelic exclusion. Indeed, in T cells, PKD1 is known to bind DAG, a product of PLCγ, and mice expressing cytosol-targeted active PKD1 can suppress V_β to DJ_β rearrangements of the *TCRβ* locus (161, 162).

After the clonal expansion of mIgμ producers, pre-B cells arrest in G1 and become small pre-B cells. Because pre-BCR signaling terminates the transcription of the genes encoding *λ5* and *VpreB*, it had been proposed that this transition to small pre-B cells is caused by the transcriptional silencing of surrogate light chain genes. Indeed, *Btk*-, *BLNK*-, and *IRF4/IRF8*-deficient mice have impaired pre-BCR downregulation and manifest a hyperplastic pre-B cell phenotype (163, 164). The resulting chronic pre-B cell proliferation seems to allow for secondary genetic mutations, with pre-B cell lymphomas developing in these mice within weeks (165). However, the enforced expression of surrogate light chains beyond the large, cycling pre-B cells turn out to have no apparent effect on pre-B cell proliferation and subsequent differentiation, despite the high expression of the pre-BCR (166), thereby calling the above transcriptional model into question. We propose that instead of the regulation of pre-BCR expression, pre-BCR signaling mediates rapid and transient expression of key transcription factors for proliferation, which might explain why pre-B cells become arrested in the G1 state. According to this model, when the amount of these factors drops below a critical level, expression of proliferative genes is downregulated, and that of antiproliferative genes is possibly upregulated, together leading pre-B cells into a quiescent state. The downregulation of IL-7 responsiveness in pre-B cells might also contribute to this quiescence. In this regard, pre-B cells are in the process of moving away from IL-7-expressing stromal cells in the bone marrow (**Figure 5*b***), which in turn might contribute to conferring attenuated IL-7 responsiveness on pre-B cells.

Upon the cessation of pre-B cell proliferation, the small pre-B cells induce *Igκ* locus activation and V_κ to J_κ recombination, resulting in the synthesis and cell surface expression of the IgM BCR (167). Signaling by the pre-BCR and loss of IL-7 signaling together enhance the accessibility of the *Igκ* locus and its recombination. These two pathways act via distinct mechanisms to regulate such processes. The *Igκ* locus contains two distinct transcriptional enhancers, the intronic enhancer (*iEκ*) and the 3′ enhancer (*3′Eκ*), which function to regulate recombination. The expression of IRF4, a regulatory transcription factor, is induced by signaling through the pre-BCR, and together with another transcription factor, PU.1, it interacts with the *3′Eκ* (164, 168). Increased binding of these proteins to the *3′Eκ* is associated with its increased accessibility to restriction endonucleases, as well as increased association with acetylated histones in B cells. Indeed, the overexpression of IRF4 in an *IRF4*$^{-/-}$*IRF8*$^{-/-}$ background resulted in high levels of *Igκ* germline transcripts and preferentially stimulated histone H4 acetylation at the *3′Eκ*. In contrast, lowering the IL-7 signaling preferentially induces histone acetylation at the iEκ (169). Although the mechanisms are not entirely clear, the lowered IL-7 signaling appears to facilitate binding of the transcription factor E2A to the *iEκ*, which in turn is required for *Igκ* recombination in pre-B cells. Thus, IL-7 signaling impacts Ig gene rearrangement in two opposite ways, depending on the B cell differentiation states: IL-7 signaling in pro-B cells enhances histone acetylation at distal V_H genes (as discussed above), whereas it inhibits histone acetylation at iEκ in pre-B cells.

iEκ: the intronic enhancer

Similar to the FoxP1-mediated regulation of *Rag1/Rag2* transcription in *IgH* chain recombination, Foxo1 appears to be involved in *IgL* chain gene recombination through regulating, in part, the transcription of *Rag1/Rag2* (170, 171). Foxo1 has an interesting mode of regulation, which may dictate its stage-specific role in Ig gene rearrangement. The activation of PI3K and subsequent Akt activation lead to the phosphorylation of Foxo1 and to its degradation. This precludes the accumulation of Foxo1 protein in the nucleus, thereby blocking its function. Hence, although not completely proven, Foxo1's involvement in *IgH* chain gene recombination is unlikely (172), given that PI3K and Akt are highly activated by IL-7R signaling in pro-B cells, which are actively undergoing V_H to DJ_H recombination. In contrast, in the case of the pre-B to immature B cell transition, the expression of pre-BCR on large cycling pre-B cells induces PI3K-Akt activation, turning off Foxo1 function. When this proliferation ceases and the cells become small pre-B cells, PI3K is no longer activated, thereby releasing the Akt-mediated inhibition on Foxo1 and allowing it to participate in *IgL* chain gene recombination (172).

To maintain the one cell–one antibody rule, allelic exclusion must be imposed on light as well as heavy chain genes (2). One of the mechanisms that contributes to light-chain allelic exclusion is asymmetric demethylation of the *Igκ* alleles. Asymmetric demethylation is thought to render one of the two *Igκ* alleles preferentially accessible for *VJκ* rearrangement.

Immature B Cell Stage

Immature B cells are the first B lineage cells to express surface BCR, and they display surface IgM but little or no IgD (**Figure 5*a***). B cells remain in the immature compartment for 3.5 days on average.

Similar to the pre-BCR, the BCR on the B cell surface is thought to be capable of ligand-independent signaling (termed the tonic BCR signal), based on inducible BCR-ablation studies together with biochemical evidence that expression of the BCR, per se, induces tyrosine phosphorylation (4, 173, 174). The data from genetic manipulations of the signaling subunit Igα-Igβ also support this concept. In the absence of the Igα cytoplasmic domain, immature B cell development was perturbed (175, 176). Conversely, expression of a plasma membrane–targeted Igα-Igβ chimeric protein (considered a gain-of-function mutant of Igα/Igβ) in BCR-deficient (*μMT*-derived) bone marrow progenitor cells was sufficient to generate mature follicular $CD23^+$ B cells (177).

Several recent studies have provided fresh insight into the nature of the BCR tonic signal. Using an in vitro culture system, Keren et al. (178) showed that a reduction in the level of tonic signaling (achieved using PI3K inhibitors) resulted in increased Rag2 levels and new *IgL* gene recombination. Similarly, Tze et al. (179) examined the effect of the loss of the BCR on the differentiation state of B cells using an inducible Cre-loxP system to eliminate the BCR. Ablation of BCR expression resulted in B cells reverting to a less-differentiated earlier phenotype, as evidenced by the reexpression of several pro- and pre-B cell–associated genes, including *Rag1*, *Rag2*, *λ5*, and *VpreB*. Furthermore, under conditions in which BCR expression was retained, the addition of PTK and PI3K inhibitors attenuates the BCR-mediated tonic signal, thereby promoting the accumulation of new *IgL* gene recombination, too (179). These studies, together with the previous suggestion that a lack of BCR tonic signaling traps developing B cells in a compartment in which they would continue to undergo secondary recombination (180, 181), substantiate the concept that the strength of BCR-mediated tonic signaling is a critical sensor for B cells in their fate decision between pre-B and immature B cell stages. Although transient inhibition of PI3K activity in immature B cells can drive B cells to attempt more rounds of *IgL* rearrangements (see above), continued PI3K inhibition eventually halts immature B cell development, probably because of the lack of vital survival signals. Indeed, $BCAP^{-/-}CD19^{-/-}$ mice have severe defects in the generation of immature and mature B cells, as well as in PI3K activation, and this developmental defect was partly relieved by the introduction of a constitutively active form of PI3K (81). Mice deficient in the *p85α* subunit of PI3K also displayed a defect in immature B cells.

Cell surface expression of an autoreactive BCR on immature B cells leads to the internalization of the self-antigen-BCR complexes and to the activation of intracellular signals that upregulate Rag1/Rag2 expression, halts differentiation, and initiates secondary *Vκ* rearrangements that replace the original *VκJκ* rearrangement. In contrast to B cell anergy and deletion mechanisms, this type of tolerance mechanism, termed receptor editing, spares autoreactive B cells by replacing their receptors and is therefore an example of molecular selection (**Figure 5*a***). Amin & Schlissel (170) have proposed that regulation of Foxo1 participates in the receptor editing process. The binding of self-antigen can probably induce antigen-BCR internalization, thereby facilitating nuclear localization of Foxo1 and reinducing Rag1/Rag2 expression and *Igκ* rearrangements.

B Cell Development in the Periphery

In the case of conventional B2 B cells, immature B cells that emigrate from the bone marrow to the periphery are referred to as transitional 1 and 2 (T1 and T2) B cells (**Figure 5*a***). Developmentally, T1 B cells appear to precede T2 B cells, which, in turn, are considered as the immediate precursors of naive mature B cells. T1 and T2 B cells are short-lived, and only 10–30% of these cells enter the long-lived (15–20 weeks in the case of mice) mature peripheral B cell compartment. In addition to a functional BCR, immature B cells require BAFF-mediated survival signals for full maturation. Indeed, B cell maturation in *BAFF*-deficient mice was impaired beyond the T1 stage. Current evidence indicates that all three BAFF receptors (BAFFR, BCMA, and TACI) are expressed on B cells at differing levels, depending on their maturation and/or activation stage (182). For instance, BCR ligation upregulates BAFFR expression on B cells, which promotes increased sensitivity to BAFF-mediated survival signals. Among BAFFR, BCMA, and TACI, BAFFR is the key receptor that triggers BAFF-mediated survival of immature B cells, as mice deficient in this receptor phenocopy the *BAFF*-null mice (183). Furthermore, in vitro and in vivo experiments demonstrate that T2 B cells are critical targets for BAFF effects on B cell development.

Recent investigations have elucidated the pathways that mediate BAFFR's prosurvival signaling. The major pathway involves activation of the so-called noncanonical NF-κB pathway (the processing of NF-κB2 and the nuclear translocation of the p52/RelB heterodimer) (184, 185), although weak activation of the canonical NF-κB pathway (nuclear translocation of the p50/RelA or p50/c-Rel heterodimer) occurs to some extent (186–189). The BAFFR has only a single TRAF-binding site, which is specific for TRAF3 (190). Unlike other TRAFs (such as TRAF2, TRAF5, and TRAF6), TRAF3 does not activate the canonical NF-κB or JNK pathway (191). Instead, TRAF3, in the resting state, suppresses the noncanonical NF-κB pathway by binding NIK and targeting it for proteosomal degradation (192). NIK is responsible for directly phosphorylating and activating IKKα and the subsequent activation of the noncanonical pathway (193, 194). Activated BAFFR recruits TRAF3, allowing B cells to terminate TRAF3-mediated degradation of NIK. NIK then accumulates and activates IKKα and the downstream noncanonical pathway. Indeed, B cells that lack TRAF3 show greatly elevated levels of NIK and NF-κB2 processing (195). More significantly, the B cell developmental defect in $BAFF^{-/-}$ mice was corrected by the loss of TRAF3, formally demonstrating the importance of the BAFFR-TRAF3-noncanonical NF-κB pathway in the development of mature B cells. TRAF3-mediated NIK degradation is likely mediated by the TRAF2-associated Ub ligase c-IAP1, although how TRAF3 regulates TRAF2 is not clear. In this context, TRAF2, TRAF3, and c-IAP1 function as suppressors of the noncanonical NF-κB pathway in B cells (196). In addition to the activation of the noncanonical NF-κB pathway, BAFFR regulates B cell survival by regulating the nuclear localization of PKCδ (197).

BCR signaling (presumably like the ligand-independent tonic signal as mentioned above) appears to be an important determinant in the transition from T1/T2 B cells to mature B2 B cells. The loss of BCR expression by conditional IgM ablation aborts all further development beyond the transitional stage (198). In addition, many mutations that affect BCR signaling pathways also interfere with this transition. In the absence of *Btk*, *BLNK*, *BCAP*, *PLCγ2*, or *Vav1/Vav2/Vav3*, BCR signaling is insufficient to induce T1/T2 B cells to differentiate into mature B cells (199). One of the critical pathways downstream of these signaling molecules is the canonical NF-κB activation pathway. The importance of this pathway has been recently highlighted in studies using mice deficient in CARMA1 or IKKγ; these mice have a decreased number of mature B cells (200). Once CARMA1 is phosphorylated by BCR-activated PKCβ, this adaptor molecule forms a scaffold for other molecules including Bcl10, MALT1, and TRAF6/2, thereby activating the

IKKα/IKKβ/IKKγ complex and facilitating the nuclear translocation of p50/RelA or p50/c-Rel heterodimers (canonical NF-κB pathway) (201). Some of the BCR signaling molecules also participate in BAFFR signaling. For example, PLCγ2 is known to be involved in BAFFR-mediated signaling, directly or indirectly, in addition to its involvement in BCR-mediated canonical NF-κB activation (202). Rac1, a downstream effector in the Vav family, mediates the BCR-induced upregulation of BAFFR, thereby augmenting the BAFFR signaling (203). Together, BAFFR and BCR likely predominantly utilize the noncanonical and canonical NF-κB pathway, respectively, both of which are essential to generate a sufficient number of mature B cells.

Mutations in *CARMA1*, *Bcl10*, or *MALT1* result in a relatively mild defect in conventional B2 B cell development, whereas these mutations lead to a complete loss of B1 B cells in the peritoneal cavity (93). Conversely, B1 B cell development remains unaffected by the disruption of *BAFF* or *BAFFR* (204). Given that the repertoire of B1 B cells is enriched in autoreactive BCRs (205), these observations suggest that B1 B cells require comparatively strong BCR signaling for their development and/or maintenance, which can be provided by strong BCR crosslinking induced by autoantigens. For B2 B cells, in contrast, such strong BCR crosslinking by autoantigens would lead to deletion in order to purge the autoreactive BCR repertoire. During transition of the T1/T2 to mature B2 B cells, the ligand-independent BCR-mediated survival signal provided by the canonical NF-κB pathway might not be sufficient by itself to generate a sufficient number of long-lived mature B cells. For ensuring such longevity, the B2 B cells additionally require a BAFFR-mediated survival signal provided by the noncanonical NF-κB pathway.

B CELL FATE DECISION AFTER ANTIGEN ENCOUNTER

After naive B2 B cells bind protein antigens, they upregulate the expression of CCR7 and are attracted by a gradient of CCL21 to the outer T cell zones of secondary lymphoid tissues, where they elicit T cell help (206, 207). In this location, B cells form dynamic conjugates with T cells, receive cognate T cell help, and differentiate along one of two pathways: a follicular pathway, which gives rise to GCs, and an extrafollicular pathway, which gives rise to short-lived PCs (208). In the extrafollicular pathway, antigen-specific B cells leave the T cell zone and localize to the splenic bridging channels or the lymph-node medullary cords, where they form extrafollicular foci of short-lived PCs that produce low-affinity antibody. The few antigen-specific B cells that seed the follicules as GC founder cells undergo intense proliferation and then differentiate into high-affinity memory B cells and long-lived PCs (209).

In the case of TI type II antigens (which are characterized by repeating determinants on a large polysaccharide backbone), the extrafollicular pathway is initiated, and the plasmablasts are generated in splenic bridging channels and the lymph-node medullary cords (210). A CD11c^{high} DC population is found in these regions and is thought to be essential for the survival of plasmablasts by providing BAFF and APRIL (211). Under physiological circumstances, the GC reaction is believed not to occur in response to the TI type II antigens.

Initiation of GC Responses

When an antigen-stimulated B cell meets an activated effector T cell at the outer T cell zone, the interaction between the TCR on the T cell and MHC class II–peptide complexes on the B cell is critical for providing T cell help to the B cell; however, many other molecules play essential roles in the subsequent GC formation (210, 212). The importance of the interaction between CD40L and CD40 has been well recognized; CD40 is constitutively expressed on B cells, and CD40L is upregulated on T cells following their activation by DCs. Mice deficient in either *CD40* or *CD40L* are unable to mount a sufficient primary response or a recall response to TD antigens and do not form GCs

(213). Similarly, in humans, defective *CD40L* expression results in the X-linked form of hyper IgM syndrome. B cells in these patients are unable to undergo Ig class switching due to the lack of the CD40L-CD40 interaction. In vitro, the ligation of CD40 on B cells stimulates their survival, proliferation, and differentiation; promotes Ig isotype switching; and induces the upregulation of surface molecules involved in antigen presentation.

The CD40-associated TRAF2, TRAF3, and TRAF6 initiate the NF-κB (both canonical and noncanonical), JNK, and p38 pathways (213, 214). MEKK1, a member of the MAP3K family, is associated with TRAF2 in CD40 signaling and is required for the optimal activation of JNK and p38, but it is not needed for NF-κB activation (215). Although it has not been tested directly, TAK1, another MAP3K member, is likely involved in canonical NF-κB activation in CD40 signaling (119). Probably as a result of defective CD40 signaling, B cells harboring defective TAK1 or MEKK1 do not generate GC B cells and subsequent TD humoral responses. Recent studies have revealed the existence of negative signaling adaptor molecules, Act1 (216) and BANK (217), in CD40 and BAFFR signaling. As mentioned above, the ligation of BAFFR leads to TRAF3 binding to the receptor, which is required to terminate TRAF3-mediated degradation of NIK. The recruitment of Act1 to the BAFFR-TRAF3 complex may provide the negative signal for subsequent NIK activation. In contrast to Act1's involvement in both CD40 and BAFFR signaling, BANK plays a negative role only in CD40 signaling, presumably through the inhibition of CD40-mediated Akt activation (217).

In B cells, Bcl6 is a master regulator of GC commitment, maintenance, and suppression of PC differentiation (212, 218). Thus, it is important to clarify when and how Bcl6 is turned on and off. However, these questions have not yet been adequately addressed. With regard to the mechanisms by which Bcl6 is turned off, signaling through the BCR and CD40 has been implicated. BCR stimulation may lead to Ub-mediated proteosomal degradation of Bcl6 following its phosphorylation by ERK1/ERK2. Signaling through CD40 results in the transcriptional silencing of *Bcl6* through NF-κB-mediated activation of IRF4 (212, 219). Together, these observations suggest that signaling through BCR and CD40 is required for both GC development and, paradoxically, for the termination of GC reactions, too.

Events During the GC Reaction

Proliferating GC B cells, which are known as centroblasts, undergo somatic hypermutation of their Ig variable region gene segments (212, 220). Centroblasts exit the cell cycle to become centrocytes, and if they bind antigen that is associated with FDCs, they receive survival signals. The cells can then differentiate into long-lived PCs and memory B cells or undergo further rounds of somatic hypermutation (208, 221). Previously, T helper (Th) 1 and 2 effector cells were thought to regulate B cell responses. For example, Th1-derived IFN-γ regulates IgG2a production, whereas Th2-derived IL-4 is critical for IgG1 and IgE production in mice (208). The recent identification of a new subset of T cells, termed T follicular helper cells (T_{FH} cells), has provided a fresh insight into how GC B cells are maintained and differentiated (218, 222–225). These T_{FH} cells are present in GCs and are characterized by their expression of the CXCR5 chemokine receptor. Investigators now think that these cells regulate humoral immunity, especially GC reactions (**Figure 6**). Two types of cells are thought to participate in the development and/or maintenance of T_{FH} cells: $CD4^+CD3^-$ accessory cells and GC B cells. The $CD4^+CD3^-$ cells present in the T cell zone–B cell follicle boundary probably provide signals through OX40 and CD30 expressed on the surface of T_{FH} cells (226). Indeed, naive T cells that are stimulated by DCs transfected with OX40L upregulate CXCR5 expression (227), and mice that overexpress OX40L on the surface of DCs have an increased number of T_{FH} cells (228). In the case of GC B cells, interaction between ICOS on T cells and ICOSL on GC B cells likely

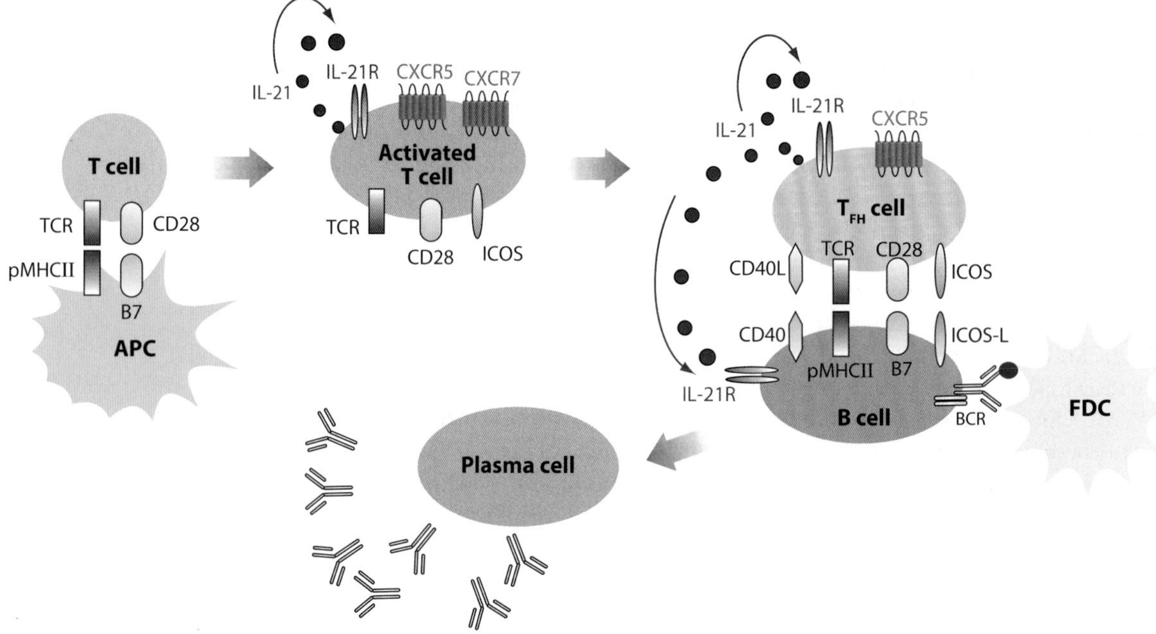

Figure 6

Interactions between B cells and T follicular helper cells (T_{FH} cells) during T-dependent immune responses. In the T cell zone of lymphoid tissues, mature DCs expressing B7.1 and B7.2 present peptide–MHC class II (pMHCII) ligand to the T cell receptor (TCR) of naive $CD4^+$ T cells. Activated $CD4^+$ T cells produce IL-21 and induce the expression of CD28 and ICOS. The sustained signaling of activated $CD4^+$ T cells through the TCR, CD28, and IL-21R in the T cell zone and at the T cell–B cell interface leads to the modulation of the expression of chemokine receptors such as CXCR5 and CCR7 and costimulatory receptors including ICOS, CD40L, and OX40. Although it is still unclear how T_{FH} cells develop, the migration of T_{FH} cells to follicles and the delivery of T cells help support the selection and differentiation of activated B cells in germinal centers. APC, antigen-presenting cell; FDC, follicular dendritic cell.

provides maintenance signals to T_{FH} cells because B cells devoid of ICOSL cannot generate sufficient numbers of T_{FH} cells (218).

Several molecules are crucial for mediating T_{FH} cell help for B cells and B cell help for T_{FH} cells during GC reactions (**Figure 6**). Although the interaction between CD40 and CD40L is essential to initiate GC reactions (as discussed above), this interaction is also important for the maintenance of GC reactions in that established GCs can be disrupted using a CD40L blocking antibody (229).

ICOS is a CD28-like molecule, and it is one of the most important molecules expressed on T_{FH} cells for TD antibody responses. Its ligand, ICOSL, is expressed by antigen-presenting cells, including GC B cells. Mice deficient in ICOS and ICOSL cannot form GCs or undergo Ig class switching (230–232). Conversely, when the negative regulation of ICOS by the Ub ligase Roquin E3 is impaired, there is an increased number of T_{FH} cells and increased IL-21 production (218, 233). The connection between ICOS and IL-21 in T cells has been clarified; the ICOS-ICOSL interaction is necessary for IL-21 expression by T cells (234). Given that T_{FH} cells can be generated in the presence of IL-21 in vitro and that T_{FH} cells express IL-21R, it seems reasonable to anticipate that, once naive T cells are activated through their TCR and ICOS, they will secrete IL-21, which in turn may function in a paracrine fashion to regulate T_{FH} cell development (207). Because high levels of IL-21R are also expressed on the surface of most B cells, IL-21 secreted by T_{FH} cells also impacts B cells (234–236). Indeed,

T_{FH} cell: T follicular helper cell

B cells cultured with a CD40 agonistic antibody showed enhanced proliferation and differentiation into ASCs, secreting all antibody isotypes when IL-21 was added to the cultures (237).

Signals through the BCR are thought to regulate the activity of GC B cells in several ways. One important outcome of the BCR signal is to provide survival and proliferative signals, thereby contributing to the generation and maintenance of GC B cells. Other cell surface molecules important in this process include CD45 or CD19; mice deficient in these proteins cannot generate sufficient survival signals, resulting in defective GC formation. In addition, the calcineurin-regulated transcription factor Mef2c is thought to function as a downstream target of the calcium/NFAT axis and has been shown to be critical for BCR-mediated proliferation and survival (238). Consequently, the B cell–specific deletion of Mef2c results in decreased GC formation, leading to lower TD antibody responses (238).

CONCLUSION

Signaling by the BCR and various coreceptors establishes a number of distinct checkpoints in the B cell pathway to ensure that B cell development occurs normally and to shape the correct naive BCR repertoire and subsequent BCR-triggered antibody responses. Additional work in this area is required to define the interconnections among the membrane, cytoplasmic, and nuclear events that set the thresholds for these checkpoints in distinct populations of developing and responding B cells.

DISCLOSURE STATEMENT

The authors are not aware of any affiliations, memberships, funding, or financial holdings that might be perceived as affecting the objectivity of this review.

ACKNOWLEDGMENTS

We acknowledge Mari Kurosaki for her help in creating **Figure 1** and compiling the references and members of our laboratory who shared their unpublished observations. We are grateful to Dr. Peter Burrows for critical discussions and Drs. S. Ishido and M. Hoshino for sharing their unpublished results and for critical discussions. Work from our laboratory was supported by grants from the Ministry of Education, Science, Sports, and Culture of Japan, the Naitoh Memorial Foundation, the Takeda Foundation, the Uehara Foundation, the Mochida Foundation, the NOVARTIS Foundation (Japan), the Human Frontier Science Program, the Hoh-ansha Foundation, and the Ono Medical Research Foundation.

LITERATURE CITED

1. Niiro H, Clark EA. 2002. Regulation of B-cell fate by antigen-receptor signals. *Nat. Rev. Immunol.* 2:945–56
2. Meffre E, Casellas R, Nussenzweig MC. 2000. Antibody regulation of B cell development. *Nat. Immunol.* 1:379–85
3. Monroe JG. 2006. ITAM-mediated tonic signalling through pre-BCR and BCR complexes. *Nat. Rev. Immunol.* 6:283–94
4. Kurosaki T. 2002. Regulation of B-cell signal transduction by adaptor proteins. *Nat. Rev. Immunol.* 2:354–63
5. Seet BT, Dikic I, Zhou MM, Pawson T. 2006. Reading protein modifications with interaction domains. *Nat. Rev. Mol. Cell Biol.* 7:473–83
6. Chen CZ, Li L, Lodish HF, Bartel DP. 2004. MicroRNAs modulate hematopoietic lineage differentiation. *Science* 303:83–86

7. Chen CZ, Lodish HF. 2005. MicroRNAs as regulators of mammalian hematopoiesis. *Semin. Immunol.* 17:155–65
8. Lodish HF, Zhou B, Liu G, Chen CZ. 2008. Micromanagement of the immune system by microRNAs. *Nat. Rev. Immunol.* 8:120–30
9. Jackson RJ, Standart N. 2007. How do microRNAs regulate gene expression? *Science STKE* 2007:re1
10. Xiao C, Calado DP, Galler G, Thai TH, Patterson HC, et al. 2007. MiR-150 controls B cell differentiation by targeting the transcription factor c-Myb. *Cell* 131:146–59
11. Vigorito E, Perks KL, Abreu-Goodger C, Bunting S, Xiang Z, et al. 2007. microRNA-155 regulates the generation of immunoglobulin class-switched plasma cells. *Immunity* 27:847–59
12. Thai TH, Calado DP, Casola S, Ansel KM, Xiao C, et al. 2007. Regulation of the germinal center response by microRNA-155. *Science* 316:604–8
13. Li QJ, Chau J, Ebert PJ, Sylvester G, Min H, et al. 2007. miR-181a is an intrinsic modulator of T cell sensitivity and selection. *Cell* 129:147–61
14. Calin GA, Croce CM. 2006. MicroRNA signatures in human cancers. *Nat. Rev. Cancer* 6:857–66
15. Teng G, Hakimpour P, Landgraf P, Rice A, Tuschl T, et al. 2008. MicroRNA-155 is a negative regulator of activation-induced cytidine deaminase. *Immunity* 28:621–29
16. Dorsett Y, McBride KM, Jankovic M, Gazumyan A, Thai TH, et al. 2008. MicroRNA-155 suppresses activation-induced cytidine deaminase-mediated Myc-Igh translocation. *Immunity* 28:1–9
17. Leonard TA, Hurley JH. 2007. Two kinase family dramas. *Cell* 129:1037–38
18. Shinohara H, Kurosaki T. 2006. Genetic analysis of B cell signaling. *Subcell. Biochem.* 40:145–87
19. Deindl S, Kadlecek TA, Brdicka T, Cao X, Weiss A, Kuriyan J. 2007. Structural basis for the inhibition of tyrosine kinase activity of ZAP-70. *Cell* 129:735–46
20. Kurosaki T, Maeda A, Ishiai M, Hashimoto A, Inabe K, Takata M. 2000. Regulation of the phospholipase C-γ2 pathway in B cells. *Immunol. Rev.* 176:19–29
21. Mackintosh C. 2004. Dynamic interactions between 14–3–3 proteins and phosphoproteins regulate diverse cellular processes. *Biochem. J.* 381:329–42
22. Tang X, Gao JS, Guan YJ, McLane KE, Yuan ZL, et al. 2007. Acetylation-dependent signal transduction for type I interferon receptor. *Cell* 131:93–105
23. Sampath SC, Marazzi I, Yap KL, Sampath SC, Krutchinsky AN, et al. 2007. Methylation of a histone mimic within the histone methyltransferase G9a regulates protein complex assembly. *Mol. Cell* 27:596–608
24. Su IH, Tarakhovsky A. 2005. Epigenetic control of B cell differentiation. *Semin. Immunol.* 17:167–72
25. Chowdhury D, Sen R. 2003. Transient IL-7/IL-7R signaling provides a mechanism for feedback inhibition of immunoglobulin heavy chain gene rearrangements. *Immunity* 18:229–41
26. Johnson K, Pflugh DL, Yu D, Hesslein DG, Lin KI, et al. 2004. B cell-specific loss of histone 3 lysine 9 methylation in the V(H) locus depends on Pax5. *Nat. Immunol.* 5:853–61
27. Osipovich O, Milley R, Meade A, Tachibana M, Shinkai Y, et al. 2004. Targeted inhibition of V(D)J recombination by a histone methyltransferase. *Nat. Immunol.* 5:309–16
28. Haglund K, Dikic I. 2005. Ubiquitylation and cell signaling. *EMBO J.* 24:3353–59
29. Pickart CM. 2001. Mechanisms underlying ubiquitination. *Annu. Rev. Biochem.* 70:503–33
30. Müller S, Hoege C, Pyrowolakis G, Jentsch S. 2001. SUMO, ubiquitin's mysterious cousin. *Nat. Rev. Mol. Cell Biol.* 2:202–10
31. Hicke L, Schubert HL, Hill CP. 2005. Ubiquitin-binding domains. *Nat. Rev. Mol. Cell Biol.* 6:610–21
32. Sun SC. 2008. Deubiquitylation and regulation of the immune response. *Nat. Rev. Immunol.* 8:501–11
33. Song J, Durrin LK, Wilkinson TA, Krontiris TG, Chen Y. 2004. Identification of a SUMO-binding motif that recognizes SUMO-modified proteins. *Proc. Natl. Acad. Sci. USA* 101:14373–78
34. Hecker CM, Rabiller M, Haglund K, Bayer P, Dikic I. 2006. Specification of SUMO1- and SUMO2-interacting motifs. *J. Biol. Chem.* 281:16117–27
35. Pfander B, Moldovan GL, Sacher M, Hoege C, Jentsch S. 2005. SUMO-modified PCNA recruits Srs2 to prevent recombination during S phase. *Nature* 436:428–33
36. Papouli E, Chen S, Davies AA, Huttner D, Krejci L, et al. 2005. Crosstalk between SUMO and ubiquitin on PCNA is mediated by recruitment of the helicase Srs2p. *Mol. Cell* 19:123–33

37. Gazumyan A, Reichlin A, Nussenzweig MC. 2006. Igβ tyrosine residues contribute to the control of B cell receptor signaling by regulating receptor internalization. *J. Exp. Med.* 203:1785–94
38. Tolar P, Sohn HW, Pierce SK. 2005. The initiation of antigen-induced B cell antigen receptor signaling viewed in living cells by fluorescence resonance energy transfer. *Nat. Immunol.* 6:1168–76
39. Sohn HW, Tolar P, Jin T, Pierce SK. 2006. Fluorescence resonance energy transfer in living cells reveals dynamic membrane changes in the initiation of B cell signaling. *Proc. Natl. Acad. Sci. USA* 103:8143–48
40. Harwood NE, Batista FD. 2008. New insights into the early molecular events underlying B cell activation. *Immunity* 28:609–19
41. Dustin ML, Dustin LB. 2001. The immunological relay race: B cells take antigen by synapse. *Nat. Immunol.* 2:480–82
42. Saito T, Yokosuka T. 2006. Immunological synapse and microclusters: the site for recognition and activation of T cells. *Curr. Opin. Immunol.* 18:305–13
43. Weber M, Treanor B, Depoil D, Shinohara H, Harwood NE, et al. 2008. Phospholipase C-γ2 and Vav cooperate within signaling microclusters to propagate B cell spreading in response to membrane-bound antigen. *J. Exp. Med.* 205:853–68
44. Depoil D, Fleire S, Treanor BL, Weber M, Harwood NE, et al. 2008. CD19 is essential for B cell activation by promoting B cell receptor-antigen microcluster formation in response to membrane-bound ligand. *Nat. Immunol.* 9:63–72
45. Hou P, Araujo E, Zhao T, Zhang M, Massenburg D, et al. 2006. B cell antigen receptor signaling and internalization are mutually exclusive events. *PLoS Biol.* 4:e200
46. Hikida M, Kurosaki T. 2005. Regulation of phospholipase C-γ2 networks in B lymphocytes. *Adv. Immunol.* 88:73–96
47. Sugawara H, Kurosaki M, Takata M, Kurosaki T. 1997. Genetic evidence for involvement of type 1, type 2 and type 3 inositol 1,4,5-trisphosphate receptors in signal transduction through the B-cell antigen receptor. *EMBO J.* 16:3078–88
48. Putney JW. 1986. A model for receptor-regulated calcium entry. *Cell Calcium* 7:1–12
49. Roos J, DiGregorio PJ, Yeromin AV, Ohlsen K, Lioudyno M, et al. 2005. STIM1, an essential and conserved component of store-operated Ca^{2+} channel function. *J. Cell Biol.* 169:435–45
50. Liou J, Kim ML, Heo WD, Jones JT, Myers JW, et al. 2005. STIM is a Ca^{2+} sensor essential for Ca^{2+}-store-depletion-triggered Ca^{2+} influx. *Curr. Biol.* 15:1235–41
51. Feske S, Gwack Y, Prakriya M, Srikanth S, Puppel SH, et al. 2006. A mutation in Orai1 causes immune deficiency by abrogating CRAC channel function. *Nature* 441:179–85
52. Vig M, Peinelt C, Beck A, Koomoa DL, Rabah D, et al. 2006. CRACM1 is a plasma membrane protein essential for store-operated Ca^{2+} entry. *Science* 312:1220–23
53. Oritani K, Kincade PW. 1996. Identification of stromal cell products that interact with pre-B cells. *J. Cell Biol.* 134:771–82
54. Baba Y, Nishida K, Fujii Y, Hirano T, Hikida M, Kurosaki T. 2008. Essential function for the calcium sensor STIM1 in mast cell activation and anaphylactic responses. *Nat. Immunol.* 9:81–88
55. Oh-hora M, Yamashita M, Hogan PG, Sharma S, Lamperti E, et al. 2008. Dual functions for the endoplasmic reticulum calcium sensors STIM1 and STIM2 in T cell activation and tolerance. *Nat. Immunol.* 9:432–43
56. Varga-Szabo D, Braun A, Kleinschnitz C, Bender M, Pleines I, et al. 2008. The calcium sensor STIM1 is an essential mediator of arterial thrombosis and ischemic brain infarction. *J. Exp. Med.* 205:1583–91
57. Baba Y, Hayashi K, Fujii Y, Mizushima A, Watarai H, et al. 2006. Coupling of STIM1 to store-operated Ca^{2+} entry through its constitutive and inducible movement in the endoplasmic reticulum. *Proc. Natl. Acad. Sci. USA* 103:16704–9
58. Putney JW. 2007. Recent breakthroughs in the molecular mechanism of capacitative calcium entry (with thoughts on how we got here). *Cell Calcium* 42:103–10
59. Hewavitharana T, Deng X, Soboloff J, Gill DL. 2007. Role of STIM and Orai proteins in the store-operated calcium signaling pathway. *Cell Calcium* 42:173–82
60. Brandman O, Liou J, Park WS, Meyer T. 2007. STIM2 is a feedback regulator that stabilizes basal cytosolic and endoplasmic reticulum Ca^{2+} levels. *Cell* 131:1327–39

61. Zhang SL, Yeromin AV, Zhang XH, Yu Y, Safrina O, et al. 2006. Genome-wide RNAi screen of Ca^{2+} influx identifies genes that regulate Ca^{2+} release-activated Ca^{2+} channel activity. *Proc. Natl. Acad. Sci. USA* 103:9357–62
62. Peinelt C, Vig M, Koomoa DL, Beck A, Nadler MJ, et al. 2006. Amplification of CRAC current by STIM1 and CRACM1 (Orai1). *Nat. Cell Biol.* 8:771–73
63. Vig M, DeHaven WI, Bird GS, Billingsley JM, Wang H, et al. 2008. Defective mast cell effector functions in mice lacking the CRACM1 pore subunit of store-operated calcium release-activated calcium channels. *Nat. Immunol.* 9:89–96
64. Gwack Y, Srikanth S, Oh-hora M, Hogan PG, Lamperti ED, et al. 2008. Hair loss and defective T and B cell function in mice lacking ORAI1. *Mol. Cell. Biol.* 28:5209–22
65. Huang GN, Zeng W, Kim JY, Yuan JP, Han L, et al. 2006. STIM1 carboxyl-terminus activates native SOC, I(crac) and TRPC1 channels. *Nat. Cell Biol.* 8:1003–10
66. Liao Y, Erxleben C, Yildirim E, Abramowitz J, Armstrong DL, Birnbaumer L. 2007. Orai proteins interact with TRPC channels and confer responsiveness to store depletion. *Proc. Natl. Acad. Sci. USA* 104:4682–87
67. Crabtree GR, Olson EN. 2002. NFAT signaling: choreographing the social lives of cells. *Cell* 109(Suppl.):S67–79
68. Timmerman LA, Healy JI, Ho SN, Chen L, Goodnow CC, Crabtree GR. 1997. Redundant expression but selective utilization of nuclear factor of activated T cells family members. *J. Immunol.* 159:2735–40
69. Ranger AM, Oukka M, Rengarajan J, Glimcher LH. 1998. Inhibitory function of two NFAT family members in lymphoid homeostasis and Th2 development. *Immunity* 9:627–35
70. Yoshida H, Nishina H, Takimoto H, Marengère LE, Wakeham AC, et al. 1998. The transcription factor NF-ATc1 regulates lymphocyte proliferation and Th2 cytokine production. *Immunity* 8:115–24
71. Peng SL, Gerth AJ, Ranger AM, Glimcher LH. 2001. NFATc1 and NFATc2 together control both T and B cell activation and differentiation. *Immunity* 14:13–20
72. Winslow MM, Gallo EM, Neilson JR, Crabtree GR. 2006. The calcineurin phosphatase complex modulates immunogenic B cell responses. *Immunity* 24:141–52
73. Sciammas R, Shaffer AL, Schatz JH, Zhao H, Staudt LM, Singh H. 2006. Graded expression of interferon regulatory factor-4 coordinates isotype switching with plasma cell differentiation. *Immunity* 25:225–36
74. Klein U, Casola S, Cattoretti G, Shen Q, Lia M, et al. 2006. Transcription factor IRF4 controls plasma cell differentiation and class-switch recombination. *Nat. Immunol.* 7:704–6
75. Tedder TF, Inaoki M, Sato S. 1997. The CD19-CD21 complex regulates signal transduction thresholds governing humoral immunity and autoimmunity. *Immunity* 6:107–18
76. Brooks SR, Li X, Volanakis EJ, Carter RH. 2000. Systematic analysis of the role of CD19 cytoplasmic tyrosines in enhancement of activation in Daudi human B cells: clustering of phospholipase C and Vav and of Grb2 and Sos with different CD19 tyrosines. *J. Immunol.* 164:3123–31
77. Fujimoto M, Fujimoto Y, Poe JC, Jansen PJ, Lowell CA, et al. 2000. CD19 regulates Src family protein tyrosine kinase activation in B lymphocytes through processive amplification. *Immunity* 13:47–57
78. Tuveson DA, Carter RH, Soltoff SP, Fearon DT. 1993. CD19 of B cells as a surrogate kinase insert region to bind phosphatidylinositol 3-kinase. *Science* 260:986–89
79. Okada T, Maeda A, Iwamatsu A, Gotoh K, Kurosaki T. 2000. BCAP: the tyrosine kinase substrate that connects B cell receptor to phosphoinositide 3-kinase activation. *Immunity* 13:817–27
80. Inabe K, Ishiai M, Scharenberg AM, Freshney N, Downward J, et al. 2002. Vav3 modulates B cell receptor responses by regulating phosphoinositide 3-kinase activation. *J. Exp. Med.* 195:189–200
81. Aiba Y, Kameyama M, Yamazaki T, Tedder TF, Kurosaki T. 2008. Regulation of B-cell development by BCAP and CD19 through their binding to phosphoinositide 3-kinase. *Blood* 111:1497–503
82. Fruman DA, Snapper SB, Yballe CM, Davidson L, Yu JY, et al. 1999. Impaired B cell development and proliferation in absence of phosphoinositide 3-kinase p85α. *Science* 283:393–97
83. Akagi T, Motegi M, Tamura A, Suzuki R, Hosokawa Y, et al. 1999. A novel gene, *MALT1* at 18q21, is involved in t(11;18) (q21;q21) found in low-grade B-cell lymphoma of mucosa-associated lymphoid tissue. *Oncogene* 18:5785–94
84. Janas ML, Hodson D, Stamataki Z, Hill S, Welch K, et al. 2008. The effect of deleting p110δ on the phenotype and function of PTEN-deficient B cells. *J. Immunol.* 180:739–46

85. Anzelon AN, Wu H, Rickert RC. 2003. Pten inactivation alters peripheral B lymphocyte fate and reconstitutes CD19 function. *Nat. Immunol.* 4:287–94
86. Yanaba K, Bouaziz JD, Haas KM, Poe JC, Fujimoto M, Tedder TF. 2008. A regulatory B cell subset with a unique CD1dhiCD5+ phenotype controls T cell-dependent inflammatory responses. *Immunity* 28:639–50
87. Suzuki A, Kaisho T, Ohishi M, Tsukio-Yamaguchi M, Tsubata T, et al. 2003. Critical roles of Pten in B cell homeostasis and immunoglobulin class switch recombination. *J. Exp. Med.* 197:657–67
88. Li Q, Verma IM. 2002. NF-κB regulation in the immune system. *Nat. Rev. Immunol.* 2:725–34
89. Gerondakis S, Grumont R, Gugasyan R, Wong L, Isomura I, et al. 2006. Unravelling the complexities of the NF-κB signalling pathway using mouse knockout and transgenic models. *Oncogene* 25:6781–99
90. Hayden MS, Ghosh S. 2008. Shared principles in NF-κB signaling. *Cell* 132:344–62
91. Hacker H, Karin M. 2006. Regulation and function of IKK and IKK-related kinases. *Science STKE* 2006:re13
92. Saijo K, Mecklenbrauker I, Santana A, Leitger M, Schmedt C, Tarakhovsky A. 2002. Protein kinase C β controls nuclear factor κ B activation in B cells through selective regulation of the IκB kinase α. *J. Exp. Med.* 195:1647–52
93. Thome M. 2004. CARMA1, BCL-10 and MALT1 in lymphocyte development and activation. *Nat. Rev. Immunol.* 4:348–59
94. Dierlamm J, Baens M, Wlodarska I, Stefanova-Ouzounova M, Hernandez JM, et al. 1999. The apoptosis inhibitor gene *API2* and a novel 18q gene, *MLT*, are recurrently rearranged in the t(11;18)(q21;q21) associated with mucosa-associated lymphoid tissue lymphomas. *Blood* 93:3601–9
95. Zhang Q, Siebert R, Yan M, Hinzmann B, Cui X, et al. 1999. Inactivating mutations and overexpression of *BCL10*, a caspase recruitment domain-containing gene, in MALT lymphoma with t(1;14)(p22;q32). *Nat. Genet.* 22:63–68
96. Willis TG, Jadayel DM, Du MQ, Peng H, Perry AR, et al. 1999. Bcl10 is involved in t(1;14)(p22;q32) of MALT B cell lymphoma and mutated in multiple tumor types. *Cell* 96:35–45
97. Morgan JA, Yin Y, Borowsky AD, Kuo F, Nourmand N, et al. 1999. Breakpoints of the t(11;18)(q21;q21) in mucosa-associated lymphoid tissue (MALT) lymphoma lie within or near the previously undescribed gene *MALT1* in chromosome 18. *Cancer Res.* 59:6205–13
98. Uren AG, O'Rourke K, Aravind LA, Pisabarro MT, Seshagiri S, et al. 2000. Identification of paracaspases and metacaspases: two ancient families of caspase-like proteins, one of which plays a key role in MALT lymphoma. *Mol. Cell* 6:961–67
99. Streubel B, Lamprecht A, Dierlamm J, Cerroni L, Stolte M, et al. 2003. T(14;18)(q32;q21) involving *IGH* and *MALT1* is a frequent chromosomal aberration in MALT lymphoma. *Blood* 101:2335–39
100. Lenz G, Davis RE, Ngo VN, Lam L, George TC, et al. 2008. Oncogenic CARD11 mutations in human diffuse large B cell lymphoma. *Science* 319:1676–79
101. Shinohara H, Yasuda T, Aiba Y, Sanjo H, Hamadate M, et al. 2005. PKCβ regulates BCR-mediated IKK activation by facilitating the interaction between TAK1 and CARMA1. *J. Exp. Med.* 202:1423–31
102. Shinohara H, Maeda S, Watarai H, Kurosaki T. 2007. IκB kinase β-induced phosphorylation of CARMA1 contributes to CARMA1 Bcl10 MALT1 complex formation in B cells. *J. Exp. Med.* 204:3285–93
103. Wegener E, Oeckinghaus A, Papadopoulou N, Lavitas L, Schmidt-Supprian M, et al. 2006. Essential role for IκB kinase β in remodeling Carma1-Bcl10-Malt1 complexes upon T cell activation. *Mol. Cell* 23:13–23
104. Lobry C, Lopez T, Israel A, Weil R. 2007. Negative feedback loop in T cell activation through IκB kinase-induced phosphorylation and degradation of Bcl10. *Proc. Natl. Acad. Sci. USA* 104:908–13
105. Rebeaud F, Hailfinger S, Posevitz-Fejfar A, Tapernoux M, Moser R, et al. 2008. The proteolytic activity of the paracaspase MALT1 is key in T cell activation. *Nat. Immunol.* 9:272–81
106. Coornaert B, Baens M, Heyninck K, Bekaert T, Haegman M, et al. 2008. T cell antigen receptor stimulation induces MALT1 paracaspase-mediated cleavage of the NF-κB inhibitor A20. *Nat. Immunol.* 9:263–71
107. Heyninck K, Beyaert R. 2005. A20 inhibits NF-κB activation by dual ubiquitin-editing functions. *Trends Biochem. Sci.* 30:1–4

108. Thome M, Weil R. 2007. Post-translational modifications regulate distinct functions of CARMA1 and BCL10. *Trends Immunol.* 28:281–88
109. Karin M, Ben-Neriah Y. 2000. Phosphorylation meets ubiquitination: the control of NF-κB activity. *Annu. Rev. Immunol.* 18:621–63
110. Jun JE, Wilson LE, Vinuesa CG, Lesage S, Blery M, et al. 2003. Identifying the MAGUK protein Carma-1 as a central regulator of humoral immune responses and atopy by genome-wide mouse mutagenesis. *Immunity* 18:751–62
111. Adhikari A, Xu M, Chen ZJ. 2007. Ubiquitin-mediated activation of TAK1 and IKK. *Oncogene* 26:3214–26
112. Ikeda F, Dikic I. 2006. CYLD in ubiquitin signaling and tumor pathogenesis. *Cell* 125:643–45
113. Simonson SJ, Wu ZH, Miyamoto S. 2007. CYLD: a DUB with many talents. *Dev. Cell* 13:601–3
114. Trompouki E, Hatzivassiliou E, Tsichritzis T, Farmer H, Ashworth A, et al. 2003. CYLD is a deubiquitinating enzyme that negatively regulates NF-κB activation by TNFR family members. *Nature* 424:793–96
115. Brummelkamp TR, Nijman SM, Dirac AM, Bernards R. 2003. Loss of the cylindromatosis tumour suppressor inhibits apoptosis by activating NF-κB. *Nature* 424:797–801
116. Kovalenko A, Chable-Bessia C, Cantarella G, Israel A, Wallach D, Courtois G. 2003. The tumour suppressor CYLD negatively regulates NF-κB signalling by deubiquitination. *Nature* 424:801–5
117. Jin W, Reiley WR, Lee AJ, Wright A, Wu X, et al. 2007. Deubiquitinating enzyme CYLD regulates the peripheral development and naive phenotype maintenance of B cells. *J. Biol. Chem.* 282:15884–93
118. Hovelmeyer N, Wunderlich FT, Massoumi R, Jakobsen CG, Song J, et al. 2007. Regulation of B cell homeostasis and activation by the tumor suppressor gene CYLD. *J. Exp. Med.* 204:2615–27
119. Sato S, Sanjo H, Takeda K, Ninomiya-Tsuji J, Yamamoto M, et al. 2005. Essential function for the kinase TAK1 in innate and adaptive immune responses. *Nat. Immunol.* 6:1087–95
120. Nagaoka H, Takahashi Y, Hayashi R, Nakamura T, Ishii K, et al. 2000. Ras mediates effector pathways responsible for pre-B cell survival, which is essential for the developmental progression to the late pre-B cell stage. *J. Exp. Med.* 192:171–82
121. Oh-hora M, Johmura S, Hashimoto A, Hikida M, Kurosaki T. 2003. Requirement for Ras guanine nucleotide releasing protein 3 in coupling phospholipase C-γ2 to Ras in B cell receptor signaling. *J. Exp. Med.* 198:1841–51
122. Ehrhardt A, David MD, Ehrhardt GR, Schrader JW. 2004. Distinct mechanisms determine the patterns of differential activation of H-Ras, N-Ras, K-Ras 4B, and M-Ras by receptors for growth factors or antigen. *Mol. Cell. Biol.* 24:6311–23
123. Teixeira C, Stang SL, Zheng Y, Beswick NS, Stone JC. 2003. Integration of DAG signaling systems mediated by PKC-dependent phosphorylation of RasGRP3. *Blood* 102:1414–20
124. Hashimoto A, Okada H, Jiang A, Kurosaki M, Greenberg S, et al. 1998. Involvement of guanosine triphosphatases and phospholipase C-γ2 in extracellular signal-regulated kinase, c-Jun NH_2-terminal kinase, and p38 mitogen-activated protein kinase activation by the B cell antigen receptor. *J. Exp. Med.* 188:1287–95
125. Aiba Y, Oh-hora M, Kiyonaka S, Kimura Y, Hijikata A, et al. 2004. Activation of RasGRP3 by phosphorylation of Thr-133 is required for B cell receptor-mediated Ras activation. *Proc. Natl. Acad. Sci. USA* 101:16612–17
126. Zheng Y, Liu H, Coughlin J, Zheng J, Li L, Stone JC. 2005. Phosphorylation of RasGRP3 on threonine 133 provides a mechanistic link between PKC and Ras signaling systems in B cells. *Blood* 105:3648–54
127. Dong C, Davis RJ, Flavell RA. 2002. MAP kinases in the immune response. *Annu. Rev. Immunol.* 20:55–72
128. Trombetta ES, Mellman I. 2005. Cell biology of antigen processing in vitro and in vivo. *Annu. Rev. Immunol.* 23:975–1028
129. Vascotto F, Lankar D, Faure-Andre G, Vargas P, Diaz J, et al. 2007. The actin-based motor protein myosin II regulates MHC class II trafficking and BCR-driven antigen presentation. *J. Cell Biol.* 176:1007–19
130. Clark MR, Massenburg D, Siemasko K, Hou P, Zhang M. 2004. B-cell antigen receptor signaling requirements for targeting antigen to the MHC class II presentation pathway. *Curr. Opin. Immunol.* 16:382–87

131. Miaczynska M, Christoforidis S, Giner A, Shevchenko A, Uttenweiler-Joseph S, et al. 2004. APPL proteins link Rab5 to nuclear signal transduction via an endosomal compartment. *Cell* 116:445–56
132. Chaturvedi A, Dorward D, Pierce SK. 2008. The B cell receptor governs the subcellular location of Toll-like receptor 9 leading to hyperresponses to DNA-containing antigens. *Immunity* 28:799–809
133. Ahmad-Nejad P, Hacker H, Rutz M, Bauer S, Vabulas RM, Wagner H. 2002. Bacterial CpG-DNA and lipopolysaccharides activate Toll-like receptors at distinct cellular compartments. *Eur. J. Immunol.* 32:1958–68
134. Stoddart A, Jackson AP, Brodsky FM. 2005. Plasticity of B cell receptor internalization upon conditional depletion of clathrin. *Mol. Biol. Cell* 16:2339–48
135. Zhang M, Veselits M, O'Neill S, Hou P, Reddi AL, et al. 2007. Ubiquitinylation of Igβ dictates the endocytic fate of the B cell antigen receptor. *J. Immunol.* 179:4435–43
136. Le Roux D, Lankar D, Yuseff MI, Vascotto F, Yokozeki T, et al. 2007. Syk-dependent actin dynamics regulate endocytic trafficking and processing of antigens internalized through the B-cell receptor. *Mol. Biol. Cell* 18:3451–62
137. Mellman I, Steinman RM. 2001. Dendritic cells: specialized and regulated antigen processing machines. *Cell* 106:255–58
138. Matsuki Y, Ohmura-Hoshino M, Goto E, Aoki M, Mito-Yoshida M, et al. 2007. Novel regulation of MHC class II function in B cells. *EMBO J.* 26:846–54
139. Matthias P, Rolink AG. 2005. Transcriptional networks in developing and mature B cells. *Nat. Rev. Immunol.* 5:497–508
140. Jung D, Giallourakis C, Mostoslavsky R, Alt FW. 2006. Mechanism and control of V(D)J recombination at the immunoglobulin heavy chain locus. *Annu. Rev. Immunol.* 24:541–70
141. Chowdhury D, Sen R. 2004. Regulation of immunoglobulin heavy-chain gene rearrangements. *Immunol. Rev.* 200:182–96
142. Zhang J, Grindley JC, Yin T, Jayasinghe S, He XC, et al. 2006. PTEN maintains haematopoietic stem cells and acts in lineage choice and leukaemia prevention. *Nature* 441:518–22
143. Labrie JE 3rd, Borghesi L, Gerstein RM. 2005. Bone marrow microenvironmental changes in aged mice compromise V(D)J recombinase activity and B cell generation. *Semin. Immunol.* 17:347–55
144. Nagasawa T. 2006. Microenvironmental niches in the bone marrow required for B-cell development. *Nat. Rev. Immunol.* 6:107–16
145. Bates JG, Cado D, Nolla H, Schlissel MS. 2007. Chromosomal position of a VH gene segment determines its activation and inactivation as a substrate for V(D)J recombination. *J. Exp. Med.* 204:3247–56
146. Bolland DJ, Wood AL, Johnston CM, Bunting SF, Morgan G, et al. 2004. Antisense intergenic transcription in V(D)J recombination. *Nat. Immunol.* 5:630–37
147. Liu H, Schmidt-Supprian M, Shi Y, Hobeika E, Barteneva N, et al. 2007. Yin Yang 1 is a critical regulator of B-cell development. *Genes Dev.* 21:1179–89
148. Xu CR, Schaffer L, Head SR, Feeney AJ. 2008. Reciprocal patterns of methylation of H3K36 and H3K27 on proximal vs distal IgVH genes are modulated by IL-7 and Pax5. *Proc. Natl. Acad. Sci. USA* 105:8685–90
149. Hu H, Wang B, Borde M, Nardone J, Maika S, et al. 2006. Foxp1 is an essential transcriptional regulator of B cell development. *Nat. Immunol.* 7:819–26
150. Martensson IL, Keenan RA, Licence S. 2007. The pre-B-cell receptor. *Curr. Opin. Immunol.* 19:137–42
151. Abram CL, Lowell CA. 2007. The expanding role for ITAM-based signaling pathways in immune cells. *Science STKE* 2007:re2
152. Ohnishi K, Melchers F. 2003. The nonimmunoglobulin portion of λ5 mediates cell-autonomous pre-B cell receptor signaling. *Nat. Immunol.* 4:849–56
153. Bankovich AJ, Raunser S, Juo ZS, Walz T, Davis MM, Garcia KC. 2007. Structural insight into pre-B cell receptor function. *Science* 316:291–94
154. Meixlsperger S, Kohler F, Wossning T, Reppel M, Muschen M, Jumaa H. 2007. Conventional light chains inhibit the autonomous signaling capacity of the B cell receptor. *Immunity* 26:323–33
155. Saijo K, Schmedt C, Su IH, Karasuyama H, Lowell CA, et al. 2003. Essential role of Src-family protein tyrosine kinases in NF-κB activation during B cell development. *Nat. Immunol.* 4:274–79
156. Yasuda T, Sanjo H, Pages G, Kawano Y, Karasuyama H, et al. 2008. Erk kinases link pre-B cell receptor signaling to transcriptional events required for early B cell expansion. *Immunity* 28:499–508

157. Shaw AC, Swat W, Ferrini R, Davidson L, Alt FW. 1999. Activated Ras signals developmental progression of recombinase-activating gene (RAG)-deficient pro-B lymphocytes. *J. Exp. Med.* 189:123–29
158. Chen HC, Byrd JC, Muthusamy N. 2006. Differential role for cyclic AMP response element binding protein-1 in multiple stages of B cell development, differentiation, and survival. *J. Immunol.* 176:2208–18
159. Schweighoffer E, Vanes L, Mathiot A, Nakamura T, Tybulewicz VL. 2003. Unexpected requirement for ZAP-70 in pre-B cell development and allelic exclusion. *Immunity* 18:523–33
160. Wen R, Chen Y, Schuman J, Fu G, Yang S, et al. 2004. An important role of phospholipase Cγ1 in pre-B-cell development and allelic exclusion. *EMBO J.* 23:4007–17
161. Marklund U, Lightfoot K, Cantrell D. 2003. Intracellular location and cell context-dependent function of protein kinase D. *Immunity* 19:491–501
162. Spitaler M, Emslie E, Wood CD, Cantrell D. 2006. Diacylglycerol and protein kinase D localization during T lymphocyte activation. *Immunity* 24:535–46
163. Kurosaki T. 2000. Functional dissection of BCR signaling pathways. *Curr. Opin. Immunol.* 12:276–81
164. Lu Q, Hope LW, Brasch M, Reinhard C, Cohen SN. 2003. TSG101 interaction with HRS mediates endosomal trafficking and receptor down-regulation. *Proc. Natl. Acad. Sci. USA* 100:7626–31
165. Jumaa H, Bossaller L, Portugal K, Storch B, Lotz M, et al. 2003. Deficiency of the adaptor SLP-65 in pre-B-cell acute lymphoblastic leukaemia. *Nature* 423:452–56
166. van Loo PF, Dingjan GM, Maas A, Hendriks RW. 2007. Surrogate-light-chain silencing is not critical for the limitation of pre-B cell expansion but is for the termination of constitutive signaling. *Immunity* 27:468–80
167. Geier JK, Schlissel MS. 2006. Pre-BCR signals and the control of Ig gene rearrangements. *Semin. Immunol.* 18:31–39
168. McDevit DC, Perkins L, Atchison ML, Nikolajczyk BS. 2005. The Igκ 3′ enhancer is activated by gradients of chromatin accessibility and protein association. *J. Immunol.* 174:2834–42
169. Johnson K, Hashimshony T, Sawai CM, Pongubala JM, Skok JA, et al. 2008. Regulation of immunoglobulin light-chain recombination by the transcription factor IRF-4 and the attenuation of interleukin-7 signaling. *Immunity* 28:335 45
170. Amin RH, Schlissel MS. 2008. Foxo1 directly regulates the transcription of recombination-activating genes during B cell development. *Nat. Immunol.* 9:613–22
171. Herzog S, Hug E, Meixlsperger S, Paik JH, DePinho RA, et al. 2008. SLP-65 regulates immunoglobulin light chain gene recombination through the PI(3)K-PKB-Foxo pathway. *Nat. Immunol.* 9:623–31
172. Dengler HS, Baracho GV, Omori SA, Bruckner S, Arden KC, et al. 2008. Distinct functions for the transcription factor Foxo1 at various stages of B cell differentiation. *Nat. Immunol.* 9:1388–98
173. Lam KP, Kuhn R, Rajewsky K. 1997. In vivo ablation of surface immunoglobulin on mature B cells by inducible gene targeting results in rapid cell death. *Cell* 90:1073–83
174. Wienands J, Larbolette O, Reth M. 1996. Evidence for a preformed transducer complex organized by the B cell antigen receptor. *Proc. Natl. Acad. Sci. USA* 93:7865–70
175. Reichlin A, Hu Y, Meffre E, Nagaoka H, Gong S, et al. 2001. B cell development is arrested at the immature B cell stage in mice carrying a mutation in the cytoplasmic domain of immunoglobulin β. *J. Exp. Med.* 193:13–23
176. Kraus M, Saijo K, Torres RM, Rajewsky K. 1999. Ig-α cytoplasmic truncation renders immature B cells more sensitive to antigen contact. *Immunity* 11:537–45
177. Bannish G, Fuentes-Panana EM, Cambier JC, Pear WS, Monroe JG. 2001. Ligand-independent signaling functions for the B lymphocyte antigen receptor and their role in positive selection during B lymphopoiesis. *J. Exp. Med.* 194:1583–96
178. Keren Z, Diamant E, Ostrovsky O, Bengal E, Melamed D. 2004. Modification of ligand-independent B cell receptor tonic signals activates receptor editing in immature B lymphocytes. *J. Biol. Chem.* 279:13418–24
179. Tze LE, Schram BR, Lam KP, Hogquist KA, Hippen KL, et al. 2005. Basal immunoglobulin signaling actively maintains developmental stage in immature B cells. *PLoS Biol.* 3:e82
180. Yamagami T, ten Boekel E, Andersson J, Rolink A, Melchers F. 1999. Frequencies of multiple IgL chain gene rearrangements in single normal or κL chain-deficient B lineage cells. *Immunity* 11:317–27

181. Pelanda R, Schwers S, Sonoda E, Torres RM, Nemazee D, et al. 1997. Receptor editing in a transgenic mouse model: site, efficiency, and role in B cell tolerance and antibody diversification. *Immunity* 7:765–75
182. Mackay F, Silveira PA, Brink R. 2007. B cells and the BAFF/APRIL axis: fast-forward on autoimmunity and signaling. *Curr. Opin. Immunol.* 19:327–36
183. Mackay F, Schneider P, Rennert P, Browning J. 2003. BAFF AND APRIL: a tutorial on B cell survival. *Annu. Rev. Immunol.* 21:231–64
184. Claudio E, Brown K, Park S, Wang H, Siebenlist U. 2002. BAFF-induced NEMO-independent processing of NF-κ B2 in maturing B cells. *Nat. Immunol.* 3:958–65
185. Kayagaki N, Yan M, Seshasayee D, Wang H, Lee W, et al. 2002. BAFF/BLyS receptor 3 binds the B cell survival factor BAFF ligand through a discrete surface loop and promotes processing of NF-κB2. *Immunity* 17:515–24
186. Kaisho T, Takeda K, Tsujimura T, Kawai T, Nomura F, et al. 2001. IκB kinase α is essential for mature B cell development and function. *J. Exp. Med.* 193:417–26
187. Miosge LA, Blasioli J, Blery M, Goodnow CC. 2002. Analysis of an ethylnitrosourea-generated mouse mutation defines a cell intrinsic role of nuclear factor κB2 in regulating circulating B cell numbers. *J. Exp. Med.* 196:1113–19
188. Senftleben U, Cao Y, Xiao G, Greten FR, Krahn G, et al. 2001. Activation by IKKα of a second, evolutionary conserved, NF-κ B signaling pathway. *Science* 293:1495–99
189. Yamada T, Mitani T, Yorita K, Uchida D, Matsushima A, et al. 2000. Abnormal immune function of hemopoietic cells from alymphoplasia (aly) mice, a natural strain with mutant NF-κB-inducing kinase. *J. Immunol.* 165:804–12
190. Xu LG, Shu HB. 2002. TNFR-associated factor-3 is associated with BAFF-R and negatively regulates BAFF-R-mediated NF-κB activation and IL-10 production. *J. Immunol.* 169:6883–89
191. Morrison MD, Reiley W, Zhang M, Sun SC. 2005. An atypical tumor necrosis factor (TNF) receptor-associated factor-binding motif of B cell-activating factor belonging to the TNF family (BAFF) receptor mediates induction of the noncanonical NF-κB signaling pathway. *J. Biol. Chem.* 280:10018–24
192. Liao G, Zhang M, Harhaj EW, Sun SC. 2004. Regulation of the NF-κB-inducing kinase by tumor necrosis factor receptor-associated factor 3-induced degradation. *J. Biol. Chem.* 279:26243–50
193. Sasaki Y, Derudder E, Hobeika E, Pelanda R, Reth M, et al. 2006. Canonical NF-κB activity, dispensable for B cell development, replaces BAFF-receptor signals and promotes B cell proliferation upon activation. *Immunity* 24:729–39
194. Enzler T, Bonizzi G, Silverman GJ, Otero DC, Widhopf GF, et al. 2006. Alternative and classical NF-κB signaling retain autoreactive B cells in the splenic marginal zone and result in lupus-like disease. *Immunity* 25:403–15
195. Xie P, Stunz LL, Larison KD, Yang B, Bishop GA. 2007. Tumor necrosis factor receptor-associated factor 3 is a critical regulator of B cell homeostasis in secondary lymphoid organs. *Immunity* 27:253–67
196. Gardam S, Sierro F, Basten A, Mackay F, Brink R. 2008. TRAF2 and TRAF3 signal adapters act cooperatively to control the maturation and survival signals delivered to B cells by the BAFF receptor. *Immunity* 28:391–401
197. Mecklenbrauker I, Kalled SL, Leitges M, Mackay F, Tarakhovsky A. 2004. Regulation of B-cell survival by BAFF-dependent PKCδ-mediated nuclear signalling. *Nature* 431:456–61
198. Kraus M, Alimzhanov MB, Rajewsky N, Rajewsky K. 2004. Survival of resting mature B lymphocytes depends on BCR signaling via the Igα/β heterodimer. *Cell* 117:787–800
199. Monroe JG, Dorshkind K. 2007. Fate decisions regulating bone marrow and peripheral B lymphocyte development. *Adv. Immunol.* 95:1–50
200. Schulze-Luehrmann J, Ghosh S. 2006. Antigen-receptor signaling to nuclear factor kappa B. *Immunity* 25:701–15
201. Rueda D, Thome M. 2005. Phosphorylation of CARMA1: the link(er) to NF-κB activation. *Immunity* 23:551–53
202. Hikida M, Johmura S, Hashimoto A, Takezaki M, Kurosaki T. 2003. Coupling between B cell receptor and phospholipase C-γ2 is essential for mature B cell development. *J. Exp. Med.* 198:581–89
203. Walmsley MJ, Ooi SK, Reynolds LF, Smith SH, Ruf S, et al. 2003. Critical roles for Rac1 and Rac2 GTPases in B cell development and signaling. *Science* 302:459–62

204. Cancro MP. 2008. Living in context with the survival factor BAFF. *Immunity* 28:300–1
205. Jacobi AM, Diamond B. 2005. Balancing diversity and tolerance: lessons from patients with systemic lupus erythematosus. *J. Exp. Med.* 202:341–44
206. Reif K, Ekland EH, Ohl L, Nakano H, Lipp M, et al. 2002. Balanced responsiveness to chemoattractants from adjacent zones determines B-cell position. *Nature* 416:94–99
207. Vinuesa CG, Tangye SG, Moser B, Mackay CR. 2005. Follicular B helper T cells in antibody responses and autoimmunity. *Nat. Rev. Immunol.* 5:853–65
208. McHeyzer-Williams LJ, McHeyzer-Williams MG. 2005. Antigen-specific memory B cell development. *Annu. Rev. Immunol.* 23:487–513
209. Tarlinton D. 2006. B-cell memory: Are subsets necessary? *Nat. Rev. Immunol.* 6:785–90
210. Mebius RE, Kraal G. 2005. Structure and function of the spleen. *Nat. Rev. Immunol.* 5:606–16
211. MacLennan I, Vinuesa C. 2002. Dendritic cells, BAFF, and APRIL: innate players in adaptive antibody responses. *Immunity* 17:235–38
212. Klein U, Dalla-Favera R. 2008. Germinal centres: role in B-cell physiology and malignancy. *Nat. Rev. Immunol.* 8:22–33
213. Bishop GA, Hostager BS. 2001. Signaling by CD40 and its mimics in B cell activation. *Immunol. Res.* 24:97–109
214. Grammer AC, Lipsky PE. 2000. CD40-mediated regulation of immune responses by TRAF-dependent and TRAF-independent signaling mechanisms. *Adv. Immunol.* 76:61–178
215. Gallagher E, Enzler T, Matsuzawa A, Anzelon-Mills A, Otero D, et al. 2007. Kinase MEKK1 is required for CD40-dependent activation of the kinases Jnk and p38, germinal center formation, B cell proliferation and antibody production. *Nat. Immunol.* 8:57–63
216. Qian Y, Qin J, Cui G, Naramura M, Snow EC, et al. 2004. Act1, a negative regulator in CD40- and BAFF-mediated B cell survival. *Immunity* 21:575–87
217. Aiba Y, Yamazaki T, Okada T, Gotoh K, Sanjo H, et al. 2006. BANK negatively regulates Akt activation and subsequent B cell responses. *Immunity* 24:259–68
218. Vinuesa CG, Cook MC, Angelucci C, Athanasopoulos V, Rui L, et al. 2005. A RING-type ubiquitin ligase family member required to repress follicular helper T cells and autoimmunity. *Nature* 435:452–58
219. Saito M, Gao J, Basso K, Kitagawa Y, Smith PM, et al. 2007. A signaling pathway mediating downregulation of BCL6 in germinal center B cells is blocked by BCL6 gene alterations in B cell lymphoma. *Cancer Cell* 12:280–92
220. Liu YJ, Malisan F, de Bouteiller O, Guret C, Lebecque S, et al. 1996. Within germinal centers, isotype switching of immunoglobulin genes occurs after the onset of somatic mutation. *Immunity* 4:241–50
221. MacLennan IC. 1994. Germinal centers. *Annu. Rev. Immunol.* 12:117–39
222. Schaerli P, Willimann K, Lang AB, Lipp M, Loetscher P, et al. 2000. CXC chemokine receptor 5 expression defines follicular homing T cells with B cell helper function. *J. Exp. Med.* 192:1553–62
223. Breitfeld D, Ohl L, Kremmer E, Ellwart J, Sallusto F, et al. 2000. Follicular B helper T cells express CXC chemokine receptor 5, localize to B cell follicles, and support immunoglobulin production. *J. Exp. Med.* 192:1545–52
224. Kim CH, Rott LS, Clark-Lewis I, Campbell DJ, Wu L, Butcher EC. 2001. Subspecialization of $CXCR5^+$ T cells: B helper activity is focused in a germinal center-localized subset of $CXCR5^+$ T cells. *J. Exp. Med.* 193:1373–81
225. King C, Tangye SG, Mackay CR. 2008. T follicular helper (TFH) cells in normal and dysregulated immune responses. *Annu. Rev. Immunol.* 26:741–66
226. Kim MY, Gaspal FM, Wiggett HE, McConnell FM, Gulbranson-Judge A, et al. 2003. $CD4^+CD3^-$ accessory cells costimulate primed CD4 T cells through OX40 and CD30 at sites where T cells collaborate with B cells. *Immunity* 18:643–54
227. Flynn S, Toellner KM, Raykundalia C, Goodall M, Lane P. 1998. CD4 T cell cytokine differentiation: The B cell activation molecule, OX40 ligand, instructs CD4 T cells to express interleukin 4 and upregulates expression of the chemokine receptor, Blr-1. *J. Exp. Med.* 188:297–304
228. Brocker T, Gulbranson-Judge A, Flynn S, Riedinger M, Raykundalia C, Lane P. 1999. CD4 T cell traffic control: in vivo evidence that ligation of OX40 on CD4 T cells by OX40-ligand expressed on dendritic cells leads to the accumulation of CD4 T cells in B follicles. *Eur. J. Immunol.* 29:1610–16

229. Han S, Hathcock K, Zheng B, Kepler TB, Hodes R, Kelsoe G. 1995. Cellular interaction in germinal centers. Roles of CD40 ligand and B7-2 in established germinal centers. *J. Immunol.* 155:556–67
230. Dong C, Temann UA, Flavell RA. 2001. Cutting edge: critical role of inducible costimulator in germinal center reactions. *J. Immunol.* 166:3659–62
231. McAdam AJ, Greenwald RJ, Levin MA, Chernova T, Malenkovich N, et al. 2001. ICOS is critical for CD40-mediated antibody class switching. *Nature* 409:102–5
232. Tafuri A, Shahinian A, Bladt F, Yoshinaga SK, Jordana M, et al. 2001. ICOS is essential for effective T-helper-cell responses. *Nature* 409:105–9
233. Yu D, Tan AH, Hu X, Athanasopoulos V, Simpson N, et al. 2007. Roquin represses autoimmunity by limiting inducible T-cell costimulator messenger RNA. *Nature* 450:299–303
234. Nurieva RI, Chung Y, Hwang D, Yang XO, Kang HS, et al. 2008. Generation of T follicular helper cells is mediated by interleukin-21 but independent of T helper 1, 2, or 17 cell lineages. *Immunity* 29:138–49
235. Parrish-Novak J, Dillon SR, Nelson A, Hammond A, Sprecher C, et al. 2000. Interleukin 21 and its receptor are involved in NK cell expansion and regulation of lymphocyte function. *Nature* 408:57–63
236. Leonard WJ, Spolski R. 2005. Interleukin-21: a modulator of lymphoid proliferation, apoptosis and differentiation. *Nat. Rev. Immunol.* 5:688–98
237. Ozaki K, Spolski R, Ettinger R, Kim HP, Wang G, et al. 2004. Regulation of B cell differentiation and plasma cell generation by IL-21, a novel inducer of Blimp-1 and Bcl-6. *J. Immunol.* 173:5361–71
238. Wilker PR, Kohyama M, Sandau MM, Albring JC, Nakagawa O, et al. 2008. Transcription factor Mef2c is required for B cell proliferation and survival after antigen receptor stimulation. *Nat. Immunol.* 9:603–12

Control of Immunity by the TNFR-Related Molecule OX40 (CD134)

Michael Croft

Division of Molecular Immunology, La Jolla Institute for Allergy and Immunology, La Jolla, California 92037. email: mick@liai.org

Annu. Rev. Immunol. 2010. 28:57–78

The *Annual Review of Immunology* is online at immunol.annualreviews.org

This article's doi:
10.1146/annurev-immunol-030409-101243

0732-0582/10/0423-0057$20.00

Key Words

OX40L, costimulation, T cells, autoimmunity, infectious disease, vaccination

Abstract

TNFR/TNF superfamily members can control diverse aspects of immune function. Research over the past 10 years has shown that one of the most important and prominent interactions in this family is that between OX40 (CD134) and its partner OX40L (CD252). These molecules strongly regulate conventional CD4 and CD8 T cells, and more recent data are highlighting their ability to modulate NKT cell and NK cell function as well as to mediate cross-talk with professional antigen-presenting cells and diverse cell types such as mast cells, smooth muscle cells, and endothelial cells. Additionally, OX40-OX40L interactions alter the differentiation and activity of regulatory T cells. Blocking OX40L has produced strong therapeutic effects in multiple animal models of autoimmune and inflammatory disease, and, in line with a prospective clinical future, reagents that stimulate OX40 signaling are showing promise as adjuvants for vaccination as well as for treatment of cancer.

INTRODUCTION

OX40 (also known as ACT35, CD134, TNFRSF4) was first discovered in 1987 with an antibody (termed MRC OX40) that bound to activated rat CD4 T cells (1). OX40 is an approximately 50-kD glycoprotein and has been cloned in the rat, mouse, and human (2–4). It is a type 1 transmembrane protein of 249 amino acids, with a 49 amino acid cytoplasmic tail and a 186 amino acid extracellular region. It was initially found to have homology to NGFR (nerve growth factor receptor) and CD40 and was then classified as a member of the TNFR (tumor necrosis factor receptor) superfamily, as more proteins with sequence and structural similarity to TNFR were discovered. The gene for OX40 is clustered on human chromosome 1 (mouse chromosome 4) with several other TNFR family molecules, TNFR2, 4-1BB, HVEM, CD30, GITR, and DR3. OX40 has three complete and one truncated cysteine-rich domains that are characteristic of the TNFR superfamily.

OX40's ligand (OX40L, also known as gp34, CD252, TNFSF4) is a type II glycoprotein with a 23 amino acid cytoplasmic tail and a 133 amino acid extracellular domain. It was originally identified in 1985 on transformed T cell lines as a molecule, gp34, induced by the *tax* gene of human T cell leukemia virus (HTLV)-1 (5, 6), and then cloning of a binding partner for OX40 identified the protein gp34 as OX40L (7). It is expressed as a trimer and has a TNF homology domain; thus, it is structurally similar to other molecules of the TNF superfamily and has some sequence homology. The *OX40L* gene is on human and mouse chromosome 1, clustered with genes for two other TNF family members, *FasL* and *GITRL*. Although a number of the TNF family can bind to several partners, at present there is no evidence that OX40L can complex with anything other than OX40. Similarly, except for reports showing that feline OX40 can be a receptor for feline immunodeficiency virus (8), there are no indications of other binding partners for OX40 in human or mouse systems, including binding to other viruses. The crystallized complex of human OX40 and OX40L is a trimeric configuration of one OX40L molecule and three OX40 monomers (9). The length of the complex of the extracellular regions of OX40 bound to OX40L is approximately 80 Å, which when factored with a linker that connects to the transmembrane portion of OX40 makes the pairing compatible with bridging regions of 100–150 Å thought to exist between a number of interacting cell types, including T cells and antigen-presenting cells (APCs). This is similar to the sizes of other complexes such as those between the T cell receptor (TCR) and major histocompatibility complex (MHC) or CD28 and B7 that regulate T cell and APC activity and corresponds well with the functional data described below indicating essential costimulatory roles for the OX40-OX40L interaction in many aspects of immunity involving direct cell-cell communication.

OX40 AND OX40L EXPRESSION

The primary cell that is quoted most often as expressing OX40 is the activated T cell, and in fact some older literature stated that OX40 was T cell specific or restricted to CD4 T cells and on occasion restricted to Th2 cells. OX40 is likely predominantly expressed on activated T cells, but this includes CD4 and CD8 T cells, Th2, Th1, and Th17 cells, as well as $Foxp3^{+}CD4^{+}$ regulatory T cells (Tregs). Naive CD4 and CD8 T cells do not express OX40, nor do most memory T cells, whether central or effector memory phenotype. However, OX40 is induced with delayed kinetics after activation of naive T cells, with no real consensus in terms of timing, having been visualized anywhere from 12 h after activation to as long as 5–6 days. Memory T cells reexpress OX40 rapidly, within 1–4 h after activation. Differences between CD4 and CD8 T cells have been seen in some inflammatory situations, with OX40 expression appearing to be more transient on CD8 T cells, but it can be prolonged on CD4 T cells (10–13). Altered kinetics most likely relate to the nature of the antigen and its persistence, as well as to the inflammatory environment that accompanies antigen presentation, leading to the statement that the time and length of OX40 expression on conventional T cells cannot be generalized. Minimally, strong crosslinking of the TCR/CD3 complex can promote OX40 on CD4 and CD8 T cells, but under physiological conditions other costimulatory molecules such as CD28 contribute to the kinetics of appearance, and the cytokines IL-1, IL-2, IL-4, and TNF can enhance or prolong expression. OX40 is also found on Tregs. It is constitutively expressed on mouse natural (thymus-derived) Foxp3$^+$ T cells, but it is only inducible on human Foxp3$^+$ T cells. Other cell types can express OX40, although there is not a clear picture of when and where. These include natural killer T cells (NKT cells), neutrophils, and natural killer (NK) cells. The current ideas are that this is also induced expression, but data are not extensive at present. As described below, literature exists on the functional activity of OX40 on all of these cell types, implying that its effects are far broader than simply positively regulating conventional T cell immunity, even though most studies relate to the latter.

The primary source of OX40L is likely to be a professional APC, and it can be induced on activated B cells (14, 15), mature conventional dendritic cells (cDCs) (16, 17), Langerhans cells (18), plasmacytoid DCs (pDCs) (19, 20), and macrophages (21). Various APC maturation factors can promote OX40L, including signals through CD40, membrane B cell receptor, and several Toll-like receptors (TLR2, 4, 9), as well as inflammatory cytokines such as TSLP (thymic stromal lymphopoietin) (22) and IL-18 (23). However, additional immune cell types such as NK cells (24) and mast cells (25, 26), as well as structural cells such as vascular endothelial cells (27) and smooth muscle cells (28), can express OX40L, induced by the inflammatory cytokines GM-CSF, IL-1, and TNF (mast cells, smooth muscle cells) or by receptors such as NKG2D (NK cells). Furthermore, OX40L is inducible on some conventional activated T cells (29, 30) and on a specialized cell type called an adult lymphoid tissue inducer (LTi) that is CD4$^+$ but CD3$^-$ and maintains the integral organization of lymphoid tissue but that might also function as an APC in some instances (31, 32).

cDC/pDC: conventional/plasmacytoid dendritic cells

Both OX40 and OX40L have been visualized in situ in mouse models of disease as well as in samples from human patients. Many of these data are summarized in **Table 1**. References have been omitted owing to space limitations, although some can be found elsewhere (33). One can have the impression from reports of in vivo expression that OX40 and OX40L are quite restricted; however, most of these analyses have focused on a particular cell type without attempting to analyze other cells. Therefore, the expression of these molecules in inflamed and diseased tissue might be much broader than is reflected in **Table 1**. A number of studies have tried to determine if either molecule can be used as a marker of disease progression or severity, with varying conclusions. Certainly there is strong support that they will be found primarily during an ongoing immune response, but given the inducible and transient nature of their expression, likely dictated by multiple other inflammatory factors, it is questionable whether they will be useful as conventional clinical biomarkers. However, expression studies during the course of any disease will be extremely valuable based on their therapeutic potential. OX40L can be cleaved from the membrane of cells, likely after binding to OX40, as implied by studies of mice deficient in OX40 in which greater levels of OX40L have been noted (Croft lab, unpublished data), and therefore any analysis of OX40L in situ might have the potential to underestimate its presence. In contrast, assessing OX40 expression should not have this limitation. Moreover, OX40 could have future uses for monitoring and isolating antigen-specific human T cells in in vitro diagnostic or functional assays. OX40 has been visualized on a few presumed memory CD4 T cells in peripheral blood, often associated with CD25 expression (34), and, perhaps more significantly, OX40 is upregulated on human T cells stimulated with recall viral antigen, bacterial antigen, and autoantigen

Table 1 Reported in situ expression of OX40 and OX40L in human and animal inflammation[a]

Disease/response	Host	Organ/tissue	Cell type	OX40	OX40L
MS, EAE	Human	Blood	T cells	+	
	Mouse	CNS/spinal cord	CD4 T cells	+	
		CNS/spinal cord	CD11b+ MΦ/microglia		+
	Rat	CNS/spinal cord	CD4 T cells	+	
RA, CIA, adjuvant arthritis	Human	Blood/synovial fluid	CD4 T cells	+	
		Synovial tissue	?		+
	Mouse	Blood	CD4 T cells	+	
	Rat		CD4 T cells	+	
IBD, colitis, CD	Human	Gut	Endothelium	+	
		Lamina propria	T cells		+
	Mouse	Peyer's patches, lamina propria	CD4 T cells	+	
		Mesenteric LN	cDCs		+
Asthma	Human	Lung	Smooth muscle		+
	Mouse	Periaortic LN, lung	CD4 T cells	+	
		Periaortic LN, lung	cDCs		+
		Lung	B cells, MΦ		+
SLE, lupus nephritis, HgCl2-induced autoimmunity	Human	Kidney	Lymphocytes	+	
		Kidney	Capillary endothelium		+
		Blood	?		+
	Mouse, rat		CD4 T cells	+	
Diabetes	Human	Blood	CD4 T cells	+	
	Mouse	Pancreas	CD4 and CD8 T cells	+	
		Pancreas	cDCs		+
Heart disease (myocarditis, atherosclerosis, acute coronary syndrome)	Human	Heart	Myocytes		+
		Heart	Lymphocytes	+	
		Blood	Monocytes		+
			Platelets ?		+
	Mouse	Heart, aorta	T cells	+	
			Myocytes		+
			Endothelial cells		+
			Macrophages		+
Myasthenia gravis	Human	Blood	CD4 T cells	+	
Psoriasis	Human	Skin	CD4 and CD8 T cells	+	
			Capillary endothelium		+
Bone marrow transplants, GVHD	Human	Blood	CD4 and CD8 T cells	+	
	Mouse	Blood	CD4 and CD8 T cells	+	
	Rat	Blood	CD4 T cells	+	
Allografts	Human	Skin	CD4 T cells	+	
		Skin	Endothelial cells		+
	Mouse	Bowel	?	+	+
		Cardiac	CD4 T cells	+	
		Skin	CD4 T cells	+	

(Continued)

Table 1 (*Continued*)

Disease/response	Host	Organ/tissue	Cell type	OX40	OX40L
Tumors	Human	TIL	CD4 T cells	+	
		TDLN	CD4 T cells	+	
	Mouse	TIL	CD4 and CD8 T cells	+	
		TDLN	CD4 and CD8 T cells, NKT cells	+	
		TIL	pDCs		+
HIV	Human	Blood	CD4 T cells	+	
Vaccinia virus	Mouse	Spleen, LN	CD8 and CD4 T cells	+	
Influenza virus	Mouse		CD4 and CD8 T cells	+	
Cryptococcus neoformans	Mouse		CD4 and CD8 T cells	+	
			cDCs		+
Leishmania major	Mouse	LN	CD4 T cells	+	
		LN	cDCs		+
Nippostrongylus brasiliensis	Mouse	Spleen	cDCs		+

[a]Abbreviations: CD, Crohn's disease; CIA, collagen-induced arthritis; cDCs/pDCs, conventional/plasmacytoid dendritic cells; EAE, experimental allergic encephalomyelitis; aGVHD, acute graft-versus-host disease; cGVHD, chronic graft-versus-host disease; HIV, human immunodeficiency virus; IBD, inflammatory bowel disease; LN, lymph node; MS, multiple sclerosis; MΦ, macrophage; RA, rheumatoid arthritis; SLE, systemic lupus erythematosus; TDLN, tumor-draining lymph node; TIL, tumor-infiltrating lymphocytes.

(35, 36), again sometimes coexpressed with CD25. This latter finding suggests that OX40, in combination with other markers, might be suitable for identifying antigen-specific human T cell populations from in vitro recall assays.

FUNCTION OF OX40 ON CD4 T CELLS

One of the most recognized and accepted activities of OX40-OX40L interactions is to regulate the division and survival of conventional T cells, which has led to the often-used description of OX40 as a costimulatory receptor for T cells. Hints at this important function were provided upon the initial discovery of OX40 in rat and human systems, where enhanced in vitro proliferation of CD4 T cells was reported with agonist antibodies to OX40, or trans-stimulation with OX40L (1, 7, 37). Furthermore, interim reports identified OX40 on pathogenic CD4 T cells at the site of inflammation in a model of MS (EAE) and suggested that depletion of such cells could ameliorate disease (38, 39). However, it was only with the advent of more physiological in vitro systems, the development of OX40 and OX40L knockout animals, and in vivo use of neutralizing or agonist antibodies specific for OX40L or OX40, respectively, that the strong role of the interaction in controlling T cells was fully appreciated (10, 11, 15, 40–44). These studies directly showed either altered division and survival of CD4 T cells in the presence or absence of OX40 or OX40L or a substantial reduction in the accumulation of antigen-specific CD4 T cells in the knockout systems, as well as impaired cytokine production either in vitro or in vivo. Furthermore, the development of CD4 T cell memory was strongly impaired in the gene-deficient animals (11, 15), and initial reports were published showing that blocking the OX40-OX40L interaction prevented CD4 T cell responses and the development of inflammation in models of MS, colitis, RA, GVHD, and leishmaniasis (21, 45–48). Directly suggesting that this is at least in part a function of OX40 signaling, in vivo administration of agonist antibodies to OX40 produced a reciprocal effect with markedly enhanced numbers of primary effector and memory CD4 T cells generated when antigen was delivered in various adjuvants (11, 49).

Further supporting the idea that OX40 plays an essential role in many situations in which enhanced or deregulated T cell activity occurs, investigators showed that ligation of OX40

EAE: experimental allergic encephalomyelitis

MS: multiple sclerosis

RA: rheumatoid arthritis

GVHD: graft-versus-host disease

TRAF: TNF-associated factor

prevented and, more significantly, reversed a state of unresponsiveness in the CD4 T cell compartment in several experimental systems of tolerance (50). In line with this finding, transgenic mice in which OX40L was constitutively expressed by DCs (51) or T cells (52) were characterized by the accumulation of greatly increased numbers of effector-like CD4 T cells after injection of antigen, and in the latter by spontaneous development of interstitial pneumonia, inflammatory bowel disease, and autoantibodies, presumably as a consequence of environmental exposure to mucosal antigens and subsequent deregulation of T cells. Illustrating that this is a physiological activity of OX40 when expressed on responding CD4 T cells are data with gene-deficient TCR transgenic T cells. These data demonstrate that T cells lacking OX40 do not sustain division for long periods after antigen recognition and are unable to maintain high levels of antiapoptotic proteins, resulting in poor long-term survival of effector T cells and poor memory development (53, 54). Moreover, blocking OX40-OX40L interactions during secondary immune responses of memory CD4 T cells, or the use of memory-like T cells that cannot express OX40, has demonstrated that these molecules also strongly regulate clonal expansion of T cells to recall antigen (55). Recent data suggest that it is the effector memory subset of CD4 T cells that is primarily regulated by OX40 (56), although more studies are needed in this area before concluding that central memory CD4 T cells do not use or require OX40 as a costimulatory receptor. Reports using human CD4 T cells cultured in vitro have supported the mouse studies, showing that OX40-OX40L interactions can again control division and survival (24, 25, 37, 57–59), and two recent preclinical studies in nonhuman primates, either stimulating OX40 or blocking OX40L, describe strong effects on the development of CD4 T cell responses (60, 61). Collectively, these studies demonstrate that OX40 and OX40L dictate the number of effector (protective or pathogenic) T cells that accumulate in primary and secondary responses, as well as determine the frequency of memory T cells that are generated.

OX40 SIGNALING IN CD4 T CELLS

Studies of the intracellular molecules engaged and targeted by OX40 have provided good rationale for the strong impact of OX40 in regulating CD4 T cells (**Figure 1**). Initial studies, largely in transient transfection systems in non-T cells, found that OX40 can bind several TNFR-associated factors, with TRAF2, 3, and 5 being the principal molecules that can be recruited to the cytoplasmic tail (62, 63) via a QEE motif that is present in other family members (64). TRAF2 and 3 have been characterized as adaptor molecules that can lead to activation of both the canonical (IKKβ-dependent) NF-κB1 pathway as well as the noncanonical (NIK/IKKα-dependent) NF-κB2 pathway. Related to the initial findings in transfection systems of NF-κB1 activity after crosslinking OX40 (62, 63) are data in physiological systems in which CD4 T cells respond to antigen. These data show that OX40 strongly contributes to the overall level of NF-κB1 activation in T cells (65). CD4 T cells that lack OX40 cannot maintain high levels of several antiapoptotic Bcl-2 family members including Bcl-2, Bcl-xL, and Bfl-1 (53), a finding that directly correlates with reduced NF-κB1 activity (65). Furthermore, reconstitution of NF-κB1 signaling in these T cells restored the expression of Bcl-2, Bcl-xL, and Bfl-1 and reversed the defect in expansion and accumulation of T cells following antigen encounter (65).

OX40 signals also control the expression of survivin, a member of the IAP (inhibitor of apoptosis) family, that is induced in the G1 phase of the cell cycle and regulates G1-S transition and hence division of T cells (66). The finding that survivin also complexes with aurora B kinase and the mammalian target of rapamycin (mTOR) provided a link to earlier work demonstrating that OX40 also controls the phosphorylation of PI-3-kinase (PI3K) and Akt (protein kinase B), upstream activators of

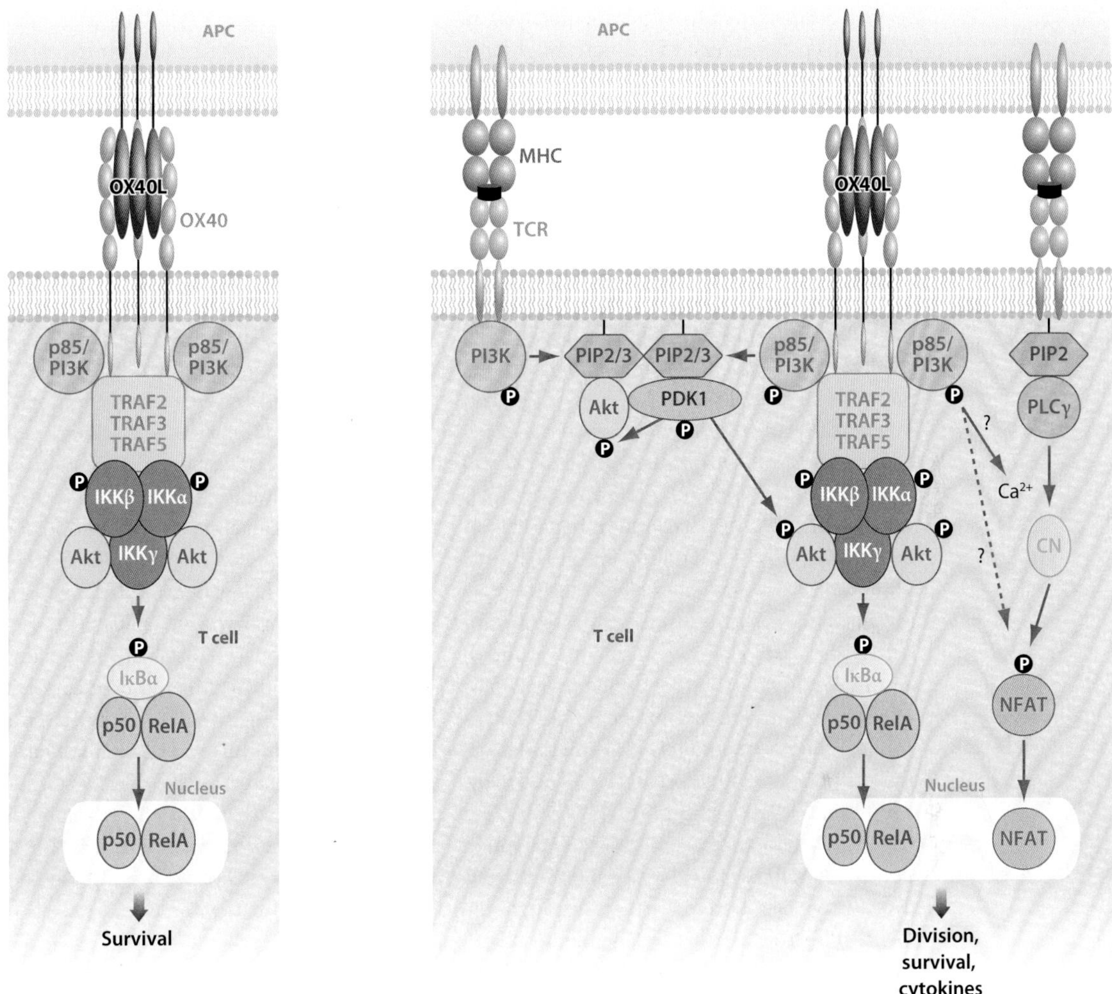

Figure 1

OX40 acts as both an independent signaling entity (*left*) and an entity augmenting antigen-driven TCR signaling (*right*). Binding of OX40L results in trimerization of OX40 monomers and the recruitment of TRAF2, 3, and 5. The sequence of events resulting in a functional OX40 signaling complex is not yet clear, but IKKα, IKKβ, IKKγ, the p85 subunit of PI3K, and Akt are found with the TRAF adaptors. The signalosome can result in phosphorylation and degradation of IκBα, leading to activation of NF-κB1 and entry of p50 and RelA into the nucleus. This is sufficient to provide survival signals to T cells in the absence of antigen recognition. NIK is most likely also recruited into the complex, although this has not been visualized at present. If NIK is recruited, this likely leads to activation of NF-κB2, which might also be necessary for transmitting survival signals. In this scenario without antigen recognition, PI3K and Akt are not activated. With antigen signaling, OX40 synergizes with the TCR to promote strong Akt phosphorylation, likely due to localization of the OX40 signalosome with PDK1 recruited by the TCR. TCR signals initiate intracellular Ca^{2+} influx, leading to NFAT dephosphorylation and nuclear entry. Through a mechanism not yet elucidated, OX40 synergizes with this process to allow greater Ca^{2+} influx and nuclear accumulation of NFAT. The combined antigen and OX40 signals in T cells can enhance expression of molecules such as survivin, cyclin A, cyclin-dependent kinases, Bcl-2 antiapoptotic molecules, cytokines, and cytokine receptors, as well as suppress Foxp3 and CTLA4 expression. (Abbreviations: TRAF, TNFR-associated factor; PI3K, PI-3-kinase; NIK, NF-κB-inducing kinase; IKKs, IκB kinases; NFAT, nuclear factor of activated T cell; PDK1, 3-phosphoinositide-dependent kinase 1; CTLA4, cytotoxic T lymphocyte–associated antigen-4; PIP2/3, phosphatidylinositol 4,5-bisphosphate/3,4,5-trisphosphate; CN, calcineurin; PLCγ, phospholipase Cγ.)

mTOR (54). This finding also connected this pathway directly with cyclin A and control of several cyclin-dependent kinases involved in cell cycle progression (67). Interestingly, decreased activity of Akt and NF-κB1 coincided in CD4 T cells that cannot receive OX40 signals, and forced expression of an active version of Akt restored defective expansion and survival of OX40-deficient T cells when responding to antigen (54), mimicking the action of an active version of IKKβ (65). This suggests that Akt and NF-κB1 cooperate to transmit the essential division and survival signals imparted by OX40.

Both published and unpublished studies have now provided a model of how OX40 acts as a costimulatory receptor (**Figure 1**). Upon ligation by OX40L expressed on APCs, OX40 is recruited into lipid rafts and forms a complex with TRAF2, 3, and 5, a complex that also contains IKKα, IKKβ, and IKKγ, as well as the p85 subunit of PI3K and Akt. OX40 can have two distinct modes of action. One is as a separate signaling unit, irrespective of antigen recognition and TCR signaling, that results in the phosphorylation of IKKα/β and subsequent nuclear accumulation of the subunits of NF-κB1, p50 and RelA. OX40 can therefore act as an independent receptor, much like TNF when binding to TNFR1/2, distinct from the classical version of a costimulatory receptor, which only functions in synergy with antigen signals through the TCR. The role of this independent activity appears to be principally to provide survival signals to T cells, although this needs to be investigated in more depth and may represent a way to sustain T cell responses after antigen is cleared. Sources of OX40L that could provide this antigen-independent signal might include LTi cells, B cells, and responding T cells themselves, which all can support T cell survival at the late effector phase of immune responses (30, 31, 68). When antigen is being presented, however, ligation of OX40 provides additional signals that are completely dependent on TCR signaling, one of which is focused on enhancing activation of the Akt pathway. This enhanced Akt activation will provide initial antigen-driven proliferative signals that further synergize with NF-κB1-driven growth and survival signals. Additionally, through an unknown mechanism, OX40 can also enhance TCR-induced calcium influx, leading to strong nuclear accumulation of NFATc1 and NFATc2 that likely regulate production of cytokines (69). TRAF2 is critical for the functional OX40 signaling complex in that it cannot form if TRAF2 is knocked down (T. So and M. Croft, unpublished observations), an observation that correlates with data demonstrating that CD4 T cells from a dominant-negative TRAF2 transgenic mouse were refractory to OX40 signals that drove generation of both effector and memory T cells (70).

OX40 can also result in activation of NIK and phosphorylation of IKKα, which leads to processing of p100 to p52 and hence to activation of noncanonical NF-κB2 (T. So and M. Croft, unpublished observation). The exact role played by TRAF3 and TRAF5 in the OX40 signaling complex is not clear. TRAF3 can complex with NIK and result in its degradation, meaning that NIK is not available for downstream effects. TRAF3 likely cooperates with TRAF2 in allowing OX40 to recruit NIK and then in allowing NIK to be released, remain intact, and become activated to drive the NF-κB2 pathway. What this controls in terms of functionality is not currently known, but NF-κB1 and NF-κB2 may synergize to fully provide division and survival signals through OX40.

CONTROL OF CYTOKINES AND T HELPER DIFFERENTIATION

Although direct intracellular signaling from OX40 can explain many of this receptor's effects on regulating T cell division and survival, other indirect activities related to modulating cytokine production or cytokine receptor signaling further contribute to these processes as well as to the balance between CD4 T helper (Th) subsets that arise. OX40-OX40L interactions minimally impact initial IL-2 production from naive CD4 T cells, a phenomenon largely controlled by CD28 (10, 53), but OX40 signals can strongly promote IL-2 from effector T cells (10), as well as enhance expression of

IL-2Rα that leads to gain of effector function typified by the ability to make IFN-γ upon exposure to cytokines such as IL-12 and IL-18 (71, 72). Other described activities that might contribute to the process of CD4 T cell differentiation include promoting IL-12Rβ2 expression (73) and blocking upregulation of CTLA4 (70), Foxp3 (74–76), and IL-10 (77). Given that CTLA4, Foxp3, and IL-10 are best characterized as suppressive molecules, inhibiting their expression would aid in driving a strong response of conventional CD4 T cells. Activation of Akt can block phosphorylation of Smad proteins that are required for TGF-βR to induce Foxp3, and therefore this might be one mechanism by which OX40 signals suppress Foxp3 expression (i.e., Treg generation). However, in one system, suppression of Foxp3 by OX40 was in part indirect, dependent on production of both IL-4 and IFN-γ (78), again implying that OX40-OX40L modulation of the cytokine environment can influence both the magnitude and the nature of the CD4 T cell response. How OX40 might antagonize IL-10 is not known, but this was illustrated in systems where vitamin D3 and dexamethasone were added into culture to induce Tregs that make IL-10 (77). This suggests either a novel action in blocking signaling through the receptors for these molecules or again an indirect effect related to production of Th1- or Th2-directive cytokines that could antagonize IL-10.

In naive CD4 T cells, under neutral conditions, OX40 engagement can preferentially lead to the generation of Th2 cells, driven by autocrine IL-4 and related to enhanced calcium/NFATc signaling, a phenotype again observed in both mouse and human systems (22, 40, 69, 79). However, the production of either IL-12 or IFN-α can overcome this Th2-directive action and result in the promotion, by OX40, of Th1 responses (19, 22, 80, 81). In one in vitro system, OX40 also antagonized the induction of Th17 cells, and this effect was mediated by autocrine IFN-γ (82). This action does not correlate with in vivo data showing that OX40 is necessary for EAE (21, 83) or in models of RA (48, 84), both Th17-controlled diseases. However, it again illustrates the ability of OX40-OX40L interactions to influence the immediate cytokine environment that might then influence Th differentiation. Certainly, ligation of OX40 can directly induce Th2, Th1, and Th17 cytokines in some situations (10, 23, 80, 85). Here the potential contribution of reverse signals through OX40L should be considered. Although much of the activity of OX40-OX40L interactions can be attributed to OX40 signaling, OX40L clearly can produce functional effects, as illustrated when crosslinked on cDCs and pDCs, B cells, and smooth muscle cells (14, 16, 28). This relates largely to production of cytokines such as IL-12, IL-6, IL-1, TNF, and IFN-α (16, 28, 86), several of which have strong activities in directing differentiation into various Th subsets (e.g., IL-12 or IFN-α for Th1; IL-6 for Th17). How OX40L transmits signals to promote proinflammatory cytokines is not known, but some studies have found alterations in PKCβ2, c-Jun, and c-Fos after OX40L is crosslinked (28, 87).

Thus, OX40-OX40L interactions have the ability to enhance an ongoing immune response regardless of the type of polarized response, both by imparting division and survival signals to differentiating or already differentiated T cells, by blocking the induction of $Foxp3^+$ or $IL\text{-}10^+$ Tregs, and by synergizing with and enhancing production of differentiative cytokines to additionally polarize the responses. This is clearly illustrated in disease studies in which the absence of OX40-OX40L interactions reduces clinical symptoms that are driven by Th1, Th2, and Th17 cells (**Table 2**).

REGULATION OF CD8 T CELLS

Studies of CD8 T cells have generally lagged behind those of CD4 T cells. As noted above, most of the initial pioneering work on OX40 and OX40L was directed to CD4 T cells, and the reports that addressed the activity of CD8 T cells largely yielded negative data. For example, OX40L transgenic animals did not demonstrate any appreciably enhanced accumulation

Table 2 Effect of manipulating OX40-OX40L interactions on inflammation and disease[a]

Inflammatory response	Host/treatment	Effect on disease or cellular immunity
EAE	OX40/L$^{-/-}$	Reduced CNS disease, CD4 T cells, IFN-γ, IL-2, IL-6
	OX40L block	Reduced CNS disease, CD4 T cells
	OX40L-Tg	Enhanced CNS disease
Lung inflammation	OX40/L$^{-/-}$	Reduced asthma, eosinophils, CD4 T cells, Th2 cytokines
	OX40L block	Reduced asthma, eosinophils, CD4 T cells, Th2 cytokines
	OX40L-Tg	Spontaneous interstitial pneumonia
Diabetes (NOD)	OX40L$^{-/-}$	No pancreatic islet destruction, no increased blood glucose
	OX40L block	Reduced diabetes incidence, insulitis
Atherosclerosis	OX40L$^{-/-}$	Reduced lesions
	OX40L block	Reduced lesions, Th2 cytokines
	OX40L-Tg	Enhanced lesions
GVHD/transplantation	OX40/L$^{-/-}$	Reduced disease, rejection, infiltration, CD4/CD8 T cells
	OX40L block	Reduced disease, infiltration, CD4/CD8 T cells, B cells, IFN-γ
IBD/colitis	OX40L block	Decreased gut infiltration, CD4/CD8 T cells, cDC, IFN-γ
	OX40L-Tg	Spontaneous gut infiltration
Contact hypersensitivity	OX40L$^{-/-}$	Reduced inflammation, CD4 T cells
	OX40L-Tg	Enhanced inflammation, T cell response
Arthritis	OX40L block	Reduced joint swelling, CD4 T cells, IFN-γ
EAC	OX40L block	Reduced eosinophilia, IL-5
$HgCl_2$ autoimmunity	OX40L block	Reduced Th2 cytokines, weight loss, mortality
Viral—LCMV	OX40$^{-/-}$	Normal primary and memory CD8, normal Ig
VSV	OX40$^{-/-}$	Normal Ig
Theilers V	OX40$^{-/-}$	Normal primary CD8, normal Ig
Influenza V	OX40/L$^{-/-}$	Normal primary CD8, reduced CD4 and memory CD8
	OX40L block	Reduced lung inflammation, CD4 and CD8 T cells
mCMV	OX40$^{-/-}$	Normal primary CD8, reduced memory CD8 and CD4
VACV	OX40$^{-/-}$	Reduced primary CD8/CD4, reduced memory CD8 and CD4
Parasite		
Heligmosomoides polygyrus	OX40L$^{-/-}$	Decreased worm expulsion, reduced Th2 cytokines
Nippostrongylus brasiliensis	OX40$^{-/-}$	Normal Th2 cytokines
Leishmania major	OX40L block	Reduced disease, decreased Th2 cytokines
	OX40L-Tg	Enhanced susceptibility to disease, increased Th2 cytokines
Listeria monocytogenes	OX40$^{-/-}$	Normal primary CD8, reduced memory CD8

[a]Abbreviations: EAC, experimental allergic conjunctivitis; EAE, experimental allergic encephalomyelitis; GVHD, graft-versus-host disease; IBD, inflammatory bowel disease; LCMV, lymphocytic choriomeningitis virus; mCMV, mouse cytomegalovirus; OX40/L$^{-/-}$, OX40- and OX40L-deficient; OX40L-Tg, OX40L transgenic; VACV, vaccinia virus; VSV, vesicular stomatitis virus.

of activated CD8 T cells (51, 52), and brief analyses of OX40 and OX40L knockouts infected with three viruses (LCMV, influenza, and Theiler's murine encephalomyelitis virus) did not reveal a pronounced defect in the generation of cytotoxic T lymphocytes (CTLs) (42, 44). This finding led some to suggest that OX40-OX40L interactions did not regulate CD8 T cells. Only with more defined systems and in-depth studies have investigators come to the conclusion that these molecules can also strongly dictate the magnitude of CD8 T cell responses.

LCMV: lymphocytic choriomeningitis virus

The initial data showing that OX40-OX40L interactions directly enhanced priming of CD8 T cells came from systems where OX40-deficient TCR transgenic CD8 T cells were tracked in vivo responding to antigen in adjuvant, expressed on tumor cells, and delivered by nonreplicating adenovirus (12, 88, 89).

Each showed defective expansion or survival of the CD8 T cells, largely mimicking data in CD4 systems. Thus, OX40 likely plays an analogous role on CD8 T cells compared with that on CD4 T cells, although no signaling studies have yet been performed to prove definitively that there are common intracellular targets. Studies of human CD8 T cells in vitro have supported this conclusion, showing that OX40 can be induced within 1–2 days of activation and that OX40L expressed on DCs can support growth and differentiation of these cells (90). Other data have shown defects in CD8 T cell responses in OX40L-deficient mice in contact hypersensitivity reactions and allograft rejection (15, 43), although these results may reflect an action on CD4 T cells that may be required to help the CTL response. Furthermore, there are now many reports of increased accumulation or activity of CD8 T cells in mice injected with agonist antibodies to OX40, either in simple systems or with viral infection or tumor inoculation. Although unclear, some of these findings might reflect a direct action of the antibody on the CD8 T cell (81, 88, 91–93); however, several studies also showed that depleting CD4 T cells abrogated CTL priming (94–98). This again suggests that OX40 can function on two levels to augment CD8 immunity directly and indirectly through CD4 T cells. How OX40 enhances CD4 T cell help for CD8 T cells has not been studied.

Whereas the initial reports of pathogens provided negative data with regard to OX40-OX40L, more recent studies have focused on long-term CD8 memory and recall immunity and found strong roles. One report of influenza virus infection demonstrated reduced accumulation of memory CD8 T cells in OX40L-deficient animals, along with reduced secondary expansion of these cells, even though primary CTL generation was normal (99). Blocking OX40-OX40L interactions also prevented weight loss and cachexia induced by intranasal influenza infection, which correlated with reduced accumulation of CD4 and CD8 T cells within the lung (100). Similarly, antigen-specific CD8 T cell populations that persisted long term after mouse cytomegalovirus (mCMV) or *Listeria monocytogenes* infection were reduced in size in OX40-deficient mice, even though acute virus- and bacteria-reactive CD8 populations developed normally (97, 101). A variation of this was found with vaccinia virus (VACV), in which case defective memory generation was again apparent, but the primary CD8 T cell response was also compromised in the absence of OX40 (13). Furthermore, in human in vitro systems, OX40 signals can directly enhance the expansion of several virus-specific memory CD8 T cell populations (HIV, EBV, flu), although its effects are mild without synergistic signals from the costimulatory molecules CD28 and 4-1BB (102), or again OX40 can indirectly promote CD8 T cell priming through augmenting CD4 T cell help (35). Even though a common theme is emerging that OX40-OX40L interactions often are necessary for CD8 memory, persistence of CD8 T cells, and recall activity, it is not clear why they are only sometimes required for the initial development of antigen-reactive CD8 T cell populations (**Table 2**). The use of OX40 likely depends on the length of time it is expressed on CD8 T cells. This in turn likely depends on the availability of CD4 T cell help to augment CTL generation and on the availability or extent of signaling of inflammatory cytokines such as IL-7, IL-15, and IFN-α. The latter control responses to infectious agents and are required for T cell longevity, and signals from their receptors might directly or indirectly affect OX40 expression or OX40 signaling on the CD8 T cell.

mCMV: mouse cytomegalovirus

VACV: vaccinia virus

CONTROL OF OTHER INFLAMMATORY CELL TYPES

OX40 or OX40L can be expressed on a number of other cell types that control aspects of immune functionality (**Figure 2**). As noted above, OX40L has been found in vivo or in vitro on cells as diverse as mast cells, smooth muscle cells, vascular endothelium, and LTi cells. The most obvious role that this OX40L might serve would be to provide signals through

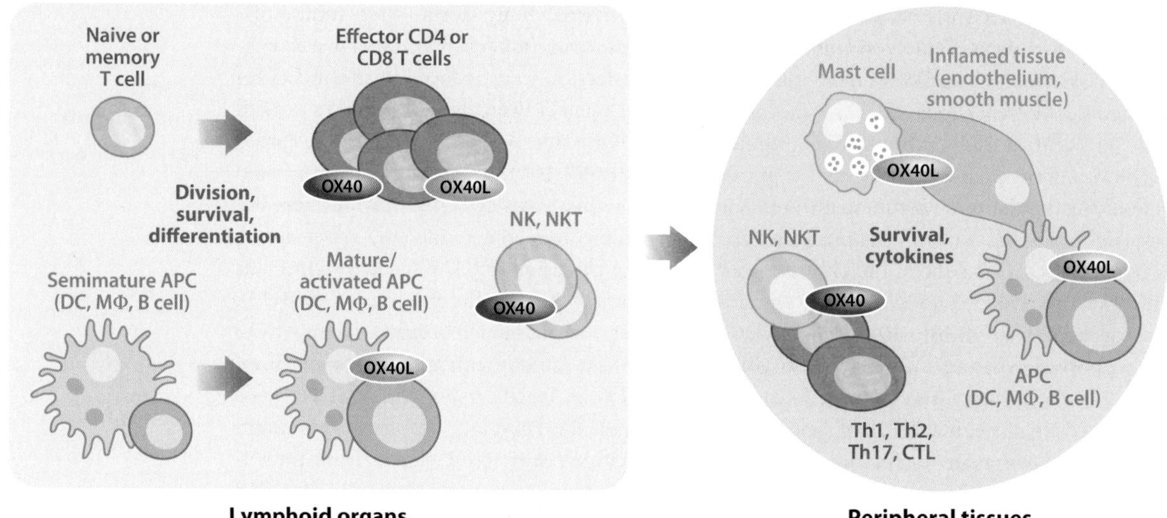

Figure 2

OX40-OX40L interactions regulate functional activity of effector CD4 and CD8 T cells, NK cells, and NKT cells. OX40 is not expressed on naive or memory CD4 or CD8 T cells but is induced after antigen recognition. Similarly, OX40L is inducible on professional APCs (DCs, macrophages, B cells) after they mature and receive activating stimuli. The interaction of these cell types primarily allows OX40 to engage its signaling pathways, targeting division and survival proteins in the activated T cells, which leads to clonal expansion and the development of high frequencies of effector cells. OX40 may also regulate differentiation in the T cells depending on other inflammatory factors. Reverse signaling through OX40L to the APC most likely also contributes to these processes through inducing inflammatory cytokines. Interactions between NK cells and T cells or APCs, or between NKT cells and APCs, can also involve OX40-OX40L interactions, promoting direct cellular activity to NK and NKT cells and perhaps survival signals, as well as provide cytokine feedback loops that will further augment T cell priming. Within inflamed tissue, varied cell types have the potential to express OX40L, including activated endothelium, smooth muscle, and innate cells such as mast cells. Through additional bi-directional interactions with OX40, this OX40L likely potentiates local tissue inflammation by maintaining the effector cells and leading to production of proinflammatory events in the tissue-resident cells.

OX40 to conventional CD4 and CD8 T cells at inflammatory sites to maintain or promote the T cell response. This could primarily involve the antigen-independent NF-κB signal that OX40-OX40L interactions can generate, although antigen presentation to CD8 T cells is a possibility, and reports of inducible class II MHC expression by some of these cell types imply presentation is also possible to CD4 T cells. Certainly, in vitro studies have shown that mast cells (25, 26), LTi cells (31, 103), and endothelial cells (57, 104) can provide costimulatory signals from OX40L for enhancing proliferation, survival, or cytokine production by T cells, although in vivo studies demonstrating these phenomena are lacking. OX40L reverse signaling into these cells might also control aspects of their cellular metabolism, although data related to this are limited to, for example, artificial crosslinking studies showing induction of chemokines such as CCL5 by endothelial cells (87, 105).

Activated NK cells also express OX40L (24, 106), which again can provide costimulatory signals to CD4 T cells in vitro (24). OX40-OX40L interactions can also augment NK function. OX40 was visualized on NK cells, and coculture of these cells with activated pDCs that expressed OX40L resulted in IFN-γ production, implying a direct effect of OX40 signals into the NK cell, but also potentially related to reverse signaling through OX40L on pDCs (20).

In line with this finding, several recent studies have focused on control of invariant NKT cells. Similar to the case with NK cells, coculture of pDCs with NKT cells resulted in OX40-dependent IFN-γ production (107), and cDCs that expressed OX40L and presented lipid antigen in the context of CD1d promoted OX40-dependent IFN-γ from NKT cells in vivo in a tumor model (108). As an extension of this crossregulation, OX40-OX40L interactions were also required for local production of IFN-α by pDC in a model of LCMV infection, with the implication that OX40 is provided by NKT cells in this setting and that the active signal is through OX40L to pDC (86). Lastly, other data have highlighted the potential for OX40 to control neutrophil activity. Ligation of OX40 on human neutrophils resulted in enhanced survival, which correlated with reduced activation of caspase 3, as well as with augmented levels of antiapoptotic and suppressed cleavage of proapoptotic Bcl-2 members (109). Although these data on NK cells, NKT cells, and neutrophils are not extensive, they certainly warrant additional attention and imply a broad base for how OX40-OX40L interactions might control both adaptive and innate immunity.

OX40 AS A THERAPEUTIC ADJUVANT

The strong activity of OX40-OX40L interactions in driving CD4 and CD8 T cells and the insights into augmentation of NK and NKT cell activity suggest that OX40 is a potential adjuvant that could be used as a target in vaccination strategies or therapeutic applications to promote protection against pathogens. Although control of acute viral replication, as alluded to above, is not affected by the inhibition of endogenous OX40-OX40L, and although control of initial parasite burden in several models with helminths is variably dependent on these molecules (42, 110–112), reagents that promote signals through OX40 are nonetheless attractive for enhancing protective immunity to infection. Several examples suggest promise in this area. With pulmonary growth of *Cryptococcus neoformans*, treatment with a stimulatory OX40L.Ig fusion protein promoted fungal clearance (113). Immunotherapy with OX40L.Ig in combination with anti-CTLA4 enhanced CD4 T cell responses, granuloma formation, and killing of *Leishmania donovani* (114). Targeting OX40 alone or with another TNFR family member, 4-1BB, during vaccination with a poxvirus vector expressing a nominal antigen strongly enhanced memory T cell responses to that antigen (96), a finding that is in line with earlier work showing that agonist antibodies to OX40 enhanced memory generation (11, 49). Anti-OX40 also promoted SIV gp130-specific T cell and antibody responses in rhesus monkeys (60), and, similarly, inclusion of the *OX40L* gene in a plasmid DNA vaccine encoding hepatitis B surface antigen (HBsAg) enhanced primary CD4 and CD8 T cell responses against this antigen, as well as long-term memory (115). Additionally, agonist antibodies to OX40 elicit strong antiviral CD4 and CD8 T cell responses when injected at the time of infection with live mCMV, resulting in enhanced clearance of the virus (97, 116). Lastly, recent data found that protection against lethal challenge with live VACV, after vaccination with a CD8 T cell epitope of VACV, was fully dependent on endogenous OX40-OX40L interactions (13), also suggesting that targeting OX40 would further promote protective memory if agonist reagents were given as part of a vaccine.

Another obvious application of OX40 agonist strategies is to augment antiself responses to tumor-associated antigens. This is an area that has received strong interest over the past eight or nine years, initiated by studies from Weinberg that showed OX40 was expressed on tumor-infiltrating T cells from patients with head and neck carcinoma or melanoma (117), and subsequently by studies showing that agonists of OX40 could augment protection against growth of melanoma, breast and colon carcinoma, and sarcoma in the mouse (118). These findings have been expanded in many tumor models to thymoma, glioma, B lymphoma, renal carcinoma, and prostate cancer. The tumor literature has been reviewed elsewhere (33, 119) and is not reiterated here except to point out that the effectiveness of targeting OX40 in isolation has been quite variable depending on the model system (solid tumor, metastases, prophylactic versus therapeutic treatment, highly immunogenic versus weakly immunogenic). Agonist antibodies to OX40 are currently in phase I clinical trials for cancer, but recent and current efforts are being focused on combining OX40 agonists, or tumor transfection protocols to express OX40L, with other forms of treatment, such as DC vaccines, adoptive T cell immunotherapy, and treatment with cytokines such as GM-CSF and IL-12. Because of the complexity of eliciting tumor-reactive T cells, along with NK and NKT cells that might be required for effective targeting of a tumor, in a cancer setting OX40 will likely only be a truly effective adjuvant if combined with other immune-based treatments. New soluble reagents are being developed, such as RNA aptamers that bind OX40 (120) and oligomeric OX40L.Ig fusion proteins (121, 122), which might be promising if they exhibit enhanced agonist activity.

As discussed briefly above, one advantage of targeting OX40 in cancer, or as an adjuvant for infectious disease, is the idea that its signals can antagonize the induction of adaptive Tregs (74, 75, 77). Moreover, other literature has indicated that OX40 signaling can prevent suppression mediated by already differentiated adaptive or thymus-derived $CD25^+Foxp3^+$ Tregs, either simply by making effector T cells resistant to suppression or by directly blocking Treg suppressive activity. The latter has been seen in basic model systems (75, 123, 124) as well as in a recent tumor model (125). However, one potential complication worth mentioning in terms of adjuvant therapy also relates to Tregs and to several studies that have shown some activity of OX40 in promoting the growth or survival of these cells (124, 126, 127), analogous to its effects on conventional CD4 and CD8 T cells. Adult OX40 and OX40L knockout animals essentially have normal numbers of $Foxp3^+$ Tregs, suggesting that OX40 is not a natural survival factor for this subset. However, reagents that target OX40 may have concomitant effects in both transiently blocking suppressive activity as well as promoting the expansion or survival of these cells. Depending on the predominant and relative activity of OX40 signals to conventional T cells, NKT cells, and NK cells, a stimulatory action on Tregs might then impair the ability of agonist reagents to function effectively as adjuvants. However, given the well-known strong activity of OX40 agonists in promoting expansion of conventional CD4 and CD8 T cells and immunity in both basic and applied systems, a positive effect on Tregs may be a minor issue. This was illustrated in a recent paper in a tumor model in which anti-OX40 combined with cyclophosphamide-induced expansion of $Foxp3^+$ Treg numbers when analyzed in peripheral tissues. However, fewer Tregs were found to accumulate at the tumor site in the same mice, and there was also a substantial increase in CD8 effector T cells, which correlated with a strong therapeutic activity of this combination treatment on tumor growth (128).

OX40 AND OX40L AS THERAPEUTIC TARGETS FOR INFLAMMATORY DISEASE

Lastly, research over the past 10 years has definitively shown the importance of OX40-OX40L interactions in development of immune-mediated disease. Most mouse models of autoimmunity and inflammatory disease have now been analyzed using either knockout mice or reagents that block OX40L. These studies have yielded results analogous to, and as impressive as, those that focused on CD28-B7 and CD40-CD40L interactions and that resulted in testing of CTLA4.Ig and anti-CD40L in a number of clinical trials. A strong reduction in disease severity or a complete lack of disease has been reported when OX40 or OX40L is absent or neutralized in EAE (MBP and PLP models), allergic asthma (OVA- and TSLP-induced models), colitis (RAG transfer, IL-2 knockout, hapten, and DSS models), diabetes (NOD and BDC2.5 transgenic models), arthritis (collagen-induced, IL-1Ra knockout, and adjuvant models), atherosclerosis (high fat diet–induced and

LDLR knockout models), GVHD (acute and chronic models), and allograft rejection (minor and major MHC mismatches). Again, I have omitted the details and references for these studies owing to space limitations, but they can be found in other reviews (33, 119), with a summary of the data in **Table 2**. Polymorphisms in OX40L have also now been linked to susceptibility to atherosclerosis (129) and SLE (130), although to date no study of OX40 or OX40L has been performed in mouse models of the latter. Encouragingly, a number of reports have shown that therapeutic targeting of OX40L can block ongoing disease in EAE (21), colitis (45, 131, 132), arthritis (48), asthma (55, 61), and diabetes (133) and that depletion of OX40 positive cells by drug/toxin delivery can also prevent disease in EAE (39) and arthritis (134) models. Here, the effect of OX40-OX40L interactions on Treg induction, maintenance, and function should again be highlighted. Assuming that a major physiological activity of OX40 signals is to suppress the generation of adaptive Tregs and to block suppression from both adaptive and thymus-derived Tregs, it follows that this will be a great advantage in terms of therapeutic inhibition of the OX40-OX40L interaction. Pathogenic effector cells (T cells, NK cells, NKT cells) will be neutralized, while allowing Tregs still to exist or be newly generated and retain functionality. The control of Tregs by OX40 has not yet been extensively investigated in autoimmune or inflammatory disease situations, but recent data in asthma and transplant models support this hypothesis (76, 78).

Neutralizing antibodies to OX40L are currently in phase I clinical trials for asthma, and, depending on success, most likely will be tested in other inflammatory diseases. One potential issue concerns a recent claim that OX40L was expressed on platelets from patients with acute coronary syndrome (135). Platelet expression of OX40L needs to be confirmed, but, given the prothrombotic complications that arose after treatment of patients with antibodies to CD40L, another TNF superfamily molecule that was also found on platelets, this should be followed up in future analyses.

SUMMARY POINTS

1. OX40 and OX40L are not ubiquitously expressed. They are induced on a number of lymphoid and nonlymphoid cell types, correlating with their activities in enhancing ongoing inflammation and immune function.
2. OX40-OX40L interactions exert several effects on conventional CD4 and CD8 T cells, NK cells, and NKT cells, including promoting division, survival, and differentiation, and regulating cytokine production. OX40-OX40L interactions additionally modulate the differentiation and activity of regulatory T cells.
3. OX40 targets intracellular signaling mediators that control canonical and noncanonical NF-κB, PI3K/Akt, as well as calcium/NFAT pathways. OX40L can also promote signals in APCs and nonlymphoid cells that are not yet defined but likely control production of proinflammatory cytokines
4. Many studies have analyzed the effects of removing or neutralizing OX40-OX40L interactions in autoimmune disease, inflammation, and infectious disease models with strong results. Blocking these molecules holds great promise for therapeutic manipulation of immune disease.
5. Agonist reagents to OX40 are strong adjuvants that allow development of protective T cells that can target tumors as well as pathogens.

DISCLOSURE STATEMENT

M.C. has patents on OX40 and OX40L.

ACKNOWLEDGMENTS

I would like to acknowledge all the laboratories that have contributed to the literature on OX40 and OX40L. Many references could not be included because of space restrictions, but this does not diminish their importance or value. M.C. is supported by grants AI67341, CA91837, AI49453, and AI070535 from the National Institutes of Health. This is publication #1145 from the La Jolla Institute for Allergy and Immunology.

LITERATURE CITED

1. Paterson DJ, Jefferies WA, Green JR, Brandon MR, Corthesy P, et al. 1987. Antigens of activated rat T lymphocytes including a molecule of 50000 Mr detected only on CD4 positive T blasts. *Mol. Immunol.* 24:1281–90
2. Mallett S, Fossum S, Barclay AN. 1990. Characterization of the MRC OX40 antigen of activated CD4 positive T lymphocytes—a molecule related to nerve growth factor receptor. *EMBO J.* 9:1063–68
3. Calderhead DM, Buhlmann JE, van den Eertwegh, Claassen E, Noelle RJ, Fell HP. 1993. Cloning of mouse Ox40: a T cell activation marker that may mediate T-B cell interactions. *J. Immunol.* 151:5261–71
4. Latza U, Durkop H, Schnittger S, Ringeling J, Eitelbach F, et al. 1994. The human OX40 homolog: cDNA structure, expression and chromosomal assignment of the ACT35 antigen. *Eur. J. Immunol.* 24:677–83
5. Tanaka Y, Inoi T, Tozawa H, Yamamoto N, Hinuma Y. 1985. A glycoprotein antigen detected with new monoclonal antibodies on the surface of human lymphocytes infected with human T-cell leukemia virus type-I (HTLV-I). *Int. J. Cancer* 36:549–55
6. Miura S, Ohtani K, Numata N, Niki M, Ohbo K, et al. 1991. Molecular cloning and characterization of a novel glycoprotein, gp34, that is specifically induced by the human T-cell leukemia virus type I transactivator p40tax. *Mol. Cell. Biol.* 11:1313–25
7. Baum PR, Gayle RB, Ramsdell F, Srinivasan S, Sorensen RA, et al. 1994. Molecular characterization of murine and human OX40/OX40 ligand systems: identification of a human OX40 ligand as the HTLV-1-regulated protein gp34. *EMBO J.* 13:3992–4001
8. Shimojima M, Miyazawa T, Ikeda Y, McMonagle EL, Haining H, et al. 2004. Use of CD134 as a primary receptor by the feline immunodeficiency virus. *Science* 303:1192–95
9. Compaan DM, Hymowitz SG. 2006. The crystal structure of the costimulatory OX40-OX40L complex. *Structure* 14:1321–30
10. Gramaglia I, Weinberg AD, Lemon M, Croft M. 1998. OX40 ligand: a potent costimulatory molecule for sustaining primary CD4 T cell responses. *J. Immunol.* 161:6510–17
11. Gramaglia I, Jember A, Pippig SD, Weinberg AD, Killeen N, Croft M. 2000. The OX40 costimulatory receptor determines the development of CD4 memory by regulating primary clonal expansion. *J. Immunol.* 165:3043–50
12. Bansal-Pakala P, Halteman BS, Cheng MH, Croft M. 2004. Costimulation of CD8 T cell responses by OX40. *J. Immunol.* 172:4821–25
13. Salek-Ardakani S, Moutaftsi M, Crotty S, Sette A, Croft M. 2008. OX40 drives protective vaccinia virus-specific CD8 T cells. *J. Immunol.* 181:7969–76
14. Stuber E, Neurath M, Calderhead D, Fell HP, Strober W. 1995. Cross-linking of OX40 ligand, a member of the TNF/NGF cytokine family, induces proliferation and differentiation in murine splenic B cells. *Immunity* 2:507–21
15. Murata K, Ishii N, Takano H, Miura S, Ndhlovu LC, et al. 2000. Impairment of antigen-presenting cell function in mice lacking expression of OX40 ligand. *J. Exp. Med.* 191:365–74

16. Ohshima Y, Tanaka Y, Tozawa H, Takahashi Y, Maliszewski C, Delespesse G. 1997. Expression and function of OX40 ligand on human dendritic cells. *J. Immunol.* 159:3838–48
17. Tanaka H, Demeure CE, Rubio M, Delespesse G, Sarfati M. 2000. Human monocyte-derived dendritic cells induce naive T cell differentiation into T helper cell type 2 (Th2) or Th1/Th2 effectors. Role of stimulator/responder ratio. *J. Exp. Med.* 192:405–12
18. Sato T, Ishii N, Murata K, Kikuchi K, Nakagawa S, et al. 2002. Consequences of OX40-OX40 ligand interactions in Langerhans cell function: enhanced contact hypersensitivity responses in OX40L-transgenic mice. *Eur. J. Immunol.* 32:3326–35
19. Ito T, Amakawa R, Inaba M, Hori T, Ota M, et al. 2004. Plasmacytoid dendritic cells regulate Th cell responses through OX40 ligand and type I IFNs. *J. Immunol.* 172:4253–59
20. Liu C, Lou Y, Lizee G, Qin H, Liu S, et al. 2008. Plasmacytoid dendritic cells induce NK cell-dependent, tumor antigen-specific T cell cross-priming and tumor regression in mice. *J. Clin. Investig.* 118:1165–75
21. Weinberg AD, Wegmann KW, Funatake C, Whitham RH. 1999. Blocking OX-40/OX-40 ligand interaction in vitro and in vivo leads to decreased T cell function and amelioration of experimental allergic encephalomyelitis. *J. Immunol.* 162:1818–26
22. Ito T, Wang YH, Duramad O, Hori T, Delespesse GJ, et al. 2005. TSLP-activated dendritic cells induce an inflammatory T helper type 2 cell response through OX40 ligand. *J. Exp. Med.* 202:1213–23
23. Maxwell JR, Yadav R, Rossi RJ, Ruby CE, Weinberg AD, et al. 2006. IL-18 bridges innate and adaptive immunity through IFN-γ and the CD134 pathway. *J. Immunol.* 177:234–45
24. Zingoni A, Sornasse T, Cocks BG, Tanaka Y, Santoni A, Lanier LL. 2004. Cross-talk between activated human NK cells and $CD4^+$ T cells via OX40-OX40 ligand interactions. *J. Immunol.* 173:3716–24
25. Kashiwakura J, Yokoi H, Saito H, Okayama Y. 2004. T cell proliferation by direct cross-talk between OX40 ligand on human mast cells and OX40 on human T cells: comparison of gene expression profiles between human tonsillar and lung-cultured mast cells. *J. Immunol.* 173:5247–57
26. Nakae S, Suto H, Iikura M, Kakurai M, Sedgwick JD, et al. 2006. Mast cells enhance T cell activation: importance of mast cell costimulatory molecules and secreted TNF. *J. Immunol.* 176:2238–48
27. Imura A, Hori T, Imada K, Ishikawa T, Tanaka Y, et al. 1996. The human OX40/gp34 system directly mediates adhesion of activated T cells to vascular endothelial cells. *J. Exp. Med.* 183:2185–95
28. Burgess JK, Carlin S, Pack RA, Arndt GM, Au WW, et al. 2004. Detection and characterization of OX40 ligand expression in human airway smooth muscle cells: a possible role in asthma? *J. Allergy Clin. Immunol.* 113:683–89
29. Takasawa N, Ishii N, Higashimura N, Murata K, Tanaka Y, et al. 2001. Expression of gp34 (OX40 ligand) and OX40 on human T cell clones. *Jpn. J. Cancer Res.* 92:377–82
30. Soroosh P, Ine S, Sugamura K, Ishii N. 2006. OX40-OX40 ligand interaction through T cell-T cell contact contributes to CD4 T cell longevity. *J. Immunol.* 176:5975–87
31. Kim MY, Gaspal FM, Wiggett HE, McConnell FM, Gulbranson-Judge A, et al. 2003. $CD4^+CD3^-$ accessory cells costimulate primed CD4 T cells through OX40 and CD30 at sites where T cells collaborate with B cells. *Immunity* 18:643–54
32. Kim MY, Anderson G, White A, Jenkinson E, Arlt W, et al. 2005. OX40 ligand and CD30 ligand are expressed on adult but not neonatal $CD4^+CD3^-$ inducer cells: evidence that IL-7 signals regulate CD30 ligand but not OX40 ligand expression. *J. Immunol.* 174:6686–91
33. Salek-Ardakani S, Song A, Humphreys IR, Croft M. 2006. OX40:OX40L axis: emerging targets for immunotherapy of human disease. *Curr. Immunol. Rev.* 2:37–53
34. Giacomelli R, Passacantando A, Perricone R, Parzanese I, Rascente M, et al. 2001. T lymphocytes in the synovial fluid of patients with active rheumatoid arthritis display CD134-OX40 surface antigen. *Clin. Exp. Rheumatol.* 19:317–20
35. Yu Q, Yue FY, Gu XX, Schwartz H, Kovacs CM, Ostrowski MA. 2006. OX40 ligation of $CD4^+$ T cells enhances virus-specific $CD8^+$ T cell memory responses independently of IL-2 and $CD4^+$ T regulatory cell inhibition. *J. Immunol.* 176:2486–95
36. Endl J, Rosinger S, Schwarz B, Friedrich SO, Rothe G, et al. 2006. Coexpression of CD25 and OX40 (CD134) receptors delineates autoreactive T-cells in type 1 diabetes. *Diabetes* 55:50–60
37. Godfrey WR, Fagnoni FF, Harara MA, Buck D, Engleman EG. 1994. Identification of a human OX-40 ligand, a costimulator of $CD4^+$ T cells with homology to tumor necrosis factor. *J. Exp. Med.* 180:757–62

38. Weinberg AD, Wallin JJ, Jones RE, Sullivan TJ, Bourdette DN, et al. 1994. Target organ-specific up-regulation of the MRC OX-40 marker and selective production of Th1 lymphokine mRNA by encephalitogenic T helper cells isolated from the spinal cord of rats with experimental autoimmune encephalomyelitis. *J. Immunol.* 152:4712–21
39. Weinberg AD, Bourdette DN, Sullivan TJ, Lemon M, Wallin JJ, et al. 1996. Selective depletion of myelin-reactive T cells with the anti-OX-40 antibody ameliorates autoimmune encephalomyelitis. *Nat. Med.* 2:183–89
40. Flynn S, Toellner KM, Raykundalia C, Goodall M, Lane P. 1998. CD4 T cell cytokine differentiation: the B cell activation molecule, OX40 ligand, instructs CD4 T cells to express interleukin 4 and upregulates expression of the chemokine receptor, Blr-1. *J. Exp. Med.* 188:297–304
41. Akiba H, Oshima H, Takeda K, Atsuta M, Nakano H, et al. 1999. CD28-independent costimulation of T cells by OX40 ligand and CD70 on activated B cells. *J. Immunol.* 162:7058–66
42. Pippig SD, Pena-Rossi C, Long J, Godfrey WR, Fowell DJ, et al. 1999. Robust B cell immunity but impaired T cell proliferation in the absence of CD134 (OX40). *J. Immunol.* 163:6520–29
43. Chen AI, McAdam AJ, Buhlmann JE, Scott S, Lupher ML Jr, et al. 1999. Ox40-ligand has a critical costimulatory role in dendritic cell:T cell interactions. *Immunity* 11:689–98
44. Kopf M, Ruedl C, Schmitz N, Gallimore A, Lefrang K, et al. 1999. OX40-deficient mice are defective in Th cell proliferation but are competent in generating B cell and CTL responses after virus infection. *Immunity* 11:699–708
45. Higgins LM, McDonald SA, Whittle N, Crockett N, Shields JG, MacDonald TT. 1999. Regulation of T cell activation in vitro and in vivo by targeting the OX40-OX40 ligand interaction: amelioration of ongoing inflammatory bowel disease with an OX40-IgG fusion protein, but not with an OX40 ligand-IgG fusion protein. *J. Immunol.* 162:486–93
46. Akiba H, Miyahira Y, Atsuta M, Takeda K, Nohara C, et al. 2000. Critical contribution of OX40 ligand to T helper cell type 2 differentiation in experimental leishmaniasis. *J. Exp. Med.* 191:375–80
47. Tsukada N, Akiba H, Kobata T, Aizawa Y, Yagita H, Okumura K. 2000. Blockade of CD134 (OX40)-CD134L interaction ameliorates lethal acute graft-versus-host disease in a murine model of allogeneic bone marrow transplantation. *Blood* 95:2434–39
48. Yoshioka T, Nakajima A, Akiba H, Ishiwata T, Asano G, et al. 2000. Contribution of OX40/OX40 ligand interaction to the pathogenesis of rheumatoid arthritis. *Eur. J. Immunol.* 30:2815–23
49. Maxwell J, Weinberg AD, Prell RA, Vella AT. 2000. Danger and OX40 receptor signaling synergize to enhance memory T cell survival by inhibiting peripheral deletion. *J. Immunol.* 164:107–12
50. Bansal-Pakala P, Gebre-Hiwot Jember A, Croft M. 2001. Signaling through OX40 (CD134) breaks peripheral T-cell tolerance. *Nat. Med.* 7:907–12
51. Brocker T, Gulbranson-Judge A, Flynn S, Riedinger M, Raykundalia C, Lane P. 1999. CD4 T cell traffic control: in vivo evidence that ligation of OX40 on CD4 T cells by OX40-ligand expressed on dendritic cells leads to the accumulation of CD4 T cells in B follicles. *Eur. J. Immunol.* 29:1610–16
52. Murata K, Nose M, Ndhlovu LC, Sato T, Sugamura K, Ishii N. 2002. Constitutive OX40/OX40 ligand interaction induces autoimmune-like diseases. *J. Immunol.* 169:4628–36
53. Rogers PR, Song J, Gramaglia I, Killeen N, Croft M. 2001. OX40 promotes Bcl-xL and Bcl-2 expression and is essential for long-term survival of CD4 T cells. *Immunity* 15:445–55
54. Song J, Salek-Ardakani S, Rogers PR, Cheng M, Van Parijs L, Croft M. 2004. The costimulation-regulated duration of PKB activation controls T cell longevity. *Nat. Immunol.* 5:150–58
55. Salek-Ardakani S, Song J, Halteman BS, Jember AG, Akiba H, et al. 2003. OX40 (CD134) controls memory T helper 2 cells that drive lung inflammation. *J. Exp. Med.* 198:315–24
56. Soroosh P, Ine S, Sugamura K, Ishii N. 2007. Differential requirements for OX40 signals on generation of effector and central memory $CD4^+$ T cells. *J. Immunol.* 179:5014–23
57. Kunitomi A, Hori T, Imura A, Uchiyama T. 2000. Vascular endothelial cells provide T cells with costimulatory signals via the OX40/gp34 system. *J. Leukoc. Biol.* 68:111–18
58. Ukyo N, Hori T, Yanagita S, Ishikawa T, Uchiyama T. 2003. Costimulation through OX40 is crucial for induction of an alloreactive human T-cell response. *Immunology* 109:226–31

59. Kober J, Leitner J, Klauser C, Woitek R, Majdic O, et al. 2008. The capacity of the TNF family members 4-1BBL, OX40L, CD70, GITRL, CD30L and LIGHT to costimulate human T cells. *Eur. J. Immunol.* 38:2678–88
60. Weinberg AD, Thalhofer C, Morris N, Walker JM, Seiss D, et al. 2006. Anti-OX40 (CD134) administration to nonhuman primates: immunostimulatory effects and toxicokinetic study. *J. Immunother.* 29:575–85
61. Seshasayee D, Lee WP, Zhou M, Shu J, Suto E, et al. 2007. In vivo blockade of OX40 ligand inhibits thymic stromal lymphopoietin driven atopic inflammation. *J. Clin. Investig.* 117:3868–78
62. Kawamata S, Hori T, Imura A, Takaori-Kondo A, Uchiyama T. 1998. Activation of OX40 signal transduction pathways leads to tumor necrosis factor receptor-associated factor (TRAF) 2- and TRAF5-mediated NF-κB activation. *J. Biol. Chem.* 273:5808–14
63. Arch RH, Thompson CB. 1998. 4-1BB and Ox40 are members of a tumor necrosis factor (TNF)-nerve growth factor receptor subfamily that bind TNF receptor-associated factors and activate nuclear factor κB. *Mol. Cell. Biol.* 18:558–65
64. Ye H, Park YC, Kreishman M, Kieff E, Wu H. 1999. The structural basis for the recognition of diverse receptor sequences by TRAF2. *Mol. Cell* 4:321–30
65. Song J, So T, Croft M. 2008. Activation of NF-κB1 by OX40 contributes to antigen-driven T cell expansion and survival. *J. Immunol.* 180:7240–48
66. Song J, So T, Cheng M, Tang X, Croft M. 2005. Sustained survivin expression from OX40 costimulatory signals drives T cell clonal expansion. *Immunity* 22:621–31
67. Song J, Salek-Ardakani S, So T, Croft M. 2007. The kinases aurora B and mTOR regulate the G1-S cell cycle progression of T lymphocytes. *Nat. Immunol.* 8:64–73
68. Linton PJ, Bautista B, Biederman E, Bradley ES, Harbertson J, et al. 2003. Costimulation via OX40L expressed by B cells is sufficient to determine the extent of primary CD4 cell expansion and Th2 cytokine secretion in vivo. *J. Exp. Med.* 197:875–83
69. So T, Song J, Sugie K, Altman A, Croft M. 2006. Signals from OX40 regulate nuclear factor of activated T cells c1 and T cell helper 2 lineage commitment. *Proc. Natl. Acad. Sci. USA* 103:3740–45
70. Prell RA, Evans DE, Thalhofer C, Shi T, Funatake C, Weinberg AD. 2003. OX40-mediated memory T cell generation is TNF receptor-associated factor 2 dependent. *J. Immunol.* 171:5997–6005
71. Lathrop SK, Huddleston CA, Dullforce PA, Montfort MJ, Weinberg AD, Parker DC. 2004. A signal through OX40 (CD134) allows anergic, autoreactive T cells to acquire effector cell functions. *J. Immunol.* 172:6735–43
72. Williams CA, Murray SE, Weinberg AD, Parker DC. 2007. OX40-mediated differentiation to effector function requires IL-2 receptor signaling but not CD28, CD40, IL-12Rβ2, or T-bet. *J. Immunol.* 178:7694–702
73. Ruby CE, Montler R, Zheng R, Shu S, Weinberg AD. 2008. IL-12 is required for anti-OX40-mediated CD4 T cell survival. *J. Immunol.* 180:2140–48
74. So T, Croft M. 2007. Cutting edge: OX40 inhibits TGF-β- and antigen-driven conversion of naive CD4 T cells into $CD25^+Foxp3^+$ T cells. *J. Immunol.* 179:1427–30
75. Vu MD, Xiao X, Gao W, Degauque N, Chen M, et al. 2007. OX40 costimulation turns off $Foxp3^+$ Tregs. *Blood* 110:2501–10
76. Chen M, Xiao X, Demirci G, Li XC. 2008. OX40 controls islet allograft tolerance in CD154 deficient mice by regulating $FOXP3^+$ Tregs. *Transplantation* 85:1659–62
77. Ito T, Wang YH, Duramad O, Hanabuchi S, Perng OA, et al. 2006. OX40 ligand shuts down IL-10-producing regulatory T cells. *Proc. Natl. Acad. Sci. USA* 103:13138–43
78. Duan W, So T, Croft M. 2008. Antagonism of airway tolerance by endotoxin/lipopolysaccharide through promoting OX40L and suppressing antigen-specific $Foxp3^+$ T regulatory cells. *J. Immunol.* 181:8650–59
79. Ohshima Y, Yang LP, Uchiyama T, Tanaka Y, Baum P, et al. 1998. OX40 costimulation enhances interleukin-4 (IL-4) expression at priming and promotes the differentiation of naive human $CD4^+$ T cells into high IL-4-producing effectors. *Blood* 92:3338–45
80. Rogers PR, Croft M. 2000. CD28, OX40, LFA-1, and CD4 modulation of Th1/Th2 differentiation is directly dependent on the dose of antigen. *J. Immunol.* 164:2955–63

81. De Smedt T, Smith J, Baum P, Fanslow W, Butz E, Maliszewski C. 2002. Ox40 costimulation enhances the development of T cell responses induced by dendritic cells in vivo. *J. Immunol.* 168:661–70
82. Li J, Li L, Shang X, Benson J, Merle Elloso M, et al. 2008. Negative regulation of IL-17 production by OX40/OX40L interaction. *Cell. Immunol.* 253:31–37
83. Ndhlovu LC, Ishii N, Murata K, Sato T, Sugamura K. 2001. Critical involvement of OX40 ligand signals in the T cell priming events during experimental autoimmune encephalomyelitis. *J. Immunol.* 167:2991–99
84. Horai R, Nakajima A, Habiro K, Kotani M, Nakae S, et al. 2004. TNF-α is crucial for the development of autoimmune arthritis in IL-1 receptor antagonist-deficient mice. *J. Clin. Investig.* 114:1603–11
85. Nakae S, Saijo S, Horai R, Sudo K, Mori S, Iwakura Y. 2003. IL-17 production from activated T cells is required for the spontaneous development of destructive arthritis in mice deficient in IL-1 receptor antagonist. *Proc. Natl. Acad. Sci. USA* 100:5986–90
86. Diana J, Griseri T, Lagaye S, Beaudoin L, Autrusseau E, et al. 2009. NKT cell-plasmacytoid dendritic cell cooperation via OX40 controls viral infection in a tissue-specific manner. *Immunity* 30:289–99
87. Matsumura Y, Hori T, Kawamata S, Imura A, Uchiyama T. 1999. Intracellular signaling of gp34, the OX40 ligand: induction of c-jun and c-fos mRNA expression through gp34 upon binding of its receptor, OX40. *J. Immunol.* 163:3007–11
88. Song A, Tang X, Harms KM, Croft M. 2005. OX40 and Bcl-xL promote the persistence of CD8 T cells to recall tumor-associated antigen. *J. Immunol.* 175:3534–41
89. Lee SW, Park Y, Song A, Cheroutre H, Kwon BS, Croft M. 2006. Functional dichotomy between OX40 and 4-1BB in modulating effector CD8 T cell responses. *J. Immunol.* 177:4464–72
90. Fujita T, Ukyo N, Hori T, Uchiyama T. 2006. Functional characterization of OX40 expressed on human $CD8^+$ T cells. *Immunol. Lett.* 106:27–33
91. Murata S, Ladle BH, Kim PS, Lutz ER, Wolpoe ME, et al. 2006. OX40 costimulation synergizes with GM-CSF whole-cell vaccination to overcome established $CD8^+$ T cell tolerance to an endogenous tumor antigen. *J. Immunol.* 176:974–83
92. Redmond WL, Gough MJ, Charbonneau B, Ratliff TL, Weinberg AD. 2007. Defects in the acquisition of CD8 T cell effector function after priming with tumor or soluble antigen can be overcome by the addition of an OX40 agonist. *J. Immunol.* 179:7244–53
93. Gough MJ, Ruby CE, Redmond WL, Dhungel B, Brown A, Weinberg AD. 2008. OX40 agonist therapy enhances CD8 infiltration and decreases immune suppression in the tumor. *Cancer Res.* 68:5206–15
94. Kjaergaard J, Tanaka J, Kim JA, Rothchild K, Weinberg A, Shu S. 2000. Therapeutic efficacy of OX-40 receptor antibody depends on tumor immunogenicity and anatomic site of tumor growth. *Cancer Res.* 60:5514–21
95. Lee SJ, Myers L, Muralimohan G, Dai J, Qiao Y, et al. 2004. 4-1BB and OX40 dual costimulation synergistically stimulate primary specific CD8 T cells for robust effector function. *J. Immunol.* 173:3002–12
96. Munks MW, Mourich DV, Mittler RS, Weinberg AD, Hill AB. 2004. 4-1BB and OX40 stimulation enhance CD8 and CD4 T-cell responses to a DNA prime, poxvirus boost vaccine. *Immunology* 112:559–66
97. Humphreys IR, Loewendorf A, de Trez C, Schneider K, Benedict CA, et al. 2007. OX40 costimulation promotes persistence of cytomegalovirus-specific CD8 T cells: a CD4-dependent mechanism. *J. Immunol.* 179:2195–202
98. Song A, Song J, Tang X, Croft M. 2007. Cooperation between CD4 and CD8 T cells for antitumor activity is enhanced by OX40 signals. *Eur. J. Immunol.* 37:1224–32
99. Hendriks J, Xiao Y, Rossen JW, Van Der Sluijs KF, Sugamura K, et al. 2005. During viral infection of the respiratory tract, CD27, 4-1BB, and OX40 collectively determine formation of $CD8^+$ memory T cells and their capacity for secondary expansion. *J. Immunol.* 175:1665–76
100. Humphreys IR, Walzl G, Edwards L, Rae A, Hill S, Hussell T. 2003. A critical role for OX40 in T cell-mediated immunopathology during lung viral infection. *J. Exp. Med.* 198:1237–42
101. Mousavi SF, Soroosh P, Takahashi T, Yoshikai Y, Shen H, et al. 2008. OX40 costimulatory signals potentiate the memory commitment of effector $CD8^+$ T cells. *J. Immunol.* 181:5990–6001

102. Serghides L, Bukczynski J, Wen T, Wang C, Routy JP, et al. 2005. Evaluation of OX40 ligand as a costimulator of human antiviral memory CD8 T cell responses: comparison with B7.1 and 4-1BBL. *J. Immunol.* 175:6368–77
103. Gaspal FM, Kim MY, McConnell FM, Raykundalia C, Bekiaris V, Lane PJ. 2005. Mice deficient in OX40 and CD30 signals lack memory antibody responses because of deficient CD4 T cell memory. *J. Immunol.* 174:3891–96
104. Mestas J, Crampton SP, Hori T, Hughes CC. 2005. Endothelial cell costimulation through OX40 augments and prolongs T cell cytokine synthesis by stabilization of cytokine mRNA. *Int. Immunol.* 17:737–47
105. Kotani A, Hori T, Matsumura Y, Uchiyama T. 2002. Signaling of gp34 (OX40 ligand) induces vascular endothelial cells to produce a CC chemokine RANTES/CCL5. *Immunol. Lett.* 84:1–7
106. Hanna J, Bechtel P, Zhai Y, Youssef F, McLachlan K, Mandelboim O. 2004. Novel insights on human NK cells' immunological modalities revealed by gene expression profiling. *J. Immunol.* 173:6547–63
107. Marschner A, Rothenfusser S, Hornung V, Prell D, Krug A, et al. 2005. CpG ODN enhance antigen-specific NKT cell activation via plasmacytoid dendritic cells. *Eur. J. Immunol.* 35:2347–57
108. Zaini J, Andarini S, Tahara M, Saijo Y, Ishii N, et al. 2007. OX40 ligand expressed by DCs costimulates NKT and CD4$^+$ Th cell antitumor immunity in mice. *J. Clin. Investig.* 117:3330–38
109. Baumann R, Yousefi S, Simon D, Russmann S, Mueller C, Simon HU. 2004. Functional expression of CD134 by neutrophils. *Eur. J. Immunol.* 34:2268–75
110. Ekkens MJ, Liu Z, Liu Q, Whitmire J, Xiao S, et al. 2003. The role of OX40 ligand interactions in the development of the Th2 response to the gastrointestinal nematode parasite *Heligmosomoides polygyrus*. *J. Immunol.* 170:384–93
111. Ierna MX, Scales HE, Schwarz H, Bunce C, McIlgorm A, et al. 2006. OX40 interactions in gastrointestinal nematode infection. *Immunology* 117:108–16
112. Balic A, Harcus Y, Holland MJ, Maizels RM. 2004. Selective maturation of dendritic cells by *Nippostrongylus brasiliensis*-secreted proteins drives Th2 immune responses. *Eur. J. Immunol.* 34:3047–59
113. Humphreys IR, Edwards L, Walzl G, Rae AJ, Dougan G, et al. 2003. OX40 ligation on activated T cells enhances the control of *Cryptococcus neoformans* and reduces pulmonary eosinophilia. *J. Immunol.* 170:6125–32
114. Zubairi S, Sanos SL, Hill S, Kaye PM. 2004. Immunotherapy with OX40L-Fc or anti-CTLA-4 enhances local tissue responses and killing of *Leishmania donovani*. *Eur. J. Immunol.* 34:1433–40
115. Du X, Zheng G, Jin H, Kang Y, Wang J, et al. 2007. The adjuvant effects of costimulatory molecules on cellular and memory responses to HBsAg DNA vaccination. *J. Gene Med.* 9:136–46
116. Humphreys IR, de Trez C, Kinkade A, Benedict CA, Croft M, Ware CF. 2007. Cytomegalovirus exploits IL-10-mediated immune regulation in the salivary glands. *J. Exp. Med.* 204:1217–25
117. Vetto JT, Lum S, Morris A, Sicotte M, Davis J, et al. 1997. Presence of the T-cell activation marker OX-40 on tumor infiltrating lymphocytes and draining lymph node cells from patients with melanoma and head and neck cancers. *Am. J. Surg.* 174:258–65
118. Weinberg AD, Rivera MM, Prell R, Morris A, Ramstad T, et al. 2000. Engagement of the OX-40 receptor in vivo enhances antitumor immunity. *J. Immunol.* 164:2160–69
119. Croft M. 2009. The role of TNF superfamily members in T-cell function and diseases. *Nat. Rev. Immunol.* 9:271–85
120. Dollins CM, Nair S, Boczkowski D, Lee J, Layzer JM, et al. 2008. Assembling OX40 aptamers on a molecular scaffold to create a receptor-activating aptamer. *Chem. Biol.* 15:675–82
121. Morris NP, Peters C, Montler R, Hu HM, Curti BD, et al. 2007. Development and characterization of recombinant human Fc:OX40L fusion protein linked via a coiled-coil trimerization domain. *Mol. Immunol.* 44:3112–21
122. Muller N, Wyzgol A, Munkel S, Pfizenmaier K, Wajant H. 2008. Activity of soluble OX40 ligand is enhanced by oligomerization and cell surface immobilization. *FEBS J.* 275:2296–304
123. Valzasina B, Guiducci C, Dislich H, Killeen N, Weinberg AD, Colombo MP. 2005. Triggering of OX40 (CD134) on CD4$^+$CD25$^+$ T cells blocks their inhibitory activity: a novel regulatory role for OX40 and its comparison with GITR. *Blood* 105:2845–51

124. Kroemer A, Xiao X, Vu MD, Gao W, Minamimura K, et al. 2007. OX40 controls functionally different T cell subsets and their resistance to depletion therapy. *J. Immunol.* 179:5584–91

125. Piconese S, Valzasina B, Colombo MP. 2008. OX40 triggering blocks suppression by regulatory T cells and facilitates tumor rejection. *J. Exp. Med.* 205:825–39

126. Takeda I, Ine S, Killeen N, Ndhlovu LC, Murata K, et al. 2004. Distinct roles for the OX40-OX40 ligand interaction in regulatory and nonregulatory T cells. *J. Immunol.* 172:3580–89

127. Hippen KL, Harker-Murray P, Porter SB, Merkel SC, Londer A, et al. 2008. Umbilical cord blood regulatory T-cell (Treg) expansion and functional effects of tumor necrosis factor receptor family members OX40 and 4-1BB expressed on artificial antigen-presenting cells. *Blood* 112:2847–57

128. Hirschhorn-Cymerman D, Rizzuto GA, Merghoub T, Cohen AD, Avogadri F, et al. 2009. OX40 engagement and chemotherapy combination provides potent antitumor immunity with concomitant regulatory T cell apoptosis. *J. Exp. Med.* 206:1103–16

129. Wang X, Ria M, Kelmenson PM, Eriksson P, Higgins DC, et al. 2005. Positional identification of TNFSF4, encoding OX40 ligand, as a gene that influences atherosclerosis susceptibility. *Nat. Genet.* 37:365–72

130. Cunninghame Graham DS, Graham RR, Manku H, Wong AK, Whittaker JC, et al. 2008. Polymorphism at the TNF superfamily gene *TNFSF4* confers susceptibility to systemic lupus erythematosus. *Nat. Genet.* 40:83–89

131. Obermeier F, Schwarz H, Dunger N, Strauch UG, Grunwald N, et al. 2003. OX40/OX40L interaction induces the expression of CXCR5 and contributes to chronic colitis induced by dextran sulfate sodium in mice. *Eur. J. Immunol.* 33:3265–74

132. Totsuka T, Kanai T, Uraushihara K, Iiyama R, Yamazaki M, et al. 2003. Therapeutic effect of anti-OX40L and anti-TNF-a MAbs in a murine model of chronic colitis. *Am. J. Physiol. Gastrointest. Liver Physiol.* 284:G595–603

133. Pakala SV, Bansal-Pakala P, Halteman BS, Croft M. 2004. Prevention of diabetes in NOD mice at a late stage by targeting OX40/OX40 ligand interactions. *Eur. J. Immunol.* 34:3039–46

134. Boot EP, Koning GA, Storm G, Wagenaar-Hilbers JP, van Eden W, et al. 2005. CD134 as target for specific drug delivery to auto-aggressive $CD4^+$ T cells in adjuvant arthritis. *Arthritis. Res. Ther.* 7:R604–15

135. Liu DM, Yan JC, Wang CP, Chen GH, Ding S, et al. 2008. The clinical implications of increased OX40 ligand expression in patients with acute coronary syndrome. *Clin. Chim. Acta* 397:22–26

Functional Anatomy of T Cell Activation and Synapse Formation

David R. Fooksman, Santosh Vardhana,* Gaia Vasiliver-Shamis,* Jan Liese, David A. Blair, Janelle Waite, Catarina Sacristán, Gabriel D. Victora, Alexandra Zanin-Zhorov, and Michael L. Dustin

Department of Molecular Pathogenesis, Skirball Institute of Biomolecular Medicine, NYU School of Medicine, New York, New York 10016; email: David.Fooksman@med.nyu.edu, Santosh.Vardhana@med.nyu.edu, Gaia.Vasiliver-Shamis@med.nyu.edu, Jan.Liese@med.nyu.edu, David.Blair@med.nyu.edu, Janelle.Waite@med.nyu.edu, Catarina.Sacristan@med.nyu.edu, Gabriel.Victora@med.nyu.edu, Alexandra.Zanin-Zhorov.@med.nyu.edu, Michael.Dustin@med.nyu.edu

Annu. Rev. Immunol. 2010. 28:79–105

First published online as a Review in Advance on November 12, 2009

The *Annual Review of Immunology* is online at immunol.annualreviews.org

This article's doi:
10.1146/annurev-immunol-030409-101308

0732-0582/10/0423-0079$20.00

*These authors contributed equally.

Key Words

immunological synapse, kinapse, microcluster, TCR triggering

Abstract

T cell activation and function require a structured engagement of antigen-presenting cells. These cell contacts are characterized by two distinct dynamics in vivo: transient contacts resulting from promigratory junctions called immunological kinapses or prolonged contacts from stable junctions called immunological synapses. Kinapses operate in the steady state to allow referencing to self-peptide-MHC (pMHC) and searching for pathogen-derived pMHC. Synapses are induced by T cell receptor (TCR) interactions with agonist pMHC under specific conditions and correlate with robust immune responses that generate effector and memory T cells. High-resolution imaging has revealed that the synapse is highly coordinated, integrating cell adhesion, TCR recognition of pMHC complexes, and an array of activating and inhibitory ligands to promote or prevent T cell signaling. In this review, we examine the molecular components, geometry, and timing underlying kinapses and synapses. We integrate recent molecular and physiological data to provide a synthesis and suggest ways forward.

TCR: T cell receptor

pMHC: peptide-major histocompatibility complex

APC: antigen-presenting cell

Kinapse: a migratory, transient T cell–APC contact with information transfer

INTRODUCTION

T cells have evolved a highly efficient mechanism for finding and discriminating antigen while integrating multiple environmental cues to determine the context of these signals. Efficiency is important for T cells for several reasons: T cell receptors (TCRs) must be able to recognize a few activating peptide-MHC (pMHC) complexes (~10) in a sea of self-pMHC on the surface of an antigen-presenting cell (APC). Furthermore, the difference between an activating and nonactivating pMHC complex can be a single conservative amino acid change, sometimes translating into minor differences in affinity. Next, antigen recognition in vivo occurs on the fly as cells brush past each other at surprisingly rapid speeds. These connections, or hapsis, are necessary because the TCRs and pMHC are both membrane-anchored molecules that span a combined length of nearly 15 nm. We refer to these interactions as immunological kinapses when fleeting and immunological synapses (IS) when longer lived. In theory, each APC could be expressing different arrays of pMHC, adding to the complexity problem. Finally, TCRs are unique and clonal, generated by random swapping and editing of DNA segments prior to any exposure with cognate pMHC. Each individual must evolve their own repertoire of receptors over a period of a few weeks to optimize the thermodynamic receptor-ligand engagement process in their particular genetic background. Although the starting TCR repertoire is not entirely random and has some bias toward recognizing pMHC (1), this is still a remarkably ad hoc process compared with other receptor-ligand systems that have evolved over millions of years. Nevertheless, for the most part, these systems are highly capable of identifying rare pathogen-associated ligands while learning to ignore self and benign foreign antigens. The consequences of errors are profound: autoimmunity resulting from inappropriate recognition of self, allergies and hypersensitivity from inappropriate recognition of benign foreign antigens, and chronic infection or death because of a failure to recognize or mount an appropriate response to pathogen-associated antigens.

Therefore, and not surprisingly, the mechanisms and mystery of T cell activation have received great attention in various fields of biology and medicine for quite some time. In recent years, the ability to image T cell activation by high-resolution in vitro methods and under physiological conditions in vivo has boosted our understanding of these processes and has helped to unify a diverse but often disjointed body of biophysical and functional data. In this review, we deal with the molecular reorganization that occurs during activation, the degeneracy of this phenomenon in other synapses, and the impacts on physiological conditions in vivo. We also try to integrate how the in vitro lessons instruct us on the cellular behaviors observed in vivo.

To understand T cell activation, we must first visit the steady-state behavior of T cells in vivo. The advent of two-photon laser scanning microscopy (TPLSM) imaging of lymphocytes in vivo has exposed the physiological behavior of these cells, which have long been studied ex vivo. It has also provided a metric to evaluate the physiological relevance of divergent in vitro observations. Early studies by Cahalan, Miller, and colleagues (2, 3) illustrated that naive T cells are in constant motion, scanning the lymph node at high rates (10–15 μm/min average, 25 μm/min burst speeds) in search of antigen and danger signals and capable of contacting 5000 dendritic cells (DCs) in 1 h.

Lymphoid tissue contains a complex but stereotyped array of cells and signals that are highly compartmentalized but fluid at the same time. A common characteristic is adjacent zones dominated by T or B cells, each tethered to distinct stromal networks. T cells kinapse with fibroblastic reticular cell networks and appear to use these to access DCs that form an interdigitating network and process past or stream with other lymphocytes via transient adhesive interactions coupled to the actin cytoskeleton (4–6). These surfaces are covered with stop, go, and exit signals that T cells must integrate to decide what to do (7, 8). A major stop signal is agonist pMHC on a DC. Three phases have been described in T cell interaction with pMHC (9). Phase 1 is initial transient T cell–DC interactions characterized by continued rapid T cell migration that can last from 30 min to 8 h depending on the pMHC density. Signals in phase 1 are integrated through kinapses. Phase 2 is a period of stable T cell–DC interactions lasting ~12 h, during which cytokines such as IL-2 are produced. Signals in phase 2 are integrated through IS. Phase 3 is a return to transient T cell–DC interaction and rapid T cell migration during which the T cell divides multiple times and then exits the lymphoid tissue. The correct interpretation of these stop and go signals is critical for generation of effector and memory T cells (10). This is the environment in which T cells engage antigen. We return to the in vivo view after developing the in vitro details.

From high-resolution imaging of in vitro T cell–APC conjugates and from imaging of T cells interacting with supported bilayers, we have been able to illuminate the molecular organization of T cell activation. Fixed-cell imaging studies by Kupfer (11) revealed the formation of a bull's eye pattern with a central cluster of TCR-pMHC, defined as the cSMAC (central supramolecular activation complex), surrounded by a ring of the cognate integrin LFA-1 (lymphocyte function–associated antigen 1) and its immunoglobulin superfamily ligand ICAM-1 (intercellular adhesion molecule 1), defined as the pSMAC (peripheral SMAC). The region outside the pSMAC, which appeared to be rich in CD45, was referred to as the dSMAC (distal SMAC) (12). Contemporaneous studies with supported planar bilayers revealed a similar stable configuration of small and large adhesion molecules in activated T cell contacts, suggesting an IS (13). Dynamic studies with planar bilayers further showed that the IS is formed through a nascent intermediate in which activating TCR clusters form first in the dSMAC and then move to the cSMAC region in an F-actin-dependent process in a few minutes to form the pattern described by Kupfer (11). Formation of the IS, regardless of the size of the cSMAC, correlates with full T cell activation over a timescale of hours, leading to an initial characterization that the IS is important for sustained TCR signaling (14). We initially thought that the TCR translocation from the dSMAC to cSMAC was a one-time event driven by actinomyosin contraction (15). However, it is now clear that TCR signaling is sustained by TCRs (MCs) that are continually forming in the dSMAC and moving to the cSMAC (16). This ongoing process of cluster formation and transport often ends in TCR signal termination (16), but not always (17, 18). We discuss the sequence of T cell activation by first examining the life cycle of TCRs.

cSMAC: central supramolecular activation complex

pSMAC: peripheral supramolecular activation complex

MC: T cell receptor microcluster

Immunoreceptor tyrosine-based activation motif (ITAM): a sequence motif in the cytoplasmic domain of antigen receptors with the form $YxxLx_{(7-12)}YxxL$

THE LIFE CYCLE OF TCRs DURING T CELL ACTIVATION

TCR Triggering

T cells can coordinate responses to as few as 10 agonist peptides presented on an APC (19). The exact mechanism of initial TCR triggering is unknown and remains hotly disputed. An intriguing study recently demonstrated that nonphosphorylated immunoreceptor tyrosine-based activation motif (ITAM) tyrosines are buried in the inner leaflet of the plasma membrane based on synergy with a positively charged N-terminal sequence that interacts with acidic lipids in the inner leaflet of the plasma membrane (20). Under normal conditions the phosphorylation of the ITAMs is inhibited unless the negative charge of the plasma membrane is reduced to allow the ITAM to dissociate from the membrane and become accessible to phosphorylation. This electrostatic switch that exposes the ITAMs may be an important early event in TCR triggering.

To achieve high sensitivity, however, T cells must overcome the low affinity of TCR-pMHC interactions (21, 22). Although it is generally accepted that higher affinities tend to correlate with activating peptides, strict correlations between TCR-pMHC affinity and T cell reactivity have been described predominantly in thymocytes (23) and peripheral CD8 T cells (24). In peripheral CD4 T cells, there remains a partial discord between affinity (or off rates) of TCR to pMHC and the functional outcome for activation, and this prevents complete resolution. One example of this divergence comes from recent work from the Shaw lab that has characterized altered peptide ligands (APLs) of the cognate antigen moth cytochrome *c* (MCC) peptide, which is recognized by the AND TCR (17, 25). In these papers, the investigators showed that a peptide variant, K99A, with lower affinity for the AND TCR than cognate antigen for the AND TCR, nevertheless can induce equivalent or even elevated levels of T cell proliferation when presented by the same B cell APC as the higher-affinity MCC_{88-103}-I-E^k complex. Understanding TCR triggering is further complicated by a variance in the threshold affinities for pMHC by different TCRs for activation (26). Moreover, the orientation and footprint for binding can vary among TCR/pMHC complexes, with some alloreactive TCRs binding pMHC interfaces in unconventional orientations (27). Physical models for relating solution affinity to functional triggering are still not fully predictive, suggesting that direct measurements of interactions in contact areas are needed (see sidebar and **Figure 1**).

MEASURING 2-D AFFINITY AND KINETICS

Much of the thermodynamic and biophysical data on TCR-pMHC interactions have been measured in solution or, to put it differently, in systems where six degrees of kinetic freedom (from x, y, and z translation and x, y, and z rotation) are lost upon binding. In theory, two apposed cell membranes should constrain TCR and pMHC movement such that only three kinetic degrees of freedom (x, y translation and z rotation) are lost on binding (**Figure 1**). We quantified the 2-D interactions of CD2-CD58 adhesion molecules, which form a large central aggregate, much as the TCR forms a cSMAC (28). Within the central cluster, we determined a 2-D dissociation constant (Kd) of 1.7 molecules/μm^2 (29–31). Photobleaching experiments yielded an off rate of 0.074 s^{-1} and an on rate of 0.044 $\mu m^2/s$ (32). The off-rate value was ~100-fold slower than that predicted by solution measurements, possibly due to constrained diffusion leading to cycles of rebinding of CD2 and CD58 prior to exchange. Whether similar rebinding effects govern TCR-pMHC interaction is unknown. Estimating 2-D Kd for the 2B4 TCR interaction with I-E^k with MCC peptide 88–103 yields a value of 10 molecules/μm^2, five-fold weaker than the CD2-CD58 interaction, and the TCR also displayed slower photobleaching recovery rates, suggesting a relatively long effective lifetime compared with CD2-CD58 (14). The effective lifetime of the TCR-pMHC complex with rebinding is likely to be the important parameter for signaling through the TCR.

Microcluster Formation

Various experimental models have revealed the subtleties of TCR activation (summarized in **Table 1**). One pathway to T cell activation is based on induction of TCR clustering by cross-linking with bivalent IgG and secondary antibodies. Surface adsorbed, bivalent anti-CD3 antibodies induce actin-dependent TCR clusters (33–35). Anti-CD3 tethered to planar bilayers can also induce MCs and mature IS (36). Whether these MCs and cSMACs are the same as those induced by pMHC is not yet clear. In solution, chemically defined pMHC class II dimers with optimal spacing are the minimal soluble stimuli for CD4 T cell activation (37).

How pMHC presented by APCs or on other surfaces triggers T cell signaling is unclear. Recent studies have shown transient Ca^{2+} elevations in response to a single pMHC (19) and sustained Ca^{2+} elevation in response to chemically defined heterodimers of agonist pMHC and endogenous pMHC (38). Planar bilayers presenting pure agonist pMHC and ICAM-1 induce formation of TCR MCs within seconds of ligand engagement (14, 39). Titration studies suggest that MCs require a single pMHC complex to nucleate, and the pMHC may serially engage several TCR complexes within the same MC (40). This may be analogous to the rebinding process described above for CD2-CD58 interactions. Therefore, although a single pMHC may trigger the TCR, a multivalent TCR complex seems to form regardless. The TCR clusters may also preexist and become stabilized or rearranged in some manner by ligation (41). Transient and actin-dependent TCR microclustering is observed in the absence of pMHC by imaging (16). It is unknown if formation of nanoscale, short-lived TCR clusters would increase the avidity of initial TCR-pMHC interactions or provide intrinsic cortical tension to support low-valency interactions. Ligand may convert transient MCs that are specialized for pMHC capture into more stable MCs that are specialized for signaling and pMHC retention. Recent electron microscopy and superresolution optical imaging studies reveal a non-homogeneous distribution of TCR and the transmembrane adapter linker of activation in T cells (LAT) (42). Activation results in a convergence of discrete TCR and LAT domains (42).

Although the stoichiometry of the TCR-pMHC interaction is 1:1, we do not know how rapid binding and dissociation, combined with cytoskeletal interactions, influence the effective valency in the TCR MCs. The question of how these low-valency, low-affinity TCR-pMHC interactions lead to cluster formation is also unknown, but we know of two mechanisms by which signal initiation within MCs might be supported. First, cluster formation and T cell activation are critically dependent on the actin cytoskeleton (16, 33, 35, 39, 40). Secondly, early signal integration within clusters might be supported by size-dependent exclusion of large phosphatases such as CD45 for the life of the MC, a process now known as kinetic segregation. Springer (43) was the first to speculate that size-dependent exclusion of CD45 could be a basis for initiation of TCR signaling. Choudhuri et al. (44) provided the best evidence for the importance of this process in TCR signal integration, and Varma et al. (16) directly demonstrated exclusion of CD45 from TCR MCs.

TCR MCs are the signaling units of T cell activation. Staining of T cells interacting with planar bilayers containing agonist pMHC and ICAM-1 shows enrichment of phosphorylated Lck, ζ-associated protein 70 (ZAP-70), LAT, Src-homology 2 (SH2) domain-containing leukocyte protein of 76 KDa (SLP-76), and growth factor receptor-bound protein 2 (Grb2) signaling kinases within MCs (33, 42, 45), correlating with increasing ITAM phosphorylation. When TCR ligands are laterally mobile in a membrane, all these components move together in a MC. Soon after formation, TCR MCs transit radially and accumulate to form the cSMAC (16). MCs travel at a rate of ~1–5 μm/min along the T cell surface. Acute treatment with anti-MHC during T cell activation, which blocks new MC formation, extinguishes signaling and Ca^{2+} influx after

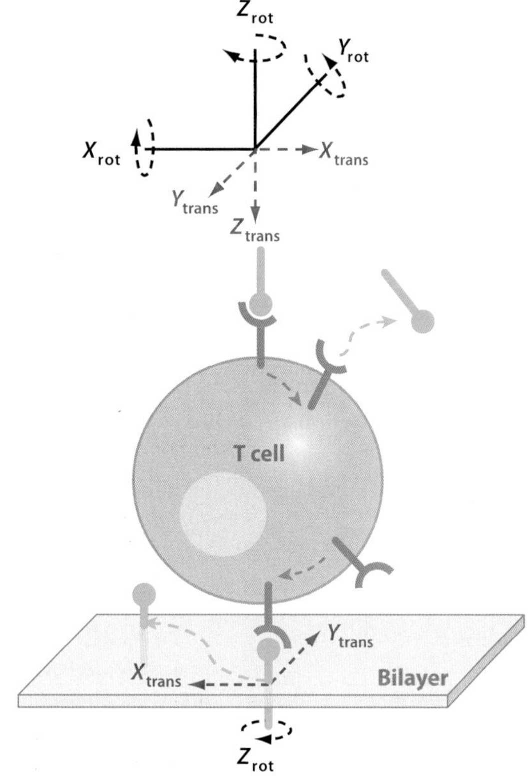

Figure 1

Receptor-ligand kinetics in solution versus membranes. In theory, dissociation constants (Kd) for bound ligands in solution are calculated based on dissociation occurring in 3-D space, with six degrees of freedom. However, some of these receptor-ligand interactions occur when two opposed cell membranes (or in this case, cell membrane and artificial lipid bilayer) are interacting. Under these circumstances, ligands are confined to 2-D translation and 1-D rotation, which may stabilize and prolong these interactions. Also, rebinding by *cis*-receptors (such as clustered TCR) can further trap ligands and generate longer binding than would be predicted in solution.

Table 1 Comparison of TCR stimuli and responses

TCR stimulus	Ligand:TCR[a]	TCR activation	Comments	Reference
Soluble				
Anti-TCR F'ab	1:1	No activation	Weak μM Kd, might not be stable; no force transduction either	196
pMHC monomers	1:1	No activation	No activation despite binding of monomers to TCR	37
Anti-CD3 antibody	2:2	Partial	Signaling not blocked by actin depolymerization drugs	197, 198
Agonist pMHC dimers	2:2	Full and sustained	Intermolecular distance, not pMHC orientation, is critical	37, 199
Agonist/endogenous pMHC heterodimers	2:2	Full and sustained	CD4 required for activation	38
Cross-linked anti-CD3	2:2+	Full and transient	CD69 upregulation	197
Plate-bound				
Anti-CD3	2:2++	Full and sustained	Stable bivalent ligand induces clustering, may generate force for mechanotransduction	33
Membrane associated				
pMHC monomers + ICAM-1 on planar bilayers	1:1++	Full and sustained if >0.2 pMHC/μm^2. Less sensitive without ICAM-1	Requires F-actin and myosin IIA	14, 16, 81
Anti-CD3 linked to Fc on APC surface	2:2++	Full and sustained	F-actin required?	200
Single pMHC on APC surface	1:1+++	Full and transient if <10 pMHC; full and sustained if >10 pMHC	Full activation achieved by 10 agonist peptides in a CD4-dependent manner (CD4 blockade raises threshold to 25 agonist peptides)	19

[a]Stoichiometry of engagement.

+ Higher-order cross-linking at optimal ratio of anti-CD3 and secondary antibody.

++ Higher-order interactions owing to distribution of receptor-ligand interactions across a 2-D interface.

+++ Higher-order interaction owing to distribution of receptor-ligand interactions across a 2-D interface and the presence of weak self-ligand interactions.

2 min (16). This latency correlates well with the time needed for existing MCs (unaffected by anti-MHC) to reach the cSMAC and terminate signaling (16). This result suggests that signaling is sustained only during the lifetime of these discrete MCs (16). Sustained signaling requires continued MC formation and continued actin polymerization.

When TCR ligands are fixed to the substrate, the TCR and ZAP-70 MCs remain fixed in place and spawn SLP-76 domains that move toward the IS center (46). Recent data have demonstrated that coupling costimulation of very late antigen-4 (VLA-4) integrin retards the cytoskeletal movements, which ultimately results in the centralization and inactivation of given SLP-76 domains (47). These findings identify a third domain of MCs enriched in SLP-76 that can persist independent of TCR MCs.

cSMAC and Signal Termination

Upon reaching the cSMAC, the signaling molecules dissociate from the TCR MCs, and signal termination and TCR degradation begin (16, 39, 45). The first clue regarding the mechanism came from detection of lysobisphosphatidic acid, which marks multivesicular bodies (MVBs) (16), at the cSMAC. Signal termination in MVBs is achieved via segregation of receptors to limiting membranes within the MVB and via fusion with lysosomes, thus isolating them from downstream kinases and adaptor proteins as soon as MVBs are formed (48). A family of proteins known as the endosomal sorting complex required for transport (ESCRT) proteins (48) are implicated in this process (S. Vardhana, K. Choudhuri, R. Varma, and M. Dustin, manuscript submitted). TSG101, the critical component of the upstream ESCRT complex ESCRT-I, is required for identification of ubiquitinated TCR MCs, for sorting them into the cSMAC compartment in the planar bilayer model, and for TCR downregulation in cellular models.

The behavior of ESCRT complexes within the IS is both domain and substrate specific. Sorting of TCR for termination of signaling and degradation occurs exclusively at the cSMAC. TCRs that do not interact with TSG101 are unable to enter the cSMAC. This is in line with prior reports demonstrating specific recruitment of MVBs to the cSMAC (16) and elevated signal transduction when engagements are restricted to the periphery, either by physical barriers (49) or by immobilized ligands (50). This is the first demonstration that ESCRT functions have been linked to protein organization within spatially segregated domains of a polarized cell interface and provides new possibilities for ESCRT proteins to respond to polarized stimuli. Importantly, ESCRT-mediated TCR sorting into the cSMAC also critically depends on ubiquitination, as neither ubiquitin-depleted nor ubiquitin-noninteracting ESCRT-I can induce cSMAC formation. It is not known how TCR signaling is sustained in the cSMAC in some situations, particularly in $CD8^+$ cytotoxic T lymphocytes (CTLs) where this signaling may play an important role in cytotoxic granule targeting to the secretory domain adjacent to the cSMAC (51). This process could be controlled at the level of ubiquitin ligases, deubiquitinating enzymes, or ubiquitin recognition, to name only three potential control points. The consequence of disabling ESCRT-I leads to chronic TCR signaling, which could be deleterious if left unchecked. Thus, the TCR signaling cascade is likely modulated rather than completely inactivated in cells displaying cSMAC-associated signaling such as CTLs.

ADDITIONAL PLAYERS OF THE SYNAPSE AND T CELL ACTIVATION

Adhesion and Costimulatory Molecules

LFA-1 engagement of ICAM-1 is essential for IS formation in vitro and in vivo and acts in several ways. Initially, these molecules serve as adhesion molecules, tethering opposing T cell and APC membranes within tens of nanometers, facilitating TCR-pMHC interactions. Engaged LFA-1 quickly consolidates into an enriched pSMAC network, which may provide the positional stability that allows it to enhance T cell sensitivity to antigen 100-fold as compared with the situation in the absence of LFA-1 engagement (52).

TCR activation induces Rap1 activation through ADAP (adhesion and degranulation–promoting adaptor protein) and SKAP55, which leads to a clustered higher-affinity LFA-1 binding of ICAM-1, referred to as inside-out signaling (53, 54). Engagement of high-affinity LFA-1 generates positive feedback on TCR-induced Ras activation by shifting Ras activation from the Golgi to the plasma membrane (55). In the thymus, this process may significantly affect negative selection, which is characterized by similar shifting of Ras activation from the Golgi to the plasma membrane (23). Linking of integrins to actin is generated by focal adhesions in many cells and involves myosin-driven recruitment and activation of force-sensitive substrates such as p130Cas, fyn, and other mediators of integrin scaffolding (56). LFA-1 microclustering and pSMAC formation are critically dependent on Talin activity but also appear to depend on myosin IIA–based contraction and may involve a role for force-sensitive substrates such as p105CasL (57; S. Vardhana, L. Santos, M. Sheetz, and M. Dustin, unpublished observations). One model for integrin activation suggested that LFA-1 was transiently released from actin to facilitate diffusion and interaction with ligands, but recent high-resolution imaging of the formation of integrin-mediated adhesion suggests that integrins are preclustered by an F-actin bundle in the lamellipodium prior to ligand binding (58).

TCR MCs also serve as sites for initiation of costimulation. The critical costimulatory receptor CD28, when engaged by its primary ligand CD80 (B7.1), is highly enriched in TCR MCs (59). Incorporation of CD28 into MCs is completely independent of its signaling, occurring in the absence of a cytoplasmic region of CD28 (59) where PKCθ (protein kinase Cθ) binds. This finding is consistent with phosphorylation-independent formation of TCR MCs (42). The CD28-CD80 complexes are transported in TCR MCs to the cSMAC, at which point they array in an annular cluster around the cSMAC, segregated from TCRs (**Figure 2**). This CD28-PKCθ compartment is actively maintained. Fluorescence recovery after photobleaching (FRAP) experiments with PKCθ or CD28 have shown that it rapidly recovers after photobleaching, indicating a dynamic enrichment in this compartment (59), and application of anti-CD3 rapidly induced loss of CD28-CD80 clusters in T cell–DC interfaces (60). This is in contrast to TCR in the cSMAC, which does not recover quickly after photobleaching (14) or dissipates upon addition of anti-pMHC antibodies (16). Although it is unclear what maintains the CD28-PKCθ annular ring around the cSMAC, it may be related to the fact that the structure is situated at the boundary between F-actin-rich and F-actin-depleted zones of the IS. Activated PKCθ is necessary for formation of cytoplasmic Bcl10/MALT1-rich foci that lead to NF-κB (nuclear factor κ-light-chain-enhancer of activated B cells) translocation into the nucleus (61).

CD2 functions equally as an adhesion and costimulatory molecule. We have recently observed the generation of novel signaling domains in response to activation of the T cell costimulatory molecule CD2 by its murine ligand, CD48. CD2 functions prominently as a costimulatory molecule by lowering the threshold for T cell activation (62). CD2 engagement induces unique phosphorylation of phospholipase γ1 (PLCγ1) via Fyn kinase (63), potentiating intracellular calcium levels above those achieved in response to TCR triggering alone. CD2 also can facilitate T cell adhesion to APCs (62). Because it spans a similar intermembrane distance as TCR-pMHC, CD2-CD58 interactions may facilitate the construction of closely apposed domains for facilitation of TCR-mediated signaling in loci that exclude phosphatases such as CD45 with large extracellular domains (28). CD2 had been described during IS formation as a large accumulation only within the cSMAC (64). However, we have found that, although a proportion of engaged CD2 is quickly routed to the cSMAC, the remainder consolidates into distinct foci within the dSMAC (S. Vardhana and M. Dustin, unpublished observations). These outer foci remain anchored in the periphery and are not translocated to the cSMAC. We have found that CD2 associates with the signaling molecule Fyn in the periphery but is largely silent in the cSMAC. Thus, engaged CD2 contributes to T cell activation in discrete ways that depend on its localization within the IS.

Inhibitory Receptors and Cosignaling

T cell activation and IS formation can be constrained by the action of inhibitory receptors. The classic example is expression of cytotoxic T lymphocyte antigen-4 (CTLA-4, CD152) on T cells after activation, which dampens signaling by a variety of mechanisms. CTLA-4 can outcompete CD28 for binding to costimulatory ligands B7-1 (CD80) and B7-2 (CD86) (65). CTLA-4 localization in synapses depends on ligand engagement (66), and ligand dosage and its engagement reduces ZAP-70 recruitment to

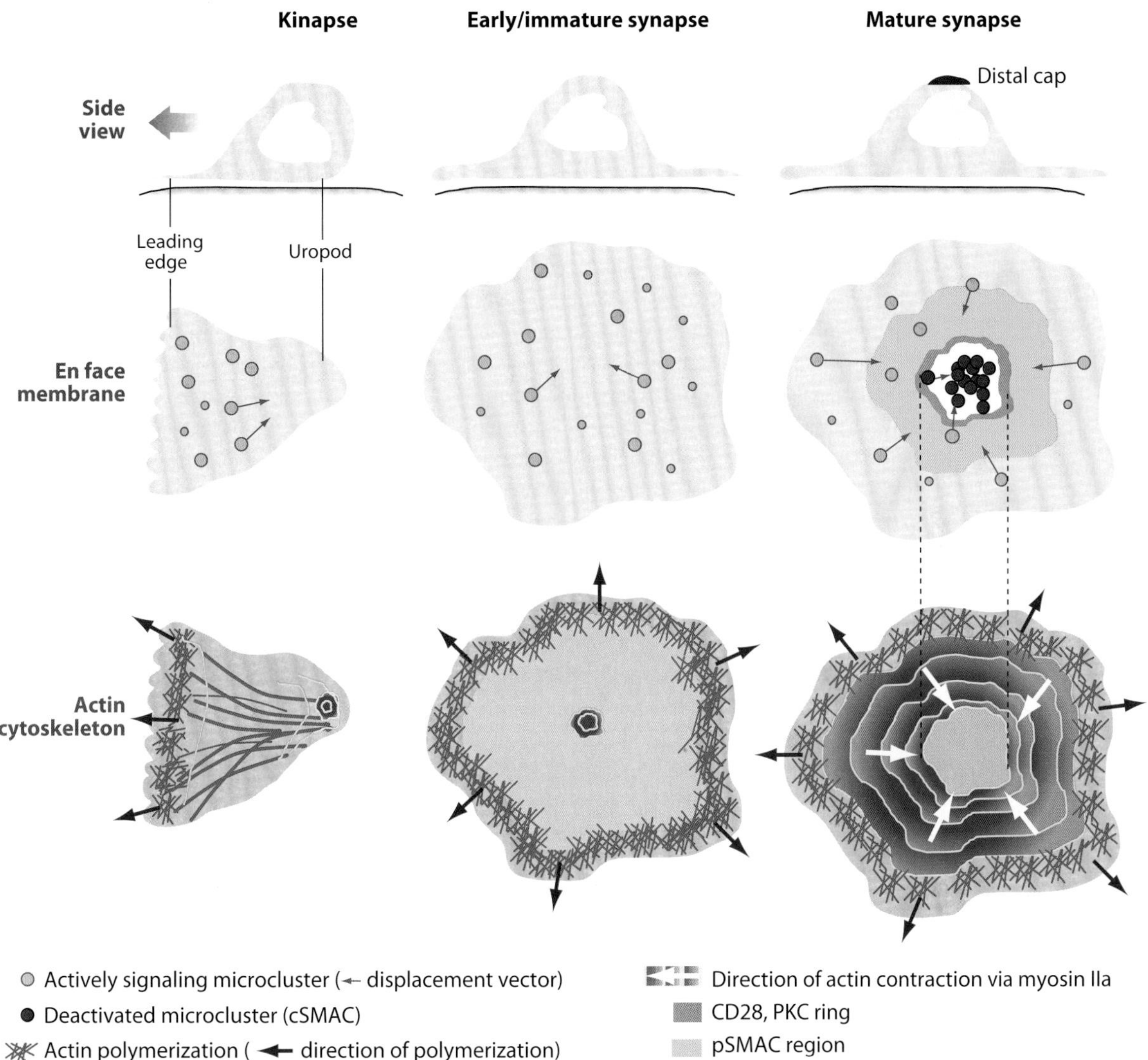

Figure 2

Spatiotemporal map of synapse formation. Side and en face views of the T cell as it engages an APC. The migrating cell has a polarized cell body with actin polymerization at the leading edge and myosin contraction at the uropod. The membrane topology in the migrating cell is poorly understood. The early/immature synapse has symmetrical actin polymerization radiating outward from the center along the perimeter of the contact surface and cytoskeletal contractions through myosin radially inward to the center. The early synapse only contains microclusters, and after a few minutes these accumulate and form the cSMAC.

MCs (67). Despite CTLA-4's effect on MC signaling, it is unknown if it colocalizes with them. It recruits SHP2 and SHP1 and blocks Akt phosphorylation (in a CD28-dependent manner for the latter), inhibiting T cell activation. Although cross-linking CD3 on previously activated mouse and human T cells reduces cell motility, coligation of CTLA-4 results in a reversal of cell arrest, with cells moving at speeds similar to that of untreated cells. Rudd (68) has proposed a reverse–stop signal model to explain this phenomenon. By increasing the rate of motility, CTLA-4 coligation increases the threshold for TCR triggering, thus decreasing the likelihood of T cell activation. We revisit the relationship between T cell arrest and activation in a later section. Mice deficient for CTLA-4 develop an aggressive autoimmune disorder characterized by inflammation and overproliferation of T cells. New cancer immunotherapies have targeted CTLA-4, which has the capacity to boost the function of tumor-infiltrating lymphocytes in patients (69).

Another inhibitory molecule involved in cosignaling in T cells is the programmed-death 1 receptor (PD-1, CD279), and, as its name suggests, it was first identified as a proapoptotic factor on CD8 T cells (70). PD-1 is part of the CD28 family, which also includes CTLA-4, ICOS (inducible T cell costimulator; CD278), and BTLA (B and T lymphocytes attenuator; CD272) (71). PD-1 has two ligands—PD-L1 (B7-H1, CD274) and PD-L2 (B7-DC, CD273)—although PD-L1 can also interact with CD80 to generate inhibitory signals (72).

Recently, PD-1 has become implicated as a marker for the "exhausted" phenotype of antigen-specific CTLs that is associated with chronic viral infections such as human immunodeficiency virus (HIV), simian immunodeficiency virus (SIV), and lymphocytic choriomeningitis virus (LCMV) clone 13 in mice (73, 74). Exhaustion has been characterized as an inability to produce effector cytokines, such as IFN-γ and IL-2, and by diminished proliferation. The level of expression of PD-1 positively correlates with the degree of functional exhaustion, but this phenotype is actively maintained by signaling. Blockade of PD-1 ligands can restore the functionality of the exhausted T cells and can curtail chronic viremia. As with a deficiency in CTLA-4, mice deficient for PD-1 also have an autoimmune disorder; however, it manifests later in life (75). PD-1 signaling inhibits CD28-dependent PI3K activation (76) and thus blocks Akt activation. The role played by PD-1 in TCR MCs is unclear. As with CTLA-4 in cancer, blockade of PD-1 signaling is being explored as a new therapy for patients with chronic viral infections (77).

Many questions remain regarding cosignaling of these receptors. For example, does PD-1 expression impair T cell arrest, as does CTLA-4 expression? From imaging experiments and affinity measurements, there seems to be a crosstalk between members of the CD28 receptor family and ligands of the B7 family. Furthermore, various receptors have nontrivial affinities for contra-ligands, and PD-L1 and PD-1 are both expressed on T cells. This suggests that these interactions may take place in homotypic (T cell–T cell) interactions or even in *cis*, e.g., between membrane projections from the same cell. Moreover, where does PD-1 localize at the IS and is its spatial and temporal control important for exerting its negative regulatory role in T cell activation? Addressing these questions will provide additional insight into how T cell activation versus inhibition is controlled. Although the inhibitory action of CTLA-4 and PD-1 may sometimes be exploited by pathogens or tumors to escape the immune response, these mechanisms are likely important in averting immunopathology.

The Actin Cytoskeleton

Actin filaments (F-actin) play a critical role throughout the various stages of T cell activation (**Figure 2**). In the steady state, actin polymerization at the leading edge and cytoskeletal contraction at the uropod mediate rapid migration during scanning (78). Upon T cell engagement of an APC bearing agonist pMHC, the T cell's machinery for locomotion is recycled for synapse formation (**Figure 2**). Globally, actin polymerization continues as before, but without T cell displacement (79). The T cell spreads a lamellar sheet over the APC surface, inducing outward, radial actin polymerization. This is coupled to contraction and centripetal flux of F-actin toward the center of the IS, which eventually becomes the cSMAC (36). Dynamic protrusion and retraction produce contractile oscillations in the lamellipodium (80). These oscillations may allow the T cell to rake the

APC surface for antigen as well as generate force transduction on the TCR, inducing triggering (81). Valitutti et al. (40) also commented on this F-actin-dependent scanning of the APC surface by T cells.

TCR signaling also induces F-actin remodeling. TCR triggering leads to LAT and SLP-76 activation, which in turn recruit Vav1, the guanine exchange factor for the Rho GTPases Cdc42 and Rac1 (82). Activated Cdc42 and Rac1 interact with WASp (Wiskott-Aldrich Syndrome protein) and the WAVE2 complex, respectively, to recruit and activate the actin-related protein 2/3 (Arp2/3) complex, leading to dendritic nucleation of F-actin (82–84). However, MC formation is independent of Src kinase activity, which indicates that actin-dependent MC formation precedes TCR signaling.

TCR triggering and MC formation depend on F-actin. Disrupting actin filaments with latrunculin A (LatA) inhibits MC formation and signaling. Antigen sensitivity is elevated in the lamellipodium, where actin polymerization is concentrated (85, 86). The stability and transit of MC to the cSMAC also depend on the actin cytoskeleton. Waves of F-actin, which can be seen flowing toward the cSMAC (87), seem to shuttle MCs to the cSMAC. The interaction of TCR MCs with actin is discontinuous, as shown by the ability of MCs to translocate around F-actin barriers (88).

The nonmuscle actin motor protein, myosin IIA, is also a key player in MC movement and signaling. This myosin isoform is the only one expressed in mouse T cells, whereas human T cells also express myosin IIB (89, 90). Myosin IIA knockdown CD4 T cells can form TCR MCs, but these MCs are barely mobile and cannot translocate efficiently to the cSMAC (91). In MCs formed in the absence of myosin IIA, there is a markedly diminished recruitment and activation of ZAP-70 and LAT (91).

Coincidentally, both MC signaling and the actin cytoskeleton terminate at the cSMAC. The mechanism that couples MC signaling to the cytoskeleton is still unclear. The void in F-actin in the cSMAC is important for localized exo- and endocytosis (92, 93). It is unclear what maintains the F-actin-free zone in the cSMAC, but this may be important for vesicle trafficking.

The Microtubule Network

The microtubule organizing center (MTOC) and microtubule network of the cell provide a molecular highway for vesicle traffic and structural support for polarized cell functions. Within seconds after TCR stimulation, the MTOC mobilizes and polarizes to the IS in T cells (94, 95). Polarization is important for efficient trafficking and directed secretion of cytolytic granules and cytokines for secretion at the synapse (95, 96).

The mechanism that initiates MTOC polarization is poorly understood. Signaling through TCR is required, with several downstream factors implicated, such as Lck, ZAP-70, LAT, SLP-76, and Ca^{2+} influx (97–99). Localized diacylglycerol production by PLCγ precedes MTOC polarization (100). The microtubule minus-end-directed motor dynein is recruited to the IS via an interaction with the adaptor ADAP, and knockdown of either protein abrogates MTOC polarization (101, 102). SLP-76 may mediate and help localize the assembly of the dynein-ADAP complex (103). Actin polymerization is also involved in MTOC polarization. Two of the formin family members, formin-like 1 (FMNL1) and Diaphanous 1 (Dia1), colocalize with the centrosome, form a ring-like structure surrounding the MTOC, and control its polarization as well as cell-mediated killing. The formin family of proteins nucleates actin into linear filaments found in actin cables, filopodia, and stress fibers (104). Branched actin structures generated by the Arp2/3 complex may not be involved in polarization (105). The plasma membrane proximal localization of the centrosome at the IS is reminiscent of centrosome positioning in basal bodies of flagella and cilia, although leukocytes lack the primary cilium that acts as sensory structures in epithelial cells. However, an evolutionary connection between the IS and sensory cilium is suggested by the recent finding that intraflagellar transport proteins play a critical role in sustaining the IS and T cell signaling (106).

Questions remain regarding the molecular mechanism and the dynamics of MTOC polarization in various aspects of the IS. How these structures function in CD4 cytokine versus CTL granule secretion is unclear. Additionally, MTOC polarization is likely involved in asymmetric cell division and segregation of polarity proteins.

Calcium and T Cell Activation

Ca^{2+} signaling is required for full T cell activation and function (107). TCR activation triggers a transient Ca^{2+} flux through release of ER stores. This opens CRAC (Ca^{2+}-release activated Ca^{2+}) channels on the plasma membrane, leading to a sustained influx of Ca^{2+} or store-operated Ca^{2+} entry (SOCE). Recently, Lewis and colleagues (108) demonstrated that stromal interaction molecule (STIM) and Orai proteins are the major players in SOCE. In response to ER store depletion, STIM proteins (primarily STIM1) form clusters that localize to sites of ER membrane association with the plasma membrane, so-called puncta (109–111). Sites of STIM1 clusters overlap with Orai1 clusters and mediate localized Ca^{2+} influx (112, 113). Direct binding of STIM1 to the cytoplasmic domain of Orai1 appears to mediate opening of the Orai channels (114, 115). In T cells, Orai1 and STIM1 are recruited to the IS in response to antigen-bearing DCs, resulting in increased local Ca^{2+} entry at the T cell–APC interface (116). STIM1 and Orai1 interact in a stable complex in puncta at the IS of Jurkat T cells, interacting with anti-CD3-coated glass (117). However, these clusters do not colocalize with TCR clusters. STIM1 and Orai1 recruitment to the IS is mediated through proximal TCR signals and is independent of sustained Ca^{2+} signaling (116, 117). Although STIM and Orai have not been directly linked to the cytoskeleton, there is evidence that their function depends on cytoskeletal components. WAVE2 is required for sustained Ca^{2+} increase (118). This may be due to a defect in localization of Ca^{2+} signaling components at the IS. In addition to STIM1 and Orai1, molecules indirectly involved in Ca^{2+} signaling translocate to the IS. Potassium channels (Kv1.3 and KCa3.1) that regulate membrane potential localize to the IS (119, 120). Mitochondria that buffer local Ca^{2+} levels also localize to the IS (121). STIM1 and Orai1 also localize to TCR-dependent cap-like structures that form outside the IS or at the distal pole. Barr et al. (117) have proposed that the formation of caps might serve as a repository for preformed channels, allowing rapid responses to additional APCs.

Overall, the function of STIM1 and Orai1 recruitment and localized Ca^{2+} entry at the synapse may serve to propagate Ca^{2+}-dependent TCR signals and facilitate long-term activation of T cells. Indeed, Ca^{2+} signaling is implicated in promoting long-lived interactions between T cells and APCs in vitro and in vivo (85, 122–124).

Asymmetric Cell Division and the IS

Although synapse formation is critically important in the initial signaling events and the activation of T cells, we and others have proposed that termination of the IS plays a role in the fate selection of effector and memory cell differentiation via asymmetric cell division (125). Asymmetric cell division is an evolutionarily conserved mechanism important in the generation of diverse cell types from a common progenitor (126). Polarity complex proteins are required to partition cell-fate determinants asymmetrically in a cell undergoing mitotic division (127, 128).

Polarity network proteins are expressed in T cells. These include proteins from the Par, Crumbs, and Scribble polarity complexes (129–132). The Par complex consists of the proteins Par3 and Par6 (127, 133) and an atypical protein kinase C-ζ (PKCζ) (134), whereas the Scribble complex is composed of the proteins Scribble, Dlg, and Lgl (128, 135). The Crumbs complex is composed of the proteins Crumbs, Pal1, and PatJ (136). The expression of these proteins during T cell activation plays an important role in both migration and the functional properties of T cells (129–131, 136). Chang and colleagues (129) demonstrated that prior to the first cell division of an activated T cell, Scribble was associated with CD3 and CD8 localization at the IS, whereas PKCζ segregated to the distal pole (opposite the IS). Upon the first division of activated $CD8^+$ T cells, the parental cells underwent asymmetric cell division with one daughter cell proximal and the other distal to the IS, and the progeny retained the unequal inheritance of the proteins, with the proximal cell inheriting greater amounts of LFA-1 and CD8 and the distal cell inheriting greater amounts of PKCζ. The proximal daughter cell had an effector phenotype, whereas the distal cell had a memory phenotype in vivo. Teixeiro et al. (137) demonstrated that T cells with a mutation in the transmembrane domain of TCRβ had defects in polarity protein distribution and could proliferate and differentiate into effector T cells, but they did not generate memory T cells. The Scribble binding partner Crtam (MHC class I–restricted T cell–associated molecule), an Ig superfamily transmembrane protein (138), may play a role in T cell polarity during the critical period prior to the first cell division (132). Collectively, these data suggest that segregation of cell polarity proteins during T cell activation may provide a means to generate divergent cell subtypes from a single naive T cell.

Although asymmetric cell division in lymphocytes can give rise to distinct lineages of T cells (i.e., effector and memory precursors) (129), it is not clear whether the daughter cells that undergo subsequent divisions continue down the pathway of asymmetric division or whether there is a molecular switch that programs the cells to divide symmetrically. Furthermore, Bannard et al. (139) have recently shown, through the use of a granzyme B cell–fate mapping system, that memory cells can arise from effector cells. This does not preclude the possibility that asymmetric cell division could occur after the first cell division in an effector precursor, giving rise to a memory cell. Alternatively, this may also indicate that there are multiple mechanisms in place for the differentiation of effector and memory cells. Understanding these aspects of dividing lymphocytes will greatly aid in the development of adoptive immunotherapy to generate antigen-specific effector cells for immediate effector function as well as long-term protection through the generation of memory cells. It will be interesting to see if these mechanisms can be exploited by means of manipulating the IS in vitro to enhance the generation of memory T cells or to identify and isolate effector or memory precursors early during the immune response for further expansion ex vivo.

EFFECTOR SYNAPSES

Many studies on the synapse have been performed with naive or resting $CD4^+$ T cells to study induction of long-term processes such as cytokine production and proliferation. Acutely activated effector T cells may also form distinct shorter-lived interactions to execute effector programs with prestored or rapidly generated proteins. The IS forms in other cell types, such as B cells, natural killer (NK) cells, and CTLs. Here we focus only on recent progress on cytotoxic, regulatory, and virological synapses (summarized in **Table 2**).

Cytotoxic T Lymphocyte Synapses

The classical view of a CTL is as a serial killer that forms a well-organized IS that is short lived (in vivo and in vitro), with a life span of 20–30 min. Similar to the $CD4^+$ T cell IS, the CTL synapse consists of the same pattern of SMACs, but it also contains a distinct secretory domain (92). The pSMAC also contributes to CTL cytolytic function in several ways. Blocking LFA-1 (CD11a/CD18) and ICAM-1 (CD54) interactions leads to decreased sensitivity and ability of CTL to lyse target cells (93, 140). Forming a complete pSMAC ring is important for CTL efficiency, and failure to do so decreases killing efficiency at least threefold (51, 140). Thus, a kinapse is not expected to be an efficient configuration for target killing.

Table 2 Comparison of various immunological synapses

Synapse	Minimum requirements for synapse formation	Site of signaling	Stability	Function, consequences, and in vivo behavior
Naive T cells	TCR-pMHC LFA-1-ICAM-1 CD28-CD80	In the periphery within MC	Periodic (break and reform IS)	Asymmetric cell division Duration of contacts with APC depends of antigen concentration
Effector CD4	TCR-pMHC LFA-1-ICAM-1	In the periphery within MC	Prolonged	Directed cytokine secretion Long-lived contacts with APC
Effector CD8 (CTL)	TCR-pMHC LFA-1-ICAM-1	cSMAC	Transient (lytic) Prolonged (stimulatory)	Release of cytolytic granules Cytokine secretion (stimulatory synapse)
Treg	TCR engagement LFA-1-ICAM-1	In the periphery within MC	Prolonged	Suppression of effector-DC contacts and effector function
HIV-1 VS	HIV-1 env gp120-CD4/ chemokine receptor LFA-1-ICAM-1	Initiated in gp120 MC and sustained in VS cSMAC	Transient	Direct secretion of viral particles and efficient Viral spread

Both actin and microtubules play a key role in cytolytic function. Upon antigen recognition on the target cell, MTOC polarizes rapidly toward the synapse. Lytic granules are trafficked to the IS along microtubules and accumulate at the interface just below the plasma membrane (51). A void of cortical actin opens up just below the cSMAC, which allows for lytic granule delivery to the target. The MTOC transiently contacts the plasma membrane at the cSMAC and directly delivers the lytic granules to the synapse (92). TCR signaling contributes to MTOC polarization through Lck and Fyn (97, 141). Lck can be found in CD8 T cell cSMACs (11). The actin cytoskeleton rearrangements upon CTL IS formation may be linked to MTOC polarization through the interaction of Cdc42 with IQGAP1 (103), a cytoskeletal regulator, which interacts with both actin and the plus-ends of microtubules (92, 142, 143). This may connect actin reorganization at the IS with MTOC polarization in a single mechanism.

Regulatory T Cell Synapses

$CD4^+CD25^+Foxp3^+$ regulatory T cells (Tregs) play a central role in the maintenance of tolerance to self-antigens and immune homeostasis. Tregs suppress the function of multiple immune cell types including conventional $CD4^+$ (Th) and $CD8^+$ cells, B cells, and DCs through an antigen receptor and cell contact–dependent mechanism (144, 145). Tregs decrease the stability of in vivo T cell–DC synapses formed by conventional T cells and other Tregs (146, 147).

Comparison of the ability of Tregs and Th cells to form an IS on supported planar bilayers revealed that human Tregs form a more stable IS than do Th. The Treg IS has less phosphorylated Src family kinases and a near absence of PKCθ and Carma-1 (A. Zanin-Zhorov, Y. Ding, M. Attur, K. Hippen, M. Brown, B. Blazar, S. Abramson, J. Lafaille, and M. Dustin, manuscript submitted). The higher IS stability seems to be mediated by the exclusion of PKCθ from the IS, which leads to attenuated NF-κB activation. NF-κB activation appears to antagonize Treg function, which is consistent with recent evidence that TNF-α directly suppresses Treg function through TNFRII signaling, which activates NF-κB and downmodulates Foxp3 expression (148). Recent studies have reported that both PKCθ and NF-κB are critical for regulating the development and expansion of Tregs but not for their suppression function in mice (149, 150).

Another example of altered TCR-induced signaling pathways in Tregs is provided by a recent study demonstrating that human Tregs fail to phosphorylate AKT upon TCR-mediated activation and that restoration of AKT activity in Tregs reversed their suppressive capacity (151). Thus, the defect in the ability of Tregs to fully activate AKT contributes to their unique suppressive function.

Synapse stabilization may enhance Treg function, as suggested by recent evidence that the IS plays an important role in Treg effects mediated through DCs (144, 152). Thus, tight regulation of NF-κB activation could be critical for Treg function, and further detailed characterization of this unique signaling induced upon IS formation in Tregs may offer new therapeutic strategies in inflammatory disease.

Virological Synapses

Viruses such as HIV-1, human T cell lymphoma virus-1 (HTLV-1), and herpes simplex virus (HSV) (153–155) have co-opted components of the IS to form a similar structure referred to as the infectious or virological synapse (VS). These processes have not been subdivided in the literature, but it is convenient to define an infectious synapse as a junction through which a virion harbored by a noninfected cell such as a DC is transferred and infects a CD4 T cell (156). The VS could then be defined as a junction for transfer of virus from an infected T cell to a noninfected T cell (153, 157). We discuss the organization and structure of the VS for HIV-1 and a model system that we have constructed in which the infected cell is replaced by a supported planar bilayer.

VS formation occurs when the HIV-1 envelope protein, gp120, is expressed on the plasma membrane of the infected cell and engages CD4 along with either CCR5 (CD195) or CXCR4 (CD184) chemokine receptors on the target cell (157–159). HIV-1 gp120 presented with ICAM-1 in a supported planar bilayer induces assembly of a VS with IS-like supramolecular structures: gp120 clusters to form a cSMAC-like structure and segregate from LFA-1-ICAM-1 that forms a pSMAC (160). A VS is transient, persisting for about 15 min (160). Soluble gp120 (and cell-free virion) can activate various intracellular signaling events in T cells and macrophages (161–164), including activation of focal adhesion kinase (FAK) (165, 166), Pyk2 (167), and the mitogen-activated protein kinase (MAPK) pathway (168, 169), as well as Ca^{2+} influx in T cells (170) and translocation of nuclear factor of activated T cells (NFAT) to the nucleus (171). T cell signaling triggered by gp120 in the context of the VS has never been studied but would be important because viral life cycle depends on T cell activation. TCR machinery is recruited and activated in the VS, but its spatial-temporal organization differs greatly from the one in the IS. A better understanding of the molecular details and biological consequences of VS may lead to the development of novel intervention strategies that block HIV-1 cell-to-cell spread within an infected host.

SYNAPSE STABILITY AND KINAPSES

We have observed that while naive T cells are forming stable synapses on supported planar bilayers, they routinely break pSMAC symmetry, migrate away, and reform synapses elsewhere with a periodicity of about 20 min (80). This interconversion between stable and migrating morphologies is reciprocally regulated by PKCθ and WASp pathways. PKCθ-deficient T cells form hyperstable synapses, whereas WASp-deficient T cells cannot reform a symmetrical IS after initial destabilization. This is consistent with Tregs having hyperstable synapses and trace levels of PKCθ at the synapse. We have suggested that PKCθ promotes destabilization via myosin IIA contraction, which favors motility. In migrating cells, myosin IIA promotes fast amoeboid locomotion by inactivating LFA-1 at the trailing edge. Similar activity may produce breaking of the LFA-1-ICAM-1-dominated pSMAC.

Contraction can reduce contact surface, leading to asymmetry in the F-actin flow leading to motion. Thus, the balance between polymerization and contraction of the actin cytoskeleton seems to control the transition between symmetric synapses and asymmetric kinapses.

The transition from migratory to stopped T cell is still poorly understood. We know Ca^{2+} signals and antigen are important for stopping. But how do these signals affect locomotion? How do antigenic signals reset actin polymerization from a migrating to a gathering orientation? Can a single MC induce stopping in vivo? Woolf et al. (172) demonstrated that solid-phase CCL21 chemokine at >100 molecules/μm^2 drives rapid migration of naive T cells in vitro without adhesion molecules. This finding enables the incorporation of a physiological go signal into in vitro models of synapse formation. We still must translate the in vitro lessons of T cell activation to the in vivo environments of the immune system.

IN VIVO SYNAPSES AND T CELL ACTIVATION

The in vivo image of T cell activation is a bit more complex. Von Andrian and colleagues (9) developed an experimental system that uses subcutaneous injection of labeled, LPS-activated DCs followed by intravenous injection of naive transgenic $CD8^+$ T cells. Using intravital TPLSM, they tracked the behavior of these cells and observed a three-phase model for T cell activation (9): During the first 8 h after entering the lymph node, the T cells establish only short-lasting contacts with DCs while upregulating activation markers. The following 12 h are characterized by the formation of stable, longer-lasting (up to 1 h or more) T cell–DC contacts and the production of cytokines. After 24 h, T cells return to their fleeting, motile behavior and start to proliferate.

In a subsequent study, they investigated the contributions of peptide quality and quantity on T cell behavior. They found that reducing the antigenic stimulus—either by using APL with lowered TCR affinities, by reducing the density of pMHC complexes per APC, or by reducing the number of antigen-bearing APCs—had the same effect of increasing the length of phase 1 (173).

In collaboration with the Nussenzweig laboratory, we utilized a system in which the antigen is targeted to endogenous DCs by coupling the peptide to an anti-DEC-205 antibody under priming (in the presence of anti-CD40 antibody) or tolerizing (without anti-CD40) conditions (174). We imaged naive T cell behavior by TPLSM and found rapid arrest after encountering antigen during the first 6 h, often near HEV sites of entry. T cells regained their motility after 18–24 h, correlating to von Andrian's phases 2 and 3, respectively. Under both tolerizing and priming conditions, T cells formed conjugates with DCs. The use of APL in this model revealed that upregulation of CD69 and retention in the lymph node was independent of the potency of the pMHC complex (124). However, only engagement with high-potency pMHC complexes leads to a Ca^{2+} fluxing and complete T cell arrest.

Several groups have established experimental model systems to study the nature of T cell–DC interactions in vivo, and differences in observations clearly reflect differences in the setup and level of stimulation established (175, 176). For example, if T cells encountered a large number of cognate pMHC complexes, they engaged more rapidly with DCs in tight contacts, which may be one explanation for the difference in our system, in which T cells arrested almost immediately after transfer. Von Andrian and colleagues (173) suggest that T cells integrate their received signals while sampling the APCs during phase 1, which leads to transition to phase 2 and T cell activation upon reaching a certain threshold. But in this context, T cells may arrest on the very first DC they encounter (177). Also, the in vivo situation is complicated by the fact that T cell arrest can be negatively regulated by CTLA-4 (178) or the presence of Tregs (146) and that chemokines present in the microenvironment (e.g., CCL21) influence the kinetics of T cell–DC interactions (179).

Effector T Cell Synapses In Vivo—Viral Activation

Viruses have adapted many immune escape mechanisms to guarantee their own propagation and spreading. Several studies have demonstrated the impact of virus infection on the formation of the IS. Most of these findings were derived from in vitro studies, which, as in the case of naive T cell activation, leave room for questioning their significance in the in vivo setting. The advent of high-resolution imaging techniques will allow us in the near future to address the role of IS formation during the immune response and during viral escape directly. A key finding was provided by Barcia et al. (180), who investigated a model of adenoviral infection of astrocytes in the central nervous system. They used Confocal imaging of brain sections from infected rats to demonstrate that the formation of the SMAC precedes the clearance of infected astrocytes. Initially, CD8 T cells exhibited a staining pattern in which phosphor-Lck and phosphor-ZAP-70 polarized toward target astrocytes. Later, TCR surrounded by an LFA-1 ring-like structure was found at contact areas with infected cells. This strongly suggests the presence of an IS in vivo.

HIV-1 also modifies the assembly of the IS (181). Most relevant for the in vivo situation, Thoulouze et al. (182) showed that HIV-1-infected T cells poorly conjugated with B cells, which serve as APCs in this setting, and TCR clustering at the site of the synapse is severely reduced. Interestingly, this was predominantly attributable to the presence of the viral protein Nef, which has a central role in HIV-1 pathogenesis. It was therefore proposed that this provides a countermechanism that prevents hyperactivation of HIV-1-infected T cells, which will lead to apoptosis and an end to the virus life cycle (181).

Another example of viral interference with the IS is respiratory syncytial virus (RSV), a common respiratory pathogen in children that impairs adaptive immune responses in vivo (183). In an in vitro system, González et al. (184) showed that RSV-infected DCs cannot stimulate T cells because of impaired IS assembly as assessed by Golgi polarization.

In Vivo T Cell–B Cell Contacts

A series of multiphoton microscopy studies have recently shed light on the similarities and differences that exist between T cell–B cell and T cell–DC synapses (185–187). T cell–B cell synapses are classically thought to occur in two spatially and temporally distinct settings: (*a*) the T:B border phase, which takes place during the first few days of an immune response, and (*b*) the germinal center (GC), which peaks at about one week later. Both stages of interaction involve previously activated T cells. During the initial phase, T cells and B cells engage in extended contacts at the border between T zone and follicle (185), some lasting for over 40 min. Similar to T cell–DC synapses, T cells also arrest on B cells, but the B cells continue to migrate, carrying the T cells with them (185). These motile conjugates have been described as serially monogamous: T cells engage a single B cell at a time but can hop to a new B cell (188). It is unclear why these conjugates continue migrating and what consequence this has on signal integration for the B and T cells. One possibility is that motility of a B cell–T cell pair may increase the likelihood that the T cell will encounter another B cell of higher affinity for the antigen (and therefore with higher surface peptide density), thus promoting partner exchange for B cells with higher-affinity B cell receptor (BCR). A caveat of this study is the use of B cells with extremely high affinity (the HEL-specific MD4 BCR) as well as on a relatively high dose of antigen; it would therefore be interesting to determine whether such extended interactions also occur in lower affinity/avidity settings.

In contrast to the extended contacts observed at the T:B border, synapses between T and B cells in the GC are much shorter lived (186). Synapses in the GC are rare and short, seldom lasting longer than 5 min (only 4%). T cells are critical to maintaining GCs, given that treatment targeting CD40-CD40L interaction between GC B and T cells extinguishes the GC rapidly (189). At the molecular level, the role of antigen-specific interactions in the GC is unclear, particularly in regulating competition between B cells expressing higher- or lower-affinity receptors. The first in vivo insight into the molecular mechanism of T cell–B cell interactions was provided by Germain and colleagues (187), who described a role for signaling lymphocyte activation molecule (SLAM)-associated protein (SAP), a T cell adaptor protein downstream of the SLAM pathway, in determining the length of T cell–B cell contacts at the T:B border. Although the duration of contacts between wild-type and SAP-deficient T cells and DCs was equivalent, knockout T cells selectively lose their ability to form extended contacts with cognate B cells between 1 and 3 days postimmunization. SAP-deficient T cells spent less time in GCs compared with wild-type T cells. SLAM receptors engage in homotypic interactions and are upregulated on GC B cells but not on DCs. The SLAM/SAP pathway may enhance the efficiency of cognate T cell–B cell engagements uniquely.

In Vivo Cytotoxic T Lymphocyte Contacts

CTLs appear to use synapse or kinapse modes of interaction with target cells in tumors or viral infection sites, respectively. CTLs interacted with tumor targets that were killed, as detected by a caspase biosensor, after ~6 h of stable contact (190). This surprisingly long duration of contact may reflect an unfavorable tumor environment. CTLs specific for LCMV were slowed in contact with infected meningeal fibroblasts but did not arrest during an immune response, leading to fatal meningitis (191). Previous histological studies in the same model capture IS-like molecule patterns (192), but this may have been misleading in the absence of dynamic information. CTLs forming kinapses are likely to be inefficient in killing, although we did not directly evaluate target killing in this study. The use of kinapses by the antiviral CTLs may reflect an initial strategy to activate innate antiviral defenses rather than directly kill the target. In contrast, innate defenses may be less effective against tumor cells, leaving killing of the tumor cells or tumor-supporting normal cells as the only effective control mechanism.

RECONCILING DIFFERENCES BETWEEN IN VIVO AND IN VITRO SYSTEMS

How does the information obtained from the in vitro systems apply to in vivo T cell activation and synapse formation? Despite a handful of static images showing synapse-like accumulations, there has been no satisfactory demonstration of the classic in vitro bull's eye by dynamic TPLSM intravital imaging. Two reasons are given for this discrepancy. The first is technical. TPLSM imaging requires high levels of fluorescent signal (millions of green fluorescent proteins), either chemical dyes or fluorescent proteins, and has worked best in cytoplasmic distributions. To visualize in situ synapses requires labeling of factors controlling T cell activation, which are present in tens of thousands of copies per cell. These have not been bright enough to visualize. But with newer generation TPLSM technology and the development of new molecular tools, the visualization of the IS at subcellular levels in vivo is in sight.

The second reason may be that the classic bull's eye is an in vitro amplification of what occurs at much smaller scales in vivo. We know that peptide dose affects the size of the cSMAC linearly (14, 45). Levels of pMHC on endogenous DCs may be lower than the levels used in our in vitro models. The rigid and flat nature of the glass-supported bilayer may also drive kinetic size segregation. Chemokinetic signals may often be absent or excessive in simplified in vitro systems. In vitro cell:cell conjugates tend to have multifocal synapses (193). Finally, we must recognize that the APC is contributing mechanical and functional contributions to IS surfaces. Recent studies have identified new roles for the APCs in modulating synapse structure and function (194, 195). We are careful to use the word amplification rather than artifact; the biology and signaling are the same, but we need to remind ourselves that the overall size/structure we see is tunable to the factors and constraints we introduce.

CONCLUDING REMARKS AND FUTURE QUESTIONS

In this review, we have tried to focus on the studies that have changed our view of the T cell synapse in the past few years. But questions remain. With the identification of the TCR MC as the quantum of signaling, the microstructure and regulation of MCs are still unknown. But with newer superresolution optical techniques, it should be possible to investigate. In vivo, the kinapse seems to rule, empirically, during early stages of signal integration and in late effector stages, when T cells seem to migrate even in the presence of antigen. The membrane protein organization of the kinapse is unknown, as is how the balance between stop and go signals is transduced. From what we know already, these pathways are redundant and reciprocal, with the balance finely tuned based on the context. We are still trying to resolve the complexity of cues and systems biology of the downstream signaling pathways that coordinate the actions of an elaborate yet elegant T cell.

DISCLOSURE STATEMENT

The authors are not aware of any affiliations, memberships, funding, or financial holdings that might be perceived as affecting the objectivity of this review.

LITERATURE CITED

1. Marrack P, Scott-Browne JP, Dai S, Gapin L, Kappler JW. 2008. Evolutionarily conserved amino acids that control TCR-MHC interaction. *Annu. Rev. Immunol.* 26:171–203
2. Miller MJ, Wei SH, Parker I, Cahalan MD. 2002. Two-photon imaging of lymphocyte motility and antigen response in intact lymph node. *Science* 296:1869–73
3. Miller MJ, Wei SH, Cahalan MD, Parker I. 2003. Autonomous T cell trafficking examined in vivo with intravital two-photon microscopy. *Proc. Natl. Acad. Sci. USA* 100:2604–9
4. Lindquist RL, Shakhar G, Dudziak D, Wardemann H, Eisenreich T, et al. 2004. Visualizing dendritic cell networks in vivo. *Nat. Immunol.* 5:1243–50
5. Bajenoff M, Egen JG, Koo LY, Laugier JP, Brau F, et al. 2006. Stromal cell networks regulate lymphocyte entry, migration, and territoriality in lymph nodes. *Immunity* 25:989–1001
6. Beltman JB, Maree AF, Lynch JN, Miller MJ, de Boer RJ. 2007. Lymph node topology dictates T cell migration behavior. *J. Exp. Med.* 204:771–80
7. Dustin ML. 2004. Stop and go traffic to tune T cell responses. *Immunity* 21:305–14
8. Pham TH, Okada T, Matloubian M, Lo CG, Cyster JG. 2008. $S1P_1$ receptor signaling overrides retention mediated by $G\alpha_i$-coupled receptors to promote T cell egress. *Immunity* 28:122–33
9. Mempel TR, Henrickson SE, Von Andrian UH. 2004. T-cell priming by dendritic cells in lymph nodes occurs in three distinct phases. *Nature* 427:154–59
10. Scholer A, Hugues S, Boissonnas A, Fetler L, Amigorena S. 2008. Intercellular adhesion molecule-1-dependent stable interactions between T cells and dendritic cells determine $CD8^+$ T cell memory. *Immunity* 28:258–70
11. Monks CR, Freiberg BA, Kupfer H, Sciaky N, Kupfer A. 1998. Three-dimensional segregation of supramolecular activation clusters in T cells. *Nature* 395:82–86
12. Freiberg BA, Kupfer H, Maslanik W, Delli J, Kappler J, et al. 2002. Staging and resetting T cell activation in SMACs. *Nat. Immunol.* 3:911–17
13. Dustin ML. 1998. Making a little affinity go a long way: a topological view of LFA-1 regulation. *Cell Adhes. Commun.* 6:255–62

14. Grakoui A, Bromley SK, Sumen C, Davis MM, Shaw AS, et al. 1999. The immunological synapse: a molecular machine controlling T cell activation. *Science* 285:221–27
15. Dustin ML, Cooper JA. 2000. The immunological synapse and the actin cytoskeleton: molecular hardware for T cell signaling. *Nat. Immunol.* 1:23–29
16. Varma R, Campi G, Yokosuka T, Saito T, Dustin ML. 2006. T cell receptor-proximal signals are sustained in peripheral microclusters and terminated in the central supramolecular activation cluster. *Immunity* 25:117–27
17. Cemerski S, Das J, Giurisato E, Markiewicz MA, Allen PM, et al. 2008. The balance between T cell receptor signaling and degradation at the center of the immunological synapse is determined by antigen quality. *Immunity* 29:414–22
18. Beal A, Anikeeva N, Varma R, Cameron TO, Norris PJ, et al. 2008. Protein kinase Cθ regulates stability of the peripheral adhesion ring junction and contributes to the sensitivity of target cell lysis by CTL. *J. Immunol.* 181:4815–24
19. Irvine DJ, Purbhoo MA, Krogsgaard M, Davis MM. 2002. Direct observation of ligand recognition by T cells. *Nature* 419:845–49
20. Xu C, Gagnon E, Call ME, Schnell JR, Schwieters CD, et al. 2008. Regulation of T cell receptor activation by dynamic membrane binding of the CD3ε cytoplasmic tyrosine-based motif. *Cell* 135:702–13
21. Matsui K, Boniface JJ, Reay PA, Schild H, Fazekas de St Groth B, Davis MM. 1991. Low affinity interaction of peptide-MHC complexes with T cell receptors. *Science* 254:1788–91
22. Corr M, Slanetz AE, Boyd LF, Jelonek MT, Khilko S, et al. 1994. T cell receptor-MHC class I peptide interactions: affinity, kinetics, and specificity. *Science* 265:946–49
23. Daniels MA, Teixeiro E, Gill J, Hausmann B, Roubaty D, et al. 2006. Thymic selection threshold defined by compartmentalization of Ras/MAPK signaling. *Nature* 444:724–29
24. Zehn D, Lee SY, Bevan MJ. 2009. Complete but curtailed T-cell response to very low-affinity antigen. *Nature* 458:211–14
25. Cemerski S, Das J, Locasale J, Arnold P, Giurisato E, et al. 2007. The stimulatory potency of T cell antigens is influenced by the formation of the immunological synapse. *Immunity* 26:345–55
26. Rudolph MG, Luz JG, Wilson IA. 2002. Structural and thermodynamic correlates of T cell signaling. *Annu. Rev. Biophys. Biomol. Struct.* 31:121–49
27. Nicholson MJ, Hahn M, Wucherpfennig KW. 2005. Unusual features of self-peptide/MHC binding by autoimmune T cell receptors. *Immunity* 23:351–60
28. Kaizuka Y, Douglass AD, Vardhana S, Dustin ML, Vale RD. 2009. The coreceptor CD2 uses plasma membrane microdomains to transduce signals in T cells. *J. Cell Biol.* 185:521–34
29. Dustin ML, Golan DE, Zhu DM, Miller JM, Meier W, et al. 1997. Low affinity interaction of human or rat T cell adhesion molecule CD2 with its ligand aligns adhering membranes to achieve high physiological affinity. *J. Biol. Chem.* 272:30889–98
30. Zhu DM, Dustin ML, Cairo CW, Thatte HS, Golan DE. 2006. Mechanisms of cellular avidity regulation in CD2-CD58-mediated T cell adhesion. *ACS Chem. Biol.* 1:649–58
31. Zhu DM, Dustin ML, Cairo CW, Golan DE. 2007. Analysis of two-dimensional dissociation constant of laterally mobile cell adhesion molecules. *Biophys. J.* 92:1022–34
32. Tolentino TP, Wu J, Zarnitsyna VI, Fang Y, Dustin ML, Zhu C. 2008. Measuring diffusion and binding kinetics by contact area FRAP. *Biophys. J.* 95:920–30
33. Bunnell S, Hong DI, Kardon JR, Yamazaki T, McGlade CJ, et al. 2002. T cell receptor ligation induces the formation of dynamically regulated signaling assemblies. *J. Cell Biol.* 158:1263–75
34. Bunnell SC, Barr VA, Fuller CL, Samelson LE. 2003. High-resolution multicolor imaging of dynamic signaling complexes in T cells stimulated by planar substrates. *Sci. STKE* 2003:PL8
35. Douglass A, Vale RD. 2005. Single-molecule microscopy reveals plasma membrane microdomains created by protein-protein networks that exclude or trap signaling molecules in T cells. *Cell* 121:937–50
36. Kaizuka Y, Douglass AD, Varma R, Dustin ML, Vale RD. 2007. Mechanisms for segregating T cell receptor and adhesion molecules during immunological synapse formation in Jurkat T cells. *Proc. Natl. Acad. Sci. USA* 104:20296–301

37. Cochran JR, Cameron TO, Stern LJ. 2000. The relationship of MHC-peptide binding and T cell activation probed using chemically defined MHC class II oligomers. *Immunity* 12:241–50
38. Krogsgaard M, Li QJ, Sumen C, Huppa JB, Huse M, Davis MM. 2005. Agonist/endogenous peptide-MHC heterodimers drive T cell activation and sensitivity. *Nature* 434:238–43
39. Campi G, Varma R, Dustin ML. 2005. Actin and agonist MHC-peptide complex-dependent T cell receptor microclusters as scaffolds for signaling. *J. Exp. Med.* 202:1031–36
40. Valitutti S, Dessing M, Aktories K, Gallati H, Lanzavecchia A. 1995. Sustained signaling leading to T cell activation results from prolonged T cell receptor occupancy. Role of T cell actin cytoskeleton. *J. Exp. Med.* 181:577–84
41. Schamel WW, Arechaga I, Risueno RM, van Santen HM, Cabezas P, et al. 2005. Coexistence of multivalent and monovalent TCRs explains high sensitivity and wide range of response. *J. Exp. Med.* 202:493–503
42. Lillemeier BF, Mörtelmaier MA, Forstner MB, Huppa JB, Groves JT, Davis MM. 2010. TCR and LAT occur in separate domains on T cell membranes, and concatenate during activation. *Nat. Immunol.* 11:90–96
43. Springer TA. 1990. Adhesion receptors of the immune system. *Nature* 346:425–34
44. Choudhuri K, Wiseman D, Brown MH, Gould K, Van Der Merwe PA. 2005. T-cell receptor triggering is critically dependent on the dimensions of its peptide-MHC ligand. *Nature* 436:578–82
45. Yokosuka T, Sakata-Sogawa K, Kobayashi W, Hiroshima M, Hashimoto-Tane A, et al. 2005. Newly generated T cell receptor microclusters initiate and sustain T cell activation by recruitment of Zap70 and SLP-76. *Nat. Immunol.* 6:1253–62
46. Bunnell S, Singer AL, Hong DI, Jacque BH, Jordan MS, et al. 2006. Persistence of cooperatively stabilized signaling clusters drives T-cell activation. *Mol. Cell. Biol.* 26:7155–66
47. Nguyen K, Sylvain NR, Bunnell SC. 2008. T cell costimulation via the integrin VLA-4 inhibits the actin-dependent centralization of signaling microclusters containing the adaptor SLP-76. *Immunity* 28:810–21
48. Williams RL, Urbe S. 2007. The emerging shape of the ESCRT machinery. *Nat. Rev. Mol. Cell Biol.* 8:355–68
49. Mossman KD, Campi G, Groves JT, Dustin ML. 2005. Altered TCR signaling from geometrically repatterned immunological synapses. *Science* 310:1191–93
50. Shen K, Thomas VK, Dustin ML, Kam LC. 2008. Micropatterning of costimulatory ligands enhances $CD4^+$ T cell function. *Proc. Natl. Acad. Sci. USA* 105:7791–96
51. Stinchcombe JC, Bossi G, Booth S, Griffiths GM. 2001. The immunological synapse of CTL contains a secretory domain and membrane bridges. *Immunity* 15:751–61
52. Bachmann MF, McKall-Faienza K, Schmits R, Bouchard D, Beach J, et al. 1997. Distinct roles for LFA-1 and CD28 during activation of naive T cells: adhesion versus costimulation. *Immunity* 7:549–57
53. Dustin ML, Springer TA. 1989. T-cell receptor cross-linking transiently stimulates adhesiveness through LFA-1. *Nature* 341:619–24
54. Wang H, Moon EY, Azouz A, Wu X, Smith A, et al. 2003. SKAP-55 regulates integrin adhesion and formation of T cell-APC conjugates. *Nat. Immunol.* 4:366–74
55. Mor A, Campi G, Du G, Zheng Y, Foster DA, et al. 2007. The lymphocyte function-associated antigen-1 receptor costimulates plasma membrane Ras via phospholipase D2. *Nat. Cell Biol.* 9:713–19
56. Sawada Y, Tamada M, Dubin-Thaler BJ, Cherniavskaya O, Sakai R, et al. 2006. Force sensing by mechanical extension of the Src family kinase substrate p130Cas. *Cell* 127:1015–26
57. Smith A, Carrasco YR, Stanley P, Kieffer N, Batista FD, Hogg N. 2005. A talin-dependent LFA-1 focal zone is formed by rapidly migrating T lymphocytes. *J. Cell Biol.* 170:141–51
58. Choi CK, Vicente-Manzanares M, Zareno J, Whitmore LA, Mogilner A, Horwitz AR. 2008. Actin and alpha-actinin orchestrate the assembly and maturation of nascent adhesions in a myosin II motor-independent manner. *Nat. Cell Biol.* 10:1039–50
59. Yokosuka T, Kobayashi W, Sakata-Sogawa K, Takamatsu M, Hashimoto-Tane A, et al. 2008. Spatiotemporal regulation of T cell costimulation by TCR-CD28 microclusters and protein kinase Cθ translocation. *Immunity* 29:589–601
60. Tseng SY, Waite JC, Liu M, Vardhana S, Dustin ML. 2008. T cell-dendritic cell immunological synapses contain TCR-dependent CD28-CD80 clusters that recruit protein kinase Cθ. *J. Immunol.* 181:4852–63

61. Rossman JS, Stoicheva NG, Langel FD, Patterson GH, Lippincott-Schwartz J, Schaefer BC. 2006. POLKADOTS are foci of functional interactions in T-cell receptor-mediated signaling to NF-κB. *Mol. Biol. Cell* 17:2166–76
62. Bachmann MF, Barner M, Kopf M. 1999. CD2 sets quantitative thresholds in T cell activation. *J. Exp. Med.* 190:1383–92
63. Espagnolle N, Depoil D, Zaru R, Demeur C, Champagne E, et al. 2007. CD2 and TCR synergize for the activation of phospholipase Cγ1/calcium pathway at the immunological synapse. *Int. Immunol.* 19:239–48
64. Singleton K, Parvaze N, Dama KR, Chen KS, Jennings P, et al. 2006. A large T cell invagination with CD2 enrichment resets receptor engagement in the immunological synapse. *J. Immunol.* 177:4402–13
65. Collins AV, Brodie DW, Gilbert RJ, Iaboni A, Manso-Sancho R, et al. 2002. The interaction properties of costimulatory molecules revisited. *Immunity* 17:201–10
66. Pentcheva-Hoang T, Egen JG, Wojnoonski K, Allison JP. 2004. B7-1 and B7-2 selectively recruit CTLA-4 and CD28 to the immunological synapse. *Immunity* 21:401–13
67. Schneider H, Valk E, da Rocha Dias S, Wei B, Rudd CE. 2005. CTLA-4 up-regulation of lymphocyte function-associated antigen 1 adhesion and clustering as an alternate basis for coreceptor function. *Proc. Natl. Acad. Sci. USA* 102:12861–66
68. Rudd CE. 2008. The reverse stop-signal model for CTLA4 function. *Nat. Rev. Immunol.* 8:153–60
69. Sarnaik AA, Weber JS. 2009. Recent advances using anti-CTLA-4 for the treatment of melanoma. *Cancer J.* 15:169–73
70. Ishida Y, Agata Y, Shibahara K, Honjo T. 1992. Induced expression of PD-1, a novel member of the immunoglobulin gene superfamily, upon programmed cell death. *EMBO J.* 11:3887–95
71. Riley JL. 2009. PD-1 signaling in primary T cells. *Immunol. Rev.* 229:114–25
72. Keir ME, Butte MJ, Freeman GJ, Sharpe AH. 2008. PD-1 and its ligands in tolerance and immunity. *Annu. Rev. Immunol.* 26:677–704
73. Day CL, Kaufmann DE, Kiepiela P, Brown JA, Moodley ES, et al. 2006. PD-1 expression on HIV-specific T cells is associated with T-cell exhaustion and disease progression. *Nature* 443:350–54
74. Kaufmann D, Walker BD. 2009. PD-1 and CTLA-4 inhibitory cosignaling pathways in HIV infection and the potential for therapeutic intervention. *J. Immunol.* 182:5891–97
75. Nishimura H, Okazaki T, Tanaka Y, Nakatani K, Hara M, et al. 2001. Autoimmune dilated cardiomyopathy in PD-1 receptor-deficient mice. *Science* 291:319–22
76. Parry RV, Chemnitz JM, Frauwirth KA, Lanfranco AR, Braunstein I, et al. 2005. CTLA-4 and PD-1 receptors inhibit T-cell activation by distinct mechanisms. *Mol. Cell. Biol.* 25:9543–53
77. Barber DL, Wherry EJ, Masopust D, Zhu B, Allison JP, et al. 2006. Restoring function in exhausted CD8 T cells during chronic viral infection. *Nature* 439:682–87
78. Giannone G, Dubin-Thaler BJ, Rossier O, Cai Y, Chaga O, et al. 2007. Lamellipodial actin mechanically links myosin activity with adhesion-site formation. *Cell* 128:561–75
79. Bunnell S, Kapoor V, Trible RP, Zhang W, Samelson LE. 2001. Dynamic actin polymerization drives T cell receptor-induced spreading: A role for the signal transduction adaptor LAT. *Immunity* 14:315–29
80. Sims T, Soos TJ, Xenias HS, Dubin-Thaler B, Hofman JM, et al. 2007. Opposing effects of PKCθ and WASp on symmetry breaking and relocation of the immunological synapse. *Cell* 129:773–85
81. Ilani T, Vasiliver-Shamis G, Vardhana S, Bretscher A, Dustin ML. 2009. T cell antigen receptor signaling and immunological synapse stability require myosin IIA. *Nat. Immunol.* 10:531–39
82. Billadeau DD, Nolz JC, Gomez TS. 2007. Regulation of T-cell activation by the cytoskeleton. *Nat. Rev. Immunol.* 7:131–43
83. Barda-Saad M, Braiman A, Titerence R, Bunnell SC, Barr VA, Samelson LE. 2005. Dynamic molecular interactions linking the T cell antigen receptor to the actin cytoskeleton. *Nat. Immunol.* 6:80–89
84. Gomez T, Billadeau DD. 2008. T cell activation and the cytoskeleton: you can't have one without the other. *Adv. Immunol.* 97:1–64
85. Negulescu PA, Krasieva TB, Khan A, Kerschbaum HH, Cahalan MD. 1996. Polarity of T cell shape, motility, and sensitivity to antigen. *Immunity* 4:421–30
86. Wei X, Tromberg BJ, Cahalan MD. 1999. Mapping the sensitivity of T cells with an optical trap: polarity and minimal number of receptors for Ca^{2+} signaling. *Proc. Natl. Acad. Sci. USA* 96:8471–76

87. Kaizuka Y, Douglass AD, Varma R, Dustin ML, Vale RD. 2007. Mechanisms for segregating T cell receptor and adhesion molecules during immunological synapse formation in Jurkat T cells. *Proc. Natl. Acad. Sci. USA* 104:20296–301
88. DeMond AL, Mossman KD, Starr T, Dustin ML, Groves JT. 2008. T cell receptor microcluster transport through molecular mazes reveals mechanism of translocation. *Biophys. J.* 94:3286–92
89. Jacobelli J, Chmura SA, Buxton DB, Davis MM, Krummel MF. 2004. A single class II myosin modulates T cell motility and stopping, but not synapse formation. *Nat. Immunol.* 5:531–38
90. Morin NA, Oakes PW, Hyun YM, Lee D, Chin EY, et al. 2008. Nonmuscle myosin heavy chain IIA mediates integrin LFA-1 de-adhesion during T lymphocyte migration. *J. Exp. Med.* 205:195–205
91. Ilani T, Vasiliver-Shamis G, Vardhana S, Bretscher A, Dustin ML. 2009. TCR signaling and immunological synapse stability requires myosin IIA. *Nat. Immunol.* 10:531–39
92. Stinchcombe JC, Majorovits E, Bossi G, Fuller S, Griffiths GM. 2006. Centrosome polarization delivers secretory granules to the immunological synapse. *Nature* 443:462–65
93. Beal AM, Anikeeva N, Varma R, Cameron TO, Norris PJ, et al. 2008. Protein kinase Cθ regulates stability of the peripheral adhesion ring junction and contributes to the sensitivity of target cell lysis by CTL. *J. Immunol.* 181:4815–24
94. Geiger B, Rosen D, Berke G. 1982. Spatial relationships of microtubule-organizing centers and the contact area of cytotoxic T lymphocytes and target cells. *J. Cell Biol.* 95:137–43
95. Kupfer A, Dennert G, Singer SJ. 1983. Polarization of the Golgi apparatus and the microtubule-organizing center within cloned natural killer cells bound to their targets. *Proc. Natl. Acad. Sci. USA* 80:7224–28
96. Kupfer A, Mosmann TR, Kupfer H. 1991. Polarized expression of cytokines in cell conjugates of helper T cells and splenic B cells. *Proc. Natl. Acad. Sci. USA* 88:775–79
97. Lowin-Kropf B, Shapiro VS, Weiss A. 1998. Cytoskeletal polarization of T cells is regulated by an immunoreceptor tyrosine-based activation motif-dependent mechanism. *J. Cell Biol.* 140:861–71
98. Spitaler M, Emslie E, Wood CD, Cantrell D. 2006. Diacylglycerol and protein kinase D localization during T lymphocyte activation. *Immunity* 24:535–46
99. Kuhne MR, Lin J, Yablonski D, Mollenauer MN, Ehrlich LI, et al. 2003. Linker for activation of T cells, ζ-associated protein-70, and Src homology 2 domain-containing leukocyte protein-76 are required for TCR-induced microtubule-organizing center polarization. *J. Immunol.* 171:860–66
100. Quann EJ, Merino E, Furuta T, Huse M. 2009. Localized diacylglycerol drives the polarization of the microtubule-organizing center in T cells. *Nat. Immunol.* 10:627–35
101. Combs J, Kim SJ, Tan S, Ligon LA, Holzbaur EL, Kuhn J, Poenie M. 2006. Recruitment of dynein to the Jurkat immunological synapse. *Proc. Natl. Acad. Sci. USA* 103:14883–88
102. Martin-Cofreces NB, Robles-Valero J, Cabrero JR, Mittelbrunn M, Gordon-Alonso M, et al. 2008. MTOC translocation modulates IS formation and controls sustained T cell signaling. *J. Cell Biol.* 182:951–62
103. Huse M, Quann EJ, Davis MM. 2008. Shouts, whispers and the kiss of death: directional secretion in T cells. *Nat. Immunol.* 9:1105–11
104. Faix J, Grosse R. 2006. Staying in shape with formins. *Dev. Cell* 10:693–706
105. Gomez TS, Kumar K, Medeiros RB, Shimizu Y, Leibson PJ, Billadeau DD. 2007. Formins regulate the actin-related protein 2/3 complex-independent polarization of the centrosome to the immunological synapse. *Immunity* 26:177–90
106. Finetti F, Rossi Paccani S, Riparbelli MG, Giacomello E, Perinetti G, et al. 2009. Intraflagellar transport is required for polarized recycling of the TCR/CD3 complex to the immune synapse. *Nat. Cell Biol.* 11:1332–39
107. Feske S. 2007. Calcium signaling in lymphocyte activation and disease. *Nat. Rev. Immunol.* 7:690–702
108. Lewis RS. 2007. The molecular choreography of a store-operated calcium channel. *Nature* 446:284–87
109. Muik M, Frischauf I, Derler I, Fahrner M, Bergsmann J, et al. 2008. Dynamic coupling of the putative coiled-coil domain of ORAI1 with STIM1 mediates ORAI1 channel activation. *J. Biol. Chem.* 283:8014–22

110. Stathopulos PB, Li GY, Plevin MJ, Ames JB, Ikura M. 2006. Stored Ca^{2+} depletion-induced oligomerization of stromal interaction molecule 1 (STIM1) via the EF-SAM region: An initiation mechanism for capacitive Ca^{2+} entry. *J. Biol. Chem.* 281:35855–62
111. Wu MM, Buchanan J, Luik RM, Lewis RS. 2006. Ca^{2+} store depletion causes STIM1 to accumulate in ER regions closely associated with the plasma membrane. *J. Cell Biol.* 174:803–13
112. Luik RM, Wu MM, Buchanan J, Lewis RS. 2006. The elementary unit of store-operated Ca^{2+} entry: local activation of CRAC channels by STIM1 at ER-plasma membrane junctions. *J. Cell Biol.* 174:815–25
113. Xu P, Lu J, Li Z, Yu X, Chen L, Xu T. 2006. Aggregation of STIM1 underneath the plasma membrane induces clustering of Orai1. *Biochem. Biophys. Res. Commun.* 350:969–76
114. Vig M, Kinet JP. 2009. Calcium signaling in immune cells. *Nat. Immunol.* 10:21–27
115. Park CY, Hoover PJ, Mullins FM, Bachhawat P, Covington ED, et al. 2009. STIM1 clusters and activates CRAC channels via direct binding of a cytosolic domain to Orai1. *Cell* 136:876–90
116. Lioudyno MI, Kozak JA, Penna A, Safrina O, Zhang SL, et al. 2008. Orai1 and STIM1 move to the immunological synapse and are up-regulated during T cell activation. *Proc. Natl. Acad. Sci. USA* 105:2011–16
117. Barr VA, Bernot KM, Srikanth S, Gwack Y, Balagopalan L, et al. 2008. Dynamic movement of the calcium sensor STIM1 and the calcium channel Orai1 in activated T-cells: puncta and distal caps. *Mol. Biol. Cell* 19:2802–17
118. Nolz JC, Gomez TS, Zhu P, Li S, Medeiros RB, et al. 2006. The WAVE2 complex regulates actin cytoskeletal reorganization and CRAC-mediated calcium entry during T cell activation. *Curr. Biol.* 16:24–34
119. Panyi G, Vamosi G, Bacso Z, Bagdany M, Bodnar A, et al. 2004. Kv1.3 potassium channels are localized in the immunological synapse formed between cytotoxic and target cells. *Proc. Natl. Acad. Sci. USA* 101:1285–90
120. Nicolaou SA, Neumeier L, Peng Y, Devor DC, Conforti L. 2007. The Ca^{2+}-activated K^+ channel KCa3.1 compartmentalizes in the immunological synapse of human T lymphocytes. *Am. J. Physiol. Cell Physiol.* 292:C1431–39
121. Quintana A, Schwindling C, Wenning AS, Becherer U, Rettig J, et al. 2007. T cell activation requires mitochondrial translocation to the immunological synapse. *Proc. Natl. Acad. Sci. USA* 104:14418–23
122. Bhakta NR, Oh DY, Lewis RS. 2005. Calcium oscillations regulate thymocyte motility during positive selection in the three-dimensional thymic environment. *Nat. Immunol.* 6:143–51
123. Wei SH, Safrina O, Yu Y, Garrod KR, Cahalan MD, Parker I. 2007. Ca^{2+} signals in $CD4^+$ T cells during early contacts with antigen-bearing dendritic cells in lymph node. *J. Immunol.* 179:1586–94
124. Skokos D, Shakhar G, Varma R, Waite JC, Cameron TO, et al. 2007. Peptide-MHC potency governs dynamic interactions between T cells and dendritic cells in lymph nodes. *Nat. Immunol.* 8:835–44
125. Dustin ML, Chan AC. 2000. Signaling takes shape in the immune system. *Cell* 103:283–94
126. Horvitz HR, Herskowitz I. 1992. Mechanisms of asymmetric cell division: two Bs or not two Bs, that is the question. *Cell* 68:237–55
127. Kemphues KJ, Priess JR, Morton DG, Cheng NS. 1988. Identification of genes required for cytoplasmic localization in early *C. elegans* embryos. *Cell* 52:311–20
128. Assemat E, Bazellieres E, Pallesi-Pocachard E, Le Bivic A, Massey-Harroche D. 2008. Polarity complex proteins. *Biochim. Biophys. Acta* 1778:614–30
129. Chang JT, Palanivel VR, Kinjyo I, Schambach F, Intlekofer AM, et al. 2007. Asymmetric T lymphocyte division in the initiation of adaptive immune responses. *Science* 315:1687–91
130. Giagulli C, Scarpini E, Ottoboni L, Narumiya S, Butcher EC, et al. 2004. RhoA and ζ PKC control distinct modalities of LFA-1 activation by chemokines: critical role of LFA-1 affinity triggering in lymphocyte in vivo homing. *Immunity* 20:25–35
131. Ludford-Menting MJ, Oliaro J, Sacirbegovic F, Cheah ET, Pedersen N, et al. 2005. A network of PDZ-containing proteins regulates T cell polarity and morphology during migration and immunological synapse formation. *Immunity.* 22:737–48
132. Yeh J, Sidhu SS, Chan AC. 2008. Regulation of a late phase of T cell polarity and effector functions by Crtam. *Cell* 132:846–59

133. Etemad-Moghadam B, Guo S, Kemphues KJ. 1995. Asymmetrically distributed PAR-3 protein contributes to cell polarity and spindle alignment in early *C. elegans* embryos. *Cell* 83:743–52
134. Tabuse Y, Izumi Y, Piano F, Kemphues KJ, Miwa J, Ohno S. 1998. Atypical protein kinase C cooperates with PAR-3 to establish embryonic polarity in *Caenorhabditis elegans*. *Development* 125:3607–14
135. Iden S, Collard JG. 2008. Crosstalk between small GTPases and polarity proteins in cell polarization. *Nat. Rev. Mol. Cell Biol.* 9:846–59
136. Humbert PO, Dow LE, Russell SM. 2006. The Scribble and Par complexes in polarity and migration: friends or foes? *Trends Cell Biol.* 16:622–30
137. Teixeiro E, Daniels MA, Hamilton SE, Schrum AG, Bragado R, et al. 2009. Different T cell receptor signals determine $CD8^+$ memory versus effector development. *Science* 323:502–5
138. Kennedy J, Vicari AP, Saylor V, Zurawski SM, Copeland NG, et al. 2000. A molecular analysis of NKT cells: identification of a class-I restricted T cell-associated molecule (CRTAM). *J. Leukoc. Biol.* 67:725–34
139. Bannard O, Kraman M, Fearon DT. 2009. Secondary replicative function of $CD8^+$ T cells that had developed an effector phenotype. *Science* 323:505–9
140. Anikeeva N, Somersalo K, Sims TN, Thomas VK, Dustin ML, Sykulev Y. 2005. Distinct role of lymphocyte function-associated antigen-1 in mediating effective cytolytic activity by cytotoxic T lymphocytes. *Proc. Natl. Acad. Sci. USA* 102:6437–42
141. Martin-Cofreces NB, Sancho D, Fernandez E, Vicente-Manzanares M, Gordon-Alonso M, et al. 2006. Role of Fyn in the rearrangement of tubulin cytoskeleton induced through TCR. *J. Immunol.* 176:4201–7
142. Fukata M, Watanabe T, Noritake J, Nakagawa M, Yamaga M, et al. 2002. Rac1 and Cdc42 capture microtubules through IQGAP1 and CLIP-170. *Cell* 109:873–85
143. Lansbergen G, Akhmanova A. 2006. Microtubule plus end: a hub of cellular activities. *Traffic* 7:499–507
144. Sakaguchi S, Yamaguchi T, Nomura T, Ono M. 2008. Regulatory T cells and immune tolerance. *Cell* 133:775–87
145. Shevach EM. 2009. Mechanisms of $Foxp3^+$ T regulatory cell-mediated suppression. *Immunity* 30:636–45
146. Tadokoro CE, Shakhar G, Shen S, Ding Y, Lino AC, et al. 2006. Regulatory T cells inhibit stable contacts between $CD4^+$ T cells and dendritic cells in vivo. *J. Exp. Med.* 203:505–11
147. Tang Q, Adams JY, Tooley AJ, Bi M, Fife BT, et al. 2006. Visualizing regulatory T cell control of autoimmune responses in nonobese diabetic mice. *Nat. Immunol.* 7:83–92
148. Valencia X, Stephens G, Goldbach-Mansky R, Wilson M, Shevach EM, Lipsky PE. 2006. TNF downmodulates the function of human $CD4^+CD25^{hi}$ T-regulatory cells. *Blood* 108:253–61
149. Gupta S, Manicassamy S, Vasu C, Kumar A, Shang W, Sun Z. 2008. Differential requirement of PKC-θ in the development and function of natural regulatory T cells. *Mol. Immunol.* 46:213–24
150. Lu LF, Gondek DC, Scott ZA, Noelle RJ. 2005. NFκB-inducing kinase deficiency results in the development of a subset of regulatory T cells, which shows a hyperproliferative activity upon glucocorticoid-induced TNF receptor family-related gene stimulation. *J. Immunol.* 175:1651–57
151. Crellin NK, Garcia RV, Levings MK. 2007. Altered activation of AKT is required for the suppressive function of human $CD4^+CD25^+$ T regulatory cells. *Blood* 109:2014–22
152. Sarris M, Andersen KG, Randow F, Mayr L, Betz AG. 2008. Neuropilin-1 expression on regulatory T cells enhances their interactions with dendritic cells during antigen recognition. *Immunity* 28:402–13
153. Igakura T, Stinchcombe JC, Goon PK, Taylor GP, Weber JN, et al. 2003. Spread of HTLV-I between lymphocytes by virus-induced polarization of the cytoskeleton. *Science* 299:1713–16
154. Jolly C, Sattentau QJ. 2004. Retroviral spread by induction of virological synapses. *Traffic* 5:643–50
155. Aubert M, Yoon M, Sloan DD, Spear PG, Jerome KR. 2009. The virological synapse facilitates herpes simplex virus entry into T cells. *J. Virol.* 83:6171–83
156. McDonald D, Wu L, Bohks SM, KewalRamani VN, Unutmaz D, Hope TJ. 2003. Recruitment of HIV and its receptors to dendritic cell-T cell junctions. *Science* 300:1295–97
157. Jolly C, Kashefi K, Hollinshead M, Sattentau QJ. 2004. HIV-1 cell to cell transfer across an Env-induced, actin-dependent synapse. *J. Exp. Med.* 199:283–93
158. Chen P, Hubner W, Spinelli MA, Chen BK. 2007. Predominant mode of human immunodeficiency virus transfer between T cells is mediated by sustained Env-dependent neutralization-resistant virological synapses. *J. Virol.* 81:12582–95

159. Jolly C, Mitar I, Sattentau QJ. 2007. Adhesion molecule interactions facilitate human immunodeficiency virus type 1-induced virological synapse formation between T cells. *J. Virol.* 81:13916–21
160. Vasiliver-Shamis G, Tuen M, Wu TW, Starr T, Cameron TO, et al. 2008. Human immunodeficiency virus type 1 envelope gp120 induces a stop signal and virological synapse formation in noninfected $CD4^+$ T cells. *J. Virol.* 82:9445–57
161. Cicala C, Arthos J, Martinelli E, Censoplano N, Cruz CC, et al. 2006. R5 and X4 HIV envelopes induce distinct gene expression profiles in primary peripheral blood mononuclear cells. *Proc. Natl. Acad. Sci. USA* 103:3746–51
162. Cicala C, Arthos J, Selig SM, Dennis G Jr, Hosack DA, et al. 2002. HIV envelope induces a cascade of cell signals in nonproliferating target cells that favor virus replication. *Proc. Natl. Acad. Sci. USA* 99:9380–85
163. Lee C, Liu QH, Tomkowicz B, Yi Y, Freedman BD, Collman RG. 2003. Macrophage activation through CCR5- and CXCR4-mediated gp120-elicited signaling pathways. *J. Leukoc. Biol.* 74:676–82
164. Weissman D, Rabin RL, Arthos J, Rubbert A, Dybul M, et al. 1997. Macrophage-tropic HIV and SIV envelope proteins induce a signal through the CCR5 chemokine receptor. *Nature* 389:981–85
165. Cicala C, Arthos J, Rubbert A, Selig S, Wildt K, et al. 2000. HIV-1 envelope induces activation of caspase-3 and cleavage of focal adhesion kinase in primary human $CD4^+$ T cells. *Proc. Natl. Acad. Sci. USA* 97:1178–83
166. Cicala C, Arthos J, Ruiz M, Vaccarezza M, Rubbert A, et al. 1999. Induction of phosphorylation and intracellular association of CC chemokine receptor 5 and focal adhesion kinase in primary human $CD4^+$ T cells by macrophage-tropic HIV envelope. *J. Immunol.* 163:420–26
167. Davis CB, Dikic I, Unutmaz D, Hill CM, Arthos J, et al. 1997. Signal transduction due to HIV-1 envelope interactions with chemokine receptors CXCR4 or CCR5. *J. Exp. Med.* 186:1793–98
168. Del Corno M, Liu QH, Schols D, de Clercq E, Gessani S, et al. 2001. HIV-1 gp120 and chemokine activation of Pyk2 and mitogen-activated protein kinases in primary macrophages mediated by calcium-dependent, pertussis toxin-insensitive chemokine receptor signaling. *Blood* 98:2909–16
169. Lee C, Tomkowicz B, Freedman BD, Collman RG. 2005. HIV-1 gp120-induced TNF-α production by primary human macrophages is mediated by phosphatidylinositol-3 (PI-3) kinase and mitogen-activated protein (MAP) kinase pathways. *J. Leukoc. Biol.* 78:1016–23
170. Melar M, Ott DE, Hope TJ. 2007. Physiological levels of virion-associated human immunodeficiency virus type 1 envelope induce coreceptor-dependent calcium flux. *J. Virol.* 81:1773–85
171. Cicala C, Arthos J, Censoplano N, Cruz C, Chung E, et al. 2006. HIV-1 gp120 induces NFAT nuclear translocation in resting $CD4^+$ T-cells. *Virology* 345:105–14
172. Woolf E, Grigorova I, Sagiv A, Grabovsky V, Feigelson SW, et al. 2007. Lymph node chemokines promote sustained T lymphocyte motility without triggering stable integrin adhesiveness in the absence of shear forces. *Nat. Immunol.* 8:1076–85
173. Henrickson SE, Mempel TR, Mazo IB, Liu B, Artyomov MN, et al. 2008. T cell sensing of antigen dose governs interactive behavior with dendritic cells and sets a threshold for T cell activation. *Nat. Immunol.* 9:282–91
174. Shakhar G, Lindquist RL, Skokos D, Dudziak D, Huang JH, et al. 2005. Stable T cell-dendritic cell interactions precede the development of both tolerance and immunity in vivo. *Nat. Immunol.* 6:707–14
175. Henrickson SE, von Andrian UH. 2007. Single-cell dynamics of T-cell priming. *Curr. Opin. Immunol.* 19:249–58
176. Celli S, Garcia Z, Beuneu H, Bousso P. 2008. Decoding the dynamics of T cell-dendritic cell interactions in vivo. *Immunol. Rev.* 221:182–87
177. Celli S, Lemaitre F, Bousso P. 2007. Real-time manipulation of T cell-dendritic cell interactions in vivo reveals the importance of prolonged contacts for $CD4^+$ T cell activation. *Immunity* 27:625–34
178. Schneider H, Downey J, Smith A, Zinselmeyer BH, Rush C, et al. 2006. Reversal of the TCR stop signal by CTLA-4. *Science* 313:1972–75
179. Friedman RS, Jacobelli J, Krummel MF. 2006. Surface-bound chemokines capture and prime T cells for synapse formation. *Nat. Immunol.* 7:1101–8
180. Barcia C, Thomas CE, Curtin JF, King GD, Wawrowsky K, et al. 2006. In vivo mature immunological synapses forming SMACs mediate clearance of virally infected astrocytes from the brain. *J. Exp. Med.* 203:2095–107

181. Fackler OT, Alcover A, Schwartz O. 2007. Modulation of the immunological synapse: a key to HIV-1 pathogenesis? *Nat. Rev. Immunol.* 7:310–17
182. Thoulouze MI, Sol-Foulon N, Blanchet F, Dautry-Varsat A, Schwartz O, Alcover A. 2006. Human immunodeficiency virus type-1 infection impairs the formation of the immunological synapse. *Immunity* 24:547–61
183. Vallbracht S, Unsold H, Ehl S. 2006. Functional impairment of cytotoxic T cells in the lung airways following respiratory virus infections. *Eur. J. Immunol.* 36:1434–42
184. Gonzalez PA, Prado CE, Leiva ED, Carreno LJ, Bueno SM, et al. 2008. Respiratory syncytial virus impairs T cell activation by preventing synapse assembly with dendritic cells. *Proc. Natl. Acad. Sci. USA* 105:14999–5004
185. Okada T, Miller MJ, Parker I, Krummel MF, Neighbors M, et al. 2005. Antigen-engaged B cells undergo chemotaxis toward the T zone and form motile conjugates with helper T cells. *PLoS Biol.* 3:e150
186. Allen CD, Okada T, Tang HL, Cyster JG. 2007. Imaging of germinal center selection events during affinity maturation. *Science* 315:528–31
187. Qi H, Cannons JL, Klauschen F, Schwartzberg PL, Germain RN. 2008. SAP-controlled T-B cell interactions underlie germinal center formation. *Nature* 455:764–69
188. Cahalan MD, Parker I, Wei SH, Miller MJ. 2003. Real-time imaging of lymphocytes in vivo. *Curr. Opin. Immunol.* 15:372–77
189. Takahashi Y, Dutta PR, Cerasoli DM, Kelsoe G. 1998. In situ studies of the primary immune response to (4-hydroxy-3-nitrophenyl)acetyl. V. Affinity maturation develops in two stages of clonal selection. *J. Exp. Med.* 187:885–95
190. Breart B, Lemaitre F, Celli S, Bousso P. 2008. Two-photon imaging of intratumoral $CD8^+$ T cell cytotoxic activity during adoptive T cell therapy in mice. *J. Clin. Invest.* 118:1390–97
191. Kim JV, Kang SS, Dustin ML, McGavern DB. 2009. Myelomonocytic cell recruitment causes fatal CNS vascular injury during acute viral meningitis. *Nature* 457:191–95
192. McGavern DB, Christen U, Oldstone MB. 2002. Molecular anatomy of antigen-specific $CD8^+$ T cell engagement and synapse formation in vivo. *Nat. Immunol.* 3:918–25
193. Brossard C, Feuillet V, Schmitt A, Randriamampita C, Romao M, et al. 2005. Multifocal structure of the T cell–dendritic cell synapse. *Eur. J. Immunol.* 35:1741–53
194. Bloom O, Unternaehrer JJ, Jiang A, Shin JS, Delamarre L, et al. 2008. Spinophilin participates in information transfer at immunological synapses. *J. Cell Biol.* 181:203–11
195. Fooksman DR, Shaikh SR, Boyle S, Edidin M. 2009. Cutting edge: phosphatidylinositol 4,5-bisphosphate concentration at the APC side of the immunological synapse is required for effector T cell function. *J. Immunol.* 182:5179–82
196. Yoon ST, Dianzani U, Bottomly K, Janeway CA Jr. 1994. Both high and low avidity antibodies to the T cell receptor can have agonist or antagonist activity. *Immunity* 1:563–69
197. Bekoff M, Kubo R, Gray HM. 1986. Activation requirements for normal T cells: accessory cell-dependent and -independent stimulation by antireceptor antibodies. *J. Immunol.* 137:1411–19
198. Wolff CH, Hong SC, von Grafenstein H, Janeway CA Jr. 1993. TCR-CD4 and TCR-TCR interactions as distinctive mechanisms for the induction of increased intracellular calcium in T-cell signaling. *J. Immunol.* 151:1337–45
199. Cochran JR, Cameron TO, Stone JD, Lubetsky JB, Stern LJ. 2001. Receptor proximity, not intermolecular orientation, is critical for triggering T-cell activation. *J. Biol. Chem.* 276:28068–74
200. Yokoyama WM, Koning F, Kehn PJ, Pereira GM, Stingl G, et al. 1988. Characterization of a cell surface-expressed disulfide-linked dimer involved in murine T cell activation. *J. Immunol.* 141:369–76

How Bacterial Carbohydrates Influence the Adaptive Immune System

Fikri Y. Avci and Dennis L. Kasper

Channing Laboratory, Department of Medicine, Brigham & Women's Hospital, and Department of Microbiology and Molecular Genetics, Harvard Medical School, Boston, Massachusetts 02115; email: favci@rics.bwh.harvard.edu, dennis_kasper@hms.harvard.edu

Annu. Rev. Immunol. 2010. 28:107–30

First published online as a Review in Advance on November 12, 2009

The *Annual Review of Immunology* is online at immunol.annualreviews.org

This article's doi: 10.1146/annurev-immunol-030409-101159

0732-0582/10/0423-0107$20.00

Key Words

glycoconjugate vaccines, zwitterionic polysaccharides, antigen presentation, MHCII pathway, bacterial carbohydrates

Abstract

The capsular polysaccharides (CPSs) of most pathogenic bacteria are T cell–independent antigens whose conjugation to carrier proteins evokes a carbohydrate-specific response eliciting T cell help. However, certain bacterial CPSs, known as zwitterionic polysaccharides (ZPSs), activate the adaptive immune system through processing by antigen-presenting cells and presentation by the major histocompatibility complex class II pathway to $CD4^+$ T cells. This discovery was the first mechanistic insight into how carbohydrates—a class of biological molecules previously thought to be T cell independent—can in fact activate T cells. Through their ability to activate $CD4^+$ T cells, ZPSs direct the cellular and physical maturation of the developing immune system. In this review, we explore the still-enigmatic relations between CPSs and the adaptive immune machinery at the cellular and molecular levels, and we discuss how new insights into the biological impact of ZPSs expand our concepts of the role of carbohydrates in microbial interactions with the adaptive immune system.

CPS: bacterial capsular polysaccharide

INTRODUCTION

Most pathogenic bacteria express large-molecular-weight (large-MW) surface polysaccharides, usually in the form of a capsule that coats the bacterial surface. A quick PubMed search on bacterial capsular polysaccharides (CPSs) indicates that an awareness of these molecules existed in the early 1920s. When the pneumococcal type XIV CPS was purified in 1938 (1), it was described as a polysaccharide composed of glucose, amino sugars, and acetyl groups, with an absence of uronic acids. Three decades after its first purification, this polysaccharide was shown to comprise a tetrasaccharide repeating unit, →4β-Glc(1→6)β-GlcNAc(1→3)[β-Gal1→4]β-Gal1→ (2). Thanks to advances in structural biochemistry and carbohydrate chemistry, more than 90 *Streptococcus pneumoniae* CPSs and other bacterial polysaccharides have been chemically characterized to date (3). Structural knowledge of these CPSs has allowed investigators to uncover mechanisms by which the human immune system deals with many bacterial pathogens.

CPSs offer substantial protection to bacterial pathogens against phagocytosis by migrating phagocytes and tissue-fixed macrophages—cells constituting a crucial host defense mechanism that limits microbial growth and spread and that probably accounts for much of the host's ability to ward off microorganism-induced diseases (4). This resistance to phagocytosis is conferred primarily by preventing innate host opsonins, such as C3 and its degradation fragments, from coating microorganisms. Complement deposition promotes bacterial uptake by phagocytes via complement receptors. CPSs inhibit this process by several mechanisms (4): (*a*) Some capsules physically mask subcapsular components of the cell that activate the alternative complement pathway independent of antibody; (*b*) capsules containing sialic acid cause preferential binding of serum proteins that specifically inhibit amplification of the alternative pathway of complement (5); (*c*) some capsules lessen the microorganisms' binding affinity for factor B compared with that of unencapsulated strains; therefore, amplification of C3B deposition via the alternative complement pathway is not promoted, and complement deposition is insufficient for phagocytosis. Induction of antibodies to CPS by immunization is an elegant strategy that has been applied for more than half a century to protect hosts against bacterial invasion by enhancing bacterial phagocytosis (6, 7).

Specific polysaccharide structures functioning in different ways to affect bacterial interactions with the immune system represent a paradigm for the way fine structures of carbohydrates dictate the characteristics—and indeed the very nature—of immune responses (see sidebar, Nomenclature of Monosaccharides, and **Figure 1**). Certain structural features of CPSs, such as variations in repeating unit composition, ring forms, glycosidic linkage positions, anomeric-center configurations, and conformations, contribute to differences in the immune response to these polysaccharides. The way in which slight structural differences can give rise to distinct immune responses is illustrated by the group B and C polysaccharides of *Neisseria meningitidis*. The meningococcal group B polysaccharide is composed of →8)α-D-Neu*p*Ac(2→ repeating units, whereas the group C polysaccharide has the repeating unit structure →9)α-D-Neu*p*Ac(2→; the only difference is the α 2→8 versus α 2→9 glycosidic

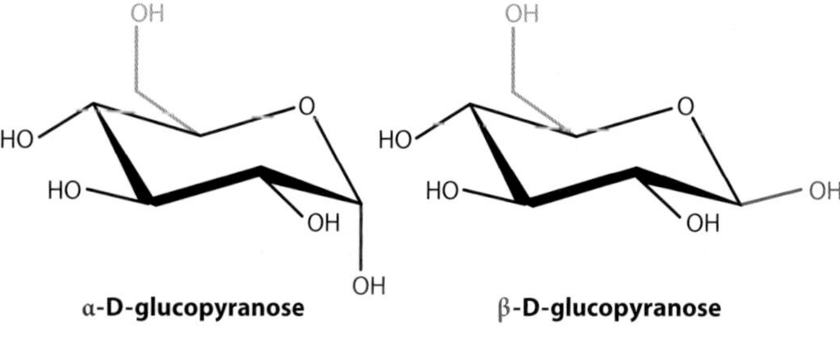

Figure 1

The α and β configurations of glucopyranose (hexacyclic glucose). In the α anomer, the -OH substituent on the anomeric carbon, rests on the opposite side (*trans*) of the ring from the CH_2OH side branch, and in the β anomer, the anomeric hydroxyl sits on the same side (*cis*) of the plane of the ring.

linkages between the sialic acid repeating sugars (8). Amazingly, the group C polysaccharide is an immunogenic molecule in human adults, whereas the group B polysaccharide is completely nonimmunogenic, failing to induce an antibody response. This difference may be due to the existence of structures identical to the repeating unit of the group B polysaccharide in mammalian tissues; thus, the group B molecule is not recognized as foreign by the immune system.

Group B *Streptococcus* (GBS) CPSs of types Ia and Ib serve as striking examples of how small differences in the structure of polysaccharides influence immune recognition. In this case, each polysaccharide has five identical sugars in its repeating units, all linked identically except for a single β1→4 versus β1→3 linkage of Gal*p* to GlcNAc in the side chain of the repeating sugar structure (**Figure 2**). This single linkage difference leads to distinct antibody responses that are not cross-protective (9). Structural features of most bacterial polysaccharides have been reviewed in detail by Ovodov (10).

Over the past two decades, we have defined another structural attribute—charge motif—that significantly influences immunologic responses to CPSs (11–13). Certain CPSs—e.g., polysaccharide A (PSA) of the common intestinal gram-negative obligate anaerobe *Bacteroides fragilis*—activate the innate immune system through Toll-like receptors (TLRs), and the innate immune system works in conjunction with the adaptive immune system in responding to these molecules (11–14). PSA is processed by antigen-presenting cells (APCs) and presented through the major histocompatibility complex class II (MHCII) pathway to $CD4^+$ T cells, which are consequently activated (14). Biochemical analysis of purified PSA established that its novel immunologic activities result from a unique structural feature: a zwitterionic charge motif (12).

In this review, we explore the molecular and cellular mechanisms by which bacterial CPSs regulate the adaptive immune system, focusing on the structural features and immunologic relevance of glycoconjugate vaccines and zwitterionic polysaccharides (ZPSs).

NOMENCLATURE OF MONOSACCHARIDES

Monosaccharides are polyhydroxycarbonyl compounds composed of two or more hydroxyl groups and a carbonyl group that can be either a ketone (called ketose) or an aldehyde (called aldose). Monosaccharides are classified according to several characteristics; one is the size of the ring when they are in cyclic form, and another is the stereocenters (stereocenter is any point in a molecule bearing groups such that an interchanging of any two groups leads to a stereoisomer). A monosaccharide ring with five atoms is called a furanose, and a ring with six atoms is called a pyranose. Monosaccharides are also classified with the stereocenters they contain. The letters D or L assigned to the monosaccharides arise from the orientation of the asymmetric carbon furthest from the carbonyl group. During the conversion from straight-chain form to cyclic form, the carbon atom containing the carbonyl oxygen, called the anomeric carbon, may take two possible configurations called anomers (see **Figure 1**). Representatives of the monosaccharide building blocks discussed in this review include GlcpNAc, N-Acetylglucopyranose; Neu*p*Ac, N-Acetylneuraminic acid; AATp, 2-acetamido-4-amino-2,4,6-trideoxygalactopyranose; and Galf, Galactofuranose.

GLYCOCONJUGATE VACCINES: A MILESTONE IN PROTECTION AGAINST ENCAPSULATED BACTERIA

Most bacterial CPSs are T cell–independent antigens (15–20) that induce specific IgM responses, with minimal IgG class switching. Immunization with pure CPSs fails to induce a booster response because of a lack of sustained T cell memory. Although these bacterial surface molecules have been identified as potent vaccine candidates, their inability to induce the activation of adaptive immune machinery is a major impediment to their use in pure form. CPSs cannot stimulate the immune responses of people in high-risk age groups, such as children less than two years old and the elderly. In the early 1980s, inspired by the hapten-carrier protein conjugation strategy (21, 22), CPSs of bacterial

MHCII: major histocompatibility complex class II

ZPS: zwitterionic polysaccharide

Hapten: a molecule that can elicit an immune response only when attached to a large carrier such as a protein

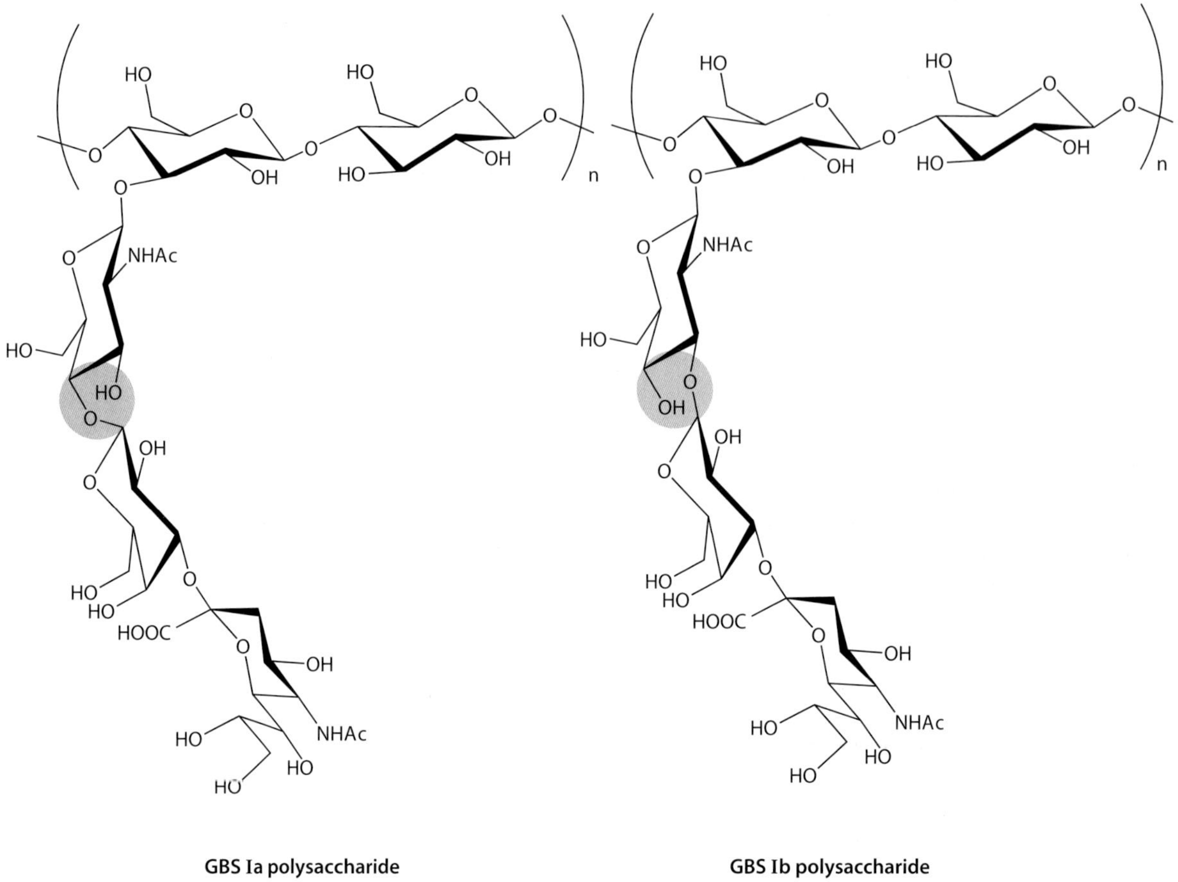

GBS Ia polysaccharide

GBS Ib polysaccharide

Figure 2

Chemical structures of the repeating units of group B streptococcal (GBS) capsular polysaccharides of types Ia and Ib. These two polysaccharides differ only in the glycosidic linkages between the side chain galactose and *N*-acetyl glucosamine residues ($\beta 1 \rightarrow 4$ versus $\beta 1 \rightarrow 3$, respectively, as highlighted by red shading in the figure) (9).

targets were coupled to carrier proteins possessing T cell peptide epitopes (3, 9, 23, 24). Immunization with glycoconjugate vaccines relies on the elicitation of T cell help for polysaccharide antigens, with promotion of polysaccharide-specific IgM-to-IgG switching, long-lived responses, and immunogenicity in children and the elderly. Over the past 20 years, several glycoconjugate vaccine constructs have been introduced into clinical use (25) and have played an enormous role in preventing infectious diseases caused by highly virulent pathogens such as *Haemophilus influenzae*, *S. pneumoniae*, and *N. meningitidis* (3, 25).

Structural Characteristics of Glycoconjugate Vaccines

Glycoconjugate vaccine design has traditionally been highly empirical. Relatively little systematic work has been done on the carbohydrate portion of these vaccines or on the coupling technology used in their development, nor have other variables (e.g., molar ratio optimization, epitope size, chain length, and carbohydrate modification) been systematically studied. The conjugation of carrier proteins to the polysaccharide has been accomplished by a number of techniques, including the reaction of amino side chains on the lysine or arginine residues of the proteins either with the activated carboxylate groups on polysaccharide chains (i.e., carbodiimide coupling) or with aldehyde groups generated by the oxidation of 1,2-diols on the sugar chains (i.e., reductive amination). These coupling reactions yield highly complex, matrix-like structures that are extremely hard to characterize. As we discuss below, efforts have been made over the past decade to improve the immunogenicity of glycoconjugates by designing and synthesizing new generation vaccines.

Traditionally, the quality of vaccine constructs has been evaluated only by their immunologic properties and not by their physicochemical properties. However, an increasing number of sophisticated analytical techniques, including nuclear magnetic resonance (NMR) spectroscopy, are being applied to the quality control of glycoconjugate vaccines. The applications include but are not limited to identification and identity testing of the glycan component, identification and quantification of impurities, quantification of polysaccharide-protein ratios, and detection and quantification of polysaccharide degradation and depolymerization after conjugation (26). Recently, NMR spectroscopy has been used for systematic physicochemical characterization of meningococcal vaccines, with determination of the identity and O-acetyl distribution of conjugated polysaccharides; size-exclusion chromatography coupled to multi-angle laser light scattering detection (SEC-MALLS) has been used for evaluation of the molecular size and distribution of different sized polymers; circular dichroism and fluorescence microscopy have been used for the conformational analysis of carrier proteins; and liquid chromatography coupled to mass spectrometry (LC-MS) has been used to assess the covalent linkages between the polysaccharide and the carrier protein (27).

Cooperation of B and T Lymphocytes: A Critical Factor in Recruitment of T Cell Help by Glycoconjugate Vaccines

In the early 1970s, Mitchison (21, 22), conducting studies in which mice were immunized with various hapten-carrier conjugates and boosted either with different conjugates or with transferred lymphocytes from primed mice, made an important discovery about hapten-carrier protein conjugates. These studies identified two kinds of cells, one recognizing the hapten and the other recognizing the carrier; these cells, which were then called antibody-forming cell precursor (AFCP) and helper cells, are now known as B cells and helper T cells, respectively. This discovery, called the "cellular cooperation hypothesis," laid the groundwork for our understanding of how B and T cells collaborate to generate the humoral immune response.

NMR spectroscopy: nuclear magnetic resonance spectroscopy

The current understanding of the activation of the adaptive immune system by glycoconjugate vaccines is based on research with haptens conjugated to carrier proteins. The traditional explanation for the mechanism of induction of polysaccharide-specific antibodies by glycoconjugates is that these vaccines generate T cell help through several steps. Polysaccharide-protein conjugates bind to the B cell receptor (BCR) of polysaccharide-specific pre-B cells and are taken into the endosome. Once inside the cell, the protein portion is digested by proteases to release peptide epitopes, which bind to MHCII by replacing the self-peptide. The peptide from the vaccine carrier protein is presented to the $\alpha\beta$ receptor of $CD4^+$ T cells in the context of the MHCII molecule. Peptide/MHCII-activated T cells release cytokines to stimulate B cell maturation and induce immunoglobulin class switching from IgM to polysaccharide-specific IgG (**Figure 3**). Although efforts have been made to test this hypothesis at the cellular level (20), the precise molecular mechanisms underlying glycoconjugate processing and presentation in the MHCII pathway have not yet been fully dissected. It will be critical to learn what happens to the carbohydrate in the endosome. The polysaccharide is covalently linked to the carrier protein, usually by a very strong chemical bond such as a secondary amine. The chemical conditions in the endolysosome may be sufficient to oxidize the carbohydrate or enzymatically digest the protein but are not sufficient to break

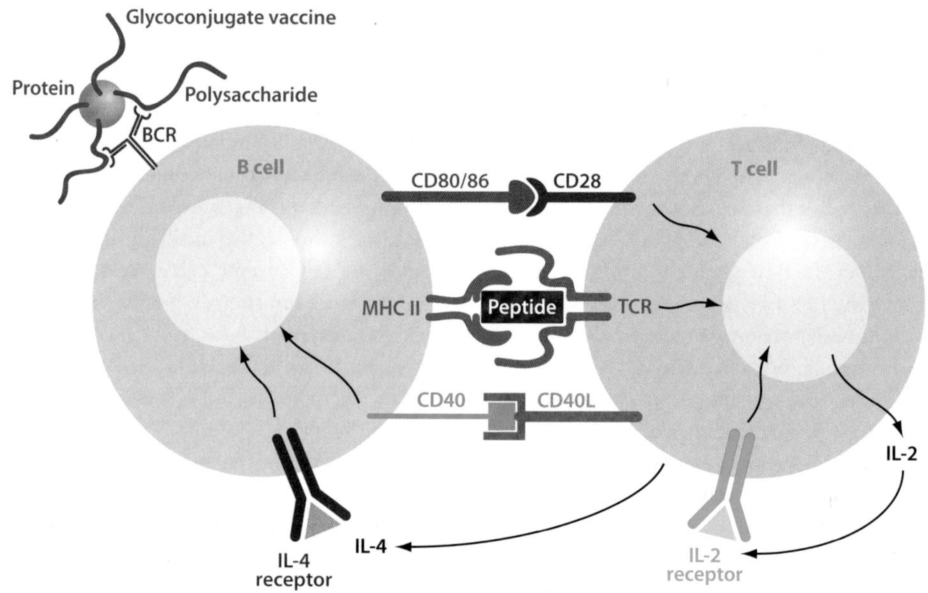

Figure 3

Immunization with a glycoconjugate vaccine results in bidirectional activation of B cells and T cells. As we currently understand the process, the glycoconjugate enters the B cell by binding to the polysaccharide-specific B cell receptor (BCR). The T cell epitope of the carrier protein generated in the endosome then binds to the MHCII molecule to be presented on the cell surface. Recognition of the peptide epitope by the $\alpha\beta$ TCR on the $CD4^+$ T cell, along with the interaction of costimulatory molecules CD80/86 with CD28, permits the activation of the T cell, leading to the secretion of IL-2 and upregulation of the IL-2 receptor on the T cell. Finally, the activated T cell secretes IL-4 and upregulates CD40L to activate the B cell through CD40-CD40L binding and signaling via the IL-4 receptor, giving rise to polysaccharide-specific, high-affinity antibody (IgG) secretion by the B cell (20).

the bonds created by linking carbohydrate to protein.

Beyond the contact of the peptide/MHCII with the T cell receptor (TCR), additional signals are essential in eliciting $CD4^+$ T cell help for the B cell. A number of ligand-receptor pairs that contribute in either a positive or a negative way to T cell help have been characterized. These molecules include CD80 (B7-1), CD86 (B7-2), CD28, CTLA4 (cytotoxic T lymphocyte–associated antigen 4), CD40L, CD40, ICOS (inducible T cell costimulator), ICOSL, PD1 (programmed death 1), and PD2.

The specific B cell–T cell interactions induced by glycoconjugate vaccines have been illustrated in studies of the immunization of mice deficient in several key membrane molecules associated with antibody induction, including MHCII, TCR, B7, CD28, and CD40L. As a model glycoconjugate vaccine, a GBS type III polysaccharide–tetanus toxoid conjugate (GBSIII-TT) was used. The results revealed a cellular signaling pathway for the induction of a polysaccharide-specific adaptive immune response. Thus, T cell help is recruited through presentation of processed antigen to TCRs by APCs in the context of MHCII molecules (signal 1), interaction of costimulatory molecules CD80 and CD86 on APCs with CD28 on T cells (signal 2), and B cell stimulation through interaction of CD40 with CD40L on activated T cells (signal 3). The interaction of CD80/86 with CD28 induces secretion of IL-2 by T cells; IL-2 then stimulates the proliferation of T cells through binding with the IL-2 receptor on the T cell surface. As a consequence of CD40-CD40L interaction between T and B cells, IL-4 is secreted by T cells and

TCR: T cell receptor

stimulates B cells by binding to the IL-4 receptor on the B cell surface. Stimulation of B cells by T cells induces IgM-to-IgG class switching on B cells, resulting in polysaccharide-specific IgG secretion by B cells.

The influence of B cell–T cell interaction on the quality of the immune response generated by conjugate vaccines has been documented by Perez-Melgosa and colleagues (28). Conjugate vaccines based on *H. influenzae* type b CPS (PRP) and various carrier proteins elicit protective antibody responses to PRP in infants only when multiple doses are given; the sole exception to this rule is for PRP conjugated to meningococcal Outer-membrane proteins (Omps), of which a single dose is sufficient to induce protection. The mechanism underlying this observation is the enhancement of CD40 ligand–mediated, T cell–dependent antibody production by Omps.

Characterizing the influence of carrier proteins on the immunogenicity of glycoconjugate vaccines is crucial for a better understanding of the mechanism of action of these vaccines and to the design of more immunogenic vaccines, as exemplified by the conjugation of PRP with Omps (28). In the conjugate vaccines that have been clinically applied thus far, the chosen carriers have been highly immunogenic modified bacterial proteins, including tetanus toxoid (TT), mutated diphtheria toxin (CRM197), or the Omps of *N. meningitidis*. The logic behind this choice is that most individuals have previously been immunized with these proteins, and therefore the response to the polysaccharide can potentially be improved by preexisting immunity to the carrier protein. However, this logic is not valid in some situations (29, 30). In a phenomenon called carrier-induced epitope suppression (CIES), individuals previously immunized with a carrier protein may show inhibited immune responses to the polysaccharide when immunized with a glycoconjugate vaccine containing that protein. CIES has been observed primarily with peptide haptens rather than with polysaccharide haptens and thus is thought to arise from competition among peptide haptens bound to carrier proteins for a limited number of carrier-specific helper T cells. Carrier-specific suppressor T cells also play a role in CIES (30). The impact of consecutive or concurrent administration of the same carrier proteins has not yet been dissected in mechanistic terms. Both enhancement and inhibition of polysaccharide-specific immune responses attributable to carrier proteins have been reported; however, because of a lack of understanding of these interactions at a molecular level, the immunologic basis of carrier responses remains unexplained (30).

Current Trends in Glycoconjugate Design

Although the value of glycoconjugate vaccines that are in clinical use has been decisively established, the synthesis of structurally well-defined conjugates is necessary not only to improve current vaccines but also to determine the structural features that govern antibody response. Current-generation glycoconjugate vaccines are typically prepared by polysaccharide modification at multiple sites, with subsequent coupling to proteins randomly in a cluster form. Consideration of critical factors such as the nature of the carrier, the ratio of carrier to polysaccharide, and the optimal types of linkages between these molecules would greatly enhance the immunologic properties of glycoconjugate vaccines. The past decade has seen progress from empirical toward rational design of conjugate vaccines. Studies have focused mainly on two aspects of these vaccines: conjugation chemistry and the nature of the carrier protein.

As has been mentioned, current conjugation chemistry requires polysaccharide modifications (e.g., random oxidation of the sugar chain) that alter natural epitopes, with consequent generation of low-affinity antibodies to the native polysaccharide. In addition, random conjugation between activated groups along the length of multiple repeating units of a polysaccharide and random active sites on a protein (e.g., all lysine residues) is difficult to reproduce from batch to batch in a clinical vaccine preparation. To overcome these obstacles, glycoconjugate vaccines have been prepared by chemically controlled coupling of polysaccharides or of the oligosaccharides derived from CPSs to carriers through their reducing ends via linker molecules (31–33). These conjugates have proven valuable not only as new vaccine candidates for clinical use but also as molecular probes used in the mapping of antigenic determinants of CPSs (to optimize vaccine configuration) and in studies of the molecular mechanisms of antibody and cellular responses to conjugate vaccines (33).

Linker technology also affects particular peptide epitopes in carrier proteins in conjugate vaccine constructs. Presentation of a conjugate-vaccine peptide generated in APCs to T cells is critical to the induction of an immune response to the polysaccharide. Thus, optimization of peptide presentation could potentially increase the immunogenicity of conjugate vaccines. The best approach is to couple polysaccharides to specific peptide epitopes of carrier proteins rather than to intact proteins, thereby allowing the presentation of a significantly larger number of peptides to T cells than in the intact protein conjugates. Moreover, carrier-specific antibody generation might be avoided with this technique. There are numerous examples of successful conjugation of peptides to polysaccharides through linker molecules (32, 34–36). One clever strategy has been to use recombinant carrier proteins constructed to contain strings of 6, 10, or 19 human $CD4^+$ T cell epitopes from various antigenic proteins (36). In each construct, separation of epitopes by the Lys-Gly spacer provides flexibility to the polyepitope and allows conjugation of the polysaccharide to the amino side chains of the lysine spacers. Thus, these synthetic polypeptide carriers can be recognized by most human MHCII haplotypes, and glycoconjugate vaccines prepared with these carriers elicit strong protective antibody responses and do not induce carrier-specific suppression of antibodies to the polysaccharide. Finally, rapid and efficient expression of these polypeptide carriers in *Escherichia coli* makes them especially attractive for use in glycoconjugate vaccine production.

Preliminary Evidence for MHCII Presentation of Carbohydrates in Conjugate Vaccines

In glycoconjugate vaccines, the type of response generated to T helper epitopes is a critical factor in improving immunogenicity over that of unconjugated polysaccharides. A recent study involving only microscopy techniques yielded preliminary data suggesting that the carbohydrate portion of a glycoconjugate vaccine may be presented on the surface of APCs in the context of the MHCII molecule (37). To elucidate this possibility, we review the relevant data on how one group of polysaccharides—the ZPSs—is processed and presented by APCs and recognized by $CD4^+$ T cells.

ZWITTERIONIC POLYSACCHARIDES: CARBOHYDRATES RECOGNIZED BY T CELLS

The adaptive arm of the immune system facilitates immunity through T cell recognition of foreign antigens. Although T cells have evolved to possess a repertoire of receptors that recognize epitopes of all biopolymers, the traditional paradigm has long dictated that only peptide epitopes of protein antigens are presented to and recognized by T cells. Over the past decade, studies have shown that peptides are not, in fact, the only antigens capable of being recognized by T cells. Several reports have described glycopeptide and glycolipid processing and MHCI/MHCII/CD1 presentation and recognition by T cells (38–44). MHCI binds to the glycopeptides—and not just the peptide portion—of these types of epitopes. In addition, TCR binding to processed glycopeptides depends on contact of the receptor with the epitope formed by both the glycan and the peptide that is bound to MHC (38). For instance, Holmdahl and colleagues (42, 43) showed that epitope glycosylation plays a critical role in T cell recognition of type II collagen (CII). These investigators found that the immunodominant T cell epitope in healthy joint cartilage of humans and rats is O-glycosylated. Studies of glycopeptide epitopes derived from tumor antigen mucin-like glycoprotein 1 (MUC1) are particularly important (39). In tumor cells, protein glycosylation forms tumor-specific glycopeptide epitopes that can be recognized by $CD4^+$ T cells (40, 41). The MHC-like CD1 molecule also presents lipids and glycolipids to γδ TCR-positive and invariant natural killer T (iNKT) cells (44). These studies illustrate that when a glycopeptide or a glycolipid epitope is introduced to the adaptive immune machinery by APCs, it is specifically recognized by T cells. The ZPSs are the newest (and surprising) members of the new generation of antigens with T cell epitopes. Most bacterial polysaccharides are either neutral or negatively charged (**Figure 2**) (10) and are well characterized as T cell–independent antigens. In contrast, a few bacterial polysaccharides contain both positive charges (e.g., free amino groups) and negative charges (e.g., carboxylate or phosphate groups) in their repeating units (45). These ZPSs include *Staphylococcus aureus* type 5 and type 8 polysaccharides (CP5 and CP8) (46, 47); *S. pneumoniae* type 1 polysaccharide (Sp1) (48); and PSA from *B. fragilis*, which is the best studied of all ZPSs (13, 14). ZPSs elicit immune responses that are unique among bacterial polysaccharides; as discussed below, the most prominent feature of these responses is the activation of T cells in the absence of carrier proteins.

Structural Characteristics of ZPS-MHCII Interactions

Sequencing of the *B. fragilis* genome (49, 50) revealed biosynthetic loci for the production of eight different CPSs (designated PSA through PSH). Expression of these polysaccharides is phase varied and, for seven of the eight carbohydrates, depends on the direction of an inverted repeat in the promoter region. Of the eight polysaccharides, PSA is the most abundant.

High-resolution NMR studies revealed the chemical composition of PSA and demonstrated both positively and negatively charged motifs on each repeating unit (51). PSA, a tetrasaccharide consisting of repeating units composed of −3)-α-D-AATp-(1–4)[β-D-Galf(1–3)]-α-D-GalpNac(1–3)-β-D-Galp(1- (**Figure 4*a***), has a molecular size of ~110 kDa (51).

The predominant feature shared by MHCII-binding carbohydrates is their zwitterionic structure (**Figure 4*a*** and **4*b***). As detailed below, ZPSs are depolymerized in the endosomes of APCs into molecules of ~10–15 kDa; these molecules bind to MHCII proteins (14, 48). Studies of PSA showed that removal of either its negative or its positive charge eliminates its MHCII binding and thus its recognition by T cells (12, 14). These exciting findings have prompted discussions about the nature of the interaction/binding of processed ZPSs with MHC proteins and about the interaction of the MHCII-bound carbohydrate epitope and the αβ TCR. Several studies have suggested explanations for ZPS-MHCII interactions (52–54); the activation of TCRs by ZPSs is not yet understood at the molecular level.

Peptides bind to MHCII molecules in an extended conformation along the binding groove of MHCII, which is formed by two parallel α helices sitting atop a β sheet. Because the binding groove of the MHCII molecule is open at both ends, MHCII-bound peptides are not limited in size. Thus, peptides that bind to MHCII molecules are variable in length. Peptides fit into the binding groove of MHCII in a linear, unfolded fashion through their anchor residues at various distances from the ends of the peptide (4). The common anchor residues of MHCII-binding peptides include an acidic (negatively charged) amino acid at position 4 and a basic (positively charged) amino acid at position 6 (with positions designated according to the order of amino acids in contact with the binding groove of MHCII) (4). An obvious issue is the degree to which ZPS-MHCII and peptide-MHCII complexes are similar. It is well

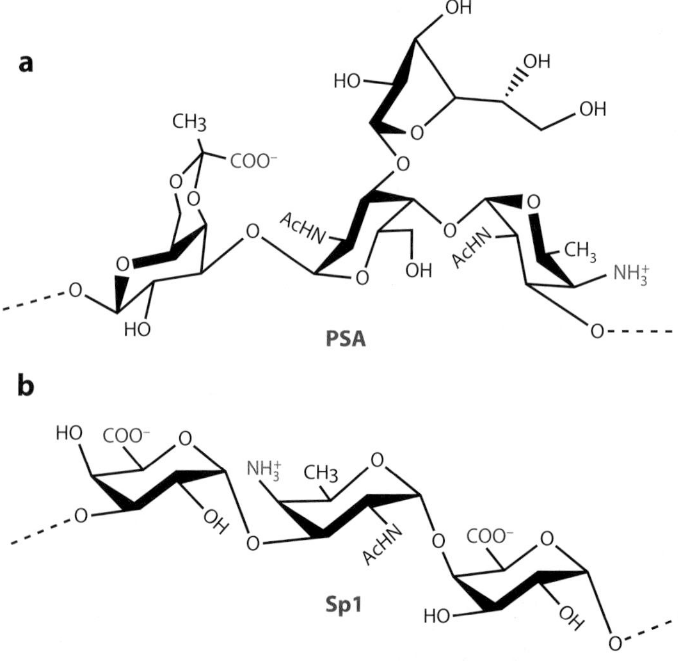

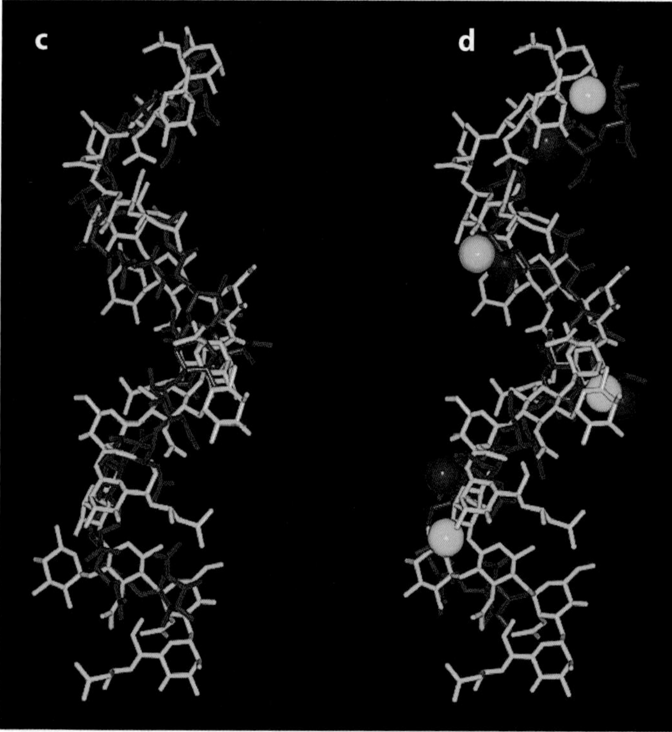

established that both negative and positive charges are required for ZPS binding to MHCII. Alteration of the zwitterionic charge motif on these antigens by N-acetylation (which eliminates the positive charge) or carbodiimide reduction (which eliminates the negative charge) results in the loss of T cell stimulatory activity (11). A recent study showed, by confocal microscopy, that both N-acetylated PSA (negatively charged) and carbodiimide-treated PSA (positively charged) are taken up into the endosome of APCs but that, unlike zwitterionic PSA, neither of these charge-modified polysaccharides is presented on the surface of the APC (**Figure 5**) (55). It remains unclear whether the zwitterionic charge motif is solely responsible for binding (electrostatically) to MHCII or is needed for a particular three-dimensional (3-D) conformation that facilitates the binding of processed ZPSs to MHCII.

The 3-D conformations of two ZPSs that are very different from each other in primary structure (e.g., monosaccharide composition)—Sp1 of *S. pneumoniae* and PSA2 of *B. fragilis*—were determined by a combination of NMR spectroscopy experiments and molecular dynamics calculations (52, 53). The two ZPSs have almost identical 3-D conformations: an extended right-handed helix with eight monosaccharide residues per turn and a pitch of 20 Å (**Figure 4*c*** and **4*d***). Positive and negative charges alternate

Figure 4

Structural features of zwitterionic polysaccharides PSA and Sp1. Chemical structures of the tetrasaccharide repeating unit of PSA (*a*) and the trisaccharide repeating unit of Sp1 (*b*) are shown. Positively charged amino groups are labeled in blue and negatively charged carboxylate groups in red. Three-dimensional conformational structures of Sp1 (*purple*) and PSA2 (*light blue*) are shown superimposed on the basis of their glycosidic oxygen atoms (*c*) and their amino groups (*d*). Purple and light blue dots represent positive charges from Sp1 and PSA2, respectively. Sp1 and PSA2 display a similar zigzag positive-charge pattern with nearly equidistant charge separation of 15 Å (52, 53). The images in parts (*c*) and (*d*) of this figure are reproduced, with permission, from *Biochemistry*, Reference 53.

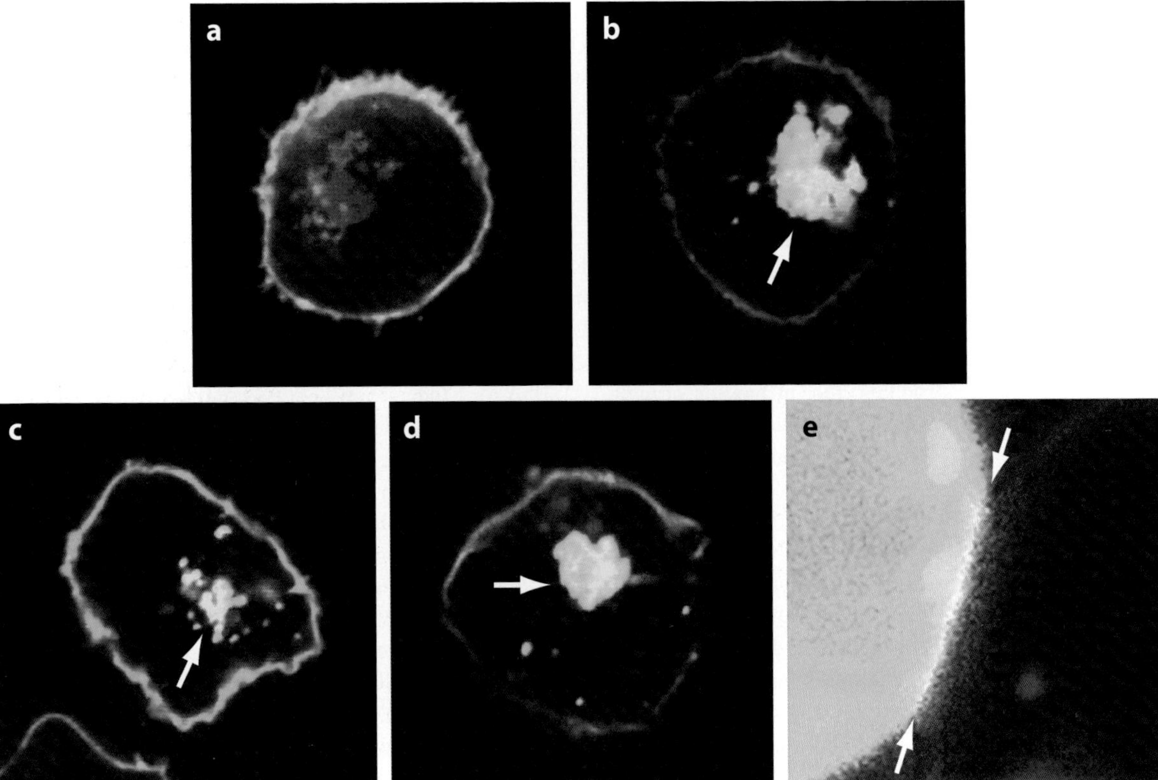

Figure 5

(*a–d*) Confocal microscopy images illustrate the role of zwitterionic charges in the uptake and presentation of PSA by antigen-presenting cells (APCs) (Raji B cell line) in the context of MHCII (55). PSA (*a*) and its derivatives missing negative, positive, or both charges (*b*, *c*, and *d*, respectively) are labeled in red; MHCII (*a–d*) is labeled in green; and yellow areas show colocalization of the two. All polysaccharides are taken up by the APCs (endosomal colocalization in *a–d*). Although depolymerized PSA colocalizes with MHCII both in the endosomes and on the cell surface (*a*), none of the charge-modified PSA derivatives—negatively charged N-acetylated PSA (*b*), positively charged carboxylate-reduced PSA (*c*), or N-acetylated, carboxylate-reduced neutral PSA (*d*)—colocalizes with the MHCII molecule on the APC surface. (*e*) White area of trilocalization (*arrows*) of PSA (*blue*), MHCII (*red*), and the αβ TCR (*green*). The αβ TCR interacts in a cognate fashion with PSA in the context of MHCII (12). The images in this figure are reproduced, with permission, from *Cell* and *Glycobiology*, References 12 and 55.

along the sides of the helical chains and are exposed on the outermost surface of helices. Moreover, the two molecules display a similar positive charge pattern with equidistant amino group separation of ~15 Å (**Figure 4*d***). The 3-D conformational similarity between ZPSs may account for their common T cell–stimulating activity. Conformational models of PSA2 interacting with hypothetical α helices (10–14 amino acids long) may suggest a mechanism for ZPS-MHCII interaction (52). Supporting evidence for this possibility was provided by Cobb and colleagues (54), who compared circular dichroism profiles of PSA derivatives to study the effects of charge and size on the 3-D conformation and consequently on MHCII-binding ability. First, these investigators showed that PSA forms a helical structure remarkably similar to that of proteins rich in α helical content. This helical structure is not found with PSA fragments of fewer than three repeating units. Studies of circular dichroism spectra showed that positively charged, negatively charged, and neutral PSA derivatives all failed to form helical

HLA-DR: a human leukocyte antigen (MHCII) molecule

conformations. These researchers also demonstrated that changes in 3-D conformation of PSA correlate with its binding to MHCII. Using an ELISA-based technique, they demonstrated that PSA derivatives smaller than three repeating units and derivatives with neutral, negative, or positive charges do not bind to MHCII, whereas zwitterionic PSA fragments ranging in size from 3 to 30 kDa do. It is interesting that higher-MW PSA fragments bind to MHCII very modestly compared with fragments of 3–30 kDa. The authors stated that the less efficient binding of high-MW PSA to MHCII is not attributable to a lack of helical structure but perhaps is due to masking of the binding domain of PSA by a higher-order structure that has not yet been identified. This study strongly supports the hypothesis that PSA must maintain a helical content to enable MHCII binding and that the zwitterionic charge motif is critical for the formation of a helical structure. These observations correlate well with the in vivo binding of processed zwitterionic PSA (10–15 kDa) with MHCII in the endosome of APCs (12, 13).

In addition to providing the right 3-D conformation for binding, zwitterionic charges on PSA may facilitate binding to MHCII through electrostatic interactions. Cobb & Kasper (55) used various concentrations of sodium chloride to inhibit the interactions of MHCII molecules and various antigens. Unlike the MHCII-bound myelin basic protein T cell epitope (MBPp) or the superantigen staphylococcal enterotoxin A (SEA), both of which were unaffected by the addition of salt, PSA was inhibited significantly (by 60%) in terms of MHCII binding by the addition of salt, which blocked electrostatic PSA-MHCII interactions (55). In addition, an acidic medium favored MHCII binding of PSA. The binding of MHCII with PSA, peptide (MBPp), and superantigen (SEA) was compared at pH 5.0 and pH 7.3. Although MBPp and SEA binding affinity was similar at the two pH values, that of PSA was sensitive to pH, with a fivefold higher binding affinity in acidic medium. The requirements for an acidic environment for processing into smaller-MW polysaccharides suggest that PSA, like protein, is processed within the endolysosome of the MHCII pathway and is bound to MHCII in the acidic endosome. These experiments and several other published studies eliminated the possibility that ZPSs are superantigens (13, 14, 56, 57).

Among the human MHCII proteins, HLA-DR was shown to be responsible for presenting processed PSA to $CD4^+$ T cells (12). Further exploration of allelic selectivity showed that preprocessed PSA (chemically depolymerized into 15-kDa fragments) binds to HLA-DR2 with an affinity (K_d = 0.31 μM) sixfold and threefold higher, respectively, than what it shows for HLA-DR1 (K_d = 1.9 μM) or HLA-DR4 (K_d = 1.0 μM) (55). The binding affinity of PSA was ~15-fold higher than that of both MBPp and SEA. Of even greater interest, PSA bound to HLA-DR with 1:1 stoichiometry (just like the peptide antigen MBPp), whereas the superantigen SEA had a binding stoichiometry of 1–2:1. To elucidate the binding position of PSA on the MHCII molecule, competition experiments were performed wherein increasing concentrations of PSA were added to MHCII preloaded with either peptide (MBPp) or superantigen (SEA). Remarkably, with regard to MHCII binding, PSA outcompeted peptide and SEA by ~75% and 80%, respectively. These findings may suggest that PSA binds both in the MHCII groove (like peptides) and outside the groove (mimicking superantigens). Another possible explanation for this observation is that PSA induces a conformational shift in MHCII that disrupts peptide and superantigen interactions.

A conclusive and direct explanation for the molecular interactions of ZPSs and MHCII can be obtained only by crystallography experiments. A cocrystal of a processed ZPS bound to an MHCII molecule would reveal all the molecular requirements for MHCII-ZPS binding. Crystallization of biomolecules is achieved by the use of structurally well-defined single molecules. There are extremely few examples of cocrystals of carbohydrates with their binding proteins. Current knowledge of carbohydrate chemistry is very limited, and chemical synthesis of high-MW complex carbohydrate structures is extremely challenging. So far, investigators have succeeded in synthesizing one fully protected tetrasaccharide repeating unit of PSA (58). Because of the obstacles encountered in synthesizing pure, single-molecule ZPS epitopes that can be recognized by T cells, cocrystals of MHCII-processed carbohydrate complex have not yet been created.

Processing and Presentation of ZPSs by the MHCII Pathway

As described above, at the molecular level, PSA shows similarities to peptides in binding to MHCII. At the cellular level, PSA is handled by the MHCII pathway in a manner similar to that documented for traditional protein antigens (12). This process involves several steps: (*a*) PSA is taken into the endosome of APCs; (*b*) PSA is processed into low-MW T cell epitopes in the endolysosome; (*c*) endolysosomes containing processed PSA fuse with exocytic vesicles containing self-peptide (CLIP)–bound HLA-DR (in humans), creating the MIIC (MHCII-containing) vesicle; (*d*) acidification of MIIC initiates HLA-DM-mediated exchange of CLIP with processed PSA on HLA-DR; and (*e*) PSA-loaded HLA-DR is presented on the surface of an APC to be recognized by a $CD4^+$ T cell (**Figure 6*a***). We next discuss these steps in more detail.

The first step is the uptake of antigen by APCs. PSA is endocytosed by professional APCs such as dendritic cells (DCs), B cells, and macrophages (12, 13, 59). Confocal microscopy experiments have shown that PSA is taken up by APCs with rapid kinetics and colocalizes with the endosomal marker lysosome-associated membrane protein 1 (LAMP-1) (12). No published data elucidate PSA uptake by APCs. However, preliminary data obtained in our laboratory indicate that a receptor-independent mechanism, most likely macropinocytosis, is involved (M. Kazmierczak, unpublished observations).

Once in the endosome, PSA is depolymerized by a novel mechanism that is quite distinct from that used in the processing of protein antigens. As is well established, peptides presented by MHCII are generated in acidified endocytic vesicles. As the protein is engulfed by the cell, a progressive decrease in the pH of the endosome activates the acid proteases (e.g., cathepsins) that reside in these vesicles, and these enzymes degrade the protein to generate peptide epitopes (4). The tenets of classic cell biology would dictate that eukaryotic APCs do not possess a sufficient number of highly specific glycosidic enzymes (or any other means) to process the diverse carbohydrates presented by microorganisms within an APC. However, as we have shown for ZPSs, chemical degradation of these molecules in endosomes can produce smaller derivatives (13, 48). PSA is depolymerized from ~110 kDa to ~15 kDa in the endosomes. Incubation of radiolabeled PSA ($[^3H]$PSA) with various APCs and extraction of the endosomal compartments yield degraded PSA detectable by gel filtration chromatography.

Monosaccharide composition and glycosidic linkages in bacterial carbohydrates are generally very different from and frequently more complex than in the polysaccharide structures of eukaryotic cells. Bacterial ZPSs are therefore resistant to depolymerization by eukaryotic glycosidases. PSA processing was found to be independent of enzymatic degradation (13). After careful exploration of possible environmental factors in PSA depolymerization (e.g., pH, reducing or oxidizing conditions), investigators concluded that PSA and other polysaccharides are susceptible to oxidative cleavage in vitro by certain reactive oxygen species and reactive nitrogen species. To determine the role of oxidation on PSA processing for presentation to T cells in vivo, PSA was introduced into knockout mice lacking NADPH oxidase (the enzyme responsible for the generation of superoxide) and knockout mice lacking inducible nitric oxide synthase [iNOS, the enzyme responsible for the generation of nitric oxide (NO)]. As

CLIP (class II-associated invariant chain peptide): CLIP binds to the MHCII groove and remains there until the MHCII receptor is fully assembled; this prevents the binding of an antigen prematurely, which would disrupt the synthesis of MHCII

LAMP-1: lysosomal-associated membrane protein 1

NADPH (nicotinamide adenine dinucleotide phosphate) oxidase: a membrane-bound enzyme complex that generates superoxide by transferring electrons from NADPH to molecular oxygen to produce the superoxide

iNOS (inducible nitric oxide synthase): produces nitric oxide by catalyzing a five-electron oxidation of a guanidino nitrogen of L-arginine

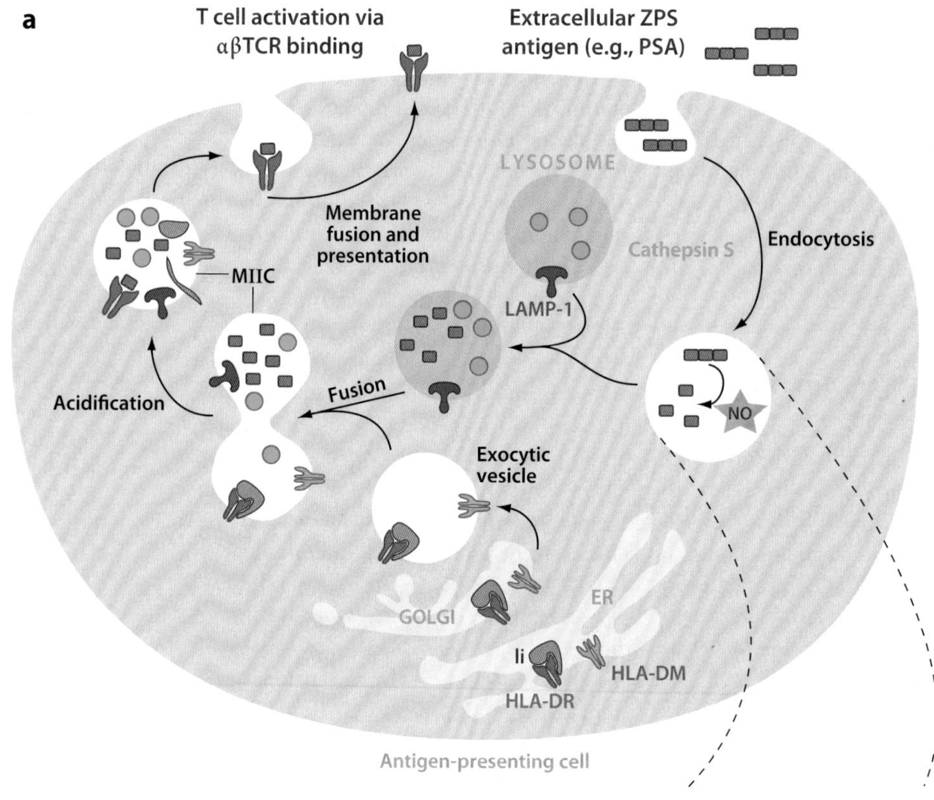

Figure 6

(*a*) Schematic of ZPS processing and presentation by the MHCII pathway (12). Extracellular ZPS is endocytosed by the antigen-binding cell (APC) and processed into smaller-molecular-weight polysaccharides (~15 kDa) by inducible nitric oxide synthase (iNOS)–mediated oxidative depolymerization (chemical reaction is shown in *b*). The endosome containing processed ZPS then fuses with the resident lysosome and the exocytic vesicle to form the MIIC vesicle containing HLA-DR, HLA-DM, LAMP-1 (lysosome-associated membrane protein 1), and processed polysaccharide. Finally, the processed polysaccharide is loaded onto HLA-DR with the aid of HLA-DM and is presented on the surface of the APC to be recognized by the αβ TCR. (*b*) Deamination of the AAT*p* residue in one repeating unit of PSA, leading to depolymerization of PSA in the endosomes of APCs (13). The positively charged amino group is lost by this reaction only at the cleavage site corresponding to one repeating unit in each processed molecule (containing ~16 repeating units).

an in vivo readout for T cell activation, an intraabdominal abscess mouse model was used. Previously, investigations had shown that in vivo abscesses formed by *B. fragilis* require the activation of $CD4^+$ T cells by PSA (11) (explained in more detail below). In this model, PSA is administered intraperitoneally, along with sterile cecal contents, and sterile abscesses form if PSA is processed and activates $CD4^+$ T cells. When injected with PSA, all $NADPH^{-/-}$ mice formed abscesses, whereas $iNOS^{-/-}$ mice did not. When injected with preprocessed (15-kDa) PSA, however, the $iNOS^{-/-}$ mice did develop abscesses. These results clearly demonstrate that APCs need iNOS for processing of PSA and for activation of $CD4^+$ T cells (13).

After exposure of APCs to microbial products, iNOS is upregulated and catalyzes the oxidation of L-arginine to form NO (60). These events in response to PSA served as evidence for the role of NO in PSA processing (13). Further studies defined the mechanism of NO-dependent PSA processing (13), using $CD11c^+$ DCs as APCs. First, DCs from wild-type and $iNOS^{-/-}$ mice were incubated either with PSA or with N-acetyl PSA (in which positively charged free amino groups had been blocked with N-acetylation). PSA was depolymerized to a much greater extent in DCs from wild-type mice than in DCs from $iNOS^{-/-}$ mice; however, N-acetyl PSA was degraded minimally in both wild-type and $iNOS^{-/-}$ DCs. This experiment suggested that the depolymerization of PSA is mediated by NO and that free amino groups are necessary for NO degradation. These studies also showed that NO-dependent depolymerization of PSA occurs through a deamination reaction. It is well established that NO-derived deaminative degradation of polysaccharides requires free amino or N-sulfo groups on sugar units, whereas N-acetyl sugars are resistant to deamination (61).

Deamination is also crucial for the activation of T cells by PSA. In vitro, PSA induces the proliferation of $CD4^+$ T cells when T cells from either wild-type or $iNOS^{-/-}$ mice are incubated with PSA in the presence of DCs from wild-type mice. $CD4^+$ T cells do not proliferate when incubated with the polysaccharide in the presence of $iNOS^{-/-}$ DCs. However, if T cells are stimulated with preprocessed PSA (in vitro, NO degrades PSA into fragments of ~15 kDa), they proliferate to the same extent upon coculture with either $iNOS^{-/-}$ or wild-type DCs. This in vitro experiment correlated with the in vivo abscess formation experiment described above.

Abscess: a collection of pus that has accumulated in a cavity formed by the tissue on the basis of an infectious process

The [^{1}H]NMR spectra of PSA and the NO-degraded product (PSA-NO) are identical. Thus, deamination of PSA does not alter its repeating unit structure except at cleavage sites. Furthermore, critical charges on amino and carboxylate groups remain intact after NO depolymerization. In short, processing of PSA in the endosomes of APCs is based on a chemical reaction called deaminative cleavage, and this reaction is mediated by iNOS-generated NO (**Figure 6*b***). This study served as the first demonstration of a mechanism for bacterial polysaccharide processing through the MHCII pathway (13).

Once PSA is processed in the endosome of the APC, endosomes are fused with lysosomes and exocytic vesicles to form the MIIC vesicle carrying HLA-DR and the accessory molecule HLA-DM. HLA-DM plays a critical role in peptide presentation by MHCII, facilitating dissociation of the MHCII self-peptide CLIP, which permits binding of processed endosomal peptides. Cobb and colleagues (12, 55) described the role of HLA-DM in PSA presentation as very similar to that in peptide presentation. In vitro, PSA binding of MHCII was greatly catalyzed by the presence of HLA-DM. In an ex vivo PSA presentation assay, MHCII complexes of processed PSA were immunoprecipitated from either wild-type or $HLA\text{-}DM^{-/-}$ primary splenocytes. Significantly less carbohydrate was detected in immunoprecipitates from $HLA\text{-}DM^{-/-}$ cells. Finally, in an in vivo T cell activation assay, abscess induction by PSA was reduced in mice lacking the HLA-DM protein (55).

The presentation of PSA-loaded MHCII on the surface of APCs was demonstrated by both confocal microscopy and coimmunoprecipitation. Confocal images of APCs incubated with fluorescently labeled PSA showed that this polysaccharide colocalizes with the MHCII protein on the surface of APCs (**Figure 5**). When these APCs are treated with drugs blocking the MHCII pathway at different stages (e.g., with colchicine, which inhibits endocytosis by blocking microtubule polymerization, or with bafilomycin A1, which inhibits loading of PSA on MHCII by blocking acidification of the MIIC vesicle—an event required for HLA-DM-mediated removal of self-peptide CLIP on MHCII), presentation of PSA on the cell surface was dramatically diminished. Although confocal microscopy images showing colocalization of PSA with MHCII suggested that PSA is bound to MHCII, these images could not definitively confirm binding on the cell surface because the resolution in fluorescence microscopy is not high enough to reveal molecular interactions. To resolve this issue, a coimmunoprecipitation experiment was done. After incubation of APCs with radiolabeled PSA, surface-bound MHCII molecules were precipitated with an antibody to the MHCII protein, and a PSA fragment of ~15 kDa was shown to be bound to these surface-bound MHCII molecules (13).

Finally, engagement of surface MHCII proteins of PSA-treated APCs with the αβ TCR on the surface of CD4$^+$ T cells was documented by confocal microscopy (**Figure 5*e***). Trilocalization of MHCII, PSA, and the αβ TCR suggested that PSA induces APC–T cell engagement through binding to both MHCII and the αβ TCR. These results illustrate how ZPSs can be presented by MHCII molecules to activate CD4$^+$ T cells in a paradigm that represents an alternative to conventional protein-antigen processing and presentation by the MHCII pathway. Although the direct interaction of ZPSs with αβ T cells is an established fact, our knowledge of the molecular nature of ZPS–T cell engagement is very limited. So far, there have been two attempts to generate ZPS-specific T cell clones (56, 62). PSA- and Sp1-reactive T cell hybridomas were generated by cell fusion of in vitro–activated T cells and a mouse thymoma cell line (62). These polyclonal T cells are reactive with a variety of other ZPSs but not with non-ZPSs, a result indicating cross-reactivity between ZPSs. In addition, ZPS-reactive T cell hybridomas were transferred to recipient rats, and the function of the ZPS-reactive T cell hybridomas was evaluated in vivo. Recipient rats were challenged with *B. fragilis*, and protection against intraabdominal abscess formation was assessed. This work confirmed the modulatory role of ZPS-specific T cells in abscess formation. More recently, investigators showed that intraperitoneal Sp1 injection into mice results in the accumulation of Th1- and Th17-polarized CD4$^+$CD44^{high}CD62^{low}CD25^{neg} memory T cells (56). Furthermore, stimulation of CD4$^+$ T cells with Sp1 induces oligoclonal expansion of these cells within the TCR β chain variable region (TCR BV) families. Sp1-mediated CD4$^+$ T cell proliferation (like that following stimulation of CD4$^+$ T cells with classical protein antigens) yields a nonrestricted Vβ repertoire in vivo and in vitro. In contrast, superantigens induce a polyclonal response within a restricted number of specific TCR BV families (56). Oligoclonal expansion of polysaccharide-activated CD4$^+$ T cells suggests ZPS recognition by the TCR antigen-binding domain.

Chemical Modification of T Cell–Independent Polysaccharides

After the discovery of MHCII-dependent CD4$^+$ T cell activation by ZPSs, a follow-up study showed that chemical introduction of zwitterionic motifs into anionic bacterial polysaccharides generates chemically modified ZPSs that execute biological functions quite similar to those performed by natural ZPSs (63). The naturally anionic GBS type 1b and type III polysaccharides were chemically modified to possess a zwitterionic charge motif. These chemically derived ZPSs upregulated the expression of MHCII in APCs through the TLR2 receptor in APCs and induced the proliferation of CD4$^+$ T cells. These activities were similar to what has been described for natural ZPSs.

Removal of either charge on these molecules resulted in the termination of T cell–dependent activity. This study expanded the observations made with natural ZPSs such as PSA.

Immunologic Significance of T Cell Activation by PSA

Intraabdominal abscess formation is one of the most common problems encountered after surgery involving the peritoneum. In a rat model simulating human intraabdominal sepsis, *B. fragilis*, in contrast to other anaerobic bacterial species, has the distinct ability to induce experimental abscesses when implanted into the peritoneal cavity along with sterile cecal contents. The organism alone does not induce abscesses (64, 65). However, prophylactic or therapeutic subcutaneous administration of PSA (by itself, without sterile cecal contents) aborts the formation of intraabdominal abscesses in rats challenged with *B. fragilis* or with other intestinal bacteria capable of synergistically stimulating abscess formation (66). Studies aimed at understanding the cellular basis of this protection against abscess formation demonstrated that splenic T cells from PSA-treated animals confer protection when transferred to animals challenged with these abscess-inducing bacteria (67–69). These studies demonstrated that PSA possesses novel immunomodulatory properties affecting T cell function. A review by Mazmanian & Kasper (70) explains in detail the T cell–dependent immunomodulatory role of PSA in intraabdominal abscess formation.

In an effort to understand whether the mechanism of protection by ZPSs (PSA and Sp1) against abscess formation would also apply to surgical adhesion formation in vivo, Ruiz-Perez and colleagues (71) studied a rodent model of fibrosis. They found that a distinct population of $CD4^+$ $CD45RB^{lo}$ T cells produces IL-10 in response to ZPSs and is responsible for protection in the fibrosis model. Moreover, in this study, IL-10 was shown to be responsible for ZPS-mediated protection against the formation of intraabdominal abscesses. $CD4^+$ $CD45RB^{lo}$ T cells from ZPS-treated mice were transferred to naive mice 4 h before abscess-inducing *B. fragilis* injection. Transfer of these T cells prevented the formation of intraabdominal abscess in recipient mice. The demonstration that ZPSs induce production of IL-10 and that this process is required for protection against T cell–mediated inflammation is a milestone in delineating the immunomodulatory roles of these polysaccharides. Therefore, as far as abscess induction, ZPSs are important (12), but ZPSs have no defined role in adhesion induction (71). However, in terms of protection against abscesses and adhesions, ZPSs such as PSA and Sp1 seem to induce identical protective mechanisms (66, 71). Another example of the T cell–mediated protective activity of ZPSs relates to inflammatory bowel disease (72). Wild-type *B. fragilis* protects mice from experimental colitis induced by *Helicobacter hepaticus*, a commensal bacterium with pathogenic potential, whereas the ΔPSA strain of *B. fragilis*, which lacks PSA on its capsule, is not protective; thus, protection is mediated by PSA. Like the protection provided by PSA against intraabdominal abscess formation and surgical fibrosis (71), this protection against inflammatory bowel disease entails a functional requirement for IL-10-producing $CD4^+$ T cells (**Figure 7**).

ZPSs are key contributors to symbiosis during commensalism. Commensalism is critical to the development of a balanced immune system. PSA—produced by *B. fragilis*, a prominent component of the gut microflora—is the archetypical molecule that stimulates the immune system to balance its $CD4^+$ T cell lineages (59). Intestinal monocolonization of previously germ-free mice with PSA-expressing *B. fragilis* directs maturation of the immune system. Monoassociation of germ-free mice with a PSA-bearing *B. fragilis* strain (wild type) corrects systemic T cell deficiencies, redresses Th1/Th2 imbalances, and directs lymphoid organogenesis (**Figure 7**) (59). These effects are not found in germ-free mice monoassociated with an isogenic *B. fragilis* mutant incapable of synthesizing PSA. Identified as a TLR2 agonist, PSA coordinates an innate and adaptive immune response

Colitis: chronic inflammation of the colon

Germ-free mice: mice lacking commensal/pathogenic bacteria in their gastrointestinal tract (sterile mice)

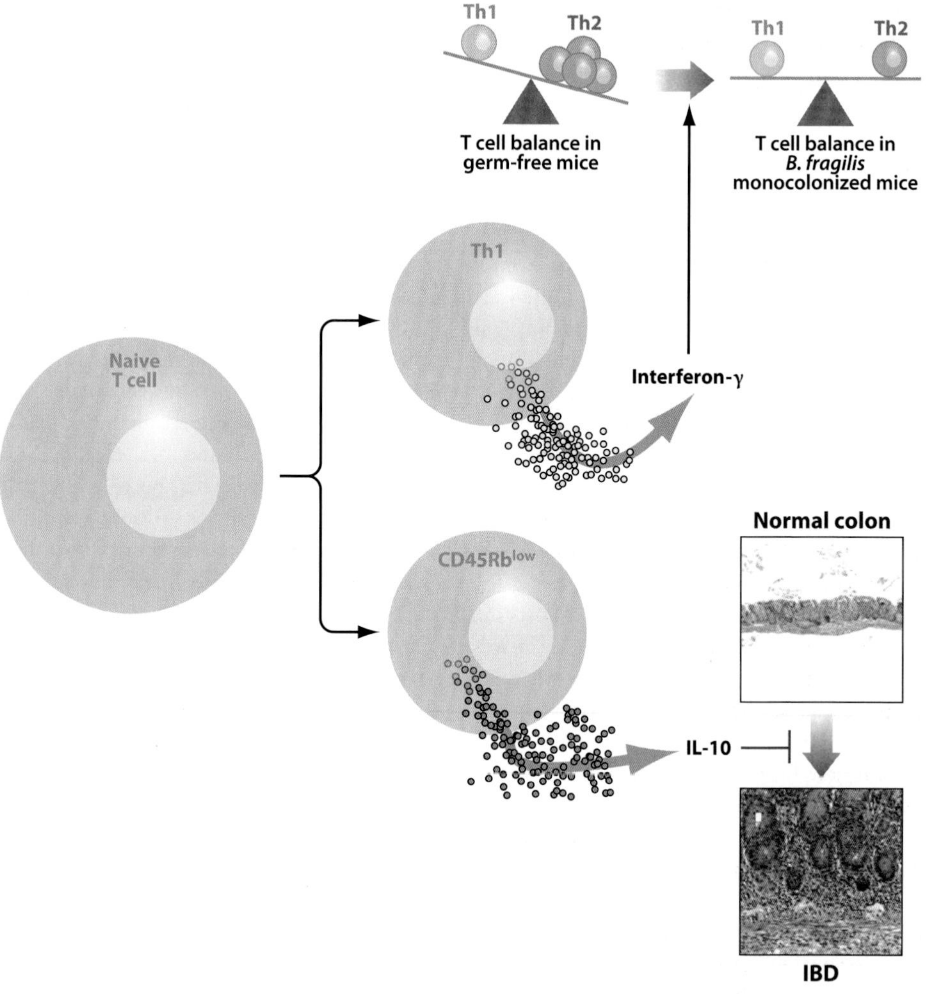

Figure 7

Current scope of PSA's biologic role as an immunomodulator. Monoassociation of germ-free mice with a PSA-bearing *B. fragilis* strain (wild type) corrects systemic T cell deficiencies, redresses Th1/Th2 imbalances, and directs lymphoid organogenesis (*upper right*) (59). PSA confers protection against inflammatory bowel disease (IBD) through a functional requirement for IL-10-producing $CD4^+$ $CD45RB^{low}$ T cells (*lower right*) (72).

that results in the production of interferon-γ, a key factor in the Th1 differentiation observed in colonization studies (14). An important and as yet unresolved issue is whether a single type or multiple types of $CD4^+$ T cells are responsible for inducing both Th1 and IL-10 cytokine production. It remains unclear whether PSA activates the same cell to do different things (depending on other environmental signals) or whether it activates different cells through either the same or different mechanisms.

Very recently, PSA has been used as a carrier molecule to induce an adaptive immune response to Tn-hapten—a tumor-associated carbohydrate antigen—in an effort to develop a novel cancer immunotherapy (73). This study demonstrates the design, synthesis, and immunologic evaluation of an entirely carbohydrate vaccine candidate.

SUMMARY AND CONCLUSION

Virtually all biological functions are regulated directly or indirectly by proteins. While an understanding of biological phenomena requires the investigation of proteins, the best-studied and most appreciated biopolymers, scientists have increasingly realized that biological events cannot be explained solely by the functions of proteins. Fine tuning of the system requires the involvement of other biomolecules, such as carbohydrates and lipids. This broadened perspective has stimulated investigations of these previously underappreciated bioregulators. The biological significance of carbohydrates—both in pure form and in association with other molecules—is now quite clear. In this article, we have reviewed several newly discovered aspects of carbohydrate interactions with the adaptive immune system.

In the past decade, paradigm-shifting observations have been made by investigators studying the unique bacterial capsules called ZPSs. Contrary to prior concepts, the ZPSs are now known to be processed and presented by APCs and to be recognized by T cells of the adaptive immune system. We have learned that, after entering APCs, carbohydrates are processed to smaller molecular size within the endosome via chemical mechanisms that are initiated with the oxidative burst and depend on reactive oxygen species and reactive nitrogen species. ZPSs such as PSA from *B. fragilis* are able to bind to MHCII within the endosome through electrostatic forces. When binding to MHCII takes place, these carbohydrates can be presented to and activate T cells, eliciting important immune responses. As discussed at length in this review, significant progress has been made in understanding the molecular requirements for ZPS stimulation of the adaptive immune system. However, many points remain to be clarified, including the precise physical-chemical and structural characteristics of the interactions of ZPSs, MHCII molecules, and TCRs. Crystal structures of MHCII-bound ZPS epitopes in contact with the TCR will help elucidate the exact nature of these interactions, but the ability of carbohydrate chemists to synthesize the molecules necessary for these studies is limited at this point. ZPS-specific T cell clones could also reveal the characteristics of ZPS activation of T cells. However, the creation of such clones is particularly challenging given their predilection to induce IL-10, which downregulates IL-2 and therefore turns off the T cell's proliferative capacity.

ZPSs play a unique role in regulating intraabdominal abscess formation. On the one hand, ZPSs are required for the induction of abscesses when injected along with sterile cecal contents (12). On the other hand, when given alone to rodents that are subsequently challenged with live bacteria, regardless of species, they protect against the induction of abscesses (66). This protective effect is also seen in models of surgical adhesion formation (71) and inflammatory bowel disease (72). These polysaccharides can also stimulate the development of a well-balanced immune system. An in-depth understanding of the interactions of this unique class of biological molecules with the immune system is likely to provide new opportunities to combat infections through regulation of immune responses (74). Most pathogens are coated with carbohydrates (e.g., bacterial CPSs), which are major virulence factors and excellent vaccine targets. To enable the adaptive immune system to recognize carbohydrates, scientists developed glycoconjugation. In glycoconjugate vaccines, peptides generated from the protein portion are presented to $CD4^{+}$ T cells; thus, T cell help is recruited and the production of IgG antibody to the polysaccharide by B cells is induced. Despite substantial progress in the prevention of infectious diseases, the success of current glycoconjugates varies with the population being immunized and with the characteristics of the specific vaccine. Persistent problems include (*a*) the need for booster doses, (*b*) poor immunogenicity in the elderly and in patients with underlying B lymphocyte defects, (*c*) the relatively short duration of immunity, (*d*) instances in which nonprotective antibodies—but not most opsonic IgG subclasses—are produced, and (*e*) the highly complicated heterogeneous structures of conjugates, which can result in much less efficient immunity to the polysaccharide and undesired immunity to the carrier protein (3, 7). Construction of glycoconjugates has been a random process in which two molecules (a carbohydrate and a protein) have been linked without optimization of the design on the basis of solid scientific principles. An understanding of the basic mechanisms governing glycoconjugate processing and presentation may be crucial for the creation of a new generation of glycoconjugate vaccines whose chemical and physical properties are specifically designed to enhance immunogenicity markedly.

FUTURE CONSIDERATIONS

Advances in the biology, chemistry, and immunology of carbohydrates have yielded novel insights into how this important class of biological molecules interfaces with the immune system in ways that were not previously appreciated. In this article, we have reviewed some of the data showing that ZPSs are actually processed and presented by the MHCII pathway and that these events result in the induction of T cell responses that are important in the development of a mature and well-balanced immune system as well as in the prevention of immune-mediated inflammatory diseases. The recognition of carbohydrates by T cells and the biologically important responses that result present an opportunity to study other functions of these biomolecules, such as the way in which the immune system recognizes glycoproteins on infectious organisms and the mechanisms by which the immune system responds to glycoconjugate vaccines. It has become clear in recent years that many bacteria (as well as viruses, fungi, and parasites) are decorated with carbohydrates. There are large gaps in our knowledge of how these molecules regulate the response to microorganisms. A better understanding of these interactions is likely to facilitate the development of drugs and vaccines for the treatment and prevention of infectious and autoimmune diseases.

DISCLOSURE STATEMENT

The authors are not aware of any affiliations, memberships, funding, or financial holdings that might be perceived as affecting the objectivity of this review.

ACKNOWLEDGMENTS

We thank Ms. Julie McCoy for her editorial assistance and Tom DiCesare for his excellent art work. We apologize to all the investigators whose research could not be cited because of the space limitations.

LITERATURE CITED

1. Hoagland CL, Beeson PB, Goebel WF. 1938. The capsular polysaccharide of the type XIV pneumococcus and its relationship to the specific substances of human blood. *Science* 88:261–63
2. Lindberg B, Lonngren J, Powell DA. 1977. Structural studies on the specific type-14 pneumococcal polysaccharide. *Carbohydr. Res.* 58:177–86
3. Weintraub A. 2003. Immunology of bacterial polysaccharide antigens. *Carbohydr. Res.* 338:2539–47
4. Janeway CA, Travers P, Walport M, Chlomchik M. 2005. *Immunobiology*. New York: Garland Sci. 6th ed.
5. Edwards MS, Nicholson-Weller A, Baker CJ, Kasper DL. 1980. The role of specific antibody in alternative complement pathway-mediated opsonophagocytosis of Type III Group B *Streptococcus*. *J. Exp. Med.* 151:1275–87

6. MacLeod CM, Hodges RG, Heidelberger M, Bernhard WG. 1945. Prevention of pneumococcal pneumonia by immunization with specific capsular polysaccharides. *J. Exp. Med.* 82:445–65
7. Lucas AH, Apicella MA, Taylor CE. 2005. Carbohydrate moieties as vaccine candidates. *Clin. Infect. Dis.* 41:705–12
8. Bhattacharjee AK, Jennings HJ, Kenny CP, Martin A, Smith IC. 1975. Structural determination of the sialic acid polysaccharide antigens of *Neisseria meningitidis* serogroups B and C with carbon 13 nuclear magnetic resonance. *J. Biol. Chem.* 250:1926–32
9. Wessels MR, Paoletti LC, Rodewald AK, Michon F, DiFabio J, et al. 1993. Stimulation of protective antibodies against type Ia and Ib group B streptococci by a type Ia polysaccharide-tetanus toxoid conjugate vaccine. *Infect. Immun.* 61:4760–66
10. Ovodov YS. 2006. Bacterial capsular antigens. Structural patterns of capsular antigens. *Biochemistry* 71:937–54
11. Tzianabos AO, Onderdonk AB, Rosner B, Cisneros RL, Kasper DL. 1993. Structural features of polysaccharides that induce intra-abdominal abscesses. *Science* 262:416–19
12. Cobb BA, Wang Q, Tzianabos AO, Kasper DL. 2004. Polysaccharide processing and presentation by the MHCII pathway. *Cell* 117:677–87
13. Duan J, Avci FA, Kasper DL. 2008. Microbial carbohydrate depolymerization by antigen-presenting cells: deamination prior to presentation by the MHCII pathway. *Proc. Natl. Acad. Sci. USA* 105:5183–88
14. Wang Q, McLoughlin RM, Cobb BA, Charrel-Dennis M, Zaleksi KJ, et al. 2006. A bacterial carbohydrate links innate and adaptive responses through Toll-like receptor 2. *J. Exp. Med.* 203:2853–63
15. Lesinski GB, Westerink MA. 2001. Vaccines against polysaccharide antigens. *Curr. Drug Targets Infect. Disord.* 1:325–34
16. Coutinho A, Moller G. 1973. B cell mitogenic properties of thymus-independent antigens. *Nat. New Biol.* 245:12–14
17. Coutinho A, Moller GJA, Bullock WW. 1973. In vitro activation of mouse lymphocytes in serum-free medium: effect of T and B cell mitogens on proliferation and antibody synthesis. *Eur. J. Immunol.* 3:299–306
18. McGhee JR, Michalek SM, Kiyono H, Eldridge JH, Colwell DE, et al. 1984. Mucosal immunoregulation: environmental lipopolysaccharide and GALT T lymphocytes regulate the IgA response. *Microbiol. Immunol.* 28:261–80
19. Barrett DJ. 1985. Human immune responses to polysaccharide antigens: an analysis of bacterial polysaccharide vaccines in infants. *Adv. Pediatr.* 32:139–58
20. Guttormsen H-K, Sharpe AH, Chandraker AK, Brigtsen AK, Sayegh MH, Kasper DL. 1999. Cognate stimulatory B-cell-T-cell interactions are critical for T-cell help recruited by glycoconjugate vaccines. *Infect. Immun.* 67:6375–84
21. Mitchison NA. 1971. The carrier effect in the secondary response to hapten-protein conjugates. II. Cellular cooperation. *Eur. J. Immunol.* 1:18–25
22. Mitchison NA. 1971. The carrier effect in the secondary response to hapten-protein conjugates. I. Measurement of the effect with transferred cells and objections to the local environment hypothesis. *Eur. J. Immunol.* 1:10–17
23. Beuvery EC, Van Rossum F, Nagel J. 1982. Comparison of the induction of immunoglobulin M and G antibodies in mice with purified pneumococcal type III and meningococcal group C polysaccharides and their protein conjugates. *Infect. Immun.* 37:15–22
24. Schneerson R, Barrera O, Sutton A, Robbins JB. 1980. Preparation, characterization, and immunogenicity of *Haemophilus influenzae* type b polysaccharide-protein conjugates. *J. Exp. Med.* 152:361–76
25. Trotter CL, McVernon J, Ramsay ME, Whitney CG, Mulholland EK, et al. 2008. Optimising the use of conjugate vaccines to prevent disease caused by *Haemophilus influenzae* type b, *Neisseria meningitidis* and *Streptococcus pneumoniae*. *Vaccine* 26:4434–45
26. Jones C. 2005. NMR assays for carbohydrate-based vaccines. *J. Pharm. Biomed. Anal.* 38:840–50
27. Bardotti A, Averani G, Berti F, Berti S, Carinci V, et al. 2008. Physicochemical characterization of glycoconjugate vaccines for prevention of meningococcal diseases. *Vaccine* 26:2284–96

28. Perez-Melgosa M, Ochs HD, Linsley PS, Laman JD, Meurs M, et al. 2001. Carrier-mediated enhancement of cognate T cell help: the basis for enhanced immunogenicity of meningococcal outer membrane protein polysaccharide conjugate vaccine. *Eur. J. Immunol.* 31:2373–81
29. Peeters CC, Tenbergen-Meekes AM, Poolman JT, Beurret M, Zegers BJ, Rijkers GT. 1991. Effect of carrier priming on immunogenicity of saccharide-protein conjugate vaccines. *Infect. Immun.* 59:3504–10
30. Pöllabauer EM, Petermann R, Ehrlich HJ. 2009. The influence of carrier protein on the immunogenicity of simultaneously administered conjugate vaccines in infants. *Vaccine* 27:1674–79
31. Dziadek S, Jacques S, Bundle DR. 2008. A novel linker methodology for the synthesis of tailored conjugate vaccines composed of complex carbohydrate antigens and specific T_H-cell peptide epitopes. *Chemistry* 19:5908–17
32. Könen-Waisman S, Cohen A, Fridkin M, Cohen IR. 1999. Self heat-shock protein (hsp60) peptide serves in a conjugate vaccine against a lethal pneumococcal infection. *J. Infect. Dis.* 179:403–13
33. Wang JY, Chang AH, Guttormsen HK, Rosas AL, Kasper DL. 2003. Construction of designer glycoconjugate vaccines with size-specific oligosaccharide antigens and site-controlled coupling. *Vaccine* 21:1112–17
34. Amir-Kroll H, Riveron L, Sarmiento ME, Sierra G, Acosta A, Cohen IR. 2006. A conjugate vaccine composed of a heat shock protein 60 T-cell epitope peptide (p458) and *Neisseria meningitidis* type B capsular polysaccharide. *Vaccine* 24:6555–63
35. Cohen N, Stolarsky-Bennun M, Amir-Kroll H, Margalit R, Nussbaum G, et al. 2008. Pneumococcal capsular polysaccharide is immunogenic when present on the surface of macrophages and dendritic cells: TLR4 signaling induced by a conjugate vaccine or by lipopolysaccharide is conducive. *J. Immunol.* 180:2409–18
36. Falugi F, Petracca R, Mariani M, Luzzi E, Mancianti S, et al. 2001. Rationally designed strings of promiscuous $CD4^+$ T cell epitopes provide help to *Haemophilus influenzae* type b oligosaccharide: a model for new conjugate vaccines. *Eur. J. Immunol.* 31:3816–24
37. Lai Z, Schreiber JR. 2009. Antigen processing of glycoconjugate vaccines; the polysaccharide portion of the pneumococcal CRM(197) conjugate vaccine colocalizes with MHC II on the antigen processing cell surface. *Vaccine* 27:3137–44
38. Haurum JS, Arsequell G, Lellouch AC, Wong SYC, Dwek RA, et al. 1994. Recognition of carbohydrate by major histocompatibility complex class I-restricted, glycopeptide-specific cytotoxic T lymphocytes. *J. Exp. Med.* 180:739–44
39. Hanish F-G, Ninkovic T. 2006. Immunology of O-glycosylated proteins: approaches to the design of a MUC1 glycopeptide-based tumor vaccine. *Curr. Protein Peptide Sci.* 7:307–15
40. Werdelin O, Meldal M, Jensen T. 2002. Processing of glycans on glycoprotein and glycopeptide antigens in antigen-presenting cells. *Proc. Natl. Acad. Sci. USA* 99:9611–13
41. Vlad AM, Muller S, Cudic M, Paulsen H, Otvos L, et al. 2002. Complex carbohydrates are not removed during processing of glycoproteins by dendritic cells: processing of tumor antigen MUC1 glycopeptides for presentation to major histocompatibility complex class II-restricted T cells. *J. Exp. Med.* 196:1435–46
42. Dzhambazov B, Holmdahl M, Yamada H, Lu S, Vestberg M, et al. 2005. The major T cell epitope on type II collagen is glycosylated in normal cartilage but modified by arthritis in both rats and humans. *Eur. J. Immunol.* 35:357–66
43. Corthay A, Backlund J, Broddefalk J, Michaelsson E, Goldschmiddt T, et al. 1998. Epitope glycosylation plays a critical role for T cell recognition of type II collagen in collagen-induced arthritis. *Eur. J. Immunol.* 28:2580–90
44. Brigl M, Brenner MB. 2004. CD1: antigen presentation and T cell function. *Annu. Rev. Immunol.* 22:817–90
45. Cobb BA, Kasper DL. 2005. Zwitterionic capsular polysaccharides: the new MHCII-dependent antigens. *Cell. Microbiol.* 7:1398–403
46. Tzianabos AO, Wang JY, Lee JC. 2001. Structural rationale for the modulation of abscess formation by *Staphylococcus aureus* capsular polysaccharides. *Proc. Natl. Acad. Sci. USA* 98:9365–70
47. McLoughlin RM, Lee JL, Kasper DL, Tzianabos AO. 2008. IFN-γ regulated chemokine production determines the outcome of *Staphylococcus aureus* Infection1. *J. Immunol.* 181:1323–32

48. Velez CD, Lewis CJ, Kasper DL, Cobb BA. 2009. Type I *Streptococcus pneumoniae* carbohydrate utilizes a nitric oxide and MHC II-dependent pathway for antigen presentation. *Immunology* 127:73–82
49. Comstock LE, Kasper DL. 2006. Bacterial glycans: key mediators of diverse host immune responses. *Cell* 126:847–50
50. Krinos CM, Coyne MJ, Weinacht KG, Tzianabos AO, Kasper DL, Comstock LE. 2001. Extensive surface diversity of a commensal microorganism by multiple DNA inversions. *Nature* 414:555–58
51. Baumann H, Tzianabos AO, Brisson JR, Kasper DL, Jennings HJ. 1992. Structural elucidation of two capsular polysaccharides from one strain of *Bacteroides fragilis* using high-resolution NMR spectroscopy. *Biochemistry* 31:4081–89
52. Wang JY, Kalka-Moll WM, Roehrl MH, Kasper DL. 2000. Structural basis of the abscess-modulating polysaccharide A2 from *Bacteroides fragilis*. *Proc. Natl. Acad. Sci. USA* 97:13478–83
53. Choi YH, Roehrl MH, Kasper DL, Wang JY. 2002. A unique structural pattern shared by T-cell-activating and abscess-regulating zwitterionic polysaccharides. *Biochemistry* 41:15144–51
54. Kreisman LS, Friedman JH, Neaga A, Cobb BA. 2007. Structure and function relations with a T-cell-activating polysaccharide antigen using circular dichroism. *Glycobiology* 17:46–55
55. Cobb BA, Kasper DL. 2008. Characteristics of carbohydrate antigen binding to the presentation protein HLA-DR. *Glycobiology* 18:707
56. Groneck L, Schrama D, Fabri M, Stephen TL, Harms F, et al. 2009. Oligoclonal $CD4^+$ T cells promote host memory immune responses to zwitterionic polysaccharide of *Streptococcus pneumoniae*. *Infect. Immun.* 77:3705–12
57. Kalka-Moll WM, Tzianabos AO, Bryant PW, Niemeyer M, Ploegh HL, Kasper DL. 2002. Zwitterionic polysaccharides stimulate T cells by MHC class II-dependent interactions. *J. Immunol.* 169:6149–53
58. van den Bosa LJ, Boltjea TJ, Provoosta T, Mazurekb J, Overkleefta HS, van der Marela GA. 2007. A synthetic study towards the PSA1 tetrasaccharide repeating unit. *Tetrahedron Lett.* 48:2697–700
59. Mazmanian SK, Liu CH, Tzianabos AO, Kasper DL. 2005. An immunomodulatory molecule of symbiotic bacteria directs maturation of the host immune system. *Cell* 122:107–18
60. Kolios G, Valatas V, Ward SG. 2004. Nitric oxide in inflammatory bowel disease: a universal messenger in an unsolved puzzle. *Immunology* 113:427–37
61. Vilar RE, Ghael D, Li M, Bhagat DD, Arrigo LM, et al. 1997. Nitric oxide degradation of heparin and heparan sulfate. *Biochem. J.* 324:473–79
62. Stingele F, Corthesy B, Kusy N, Porcelli SA, Kasper DL, Tzianabos AO. 2004. Zwitterionic polysaccharides stimulate T cells with no preferential Vβ usage and promote anergy, resulting in protection against experimental abscess formation. *J. Immunol.* 172:1483–90
63. Gallorini S, Berti F, Parente P, Baronio R, Aprea S, et al. 2007. Introduction of zwitterionic motifs into bacterial polysaccharides generates TLR2 agonists able to activate APCs. *J. Immunol.* 179:8208–15
64. Kasper DL, Onderdonk AB, Crabb J, Bartlett JG. 1979. Protective efficacy of immunization with capsular antigen against experimental infection with *Bacteroides fragilis*. *J. Infect. Dis.* 140:724–31
65. Onderdonk AB. 1979. Experimental animal models for anaerobic infections. *Rev. Infect. Dis.* 1:291–301
66. Tzianabos AO, Kasper DL, Cisneros RL, Smith RS, Onderdonk AB. 1995. Polysaccharide-mediated protection against abscess formation in experimental intra-abdominal sepsis. *J. Clin. Invest.* 96:2727–31
67. Tzianabos AO, Onderdonk AB, Smith RS, Kasper DL. 1994. Structure-function relationships for polysaccharide-induced intra-abdominal abscesses. *Infect. Immun.* 62:3590–93
68. Tzianabos AO, Russell PR, Onderdonk AB, Gibson FC 3rd, Cywes C, et al. 1999. IL-2 mediates protection against abscess formation in an experimental model of sepsis. *J. Immunol.* 163:893–97
69. Tzianabos AO, Finberg RW, Wang Y, Chan M, Onderdonk AB, et al. 2000. T cells activated by zwitterionic molecules prevent abscesses induced by pathogenic bacteria. *J. Biol. Chem.* 275:6733–40
70. Mazmanian SK, Kasper DL. 2006. The love-hate relationship between bacterial polysaccharides and the host immune system. *Nat. Rev. Immunol.* 6:849–58
71. Ruiz-Perez B, Chung DR, Sharpe AH, Yagita H, Kalka-Moll W, et al. 2005. Modulation of surgical fibrosis by microbial zwitterionic polysaccharides. *Proc. Natl. Acad. Sci. USA* 102:16753–58

72. Mazmanian SK, Round JL, Kasper DL. 2008. A microbial symbiosis factor prevents intestinal inflammatory disease. *Nature* 453:620–25

73. De Silva RA, Wang Q, Chidley T, Appulage DK, Andreana PR. 2009. Immunological response from an entirely carbohydrate antigen: design of synthetic vaccines based on Tn-PS A1 conjugates. *J. Am. Chem. Soc.* 131:9622–23

74. Tzianabos AO, Wang JY, Kasper DL. 2003. Biological chemistry of immunomodulation by zwitterionic polysaccharides. *Carbohydr. Res.* 338:2531–38

Properdin: Emerging Roles of a Pattern-Recognition Molecule

Claudia Kemper,[1] John P. Atkinson,[2] and Dennis E. Hourcade[2]

[1]MRC Centre for Transplantation, King's College London, SE1 9RT United Kingdom; email: claudia.kemper@kcl.ac.uk

[2]Department of Medicine/Division of Rheumatology, Washington University School of Medicine, St. Louis, Missouri 63110; email: jatkinso@dom.wustl.edu; dhourcad@dom.wustl.edu

Annu. Rev. Immunol. 2010. 28:131–55

First published online as a Review in Advance on November 30, 2009

The *Annual Review of Immunology* is online at immunol.annualreviews.org

This article's doi:
10.1146/annurev-immunol-030409-101250

0732-0582/10/0423-0131$20.00

Key Words

apoptosis, complement, neutrophil granules, pattern recognition

Abstract

Complement is an innate immune system that is a first line of defense against pathogens and facilitates elimination of apoptotic and injured cells. During complement activation, the complement convertases are assembled on target surfaces and initiate their proteolytic activities, a process that marks targets for phagocytosis and/or lysis. The complement alternative activation pathway has been implicated in a number of autoimmune conditions including arthritis and age-related macular degeneration. Properdin, a plasma component that is also released by activated neutrophils, is critical in the stabilization of alternative pathway convertases. Recently, it has been shown that properdin is also a pattern-recognition molecule that binds to certain microbial surfaces, apoptotic cells, and necrotic cells. Once bound to a surface, properdin can direct convertase formation and target uptake. New studies are now focusing on a role for properdin in inflammatory and autoimmune diseases. This review examines the new properdin findings and their implications.

Innate immunity: immediate immune response that is mediated via the recognition of pathogens through germ-line encoded pattern-recognition receptors

Adaptive immunity: immune response involving B and T lymphocyte activation leading to immunological memory with the generation of B lymphocyte clones having somatically recombined receptors

Opsonin: proteins that bind to the surface of a particle and enhance its uptake by phagocytes; includes IgG and complement activation fragments (including C4b, C3b, iC3b, C3dg, and C3d)

INTRODUCTION

"In all affairs it's a healthy thing now and then to hang a question mark on the things you have long taken for granted." —Bertrand Russell

Complement is an innate defense system that is found in vertebrate and invertebrate animals. Complement was defined more than one hundred years ago by Bordet as one of two distinguishable blood components that together had the capacity to lyse certain bacteria (1). One component (later described by Paul Ehrlich as antibody) was increased by immunization, reacting specifically with the immunizing organism, and was relatively heat stable; in contrast, the "complementing factor" was equivalent in activity in immune and nonimmune animals and was heat labile. Today, we know the bacteria:antibody complexes formed in this reaction activate the complement classical pathway (CP). CP activation is amplified by the complement alternative pathway (AP), and the membrane attack complex (MAC) is formed (2). Indeed, complementing factor is now known to consist of more than a dozen soluble proteins!

The complement system appears to have arisen to defend the host against infection: Humans completely deficient in key complement components are highly prone to infections with pyogenic bacteria. The complement proteins are at their highest concentrations in blood (in a standard whole complement assay, red blood cells are lysed at a 1/100 to 1/200 dilution of serum) (3). Thus, the primary biologic function of complement is to protect the intravascular compartment (hemolymph or blood) from infection. In that respect, complement is the premier guardian of the intravascular space. However, complement activity clearly goes well beyond this simple sentinel function in innate immunity and also plays vital roles in adaptive immunity and immune homeostasis (4–6). Here we review the current understanding of the complement system, focusing on the recently emerging roles of properdin, a complement protein that has been the subject of controversy several times since its discovery more than 50 years ago.

THE COMPLEMENT SYSTEM

Pathogen Recognition/Elimination and the Induction of the Inflammatory Reaction

Complement activation is precipitated by specific molecular recognition events. In some cases, recognition is mediated by antibody that may bind to a single pathogenic antigen, whereas in other cases recognition is performed by complement components with pattern-recognition activity that may bind a class of microbial targets. Several activation pathways have been identified (7) (**Figure 1**): the CP is activated by antigen:antibody complexes and certain other molecular patterns, the lectin pathway (LP) responds to mannose-containing polysaccharides (specifically those found on pathogen surfaces), and the AP is engaged by a variety of microbial surfaces. More recently, it has been shown that complement activation is also promoted by properdin:target complexes (see below) (8–10) and, in some situations, by several fluid phase serine proteases (11).

Although each complement activation pathway is triggered by a distinct set of activators, all culminate in the formation of the convertases, the major enzymes of the cascade (13, 14), and the generation of the opsonin C3b. The C3 convertase cleaves C3 at a single site, thereby generating the C3a and C3b fragments. This process exposes in the C3b fragment a highly reactive thiolester that can form a covalent bond to a nearby target surface, and the target-bound C3b that results can initiate assembly of additional C3 convertases (the AP amplification loop). C3b opsonization is rapid and robust; up to 10^7 C3b molecules are deposited on a target within 5 min (12). C3b can also bind directly to C3 convertase to form the C5 convertase, which cleaves C5 at a single site to produce C5a and C5b (13, 14). Formation of the MAC (**Figure 2**) begins in the fluid phase with the association of C5b with complement components C6 and C7. The resulting C5b67 complex inserts into the microbial membrane where

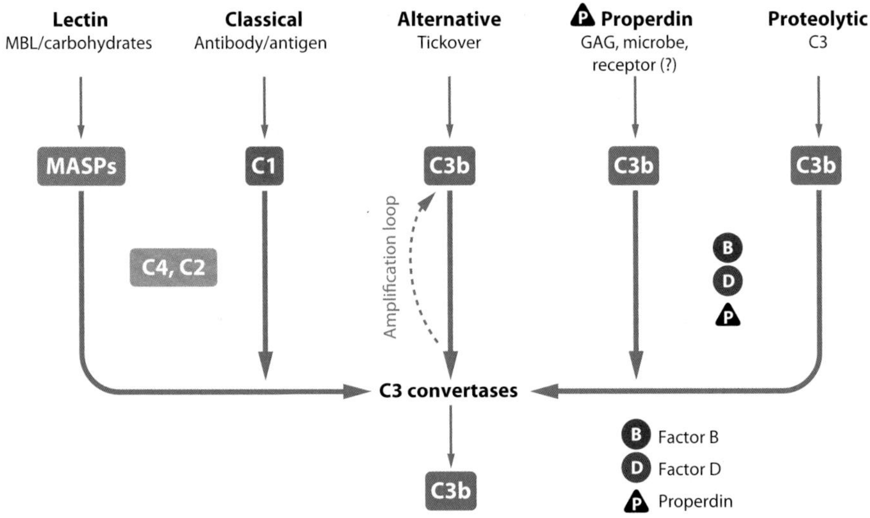

Figure 1

The complement activation pathways. Complement is activated through several distinct cascades: the lectin, classical, alternative, and properdin pathways. In addition, direct cleavage of C3 (or C5) occurs through a number of proteases including the kinin-generating proteases kallikrein and thrombin. The initial deposition of C3b on a target surface initiates the feedback amplification loop, which potentiates complement activation dramatically. All activation conditions culminate in the formation of the major opsonin and complement effector molecule C3b. (Abbreviations: MBL, mannose-binding lectin; MASP, MBL-associated serine protease; GAG, glycosaminoglycan.)

it binds C8 and C9. The completed MAC then promotes membrane disruption and cell lysis (13, 14).

Opsonized targets are also recognized by complement receptors expressed on several distinct cell populations. Complement receptors on red blood cells bind C3b-coated targets (a reaction known as immune adherence) and transport them to phagocytes in the liver and spleen (15). Complement receptors on phagocytes facilitate target uptake and clearance in these organs or in inflamed tissues (16–18) (**Figure 2**). The lytic pathway was first thought to be the key to complement antimicrobial activity. However, nearly a half-century later, immune adherence and subsequent phagocytic ingestion are thought to be of greater importance.

In addition, the concurrent generation of the anaphylatoxins C3a and C5a during C3 and C5 cleavage ensures the timely recruitment and activation of immunocompetent cells (including phagocytic cells) to the site of pathogen invasion: C5a is a powerful chemoattractant for most leukocytes (19, 20). C3a directs bactericidal activity (21). In addition, both C3a and C5a induce smooth muscle cell contraction and increased vascular permeability as well as degranulation of endothelial cells, mast cells (histamine release), and phagocytes, which leads to a protective acute inflammatory reaction, another major function of complement activation (21, 22) (**Figure 2**).

The Instruction of Adaptive Immunity

The adaptive immune response is largely dependent on the capacity of the innate immune system to distinguish self from nonself (4, 5, 23). The functional interplay between complement and adaptive immunity (**Figure 2**) was first explored in the early 1970s: Eden, Nussenzweig, and their collaborators observed that B cells bind C3 fragments on their surface (24), whereas Pepys discovered that the B cell response against T cell–dependent antigens is

Immune adherence: the binding of opsonized antigens or immune complexes to complement receptors expressed on cells such as erythrocytes, B cells, follicular dendritic cells, monocytes, and macrophages

Anaphylatoxins: the proinflammatory complement activation fragments C3a and C5a, which mediate an inflammatory response through cell activation to induce, for example, chemotaxis and histamine release

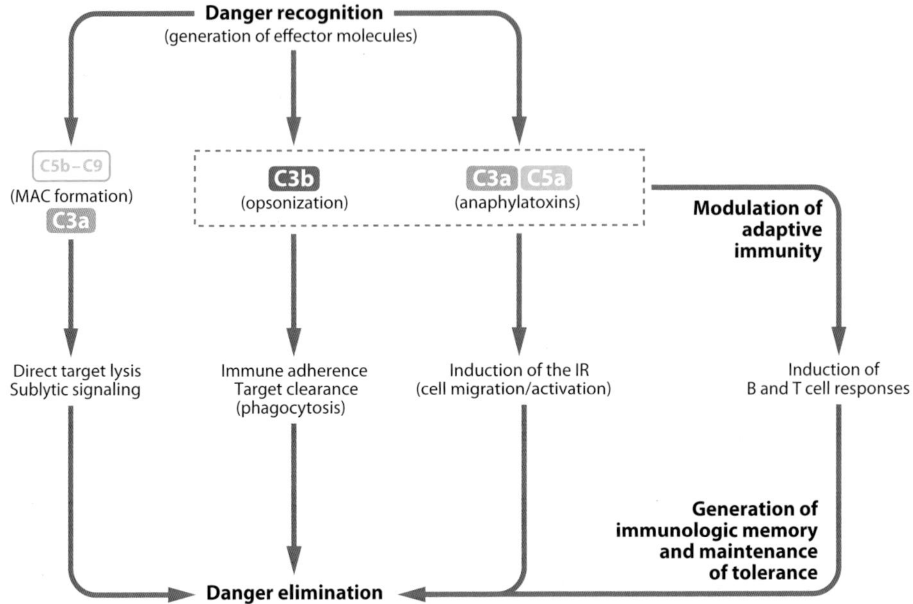

Figure 2

Complement effector functions. Recognition of danger by complement (**Figure 1**) leads to the generation of complement effector molecules/pathways. This includes the direct lysis of a pathogen, the uptake/clearance of dangerous targets, and the recruitment and activation of immunocompetent cells to the site of inflammation. In addition, complement effector molecules (C3b/C4b degradation products and C3a/C5a) aid in B and T cell activation and are required for optimal induction of the T and B cell memory pool as well as for the generation of tolerance to self-antigens. (Abbreviations: MAC, membrane attack complex; IR, immune response.)

impaired in C3-deficient mice (25). Together, these findings clearly indicated an essential role for C3 in B cell activity. Subsequent studies by Fearon and collaborators established the C3d-binding complement receptor CD21 (CR2) as a key component in the complement-mediated modulation of B cell responses (26). CD21 forms a functional receptor group on B cells with CD19 and CD81.This coreceptor complex engages with antigen opsonized with C3d (and related fragments C3dg and C3bi) during B cell receptor (BCR) stimulation (27). This signal functions as adjuvant and lowers the threshold for B cell activation and antibody production 10- to 10,000-fold, promoting the clonal expansion of B cells producing antibodies with great specificity for the recognized antigen (28). In addition, CD21 facilitates antigen localization to follicular dendritic cells (FDCs) within lymphoid follicles (29, 30) and plays a role in the promotion of an optimal B cell memory pool (31), that is, the production of natural antibody (32, 33), as well as in the induction and maintenance of B cell tolerance (34, 35).

Adjuvant: substance that enhances the immunogenicity of an antigen

Complement also is important for optimal T cell function (4, 6, 36, 37). In this regard, two distinct mechanisms have been proposed: In the first case, complement activation products modulate T cell activity indirectly via their effects on antigen-presenting cells (APCs), the cells that mediate antigen:T cell interactions. In the second case, complement fragments may directly impact T cell functions.

APCs express a wide range of complement receptors and complement regulatory proteins, which makes them ideally equipped to sense and respond to complement activation in the environment. Association of antigen with C3 fragments is instrumental for optimal antigen recognition and processing by APCs: C3 deficiency leads to reduced antigen presentation and in turn to impaired T cell immunity (38–41). Moreover, full maturation of dendritic cells (DCs) upon antigen uptake does not occur in C3-deficient mice (42–44).

Of the complement activation fragments that modulate APC functions, the anaphylatoxins play a particularly important role: C3a/C5a receptors are instrumental in the regulation of cytokine production by APCs (specifically IL-12), dramatically impacting Th1 or Th2 lineage development, pathogen clearance, and allergy onset and development (45–48). In addition, CD4 and CD8 T cell responses are diminished in mice deficient in the anaphylatoxin C3a/C5a receptors (or treated with peptide antagonist) as well as in animals deficient in complement regulators (see below) that control the availability of these complement activation fragments (45, 46, 49, 50). Also, the C3a/C5a intracellular signaling pathways on APCs intersect with those of the Toll-like receptor (TLR) family (51, 52).

Complement also influences T cells directly (6): Activation of the complement receptors and regulators located on the T cell surface impacts cell proliferation, cell viability, and IFN-γ production (53–56). Complement:T cell interactions may also regulate and downmodulate successful effector T responses, providing essential dampeners to inflammatory immune reactions. Activation of membrane cofactor protein (MCP, CD46), a complement regulator, in the presence of IL-2 during T cell activation induces the development/activation of adaptive IL-10-secreting and granzyme B–expressing regulatory T cells (57, 58). These cells can suppress the activation of bystander T cells via immunosuppressive IL-10, direct killing, and the consumption of IL-2. Similarly, crosslinking of complement receptor 1 (CR1, CD35) during T cell activation decreases cell proliferation and IL-2 production (59). The suppression of immune reactions by complement may be an essential step in the timely resolution of an immune response, which is vital in the prevention of tissue damage and autoimmunity.

Regulators Protect Host Tissue from Complement-Mediated Damage

Complement activity is controlled by a group of regulatory proteins (the regulators of complement activation or RCA proteins) that protects host cells and tissues from complement-mediated damage (60). When the RCA proteins misfunction, serious tissue injury can result. The RCA proteins control complement activation by inhibiting convertase assembly and stability via two critical mechanisms (**Figure 3**): (*a*) The RCA proteins decay accelerating factor (DAF, CD55), factor H, and CR1 dissociate Bb from AP convertase (61). This reaction terminates convertase activity, and Bb cannot reassociate freely with C3b, although the remaining C3b does provide a site for the formation of a new convertase. (*b*) The RCA proteins MCP, CR1, and factor H each can serve as cofactor for the cleavage of C3b by the fluid phase protease factor I (61). Convertase can no longer form from the iC3b fragment that results. Some cofactor proteins also permit further cleavage of iC3b, leading to C3d and C3dg. The RCA proteins also direct similar regulatory reactions to C4b and the CP convertases. In addition, CD59, a membrane-bound non-RCA protein, protects host tissue by blocking the assembly of the MAC (61).

Toll-like receptor (TLR): a family of cell surface or cell compartment-bound innate danger recognition receptors that detect a wide range of pathogenic pathogen-associated molecular patterns and some endogenous ligands

THE EMERGING CASE OF PROPERDIN AS A NOVEL PATTERN-RECOGNITION MOLECULE

Properdin and the Alternative Pathway: Historical Perspective

For 50 years, complement was thought to function only in response to antigen:antibody complexes. That view began to change in 1954 because of work by Louis Pillemer and collaborators at the Western Reserve University (now Case Western University) (62). They reported the serum-dependent activation of complement on a number of specific targets, including bacteria, viruses, certain red blood cells, and zymosan, all apparently in the absence of

a

Cofactor activity

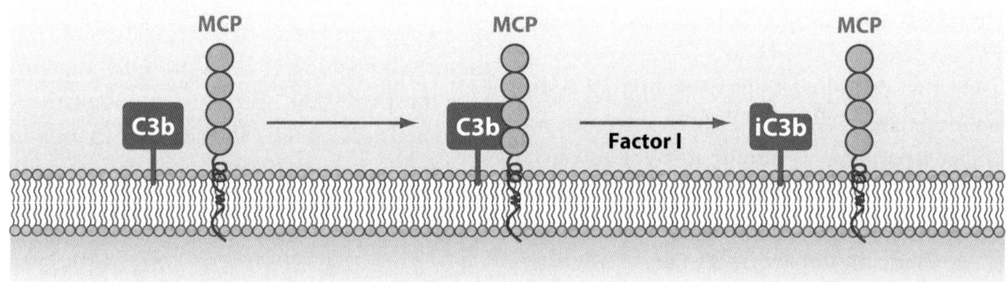

b

Decay acceleration activity

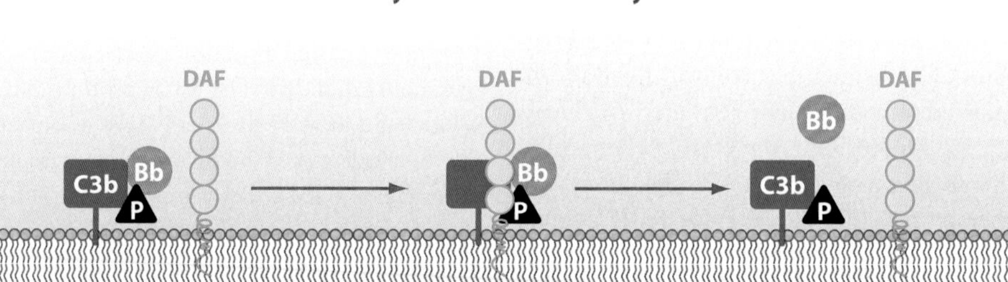

Figure 3

Regulation of complement activation. (*a*) Cofactor activity. Membrane cofactor protein (MCP, CD46) associates with C3b, promoting the proteolytic cleavage of C3b by factor I. (*b*) Decay acceleration activity. Decay accelerating factor (DAF, CD55) associates with C3bBbP and accelerates the dissociation of the Bb subunit.

antibody. A new serum protein, properdin (named after the Latin word *perdere*, to destroy), played an essential role in these reactions. Pillemer and collaborators proposed a simple model to account for their observations: (*a*) Properdin bound its various targets, and (*b*) properdin-target complexes activated complement.

The "properdin system" attracted a great deal of interest as it represented the first example of natural (innate) immunity (63). When, however, critical evidence for the new system was examined by other investigators, important questions arose. Robert Nelson, in particular, provided strong evidence that Pillemer's properdin preparations were likely contaminated by antibodies, so the reactions Pillemer and his coauthors regarded as novel could be explained by the known complement system (64). Following Pillemer's untimely death in 1957 (65), properdin was largely dismissed by the scientific community (66).

Interest in properdin was renewed in the 1970s when several reports indicated the likely existence of an antibody-independent complement activation pathway (66). With the use of purified complement proteins, the alternative activation pathway was elucidated (67, 68) (**Figure 4*a***): Nascent C3b, produced by constant turnover (tickover) of fluid phase C3, binds covalently to a target and engages

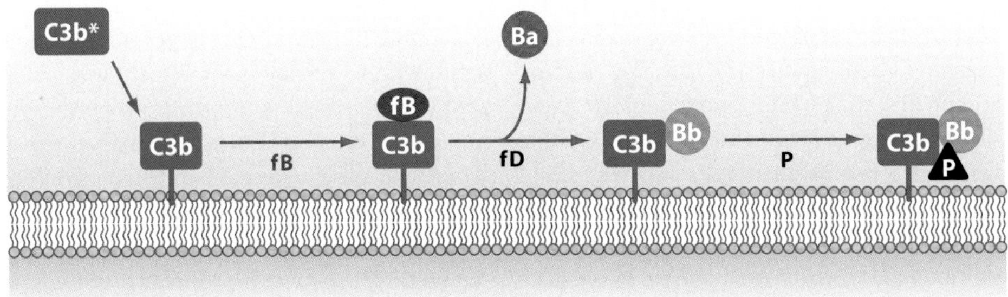

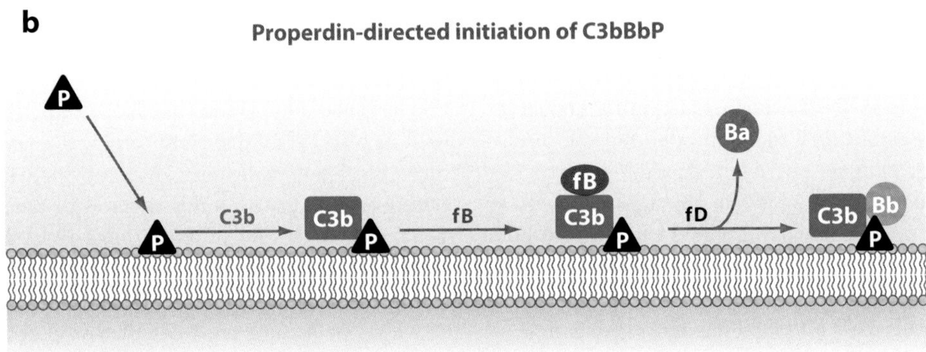

Figure 4

Assembly of the alternative pathway C3 convertase (C3bBbP) on a target surface. (*a*) Initiation of convertase assembly by nonspecific covalent binding of nascent C3b (C3b*) to the target. (*b*) Initiation of convertase assembly by the specific noncovalent binding of properdin to the target. Figure derived from Reference 9 (copyright 2007, The American Association of Immunologists, Inc.).

factor B, an inactive serine protease. The C3bB complex is cleaved by factor D in the presence of Mg^{2+} at a single site in the factor B subunit, resulting in the release of the factor B amino-terminal fragment (Ba) and the activation of the serine protease domain, which can now cleave C3. C3bBb is a short-lived complex [$T_{1/2} \sim$ 90 sec (69, 70)] that is stabilized 5- to 10-fold by subsequent association with properdin (71).

Once the AP was firmly established, the work of Pillemer was considered to be vindicated (66), although properdin did not play as significant a role in the new model as Pillemer originally envisioned (62). In retrospect, Pillemer and collaborators had never established unequivocal evidence for direct properdin:target interaction, and the serum properdin found to be bound to zymosan or to other targets was accounted for by a more complex process that required other serum components.

Pillemer Revisited: Properdin Recognizes Targets and Initiates Convertase Assembly

Although properdin was accepted as the only positive regulator of complement, it was regarded as relatively unimportant in part because AP activation could proceed in vitro without it.

Lipopolysaccharide (LPS): a major surface component of the enteric bacteria that consists of a lipid anchor, a "core" oligosaccharide, and a highly repeated pentasaccharide or O antigen

Recently, the concept of properdin as a pattern-recognition molecule emerged from a series of studies designed to better characterize the C3b/properdin interaction during convertase assembly. These studies (8), utilizing surface plasmon resonance (SPR) methodology, confirmed that properdin bound C3bB and C3bBb much more readily than C3b and that multivalent properdin:C3b interactions were far more stable than univalent properdin:C3b interactions (72). Novel observations were also made: (*a*) Properdin was covalently attached to a biosensor chip and treated with purified complement proteins, initially C3b followed by a mixture of factor B and factor D or all three purified proteins together. Either way, C3bBbP was formed, a clear demonstration that properdin could provide a platform for convertase assembly. (*b*) Properdin bound to the biosensor chip via one ligand-binding site provided additional sites for C3b binding and C3bBb assembly. These new findings led to the proposal that properdin bound to an activating surface via either C3b, C3bB, and/or C3bBb creates new points for C3b binding and convertase assembly. By this view, properdin would both stabilize preformed convertase and promote further convertase assembly and C3b deposition.

The SPR model (8) (**Figure 4*b***) seemed somewhat reminiscent of the ill-fated two-step model that Pillemer and collaborators proposed for properdin function more than 50 years earlier: that is, properdin binds its target and properdin-target complexes activate complement (62). However, while the SPR experiments clearly demonstrated that surface-bound properdin can provide a platform to initiate C3bBbP assembly from purified C3b, factor B, and factor D, it was not apparent that this process could occur in biological fluids, where C3b is limited, nor was it known that properdin itself would bind to targets. These two questions were soon addressed.

C3 slowly and continuously undergoes autoactivation (tickover), forming a C3b-like form that activates the AP and creates a pool of C3b in bodily fluids (13, 14). Thus, in principle, properdin could direct convertase formation by recruiting fluid phase C3b from that pool. In practice, however, would there be sufficient C3b to permit properdin-directed convertase formation? To answer that question, a bifunctional recombinant protein was generated that consisted of a human properdin domain fused to a single chain Fv domain that recognizes the abundant mouse erythrocyte (E_m) surface antigen glycophorin A (**Figure 5*a***) (9). The bifunctional protein was used to tag a potential target, E_m, with properdin, and tagged E_m was treated with human serum. Serum deficient in C8 was used to prevent cell lysis. Analysis of the resulting erythrocytes showed that properdin bound to the E_m promoted serum-dependent deposition of complement activation products in the absence of CP or LP function (**Figure 5*b***). When normal serum was used in place of C8-deficient serum, the erythrocytes lysed, indicating that complement activation culminated in the assembly of functional MACs. A similar bifunctional reagent, made with an antihuman targeting domain, directed human complement activation on E_{hu} (9). Thus, it became apparent that properdin bound to a target surface could initiate complement activation using the proteins present in serum.

Properdin Recognizes Dangerous Nonself

Once it was discovered that properdin bound to a biosensor can direct the assembly of the C3 convertase with C3b recruited from the serum pool, studies were undertaken to determine whether properdin could bind microbial targets (9). To that end, the standard AP targets, zymosan and rabbit erythrocytes (E_r), were compared to sheep erythrocytes (E_s, the standard non-AP activator). The AP targets, zymosan and E_r, bound properdin in a standard AP buffer, whereas E_s (the CP activator) did not bind properdin. Properdin also attached to *Neisseria gonorrhoeae* and to lipopolysaccharide (LPS)-defective *Escherichia coli* and *Salmonella typhimurium* but not to *E. coli* or *S. typhimurium* with wild-type LPS (9). In a

a Construction of a single chain Fv-properdin that binds an E surface antigen

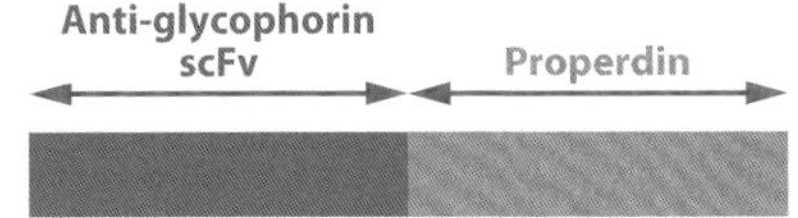

b Properdin-directed activation and lysis of E

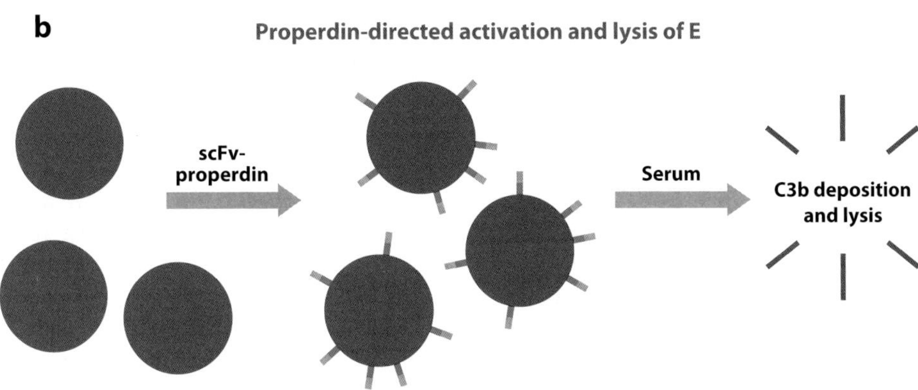

Figure 5

Properdin-tagged erythrocytes activate complement. (*a*) A bifunctional protein was constructed from coding sequences of properdin and a single chain antibody (scFv) that recognizes glycophorin, a red blood cell (E) surface antigen; (*b*) E bound by bifunctional proteins described in *a* are treated with serum, resulting in C3b deposition and cell lysis.

separate study, Kimura et al. (73) showed purified properdin bound to LPS-coated microtiter wells. In all cases tested (zymosan, *Neisseria*, and LPS-coated microtiter wells), the properdin:target complexes promoted C3bBbP assembly in the presence of properdin-deficient serum. Taken together, these studies indicate that properdin recognizes a variety of nonself antigens/structures and functions as an initiation point for the AP convertase on potentially dangerous targets. This new aspect of properdin activity became the starting point for further inquiries (below).

Properdin Recognizes Altered Self

Complement likely evolved in relatively simple multicellular organisms as a system dedicated only to antimicrobial defense (dangerous nonself). As life forms became increasingly complex, it became pertinent for the complement system to recognize and respond to altered and dangerous self. Apoptosis (programmed cell death) is a fundamental biological process in which harmful or obsolete cells are safely eliminated (74–77). Apoptosis plays critical roles in morphogenesis, cellular homeostasis, regulation of cellular immunity, and the removal of injured and virus-infected cells (74, 76). Complement has been known for many years to play a role in the recognition and removal of apoptotic cells (78, 79). Surface remodeling (membrane flip-flop) that occurs during apoptosis appears to facilitate C1q and/or mannose-binding lectin (MBL) recognition, leading ultimately to opsonization with C3 activation fragments. These C3 fragments are, in turn, recognized by the complement receptors CR3 (CD11b), CR4 (CD11c), and CRIg—expressed by phagocytes and scavenger cells—and this interaction mediates the uptake and clearance of the dying cells (16–18, 79).

Apoptosis: a naturally occurring process of controlled or programmed cell death that is fundamental in many biological processes including development and immune homeostasis and does not generally evoke an inflammatory immune response

Necrosis: premature cell death induced through external factors such as trauma, infection, or toxins inducing an inflammatory response that is the underlying reason for a number of (autoimmune) diseases

Phagocytosis: the controlled uptake and digestion of cells, cell particles, or pathogens by specialized cells such as macrophages, neutrophils, or dendritic cells

Apoptosis also plays a critical role in shaping and controlling the immune response. For example, T cell populations that have expanded in response to specific antigens and have performed their effector functions finally undergo apoptosis, thereby limiting their physiologic impact (74, 80). Experiments were initiated to determine whether properdin might be involved in the recognition and clearance of apoptotic T cells (10). Primary T cells were isolated, activated in vitro, and treated with either staurosporin or anti-Fas monoclonal antibody to induce apoptosis or with H_2O_2 to induce necrosis. The major findings include the following: (*a*) Properdin binds early apoptotic T cells but not resting T cells, activated (live) T cells, or necrotic T cells; (*b*) surface-bound properdin directs deposition of C3b activation fragments on apoptotic T cells under conditions that exclude CP or LP participation; (*c*) properdin bound to apoptotic cells promotes their phagocytic uptake by macrophages and DCs; and (*d*) although maximum uptake is dependent on complement activation, properdin bound to apoptotic T cells enhances their uptake in the absence of complement activation or other serum proteins. This result, together with the observation that macrophages and DCs can bind properdin, strongly suggests that properdin:target complexes direct phagocytosis without further complement involvement.

From the T cell findings, investigators have proposed that properdin promotes phagocytosis of apoptotic T cells by two different mechanisms (10). In one case, properdin binds to apoptotic T cells and initiates in situ complement activation. The surface-bound C3b and iC3b that is generated then mediates contact with phagocytes via the phagocyte receptors CR3 and CRIg. Downregulation, shedding, or redistribution of complement regulatory molecules may facilitate this process (81, 82). In the second case, properdin binds to apoptotic T cells and mediates contact with phagocytes directly. In this scenario, properdin functions as a bridging protein that can promote phagocytosis in the absence of further complement activation. Direct properdin:phagocyte interaction would require the presence of properdin receptors on the phagocyte surface—however, such a receptor has yet to be identified.

Properdin-dependent recognition and clearance of apoptotic cells may be promoted by neutrophils, whose granules are a major source of properdin. Incubation of apoptotic T cells with freshly stimulated neutrophils leads to release of properdin from the neutrophils and subsequent deposition of properdin on the T cell surface. Importantly, properdin binding is independent of complement activation because concomitant C3b deposition is not observed. Minimal properdin is deposited on nonapoptotic T cells incubated with activated neutrophils or when apoptotic T cells are incubated with nonactivated neutrophils. These results indicate that properdin freshly expelled by degranulating neutrophils, like purified properdin, readily binds apoptotic T cells (10).

Although apoptosis is characterized by dramatic cell reorganization, the cell itself remains intact (74, 80). In contrast, necrosis involves interruption of the cell membrane and release of interior contents (76). Necrosis is a consequence of gross cell injury, but it is also the natural endpoint of apoptosis. Such cells are especially dangerous because they may induce harmful inflammatory reactions (76). Necrotic cells are recognized by the complement proteins C1q and MBL, as well as by a number of noncomplement proteins, which promote their clearance (79). Xu et al. (83) showed that human properdin can also recognize damaged (heat-treated) necrotic mouse splenocytes. Importantly, properdin would bind to the injured splenocytes whether they were derived from C3-deficient or wild-type mice, thereby conclusively demonstrating that properdin can bind its targets without C3b mediation. They also showed that properdin binds several different cultured human cell types damaged by repeated freeze/thaw cycles and also to late-stage apoptotic cells. Consistent with the previous studies, properdin bound to a target cell can direct complement activation.

Properdin has not been reported to bind to healthy primary cells: Properdin does not bind primary human red blood cells (9), B cells or T cells (10), kidney cells (84), or mouse splenocytes (83). Properdin does, however, bind a subset of healthy cultured cells including immortalized human kidney cells (84) and Chinese hamster ovary (CHO) cells (10), as well as certain malignant T cell and breast tumor lines. These latter cases suggest that properdin may also recognize cells undergoing malignant transformation. Sjoblom et al. (85) compared the sequences of over 13,000 genes from primary breast tumors and lines to equivalent gene sequences from normal tissue. Genes were identified that had mutated to a significant degree during tumorigenesis and therefore may normally play a protective role. The properdin gene was in this group. Thus, in some cases the properdin gene may be activated during tumorigenesis, with the resulting properdin protein exported to the cell surface, tagging it for clearance.

Properdin Structure

Properdin is composed of identical 53-kDa protein subunits (86). Each subunit is rod-like, approximately 26 nm in length and 2.5 nm in diameter (87). The properdin subunits associate head-to-tail to form cyclic dimers, trimers, and tetramers that resemble rods, triangles, and squares, respectively (**Figure 6*a***) (87). Properdin function is dependent on its polymeric nature: Specific activity of properdin increases with size, with the tetramer being approximately tenfold more active compared to the dimer (88). Farries et al. (72) proposed a model for properdin:convertase interactions that is based on multiple properdin:ligand interactions.

The properdin protein is composed exclusively of seven thrombospondin repeats (TSRs) of type 1 (86, 89). Structural studies indicate the TSR is an independently folded module that consists of three antiparallel strands held together by three disulfides (90) (**Figure 6*b***). The amino terminal or A strand is irregular in structure, whereas the B and C strands associate as beta sheet elements. The properdin TSRs are numbered in order from the N terminus,

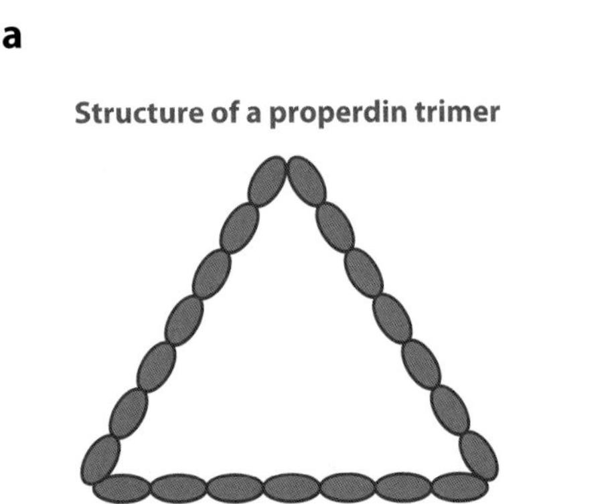

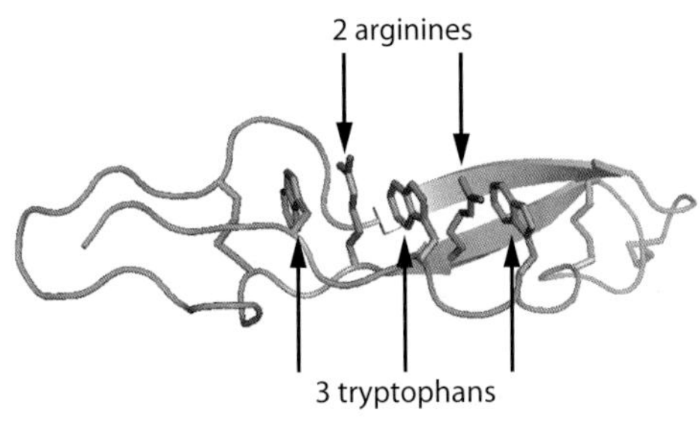

Figure 6

(*a*) Properdin is formed by head-to-tail association of identical monomers. Each properdin monomer is composed of seven thrombospondin repeat (TSR) type I domains. (*b*) A TSR domain with the proposed key arginine and tryptophan side chains. The two arginines are approximately 9 Å apart and are proposed to interact at target surfaces with pairs of negatively charged chemical groups such as sulfates. The structure was generated using PyMOL (128).

Glycosaminoglycan (GAG): a family of linear polysaccharides that are often linked to proteins to form proteoglycans

TSR 0 followed by TSR 1–6. This is because TSR 0 was not immediately recognized from its amino acid sequence as a TSR owing to a large deletion located in the A strand. Recent analysis indicates that TSR 0 indeed carries the essential TSR structural elements (89), and the domain was named TSR 0 to avoid renumbering the others.

TSR-containing proteins are prevalent in animals and certain protozoans, forming a TSR "superfamily" and serving in development, angiogenesis, tumor progression, axon guidance, activation of TGF-β, and wound healing (91). There are at least 41 members of the human TSR superfamily (90), and most are chimeric in structure. Although TSR domains mediate protein:ligand interactions, many are involved in cell attachment and extracellular matrix interactions including the three TSRs in thrombospondin 1, TSR 5 of F-spondin, several TSRs in the ADAMST proteins, and the TSR of the *Plasmodium* protein TRAP (91). Of particular interest, TSRs in thrombospondin (92), TRAP (93), and other superfamily proteins (91) bind to surface glycosaminoglycans (GAGs).

Properdin Recognizes and Binds to GAGs

GAGs are linear polysaccharides composed of repeating disaccharide units that are variously modified with sulfate groups (94). Major GAGs include heparan sulfate and chondroitin sulfate. Protein:GAG conjugates (proteoglycans) are synthesized by and present on most mammalian cells and play major roles in cell signaling and morphogenesis through their specific GAG structures. A previous study showed that properdin binds heparin (95). Thus, it was determined whether properdin might bind cells via the GAG chains of surface proteoglycans.

Wild-type and GAG-defective CHO cells have been used to study the role of proteoglycan GAG structures during a wide variety of cell functions (96). Analysis of properdin binding utilizing a series of CHO cells demonstrated that properdin binds via heparan sulfate and chondroitin sulfate proteoglycan chains. Moreover, properdin binding to wild-type CHO cells was diminished when the sulfation of GAGs was inhibited by sodium chlorate pretreatment, results indicating that properdin:GAG recognition is mediated in part by the GAG sulfate moieties (10). Interestingly, properdin likely recognizes apoptotic T cells via a similar mechanism: While GAG-defective T cells were not available for analysis, properdin binding was diminished when T cells were pretreated with sodium chlorate prior to the induction of apoptosis. Moreover, soluble GAGs, especially chondroitin sulfate C and E, inhibited properdin recognition of apoptotic T cells (10).

The detailed three-dimensional structure of properdin has not yet been resolved, but structures of other TSRs have been deduced. In the case of TSR 2 and 3 of thrombospondin, a protein surface containing disulfide-stabilized alternating arginine and tryptophan side chains has been proposed as a GAG-binding face (90, 93). In particular, the distance between the arginines (~9 Å) matches closely the length of a GAG disaccharide unit, suggesting that the interaction between TSR and sulfated GAG could be determined in part by electrostatic interactions between the TSR arginine side chains and adjacent GAG sulfates (**Figure 6*b***). Similar structures likely mediate properdin:GAG interactions because the critical arginines and tryptophans are conserved in 5 of 7 properdin TSRs (86).

Properdin:GAG interactions may account for properdin recognition of mammalian cells, but there is no evidence for GAGs on the bacteria used in the properdin studies (9). Thus, properdin must recognize other biochemical targets on those microbial surfaces. Kimura et al. (73) showed that properdin can bind microtiter wells coated with LPS. In addition, Xu et al. (83) provided evidence that properdin recognizes necrotic cells via surface DNA. Like the GAGs, these other potential properdin ligands are polyanionic. The properdin residues proposed to bind the sulfate moieties of GAGs may also mediate properdin interactions with LPS and DNA.

Regulation of Properdin Target Recognition Activity

Although apoptotic T cells bind readily to purified properdin that has been derived from serum and to properdin freshly released from neutrophils, they bind poorly to properdin present in unfractionated C3-deficient serum (10). Similarly, purified but not serum properdin binds certain gram-negative bacteria (9) and LPS-coated microtiter wells (73). These observations suggest serum-level inhibition of properdin:target recognition, either by competition with other pattern-recognition molecules for binding sites or by direct association of properdin with inhibitory agents.

Complement activation is controlled in part by soluble inhibitors that function to protect self-tissue from complement-mediated damage: factor H regulates AP activation, and C4b-binding protein regulates CP and LP activation (61). By analogy, we would expect serum-based control of properdin-directed complement activation. Because properdin is found at a relatively low concentration in plasma [4–6 μg/ml, (97)], changes in its local concentration could significantly impact local levels of AP activation—thus, properdin may successfully compete with other serum proteins for ligand sites when local properdin concentration is relatively high (either in the fluid phase or on a surface).

In contrast to most other complement proteins, properdin is not produced primarily in the liver. Properdin is constantly synthesized and secreted by monocytes/macrophages and T cells (98, 99). Interestingly, properdin is also synthesized at some point during neutrophil biogenesis: Though properdin does not appear to be made by mature neutrophils, it is found stored in neutrophil secondary granules. Moreover, the stored properdin is released upon cell stimulation (100). The release of properdin from neutrophils may be a major determinant of local AP activity (101). Investigators have recently shown that properdin is also stored by mast cells (102), suggesting that a similar scenario may apply to mast cell properdin. By this view, properdin-dependent recognition is largely mediated by the local release of stored properdin (**Figure 7**), whereas plasma properdin functions primarily to stabilize C3 convertases. Alternatively, stored properdin may be structurally different than serum properdin, either in its multimeric structure or in its posttranslational modifications. All properdin structure information has been derived from serum properdin. Thus, the future structural analysis of neutrophil/mast cell–derived properdin may deliver valuable clues to properdin function and regulation.

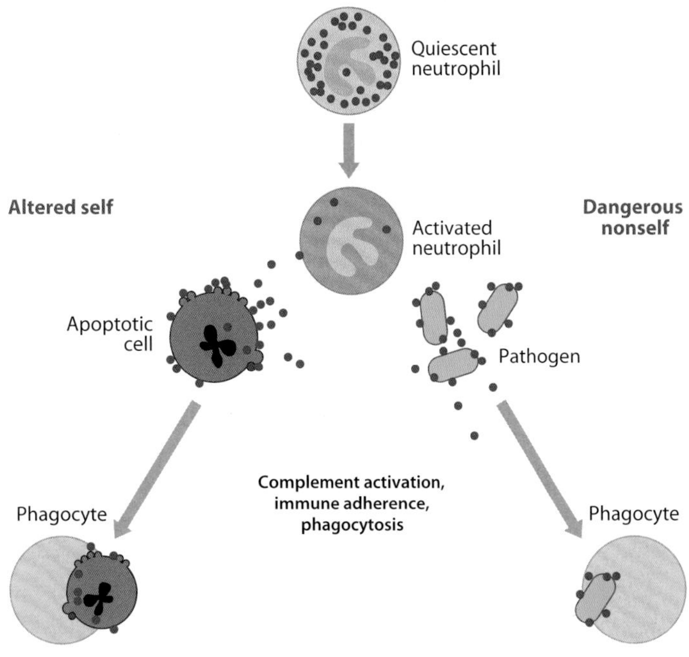

Figure 7

New model for properdin action. Properdin released from activated neutrophils binds to altered self (apoptotic cells) and dangerous nonself (microbial pathogens) cells, marking them for complement activation. Targets are then shuttled to the liver and spleen via red blood cell receptors (immune adherence) and undergo phagocytosis.

PROPERDIN AND DISEASE

Properdin and Infection

Complement-deficient individuals are highly vulnerable to *Neisseria meningitides* infection, with meningococcal disease frequencies at least

Lipooligosaccharide (LOS): a major surface component of *Neisseria* bacteria that consists of a lipid anchor and a "core" oligosaccharide

1000-fold greater than in normal individuals (103). Properdin-deficient individuals are similarly prone, with a disease frequency 3000-fold greater than normal and a mortality rate per disease episode of 34–63% (versus ~19% for normal individuals). Because properdin is encoded by a single gene carried on the short arm of the X chromosome (104), properdin-deficient individuals are usually found through analyses of families with multiple cases of fulminate male-specific meningococcal disease (103).

Properdin deficiency has been documented in over 25 families, and nearly all known properdin-deficient individuals are male (103, 105). There are three distinguishable deficient phenotypes [reviewed by Fijen et al. (105)]: In type 1 deficiency, the plasma is devoid of properdin; in type 2 deficiency, plasma properdin is greatly diminished (1–10% of normal values); finally, type 3 deficiency results in normal amounts of plasma properdin but the properdin is inactive. Most analyzed cases of properdin deficiency are of the type 1 phenotype, and in many of those cases the mutant properdin protein is truncated by a premature stop codon or interrupted by a frameshift mutation.

Properdin deficiency has also been associated with nonmeningococcal infections. In a recent report (106), properdin deficiency was associated with recurrent otitis media and pneumonia. Both CP and LP functions appeared normal in the four affected individuals, whereas AP activity was <2% of normal levels. The affected individuals carried a properdin gene encoding a protein that was truncated in TSR 3 and, therefore, properdin was expected to be nonfunctional. Recent studies that utilize properdin-deficient mice provide further evidence for properdin involvement in the clearance of infections. Stover et al. (102) showed that properdin-deficient mice were more vulnerable to polymicrobial septic peritonitis. In addition, if properdin plays an important role in bacterial clearance, then pathogens likely evolved measures to interfere with or avoid properdin function. The O antigen of gram-negative bacteria inhibits properdin:bacterial interactions (9) and may represent such an example. In another case, *Streptococcus pyogenes* produces exotoxin B (SPE B), a cysteine protease that degrades properdin and inhibits complement activation and complement-mediated phagocytosis (107). However, though SPE B appears to be a critical virulence factor, it targets a number of other host proteins as well, and thus the biological significance of its antiproperdin activity awaits further investigation.

Properdin plays important roles in antibacterial defense, but it is not yet certain whether pattern recognition is involved. In one case, Spitzer et al. (9) showed that *E. coli* strains with truncated LPS activate the AP very rapidly and also bind purified properdin readily, whereas wild-type strains activate the AP slowly and do not bind purified properdin. In another case, Kimura et al. (73) demonstrated that lipooligosaccharide (LOS), which is structurally similar to the truncated LPS, induces plasma C3 activation in wild-type mice but not in properdin-deficient animals. In both cases, the AP may be initiated by properdin:target recognition. Similarly, the recently described LPS-based ELISA assay of AP activity has been observed to be better at distinguishing properdin-deficient from wild-type sera than are the standard hemolytic assays (108, 109), possibly because properdin mutations that specifically disrupt target recognition may interfere with the LPS-based ELISA but not with the hemolysis assay (73, 109). A detailed structure/function analysis of the active sites of normal properdin and naturally occurring properdin mutants should help clarify these issues.

Properdin and Inflammatory/Autoimmune Diseases

The immune system is a potent weapon against dangerous intruders, but when not appropriately regulated it can turn against the host. Inappropriate activation or dysregulation of the complement AP is a critical factor in a number of autoimmune and injury states (110). The strongest evidence for AP involvement in many of these disease and/or injury states has been derived from analyses of wild-type versus fB null or fD null animals, but the specific mechanism(s) that direct(s) AP activation remain(s) unclear. In principle, properdin activity likely would be critical in all these cases, but in practice, with few exceptions, direct information pertaining to properdin involvement is sparse.

Proteinuria is regarded as a major contributor to tubulointerstitial injury associated with chronic kidney disease, and evidence has accumulated that unwanted complement activation is an underlying cause. Gaarkeuken et al. (84) hypothesized that properdin serves to focus complement activation on the tubular surface of affected patients. They demonstrated that (*a*) properdin is present on the tubular brush border of proteinuric human kidney biopsies but absent from normal kidney tissue; (*b*) purified properdin binds primary and immortalized proximal tubular epithelial cells (PTEC) but not members of a panel of immortalized human cell lines derived from other tissues; and (*c*) PTEC undergo C3 deposition when treated with human serum. Deposition was greatly diminished if properdin-depleted serum was used but could be regained if cells were pretreated with purified properdin prior to their exposure to properdin-depleted serum. This work clearly demonstrates the capacity of purified properdin to bind directly to kidney-derived epithelial cells and form a focal point for complement activation, but it has not yet been determined whether C3 is necessary to mediate initial properdin binding in the patient samples or in the treatment of cells with whole serum. Therefore, it is not yet clear what initiates properdin binding to the tubular cells.

Another recent analysis indicates that the AP plays a major role in the development of abdominal aortic aneurysms (AAAs). Pagano et al. (111) used an elastase-induced AAA mouse model and demonstrated that C5a and C3a, generated by AP activation, provide the signals to recruit neutrophils [which are another important mediator of the disease (112)] to the aortic wall. In this case, neutrophils may amplify AP activation by release of properdin (101). Significantly, Pagano et al. also examined the complement proteins deposited in human AAA specimens. Although C3, C4, factor B, properdin, and C5–9 neoantigen (a MAC antigen) were present throughout all layers of the aortic wall, C3, C4, and factor B were located predominantly along the medial and adventitial layers, whereas properdin and C5–9 neoantigen were also prominent along the luminal side (**Figure 8**). This finding suggests (but does not prove) that properdin could serve to

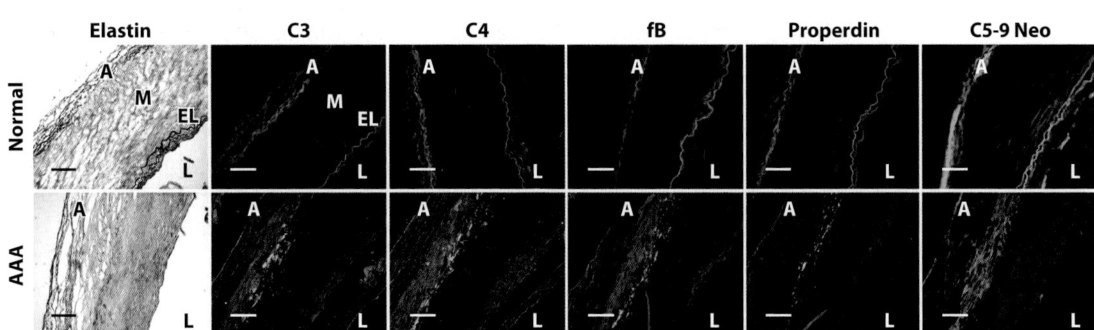

Figure 8

The alternative pathway is activated in human abdominal aortic aneurysms (AAAs). Immunohistochemistry of human aortic tissues reveals abundant C3, C4, fB, properdin, and C5–9 neoantigen (*red*) throughout all layers of aortic tissues in AAA but not in normal aortas. (A, adventitia; M, media; EL, elastic lamella; L, lumen.) Elastin in the aortic wall was detected by VVG (Verhoeff-Van Gieson) stain. The extensive remodeling in AAA obscures the distinct layers of the aortic wall. The elastic fibers autofluoresce (*green*). Scale bar, 0.2 mm. Photomicrographs shown are representative of three human AAA specimens. Figure derived from Reference 111.

focus complement activity on the luminal side and, thus, contribute to chronic inflation in the vasculature wall, a critical part of the pathologic process in this common disease.

Harmful inflammatory and autoimmune reactions may be initiated when cell integrity is breached as in late apoptosis and secondary necrosis (80). For example, systemic lupus erythematosus may be initiated by such events (113). Given the capacity for properdin to recognize and promote the elimination of apoptotic cells (above), it may be expected that properdin deficiency would have a significant impact on the safe removal of apoptotic and necrotic cells and, thus, be a cause of autoimmunity. No such relationship has yet been observed, however. Several explanations are possible:

1. Critical biological functions are often mediated by redundant pathways. In the case of apoptotic cell clearance, several other proteins, including the class B scavenger receptor (CD36), the classic phosphatidyl serine receptor, β_2-glycoprotein, and milk-fat globule epidermal growth factor 8 (MFGE8), recognize dying cells and promote their removal (114–116). Therefore, the effects of properdin deficiency on autoimmunity might be subtle unless some of these additional pathways are also compromised. It is also noteworthy that properdin may bind to only certain apoptotic cells: Thus far, properdin has been shown to recognize only apoptotic T cells (10), and properdin deficiency may therefore result in more limited effects on autoimmunity.
2. Harmful autoimmune reactions may be partially dependent on normal properdin activity: Renal disease in the mouse MRL/*lpr* lupus nephritis model is dependent on the AP convertase components factor B (117) and factor D (118) for the induction of pathologic complement deposition and cell death. Given that properdin is also important for convertase assembly, properdin deficiency could both impair the normal elimination of apoptotic cells and also protectively limit AP activation and, therefore, the capacity of necrotic cells to initiate inflammation. In fact, nearly all the properdin mutations reported were identified because of resulting meningococcal infection (103, 119). One might speculate that properdin mutations that interfere only with the recognition of apoptotic cells would more likely be susceptible to risk factors for autoimmunity than those causing complete properdin deficiency. Such mutations would not be identified as in the previous studies because they would not necessarily impart sensitivity to meningococcal disease.

PROPERDIN: OTHER FUNCTIONS?

The Removal of Debris

Higher organisms constantly generate undesirable matter, including oxidized lipids, lipoproteinaceous particles, misfolded and/or nondegradable proteins, and the membrane fragments and macromolecules released from damaged cells and lysed microbes. Presumably, this potentially dangerous debris should be eliminated without excessive tissue damage and without initiating autoimmune reactions. By the long-standing models, debris particles are recognized directly by complement, become opsonized with C3b and/or C4b, and undergo immune adherence, phagocytic uptake, and clearance. There is another possibility, based on the capacity of properdin to recognize danger-associated molecular patterns, that begins with complement-mediated recognition of an unrelated target (**Figure 9**): Once any target has activated complement, the AP amplification loop is engaged and the target surface becomes coated with properdin as well as with C3b. Because properdin can interact with a variety of polyanionic macromolecules (LPS, DNA, sulfatides), any properdin-opsonized target, in principle, should bind to polyanionic materials.

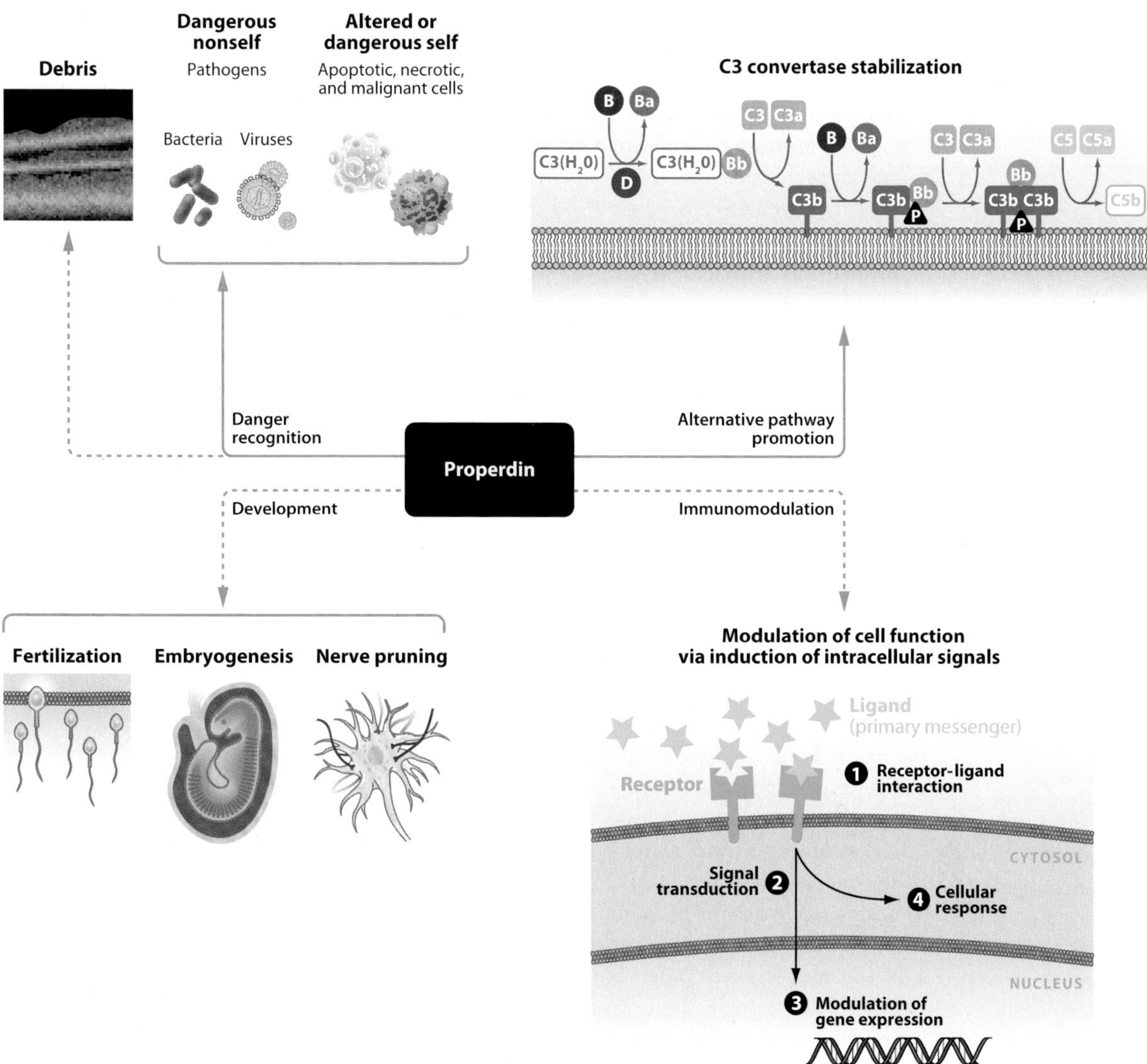

Figure 9

Properdin: established and potentially novel functions. Properdin recognizes danger signals on pathogens (*Neisseria*, *E. coli*, yeasts) and on dangerously altered self (i.e., apoptotic, necrotic, injured, or malignant) cells via the detection of certain GAGs. Properdin may also play a role in the recognition and removal of cellular debris. The properdin:target interaction induces rapid alternative pathway activation as well as target clearance by phagocytes. In addition, properdin stabilizes C3 convertases already formed on target surfaces and thereby promotes alternative pathway activation. Recognition of properdin by phagocytes/antigen-presenting cells (that is, DCs) induces intracellular signals within the DCs leading to modulation of cell function. Recent literature also suggests that properdin may be involved in developmental processes including fertilization and tissue/organ development. The solid arrows depict established functions of properdin, and the dashed arrows indicate potential novel functions.

In this scenario, the opsonized target acts as a debris magnet. It would bind to nearby polyanions that would be taken up by phagocytes along with the target. In the case of immune clearance, opsonized targets would become engaged to red blood cell receptors and continue to accumulate debris as they are shuttled through the intravasculature space to the liver or spleen for clearance. By this mechanism, elimination of pathogens or antigen:antibody complexes would also result in the removal of other undesirable material normally generated during an inflammatory reaction or normal homeostasis.

Properdin as Intracellular Signal Inducer

Properdin-dependent uptake of apoptotic cells by phagocytes can take place independently of further complement activation (see above). This suggests that DCs and macrophages express a properdin-recognizing protein/receptor on their cell surface and that the interaction of this receptor with properdin induces intracellular signals that, at the least, induce target cell uptake (10).

Antigen uptake by DCs and macrophages leads to antigen presentation and the subsequent induction of an immunogenic or tolerogenic response—the outcome is dependent on the nature of the antigen, the presence of sufficient danger signals, and the surrounding microenvironment (that is, release of C3a and C5a, cytokines, growth factors, and others) (120). In contrast to the uptake of pathogens by phagocytes, ingestion of apoptotic cells generally induces not an inflammatory but rather a tolerogenic response (120). Given that complement is involved in the instruction of the immune response at many levels including induction, control, and contraction (6), it is feasible that the tagging of apoptotic cells with properdin may not only induce their uptake but also transmit an instructing signal into the DC (**Figure 9**). This has indeed been shown for another complement component: The binding of iC3b to its receptor CR3 on DCs induces tolerogenic DCs that are unable to induce an effector T cell response (121, 122). Consequently, engagement of a properdin receptor on APCs in a steady-state or in the absence of sufficient additional danger signals may also be important in the maintenance of tolerance to self antigens.

Potential Crosstalk with Other Sentinel Systems

Misinterpretation of a signal derived from nondangerous nonself by complement is detrimental and can lead to chronic inflammation. However, failure to detect the presence of a pathogen may lead to uncontrolled infection and death. By this view, if properdin, as with CR3 (121, 122), is indeed involved in inducing tolerance or dampening inflammatory responses, its signaling pathways are likely susceptible to modulation by other danger-signaling pathways [i.e., TLRs, the Nod receptor system (23)] to ensure that the presence of real danger does not go undetected. Such cross-communication has been shown for the anaphylatoxin C5a receptor and TLRs and is important in optimized APC maturation and the induction of appropriate effector T cell responses (51, 123). In addition, we propose that, beside properdin's potential cross-signaling with other sentinel systems, a better understanding of the action and functional interrelationship of properdin with other complement regulatory proteins (i.e., CD46 and CD55) and receptors (which ultimately regulate the availability of complement activation fragments) may provide a platform to control properdin function for potential therapeutic usage.

Possible Roles in Development

Although complement is a first line of defense against pathogens and participates in the recognition and removal of altered self and cell debris, complement can also serve developmental functions. For example, during development of the neural network, certain synapses undergo a pruning process that eliminates most of the electrophysiologically weak connections and reorganizes the remaining strong circuits (124). Stevens et al. (125) examined development of the visual system in the mouse and discovered that complement plays an essential role in this process. In another example, Riley-Vargas et al. (126) showed that the inner acrosomal membrane of human sperm, exposed after the sperm makes contact with the zona pellucida, is subject to efficient localized complement activation that is then arrested after C3 deposition. It was proposed that this "limited and restricted" complement activation facilitated further sperm:egg interactions. McLin and collaborators undertook a systematic analysis of complement gene expression during embryonic development of the African clawed frog, *Xenopus laevis* (127). Several remarkable patterns were observed during early development including that of properdin, which is expressed in the neural plate and neural precursor tissue and later in the hindbrain and developing lens. Given the capacity of properdin to recognize cell surfaces, properdin may serve during development to mediate cell:cell interactions, either directly or through limited and restricted AP activation (**Figure 9**) (126). These few cases could portend many more examples once the possible involvement of complement in developmental processes is more widely considered.

CONCLUDING REMARKS

Host survival is dependent on the rapid recognition and elimination of harmful entities including pathogens and necrotic, malignant, or infected cells. The innate immune system constantly monitors a spectrum of biological agents including those of self, altered self, and nonself. Here, we review the recent findings indicating that the complement protein properdin is a pattern-recognition molecule that can distinguish nonself and altered self from self. Targets tagged with properdin are marked for clearance by scavenger cells, even in the absence of complement activation. Therefore, properdin could play multiple roles in the safe elimination of dangerous agents. Nevertheless, though the current evidence presents a compelling case for the importance of properdin in host defense and disease, the mechanism(s) underlying its critical activities in vivo are not yet well established. These important issues await future studies.

SUMMARY POINTS

1. Properdin is a pattern-recognition molecule that recognizes microbial surfaces and apoptotic, necrotic, and certain malignant cells.
2. Once bound to a target, properdin can initiate the assembly of C3 and C5 convertases, leading to target uptake and/or lysis.
3. Properdin can bind cells via GAG chains of surface proteoglycans.
4. Properdin bound to a target can mediate phagocytic uptake without further participation of complement proteins.
5. Properdin released from activated neutrophils may play a major role in pattern recognition, whereas plasma properdin may primarily stabilize convertase.
6. Properdin pattern recognition activity may play a role in inflammatory/autoimmune diseases.

FUTURE ISSUES

1. What is the role of properdin in human disease? (This issue will soon be elucidated in part using properdin-deficient mice and mouse disease models.)
2. What is the function of serum properdin compared with the properdin released from storage granules of cells?

3. Is properdin pattern recognition activity regulated in the blood?
4. Is properdin a signaling molecule? Are there properdin receptors?
5. Are certain properdin mutations risk factors for autoimmune disease?
6. Does properdin recognize virus-infected cells and/or malignant cells?
7. Does properdin play a role in mammalian development?
8. Will properdin be a useful therapeutic target?

DISCLOSURE STATEMENT

The authors are not aware of any affiliations, memberships, funding, or financial holdings that might be perceived as affecting the objectivity of this review.

ACKNOWLEDGMENTS

We gratefully acknowledge our properdin collaborators, Dirk Spitzer, Lynne Mitchell, and LiJuan Zhang, and all our colleagues who have offered their valuable insights and/or reagents. We thank Madonna Bogacki for help with the manuscript. We were supported by NIH grant R01 AI051436-07 (to D.E.H.), NIH grant U 19 AI070489 (to J.P.A.), the American Asthma Foundation (to J.P.A.), and the Kidney Patient Association UK (C.K.). The content of this review is solely the responsibility of the authors and does not necessarily represent the official views of the National Institute of Allergy and Infectious Diseases or the National Institutes of Health.

LITERATURE CITED

1. Whaley K. 1985. An introduction to the complement system. In *Methods in Complement for Clinical Immunologists*, ed. K Whaley, pp. 1–20. Edinburgh: Churchill Livingstone
2. Volanakis JE. 1998. Overview of the complement system. See Reference 7, pp. 9–32
3. Whaley K. 1985. Measurement of complement. In *Methods in Complement for Clinical Immunologists*, ed. K Whaley, pp. 77–139. New York: Churchill Livingstone
4. Carroll MC. 2004. The complement system in regulation of adaptive immunity. *Nat. Immunol.* 5:981–86
5. Fearon DT, Locksley RM. 1996. The instructive role of innate immunity in the acquired immune response. *Science* 272:50–54
6. Kemper C, Atkinson JP. 2007. T-cell regulation: with complements from innate immunity. *Nat. Rev. Immunol.* 7:9–18
7. Volanakis JE, Frank MM. 1998. *The Human Complement System in Health and Disease*. New York: Marcel Dekker
8. Hourcade D. 2006. The role of properdin in the assembly of the alternative pathway C3 convertases of complement. *J. Biol. Chem.* 281:2128–32
9. **Spitzer D, Mitchell LM, Atkinson JP, Hourcade DE. 2007. Properdin can initiate complement activation by binding specific target surfaces and providing a platform for de novo convertase assembly. *J. Immunol.* 179:2600–8**
10. **Kemper C, Mitchell LM, Zhang L, Hourcade DE. 2008. The complement protein properdin binds apoptotic T cells and promotes complement activation and phagocytosis. *Proc. Natl. Acad. Sci. USA* 105:9023–28**
11. Markiewski MM, Nilsson B, Ekdahl KN, Mollnes TE, Lambris JD. 2007. Complement and coagulation: strangers or partners in crime? *Trends Immunol.* 28:184–92

9. Demonstrates that purified properdin binds certain microbial surfaces and provides a platform for the assembly of functional convertases.

10. Shows that properdin binds apoptotic T cells and malignant cells and can promote phagocytosis without additional complement proteins.

12. Ollert MW, Kadlec JV, David K, Petrella EC, Bredehorst R, Vogel C-W. 1994. Antibody-mediated complement activation on nucleated cells. A quantitative analysis of the individual reaction steps. *J. Immunol.* 153:2213–21
13. Walport MJ. 2001. Complement. First of two parts. *N. Engl. J. Med.* 344:1058–66
14. Walport MJ. 2001. Complement. Second of two parts. *N. Engl. J. Med.* 344:1140–44
15. Davies KA, Walport MJ. 1998. Processing and clearance of immune complexes by complement and the role of complement in immune complex diseases. See Reference 7, pp. 423–53
16. Wright SD, Silverstein SC. 1983. Receptors for C3b and C3bi promote phagocytosis but not the release of toxic oxygen from human phagocytes. *J. Exp. Med.* 158:2016–23
17. Mevorach D, Mascarenhas JO, Gershov D, Elkon KB. 1998. Complement-dependent clearance of apoptotic cells by human macrophages. *J. Exp. Med.* 188:2313–20
18. Helmy KY, Katschke KJ Jr, Gorgani NN, Kljavin NM, Elliott JM, et al. 2006. CRIg: a macrophage complement receptor required for phagocytosis of circulating pathogens. *Cell* 124:915–27
19. Gerard NP, Gerard C. 1991. The chemotactic receptor for human C5a anaphylatoxin. *Nature* 349:614–17
20. Wetsel RA. 1995. Structure, function and cellular expression of complement anaphylatoxin receptors. *Curr. Opin. Immunol.* 7:48–53
21. Klos A, Tenner AJ, Johswich KO, Ager RR, Reis ES, Kohl J. 2009. The role of the anaphylatoxins in health and disease. *Mol. Immunol.* 46:2753–66
22. Guo RF, Ward PA. 2005. Role of C5a in inflammatory responses. *Annu. Rev. Immunol.* 23:821–52
23. Medzhitov R, Janeway C Jr. 2000. Innate immunity. *N. Engl. J. Med.* 343:338–44
24. Nussenzweig V, Bianco C, Dukor P, Eden A. 1971. Receptors for C3 on B lymphocytes: possible role in the immune response. In *Progress in Immunology*, ed. DB Amos, pp. 73–81. New York: Academic
25. Pepys MB. 1972. Role of complement in induction of the allergic response. *Nat. New Biol.* 237:157–59
26. Fearon DT, Wong WW. 1983. Complement ligand-receptor interactions that mediate biological responses. *Annu. Rev. Immunol.* 1:243–71
27. Fearon DT, Carter RH. 1995. The CD19/CR2/TAPA-1 complex of B lymphocytes: linking natural to acquired immunity. *Annu. Rev. Immunol.* 13:127–49
28. Dempsey PW, Allison ME, Akkaraju S, Goodnow CC, Fearon DT. 1996. C3d of complement as a molecular adjuvant: bridging innate and acquired immunity. *Science* 271:348–50
29. Molina H, Holers VM, Li B, Fang Y-F, Mariathasan S, et al. 1996. Markedly impaired humoral immune response in mice deficient in complement receptors 1 and 2. *Proc. Natl. Acad. Sci. USA* 93:3357–61
30. Fang Y, Xu C, Fu YX, Holers VM, Molina H. 1998. Expression of complement receptors 1 and 2 on follicular dendritic cells is necessary for the generation of a strong antigen-specific IgG response. *J. Immunol.* 160:5273–79
31. Barrington RA, Pozdnyakova O, Zafari MR, Benjamin CD, Carroll MC. 2002. B lymphocyte memory: role of stromal cell complement and FcγRIIB receptors. *J. Exp. Med.* 196:1189–99
32. Fleming SD, Shea-Donohue T, Guthridge JM, Kulik L, Waldschmidt TJ, et al. 2002. Mice deficient in complement receptors 1 and 2 lack a tissue injury-inducing subset of the natural antibody repertoire. *J. Immunol.* 169:2126–33
33. Reid RR, Woodcock S, Shimabukuro-Vornhagen A, Austen WG Jr, Kobzik L, et al. 2002. Functional activity of natural antibody is altered in Cr2-deficient mice. *J. Immunol.* 169:5433–40
34. Prodeus AP, Goerg S, Shen LM, Pozdnyakova O, Chu L, et al. 1998. A critical role for complement in maintenance of self-tolerance. *Immunity* 9:721–31
35. Pappworth IY, Kulik L, Haluszczak C, Reuter JW, Holers VM, Marchbank KJ. 2009. Increased B cell deletion and significantly reduced auto-antibody titer due to premature expression of human complement receptor 2 (CR2, CD21). *Mol. Immunol.* 46:1042–49
36. Morgan BP, Marchbank KJ, Longhi MP, Harris CL, Gallimore AM. 2005. Complement: central to innate immunity and bridging to adaptive responses. *Immunol. Lett.* 97:171–79
37. Longhi MP, Harris CL, Morgan BP, Gallimore A. 2006. Holding T cells in check—a new role for complement regulators? *Trends Immunol.* 27:102–8
38. Kopf M, Abel B, Gallimore A, Carroll MC, Bachmann MF. 2002. Complement component C3 promotes T-cell priming and lung migration to control acute influenza virus infection. *Nat. Med.* 8:373–78

39. Stager S, Alexander J, Kirby AC, Botto M, Van Rooijen N, et al. 2003. Natural antibodies and complement are endogenous adjuvants for vaccine-induced CD8+ T-cell responses. *Nat. Med.* 9:1287–92
40. Suresh M, Molina H, Salvato MS, Mastellos D, Lambris JD, Sandor M. 2003. Complement component 3 is required for optimal expansion of CD8 T cells during a systemic viral infection. *J. Immunol.* 170:788–94
41. Verschoor A, Brockman MA, Gadjeva M, Knipe DM, Carroll MC. 2003. Myeloid C3 determines induction of humoral responses to peripheral herpes simplex virus infection. *J. Immunol.* 171:5363–71
42. Jacquier-Sarlin MR, Gabert FM, Villiers MB, Colomb MG. 1995. Modulation of antigen processing and presentation by covalently linked complement C3b fragment. *Immunology* 84:164–70
43. Kerekes K, Cooper PD, Prechl J, Jozsi M, Bajtay Z, Erdei A. 2001. Adjuvant effect of gamma-inulin is mediated by C3 fragments deposited on antigen-presenting cells. *J. Leukoc. Biol.* 69:69–74
44. Zhou W, Patel H, Li K, Peng Q, Villiers MB, Sacks SH. 2006. Macrophages from C3-deficient mice have impaired potency to stimulate alloreactive T cells. *Blood* 107:2461–69
45. Drouin SM, Corry DB, Kildsgaard J, Wetsel RA. 2001. Cutting edge: the absence of C3 demonstrates a role for complement in Th2 effector functions in a murine model of pulmonary allergy. *J. Immunol.* 167:4141–45
46. Gerard NP, Gerard C. 2002. Complement in allergy and asthma. *Curr. Opin. Immunol.* 14:705–8
47. Kohl J, Baelder R, Lewkowich IP, Pandey MK, Hawlisch H, et al. 2006. A regulatory role for the C5a anaphylatoxin in type 2 immunity in asthma. *J. Clin. Invest.* 116:783–96
48. Hawlisch H, Belkaid Y, Baelder R, Hildeman D, Gerard C, Kohl J. 2005. C5a negatively regulates Toll-like receptor 4-induced immune responses. *Immunity* 22:415–26
49. Kim AH, Dimitriou ID, Holland MC, Mastellos D, Mueller YM, et al. 2004. Complement C5a receptor is essential for the optimal generation of antiviral CD8+ T cell responses. *J. Immunol.* 173:2524–29
50. Fang C, Miwa T, Shen H, Song WC. 2007. Complement-dependent enhancement of CD8+ T cell immunity to lymphocytic choriomeningitis virus infection in decay-accelerating factor-deficient mice. *J. Immunol.* 179:3178–86
51. Hawlisch H, Kohl J. 2006. Complement and Toll-like receptors: key regulators of adaptive immune responses. *Mol. Immunol.* 43:13–21
52. Zhang X, Kimura Y, Fang C, Zhou L, Sfyroera G, et al. 2007. Regulation of Toll-like receptor-mediated inflammatory response by complement in vivo. *Blood* 110:228–36
53. Heeger PS, Lalli PN, Lin F, Valujskikh A, Liu J, et al. 2005. Decay-accelerating factor modulates induction of T cell immunity. *J. Exp. Med.* 201:1523–30
54. Liu J, Miwa T, Hilliard B, Chen Y, Lambris JD, et al. 2005. The complement inhibitory protein DAF (CD55) suppresses T cell immunity in vivo. *J. Exp. Med.* 201:567–77
55. Longhi MP, Sivasankar B, Omidvar N, Morgan BP, Gallimore A. 2005. Cutting edge: murine CD59a modulates antiviral CD4+ T cell activity in a complement-independent manner. *J. Immunol.* 175:7098–102
56. Strainic MG, Liu J, Huang D, An F, Lalli PN, et al. 2008. Locally produced complement fragments C5a and C3a provide both costimulatory and survival signals to naive CD4+ T cells. *Immunity* 28:425–35
57. Kemper C, Chan AC, Green JM, Brett KA, Murphy KM, Atkinson JP. 2003. Activation of human CD4+ cells with CD3 and CD46 induces a T-regulatory cell 1 phenotype. *Nature* 421:388–92
58. Grossman WJ, Verbsky JW, Barchet W, Colonna M, Atkinson JP, Ley TJ. 2004. Human T regulatory cells can use the perforin pathway to cause autologous target cell death. *Immunity* 21:589–601
59. Wagner C, Hansch GM. 2006. Receptors for complement C3 on T-lymphocytes: relics of evolution or functional molecules? *Mol. Immunol.* 43:22–30
60. Hourcade D, Holers VM, Atkinson JP. 1989. The regulators of complement activation (RCA) gene cluster. *Adv. Immunol.* 45:381–416
61. Liszewski MK, Atkinson JP. 1998. Regulatory proteins of complement. See Reference 7, pp. 149–66

62. The first description of properdin and the complement AP.

62. **Pillemer L, Blum L, Lepow IH, Ross OA, Todd EW, Wardlaw AC. 1954. The properdin system and immunity. I. Demonstration and isolation of a new serum protein, properdin, and its role in immune phenomena. *Science* 120:279–85**
63. Ratnoff WD. 1980. A war with the molecules: Louis Pillemer and the history of properdin. *Perspect. Biol. Med.* 23:638–57

64. Nelson RA Jr. 1958. An alternative mechanism for the properdin system. *J. Exp. Med.* 108:515–35
65. Ecker EE. 1958. Louis Pillemer, 1908–1957. *J. Immunol.* 80:415–16
66. Lepow IH. 1980. Presidential address to American Association of Immunologists in Anaheim, California, April 16, 1980. Louis Pillemer, Properdin, and scientific controversy. *J. Immunol.* 125:471–75
67. Fearon DT. 1979. Activation of the alternative complement pathway. *CRC Crit. Rev. Immunol.* 1:1–32
68. Pangburn MK, Muller-Eberhard HJ. 1984. The alternative pathway of complement. *Springer Semin. Immunopathol.* 7:163–92
69. Pangburn MK, Muller-Eberhard HJ. 1986. The C3 convertase of the alternative pathway of human complement. Enzymic properties of the bimolecular proteinase. *Biochem. J.* 235:723–30
70. Medicus RG, Gotze O, Muller-Eberhard HJ. 1976. Alternative pathway of complement: recruitment of precursor properdin by the labile C3/C5 convertase and the potentiation of the pathway. *J. Exp. Med.* 144:1076–93
71. **Fearon DT, Austen KF. 1975. Properdin: binding to C3b and stabilization of the C3b-dependent C3 convertase. *J. Exp. Med.* 142:856–63**
72. **Farries TC, Lachmann PJ, Harrison RA. 1988. Analysis of the interactions between properdin, the third component of complement (C3), and its physiological activation products. *Biochem. J.* 252:47–54**
73. Kimura Y, Miwa T, Zhou L, Song WC. 2008. Activator-specific requirement of properdin in the initiation and amplification of the alternative pathway complement. *Blood* 11:732–40
74. Kerr JF, Wyllie AH, Currie AR. 1972. Apoptosis: a basic biological phenomenon with wide-ranging implications in tissue kinetics. *Br. J. Cancer* 26:239–57
75. Krammer PH. 2000. CD95's deadly mission in the immune system. *Nature* 407:789–95
76. Savill J, Fadok V. 2000. Corpse clearance defines the meaning of cell death. *Nature* 407:784–88
77. Huynh ML, Fadok VA, Henson PM. 2002. Phosphatidylserine-dependent ingestion of apoptotic cells promotes TGF-β1 secretion and the resolution of inflammation. *J. Clin. Invest.* 109:41–50
78. Nauta AJ, Daha MR, van Kooten C, Roos A. 2003. Recognition and clearance of apoptotic cells: a role for complement and pentraxins. *Trends Immunol.* 24:148–54
79. Roos A, Xu W, Castellano G, Nauta AJ, Garred P, et al. 2004. Mini-review: a pivotal role for innate immunity in the clearance of apoptotic cells. *Eur. J. Immunol.* 34:921–29
80. Savill J, Dransfield I, Gregory C, Haslett C. 2002. A blast from the past: clearance of apoptotic cells regulates immune responses. *Nat. Rev. Immunol.* 2:965–75
81. Jones J, Morgan BP. 1995. Apoptosis is associated with reduced expression of complement regulatory molecules, adhesion molecules and other receptors on polymorphonuclear leucocytes: functional relevance and role in inflammation. *Immunology* 86:651–60
82. Elward K, Griffiths M, Mizuno M, Harris CL, Neal JW, et al. 2005. CD46 plays a key role in tailoring innate immune recognition of apoptotic and necrotic cells. *J. Biol. Chem.* 280:36342–54
83. Xu W, Berger SP, Trouw LA, de Boer HC, Schlagwein N, et al. 2008. Properdin binds to late apoptotic and necrotic cells independently of C3b and regulates alternative pathway complement activation. *J. Immunol.* 180:7613–21
84. Gaarkeuken H, Siezenga MA, Zuidwijk K, van Kooten C, Rabelink TJ, et al. 2008. Complement activation by tubular cells is mediated by properdin binding. *Am. J. Physiol. Renal. Physiol.* 295:F1397–403
85. Sjoblom T, Jones S, Wood LD, Parsons DW, Lin J, et al. 2006. The consensus coding sequences of human breast and colorectal cancers. *Science* 314:268–74
86. **Nolan KF, Schwaeble W, Kaluz S, Dierich MP, Reid KB. 1991. Molecular cloning of the cDNA coding for properdin, a positive regulator of the alternative pathway of human complement. *Eur. J. Immunol.* 21:771–76**
87. **Smith CA, Pangburn MK, Vogel CW, Muller-Eberhard HJ. 1984. Molecular architecture of human properdin, a positive regulator of the alternative pathway of complement. *J. Biol. Chem.* 259:4582–88**
88. Pangburn MK. 1989. Analysis of the natural polymeric forms of human properdin and their functions in complement activation. *J. Immunol.* 142:202–7

71. Shows that properdin binds C3b and stabilizes the AP convertase.

72. Examines properdin interactions with surface-bound C3b, C3bB and C3bBb, and proposes a model to account for properdin activity that is based on its polymeric structure.

86. Describes the cloning of the properdin cDNA and provides the first description of the properdin primary structure.

87. Provides the visualization of properdin polymeric structures.

89. Sun Z, Reid KB, Perkins SJ. 2004. The dimeric and trimeric solution structures of the multidomain complement protein properdin by X-ray scattering, analytical ultracentrifugation and constrained modelling. *J. Mol. Biol.* 343:1327–43

90. Determines the crystal structure of two TSR domains of thrombospondin.

90. Tan K, Duquette M, Liu JH, Dong Y, Zhang R, et al. 2002. Crystal structure of the TSP-1 type 1 repeats: a novel layered fold and its biological implication. *J. Cell Biol.* 159:373–82

91. Tucker RP. 2004. The thrombospondin type 1 repeat superfamily. *Int. J. Biochem. Cell Biol.* 36:969–74

92. Panetti TS, Kudryk BJ, Mosher DF. 1999. Interaction of recombinant procollagen and properdin modules of thrombospondin-1 with heparin and fibrinogen/fibrin. *J. Biol. Chem.* 274:430–37

93. Tossavainen H, Pihlajamaa T, Huttunen TK, Raulo E, Rauvala H, et al. 2006. The layered fold of the TSR domain of *P. falciparum* TRAP contains a heparin binding site. *Protein Sci.* 15:1760–68

94. Esko JD, Selleck SB. 2002. Order out of chaos: assembly of ligand binding sites in heparan sulfate. *Annu. Rev. Biochem.* 71:435–71

95. Yu H, Munoz EM, Edens RE, Linhardt RJ. 2005. Kinetic studies on the interactions of heparin and complement proteins using surface plasmon resonance. *Biochim. Biophys. Acta* 1726:168–76

96. Zhang L, Lawrence R, Frazier BA, Esko JD. 2006. CHO glycosylation mutants: proteoglycans. *Methods Enzymol.* 416:205–21

97. Nolan KF, Reid KB. 1993. Properdin. *Methods Enzymol.* 223:35–46

98. Schwaeble W, Huemer HP, Most J, Dierich MP, Strobel M, et al. 1994. Expression of properdin in human monocytes. *Eur. J. Biochem.* 219:759–64

99. Schwaeble W, Dippold WG, Schafer MK, Pohla H, Jonas D, et al. 1993. Properdin, a positive regulator of complement activation, is expressed in human T cell lines and peripheral blood T cells. *J. Immunol.* 151:2521–28

100. Demonstrates that properdin is stored in neutrophil granules and released upon cell stimulation.

100. Wirthmueller U, Dewald B, Thelen M, Schafer MK, Stover C, et al. 1997. Properdin, a positive regulator of complement activation, is released from secondary granules of stimulated peripheral blood neutrophils. *J. Immunol.* 158:4444–51

101. Proposes that properdin connects humoral and cellular immunity.

101. Schwaeble WJ, Reid KB. 1999. Does properdin crosslink the cellular and the humoral immune response? *Immunol. Today* 20:17–21

102. Stover CM, Luckett JC, Echtenacher B, Dupont A, Figgitt SE, et al. 2008. Properdin plays a protective role in polymicrobial septic peritonitis. *J. Immunol.* 180:3313–18

103. Densen P. 1989. Interaction of complement with *Neisseria meningitidis* and *Neisseria gonorrhoeae*. *Clin. Microbiol. Rev.* 2(Suppl.):S11–17

104. Goundis D, Holt SM, Boyd Y, Reid KBM. 1989. Localization of properdin structural locus to Xp11.23-Xp21.1. *Genomics* 5:56–60

105. Fijen CAP, von den Bogaard R, Schipper M, Nanhens M, Schlesinger M, et al. 1999. Properdin deficiency: molecular basis and disease association. *Mol. Immunol.* 36:863–68

106. Schejbel L, Rosenfeldt V, Marquart H, Valerius NH, Garred P. 2009. Properdin deficiency associated with recurrent otitis media and pneumonia, and identification of male carrier with Klinefelter syndrome. *Clin. Immunol.* 131:456–62

107. Tsao N, Tsai WH, Lin YS, Chuang WJ, Wang CH, Kuo CF. 2006. Streptococcal pyrogenic exotoxin B cleaves properdin and inhibits complement-mediated opsonophagocytosis. *Biochem. Biophys. Res. Commun.* 339:779–84

108. Seelen MA, Roos A, Wieslander J, Mollnes TE, Sjoholm AG, et al. 2005. Functional analysis of the classical, alternative, and MBL pathways of the complement system: standardization and validation of a simple ELISA. *J. Immunol. Methods* 296:187–98

109. Harboe M, Mollnes TE. 2008. The alternative complement pathway revisited. *J. Cell Mol. Med.* 12:1074–84

110. Holers VM. 2008. The spectrum of complement alternative pathway-mediated diseases. *Immunol. Rev.* 223:300–16

111. Pagano MB, Zhou HF, Ennis TL, Wu X, Lambris JD, et al. 2009. Complement-dependent neutrophil recruitment is critical for the development of elastase-induced abdominal aortic aneurysm. *Circulation* 119:1805–13

112. Cohen JR, Parikh S, Grella L, Sarfati I, Corbie G, et al. 1993. Role of the neutrophil in abdominal aortic aneurysm development. *Cardiovasc. Surg.* 1:373–76

113. Korb LC, Ahearn JM. 1997. C1q binds directly and specifically to surface blebs of apoptotic human keratinocytes. *J. Immunol.* 158:4525–28
114. Ren Y, Silverstein RL, Allen J, Savill J. 1995. CD36 gene transfer confers capacity for phagocytosis of cells undergoing apoptosis. *J. Exp. Med.* 181:1857–62
115. Verhoven B, Schlegel RA, Williamson P. 1995. Mechanisms of phosphatidylserine exposure, a phagocyte recognition signal, on apoptotic T lymphocytes. *J. Exp. Med.* 182:1597–601
116. Fadok VA, Bratton DL, Rose DM, Pearson A, Ezekewitz RA, Henson PM. 2000. A receptor for phosphatidylserine-specific clearance of apoptotic cells. *Nature* 405:85–90
117. Watanabe H, Garnier G, Circolo A, Wetsel RA, Ruiz P, et al. 2000. Modulation of renal disease in MRL/*lpr* mice genetically deficient in the alternative complement pathway factor B. *J. Immunol.* 164:786–94
118. Elliott MK, Jarmi T, Ruiz P, Xu Y, Holers VM, Gilkeson GS. 2004. Effects of complement factor D deficiency on the renal disease of MRL/*lpr* mice. *Kidney Int.* 65:129–38
119. Fijen CAP, Kuijper EJ, te Bulte MT, Daha MR, Dankert J. 1999. Assessment of complement deficiency in patients with meningococcal disease in the Netherlands. *Clin. Infect. Dis.* 28:98–105
120. Green DR, Ferguson T, Zitvogel L, Kroemer G. 2009. Immunogenic and tolerogenic cell death. *Nat. Rev. Immunol.* 9:353–63
121. Skoberne M, Somersan S, Almodovar W, Truong T, Petrova K, et al. 2006. The apoptotic-cell receptor CR3, but not $\alpha v\beta 5$, is a regulator of human dendritic-cell immunostimulatory function. *Blood* 108:947–55
122. Sohn J-H, Bora PS, Suk H-J, Molina H, Kaplan HJ, Bora NS. 2003. Tolerance is dependent on complement C3 fragment iC3b binding to antigen-presenting cells. *Nat. Med.* 9:206–12
123. Zhang X, Kimura Y, Fang C, Zhou L, Sfyroera G, et al. 2007. Regulation of Toll-like receptor-mediated inflammatory response by complement in vivo. *Blood* 110:228–36
124. Fourgeaud L, Boulanger LM. 2007. Synapse remodeling, compliments of the complement system. *Cell* 131:1034–36
125. Stevens B, Allen NJ, Vazquez LE, Howell GR, Christopherson KS, et al. 2007. The classical complement cascade mediates CNS synapse elimination. *Cell* 131:1164–78
126. Riley-Vargas RC, Lanzendorf S, Atkinson JP. 2005. Targeted and restricted complement activation on acrosome-reacted spermatozoa. *J. Clin. Invest.* 115:1241–49
127. McLin VA, Hu CH, Shah R, Jamrich M. 2008. Expression of complement components coincides with early patterning and organogenesis in *Xenopus laevis*. *Int. J. Dev. Biol.* 52:1123–33
128. DeLano WL. 2002. *The PyMOL Molecular Graphics System*. Palo Alto, CA: DeLano Scientific

An Integrated View of Humoral Innate Immunity: Pentraxins as a Paradigm

Barbara Bottazzi,[1] Andrea Doni,[1] Cecilia Garlanda,[1] and Alberto Mantovani[2]

[1]Laboratory for Immunology and Inflammation, IRCCS Istituto Clinico Humanitas, Rozzano (Milano) 20089, Italy; email: barbara.bottazzi@humanitas.it, andrea.doni@humanitas.it, cecilia.garlanda@humanitas.it

[2]Laboratory for Immunology and Inflammation, IRCCS Istituto Clinico Humanitas, Rozzano (Milano), and Department of Translational Medicine, University of Milano, Milano 20089, Italy; email: alberto.mantovani@humanitas.it

Annu. Rev. Immunol. 2010. 28:157–83

First published online as a Review in Advance on December 7, 2009

The *Annual Review of Immunology* is online at immunol.annualreviews.org

This article's doi:
10.1146/annurev-immunol-030409-101305

0732-0582/10/0423-0157$20.00

Key Words

C reactive protein, serum amyloid P component, ficolins, collectins, complement, phagocytes

Abstract

The innate immune system consists of a cellular and a humoral arm. Pentraxins (e.g., the short pentraxin C reactive protein and the long pentraxin PTX3) are key components of the humoral arm of innate immunity which also includes complement components, collectins, and ficolins. In response to microorganisms and tissue damage, neutrophils, macrophages, and dendritic cells are major sources of fluid-phase pattern-recognition molecules (PRMs) belonging to different molecular classes. Humoral PRMs in turn interact with and regulate cellular effectors. Effector mechanisms of the humoral innate immune system include activation and regulation of the complement cascade; agglutination and neutralization; facilitation of recognition via cellular receptors (opsonization); and regulation of inflammation. Thus, the humoral arm of innate immunity is an integrated system consisting of different molecules and sharing functional outputs with antibodies.

PRM: pattern-recognition molecule

TLR: Toll-like receptor

CRP: C reactive protein

SAP: serum amyloid P component

INTRODUCTION

Innate immunity is a first line of resistance against pathogens, and it plays a key role in the activation and orientation of adaptive immunity and in the maintenance of tissue integrity and repair. As with adaptive immunity, the innate immune system consists of a cellular and a humoral arm. Cell-associated pattern-recognition molecules (PRMs) are strategically located in different cellular compartments (plasma membrane, endosomes, cytoplasm) and belong to different molecular classes, such as the Toll-like receptors (TLRs), the NOD- and RIG-like receptors, and the scavenger receptors (**Figure 1**).

A component of the humoral innate immune system, the pentraxin C reactive protein (CRP) was the first PRM to be identified (1–4). Fluid-phase PRMs belong to different molecular families, including collectins (5), ficolins (6), and pentraxins (3). Humoral PRMs represent functional ancestors of antibodies (ante-antibodies). Whereas cellular innate immunity is currently in the research limelight, the humoral innate immune system is frequently perceived as a world apart, consisting of a heterogeneous collection of weird molecules.

Here, we review the key components and properties of the humoral arm of innate immunity, with emphasis on pentraxins, which we use as a paradigm. In particular, we surmise that humoral PRMs form an integrated system of diverse molecules, with complementary specificity, tissue distribution, and mode of production. Despite molecular diversity, humoral PRMs share a basic, evolutionarily conserved mode of action (complement activation, agglutination and neutralization, opsonization). Moreover, a bidirectional interaction between the humoral and the cellular arms sustains and regulates innate responses.

PENTRAXINS

Pentraxins constitute a superfamily of evolutionarily conserved proteins, characterized by a cyclic multimeric structure and by the presence in C terminus of a 200 amino acid pentraxin domain, with an 8 amino acid–long conserved pentraxin signature (HxCxS/TWxS, where x is any amino acid) (3, 7). They are prototypic components of the humoral arm of innate immunity. CRP and serum amyloid P component (SAP) together constitute the short pentraxin arm of the superfamily. Pentraxin 3 (PTX3) and other subsequently identified proteins (3) represent the long pentraxin arm: The members were originally identified as cytokine-inducible genes or molecules expressed in specific tissues (e.g., neurons, spermatozoa).

Pentraxins are conserved in evolution from arachnids and insects to humans. Their conservation is testimony to their role in complex organisms. Structural analysis and genetically modified mice have provided a new level of understanding of the role of pentraxins in immunity and homeostasis. Unlike the classic short pentraxins CRP and SAP, whose sequence and regulation have diverged between mouse and human, PTX3 is highly conserved in human and mouse. Thus, results obtained using genetic approaches in the mouse are likely to be informative for the function of PTX3 in human (3), whereas extrapolation from animals to human is more difficult for CRP and SAP (2).

Short Pentraxins: C Reactive Protein and Serum Amyloid P Component

The first pentraxin described was CRP, identified in human serum in the 1930s as the prototypic acute-phase response protein (1, 3). Human SAP was subsequently identified as a relative of CRP on the basis of amino acid sequence identity (51%) (8). CRP and SAP orthologs in different mammal species share substantial sequence similarity; notable differences include serum basal levels and changes during the acute-phase response, with CRP and SAP being the main acute-phase reactants in human and mouse, respectively. In the arthropod *Limulus polyphemus*, different forms of CRP and SAP were identified as abundant constituents of the hemolymph involved in recognizing and destroying pathogens.

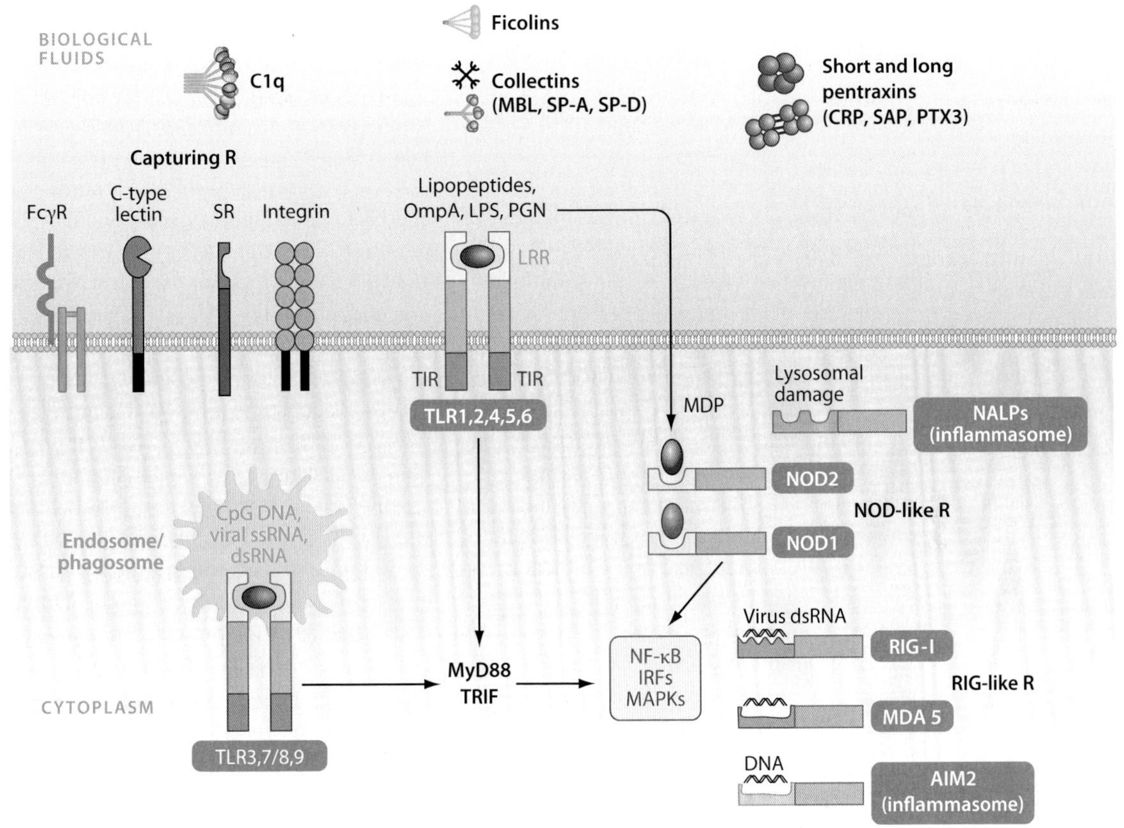

Figure 1

The humoral and cellular arms of innate immunity: a schematic view. Fluid-phase PRMs belong to different molecular families, including collectins (MBL, SP-A, SP-D), ficolins, C1q, and pentraxins (CRP, SAP, PTX3). Cell-associated PRMs are strategically located in different cellular compartments (plasma membrane, endosomes, cytoplasm) and belong to different molecular classes (e.g., TLRs, scavenger receptors, lectin receptors), some of which are shown here. The TLRs and the NOD- and RIG-like receptors are signaling receptors that lead to activation of transcription factors, including NF-κB, IRFs, and MAPKs. The scavenger receptors, C-type lectins, integrins, and FcγR are capturing receptors. TLRs recognize microbial moieties. RIG-like receptors recognize viral double-strand RNA and AIM2 recognizes DNA, inducing production of type 1 interferon. Peptidoglycan-derived units (e.g., MDP) are recognized by NODs and by NALP3, a component of the inflammasome. NALPs are also activated by different danger signals, including lysosomal damage. Conserved domains, such as the TIR domain or LRR domain, are shown. (Abbreviations used: CRP, C reactive protein; LPS, lipopolysaccharide; LRR, leucine-rich repeat; MAPK, mitogen-activated protein kinase; MBL, mannan-binding lectin; MDA5, melanoma-differentiation-associated gene 5; MDP, muramyl dipeptide; NALPs, NACHT-LRR-PYD-containing proteins; NF-κB, nuclear factor-κB; NOD, nucleotide-binding oligomerization domain; OmpA, Outer membrane protein A; PGN, peptidoglycan; PTX3, pentraxin 3; RIG-I, retinoic acid–inducible gene I; SAP, serum amyloid P component; SP-A/-D, surfactant protein A/D; SR, scavenger receptor; TIR, Toll/interleukin-1 receptor domain; TLR, Toll-like receptor; TRIF, Toll-IL-1 receptor domain-containing adaptor-inducing interferon-β.)

Structure. The *CRP* gene is located on chromosome 1q23 and is organized in two exons, the first coding for the leader peptide and the first two amino acids of the mature protein and the second coding for the remaining 204 amino acids. Human CRP is composed of five identical nonglycosylated protomers with a total molecular weight of 115 kDa. The amino acid

LPS: lipopolysaccharide

sequence includes two cysteines in positions 36 and 97 conserved in all the members of the pentraxin family and involved in intrachain disulfide bonds (9). SAP is a glycoprotein made up of five noncovalently attached subunits of 23 kDa each.

Production. CRP levels in the plasma of healthy adults are barely detectable (≤3 mg/l), but they increase as much as 1000-fold following an acute-phase stimulus as a result of accelerated rates of transcription in the liver, mainly in response to the proinflammatory cytokine IL-6 (7). Expression of CRP mRNA in tissues other than the liver has also been reported, but apparently extra hepatic sources do not contribute to CRP plasma levels. CRP has been extensively used clinically for over 75 years as a nonspecific systemic marker of infection, inflammation, and tissue damage.

SAP is produced exclusively by hepatocytes and is the main acute-phase protein in mice, whereas in human serum it is constitutively present at 30 to 50 mg/l.

Ligand specificity and function. The physiological functions attributed to pentraxins involve recognition and binding to different ligands, mostly in a Ca^{2+}-dependent manner. A list of selected ligands recognized by PTX3, CRP, and SAP is provided in **Table 1**. However, the relationship between ligand binding and function of pentraxins is a matter of debate (10).

The first ligand described for CRP was the C-polysaccharide of *Streptococcus pneumoniae*: This interaction is due to a direct binding of CRP to phosphorylcholine (PC), a major constituent of C-type capsule polysaccharides. Moreover, CRP binds various microorganisms, including fungi, yeasts, bacteria, and parasites (*Plasmodium*, *Leishmania*) through PC and carbohydrate structures, promoting phagocytosis and resistance to infections (11). Binding to bacteria is not always necessary for protection because CRP also protects mice from infection with *Salmonella typhimurium*, a pathogen to which CRP does not bind (12). Furthermore, CRP-mediated activation of the classical complement pathway (see below) has no role in protecting mice against *S. pneumoniae* infection (13).

Like CRP, SAP binds various bacteria, such as *Streptococcus pyogenes* and *Neisseria meningitidis* (14). Moreover, binding to influenza virus has also been reported (15). SAP binds to several bacteria via lipopolysaccharide (LPS) and prevents LPS-mediated complement activation and LPS toxicity (14, 16). However, for certain organisms to which SAP binds, such as *S. pyogenes* and rough strains of *Escherichia coli*, SAP enhances virulence by protecting the bacteria against phagocytosis, whereas it is protective in infection with organisms to which it does not bind, for instance *Listeria monocytogenes* (14).

CRP binds to modified low-density lipoprotein (LDL) via the PC and cholesterol moieties present on LDL (17) and colocalizes with LDL in human atherosclerotic lesions. However, CRP is neither atheroprotective nor proatherogenic in mouse models of human atherosclerosis (2). An analysis of the role of CRP as a cardiovascular risk factor (e.g., 18) is beyond the scope of this review. However, it is interesting that polymorphisms in the *CRP* gene that are associated with marked increases in CRP levels are not associated with an increased risk of ischemic vascular disease (19, 20).

Pentraxins recognize damaged cells and their constituents and are implicated in in vivo disposal of apoptotic cells. Human CRP binds to the membranes of damaged cells and apoptotic cells during late phases of apoptosis, via various phospholipids (PC and phosphoethanolamine) and small nuclear ribonucleoprotein particles and chromatin/nucleolar components that redistribute to the plasma membrane during late apoptosis (7). Human SAP binds in vivo to chromatin (21).

CRP and SAP, aggregated or attached to most of their ligands, interact with the globular head modules of C1q, the recognition subunit of the classical complement pathway (**Figure 2**), and activate the classical complement cascade (22). The three-dimensional structure of CRP shows the presence of a deep, extended cleft in each protomer on the face of

Table 1 Ligands recognized by pattern-recognition molecules

Pattern-recognition molecules	Producers[a]	Ligands
Short pentraxins (CRP, SAP)	Liver (hepatocytes)	■ Complement components (C1q, Factor H, L-ficolin, M-ficolin) ■ Microorganisms (bacteria, viruses, fungi, parasites) ■ Phosphorylcoline, carbohydrates ■ Modified LDLs ■ ECM protein (fibronectin, collagen IV, laminin, proteoglycans) ■ Amyloid fibrils ■ DNA
Long pentraxins (PTX3)	Monocytes, MΦ, PMN, EC, DC, fibroblasts, epithelial cells	■ Complement components (C1q, Factor H, L-ficolin) ■ Microorganisms (bacteria, viruses, fungi) and microbial moieties (OmpA) ■ ECM protein (IαI, TSG-6) ■ Apoptotic cells ■ FGF2
C1q	MΦ, DC, EC	■ Fc portion of immunoglobulin ■ Pentraxins (CRP, SAP, PTX3) ■ Microorganisms and microbial moieties (LPS, lipid A, Omps) ■ Aβ peptide of prions ■ ECM protein (fibronectin, laminin, fibromodulin, osteoadherin) ■ Apoptotic cells
Collectins (MBL, SP-A, SP-D)	Liver (hepatocytes), lung (type II alveolar cells), MΦ	■ Carbohydrates ■ Microorganisms and microbial moieties (LPS, LOS, LTA, PDG)
Ficolins	Liver (hepatocytes), lung (type II alveolar cells), PMN, monocytes	■ Carbohydrates ■ Microorganisms and microbial moieties (LTA, PDG, 1,3-β-D-glucan)
Properdin	Monocytes, MΦ, PMN, mast cells	■ Complement components (C3b) ■ Microorganisms, zymosan
SAA	Liver (hepatocytes, monocytes, MΦ)	■ Microorganisms and microbial moieties (OmpA)
Mindin	Spleen, lymph nodes	■ Microorganisms and microbial moieties (LPS, LTA)

[a]This column reports the main cellular sources of PRM, with particular emphasis on cells of the innate immune system.
Abbreviations: CRP, C reactive protein; DC, dendritic cell; EC, endothelial cell; ECM, extracellular matrix; IαI, inter-α-trypsin inhibitor; LDL, low-density lipoprotein; LPS, lipopolysaccharide; LOS, lipooligosaccharide; LTA, lipotheicoic acid; MΦ, macrophage; Omp, Outer membrane protein; PDG, peptidoglycan; PMN, polymorphonuclear cell; SAA, serum amyloid A; SAP, serum amyloid P component; TSG-6, TNF-α-induced protein 6.

the pentamer opposite that containing the PC-binding sites. Mutational analysis of residues participating in the formation of this pocket identified the amino acids involved in C1q binding and complement activation (23).

Complement activation by short pentraxins may be one of the mechanisms leading to the removal of cellular debris (24). When bound to self surfaces (e.g., apoptotic cells, damaged tissue), CRP activates the classical pathway of complement through interaction with C1q, but this activation is restricted to the initial stages with only little consumption of C5-C9 (25). Furthermore, surface-bound CRP inhibits the alternative pathway amplification loop, possibly through the interaction with Factor H, the

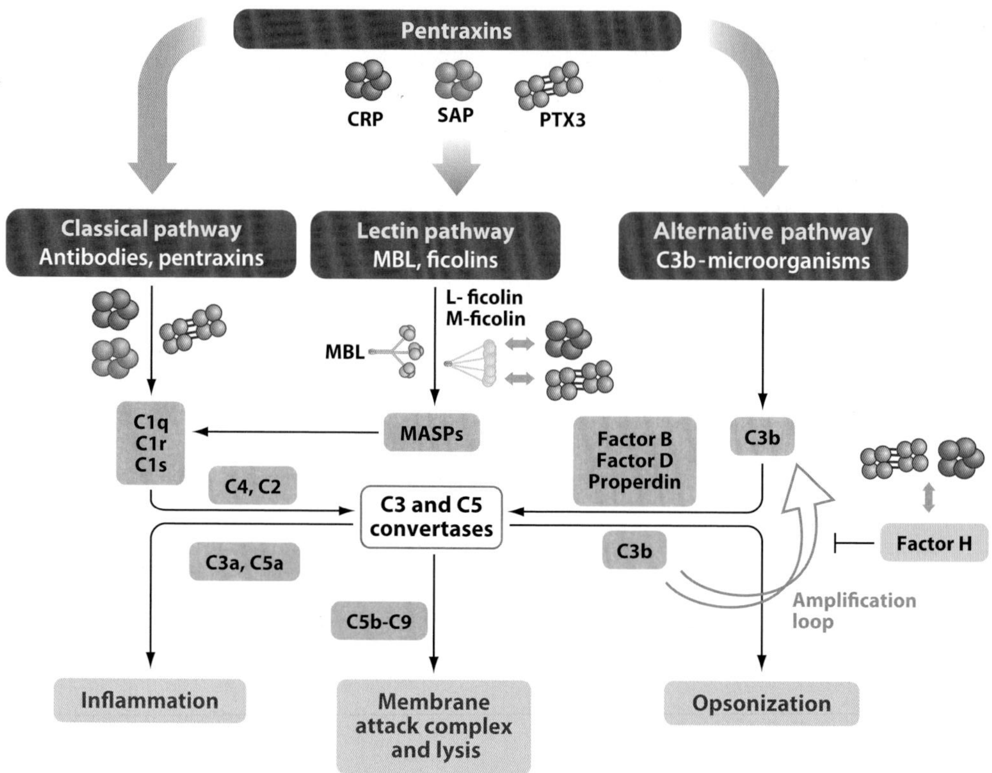

Figure 2

Roles of pentraxins in complement activation and regulation. The classical and the lectin pathways are initiated when the recognition molecules (antibodies or pentraxins and MBL or ficolins, respectively) bind to the activation structure (e.g., antigens or microbial moieties). Upon this interaction, downstream complement components are activated. C1q itself can serve as a pattern-recognition molecule. The alternative pathway is initiated by autoactivation of unstable C3 on the cell surface molecules of microorganisms. Deposition of C3b onto surfaces leads to the activation of the alternative pathway amplification loop, which involves Factor B, Factor D, and properdin. In these cascades, crucial elements are opsonization of targets, generation of proinflammatory chemotactic anafilotoxins, and formation of the membrane attack complex. Pentraxins participate in the activation and regulation of complement activation through the three pathways, by interacting with C1q (CRP, SAP, PTX3), with ficolins (CRP, PTX3), and with Factor H (CRP, PTX3).

main soluble regulator of the alternative pathway of complement activation (26), modulating complement activation. However, it is currently unclear whether this is a physiological phenomenon (27) (see Note Added in Proof). SAP binds to matrix components such as laminin, type IV collagen, fibronectin, and proteoglycans. Moreover, SAP binds to β-amyloid peptide in a Ca^{2+}-dependent manner and contributes to the pathogenesis of amyloidosis (28).

Receptors. A specific and saturable binding to all three classes of Fcγ receptors (FcγR) has been demonstrated for both CRP and SAP, and the interaction with FcγR is able to mediate phagocytosis of apoptotic cells and microorganisms, as well as mediate protective immune responses (29, 30). However, the interpretation of these data has been questioned (31). The crystal structure of human SAP in complex with the extracellular domain of FcγRIIa has recently been characterized, indicating that the contact region between the two molecules involves the ridge helices of pentameric SAP. The functional activation of FcγR-mediated phagocytosis and cytokine secretion have been described: The stoichiometry of the interaction infers the requirement for multivalent pathogen binding for receptor aggregation (32). These studies show that SAP and IgG share the binding site and compete for FcγR binding and that pentraxins inhibit immune complex–mediated phagocytosis. Thus, pentraxins possess similar functions to those of antibodies that activate both the complement and FcγR pathways.

Long Pentraxins

PTX3 is the first member of the long pentraxin subfamily, identified in the early 1990s as a new secreted protein rapidly induced by IL-1 in endothelial cells (ECs) or by TNF in fibroblasts (33, 34). Other long pentraxins were then identified (3), including guinea pig apexin, neuronal pentraxin (NP) 1 or NPTX1, NP2 (also called Narp or NPTX2), and the so-called neuronal pentraxin receptor (NPR), an integral membrane molecule belonging to the pentraxin family and capable of interacting with NP2. The general structural features of these molecules are the presence of a C-terminal pentraxin-like domain, containing the pentraxin signature, associated with a long N-terminal domain unrelated to other known proteins. The amino acid sequence identity among members of this subfamily is relatively high in the carboxy-pentraxin domain and ranges from 28% between human PTX3 and hNP1 to 68% between hNP1 and hNP2. By contrast, a low level of similarity is found between the amino-terminal domains. Ortholog molecules have been found so far for PTX3, NP1, NP2, and NPR in human, mouse, and rat, as well as in lower vertebrates such as zebra fish and puffer fish (Y. Martinez, unpublished results). Long pentraxins have been identified in *Xenopus laevis* (XL-PXN1) and in insects [e.g., *Drosophila melanogaster* B6 (Y17570)].

Recently, a search for pentraxin domain–containing sequences in databases resulted in the identification of a new long pentraxin (that we named PTX4) conserved from mammals to lower vertebrates, which clusters alone in phylogenetic analysis and has a unique pattern of mRNA expression (Y. Martinez, unpublished results).

PTX3

Structure. The human *PTX3* gene is located on chromosome 3q25 and is organized in three exons (**Figure 3**). Mature PTX3 is characterized by a long N-terminal domain (amino acids 18–179), and a pentraxin-like C-terminal domain (PTX, amino acids 179–381) (3, 33). The murine *ptx3* gene is highly homologous to the human counterpart and is located on chromosome 3. The proximal promoters of the human and murine *PTX3* genes have numerous potential enhancer-binding elements, including Pu1, AP-1, NF-κB, SP1, and NF-IL-6 sites.

A unique N-linked glycosylation site is located in the C-terminal domain at Asn220. The glycosidic moiety includes fucosylated and sialylated biantennary sugars with a minor fraction of tri- and tetraantennary glycans, whose heterogeneity depends on the cell type and inflammatory stimulus inducing PTX3 production (35). The molecule is characterized by a complex octameric structure (**Figure 3**) composed of two covalently linked tetramers (36).

Omp: outer membrane protein

PMN: polymorphonuclear neutrophil

Production. PTX3 is rapidly induced by several stimuli in different cell types (3). Peripheral blood leukocytes and myeloid dendritic cells (DCs) release PTX3 in response to proinflammatory cytokines (IL-1 and TNF-α) and agonists of TLR or following stimulation with microbial components, including LPS, lipoarabinomannan, and Outer membrane proteins (Omp) (37). PTX3 production is also stimulated by the anti-inflammatory cytokine IL-10 and by high-density lipoproteins (HDLs) (38, 39). Polymorphonuclear cells (PMNs) store PTX3 in lactoferrin-positive granules (40). Following microbial recognition by cellular pattern-recognition receptors, PTX3 is promptly released from PMN granules and localizes in neutrophil extracellular traps, where it likely contributes to the generation of an antimicrobial microenvironment essential to trap and kill microorganisms.

Other cell types can produce PTX3 in response to appropriate proinflammatory stimulation, such as vascular ECs; smooth muscle cells (SMCs); fibroblasts; adipocytes; chondrocytes; stromal, mesangial, and epithelial cells; and cells of the granulosa (reviewed in 3).

Different signaling pathways can affect PTX3 production, depending on the cell type and/or the stimuli: The NF-κB pathway is involved in regulation of PTX3 production in a model of acute myocardial ischemia and reperfusion in mice (41), whereas induction of PTX3 by HDL requires activation of the PI3K/Akt pathway through a G-coupled lysosphingolipid receptor (38). Induction of PTX3 by TNF-α in alveolar epithelial cells is mediated by the JNK pathway (42). PTX3 expression can be regulated by the chimeric transcription factor obtained by the fusion

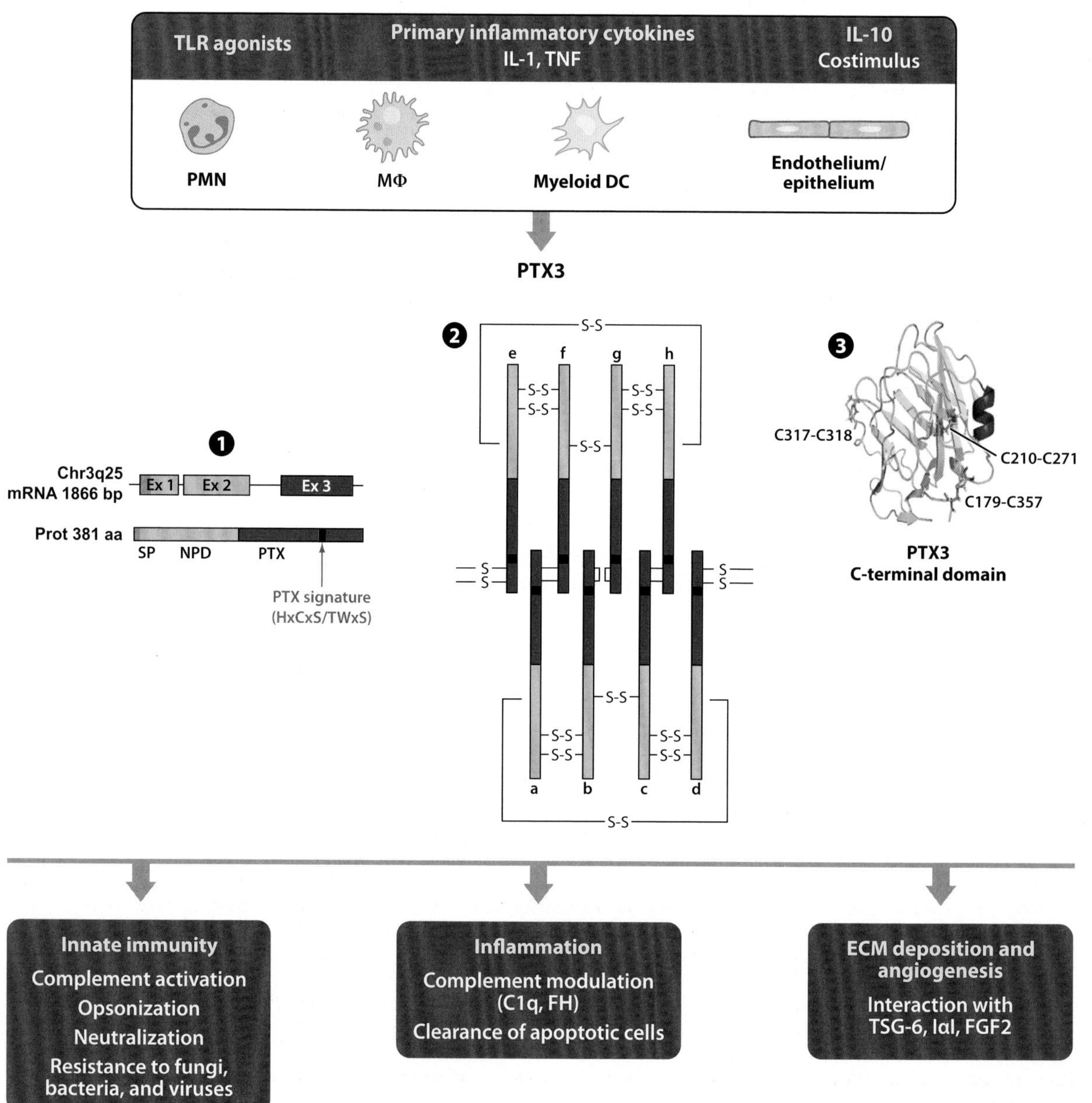

of the gene encoding the N terminus of the *FUS* (fused in liposarcoma) gene in frame to the coding region of the *CHOP* gene (C/EBP homologous protein) and involved in the pathogenesis of a subset of soft tissue sarcomas (43). Glucocorticoid hormones have divergent regulatory effects, inhibiting PTX3 production in myeloid DCs while inducing and enhancing, under inflammatory conditions, the production of the protein in fibroblasts and ECs (44). This divergent effect is likely due to differences in the way the glucocorticoid receptor acts in different cell populations, with a dimerization-dependent stimulation of PTX3 gene expression and production in nonhematopoietic cells and, on the contrary, a dimerization-independent suppression of PTX3 production in cells of hematopoietic origin (44).

Ligand specificity. The physiological functions attributed to pentraxins involve recognition and binding to different ligands, including microbial moieties, complement components, and extracellular matrix (ECM) proteins. Similarly to short pentraxins, PTX3 binds a number of selected bacteria, fungi, and viruses: A specific binding has been observed to conidia of *Aspergillus fumigatus* (45), *Paracoccidoides brasiliensis*, and zymosan (46); to selected gram-positive and gram-negative bacteria (45, 47); and finally to some viral strains, such as human and murine cytomegalovirus and influenza virus type A (IVA) (48, 49). The interaction between PTX3 and IVA occurs through binding of sialylated ligands on PTX3 to the viral hemagglutinin and results in neutralization of virus infectivity in vitro (49). Consistently, desialylated PTX3 does not bind IVA and does not neutralize virus infectivity. In addition to viral hemagglutinin, other microbial ligands have been identified. PTX3, which is produced in response to OmpA from *Klebsiella pneumoniae* in a TLR2-dependent manner, in turn binds to this microbial moiety and amplifies the TLR2-dependent inflammatory response induced upon OmpA recognition by scavenger receptors LOX-1 and SREC-I (47). Pretreatment with complement inhibitors abrogates PTX3 enhancement of OmpA proinflammatory effect, underscoring the interplay among the cellular and the humoral arms of innate immunity in recognizing microbial moieties (47, 50).

The interaction of PTX3 with the complement system has been known since the first characterization of the protein (51). PTX3 binds the first component of the classical complement cascade C1q, interacting with the C1q globular head (22, 52) but not with other components of the complement system such as C3 and C4. Interaction of PTX3 with C1q results in activation of the classical complement cascade only when C1q is plastic-immobilized, a situation that mimics C1q bound to a microbial surface. On the contrary, when interaction occurs in the fluid phase, a dose-dependent inhibition of C1q hemolytic activity is observed,

Figure 3

Cellular sources, structure, and function of the long pentraxin PTX3. PTX3 is produced by phagocytes (PMN, MΦ, myeloid DC), by ECs, and to a lesser extent by epithelial and mesenchymal cells, upon stimulation with microbial moieties (TLR agonists) or primary inflammatory cytokines (IL-1, TNF); IL-10 acts as a costimulus for proinflammatory stimuli. Human gene location and structure are shown in panel 1. The 381 amino acid–long protein consists of a signal peptide coded by exon 1, a nonpentraxin domain (NPD) coded by exon 1 and 2, a conserved pentraxin domain (PTX) coded by exon 3, which is characterized by a conserved pentraxin signature. The protein assembles in octamers consisting of 8 chains, labeled a-h in the stick diagram in panel 2, that are disulfide linked as indicated. Panel 3 is a three-dimensional model of PTX3 C-terminal domain based on CRP crystal structure (Protein Data Base code 1b09), kindly provided by Dr. A. Inforzato. Ribbons are representative of secondary structure elements. Once released, PTX3 participates in innate immune responses to fungi, bacteria, and viruses, through complement activation and regulation, microorganism opsonization, viral neutralization; and in inflammatory responses, by modulating complement activation, by participating in the clearance of apoptotic cells, and possibly by other undefined mechanisms. PTX3 also participates in extracellular matrix deposition and angiogenesis. (Abbreviations: DC, dendritic cell; EC, endothelial cell; ECM, extracellular matrix; FGF2, fibroblast growth factor 2; IL-1/-10; interleukin 1/10; IαI, inter-α-trypsin inhibitor; MΦ, macrophage; PMN, polymorphonuclear cell; TNF, tumor necrosis factor; TSG-6, TNF-α-induced protein 6.)

MΦ: macrophage

suggesting a possible inhibitory effect by competitive blocking of relevant sites (52). Similarly to CRP (26), PTX3 can interact with Factor H (53), promoting Factor H deposition on PTX3-coated surfaces and preventing an exaggerated complement activation (53). Finally, by interacting and cooperating with L-ficolin in microorganism recognition, PTX3 indirectly affects the lectin pathway (54), similarly to CRP (55, 56). Further investigation is necessary to define whether PTX3 also affects the lectin pathway of complement activation.

Assessing the capacity of PTX3 to bind secreted cytokines and growth factors, investigators found a significant interaction with fibroblast growth factor 2 (FGF2) (57). In this respect, PTX3 sequesters the growth factor in an inactive form, acting as a FGF2 decoy and tuning the neovascularization process.

PTX3 also interacts with ECM proteins such as tumor necrosis factor α-induced protein 6 (TNFAIP6 or TSG-6) and inter-α-trypsin inhibitor (IαI). The binding of PTX3 with TSG-6 and IαI is essential for the organization of the viscoelastic matrix of cumulus oophorus, and lack of PTX3 is associated with female subfertility owing to cumulus matrix instability (58, 59).

Although most of the ligands recognized by PTX3 require the full-length protein for optimal binding, IαI and FGF2 are recognized by the PTX3 N-terminal domain (57, 59) (**Figure 4**); the N-terminal domain is also mainly involved in the interaction with *A. fumigatus* conidia and with Factor H short consensus repeats 19–20 (53; B. Bottazzi, unpublished observation). The recombinant N-terminal domain can completely reconstitute the functions exerted by full-length PTX3 in terms of organization of the cumulus oophorus matrix and inhibition of FGF2-dependent proliferation of ECs (57, 59).

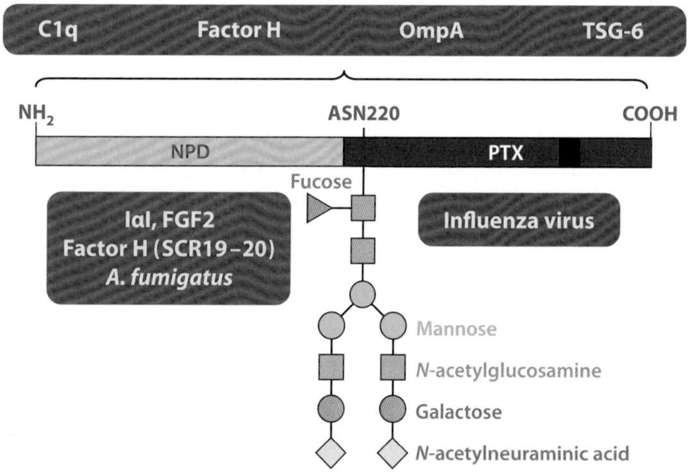

Figure 4

Role of the two PTX3 domains in recognizing ligands. The overall molecule is necessary for optimal interaction with complement components (C1q and Factor H), microbial moieties (OmpA), and the extracellular matrix protein TSG-6. Recombinant NPD can reconstitute the full-length protein in the interaction with IαI and FGF2. Interaction with conidia of *A. fumigatus* is also mediated by NPD, whereas influenza virus interacts with the sialic acid present on the glycosidic moiety at Asn220, localized in the PTX domain. (Abbreviations: TSG-6, TNF-α-induced protein 6; NPD, nonpentraxin domain; IαI, inter-α-trypsin inhibitor; FGF2, fibroblast growth factor 2.)

Receptors. The observation that MΦ display a binding site for PTX3 (45) suggested the existence of a cellular receptor for this protein. In the context of a study focused on SAP, Lu and coworkers (32) reported recently that PTX3, similarly to CRP and SAP, can interact with FcγR, particularly with FcγRIII/CD16 and FcγRII/CD32, with K_D 1.6 μM and 18.7 μM, respectively. We observed a similarly key role for CD32 in the opsonic activity of PTX3 toward *A. fumigatus* (F. Moalli, unpublished observations). Whether PTX3 receptors other than FcγR exist remains to be established.

Function. The first evidence of a role for PTX3 as a soluble PRM has been obtained in animals infected with *A. fumigatus* (45), a major opportunistic pathogen. *Ptx3*-deficient animals are more susceptible to *A. fumigatus* infection as a result of a defective recognition of conidia by alveolar MΦ and DCs; in addition, the same animals are protected by treatment with recombinant or PMN-derived PTX3 (40, 60). Accordingly, *Ptx3*-overexpressing mice have an increased phagocytic index toward the fungal pathogen *Paracoccidoides brasiliensis* compared with wild-type animals, and exogenous PTX3 can enhance the phagocytic activity of wild-type

MΦ (46). The role played by PTX3 in innate resistance to pathogens could also be exerted in an opsonization-independent manner: Overexpression of PTX3 by transgenic mice during infection with *K. pneumoniae* was associated with an enhanced ability to produce proinflammatory mediators, including nitric oxide and TNF-α and, as a consequence, with protection or faster lethality, depending on the size of inocula, even if no binding of PTX3 to *K. pneumoniae* could be demonstrated (61).

As reported for the short pentraxins, PTX3 may play a regulatory role in inflammation. The in vivo role of PTX3 in inflammatory conditions has been investigated in both transgenic mice and *ptx3*-deficient animals. An increased resistance to LPS toxicity and to cecal ligation and puncture has been observed in PTX3 transgenic mice (62), whereas *ptx3*-deficient animals display increased myocardial damage associated with increased neutrophil infiltration in a model of cardiac ischemia/reperfusion injury (41). The interaction with FGF2 is a further aspect to consider when dissecting the role of PTX3 in inflammation. At a functional level, this interaction prevents the binding of the growth factor to its cell surface receptors, thus suppressing the proangiogenic and prorestenotic activity exerted by FGF2 on ECs and SMCs, respectively. Thus, the molecular basis underlying the regulatory function of PTX3 on inflammation remains largely undefined, and further investigations are necessary to shed light on this fundamental aspect of PTX3 biology.

Emerging evidence suggests that PTX3 plays a role in the deposition of the ECM (58, 59). In particular, PTX3 is deposited in the cumulus oophorus matrix, where it interacts with the matrix proteins TSG-6 and IαI, allowing the formation of a highly organized hyaluronan-rich matrix necessary for successful ovulation and subsequent fertilization. These findings raise the possibility of a similar localization and function of this molecule in certain hyaluronic acid–enriched inflammatory tissues, such as in rheumatoid arthritis, where TSG-6 is also expressed.

Clinical studies. PTX3 is a candidate novel marker for inflammatory, infectious, and cardiovascular pathology (4). Rapidity of increase in blood, production in peripheral extrahepatic tissues, and correlation with outcome in diverse conditions encourage ongoing efforts (for review, see Reference 4). Interestingly, PTX3 polymorphisms have been associated with susceptibility to *Mycobacterium tuberculosis* (63) and female fertility (64), findings consistent with lessons learned from genetically modified mice.

COLLECTINS AND C1Q

Collectins are a family of multimeric and multifunctional PRMs in which carbohydrate recognition domains (CRDs) are found in association with collagenous structures (5, 65, 66). Nine different members have been identified so far in vertebrates, the best characterized of which is mannose-binding lectin (MBL). The other members include surfactant protein (SP)-A and SP-D; conglutinin and collectin (CL)-43 and CL-46, which are only present in bovidae; and three related human collectins, CL-P1 (placenta), CL-L1 (lung), and the very recently identified CL-K1 (kidney).

C1q's relation to the collectins is based on structure and function, except that its globular head lacks lectin activity. The complement system represents one of the major effector arms of the innate immune response against pathogens (67). The classical and the lectin pathways of complement activation are initiated when the recognition molecule, C1q and MBL or ficolins, respectively, binds to the activation structure. The analysis of the phylogeny and evolution of the classical and lectin pathways strongly suggests that C1q may have functioned as a recognition molecule of the lectin pathway, as did MBL and ficolins in innate immunity before the appearance of immunoglobulin-dependent adaptive immunity in jawed vertebrates. Only with the emergence of these species was the classical pathway established (6). In the classical pathway, the specificity of C1q for carbohydrate is recruited to recognize the Fc region of immunoglobulin.

CRD: carbohydrate recognition domain

MBL: mannose-binding lectin

C1q

Structure. C1q has a hexameric structure that looks like a bouquet of tulips under electron microscopy. Each unit is composed of an N-terminal collagen-like region that has a triple-helical structure and forms a central fibril-like region, connected by a strand to the C-terminal globular domain (gC1q). The gC1q domain has a heterotrimeric organization, formed by the C-terminal domain of three different chains (A, B, C) (68).

The gC1q domain is the main ligand recognition domain of C1q, and each of the three gC1q modules binds different ligands independently. The collagenous stalks harbor the tetramer of C1r and C1s serine proteases, and these proteases lead to assembly of the classical pathway C3 convertase, C4b2a (68).

Production. Unlike most complement proteins that are produced in the liver, C1q is predominantly synthesized by tissue MΦ, DCs, and ECs, localizing in the ECM (69). Only a fraction of C1q found in the circulation forms the C1 complex (C1qC1r2C1s2).

Ligand specificity. In addition to recognizing the Fc portion of antibodies, C1q binds to pentraxins (CRP, SAP, PTX3) through its gC1q domain (see above). gC1q also binds directly to many gram-negative bacteria through Omp, LPS, or lipid A and to viruses (e.g., gp41 of HIV-1 or gp21 of HTLV-1) (68).

C1q also interacts with misfolded proteins, such as amyloid Aβ peptide and prion proteins found in neurodegenerative diseases (68) and with several ECM proteins (such as fibromodulin, osteoadherin, fibronectin, and laminin) (70).

Finally, C1q binds via the globular head domain to surface blebs on apoptotic cells and to necrotic cells directly or through pentraxins and Ig (24). The binding sites include anionic phospholipids (phosphatidylserine), surface proteins, and DNA.

Interestingly, C1q endogenous ligands also interact with C inhibitors C4BP and Factor H. This phenomenon, which is exploited as an evasion strategy by many pathogens to avoid C attack, plays an important role in balancing C responses to endogenous ligands and preventing immunopathology (70).

Receptors. C1q binds to a wide range of cell types (PMN, monocytes, lymphocytes, DCs, ECs, and platelets), resulting in the induction of cell-specific biological responses, which include phagocytosis, chemotaxis, the generation of procoagulant activity, activation of ECs, and enhancement of FcγR- and CR1-mediated phagocytosis and superoxide production by neutrophils (71). To date, investigators have described four types of C1q-binding proteins/receptors expressed on the cell surface. These include cC1q-R/calreticulin (CRT), a 60-kDa protein (72); gC1q-R/p33, a 33-kDa homotrimeric protein (71); C1q-Rp (CD93), a 120-kDa O-sialoglycoprotein (73); and CR1 (CD35), the receptor for C3b (74). In addition to C1q, CRT reportedly serves as a receptor for collectins, such as the MBL, SP-A, SP-D, CL-43, and conglutinin, and, in association with CD91, initiates macropinocytosis and phagocytosis of apoptotic cells (72, 75, 76).

Finally, investigators have recently reported that α2β1 integrin acts as a receptor for collectins, including C1q and ficolins through their collagen domain, and that collectins behave as adhesive ligands for α2β1 integrin (77).

Function. C1q activates the classical complement pathway upon interaction with IgG- or IgM-containing immune complexes or with aggregated pentraxins. In addition, C1q is involved in maintaining immune tolerance via clearance of apoptotic cells, in phagocytosis of bacteria, and in neutralization of viruses. C1q deficiency is mainly associated with autoimmunity (e.g., systemic lupus erythematosus and glomerunephritis) and to a lesser extent to increased susceptibility to infections (e.g., *Salmonella*, malaria, polymicrobial peritonitis, and aspergillosis) (70, 78). This suggests that C1q, by activating the classical complement pathway or by acting as opsonin, is primarily involved in the handling of self ligands rather then microorganisms. Actually, promotion of apoptotic cell and debris handling is likely a major determinant of the protective role of C1q in autoimmunity (24, 70).

MBL and Surfactant Proteins

Structure. The basic building block of the collectins MBL, SP-A, and SP-D is a triple helix composed of three identical polypeptide chains (65, 79). Each chain is characterized by a modular organization consisting in a globular C-terminal CRD that mediates calcium-dependent ligand binding; a short α-helical hydrophobic neck region (24–28 amino acids long); a collagenous region containing a variable number of Gly-X-Y triplets, involved in the maintenance of shape, stability, and oligomerization; and a cysteine-rich N-terminal region of 7–28 amino acid residues, required for oligomerization. The three polypeptide chains interact to form a triple helix within the collagenous region, stabilized by hydrophobic interactions and interchain disulphide bonds. MBL and SP-A form multimers of six trimeric subunits interacting to form large oligomers resembling the typical bouquet-like structure, whereas SP-D is assembled into dodecamers of four trimeric subunits assuming a cruciform structure.

The CRDs of the different collectins are densely folded polypeptide fragments organized in trimeric clusters with relatively low affinities for a single monosaccharide but with higher affinities for clustered oligosaccharides. Several calcium-binding sites are present in the different CRDs, given that calcium is essential for maintenance of CRD folding and for interaction of collectins with immune cell surface receptors.

Production. The liver is the main source of MBL: The protein is found in normal serum at low levels, and its production increases in the course of inflammatory processes and during the acute-phase response. MBL serum concentrations are genetically controlled in the population by polymorphism/mutation in the promoter and in the coding region of the *MBL2* gene, influencing the susceptibility to and the course of different types of infections and of autoimmune, cardiovascular, and metabolic disease (80, 81).

SP-A and SP-D are synthesized in the lung by type II alveolar cells, by nonciliated respiratory epithelial cells, and by submucosal cells (65), but their expression has also been described in other human tissues, such as in the gastrointestinal tract, trachea, brain, testes, heart, kidney, and exocrine glands (82, 83). SP-D is also present in the female urogenital tract, in the placenta, and in the amniotic fluid, whereas SP-A is expressed in human chorioamniotic membranes (84).

Ligand specificity. Collectins bind complex carbohydrates and lipids on microbial surfaces (5, 65, 66) as well as LPS and lipooligosaccharide (LOS) of gram-negative bacteria and lipotheicoic acid (LTA) and peptidoglycan (PDG) of gram-positive bacteria. Highly glycosylated proteins present on the surface of fungi are targets for collectins, such as gpA from *Pneumocystis carinii*; gp55 and gp45 from *A. fumigatus*; mannoproteins and glucuronoxylomannan from the capsule of *Cryptococcus neoformans*; and mannan and β-glucan from the cell wall of *Saccharomyces cerevisiae*. Recognition of several parasites is mediated by interaction with high-mannose N-linked glycoproteins and glycolipids. SP-A also binds the P2 Omp of *Haemophilus influenzae* type A and a lipid component of *Mycoplasma pneumoniae*, whereas SP-D binds to the arabinomannan of *M. tuberculosis*.

Collectins bind selectively to several types of viruses, including cytomegalovirus, HIV, SARS coronavirus, and herpes simplex virus, by interacting with glycoproteins of the viral envelope. MBL and SP-D bind gp120, the highly mannosylated envelope protein of HIV, inhibiting HIV infectivity (65, 85).

Receptors. Although binding of collectins to microorganisms is mainly due to the recognition by the different CRDs of sugars expressed on the microbial surface, the interaction of collectins with immune and inflammatory cells occurs via binding of the collagenous tail with receptors on the cell surface. The first SP-A receptor identified is SP-R210, a 210-kDa protein expressed on alveolar type II cells and alveolar MΦ (86) involved in macrophage proliferation, uptake, and killing of bacteria (87, 88).

MBL and lung collectins interact with the C1q phagocytic receptor C1qRp (CD93) (73) and with cC1qR (CRT) (72). Although several studies describe interaction of MBL and lung collectins with C1qRp, CD93$^{-/-}$ mice are fully phagocytosis competent (73), ruling out the possibility that this is the principal cellular receptor involved in the prophagocytic effect induced by collectins. Gardai and coworkers (76) provided evidence that SP-D and SP-A can differentially bind to cell membrane receptors, through either their CRD or their collagen tail, eliciting respectively anti-inflammatory or proinflammatory responses. In accordance with this "head-and-tail" hypothesis, SP-D and SP-A interact with pathogens via their CRDs, whereas the free collagen tail binds the complex CRT/CD91, enhancing phagocytosis and proinflammatory response (76). In contrast, in the absence of a pathogen, SP-A or SP-D binds to signal regulating protein α (SIRPα) on residential alveolar MΦ via their CRD, suppressing the phagocytic function of these cells (89).

A number of other putative receptors have been identified: MBL binds to CR1, interacting with the C1q-binding site of the receptor (74); SP-A and SP-D can directly bind CD14 (90), modulating LPS-elicited responses, as well as TLR2 and TLR4 (91); finally, MBL and SP-A interact with α2β1 integrin, recently described as a novel C1q receptor (77).

Function. Collectins protect the host by recognizing conserved structures on microorganisms and cooperating with phagocytes and humoral factors (i.e., complement) in order to promote elimination of the pathogen. Three common polymorphisms have been described so far in the human *MBL2* gene, and all appear to be associated with decreased serum levels of MBL and higher susceptibility to recurrent infections (81). The uptake of pathogens is either (*a*) promoted directly, after binding of CRDs to sugars exposed on the microbial surface and interaction with one of the previously described phagocyte receptor, or (*b*) independently of microbial binding, upregulating expression of cell surface receptors on phagocytic cells (92, 93). In addition, collectins exert their effect activating complement through the lectin pathway (**Figure 2**) (see Reference 6 for a review). Collectins also play a role in the uptake of damaged cells: MBL, SP-A, and SP-D bind apoptotic cells and enhance their uptake by alveolar MΦ (72, 75).

Accumulating evidence shows that MBL is able to modulate the inflammatory response; however, its mode of action remains unexplained. MBL is able to trigger production of proinflammatory cytokines from monocytes when interacting with a pathogen such as *Neisseria meningitides* (94, 95). Recent data demonstrate that MBL and SP-D cooperate with TLR2/6 during infection with *Staphylococcus aureus*, inducing production of TNF-α independently of complement activation (96). The phagosome plays an essential role in coordinating the response, emphasizing the importance of engulfment in providing the appropriate cellular environment to facilitate synergy between defense pathways.

FICOLINS

Ficolins are proteins structurally and functionally related to collectins (5, 97). Ficolins have been identified in vertebrates, including human, rodent, pig, hedgehog, and xenopus, as well as in the invertebrate ascidian (reviewed in 97); they can recognize carbohydrate-based pathogen-associated molecular patterns on microorganisms, thus activating the lectin complement pathway.

Structure

Three ficolins have been identified in humans: L-ficolin/P35 (also known as Ficolin-2) and

H-ficolin/Hakata antigen (Ficolin-3), which are both serum proteins, and a third ficolin termed M-ficolin/P35-related antigen (Ficolin-1), not present in serum (97). The general structure of ficolins resembles that of collectins, with an N-terminal region, a collagen-like domain involved in the activation of the lectin pathway, and a C-terminal portion homologous to the fibrinogen β and γ chains (fibrinogen-like domain). The fibrinogen-like domain is organized in a globular structure similar to the CRDs of collectins, and it participates in the recognition of microbial moieties and bacteria.

L-ficolin, the first member of the family to be identified, is a multimeric protein consisting of 35-kDa subunits; the oligomeric structure is formed by crosslinking of three subunits via disulphide bridges in the N-terminal portion. The collagen domains assemble the subunits into a trimer, and four trimers assemble in a dodecamer (98). H-ficolin and M-ficolin are octadecameric proteins with similar general structures.

Two murine ficolins have been described: ficolin A, homologous of human L-ficolin, and ficolin B, homologous to human M-ficolin (99).

Production

Human L- and H-ficolin are mainly expressed in the liver and secreted into the circulation as serum lectins. In addition, production of H-ficolin also occurs in the lung, by ciliated bronchial epithelial cells, by type II alveolar epithelial cells, and by glioma cells (100). Despite the lack of a typical transmembrane domain, M-ficolin is detected on the surface of monocytes, and its expression is downregulated during monocyte differentiation. In addition, prolonged exposure to TLR ligands such as LPS and Pam_3Cys induces M-ficolin mRNA in monocyte-derived MΦ as well as in alveolar MΦ (101). M-ficolin is present in the cytoplasm of neutrophils, monocytes, and type II alveolar epithelial cells in lung, suggesting that it could also be secreted (102, 103).

Ligand Specificity

Similarly to collectins, ficolins recognize selected gram-positive and gram-negative bacteria and promote their uptake (102, 104). The fibrinogen-like domain of ficolins has a similar function as the CRD of C-type lectins and is responsible for specificity in carbohydrate recognition and binding. The structure of the recognition domain suggests that ficolins have evolved to recognize a variety of acetylated and carbohydrate targets; in particular, L-ficolin has three distinct recognition sites specialized to recognize elongated carbohydrates (105). Ficolins are characterized by a specificity for N-acetyl glucosamine residues in complex-type oligosaccharides, but not for mannose or high-mannose-type oligosaccharides (97, 106); in addition, H-ficolin binds to N-acetyl-D-galactosamine and D-fucose, whereas M-ficolin binds to sialic acid (107). Finally, L-ficolin binds microbial moieties such as PDG and LTA, as well as 1,3-β-D-glucan, the major constituent of yeast and fungal cell walls (108).

Receptors

Despite the similarities between ficolins and collectins, our knowledge of putative cellular receptor(s) is limited. As in the case of collectins and C1q, L- and H-ficolin interact with cC1qR (CRT) (109). MBL inhibits H-ficolin binding to CRT, suggesting that both proteins share a common binding site on CRT (98, 110).

Function

Data available so far indicate that ficolins may act through two routes: promoting primitive opsonophagocytosis and initiating the lectin pathway of complement activation (97, 102). Mouse ficolin B strongly aggregates *S. aureus*, and M-ficolin enhances phagocytosis of *E. coli* by U937 cells (103), whereas L-ficolin enhances the uptake of *Salmonella typhimurium* by neutrophils. Similarly to MBL, the three human ficolins bind carbohydrates on the surface of pathogens and activate the lectin pathway through attached serine proteases, MBL-associated serine proteases (MASP) (97). The complex L-ficolin/MASP binds to intact group B *streptococci* and promotes C4 consumption (106). In addition, ficolins interact with CRP, amplifying complement-mediated killing of *Pseudomonas aeruginosa* and widening the range of bacteria recognized by CRP (55, 56).

L- and H-ficolin bind apoptotic cells, leading to C3 and C4 deposition (98, 109); these data imply that ficolins could participate in the clearance of nonself, such as microorganisms and apoptotic cells, through the lectin pathway. The pattern of structures recognized by MBL and ficolins are complementary and may target different, though overlapping, microbial populations, covering a broad range of pathogens. Although genetically determined deficiency and defects of MBL are common, only recently has a frameshift mutation leading to immunodeficiency and defective activation of the lectin complement pathway been described in *FCN3*, the gene encoding H-ficolin (81, 111).

PROPERDIN

Structure

Properdin is a highly positively charged protein composed of identical 53-kDa subunits that are further composed of six globular domains that are homologous to the thrombospondin type 1 repeat and are highly mannosylated. Properdin subunits associate head to tail and form dimers, trimers, and tetramers.

Production

The biosynthesis of properdin occurs in monocytes/MΦ, T cells, neutrophils, and mast cells. In the case of neutrophils and mast cells, properdin is stored in secondary granules and rapidly released upon cell stimulation, possibly playing a major role in local alternative pathway activity (112).

Ligand Specificity and Function

Properdin is a C3b-binding protein that protects C3b from the catalytic cleavage by the complement regulators Factor H and Factor I and promotes and stabilizes C3bB as well as C3bBb (113). Properdin binds to *Neisseria gonorrhoeae*, zymosan, *E. coli*, and *Salmonella typhimurium* rough LPS strains, directing C3 deposition to the microbial surface. Accordingly, properdin-deficient individuals are particularly sensitive to meningococcal disease (114).

Interestingly, pathogens have evolved measures to interfere with properdin recognition. For instance, some tick salivary proteins bind to properdin, blocking the alternative pathway activity and possibly contributing to *Borrelia burgdorferi* (the causative agent of Lyme disease) transmission by ticks (115).

OTHER FLUID-PHASE PATTERN-RECONGITION MOLECULES

In addition to the molecular families described above, other molecules can serve as PRMs, including serum amyloid A (SAA) proteins, which are the precursors of amyloid protein A found in secondary amyloidosis, and mindin.

Serum Amyloid A

Structure. SAA proteins are members of a conserved multigene family divided into acute-phase SAA (A-SAA) and constitutive SAA (C-SAA) (116). Mammal SAA genes have four exons and encode for 104–112 amino acid, 12-kDa proteins whose tertiary structure has not yet been elucidated.

Production. A-SAA are mainly synthesized by the hepatocytes and are induced by proinflammatory stimuli, such as bacterial products and proinflammatory cytokines (IL-1β, TNF-α, and IL-6). During the acute-phase response, A-SAA plasma concentrations increase up to 1000-fold, reaching 1 mg/ml, and decline thereafter. Both A-SAA and C-SAA are also produced by SMCs, vascular cells, adipocytes, monocytes, MΦ, synovial cells, chondrocytes, and epithelial cell lines. Mouse SAA3, in particular, is the principal extrahepatic A-SAA and is secreted by MΦ (117).

Ligand specificity. SAA proteins represent innate recognition proteins for gram-negative bacteria, including *Escherichia coli, Salmonella typhimurium, Shigella flexneri, Klebsiella pneumoniae, Vibrio cholerae*, and *Pseudomonas aeruginosa*, by interacting with OmpA family members (118). SAA opsonization of recognized microorganisms increased the response of innate phagocytic cells to bacteria, with production of TNF-α, IL-10, and neutrophil reactive oxygen intermediate (119). SAA also binds to hepatitis C virus, inhibiting infection of cultured cells by blocking entry (120).

Receptors. SAA also has cytokine-like properties and can induce the secretion of proinflammatory cytokines, chemokines (IL-1β, IL-1Ra, TNF-α, IL-6, IL-8, CCL2, CCL20, IFN-γ), and soluble TNFRII, the activation of the IL-23/Th17 pathway (121), and the production of matrix metalloproteases, nitric oxide, and reactive oxygen species (122). One recognized signaling receptor responsible for these SAA properties is formyl peptide receptor-like 1/lipoxin A4 receptor (FPRL1/LXA4R), expressed by leukocytes (123, 124). Investigators have recently proposed that SAA interacts with TLR2, inducing NF-κB activation (125). Moreover, scavenger receptor B-I (SR-BI)/CD36 functions as an endocytic SAA receptor and is involved in SAA-mediated cell signaling events associated with the immune-related and inflammatory effects of SAA (126).

SAA proteins have other biological properties, including the association to HDL and lipid transport.

Mindin

Mindin (spondin-2) is a secreted protein expressed in several tissues, including the spleen and lymph nodes, and is a PRM component of the ECM involved in sensing and responding to several types of bacterial invaders (127). Mindin binds to bacteria through sugar moieties found in the bacterial cell wall (e.g., LPS and LTA), which results in the opsonization and agglutination of the bacteria, phagocytosis, and stimulated production of proinflammatory cytokines by the macrophage. Moreover, mindin interacts with influenza virus particles, directly favoring macrophage activation and in vivo clearance of influenza virus (128). Mindin comprises an N-terminal F-spondin domain and C-terminal thrombospondin type 1 repeat (TSR). The F-spondin domain mediates integrin binding, whereas the TSR domain recognizes LPS (129). Thus, mindin serves as a novel ligand for integrins, is essential in the initiation of the innate immune response, and represents a unique PRM in the ECM for microbial pathogens.

COMMON THEMES

Having summarized the molecular and functional properties of individual components of the humoral innate immune system, here we provide an overview of the ensemble, based on shared themes essential in the construction of a system.

Phagocytes as a Critical Source

Phagocytes are major players in innate immunity and a source of soluble PRMs. Members of all major classes of PRMs are produced by MΦ and myeloid DCs (e.g., PTX3, C1q, M-ficolin, properdin, CL-K1, SAA3) or stored in neutrophil granules (PTX3, M-ficolin, properdin). Thus, phagocytes serve as a source of PRMs to be produced and released at sites of innate immune reactions, much like B cells produce antibodies.

Constitutive and Inducible Production

Tonic production by epithelial tissues (the liver, lung) ensures a constitutive presence of humoral PRMs in the systemic circulation (CRP or SAP, MBL, ficolins) and at key anatomical locations such as the lungs (SP-A and SP-D). Recognition of damaged tissues or of microbical moieties triggers a massive increase of PRM levels in the systemic circulation and in tissues. A set of PRMs (e.g., the short pentraxin CRP in human, SAP in the mouse, MBL, ficolins) are produced in the liver and released in the systemic circulation as a result of a cytokine (IL-1/IL-6) amplification cascade. Diverse tissue elements and most prominently MΦ and mDCs produce PTX3, C1q, SAA3, properdin, and M-ficolin in a gene expression–dependent fashion. Finally, neutrophils act as a reservoir of ready-made PTX3, M-ficolin, and properdin for rapid release in minutes upon microbial encounter. Thus, the diverse mode of production ensures coverage of different temporal windows and body compartments (systemic circulation, mucosal surfaces, tissues) in response to microbial invasion and tissue damage.

Heterocomplexes and Cooperative Interactions

In an unexpected twist, investigators have observed that members of different classes of humoral PRMs can physically and functionally interact. Members of the ficolin (L-ficolin and H-ficolin) and pentraxin (CRP, PTX3) families can form heterocomplexes and cooperate in pathogen recognition and activation of effector functions (54, 55). Cooperative recognition is likely to expand the repertoire of molecular patterns effectively recognized by the humoral innate immune system and to diversify the effector mechanisms (e.g., classic and lectin pathway) that have been activated.

Receptors and Interplay with Cellular and Innate Immunity

Fluid-phase PRMs are recognized by cellular receptors expressed on innate immunity cells. Receptors for PRMs belong to different molecular classes (**Figure 5**). By interacting with cellular receptors directly and by triggering complement activation, PRMs facilitate recognition and effector function of phagocytes and related cells.

In addition to serving as opsonins, PRMs engage in a complex interplay with cellular PRR. Some bacterial moieties are recognized both by humoral PRMs and by members of the scavenger and TLR families, as illustrated by LTA of gram-positive bacteria (MBL, CD36, and TLR2/6) and OmpA (PTX3, SREC, LOX, and TLRs) (47, 96). Interestingly, in the context of *S. aureus* recognition, MBL facilitates TLR2/6 signaling within the phagosomal compartment (96). Thus, the cellular and the humoral arm of innate immunity are complementary and synergic in deciphering microbial patterns and regulating the innate response.

In addition to serving as opsonins, humoral PRMs have a regulatory function on cellular effectors. Lung collectins via their globular heads bind SIRPα and block production of inflammatory mediators (76); SP-A also regulates expression and signaling of TLR2 in MΦ (130). Moreover, there is extensive evidence, including from genetically modified mice, for a regulatory function of pentraxins (41; L. Deban, unpublished data). However, the molecular basis for the regulatory activity of fluid-phase humoral PRMs, reminiscent of that of antibodies (131), remains largely unclear.

Effector Functions

Humoral PRMs act by activating and regulating the complement cascade and by facilitating recognition by cellular effector cells. In addition, PRMs are multimeric and cause agglutination as well as neutralization of certain pathogens, a strategy to facilitate disposal (e.g., 15, 49). Complement activation, opsonization, agglutination, and neutralization are the effector mechanisms used by antibodies. Thus, humoral, fluid-phase PRMs share with antibodies mechanisms of action and qualify as functional ancestors of immunoglobulins (ante-antibodies). Although the building blocks (genes, molecular structures, producing cells) are different, innate and adaptive humoral

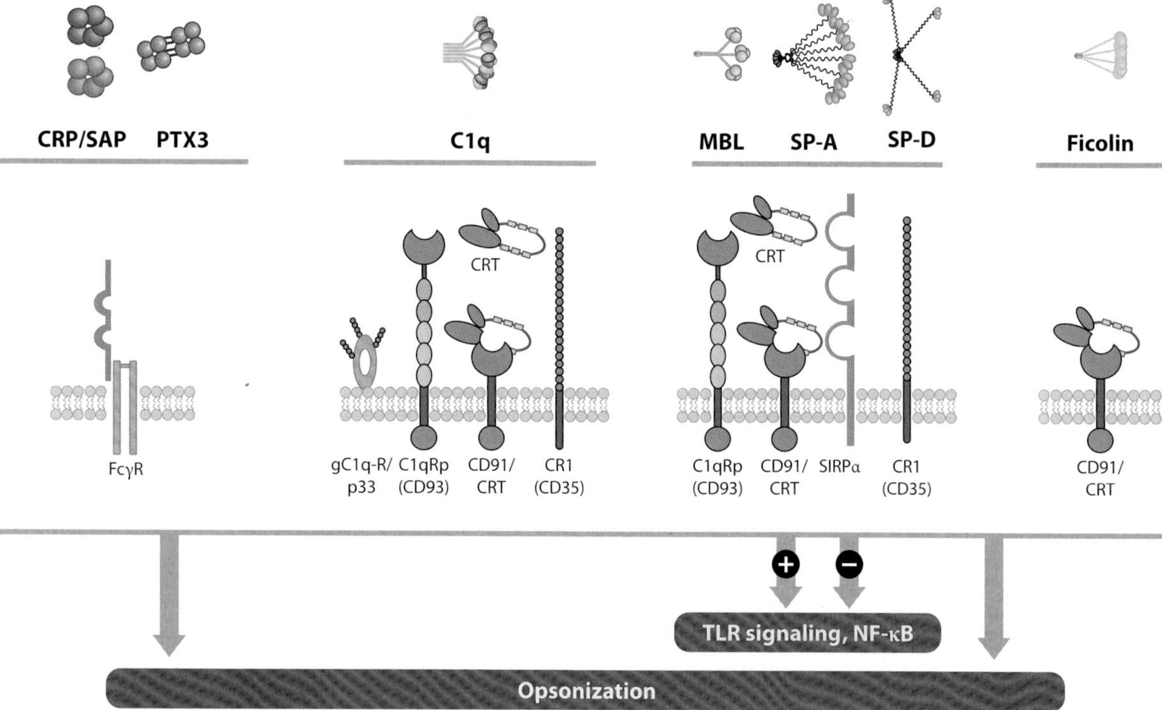

Figure 5

Receptors for humoral PRMs and interplay with cellular innate immunity. Humoral fluid-phase PRMs are recognized by different cellular receptors, some of which are reported here, belonging to different molecular classes and expressed on innate immunity cells. The same receptor can recognize different PRMs. This is the case for C1qRp (CD93) and CR1 (CD35), both recognized by C1q and collectins, and for the complex CD91/CRT, recognized by C1q, collectins, and ficolins. Other molecules are recognized by a single class of PRMs: SIRPα, recognized by SP-A and SP-D; gC1q-R/CD33, recognized by C1q; and FcγR, recognized by pentraxins. By interacting with cellular receptors, PRMs facilitate recognition and effector function of phagocytes and related cells, such as opsonization and regulation of inflammation through NF-κB signaling and TLR function (e.g., pentraxins and FcγR, SP-A and SIRPα, or CD91/calreticulin).

immunity share fundamental strategies to cope with pathogens.

CONCLUDING REMARKS: HUMORAL INNATE IMMUNITY AS AN INTEGRATED SYSTEM

Figure 6 is a schematic representation of the humoral arm of the innate immune system and of its integration with cellular effectors. Sensing microbial moieties or tissue damage by cellular receptors sets in motion and orients innate immune responses. In addition to mediating cellular responses, innate immunity cells (typically MΦ, DCs, PMNs) directly produce and release fluid-phase PRMs or induce production by other cell types (endothelia, liver, and epithelial cells at mucosal surfaces).

Humoral fluid-phase PRMs are diverse in terms of molecular structure and are released with different tempos. Neutrophil granules are a reservoir of a certain PRM (PTX3, M-ficolin, properdin) for rapid release in minutes. Early gene expression–dependent production by mononuclear phagocytes and DCs sustains levels of a wider repertoire of molecules. Finally, epithelial tissues, the liver in particular, serve as a source of delayed, systemic mass production.

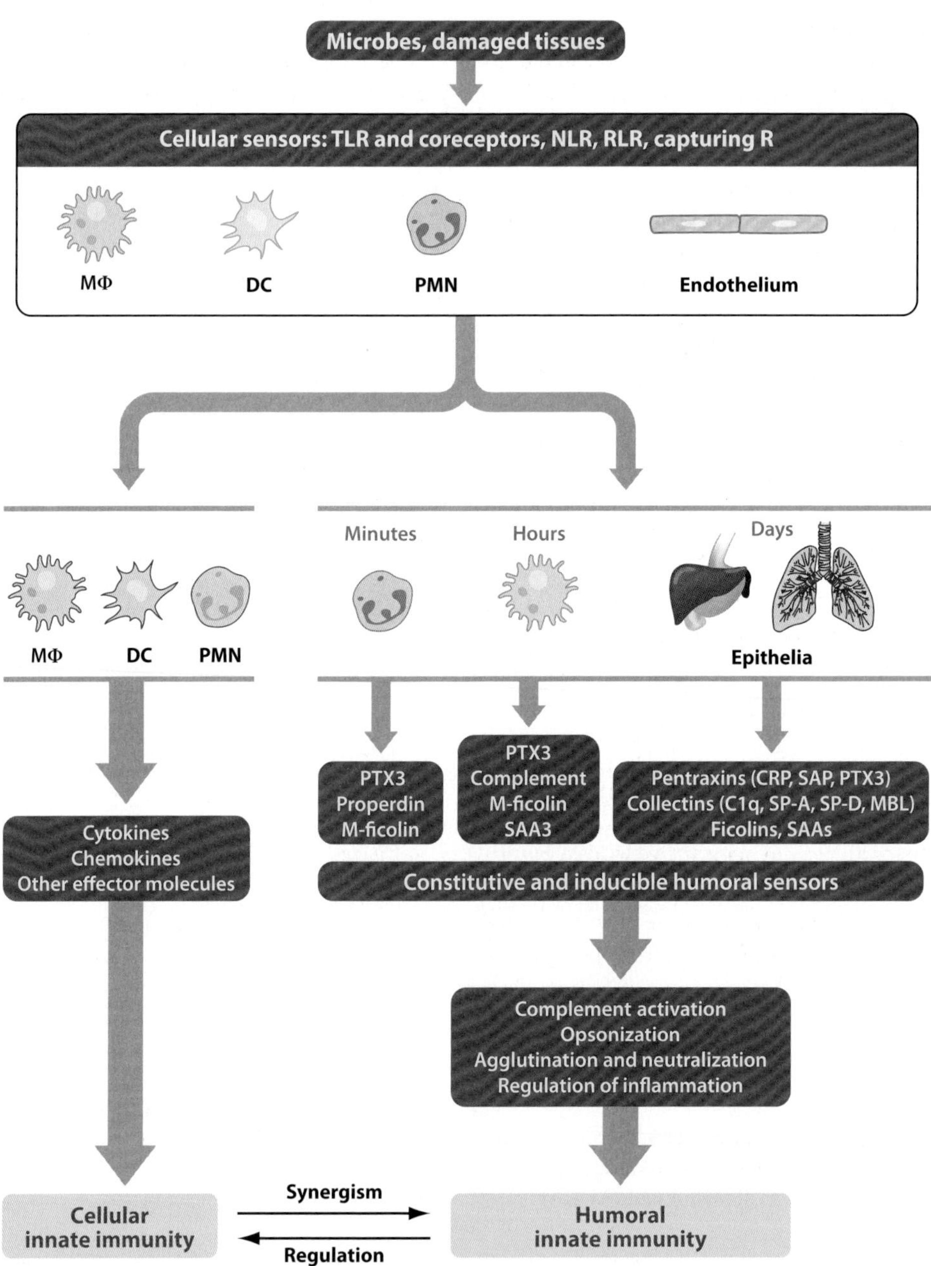

Figure 6

Humoral innate immunity as an integrated system. Humoral sensors share fundamental mechanisms of effector function: complement activation and regulation, opsonization, agglutination, virus neutralization, and regulation of inflammation. The humoral and cellular arms of innate immunity form an integrated system with synergism in deciphering microbial patterns and regulating the innate responses.

In addition to being released or produced in response to microorganisms or to tissue damage, some PRMs are produced constitutively to provide a ready-made line of defense in the circulation or in the lung, reminiscent of the function of natural antibodies.

Although structurally diverse, components of the humoral arm of innate immunity share fundamental mechanisms of effector function. They activate complement via the classical or the lectin pathway and tune the alternative pathway. Humoral PRMs have opsonic activity, facilitating recognition by phagocytes directly or via complement activation. Finally, because of their multimeric structure, they agglutinate particles, a strategy of disposal, and can have neutralizing activity on viruses. Thus, despite genetic and structural differences, the general mode of action of humoral PRMs is remarkably similar to that of antibodies.

The humoral and cellular arms of innate immunity form an integrated system with crosstalk, synergism, and regulation. In addition to being a source of humoral PRMs, innate immunity cells are regulated by PRMs, and their effector function is facilitated by the opsonic activity of fluid-phase PRMs.

Thus, although genes, cells, and molecules are different, certain elements of the overall strategy (e.g., complement activation, agglutination, opsonization, neutralization, regulation of inflammation) are conserved in evolution and shared between the humoral arm of the innate and adaptive immune system.

DISCLOSURE STATEMENT

The authors are not aware of any affiliations, memberships, funding, or financial holdings that might be perceived as affecting the objectivity of this review.

ACKNOWLEDGMENTS

This work was supported by European Research Council (Project HIIS), Istituto Superiore di Sanità, MIUR (FIRB contract RBLA039LSF), Ministero della Salute, European Union Sixth and Seventh Framework Programs (MUGEN: LSHG-CT-2005-005203; MUVAPRED: LSHP-CT-2003-503240; TOLERAGE: HEALTH-F4-2008-202156; FLUINNATE: SP5B-CT-2006-044161), Associazione Italiana per la Ricerca sul Cancro, Fondazione Telethon and Fondazione Fibrosi Cistica. We are grateful to Dr. Antonio Inforzato for discussion and for providing the structural model of PTX3. We apologize to the authors whose important work could not be included in the list of references because of space constraints.

LITERATURE CITED

1. Abernethy TJ, Avery OT. 1941. The occurrence during acute infections of a protein not normally present in the blood. I. Distribution of the reactive protein in patients' sera and the effect of calcium on the flocculation reaction with C polysaccharide of Pneumococcus. *J. Exp. Med.* 73:173–82
2. Casas JP, Shah T, Hingorani AD, Danesh J, Pepys MB. 2008. C-reactive protein and coronary heart disease: a critical review. *J. Intern. Med.* 264:295–314
3. Garlanda C, Bottazzi B, Bastone A, Mantovani A. 2005. Pentraxins at the crossroads between innate immunity, inflammation, matrix deposition, and female fertility. *Annu. Rev. Immunol.* 23:337–66
4. Mantovani A, Garlanda C, Doni A, Bottazzi B. 2008. Pentraxins in innate immunity: from C-reactive protein to the long pentraxin PTX3. *J. Clin. Immunol.* 28:1–13
5. Holmskov U, Thiel S, Jensenius JC. 2003. Collectins and ficolins: humoral lectins of the innate immune defense. *Annu. Rev. Immunol.* 21:547–78
6. Fujita T. 2002. Evolution of the lectin-complement pathway and its role in innate immunity. *Nat. Rev. Immunol.* 2:346–53

7. Pepys MB, Hirschfield GM. 2003. C-reactive protein: a critical update. *J. Clin. Invest.* 111:1805–12
8. Emsley J, White HE, O'Hara BP, Oliva G, Srinivasan N, et al. 1994. Structure of pentameric human serum amyloid P component. *Nature* 367:338–45
9. Shrive AK, Cheetham GM, Holden D, Myles DA, Turnell WG, et al. 1996. Three dimensional structure of human C-reactive protein. *Nat. Struct. Biol.* 3:346–54
10. Suresh MV, Singh SK, Ferguson DA Jr, Agrawal A. 2007. Human C-reactive protein protects mice from *Streptococcus pneumoniae* infection without binding to pneumococcal C-polysaccharide. *J. Immunol.* 178:1158–63
11. Szalai AJ. 2002. The antimicrobial activity of C-reactive protein. *Microbes Infect.* 4:201–5
12. Szalai AJ, VanCott JL, McGhee JR, Volanakis JE, Benjamin WH Jr. 2000. Human C-reactive protein is protective against fatal *Salmonella enterica* serovar typhimurium infection in transgenic mice. *Infect. Immun.* 68:5652–56
13. Suresh MV, Singh SK, Ferguson DA Jr, Agrawal A. 2006. Role of the property of C-reactive protein to activate the classical pathway of complement in protecting mice from pneumococcal infection. *J. Immunol.* 176:4369–74
14. Noursadeghi M, Bickerstaff MC, Gallimore JR, Herbert J, Cohen J, et al. 2000. Role of serum amyloid P component in bacterial infection: protection of the host or protection of the pathogen. *Proc. Natl. Acad. Sci. USA* 97:14584–89
15. Andersen O, Vilsgaard Ravn K, Juul Sorensen I, Jonson G, Holm Nielsen E, et al. 1997. Serum amyloid P component binds to influenza A virus haemagglutinin and inhibits the virus infection in vitro. *Scand. J. Immunol.* 46:331–37
16. de Haas CJ, van Leeuwen EM, van Bommel T, Verhoef J, van Kessel KP, et al. 2000. Serum amyloid P component bound to gram-negative bacteria prevents lipopolysaccharide-mediated classical pathway complement activation. *Infect. Immun.* 68:1753–59
17. Chang MK, Binder CJ, Torzewski M, Witztum JL. 2002. C-reactive protein binds to both oxidized LDL and apoptotic cells through recognition of a common ligand: phosphorylcholine of oxidized phospholipids. *Proc. Natl. Acad. Sci. USA* 99:13043–48
18. Mora S, Ridker PM. 2006. Justification for the Use of Statins in Primary Prevention: an Intervention Trial Evaluating Rosuvastatin (JUPITER)—can C-reactive protein be used to target statin therapy in primary prevention? *Am. J. Cardiol.* 97:33–41A
19. Zacho J, Tybjaerg-Hansen A, Jensen JS, Grande P, Sillesen H, et al. 2008. Genetically elevated C-reactive protein and ischemic vascular disease. *N. Engl. J. Med.* 359:1897–908
20. Melander O, Newton-Cheh C, Almgren P, Hedblad B, Berglund G, et al. 2009. Novel and conventional biomarkers for prediction of incident cardiovascular events in the community. *J. Am. Med. Assoc.* 302:49–57
21. Gillmore JD, Hutchinson WL, Herbert J, Bybee A, Mitchell DA, et al. 2004. Autoimmunity and glomerulonephritis in mice with targeted deletion of the serum amyloid P component gene: SAP deficiency or strain combination? *Immunology* 112:255–64
22. Roumenina LT, Ruseva MM, Zlatarova A, Ghai R, Kolev M, et al. 2006. Interaction of C1q with IgG1, C-reactive protein and pentraxin 3: mutational studies using recombinant globular head modules of human C1q A, B, and C chains. *Biochemistry* 45:4093–104
23. Agrawal A, Shrive AK, Greenhough TJ, Volanakis JE. 2001. Topology and structure of the C1q-binding site on C-reactive protein. *J. Immunol.* 166:3998–4004
24. Nauta AJ, Daha MR, van Kooten C, Roos A. 2003. Recognition and clearance of apoptotic cells: a role for complement and pentraxins. *Trends Immunol.* 24:148–54
25. Gershov D, Kim S, Brot N, Elkon KB. 2000. C-reactive protein binds to apoptotic cells, protects the cells from assembly of the terminal complement components, and sustains an antiinflammatory innate immune response: implications for systemic autoimmunity. *J. Exp. Med.* 192:1353–64
26. Jarva H, Jokiranta TS, Hellwage J, Zipfel PF, Meri S. 1999. Regulation of complement activation by C-reactive protein: targeting the complement inhibitory activity of factor H by an interaction with short consensus repeat domains 7 and 8–11. *J. Immunol.* 163:3957–62

27. Hakobyan S, Harris CL, Van Den Berg CW, Fernandez-Alonso MC, Goicoechea de Jorge E, et al. 2008. Complement factor H binds to denatured rather than to native pentameric C-reactive protein. *J. Biol. Chem.* 283:30451–60
28. Botto M, Hawkins PN, Bickerstaff MC, Herbert J, Bygrave AE, et al. 1997. Amyloid deposition is delayed in mice with targeted deletion of the serum amyloid P component gene. *Nat. Med.* 3:855–59
29. Bharadwaj D, Stein MP, Volzer M, Mold C, Du Clos TW. 1999. The major receptor for C-reactive protein on leukocytes is Fcγ receptor II. *J. Exp. Med.* 190:585–90
30. Mold C, Gresham HD, Du Clos TW. 2001. Serum amyloid P component and C-reactive protein mediate phagocytosis through murine FcγRs. *J. Immunol.* 166:1200–5
31. Saeland E, van Royen A, Hendriksen K, Vile-Weekhout H, Rijkers GT, et al. 2001. Human C-reactive protein does not bind to FcγRIIa on phagocytic cells. *J. Clin. Invest.* 107:641–43
32. Lu J, Marnell LL, Marjon KD, Mold C, Du Clos TW, et al. 2008. Structural recognition and functional activation of FcγR by innate pentraxins. *Nature* 456:989–92
33. Breviario F, d'Aniello EM, Golay J, Peri G, Bottazzi B, et al. 1992. Interleukin-1-inducible genes in endothelial cells. Cloning of a new gene related to C-reactive protein and serum amyloid P component. *J. Biol. Chem.* 267:22190–97
34. Lee GW, Lee TH, Vilcek J. 1993. TSG-14, a tumor necrosis factor- and IL-1-inducible protein, is a novel member of the pentaxin family of acute phase proteins. *J. Immunol.* 150:1804–12
35. Inforzato A, Peri G, Doni A, Garlanda C, Mantovani A, et al. 2006. Structure and function of the long pentraxin PTX3 glycosidic moiety: fine-tuning of the interaction with C1q and complement activation. *Biochemistry* 45:11540–51
36. Inforzato A, Rivieccio V, Morreale AP, Bastone A, Salustri A, et al. 2008. Structural characterization of PTX3 disulfide bond network and its multimeric status in cumulus matrix organization. *J. Biol. Chem.* 283:10147–61
37. Bottazzi B, Garlanda C, Cotena A, Moalli F, Jaillon S, et al. 2009. The long pentraxin PTX3 as a prototypic humoral pattern recognition receptor: interplay with cellular innate immunity. *Immunol. Rev.* 227:9–18
38. Norata GD, Marchesi P, Pirillo A, Uboldi P, Chiesa G, et al. 2008. Long pentraxin 3, a key component of innate immunity, is modulated by high-density lipoproteins in endothelial cells. *Arterioscler. Thromb. Vasc. Biol.* 28:925–31
39. Doni A, Peri G, Chieppa M, Allavena P, Pasqualini F, et al. 2003. Production of the soluble pattern recognition receptor PTX3 by myeloid, but not plasmacytoid, dendritic cells. *Eur. J. Immunol.* 33:2886–93
40. Jaillon S, Peri G, Delneste Y, Fremaux I, Doni A, et al. 2007. The humoral pattern recognition receptor PTX3 is stored in neutrophil granules and localizes in extracellular traps. *J. Exp. Med.* 204:793–804
41. Salio M, Chimenti S, De Angelis N, Molla F, Maina V, et al. 2008. Cardioprotective function of the long pentraxin PTX3 in acute myocardial infarction. *Circulation* 117:1055–64
42. Han B, Mura M, Andrade CF, Okutani D, Lodyga M, et al. 2005. TNFα-induced long pentraxin PTX3 expression in human lung epithelial cells via JNK. *J. Immunol.* 175:8303–11
43. Willeke F, Assad A, Findeisen P, Schromm E, Grobholz R, et al. 2006. Overexpression of a member of the pentraxin family (PTX3) in human soft tissue liposarcoma. *Eur. J. Cancer* 42:2639–46
44. Doni A, Mantovani G, Porta C, Tuckermann J, Reichardt HM, et al. 2008. Cell-specific regulation of PTX3 by glucocorticoid hormones in hematopoietic and nonhematopoietic cells. *J. Biol. Chem.* 283:29983–92
45. Garlanda C, Hirsch E, Bozza S, Salustri A, De Acetis M, et al. 2002. Non-redundant role of the long pentraxin PTX3 in antifungal innate immune response. *Nature* 420:182–86
46. Diniz SN, Nomizo R, Cisalpino PS, Teixeira MM, Brown GD, et al. 2004. PTX3 function as an opsonin for the dectin-1-dependent internalization of zymosan by macrophages. *J. Leukoc. Biol.* 75:649–56
47. Jeannin P, Bottazzi B, Sironi M, Doni A, Rusnati M, et al. 2005. Complexity and complementarity of outer membrane protein A recognition by cellular and humoral innate immunity receptors. *Immunity* 22:551–60
48. Bozza S, Bistoni F, Gaziano R, Pitzurra L, Zelante T, et al. 2006. Pentraxin 3 protects from MCMV infection and reactivation through TLR sensing pathways leading to IRF3 activation. *Blood* 108:3387–96

49. Reading PC, Bozza S, Gilbertson B, Tate M, Moretti S, et al. 2008. Antiviral activity of the long chain pentraxin PTX3 against influenza viruses. *J. Immunol.* 180:3391–98
50. Cotena A, Maina V, Sironi M, Bottazzi B, Jeannin P, et al. 2007. Complement dependent amplification of the innate response to a cognate microbial ligand by the long pentraxin PTX3. *J. Immunol.* 179:6311–17
51. Bottazzi B, Vouret-Craviari V, Bastone A, De Gioia L, Matteucci C, et al. 1997. Multimer formation and ligand recognition by the long pentraxin PTX3. Similarities and differences with the short pentraxins C-reactive protein and serum amyloid P component. *J. Biol. Chem.* 272:32817–23
52. Nauta AJ, Bottazzi B, Mantovani A, Salvatori G, Kishore U, et al. 2003. Biochemical and functional characterization of the interaction between pentraxin 3 and C1q. *Eur. J. Immunol.* 33:465–73
53. Deban L, Jarva H, Lehtinen MJ, Bottazzi B, Bastone A, et al. 2008. Binding of the long pentraxin PTX3 to Factor H: interacting domains and function in the regulation of complement activation. *J. Immunol.* 181:8433–40
54. Ma YJ, Doni A, Hummelshøj T, Honoré C, Bastone A, et al. 2009. Synergy between ficolin-2 and pentraxin 3 boosts innate immune recognition and complement deposition. *J. Biol. Chem.* 284:28263–75
55. Ng PM, Le Saux A, Lee CM, Tan NS, Lu J, et al. 2007. C-reactive protein collaborates with plasma lectins to boost immune response against bacteria. *EMBO J.* 26:3431–40
56. Zhang J, Koh J, Lu J, Thiel S, Leong BS, et al. 2009. Local inflammation induces complement crosstalk which amplifies the antimicrobial response. *PLoS Pathog.* 5:e1000282
57. Camozzi M, Rusnati M, Bugatti A, Bottazzi B, Mantovani A, et al. 2006. Identification of an antiangiogenic FGF2-binding site in the N terminus of the soluble pattern recognition receptor PTX3. *J. Biol. Chem.* 281:22605–13
58. Salustri A, Garlanda C, Hirsch E, De Acetis M, Maccagno A, et al. 2004. PTX3 plays a key role in the organization of the cumulus oophorus extracellular matrix and in in vivo fertilization. *Development* 131:1577–86
59. Scarchilli L, Camaioni A, Bottazzi B, Negri V, Doni A, et al. 2007. PTX3 interacts with interalpha-trypsin inhibitor: implications for hyaluronan organization and cumulus oophorus expansion. *J. Biol. Chem.* 282:30161–70
60. Gaziano R, Bozza S, Bellocchio S, Perruccio K, Montagnoli C, et al. 2004. Anti-*Aspergillus fumigatus* efficacy of pentraxin 3 alone and in combination with antifungals. *Antimicrob. Agents Chemother.* 48:4414–21
61. Soares AC, Souza DG, Pinho V, Vieira AT, Nicoli JR, et al. 2006. Dual function of the long pentraxin PTX3 in resistance against pulmonary infection with *Klebsiella pneumoniae* in transgenic mice. *Microbes Infect.* 8:1321–29
62. Dias AA, Goodman AR, Dos Santos JL, Gomes RN, Altmeyer A, et al. 2001. TSG-14 transgenic mice have improved survival to endotoxemia and to CLP-induced sepsis. *J. Leukoc. Biol.* 69:928–36
63. Olesen R, Wejse C, Velez DR, Bisseye C, Sodemann M, et al. 2007. DC-SIGN (CD209), Pentraxin 3 and vitamin D receptor gene variants associate with pulmonary tuberculosis risk in West-Africans. *Genes Immun.* 8:456–67
64. May L, Kuningas M, van Bodegom D, Meij HJ, Frolich M, et al. 2009. Genetic variation in pentraxin (PTX) 3 gene associates with PTX3 production and fertility in women. *Biol. Reprod.* doi: 10.1095/biolreprod.109.079111
65. Gupta G, Surolia A. 2007. Collectins: sentinels of innate immunity. *Bioessays* 29:452–64
66. Wright JR. 2005. Immunoregulatory functions of surfactant proteins. *Nat. Rev. Immunol.* 5:58–68
67. Lambris JD, Ricklin D, Geisbrecht BV. 2008. Complement evasion by human pathogens. *Nat. Rev. Microbiol.* 6:132–42
68. Kishore U, Gaboriaud C, Waters P, Shrive AK, Greenhough TJ, et al. 2004. C1q and tumor necrosis factor superfamily: modularity and versatility. *Trends Immunol.* 25:551–61
69. Castellano G, Woltman AM, Nauta AJ, Roos A, Trouw LA, et al. 2004. Maturation of dendritic cells abrogates C1q production in vivo and in vitro. *Blood* 103:3813–20
70. Sjoberg AP, Trouw LA, Blom AM. 2009. Complement activation and inhibition: a delicate balance. *Trends Immunol.* 30:83–90
71. Ghebrehiwet B, Peerschke EI. 2004. cC1q-R (calreticulin) and gC1q-R/p33: ubiquitously expressed multi-ligand binding cellular proteins involved in inflammation and infection. *Mol. Immunol.* 41:173–83

72. Ogden CA, deCathelineau A, Hoffmann PR, Bratton D, Ghebrehiwet B, et al. 2001. C1q and mannose binding lectin engagement of cell surface calreticulin and CD91 initiates macropinocytosis and uptake of apoptotic cells. *J. Exp. Med.* 194:781–95
73. Norsworthy PJ, Fossati-Jimack L, Cortes-Hernandez J, Taylor PR, Bygrave AE, et al. 2004. Murine CD93 (C1qRp) contributes to the removal of apoptotic cells in vivo but is not required for C1q-mediated enhancement of phagocytosis. *J. Immunol.* 172:3406–14
74. Ghiran I, Barbashov SF, Klickstein LB, Tas SW, Jensenius JC, et al. 2000. Complement receptor 1/CD35 is a receptor for mannan-binding lectin. *J. Exp. Med.* 192:1797–808
75. Vandivier RW, Ogden CA, Fadok VA, Hoffmann PR, Brown KK, et al. 2002. Role of surfactant proteins A, D, and C1q in the clearance of apoptotic cells in vivo and in vitro: calreticulin and CD91 as a common collectin receptor complex. *J. Immunol.* 169:3978–86
76. Gardai SJ, Xiao YQ, Dickinson M, Nick JA, Voelker DR, et al. 2003. By binding SIRPα or calreticulin/CD91, lung collectins act as dual function surveillance molecules to suppress or enhance inflammation. *Cell* 115:13–23
77. Zutter MM, Edelson BT. 2007. The α2β1 integrin: a novel collectin/C1q receptor. *Immunobiology* 212:343–53
78. Lu JH, Teh BK, Wang L, Wang YN, Tan YS, et al. 2008. The classical and regulatory functions of C1q in immunity and autoimmunity. *Cell. Mol. Immunol.* 5:9–21
79. Kishore U, Greenhough TJ, Waters P, Shrive AK, Ghai R, et al. 2006. Surfactant proteins SP-A and SP-D: structure, function and receptors. *Mol. Immunol.* 43:1293–315
80. Garred P, Larsen F, Seyfarth J, Fujita R, Madsen HO. 2006. Mannose-binding lectin and its genetic variants. *Genes Immun.* 7:85–94
81. Garred P, Honoré C, Ma YJ, Munthe-Fog L, Hummelshøj T. 2009. MBL2, FCN1, FCN2 and FCN3—the genes behind the initiation of the lectin pathway of complement. *Mol. Immunol.* 46:2737–44
82. Herias MV, Hogenkamp A, van Asten AJ, Tersteeg MH, van Eijk M, et al. 2007. Expression sites of the collectin SP-D suggest its importance in first line host defense: power of combining in situ hybridisation, RT-PCR and immunohistochemistry. *Mol. Immunol.* 44:3324–32
83. Madsen J, Kliem A, Tornoe I, Skjodt K, Koch C, et al. 2000. Localization of lung surfactant protein D on mucosal surfaces in human tissues. *J. Immunol.* 164:5866–70
84. Han YM, Romero R, Kim YM, Kim JS, Richani K, et al. 2007. Surfactant protein-A mRNA expression by human fetal membranes is increased in histological chorioamnionitis but not in spontaneous labor at term. *J. Pathol.* 211:489–96
85. Leth-Larsen R, Zhong F, Chow VT, Holmskov U, Lu J. 2007. The SARS coronavirus spike glycoprotein is selectively recognized by lung surfactant protein D and activates macrophages. *Immunobiology* 212:201–11
86. Chroneos ZC, Abdolrasulnia R, Whitsett JA, Rice WR, Shepherd VL. 1996. Purification of a cell-surface receptor for surfactant protein A. *J. Biol. Chem.* 271:16375–83
87. Borron P, McCormack FX, Elhalwagi BM, Chroneos ZC, Lewis JF, et al. 1998. Surfactant protein A inhibits T cell proliferation via its collagen-like tail and a 210-kDa receptor. *Am. J. Physiol.* 275:L679–86
88. Weikert LF, Lopez JP, Abdolrasulnia R, Chroneos ZC, Shepherd VL. 2000. Surfactant protein A enhances mycobacterial killing by rat macrophages through a nitric oxide-dependent pathway. *Am. J. Physiol. Lung Cell Mol. Physiol.* 279:L216–23
89. Janssen WJ, McPhillips KA, Dickinson MG, Linderman DJ, Morimoto K, et al. 2008. Surfactant proteins A and D suppress alveolar macrophage phagocytosis via interaction with SIRP α. *Am. J. Respir. Crit. Care Med.* 178:158–67
90. Sano H, Chiba H, Iwaki D, Sohma H, Voelker DR, et al. 2000. Surfactant proteins A and D bind CD14 by different mechanisms. *J. Biol. Chem.* 275:22442–51
91. Ohya M, Nishitani C, Sano H, Yamada C, Mitsuzawa H, et al. 2006. Human pulmonary surfactant protein D binds the extracellular domains of Toll-like receptors 2 and 4 through the carbohydrate recognition domain by a mechanism different from its binding to phosphatidylinositol and lipopolysaccharide. *Biochemistry* 45:8657–64
92. Kudo K, Sano H, Takahashi H, Kuronuma K, Yokota S, et al. 2004. Pulmonary collectins enhance phagocytosis of *Mycobacterium avium* through increased activity of mannose receptor. *J. Immunol.* 172:7592–602

93. Kuronuma K, Sano H, Kato K, Kudo K, Hyakushima N, et al. 2004. Pulmonary surfactant protein A augments the phagocytosis of *Streptococcus pneumoniae* by alveolar macrophages through a casein kinase 2-dependent increase of cell surface localization of scavenger receptor A. *J. Biol. Chem.* 279:21421–30
94. Chaka W, Verheul AF, Vaishnav VV, Cherniak R, Scharringa J, et al. 1997. Induction of TNF-α in human peripheral blood mononuclear cells by the mannoprotein of *Cryptococcus neoformans* involves human mannose binding protein. *J. Immunol.* 159:2979–85
95. Jack DL, Read RC, Tenner AJ, Frosch M, Turner MW, et al. 2001. Mannose-binding lectin regulates the inflammatory response of human professional phagocytes to *Neisseria meningitidis* serogroup B. *J. Infect. Dis.* 184:1152–62
96. Ip WKE, Takahashi K, Moore KJ, Stuart LM, Ezekowitz RAB. 2008. Mannose-binding lectin enhances Toll-like receptors 2 and 6 signaling from the phagosome. *J. Exp. Med.* 205:169–81
97. Fujita T, Matsushita M, Endo Y. 2004. The lectin-complement pathway—its role in innate immunity and evolution. *Immunol. Rev.* 198:185–202
98. Honore C, Hummelshoj T, Hansen BE, Madsen HO, Eggleton P, et al. 2007. The innate immune component ficolin 3 (Hakata antigen) mediates the clearance of late apoptotic cells. *Arthritis Rheum.* 56:1598–607
99. Liu Y, Endo Y, Homma S, Kanno K, Yaginuma H, et al. 2005. Ficolin A and ficolin B are expressed in distinct ontogenic patterns and cell types in the mouse. *Mol. Immunol.* 42:1265–73
100. Kuraya M, Matsushita M, Endo Y, Thiel S, Fujita T. 2003. Expression of H-ficolin/Hakata antigen, mannose-binding lectin-associated serine protease (MASP)-1 and MASP-3 by human glioma cell line T98G. *Int. Immunol.* 15:109–17
101. Frankenberger M, Schwaeble W, Ziegler-Heitbrock L. 2008. Expression of M-Ficolin in human monocytes and macrophages. *Mol. Immunol.* 45:1414–30
102. Liu Y, Endo Y, Iwaki D, Nakata M, Matsushita M, et al. 2005. Human M-ficolin is a secretory protein that activates the lectin complement pathway. *J. Immunol.* 175:3150–56
103. Teh C, Le Y, Lee SH, Lu J. 2000. M-ficolin is expressed on monocytes and is a lectin binding to N-acetyl-D-glucosamine and mediates monocyte adhesion and phagocytosis of *Escherichia coli*. *Immunology* 101:225–32
104. Tsujimura M, Miyazaki T, Kojima E, Sagara Y, Shiraki H, et al. 2002. Serum concentration of Hakata antigen, a member of the ficolins, is linked with inhibition of *Aerococcus viridans* growth. *Clin. Chim. Acta* 325:139–46
105. Garlatti V, Belloy N, Martin L, Lacroix M, Matsushita M, et al. 2007. Structural insights into the innate immune recognition specificities of L- and H-ficolins. *EMBO J.* 26:623–33
106. Aoyagi Y, Adderson EE, Rubens CE, Bohnsack JF, Min JG, et al. 2007. L-ficolin/mannose-binding lectin-associated serine protease complexes bind to group B streptococci largely through *N*-acetylneuraminic acid of capsular polysaccharide, and activate the complement pathway. *Infect. Immun.* 76:179–88
107. Endo Y, Nakazawa N, Liu Y, Iwaki D, Takahashi M, et al. 2005. Carbohydrate-binding specificities of mouse ficolin A, a splicing variant of ficolin A and ficolin B and their complex formation with MASP-2 and sMAP. *Immunogenetics* 57:837–44
108. Ma YG, Cho MY, Zhao M, Park JW, Matsushita M, et al. 2004. Human mannose-binding lectin and L-ficolin function as specific pattern recognition proteins in the lectin activation pathway of complement. *J. Biol. Chem.* 279:25307–12
109. Kuraya M, Ming Z, Liu X, Matsushita M, Fujita T. 2005. Specific binding of L-ficolin and H-ficolin to apoptotic cells leads to complement activation. *Immunobiology* 209:689–97
110. Lacroix M, Dumestre-Perard C, Schoehn G, Houen G, Cesbron JY, et al. 2009. Residue Lys57 in the collagen-like region of human L-ficolin and its counterpart Lys47 in H-ficolin play a key role in the interaction with the mannan-binding lectin-associated serine proteases and the collectin receptor calreticulin. *J. Immunol.* 182:456–65
111. Munthe-Fog L, Hummelshoj T, Honore C, Madsen HO, Permin H, et al. 2009. Immunodeficiency associated with FCN3 mutation and ficolin-3 deficiency. *N. Engl. J. Med.* 360:2637–44
112. Stover CM, Luckett JC, Echtenacher B, Dupont A, Figgitt SE, et al. 2008. Properdin plays a protective role in polymicrobial septic peritonitis. *J. Immunol.* 180:3313–18

113. Hourcade DE. 2006. The role of properdin in the assembly of the alternative pathway C3 convertases of complement. *J. Biol. Chem.* 281:2128–32
114. Spitzer D, Mitchell LM, Atkinson JP, Hourcade DE. 2007. Properdin can initiate complement activation by binding specific target surfaces and providing a platform for de novo convertase assembly. *J. Immunol.* 179:2600–8
115. Tyson KR, Elkins C, de Silva AM. 2008. A novel mechanism of complement inhibition unmasked by a tick salivary protein that binds to properdin. *J. Immunol.* 180:3964–68
116. Uhlar CM, Whitehead AS. 1999. Serum amyloid A, the major vertebrate acute-phase reactant. *Eur. J. Biochem.* 265:501–23
117. Meek RL, Eriksen N, Benditt EP. 1992. Murine serum amyloid A3 is a high density apolipoprotein and is secreted by macrophages. *Proc. Natl. Acad. Sci. USA* 89:7949–52
118. Hari-Dass R, Shah C, Meyer DJ, Raynes JG. 2005. Serum amyloid A protein binds to outer membrane protein A of gram-negative bacteria. *J. Biol. Chem.* 280:18562–67
119. Shah C, Hari-Dass R, Raynes JG. 2006. Serum amyloid A is an innate immune opsonin for Gram-negative bacteria. *Blood* 108:1751–57
120. Cai Z, Cai L, Jiang J, Chang KS, Van Der Westhuyzen DR, et al. 2007. Human serum amyloid A protein inhibits hepatitis C virus entry into cells. *J. Virol.* 81:6128–33
121. He R, Shepard LW, Chen J, Pan ZK, Ye RD. 2006. Serum amyloid A is an endogenous ligand that differentially induces IL-12 and IL-23. *J. Immunol.* 177:4072–79
122. Koga T, Torigoshi T, Motokawa S, Miyashita T, Maeda Y, et al. 2008. Serum amyloid A-induced IL-6 production by rheumatoid synoviocytes. *FEBS Lett.* 582:579–85
123. Su SB, Gong W, Gao JL, Shen W, Murphy PM, et al. 1999. A seven-transmembrane, G protein-coupled receptor, FPRL1, mediates the chemotactic activity of serum amyloid A for human phagocytic cells. *J. Exp. Med.* 189:395–402
124. He R, Sang H, Ye RD. 2003. Serum amyloid A induces IL-8 secretion through a G protein-coupled receptor, FPRL1/LXA4R. *Blood* 101:1572–81
125. He RL, Zhou J, Hanson CZ, Chen J, Cheng N, et al. 2009. Serum amyloid A induces G-CSF expression and neutrophilia via Toll-like receptor 2. *Blood* 113:429–37
126. Baranova IN, Vishnyakova TG, Bocharov AV, Kurlander R, Chen Z, et al. 2005. Serum amyloid A binding to CLA-1 (CD36 and LIMPII analogous-1) mediates serum amyloid A protein-induced activation of ERK1/2 and p38 mitogen-activated protein kinases. *J. Biol. Chem.* 280:8031–40
127. He YW, Li H, Zhang J, Hsu CL, Lin E, et al. 2004. The extracellular matrix protein mindin is a pattern-recognition molecule for microbial pathogens. *Nat. Immunol.* 5:88–97
128. Jia W, Li H, He YW. 2008. Pattern recognition molecule mindin promotes intranasal clearance of influenza viruses. *J. Immunol.* 180:6255–61
129. Li Y, Cao C, Jia W, Yu L, Mo M, et al. 2009. Structure of the F-spondin domain of mindin, an integrin ligand and pattern recognition molecule. *EMBO J.* 28:286–97
130. Henning LN, Azad AK, Parsa KV, Crowther JE, Tridandapani S, et al. 2008. Pulmonary surfactant protein A regulates TLR expression and activity in human macrophages. *J. Immunol.* 180:7847–58
131. Nimmerjahn F, Ravetch JV. 2008. Anti-inflammatory actions of intravenous immunoglobulin. *Annu. Rev. Immunol.* 26:513–33
132. Okemefuna AI, Nan R, Miller A, Gor J, Perkins SJ. 2010. Complement factor H binds at two independent sites to C-reactive protein in acute phase concentrations. *J. Biol. Chem.* 285:1053–65

NOTE ADDED IN PROOF

Okemefuna et al. (132) recently showed by analytical ultracentrifugation, surface plasmon resonance, and synchrotron X-ray scattering methods that wild-type FH interacts with native CRP in both the fluid and surface phases, definitively demonstrating that in fact the FH-CRP interaction does exist.

Early Events in B Cell Activation

Naomi E. Harwood and Facundo D. Batista

Lymphocyte Interaction Laboratory, Cancer Research UK London Research Institute, Lincoln's Inn Fields Laboratories, London WC2A 3PX, United Kingdom; email: facundo.batista@cancer.org.uk

Annu. Rev. Immunol. 2010. 28:185–210

First published online as a Review in Advance on December 8, 2009

The *Annual Review of Immunology* is online at immunol.annualreviews.org

This article's doi: 10.1146/annurev-immunol-030409-101216

0732-0582/10/0423-0185$20.00

Key Words

B cell receptor, antigen, cytoskeleton, kinetic segregation, microsignalosome

Abstract

B cell activation is initiated by the ligation of the B cell receptor (BCR) with antigen and ultimately results in the production of protective antibodies against potentially pathogenic invaders. Here we review recent literature concerned with the spatiotemporal dynamic characterization of the early molecular events of B cell activation, including the initiation of BCR triggering, the formation of BCR microclusters, and the dynamic regulation of BCR signaling. Because these events involve the considerable reorganization of molecules within the membrane, an important role for the cytoskeleton is emerging in the regulation of B cell activation. At each stage we highlight the role of the cytoskeleton, establishing its pivotal position during the initiation and regulation of B cell activation.

INTRODUCTION

BCR: B cell receptor

Immunoreceptor tyrosine activation motif (ITAM): conserved sequence of $YXXLX_{(7-12)}YXXL$ residues commonly found in the cytoplasmic tails of cell surface proteins and responsible for mediating intracellular signaling

Phospholipase Cγ2 (PLCγ2): catalyzes the hydrolysis of phosphatidylinositol 4,5-bisphosphate (PIP_2) to form inositol-1,4,5-phosphate (IP_3) and diacylglycerol (DAG)

PI3K: phosphoinositide-3-kinase

Btk: Bruton's tyrosine kinase

Blnk: B cell linker (also known as SLP-65 and BASH)

Germinal center (GC): organization of follicular B cells and follicular dendritic cells (FDCs) that forms approximately five days after immunization with antigen

B cells are a critical component of the adaptive immune system, providing both specific and long-lasting protection from a tremendously diverse range of potential pathogens. B cell activation is initiated following the recognition of antigen through the B cell receptor (BCR) and results in B cell proliferation and differentiation. Activated B cells can differentiate to form either plasma cells capable of antibody secretion or memory cells that provide long-lived protection against secondary infection. The importance of these effector cells in enhancing an individual's survival requires that the processes underlying B cell activation be both highly coordinated and precisely regulated.

Traditionally, much of our understanding concerning the molecular events underlying B cell activation was gleaned from standard biochemical characterizations in response to soluble antigen or antibodies to the BCR. These methods revealed that the BCR consists of an antigen-binding membrane immunoglobulin (mIg) component in complex with an Igα/β sheath containing immunoreceptor tyrosine activation motifs (ITAMs) and that these ITAMs enable the transmission of intracellular signaling (1). Antigen engagement leads to BCR cross-linking and phosphorylation of ITAM motifs by the Src family kinase Lyn. This phosphorylation event initiates the formation of the signalosome, an assembly of intracellular signaling molecules, such as the kinase Syk, phospholipase-Cγ2 (PLCγ2), phosphoinositide 3-kinase (PI3K), Bruton's tyrosine kinase (Btk), and Vav, alongside adaptor molecules such as B cell linker (Blnk) (2–6). The signalosome allows the coordinated regulation of downstream cellular events, including signaling through second messengers such as calcium, the induction of gene expression, and the internalization of antigen. Subsequently, antigen within endosomes is processed, loaded onto the major histocompatibility complex (MHC), and presented on the B cell surface (7, 8). This antigen presentation allows for the recruitment of cognate $CD4^+$ T helper cells to facilitate the complete activation of B cells. Depending on where the activated B cells reside, they can either rapidly produce low-affinity antibodies (9) or they can enter germinal centers (GCs) to undergo somatic hypermutation and generate antibodies with extremely high affinity (10, 11).

The identification of the important mediators and characterization of signaling pathways detailed above has provided an essential foundation for developing our understanding of how humoral immune responses are initiated. However, because these experimental approaches do not provide spatiotemporal dynamic information, they cannot be used to establish the precise molecular mechanisms underlying and regulating activation within the B cell (12). Furthermore, it is now widely accepted that the predominant form of antigen initiating B cell activation in vivo is attached to a membrane surface (13, 14). Because the recognition of physically constrained antigen involves the considerable alteration of B cell morphology, the underlying cytoskeleton likely plays a critical, but currently unappreciated, role in regulating B cell activation in vivo. Recent genetic evidence supports this view: Mutations in key cytoskeleton regulators have been associated with the development of antibody deficiency syndromes in humans (15). In this review, we discuss recent evidence garnered by using a variety of innovative imaging strategies to reveal the spatiotemporal dynamics of molecular events during B cell activation. Throughout we highlight the emerging and important role of the B cell cytoskeleton in regulating B cell activation in vivo. To conclude we describe the latest intravital investigations that have enabled the visualization of sites and mechanisms by which B cells encounter antigen in vivo.

BCR DISTRIBUTION IN RESTING B CELLS

Although understanding the state of the BCR in the resting membrane prior to antigen stimulation is critically important for characterizing the mechanism of B cell activation, this remains to be established. Native gel electrophoresis demonstrated that BCRs interact within the resting membrane, suggesting that BCRs form an oligomeric structure prior to antigen stimulation (16). However, more recently a fluorescence resonance energy transfer (FRET)-based approach detected no interaction between BCRs labeled with either Igα-CFP or Igα-YFP, suggesting that the BCR exists in a monomeric form (17). Because B cell activation is associated with an alteration in the distribution of BCR in the membrane, it is necessary to understand the dynamics of the BCR and the mechanisms regulating the distribution of the BCR in the resting B cell membrane.

Dynamic Diffusion of Proteins in the Plasma Membrane

The original fluid-mosaic model postulated by Singer & Nicholson (18) suggested a general organization for proteins and lipids in the plasma membrane. The essential features of this model have since proven to be in agreement with experimental data; however, the predicted unrestricted diffusion of membrane components within the plane of the membrane has been called into question (19). In line with this, biochemical characterizations have suggested the presence of microdomains within a membrane (20). These microdomains have differential lipid composition, and, because they are often enriched in signaling molecules such as Lyn, they may play an important role in initiating and regulating cellular activation processes (21–23). The distribution and dynamics of various transmembrane proteins in the membranes of fibroblasts have been directly visualized using single molecule tracking (24–26). Using this approach, investigators observed that single molecules were indeed free to move but within confinement zones with diameters typically between 30 and 700 nm. However, long-range diffusion across the membrane was restricted and required the molecule to jump between adjoining confinement zones. In light of these results, the authors proposed a picket-fence model to describe the movement of proteins within the membrane (27). In this model, selected transmembrane proteins delimit confinement zones acting as pickets and are anchored to the underlying cytoskeleton fence. The picket-fence model suggests a prominent role for the cytoskeleton in determining the diffusion dynamics of proteins within the plasma membrane. In line with this view, Davis and colleagues (28) have used transmission electron microscopy to demonstrate that cholesterol-enriched islands containing protein clusters are indeed rich in actin. Furthermore, using inhibitors of T cell receptor (TCR) signaling, these authors demonstrated that the cytoskeleton plays a key role in the formation and/or maintenance of these protein islands in T cells.

BCR Diffusion Is Shaped by the Cytoskeleton

In view of these observations, the cytoskeleton likely also plays a role in determining the diffusion dynamics of the BCR in the resting B cell. To test this hypothesis, we developed a two-color acquisition total internal reflection fluorescence microscopy (TIRFM) strategy to simultaneously visualize and track the BCR alongside components of the cytoskeleton (B. Treanor, D. Depoil, A. Gonzalez-Granja, P. Barral, M. Weber, O. Dushek, A. Bruckbauer & F.D. Batista, submitted manuscript). In resting B cells, BCRs that were located in actin-rich regions exhibited slower diffusion than those that were located in actin-poor regions. Furthermore, we observed that the dynamic linkage of the actin cytoskeleton with the plasma membrane through the ezrin-radixin-moesin (ERM) family of proteins establishes and gates barriers to BCR diffusion. Interestingly, disruption of this ezrin-defined actin network removes constraints to BCR diffusion and leads to initiation of intracellular calcium signaling, possibly as a result of the formation of clusters of BCR. Clearly, the cytoskeleton plays a significant role in determining the distribution and behavior of BCRs in the resting B cell prior to antigen stimulation.

Fluorescence resonance energy transfer (FRET): method that uses the efficiency of energy transfer to give an estimate of molecular distance between a fluorescence donor and acceptor

Fluid mosaic model: postulates that the plasma membrane of a cell is composed of a lipid bilayer patterned as a mosaic containing other associated macromolecules, including integral membrane proteins and glycoproteins; all components of the plasma membrane are free to move laterally within the membrane

Total internal reflection fluorescence microscopy (TIRFM): visualizes molecules in contact with a surface to a depth of approximately 200 nm

Ezrin-radixin-moesin (ERM): family of closely related proteins that function as molecular linkers between the actin cytoskeleton and components of the plasma membrane

Follicular dendritic cells (FDCs): population of cells in the GC, expressing high levels of adhesion molecules and displaying dendritic-like morphology; thought to be mesenchymal in origin

B CELL ACTIVATION IS INITIATED FOLLOWING ANTIGEN ENCOUNTER

The binding of specific antigen to the mIg component of the BCR initiates intracellular signaling and results in B cell activation. Given the propensity of multivalent, but not monovalent, soluble antigen to stimulate B cell responses (S. Minguet, M. Reth, and W. Schamel, personal communication), B cell activation was assumed to be a result of dimerization of monomeric BCR. In support of this assumption, early imaging studies demonstrated that cross-linked BCRs were located in a cap structure following stimulation with soluble multimeric antigen (29–31). Within this cap the ITAMs of numerous Igα/β sheaths are brought close together, allowing for their phosphorylation and initiating the assembly of the signalosome. Alternatively, and in light of biochemical data suggesting higher order structure of the BCR in the resting B cell membrane (16), B cell activation may be triggered by antigen binding that disrupts the existing oligomeric structure (32). However, the precise mechanism by which extracellular antigen engagement is communicated across the membrane to trigger activation processes remains unclear.

Membrane-Bound Antigen Initiates B Cell Activation In Vivo

B cells are capable of recognizing and responding to soluble antigen, and they can also recognize antigen on the surface of antigen-presenting cells (APCs), such as dendritic cells (DCs) (33, 34), follicular dendritic cells (FDCs) (35–37), and macrophages (38). However, the mechanism and cell surface receptors involved remain unclear (reviewed in 39). Membrane-bound antigen seems to represent a more effective trigger of B cell activation than does soluble antigen because the threshold of antigen required to induce activation by the former is lower than that of the latter (40–42). Indeed it is now apparent that the predominant form of antigen that mediates B cell activation in vivo is bound to a membrane surface (13, 14). In light of this, the original models proposed to describe the initiation of B cell activation in response to soluble antigen suffer from two major limitations. First, they do not consider the significant alteration in B cell morphology that is required for the recognition of antigen on a constrained surface. Second, monomeric antigen on the surface of an APC can initiate B cell activation (43), indicating that the cross-linking of BCRs may represent a later stage after the initial triggering has taken place. Interestingly, because T cells require the recognition of antigen in complex with MHC on the surface of an APC, these two factors have been considered in the development of two prominent models to explain the initiation of T cell activation. Because these models may prove useful in deriving a description of the mechanism underlying triggering of B cell activation, we discuss conformational change and kinetic segregation models in more detail below (**Figure 1**).

Conformational Change Model

In simple terms, the conformational change model supposes that the binding of antigen to the extracellular domain of the immunoreceptor is communicated to the intracellular domain through a series of conformational changes within the immunoreceptor (44, 45). This model depends on a degree of conformational flexibility within the immunoreceptor, potentially in the antigen-binding component of the TCR itself or by alteration of its interaction with the CD3 anchoring component. Following the publication of several impressive high-resolution X-ray crystallography structures (reviewed in 46, 47), this model fell out of favor. These structures, collected in the presence or absence of soluble peptide-MHC or antibodies to the TCR, indicated that although antigen binding caused localized alterations in the extracellular domains themselves, few changes were transmitted to the membrane-proximal regions (reviewed in 48, 49). However, although informative, these structural studies provide only static snapshots of the receptor conformation. Furthermore, these changes

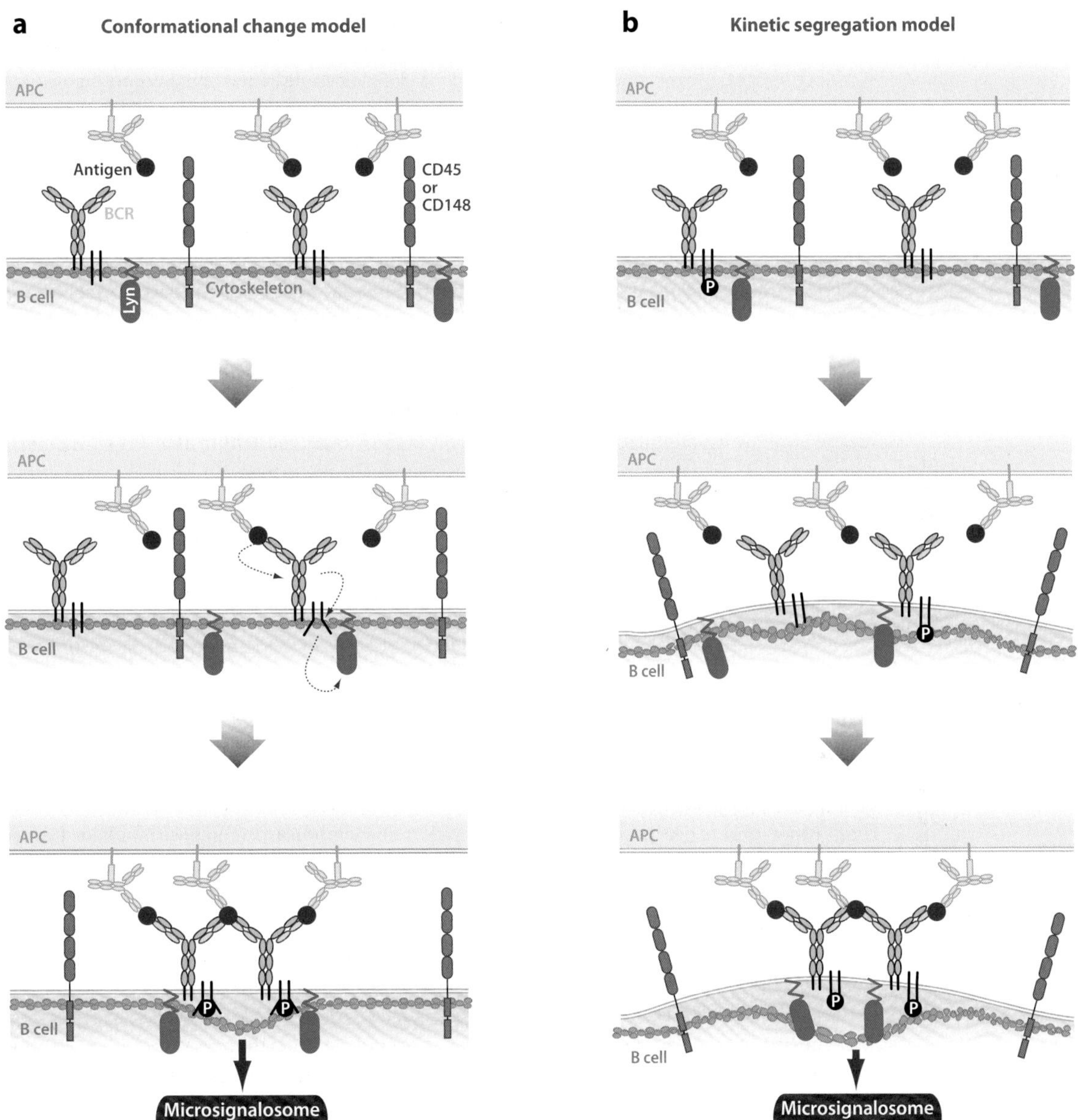

Figure 1

Two models of B cell activation in response to membrane-bound antigen. Schematic representation of two models of B cell activation in response to antigen on the surface of an antigen-presenting cell (APC). In both panels, the BCR is green, antigen is red, the cytoskeleton is brown, the Src family kinase Lyn is blue, and CD45 or CD148 is purple. (*a*) The conformational change model assumes that engagement of the BCR with antigen triggers a conformational change(s) that is transmitted through the BCR across the B cell membrane (*red dotted arrows*) to initiate recruitment of Lyn and phosphorylation of the Igα/β ITAMs, leading to the assembly of the microsignalosome. (*b*) The kinetic segregation model assumes that the exclusion of bulky phosphatases such as CD45 or CD148 from close contact sites increases the likelihood of phosphorylated BCR being found in these sites. Engagement of the BCR with specific antigen will retain phosphorylated BCRs in these close contact sites, promoting the assembly of the microsignalosome.

may not be representative of those changes induced following stimulation with physiological antigen in the context of the APC.

More recently, experimental evidence has been collected in support of the conformational change model, prompting a reevaluation of this model in the T cell field. Alarcón and colleagues (50) demonstrated that TCR engagement with ligand triggered exposure of a proline-rich region in the CD3ε component of the TCR. This conformational change occurs prior to tyrosine phosphorylation of the TCR ITAMs and results in the recruitment of the adaptor protein Nck. Interestingly, Nck has been implicated in mediating cytoskeleton reorganization following stimulation of cell surface receptors (51). In addition, Wucherpfennig's laboratory has elegantly shown that ligation of the TCR stimulates the movement of basic residues in CD3ε from contact with acidic headgroups of the inner leaflet of the plasma membrane to be exposed to the cytoplasmic milieu (52). Indeed, using nuclear magnetic resonance spectroscopy, the authors observed that this region in CD3ε containing the ITAMs became accessible to Src kinases following TCR stimulation. Interestingly, these observations point to a potential role for the precise composition and organization of lipids within the membrane in regulating activation through the immunoreceptor. Thus, these studies have stimulated a resurgence of the conformational change model to describe the initial events of T cell activation. Furthermore, this has led to the proposal that the TCR may transduce the forces created by the APC that is pulling on the receptor, leading to conformational changes in the intracellular domains (53).

Are aspects of this conformational change applicable to the initiation of B cell activation (**Figure 1*a***)? Numerous high-resolution X-ray crystallography structures are now available for Fab and Fc domains of the mIg component of the BCR. Although many Fab structures have been determined in the presence and absence of soluble antigen, they have not yet revealed significant conformational changes that can be transmitted to membrane-proximal regions in the intact BCR. However, as with the TCR, the lack of structural-based evidence at this stage does not preclude the possibility that conformational changes may contribute to the initiation of B cell activation.

Kinetic Segregation Model

An alternative model, referred to as kinetic segregation, has been proposed by Davis & van der Merwe to explain the initiation of T cell activation (54, 55). This model takes into account the kinetic properties that have been characterized for the interaction between the TCR and the antigen-loaded MHC, alongside the segregation observed within the T cell membrane early during activation.

The kinetic segregation model assumes that before antigen stimulation, the TCR diffuses through the plasma membrane coming into contact with Src family kinases such as Lck and phosphatases such as CD45. The TCR is equally likely to be found in a phosphorylated or nonphosphorylated state in the resting T cell. Proximity of an APC to the T cell establishes close contact zones through adhesion molecules such as CD2. Because CD2 is composed of short extracellular domains, transmembrane proteins with bulkier extracellular domains, including the major phosphatase CD45, are forced out of close contact regions. Thus, TCRs inside close contact zones are more likely to be phosphorylated but are free to diffuse out of these zones and become dephosphorylated by CD45. However, if the phosphorylated TCR within the close contact region binds to a specific antigen-MHC complex with a sufficiently tight affinity, it is more likely to be retained in this region. Improvement in the half-life of the phosphorylated TCR in the close contact zone leads to TCR triggering.

Several lines of evidence support the kinetic segregation model. First, the treatment of resting T cells with the phosphatase inhibitor pervandate results in the net phosphorylation of the TCR, leading to T cell triggering in the absence of antigen (56). Second, constructs of CD45 possessing altered extracellular dimensions have been generated and expressed in CD45-deficient T cells (57). Although T cells expressing CD45 truncated in the extracellular domain are unable to stimulate T cell triggering, this triggering is fully restored on expression of a chimeric CD45 with extracellular dimensions similar to native CD45. This finding demonstrates that the size-dependent exclusion of CD45 from the close contact zone is important for T cell activation. Similarly, increasing the dimensions of the antigen-MHC complex presented to the TCR abrogates T cell triggering (54). In this situation, the bulkier TCR antigen-MHC complex is less likely to be held in the close contact zone and is thus more likely to be dephosphorylated following exposure to bulky phosphatases. Finally, researchers have shown that recruiting and retaining TCR ITAMs within close contact zones are critical for triggering T cell activation (54). This demonstration involved generating a chimeric molecule containing the transmembrane and intracellular domains of TCRζ (containing ITAMs) fused to the extracellular domain CD2. T cells expressing this chimeric molecule were able to initiate TCR triggering following incubation with APCs in the absence of antigen. Thus, experimental data support major predictions of the kinetic segregation model.

Can aspects of this model be useful in deriving a description of antigen-induced activation of B cells (**Figure 1*b***)? Notably, the BCR is multivalent, binds antigen with higher affinity, and is considerably larger than the TCR. However, there is already some experimental evidence that supports aspects of the kinetic segregation model. Importantly, it appears that, similar to T cells, the phosphorylation status within the B cell is critical for the initiation of B cell activation (58). Surprisingly, CD45-deficient mice do not exhibit significantly impaired B cell responses (59, 60). Furthermore, CD45-deficient B cells are activated to the same extent as wild-type B cells in response to membrane-bound antigen (14). However, CD45 contributes approximately 90% of membrane tyrosine phosphatase activity in T cells (61), but B cells express significant amounts of the phosphatase CD148 (62). Interestingly, the extracellular domains of CD148 are bulkier than those of CD45, and both phosphatases may contribute to segregation within the B cell membrane during triggering. Similarly, B cells deficient in both CD45 and CD148 exhibit impaired immunoreceptor signaling. Thus, we should consider the presence of two bulky phosphatases when describing the triggering of B cell activation. In view of this evidence, the principles of kinetic segregation are likely to be applicable to B cells and could potentially be useful in describing the early events of B cell activation.

Overall, although the mechanism employed by B cells to trigger the initiation of B cell activation is unclear at this stage, aspects of conformational change and kinetic segregation models could contribute to our understanding of this process.

Planar lipid bilayers: experimental model system simulating APCs and allowing incorporated antigen to retain mobility in the plane of the membrane

BCR MICROCLUSTERS MEDIATE INTRACELLULAR SIGNALING FOR B CELL ACTIVATION

The establishment of a precise mechanism that triggers the earliest events of B cell activation will require the development of innovative imaging strategies to follow the spatiotemporal dynamics of molecular events. At this stage, time-lapse wide-field fluorescence microscopy and high-resolution TIRFM have enabled the direct visualization of BCR microclusters in the B cell membrane following settling on antigen-containing planar lipid bilayers (14, 63). BCR microclusters were observed to form rapidly in the B cell membrane following settling on planar lipid bilayers containing antigen. Furthermore, microclusters contain 50 to 500 molecules of BCRs, and in primary B cells can consist of IgM alone, IgD alone, or a mixture of both isotypes (14). Because BCR microcluster formation is currently the earliest observable event associated with successful B cell activation, we now discuss what is known about their formation and function because understanding these processes will help drive our understanding of the initiation of B cell activation.

Formation of BCR Microclusters

Microsignalosomes: numerous signaling-competent antigen microclusters formed throughout the contact area with APCs

BCR microclusters could potentially be formed as a result of conformational changes in the BCR and/or diffusion trapping after kinetic segregation in the B cell membrane. The formation of microclusters does not depend on signaling through the BCR because they were observed to form in membranes of Lyn-deficient B cells following antigen stimulation (64). However, because BCR microcluster formation was abrogated following treatment with actin polymerization inhibitors, this process clearly depends on rearrangements of the B cell cytoskeleton (14). Indeed, we have recently observed that the B cell cortical actin network is dynamically rearranged following antigen stimulation to form corrals around BCR microclusters (**Figure 2**; B. Treanor & F.D. Batista, unpublished observations). These F-actin corrals are responsible for restricting BCR diffusion and thus may maintain the integrity and organization of BCR microclusters. Other factors may also contribute to the formation of BCR microclusters. In line with this, the membrane-proximal Ig domain may play a role during the formation of BCR microclusters (43). Pierce and colleagues investigated the propensity of a series of constructs containing IgM domains to form BCR microclusters when expressed in the plasma cell line J558L. Interestingly, because spontaneous clustering of Cμ4 domains of the IgM was observed, investigators postulated that these domains are both necessary and sufficient for mediating formation of BCR microclusters (43). However, they noted that this likely represents a second phase during the formation of BCR microclusters following an initial accumulation and confinement of BCRs in microscopic regions within the membrane. Rearrangements in the cytoskeleton likely mediate the initial confinement of BCRs prior to the formation of BCR microclusters in the membrane.

Function of BCR Microclusters

That BCR microclusters were formed rapidly following stimulation with antigen, in concert with the initiation of calcium signaling, offered an indication of their potential function in BCR-mediated signaling during B cell activation. Early investigations demonstrated that sites of antigen accumulation coincided with the accumulation of phosphotyrosine (63) and that BCR microclusters recruited the kinase Syk and excluded the phosphatase CD45 (14). A later study showed that BCR microclusters mediate the sequential and highly coordinated recruitment of key intracellular mediators and adaptors associated with BCR signaling, including Lyn, Syk, PLCγ2, Blnk, and Vav (64). Subsequent investigations using a FRET-based imaging approach confirmed the recruitment of Lyn to BCR microclusters and suggested that membrane lipids may play a role in the regulation of this association (65). Although the recruitment of these mediators to the BCR microclusters was necessary, the induction of calcium signaling underlying B cell activation also required the enzymatic activity of these mediators (64). Interestingly, investigators also observed that individual components cooperate to promote the recruitment and retention of other components at BCR microclusters (64). Given the function of these assemblies in mediating intracellular signaling, they have been redefined as microsignalosomes. Because similar assemblies have been observed to be important for sustaining signaling in T cells (66–68), we have suggested that microsignalosomes are common units for signaling during lymphocyte activation (14, 69).

The distribution of BCR-mediated signaling among numerous smaller clusters throughout the membrane offers a distinct functional advantage in terms of flexibility of regulating signaling. This mode of signaling from spatially continuous clusters resembles that proposed in the immunon model by Vogelstein in the 1970s (70). Because observed microsignalosomes retain mobility within the B cell membrane, they can dynamically recruit or exclude positive or negative regulators of BCR signaling. For example, BCR microclusters were found to exclude the phosphatase CD45, thus favoring signaling through the BCR

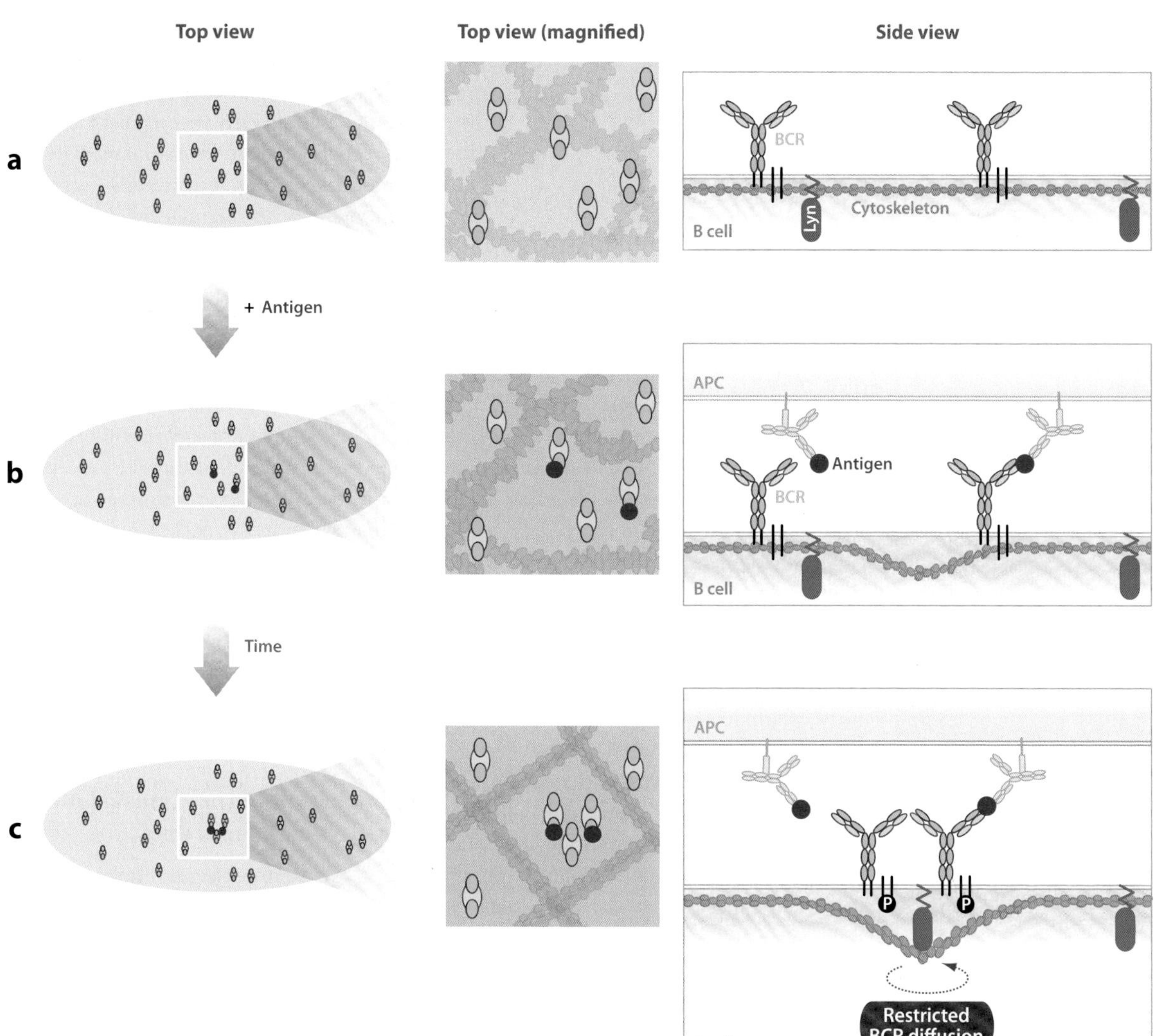

Figure 2

Formation and function of BCR microclusters. In all panels, the BCR is green, antigen is red, the cytoskeleton is brown, and the Src family kinase Lyn is blue. (*a*) In the resting B cell membrane, BCR diffusion is shaped by the density of the underlying actin-ezrin cytoskeleton network. (*b*) On initial engagement of antigen on the surface of an antigen-presenting cell (APC, not shown in top views for clarity), BCR engagement triggers local reorganization of the actin-ezrin network, leading to the formation of BCR microclusters. (*c*) Over time, BCR microclusters form, recruiting and activating various signaling molecules and adaptors. The resultant microsignalosomes trigger further reorganization of the actin-ezrin network, restricting the diffusion of BCRs from the microcluster.

(14). Indeed, recruitment of FcγRIIB to the microcluster by cross-linking with the BCR blocks processes associated with B cell activation (65). A similar mechanism for dynamic regulation through smaller signaling clusters is employed by T cells. The coreceptor CD28 mediates the recruitment of protein kinase Cθ (PKCθ) to the TCR microcluster, promoting signaling through the TCR (71). This dynamic flexibility adds an extra layer of complexity when considering the regulation of immunoreceptor signaling and emphasizes

Guanine nucleotide exchange factors (GEFs): activate G proteins, such as the Rho GTPases, by facilitating the exchange of GDP for GTP

the importance of considering spatiotemporal dynamics when investigating the events of B cell activation.

CELLULAR SPREADING PROPAGATES MICROSIGNALOSOMES FOR B CELL ACTIVATION

The formation of microsignalosomes is critical but insufficient to induce B cell activation in response to antigen. B cells must also increase the number of microsignalosomes within the membrane above the threshold required for activation (64). To achieve this, B cells undergo a cellular response, involving rapid spreading of their membranes across the antigen-containing surface (63). This spreading response is driven by BCR engagement of antigen at the leading edge of the B cell (**Figure 3**). As predicted by an in silico modeling strategy, the extent of B cell spreading is directly dependent on the affinity and density of antigen on the presenting surface. Importantly, the extent of B cell spreading influences the amount of antigen that is ultimately internalized and thus the amount of T cell help that can be recruited and the degree of B cell activation (63). Hence, this cell-spreading strategy provides a mechanism whereby B cells can undergo affinity discrimination according to properties of the antigen. Given that B cell spreading is abrogated in the presence of the Src kinase inhibitor PP1 and actin polymerization inhibitors, including latrunculin A and cytochalasin D, this cellular response is clearly dependent on signaling through the BCR and reorganization of the actin cytoskeleton (**Figure 3**).

BCR Signaling Mediates B Cell Spreading

A comprehensive genetic screen has been carried out in the DT40 B cell line to uncover the intracellular signaling molecules downstream of the BCR that are important for mediating cellular spreading (64). DT40 B cells have a high rate of homologous recombination, allowing the production of knockout cells with relative ease and the investigation of deficiencies that would otherwise be embryonically lethal in animal model systems (72). Examination of a preexisting panel of DT40 B cell knockouts deficient in various mediators of BCR signaling (73) has revealed that the kinases Lyn and Syk play an essential role in initiating the spreading response (64). Furthermore, downstream of these kinases, PLCγ2, Vav, Blnk, and Btk are critical for propagating B cell spreading. Importantly, these findings were subsequently confirmed in primary mouse B cells. However, somewhat surprisingly, the extent of spreading is not significantly compromised in the absence of all three IP_3 receptors, suggesting that B cell spreading may not exhibit the same dependency on calcium signaling as observed in T cells (74). Based on these observations, we expect that BCR signaling through microsignalosomes leads to localized reorganization of the actin cytoskeleton, allowing spreading of the B cell membrane across the antigen-containing surface (**Figure 3**).

Reorganization of the Cytoskeleton Mediates B Cell Spreading

Although roles for several key signaling molecules and adaptors in mediating B cell spreading have been identified, the precise molecular mechanism underlying cytoskeleton reorganization has not been established yet. However, scanning electron microscopy images of B cells in the steady state that are deficient in key mediators of BCR signaling show that such cells exhibit altered cellular morphology, indicative of underlying changes in the regulation of cytoskeleton organization (64). Currently, several lines of evidence point to a number of potential regulators of the cytoskeleton that may be important during B cell activation. It has been demonstrated that the activity of the guanine nucleotide exchange factor (GEF) domain of Vav is essential for mediating its role in B cell spreading. It is well established that Vav acts as a GEF for various RhoGTPases, such as Cdc42 and Rac, which play a critical role in regulating

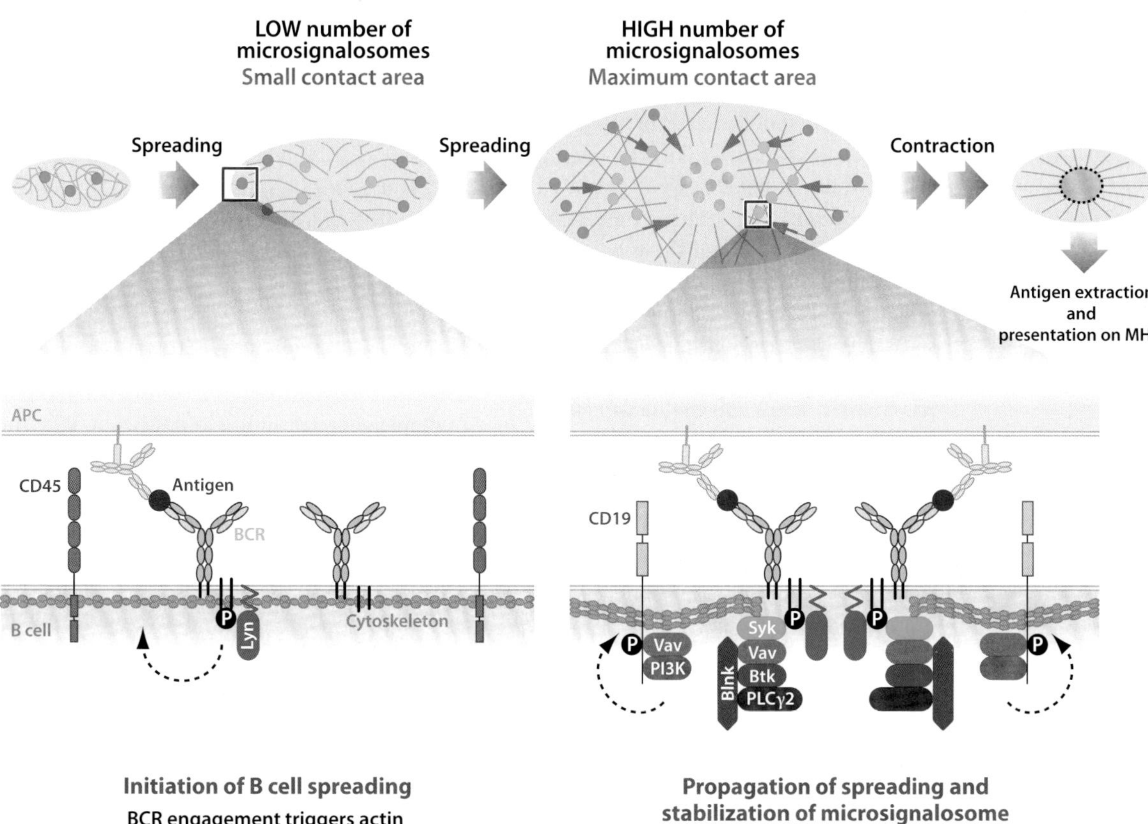

Figure 3

Spreading amplifies the number of BCR microclusters for B cell activation. The top view of B cell during spreading illustrates the formation of BCR microclusters and involvement of the underlying ezrin-actin cytoskeleton network (*brown*) (antigen-presenting cell is not shown in top views for clarity). BCR microclusters are shown in green and shaded according to their age and signaling competence. The earliest BCR microclusters formed on initial engagement of antigen (*dark green*) trigger a local reorganization of the underlying B cell actin cytoskeleton (*brown*), initiating spreading by an as yet unknown mechanism (*magnified lower left panel*). Over time, these BCR microclusters recruit various signaling molecules and adaptors, forming microsignalosomes that propagate CD19-dependent (*pink*) spreading and are stabilized through additional cytoskeleton reorganizations (*magnified lower right panel*). Microsignalosomes are moved toward the center of contact, possibly through retrograde actin flow (*arrowheads*) and coalesce in a central contact site. By this stage, BCR microclusters have lost signaling competence (*light green*) and are internalized by the B cell for antigen processing and presentation in complex with MHC to $CD4^+$ helper T cells.

cytoskeleton rearrangements (75). Indeed, Vav-regulated Rac1 activation is important during spreading of mature B cells in response to BCR capping (76). Furthermore, Vav is involved in the regulation of ezrin dephosphorylation in response to TCR signaling (77). This results in disruption of the association between the actin cytoskeleton and the plasma membrane, allowing relaxation of cellular rigidity and promoting formation of cellular conjugates. A similar mechanism may operate in B cells, given that rapid global dephosphorylation of ezrin has been observed following stimulation with soluble antigen (78). Another potential downstream mediator of the BCR signalosome involved in regulation of cytoskeleton reorganization is the B lymphocyte adaptor molecule of 32 kDa (Bam32)

(79–81). Bam32 is phosphorylated in a Src family kinase–dependent manner and recruited to the plasma membrane following BCR ligation (81), and this activation is necessary for B cell proliferation (79). Interestingly, B cells deficient in Bam32 exhibit impaired actin polymerization and antigen internalization (82). However, although these processes may be Rac-independent, the precise downstream target(s) of Bam32 remains unclear at this stage. Lastly, following BCR ligation, Lyn and Syk kinases cooperate to regulate the phosphorylation status of the leukocyte-specific homolog of cortactin HS1 (83). Because HS1 binds to actin and important actin nucleator actin-related proteins 2 and 3 (Arp2/3), HS1 may play an important role in mediating cytoskeleton reorganization following BCR stimulation. Furthermore, HS1 is required for actin reorganization following immunoreceptor stimulation in lymphocytes (84, 85). Other candidates that likely contribute to the regulation of B cell cytoskeleton reorganizations include F-actin depolymerizing and severing protein, cofilin (86, 87), and a lymphocyte-specific potential RhoGEF, DOCK8 (88); however, the importance of these remains to be established. Furthermore, because the regulation of cytoskeleton reorganization in lymphocytes is currently not well understood, other proteins that play critical roles during B cell activation may be uncovered. Given the importance of the cytoskeleton in mediating B cell activation, research in this area will be invaluable for a more comprehensive characterization of molecular events during B cell activation.

CORECEPTORS REGULATE CYTOSKELETON REORGANIZATIONS SHAPING B CELL ACTIVATION

The recognition of antigen on the surface of an APC allows the B cell to regulate the extent of activation according to the cellular context of recognition. A role is emerging for B cell coreceptors in both the positive and negative regulation of B cell activation. Here we highlight two positive coreceptors, CD19 and integrins, that facilitate B cell activation potentially through the regulation of cytoskeleton reorganizations following antigen recognition.

CD19 Is Essential for Mediating B Cell Spreading

A novel and essential role for the B cell coreceptor CD19 in mediating B cell spreading has been demonstrated elegantly by recent work (14). Previously, CD19 was most commonly known as part of a complex containing complement receptor 2 (CD21 or CR2), the tetraspanin family protein CD81, and the interferon-induced transmembrane protein leu13, which is responsible for enhancing signaling through the BCR following cross-linking by complement-coated antigen (89). Investigators observed that CD19-deficient B cells were severely impaired in the initiation of calcium signaling and spreading in response to membrane-bound antigen (14). As a result, CD19-deficient B cells were unable to gather sufficient antigen to trigger B cell activation. CD19 performs an essential role, independent of CD21, in enhancing signaling through the BCR in response to membrane-bound antigen, providing a satisfactory explanation for an anomaly that had arisen previously in the literature. Although CD19-deficient B cells make comparable responses to soluble antigen as wild-type B cells (14, 90, 91), mice lacking CD19 exhibit severely compromised immune responses to antigen (92, 93). These findings highlight not only the importance of CD19 in mediating B cell activation, but also the contribution of membrane-bound antigen recognition in vivo.

CD19 recruits intracellular mediators to facilitate BCR signaling. The extensive intracellular domain of CD19 points to a potential molecular mechanism underlying its role in facilitating signaling through the BCR in response to membrane antigen. This domain contains nine tyrosine residues, including some that can be phosphorylated to form sites capable of recruiting various intracellular signaling molecules, including Vav and PI3K (94, 95). In line with this, immunoprecipitation of CD19 yields an associated complex of proteins, such as Vav, PI3K, Lyn, and PLCγ2 (96). Furthermore, this study suggested that CD19 might form multimers in the B cell membrane, resulting in an increased affinity of these interactions. It therefore seems likely that CD19 recruits additional signaling molecules to the BCR microsignalosome (**Figure 3**). Indeed, the cooperative relationship between Vav and PLCγ2 observed within the microsignalosome lends support to this proposal (64). In addition, Vav recruitment by phosphorylated CD19 has been shown to lead to the synthesis of phosphatidylinositol 4,5-bisphosphate following the activation of phosphatidylinositol 4-phosphatase 5-kinase, thereby providing a source of PLCγ2 substrate during B cell activation (97). Thus, CD19 might play an adaptor function in B cells, homologous to the linker of T cell activation (LAT) in T cells (98).

CD19 is transiently recruited to BCR microclusters. The close proximity of CD19 and BCR during B cell activation is a central tenet of the theory that CD19 functions as a LAT-like adaptor to facilitate signaling through the BCR. Consistent with this, investigators observed that CD19 becomes transiently associated with BCR microclusters following activation with membrane antigen (14). Recently, we used two-color acquisition TIRFM to visualize simultaneously single particles of CD19 alongside BCR microclusters (D. Depoil & F.D. Batista, unpublished data). We observed that CD19 is dynamically recruited to and moves between signaling BCR microclusters following membrane-bound antigen stimulation. Indeed, as would be expected if CD19 mediates the recruitment of additional intracellular signaling molecules to facilitate BCR signaling, molecules recruited by CD19 (such as PI3K) are laterally segregated in the membrane from those recruited solely through the BCR. This mechanism elegantly illustrates the potential for dynamic regulation of BCR signaling that can be offered as a consequence of smaller signaling units compared with larger BCR-caps associated with soluble antigen stimulation.

The formation of microsignalosomes and the dynamic recruitment of CD19 provide critical boosts to the BCR signaling that are required to drive remodeling of the actin cytoskeleton, which is, in turn, required for activation in response to membrane-bound antigen (**Figure 3**). Indeed, mutations in CD19 that result in disruption of the associated cytoskeleton reorganization have been associated with the development of various antibody deficiency syndromes in humans (15).

Integrins Facilitate B Cell Activation

Mature B cells express high levels of the integrins LFA-1 (leukocyte function-associated antigen-1) and VLA-4 (very late antigen-4) on their surface. The corresponding ligands for integrins—ICAM-1 (intercellular adhesion molecule-1) for LFA-1 and VCAM-1 (vascular cell adhesion mediator-1) and fibronectin for VLA-4—are widely expressed on a variety of cell types including DCs and FDCs (99–101). The importance of such molecules in mediating processes underlying humoral immunity is underscored by the observation that the interaction between LFA-1 and ICAM-1 prevents apoptosis of B cells in the GC (102). Indeed, the integrin-binding domain of CD98hc may be necessary to allow rapid B cell proliferation (103). Recent investigations have offered insight into two molecular mechanisms that may underlie the role of integrins during B cell activation: that integrins promote B cell adhesion and that they slow inactivation of signaling microclusters.

Integrins promote B cell adhesion. Integrins lower the threshold of B cell activation by promoting B cell adhesion (104, 105). B cells are only able to form stable attachments to planar lipid bilayers containing a limited amount of antigen when the bilayers are also loaded with ICAM-1 (104). The extent to which integrin ligation promotes B cell adhesion depends on signaling through the BCR. This inside-out activation is a common mode of regulating integrin activity through alteration of conformation and/or clustering in the membrane (106, 107). The molecular mechanism underlying this activation has been investigated and reveals an important role for Src family kinases, Vav, and PI3K, following BCR engagement (108). Unexpectedly, this study also identifies a critical role for the Rho GTPase Rac2, but not Rac1, in promoting LFA-1-mediated B cell adhesion. In combination with another investigation (109), Rap1 was also established as important during B cell activation in response to particulate and cell-associated antigen. Together these observations demonstrate the importance of cytoskeleton reorganizations for promoting integrin-induced B cell adhesion potentially by facilitating B cell spreading.

Immunological synapse (IS): formed between an APC and a lymphocyte and characterized by segregation of cell surface receptors and immunoreceptors to form a bullseye-like structure in the lymphocyte membrane

Integrins slow inactivation of signaling microclusters. An alternative mechanism by which integrins can promote lymphocyte activation has been proposed based on observations in T cells. During T cell spreading, actin polymerization at the leading edge drives centripetal retrograde actin flow toward the center of contact (110). As TCR microclusters are associated with the actin cytoskeleton, the retrograde flow causes TCR microclusters to gather in the center of contact, forming a large cluster. Interestingly, this mechanism can lead to molecular segregation in the membrane if microclusters of different compositions are differentially coupled to the cytoskeleton. The tracking of TCR microclusters during T cell activation has revealed that ligation of VLA-4 slows their movement toward the central cluster (111). The retention of TCR microclusters in the periphery of the cell contact prolongs interactions between signaling molecules within the microsignalosome, promoting TCR signaling. Thus, integrins may promote lymphocyte activation by both stimulating adhesion and also attenuating cytoskeleton movements that lead to inactivation of signaling microclusters.

Whatever the relative importance of the roles played by these two contributory factors, reorganizations of the cytoskeleton clearly play a key role in promoting the early stages of B cell activation through integrins.

B CELL CONTRACTION RESULTS IN FORMATION OF THE MATURE IMMUNOLOGICAL SYNAPSE

Following rapid spreading across an antigen-containing surface, B cells undergo a more prolonged contraction phase (63). Currently, it is not clear what drives the onset of contraction or if this is simply a passive result of the completion of spreading, although preliminary evidence suggests that Vav, Grb2, and Casitas B cell lymphoma (Cbl) may be involved in mediating this process (64; M. Weber & F.D. Batista, unpublished data). The contraction response results in dramatic reorganization within the B cell membrane and formation of the mature immunological synapse (IS). The mature IS was first observed following antigen stimulation of $CD4^+$ T cells (112–114). Because the IS has since been observed in $CD8^+$ T cells (115, 116), B cells (40, 104), and natural killer cells (117), it may represent a common feature associated with lymphocyte activation. The mature IS structure consists of a central cluster containing an immunoreceptor known as the central supramolecular activation cluster (cSMAC), encircled by a ring of adhesion molecules such as LFA-1 and VLA-4, known as the peripheral SMAC (pSMAC) (114). Although the IS was first observed more than a decade ago, the precise functional segregation within regions of the IS remains unclear.

Newer Insights into the Role of the IS

Given the concentration of immunoreceptors in the cSMAC, investigators originally assumed that this compartment formed the site of active signaling. However, in view of the observation that calcium signaling is initiated more rapidly than the formation of the mature IS, it has been suggested that the cSMAC instead acts as a platform for immunoreceptor internalization and signaling termination (118). The internalization process is of particular significance in B cells because the internalization of antigen by B cells is critical for recruiting cognate $CD4^+$ T cells necessary for maximal activation (40). Interestingly, the actin-based motor protein myosin II regulates BCR internalization to MHC-containing lysosomes and is thus required for efficient antigen processing and presentation (119). Furthermore, microclusters that are rapidly formed in the periphery of the cell contact mediate immunoreceptor signaling (14, 64, 66–68). Nevertheless, because signaling has been observed in the cSMAC following stimulation with weak agonists (120), there may not be an absolute division of function between different regions of the IS.

Our understanding of the molecular mechanisms of IS formation and associated IS function is continually evolving with new data collected by increasingly intricate investigative techniques. We highlight three recent observations of particular interest in this discussion of the role of the cytoskeleton in mediating B cell activation. First, the movement of a microcluster toward the central cluster may occur not only through retrograde actin flow, but also via an active process (121). In this study, the authors observed that myosin IIA was activated in response to TCR signaling and was important for complete assembly and movement of microclusters to central clusters in T cells. Second, the cSMAC may contain subregions with distinct molecular compositions (71). Although the costimulatory receptor CD28 and the downstream mediator PKCθ were initially associated with TCR microclusters, these were subsequently segregated from the TCR following translocation to the central cluster. Interestingly, it was postulated that these different subregions are established as a result of differential regulation of transport of protein clusters, potentially through associations with the cytoskeleton. Finally, in view of the opposing roles of actinomyosin regulators PKCθ and Wiscott Aldrich Syndrome protein (WASp) in disrupting and promoting IS formation (122), Dustin (123, 124) has introduced the term kinapses to describe a mode of antigen recognition by T cells through motile contacts with APCs. The kinapse is an asymmetric structure with the uropod and lamella acting as functional homologs of the cSMAC and pSMAC of the more stable IS. In this model, the decision to commence TCR signaling through a kinapse or an IS depends on the state of symmetry/asymmetry of force-generating structures in the T cell. Taken together, these recent studies establish the variety and importance of the cytoskeleton in regulating T cell activation. It will be informative to carry out similar investigations in B cells to fully characterize the role of the cytoskeleton in processes underlying B cell activation.

THE INITIATION OF B CELL ACTIVATION IN VIVO

Although considerable detail has been uncovered concerning the molecular mechanisms of the early steps of B cell activation, little was known about how this process is initiated in vivo until relatively recently. An individual contains an enormous repertoire of B cells for protection against a plethora of pathogenic invaders. However, with this diversity, the probability that a B cell will encounter its cognate antigen is very low indeed. To improve the likelihood of such an encounter, the body localizes these events within secondary lymphoid organs, such as lymph nodes and the spleen. Most $IgM^{med}IgD^{hi}CD21^{med}CD23^{hi}$ B cells within the body are contained within secondary lymphoid tissue, spending approximately 24 h searching for cognate antigen before rejoining the circulatory system and being taken to another secondary lymphoid tissue to continue the search (125). To further increase the probability of antigen encounter, secondary lymphoid tissues are extremely well networked to at least one of the lymphatic or blood systems, which continually supply antigen to the tissue. This ensures that the activation of the specific B cell occurs within a reasonable time to minimize the probability of establishing infection.

Subcapsular sinus (SCS): a region just beneath the collagenous capsule encircling the interior of lymph node, lined by a layer of macrophages that restrict the movement of lymphatic fluid into the interior lymphatic tissue

Multiphoton microscopy (MPM): allows visualization of cellular dynamics within the correct physiological environment and in real time to a depth of approximately 200 μm

Immune complexes: comprised of antigen in complex with antibody and/or coated with complement fragments

Secondary Lymphoid Tissue Architecture

Early understanding of the initiation of humoral immune responses in vivo was based on a combination of immunohistochemistry and electron microscopy (see reviews 125–127 and references therein). Such methods provided invaluable insight into the underlying anatomy of secondary lymphoid tissues. These tissues necessarily exhibit an intricate organization in terms of their underlying anatomy because the numerous processes that they host contributing to the regulation of immune responses must be finely coordinated both spatially and temporally (128). The interior of a lymph node is divided into two discrete compartments: the outer cortex and the inner medulla (**Figure 4**). The cortex is further subdivided according to chemokine expression, consisting of follicles containing B cells and the T cell rich paracortex. The paracortex also contains high endothelial venules (HEVs) through which blood, containing lymphocytes, can enter the node. The medulla is rich in phagocytic cells, including macrophages and DCs. The lymph node is supplied with lymphatic fluid through the afferent vessel; however, as this fluid is moved around a complex network of sinuses, including the subcapsular sinus (SCS), it is not allowed to diffuse freely into the lymph node interior. The sinuses come together in the medullary region, and filtered lymphatic fluid is drained through the efferent lymph vessel. Even with a detailed anatomical description of a secondary lymphoid organ in place, investigators still lacked a clear understanding of how antigen can encounter B cells contained within the follicle.

B Cell Encounter with Small Antigen In Vivo

In recent years the development of multiphoton microscopy (MPM) has enabled the direct and dynamic visualization of immune cells within secondary lymphoid tissue in vivo (126, 129, 130). Using this approach, numerous groundbreaking studies published within the past five years have revealed that B cells encounter antigen in vivo via different mechanisms according to the properties of the antigen itself (**Figure 4**). Antigens with a molecular mass less than 70 kDa diffuse into the follicle across the SCS following entry through the afferent lymph vessel (131). Thus follicular B cells in close proximity to the SCS can acquire and present cognate antigen to $CD4^+$ T cells for maximal activation. The authors suggest that this diffusion might occur through tiny pores in the SCS (132–134), although the existence of these pores remains controversial. When considered along with the discrepancy between the hydrodynamic radii of antigens permitted entry and the potential dimensions of these pores, there may be an alternative mechanism for diffusion through the SCS. Recently, Carroll's group (135) has identified a conduit network composed of bundles of collagen fibers ensheathed with fibroreticular cells. This network transports low-molecular-mass antigen from the SCS into the follicle so that cognate B cells can acquire this antigen. Thus, this conduit network appears functionally analogous to that previously observed in the paracortex (136, 137). Interestingly, the follicular conduits may also play a role in transport of chemokines such as CXCL13 to attract B cells to likely sources of antigen. However, several questions remain to be addressed in the future including where these conduits end and if they can transport antigen directly to FDCs (39).

B Cell Encounter with Larger Antigen In Vivo

Although these two mechanisms provide potential means for follicular B cells to encounter low-molecular-mass compounds, including chemokines and toxins, most antigens encountered during immune responses have a molecular mass considerably greater than 70 kDa (**Figure 4**). Three independent studies identified a novel role for macrophages in the SCS in mediating presentation of larger antigen to follicular B cells (138–140). These studies demonstrated that particulate antigens, viral particles, and immune complexes were

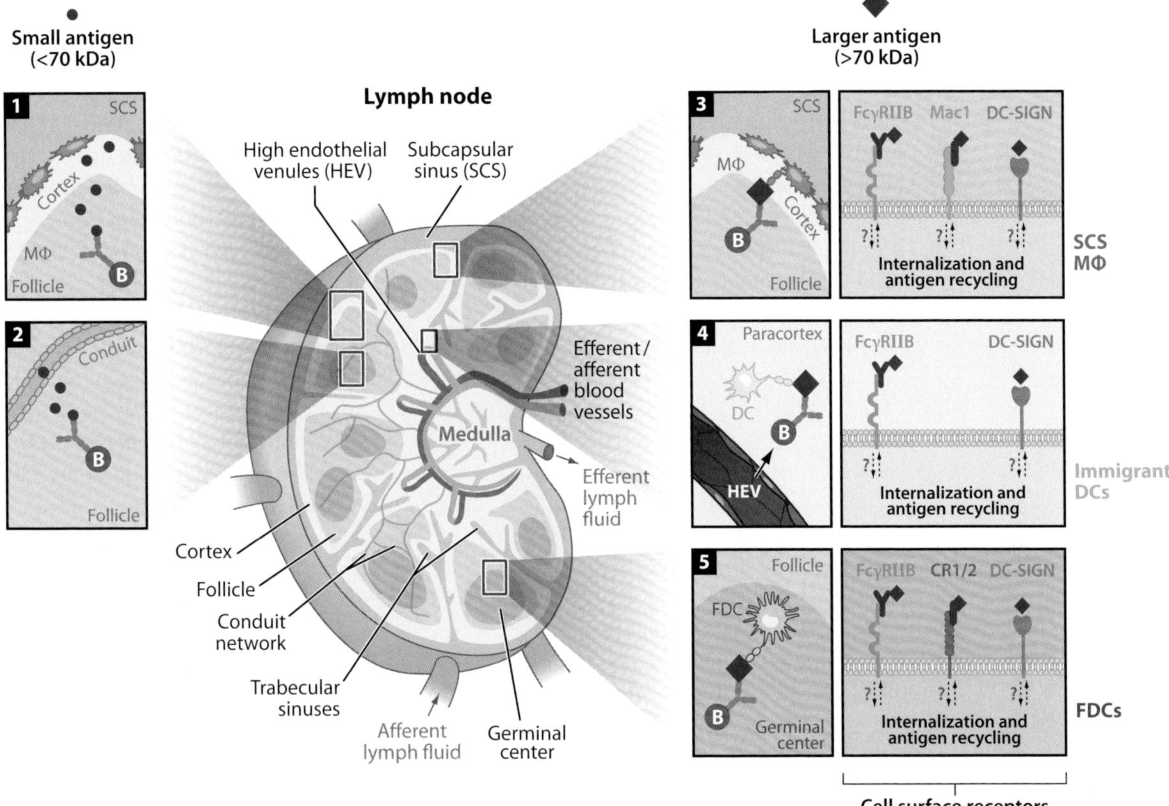

Figure 4

Antigen presentation to cognate B cells in the lymph node in vivo. Schematic view of the lymph node. Lymphatic fluid enters the lymph node through the afferent vessel, moves around the subcapsular sinus (SCS) and the trabecular sinuses through the cortex toward the medulla and then exits the node through the efferent vessel. Antigen with a molecular mass below 70 kDa (*red circles*) (such as chemokines and toxins) can enter the cortex to activate cognate B cells (*green*) contained within follicles either through (*1*) pores in the SCS or (*2*) FRC-lined conduits. In contrast, larger antigen (*red diamonds*) (such as immune complexes, viruses, or bacteria) are presented on the surface of (*3*) SCS macrophages (*blue*) to follicular B cells, (*4*) immigrant DCs (*light green*) to B cells as they enter the node through high endothelial venules (HEVs) in the paracortex, or (*5*) follicular dendritic cells (FDCs, *purple*) to B cells in the germinal center. (*Right panels*) Cell surface receptors that may play a role in cell surface presentation of larger antigen, such as immune complexes (comprising antigen in complex with either antibody and/or complement fragments), on various cell types shown in (*3-5*). These may include the antibody receptor FcγRIIB (*green*), complement receptors Mac1 (*blue*) and CR1/2 (*gray*), and/or the carbohydrate-binding receptor DC-SIGN (*brown*).

concentrated at the SCS following entry to the lymph node. Indeed, removal of these macrophages following treatment with chlorodonate liposomes resulted in global dissemination of the antigen (139). It was observed that, unlike noncognate B cells, antigen-specific follicular B cells make prolonged contact with the SCS macrophages. Thus, this $CD169^+$ population may be less efficient at phagocytosis than other macrophage populations as they present intact antigen to initiate B cell activation (141). The molecular mechanisms used by the macrophages to present antigen have not yet been established, but this presentation could occur through a variety of cell surface receptors, including macrophage adhesion molecule-1 (Mac1) for complement-coated antigen, FcγRIIB for immune complexes, and the C-type lectin DC-specific ICAM-3 grabbing nonintegrin (DC-SIGN) for carbohydrate-containing antigen (39). As a result of contact with SCS macrophages, specific B cells acquire antigen and migrate to the B-T boundary within the cortex to recruit CD4$^+$ T cell help necessary for maximal activation. This migration following antigen acquisition has been previously observed in response to immunization with soluble antigen and occurs in a CCR7-dependent manner (142). The interaction between cognate B and T cells is dependent on expression of the SLAM-associated protein (SAP) in T cells (143). Indeed, SAP-deficient T cells are unable to mediate prolonged interactions with B cells, leading to severe defects in the GC response. Interestingly, B cells arriving at the lymph node through the HEV in the paracortex may also be able to recognize intact antigen on the surface of DCs (144). Such a mechanism would leave B cells in the perfect location to receive T cell help, and, consistent with this observation, trios of B cells, T cells, and DCs have been observed in the paracortex (145). Recently, investigators showed that, following activation at the B-T cell boundary, pre-GC B cells migrate across the follicle to the periphery, where they undergo extensive proliferation prior to establishing a GC in the center of the follicle (146). Clearly, at least two alternative mechanisms exist for the activation of follicular B cells by larger antigen in vivo.

It has long been established that FDCs accumulate antigen in the form of immune complexes after the initial wave of antigen present in the lymph fluid has passed (35–37, 147, 148). Recent MPM studies have revealed that immune complexes can be transported on the surface of nonspecific B cells from SCS macrophages to FDCs (138, 140). This transport appears to depend on the expression of complement receptors on the B cell (140). A similar shuttling mechanism has been proposed to explain the transport of immune complexes by splenic marginal zone B cells to FDCs (149). It is unclear if antigen present on the surface of FDCs can mediate the activation of naive B cells, but some recent evidence suggests this possibility (150, 151). However, this mode of antigen presentation is critical for affinity maturation in the GC and the generation of extremely high-affinity antibodies. Three MPM studies were published in quick succession and have revealed the GC to be a more dynamic structure than was anticipated from early imaging work (152–154). In all three studies, B cells exhibited altered B cell morphology, suggesting a different mode by which B cells recognize antigen on the surface of FDCs.

Overall, significant progress has been made in visualizing the early stages of B cell activation in vivo. These studies not only demonstrate the importance of antigen recognition on the surface of APCs, but also confirm the significance of underlying alterations in B cell morphology that must therefore occur during physiological B cell activation.

CONCLUDING REMARKS

The recent development of innovative imaging approaches has enabled characterization of both molecular events of B cell activation and the initiation of humoral immune responses in vivo. These studies have established a pivotal role for the cytoskeleton in regulating the early events of B cell activation at various stages. The dynamic association of the cytoskeleton with the plasma membrane regulates the diffusion of the BCR in the membrane, important in determining both the distribution of BCR during triggering of B cell activation and the formation of BCR microclusters. Furthermore, the cytoskeleton, through regulation of the distribution of cell surface molecules, including CD19 and integrins, can contribute to the intricate and dynamic regulation of signaling through the BCR and the formation of the IS. Indeed, the recent visualization of antigen recognition on the surface of macrophages, DCs, and FDCs in vivo substantiates the value of investigating the events of B cell activation, in particular the cytoskeleton reorganizations, within their correct cellular context.

SUMMARY POINTS

1. In the resting B cell membrane, the state of the BCR has not been firmly established; it may exist as a monomer or as a higher-order oligomer. However, the B cell cytoskeleton clearly plays a role in regulating the dynamic distribution of the BCR in the resting B cell membrane.
2. Engagement of the BCR with antigen on the surface of an antigen-presenting cell triggers B cell activation by a mechanism potentially involving conformational changes in the BCR and/or by kinetic segregation in the B cell membrane.
3. BCR microclusters are formed rapidly throughout the contact area following stimulation with antigen on the surface of an antigen-presenting cell. The formation of BCR microclusters requires reorganization of the cytoskeleton but not BCR-mediated signaling. BCR microclusters initiate recruitment of intracellular signaling molecules and adaptors to form microsignalosomes, allowing intricate dynamic regulation of signaling through the BCR.
4. B cell activation requires spreading of the B cell membrane across the antigen-containing surface to amplify the number of microsignalosomes formed. CD19 is essential for mediating this spreading response and facilitates signaling through the BCR by recruiting intracellular molecules to microsignalosomes. The recruitment of CD19 provides the boost to BCR signaling needed to stimulate the cytoskeleton reorganization, which is required for B cell spreading and activation.
5. The contraction of the B cell membrane following spreading results in formation of the mature immunological synapse. The central cluster of BCRs in the mature immunological synapse acts as a platform for antigen internalization, which is necessary for recruitment of helper T cells and for maximal B cell activation.
6. B cell activation in vivo is initiated in secondary lymphoid organs. Recent intravital imaging has demonstrated that small antigens can diffuse directly through the subcapsular sinus or access B cells through a follicular conduit network. In contrast, larger antigens are encountered by B cells on the surface of macrophages lining the subcapsular sinus, dendritic cells in the paracortex, or on the surface of follicular dendritic cells in the germinal centers.

FUTURE ISSUES

1. A definition is needed of the precise molecular mechanism underlying triggering of B cell activation, in particular assessing the relative contribution of conformational changes and/or kinetic segregation.
2. Investigators must establish the role of the cytoskeleton and various cell surface receptors in regulating the formation and function of BCR microclusters.
3. Studies are needed that will identify and characterize regulators of the cytoskeleton that are required for organization of the rearrangements underlying early events of B cell activation in vivo.

DISCLOSURE STATEMENT

The authors are not aware of any affiliations, memberships, funding, or financial holdings that might be perceived as affecting the objectivity of this review.

ACKNOWLEDGMENTS

Cancer Research UK supports research in the Lymphocyte Interaction Laboratory. We would like to thank members of the Lymphocyte Interaction Laboratory for critical reading of the manuscript, and S. Minguet, M. Reth, and W. Schamel for helpful discussions.

LITERATURE CITED

1. Reth M. 1989. Antigen receptor tail clue. *Nature* 338:383–84
2. Dal Porto J, Gauld S, Merrell K, Mills D, Pugh-Bernard A, Cambier J. 2004. B cell antigen receptor signaling 101. *Mol. Immunol.* 41:599–613
3. DeFranco A. 1997. The complexity of signaling pathways activated by the BCR. *Curr. Opin. Immunol.* 9:296–308
4. Kurosaki T. 2002. Regulation of B-cell signal transduction by adaptor proteins. *Nat. Rev. Immunol.* 2:354–63
5. Reth M, Wienands J. 1997. Initiation and processing of signals from the B cell antigen receptor. *Annu. Rev. Immunol.* 15:453–79
6. Scharenberg A, Humphries L, Rawlings D. 2007. Calcium signaling and cell-fate choice in B cells. *Nat. Rev. Immunol.* 7:778–89
7. Lanzavecchia A. 1985. Antigen-specific interaction between T and B cells. *Nature* 314:537–39
8. Rock K, Benacerraf B, Abbas A. 1984. Antigen presentation by hapten-specific B lymphocytes. I. Role of surface immunoglobulin receptors. *J. Exp. Med.* 160:1102–13
9. MacLennan IC, Toellner KM, Cunningham AF, Serre K, Sze DM, et al. 2003. Extrafollicular antibody responses. *Immunol. Rev.* 194:8–18
10. MacLennan I. 1994. Germinal centers. *Annu. Rev. Immunol.* 12:117–39
11. Rajewsky K. 1996. Clonal selection and learning in the antibody system. *Nature* 381:751–58
12. Treanor B, Batista F. 2007. Mechanistic insight into lymphocyte activation through quantitative imaging and theoretical modelling. *Curr. Opin. Immunol.* 19:476–83
13. Carrasco YR, Batista FD. 2006. B cell recognition of membrane-bound antigen: an exquisite way of sensing ligands. *Curr. Opin. Immunol.* 18:286–91
14. **Depoil D, Fleire S, Treanor BL, Weber M, Harwood NE, et al. 2008. CD19 is essential for B cell activation by promoting B cell receptor-antigen microcluster formation in response to membrane-bound ligand. *Nat. Immunol.* 9:63–72**

14. Reveals an essential role for CD19 in B cell activation in response to membrane-bound antigen and that CD19 is dynamically recruited to signaling-active BCR microclusters.

15. Conley ME, Dobbs AK, Farmer DM, Kilic S, Paris K, et al. 2009. Primary B cell immunodeficiencies: comparisons and contrasts. *Annu. Rev. Immunol.* 27:199–227
16. Schamel W, Reth M. 2000. Monomeric and oligomeric complexes of the B cell antigen receptor. *Immunity* 13:5–14
17. Tolar P, Sohn H, Pierce S. 2005. The initiation of antigen-induced B cell antigen receptor signaling viewed in living cells by fluorescence resonance energy transfer. *Nat. Immunol.* 6:1168–76
18. Singer SJ, Nicolson GL. 1972. The fluid mosaic model of the structure of cell membranes. *Science* 175:720–31
19. Sheetz MP, Schindler M, Koppel DE. 1980. Lateral mobility of integral membrane proteins is increased in spherocytic erythrocytes. *Nature* 285:510–11
20. Simons K, Ikonen E. 1997. Functional rafts in cell membranes. *Nature* 387:569–72
21. Gupta N, DeFranco A. 2007. Lipid rafts and B cell signaling. *Semin. Cell Dev. Biol.* 18:616–26
22. Pierce S. 2002. Lipid rafts and B-cell activation. *Nat. Rev. Immunol.* 2:96–105

23. Sohn H, Tolar P, Jin T, Pierce S. 2006. Fluorescence resonance energy transfer in living cells reveals dynamic membrane changes in the initiation of B cell signaling. *Proc. Natl. Acad. Sci. USA* 103:8143–48
24. Kusumi A, Ike H, Nakada C, Murase K, Fujiwara T. 2005. Single-molecule tracking of membrane molecules: plasma membrane compartmentalization and dynamic assembly of raft-philic signaling molecules. *Semin. Immunol.* 17:3–21
25. Sako Y, Kusumi A. 1994. Compartmentalized structure of the plasma membrane for receptor movements as revealed by a nanometer-level motion analysis. *J. Cell Biol.* 125:1251–64
26. Simson R, Sheets ED, Jacobson K. 1995. Detection of temporary lateral confinement of membrane proteins using single-particle tracking analysis. *Biophys. J.* 69:989–93
27. Fujiwara T, Ritchie K, Murakoshi H, Jacobson K, Kusumi A. 2002. Phospholipids undergo hop diffusion in compartmentalized cell membrane. *J. Cell Biol.* 157:1071–81
28. Lillemeier BF, Pfeiffer JR, Surviladze Z, Wilson BS, Davis MM. 2006. Plasma membrane-associated proteins are clustered into islands attached to the cytoskeleton. *Proc. Natl. Acad. Sci. USA* 103:18992–97
29. Schreiner GF, Braun J, Unanue ER. 1976. Spontaneous redistribution of surface immunoglobulin in the motile B lymphocyte. *J. Exp. Med.* 144:1683–88
30. Unanue ER, Perkins WD, Karnovsky MJ. 1972. Ligand-induced movement of lymphocyte membrane macromolecules. I. Analysis by immunofluorescence and ultrastructural radioautography. *J. Exp. Med.* 136:885–906
31. Stackpole CW, Jacobson JB, Lardis MP. 1974. Two distinct types of capping of surface receptors on mouse lymphoid cells. *Nature* 248:232–34
32. Reth M. 2001. Oligomeric antigen receptors: a new view on signaling for the selection of lymphocytes. *Trends Immunol.* 22:356–60
33. Huang N, Han S, Hwang I, Kehrl J. 2005. B cells productively engage soluble antigen-pulsed dendritic cells: visualization of live-cell dynamics of B cell-dendritic cell interactions. *J. Immunol.* 175:7125–34
34. Wykes M, Pombo A, Jenkins C, MacPherson G. 1998. Dendritic cells interact directly with naive B lymphocytes to transfer antigen and initiate class switching in a primary T-dependent response. *J. Immunol.* 161:1313–19
35. Chen L, Frank A, Adams J, Steinman R. 1978. Distribution of horseradish peroxidase (HRP)-anti-HRP immune complexes in mouse spleen with special reference to follicular dendritic cells. *J. Cell Biol.* 79:184–99
36. Mandel T, Phipps R, Abbot A, Tew J. 1980. The follicular dendritic cell: long-term antigen retention during immunity. *Immunol. Rev.* 53:29–59
37. Tew JG, Phipps RP, Mandel TE. 1980. The maintenance and regulation of the humoral immune response: persisting antigen and the role of follicular antigen-binding dendritic cells as accessory cells. *Immunol. Rev.* 53:175–201
38. Koppel E, Wieland C, Van Den Berg V, Litjens M, Florquin S, et al. 2005. Specific ICAM-3 grabbing nonintegrin-related 1 (SIGNR1) expressed by marginal zone macrophages is essential for defense against pulmonary *Streptococcus pneumoniae* infection. *Eur. J. Immunol.* 35:2962–69
39. Batista FD, Harwood NE. 2009. The who, how and where of antigen presentation to B cells. *Nat. Rev. Immunol.* 9:15–27
40. Batista F, Iber D, Neuberger M. 2001. B cells acquire antigen from target cells after synapse formation. *Nature* 411:489–94
41. Batista F, Neuberger M. 1998. Affinity dependence of the B cell response to antigen: a threshold, a ceiling, and the importance of off-rate. *Immunity* 8:751–59
42. Batista F, Neuberger M. 2000. B cells extract and present immobilized antigen: implications for affinity discrimination. *EMBO J.* 19:513–20
43. Tolar P, Hanna J, Krueger PD, Pierce SK. 2009. The constant region of the membrane immunoglobulin mediates B cell-receptor clustering and signaling in response to membrane antigens. *Immunity* 30:44–55
44. Kuhns MS, Davis MM, Garcia KC. 2006. Deconstructing the form and function of the TCR/CD3 complex. *Immunity* 24:133–39
45. Schamel WW, Risueño RM, Minguet S, Ortíz AR, Alarcón B. 2006. A conformation- and avidity-based proofreading mechanism for the TCR-CD3 complex. *Trends Immunol.* 27:176–82

28. Used transmission electron microscopy to visualize clusters of proteins within "islands" of the T cell membrane that are associated with the cytoskeleton.

40. Demonstrates the formation of the IS in B cells before acquisition of antigen but after recognition on the APC surface.

46. Rudolph MG, Stanfield RL, Wilson IA. 2006. How TCRs bind MHCs, peptides, and coreceptors. *Annu. Rev. Immunol.* 24:419–66
47. Van Der Merwe PA. 2001. The TCR triggering puzzle. *Immunity* 14:665–68
48. Garcia KC, Teyton L, Wilson IA. 1999. Structural basis of T cell recognition. *Annu. Rev. Immunol.* 17:369–97
49. Hennecke J, Wiley DC. 2001. T cell receptor-MHC interactions up close. *Cell* 104:1–4
50. Gil D, Schamel WW, Montoya M, Sánchez-Madrid F, Alarcón B. 2002. Recruitment of Nck by CD3ε reveals a ligand-induced conformational change essential for T cell receptor signaling and synapse formation. *Cell* 109:901–12

50. Supports the conformational change model of TCR triggering.

51. Buday L. 1999. Membrane-targeting of signaling molecules by SH2/SH3 domain-containing adaptor proteins. *Biochem. Biophys. Acta* 1422:187–204
52. Xu C, Gagnon E, Call ME, Schnell JR, Schwieters CD, et al. 2008. Regulation of T cell receptor activation by dynamic membrane binding of the CD3ε cytoplasmic tyrosine-based motif. *Cell* 135:702–13
53. Ma Z, Janmey PA, Finkel TH. 2008. The receptor deformation model of TCR triggering. *FASEB J.* 22:1002–8
54. Choudhuri K, Wiseman D, Brown M, Gould K, Van Der Merwe P. 2005. T-cell receptor triggering is critically dependent on the dimensions of its peptide-MHC ligand. *Nature* 436:578–82
55. Davis S, Van Der Merwe P. 2006. The kinetic-segregation model: TCR triggering and beyond. *Nat. Immunol.* 7:803–9

55. Summarizes the experimental evidence for their kinetic segregation model to explain the mechanism of TCR triggering.

56. Secrist JP, Burns LA, Karnitz L, Koretzky GA, Abraham RT. 1993. Stimulatory effects of the protein tyrosine phosphatase inhibitor, pervanadate, on T-cell activation events. *J. Biol. Chem.* 268:5886–93
57. Irles C, Symons A, Michel F, Bakker T, Van Der Merwe P, Acuto O. 2003. CD45 ectodomain controls interaction with GEMs and Lck activity for optimal TCR signaling. *Nat. Immunol.* 4:189–97
58. Rolli V, Gallwitz M, Wossning T, Flemming A, Schamel W, et al. 2002. Amplification of B cell antigen receptor signaling by a Syk/ITAM positive feedback loop. *Mol. Cell* 10:1057–69
59. Byth K, Conroy L, Howlett S, Smith A, May J, et al. 1996. CD45-null transgenic mice reveal a positive regulatory role for CD45 in early thymocyte development, in the selection of $CD4^+CD8^+$ thymocytes, and B cell maturation. *J. Exp. Med.* 183:1707–18
60. Kishihara K, Penninger J, Wallace V, Kündig T, Kawai K, et al. 1993. Normal B lymphocyte development but impaired T cell maturation in CD45-exon6 protein tyrosine phosphatase-deficient mice. *Cell* 74:143–56
61. Mustelin T, Coggeshall K, Altman A. 1989. Rapid activation of the T-cell tyrosine protein kinase pp56lck by the CD45 phosphotyrosine phosphatase. *Proc. Natl. Acad. Sci. USA* 86:6302–6
62. Zhu J, Brdicka T, Katsumoto T, Lin J, Weiss A. 2008. Structurally distinct phosphatases CD45 and CD148 both regulate B cell and macrophage immunoreceptor signaling. *Immunity* 28:183–96
63. Fleire S, Goldman J, Carrasco Y, Weber M, Bray D, Batista F. 2006. B cell ligand discrimination through a spreading and contraction response. *Science* 312:738–41

63. Describes the identification of a novel cellular response following B cell recognition of antigen on the APC surface.

64. Weber M, Treanor B, Depoil D, Shinohara H, Harwood NE, et al. 2008. Phospholipase C-gamma2 and Vav cooperate within signaling microclusters to propagate B cell spreading in response to membrane-bound antigen. *J. Exp. Med.* 205:853–68
65. Sohn H, Pierce S, Tzeng S. 2008. Live cell imaging reveals that the inhibitory Fc{gamma}RIIB destabilizes B cell receptor membrane-lipid interactions and blocks immune synapse formation. *J. Immunol.* 180:793–99
66. Bunnell S, Hong D, Kardon J, Yamazaki T, McGlade C, et al. 2002. T cell receptor ligation induces the formation of dynamically regulated signaling assemblies. *J. Cell Biol.* 158:1263–75
67. Campi G, Varma R, Dustin M. 2005. Actin and agonist MHC-peptide complex-dependent T cell receptor microclusters as scaffolds for signaling. *J. Exp. Med.* 202:1031–36
68. Yokosuka T, Sakata-Sogawa K, Kobayashi W, Hiroshima M, Hashimoto-Tane A, et al. 2005. Newly generated T cell receptor microclusters initiate and sustain T cell activation by recruitment of Zap70 and SLP-76. *Nat. Immunol.* 6:1253–62
69. Harwood NE, Batista FD. 2008. New insights into the early molecular events underlying B cell activation. *Immunity* 28:609–19

70. Dintzis H, Dintzis R, Vogelstein B. 1976. Molecular determinants of immunogenicity: the immunon model of immune response. *Proc. Natl. Acad. Sci. USA* 73:3671–75
71. Yokosuka T, Kobayashi W, Sakata-Sogawa K, Takamatsu M, Hashimoto-Tane A, et al. 2008. Spatiotemporal regulation of T cell costimulation by TCR-CD28 microclusters and protein kinase C theta translocation. *Immunity* 29:589–601
72. Kurosaki T. 1999. Genetic analysis of B cell antigen receptor signaling. *Annu. Rev. Immunol.* 17:555–92
73. Shinohara H, Kurosaki T. 2006. Genetic analysis of B cell signaling. *Subcell. Biochem.* 40:145–87
74. Bunnell S, Kapoor V, Trible R, Zhang W, Samelson L. 2001. Dynamic actin polymerization drives T cell receptor-induced spreading: a role for the signal transduction adaptor LAT. *Immunity* 14:315–29
75. Jaffe A, Hall A. 2005. Rho GTPases: biochemistry and biology. *Annu. Rev. Cell Dev. Biol.* 21:247–69
76. Brezski R, Monroe J. 2007. B cell antigen receptor-induced Rac1 activation and Rac1-dependent spreading are impaired in transitional immature B cells due to levels of membrane cholesterol. *J. Immunol.* 179:4464–72
77. Faure S, Salazar-Fontana L, Semichon M, Tybulewicz V, Bismuth G, et al. 2004. ERM proteins regulate cytoskeleton relaxation promoting T cell-APC conjugation. *Nat. Immunol.* 5:272–79
78. Gupta N, Wollscheid B, Watts J, Scheer B, Aebersold R, DeFranco A. 2006. Quantitative proteomic analysis of B cell lipid rafts reveals that ezrin regulates antigen receptor-mediated lipid raft dynamics. *Nat. Immunol.* 7:625–33

78. Reports that the ERM protein ezrin is dephosphorylated and dissociates from membrane rafts following BCR stimulation with soluble antigen, potentially triggering membrane raft coalescence and signaling.

79. Fournier E, Isakoff S, Ko K, Cardinale C, Inghirami G, et al. 2003. The B cell SH2/PH domain-containing adaptor Bam32/DAPP1 is required for T cell-independent II antigen responses. *Curr. Biol.* 13:1858–66
80. Han A, Saijo K, Mecklenbräuker I, Tarakhovsky A, Nussenzweig M. 2003. Bam32 links the B cell receptor to ERK and JNK and mediates B cell proliferation but not survival. *Immunity* 19:621–32
81. Marshall A, Niiro H, Lerner C, Yun T, Thomas S, et al. 2000. A novel B lymphocyte-associated adaptor protein, Bam32, regulates antigen receptor signaling downstream of phosphatidylinositol 3-kinase. *J. Exp. Med.* 191:1319–32
82. Niiro H, Allam A, Stoddart A, Brodsky F, Marshall A, Clark E. 2004. The B lymphocyte adaptor molecule of 32 kilodaltons (Bam32) regulates B cell antigen receptor internalization. *J. Immunol.* 173:5601–9
83. Gomez T, McCarney S, Carrizosa E, Labno C, Comiskey E, et al. 2006. HS1 functions as an essential actin-regulatory adaptor protein at the immune synapse. *Immunity* 24:741–52
84. Hao J, Carey G, Zhan X. 2004. Syk-mediated tyrosine phosphorylation is required for the association of hematopoietic lineage cell-specific protein 1 with lipid rafts and B cell antigen receptor signalosome complex. *J. Biol. Chem.* 279:33413–20
85. Yamanashi Y, Fukuda T, Nishizumi H, Inazu T, Higashi K, et al. 1997. Role of tyrosine phosphorylation of HS1 in B cell antigen receptor-mediated apoptosis. *J. Exp. Med.* 185:1387–92
86. DesMarais V, Ghosh M, Eddy R, Condeelis J. 2005. Cofilin takes the lead. *J. Cell Sci.* 118:19–26
87. Yonezawa N, Homma Y, Yahara I, Sakai H, Nishida E. 1991. A short sequence responsible for both phosphoinositide binding and actin binding activities of cofilin. *J. Biol. Chem.* 266:17218–21
88. Randall K, Lambe T, Johnson A, Treanor B, Kucharska E, et al. 2009. Dock8 mutations cripple B cell immunological synapses, germinal centers and long-lived antibody production. *Nat Immunol.* 10:1283–91
89. Fearon D, Carroll M. 2000. Regulation of B lymphocyte responses to foreign and self-antigens by the CD19/CD21 complex. *Annu. Rev. Immunol.* 18:393–422
90. Fujimoto M, Bradney A, Poe J, Steeber D, Tedder T. 1999. Modulation of B lymphocyte antigen receptor signal transduction by a CD19/CD22 regulatory loop. *Immunity* 11:191–200
91. Sato S, Miller A, Howard M, Tedder T. 1997. Regulation of B lymphocyte development and activation by the CD19/CD21/CD81/Leu 13 complex requires the cytoplasmic domain of CD19. *J. Immunol.* 159:3278–87
92. Engel P, Zhou L, Ord D, Sato S, Koller B, Tedder T. 1995. Abnormal B lymphocyte development, activation, and differentiation in mice that lack or overexpress the CD19 signal transduction molecule. *Immunity* 3:39–50
93. Rickert R, Rajewsky K, Roes J. 1995. Impairment of T-cell-dependent B-cell responses and B-1 cell development in CD19-deficient mice. *Nature* 376:352–55

92–93. Both papers report that the deletion of CD19 in mice does not perturb the development of mature B cells but does severely effect the ability of B cells to become activated in response to T cell–dependent antigen.

94. Li X, Sandoval D, Freeberg L, Carter R. 1997. Role of CD19 tyrosine 391 in synergistic activation of B lymphocytes by coligation of CD19 and membrane Ig. *J. Immunol.* 158:5649–57
95. Tuveson D, Carter R, Soltoff S, Fearon D. 1993. CD19 of B cells as a surrogate kinase insert region to bind phosphatidylinositol 3-kinase. *Science* 260:986–89
96. Brooks S, Kirkham P, Freeberg L, Carter R. 2004. Binding of cytoplasmic proteins to the CD19 intracellular domain is high affinity, competitive, and multimeric. *J. Immunol.* 172:7556–64
97. O'Rourke L, Tooze R, Turner M, Sandoval D, Carter R, et al. 1998. CD19 as a membrane-anchored adaptor protein of B lymphocytes: costimulation of lipid and protein kinases by recruitment of Vav. *Immunity* 8:635–45
98. Zhang W, Samelson L. 2000. The role of membrane-associated adaptors in T cell receptor signaling. *Semin. Immunol.* 12:35–41
99. Freedman AS, Munro JM, Rice GE, Bevilacqua MP, Morimoto C, et al. 1990. Adhesion of human B cells to germinal centers in vitro involves VLA-4 and INCAM-110. *Science* 249:1030–33
100. Koopman G, Parmentier HK, Schuurman HJ, Newman W, Meijer CJ, Pals ST. 1991. Adhesion of human B cells to follicular dendritic cells involves both the lymphocyte function-associated antigen 1/intercellular adhesion molecule 1 and very late antigen 4/vascular cell adhesion molecule 1 pathways. *J. Exp. Med.* 173:1297–304
101. Kushnir N, Liu L, MacPherson GG. 1998. Dendritic cells and resting B cells form clusters in vitro and in vivo: T cell independence, partial LFA-1 dependence, and regulation by cross-linking surface molecules. *J. Immunol.* 160:1774–81
102. Koopman G, Keehnen RM, Lindhout E, Newman W, Shimizu Y, et al. 1994. Adhesion through the LFA-1 (CD11a/CD18)-ICAM-1 (CD54) and the VLA-4 (CD49d)-VCAM-1 (CD106) pathways prevents apoptosis of germinal center B cells. *J. Immunol.* 152:3760–67
103. Cantor J, Browne CD, Ruppert R, Féral CC, Fässler R, et al. 2009. CD98hc facilitates B cell proliferation and adaptive humoral immunity. *Nat. Immunol.* 10:412–19
104. Carrasco Y, Fleire S, Cameron T, Dustin M, Batista F. 2004. LFA-1/ICAM-1 interaction lowers the threshold of B cell activation by facilitating B cell adhesion and synapse formation. *Immunity* 20:589–99
105. Carrasco YR, Batista FD. 2006. B-cell activation by membrane-bound antigens is facilitated by the interaction of VLA-4 with VCAM-1. *EMBO J.* 25:889–99
106. Dustin ML, Springer TA. 1988. Lymphocyte function-associated antigen-1 (LFA-1) interaction with intercellular adhesion molecule-1 (ICAM-1) is one of at least three mechanisms for lymphocyte adhesion to cultured endothelial cells. *J. Cell Biol.* 107:321–31
107. Kim M, Carman CV, Springer TA. 2003. Bidirectional transmembrane signaling by cytoplasmic domain separation in integrins. *Science* 301:1720–25
108. Arana E, Vehlow A, Harwood N, Vigorito E, Henderson R, et al. 2008. Activation of the small GTPase Rac2 via the B cell receptor regulates B cell adhesion and immunological synapse formation. *Immunity* 28:88–99
109. Lin K, Freeman S, Zabetian S, Brugger H, Weber M, et al. 2008. The Rap GTPases regulate B cell morphology, immune synapse formation and signaling by particulate B cell receptor ligands. *Immunity* 28:75–87
110. Kaizuka Y, Douglass AD, Varma R, Dustin ML, Vale RD. 2007. Mechanisms for segregating T cell receptor and adhesion molecules during immunological synapse formation in Jurkat T cells. *Proc. Natl. Acad. Sci. USA* 104:20296–301
111. Nguyen K, Sylvain NR, Bunnell SC. 2008. T cell costimulation via the integrin VLA-4 inhibits the actin-dependent centralization of signaling microclusters containing the adaptor SLP-76. *Immunity* 28:810–21
112. Grakoui A, Bromley S, Sumen C, Davis M, Shaw A, et al. 1999. The immunological synapse: a molecular machine controlling T cell activation. *Science* 285:221–27
113. Krummel M, Sjaastad M, Wülfing C, Davis M. 2000. Differential clustering of CD4 and CD3ζ during T cell recognition. *Science* 289:1349–52
114. Monks C, Freiberg B, Kupfer H, Sciaky N, Kupfer A. 1998. Three-dimensional segregation of supramolecular activation clusters in T cells. *Nature* 395:82–86

115. Potter T, Grebe K, Freiberg B, Kupfer A. 2001. Formation of supramolecular activation clusters on fresh ex vivo CD8+ T cells after engagement of the T cell antigen receptor and CD8 by antigen-presenting cells. *Proc. Natl. Acad. Sci. USA* 98:12624–29
116. Stinchcombe J, Bossi G, Booth S, Griffiths G. 2001. The immunological synapse of CTL contains a secretory domain and membrane bridges. *Immunity* 15:751–61
117. Davis D, Chiu I, Fassett M, Cohen G, Mandelboim O, Strominger J. 1999. The human natural killer cell immune synapse. *Proc. Natl. Acad. Sci. USA* 96:15062–67
118. Lee K, Holdorf A, Dustin M, Chan A, Allen P, Shaw A. 2002. T cell receptor signaling precedes immunological synapse formation. *Science* 295:1539–42
119. Vascotto F, Lankar D, Faure-André G, Vargas P, Diaz J, et al. 2007. The actin-based motor protein myosin II regulates MHC class II trafficking and BCR-driven antigen presentation. *J. Cell Biol.* 176:1007–19
120. Čemerski S, Das J, Giurisato E, Markiewicz MA, Allen PM, et al. 2008. The balance between T cell receptor signaling and degradation at the center of the immunological synapse is determined by antigen quality. *Immunity* 29:414–22
121. Ilani T, Vasiliver-Shamis G, Vardhana S, Bretscher A, Dustin ML. 2009. T cell antigen receptor signaling and immunological synapse stability require myosin IIA. *Nat. Immunol.* 10:531–39
122. Sims TN, Soos TJ, Xenias HS, Dubin-Thaler B, Hofman JM, et al. 2007. Opposing effects of PKCθ and WASp on symmetry breaking and relocation of the immunological synapse. *Cell* 129:773–85
123. Dustin ML. 2008. T-cell activation through immunological synapses and kinapses. *Immunol. Rev.* 221:77–89
124. Dustin ML. 2008. Hunter to gatherer and back: immunological synapses and kinapses as variations on the theme of amoeboid locomotion. *Annu. Rev. Cell Dev. Biol.* 24:577–96
125. von Andrian UH, Mempel TR. 2003. Homing and cellular traffic in lymph nodes. *Nat. Rev. Immunol.* 3:867–78
126. Halin C, Rodrigo Mora J, Sumen C, von Andrian U. 2005. In vivo imaging of lymphocyte trafficking. *Annu. Rev. Cell Dev. Biol.* 21:581–603
127. Bajénoff M, Germain R. 2007. Seeing is believing: a focus on the contribution of microscopic imaging to our understanding of immune system function. *Eur. J. Immunol.* 37(Suppl. 1):S18–33
128. Junt T, Scandella E, Ludewig B. 2008. Form follows function: lymphoid tissue microarchitecture in antimicrobial immune defense. *Nat. Rev. Immunol.* 8:764–75
129. Cahalan M, Parker I. 2008. Choreography of cell motility and interaction dynamics imaged by two-photon microscopy in lymphoid organs. *Annu. Rev. Immunol.* 26:585–626
130. Germain R, Miller M, Dustin M, Nussenzweig M. 2006. Dynamic imaging of the immune system: progress, pitfalls and promise. *Nat. Rev. Immunol.* 6:497–507
131. Pape K, Catron D, Itano A, Jenkins M. 2007. The humoral immune response is initiated in lymph nodes by B cells that acquire soluble antigen directly in the follicles. *Immunity* 26:491–502

131. Reveals low-molecular-mass antigen diffuses from the SCS and is rapidly accumulated by follicular B cells.

132. Clark S. 1962. The reticulum of lymph nodes in mice studied with the electron microscope. *Am. J. Anat.* 110:217–57
133. Farr A, Cho Y, De Bruyn P. 1980. The structure of the sinus wall of the lymph node relative to its endocytic properties and transmural cell passage. *Am. J. Anat.* 157:265–84
134. van Ewijk W, Brekelmans P, Jacobs R, Wisse E. 1988. Lymphoid microenvironments in the thymus and lymph node. *Scanning Microsc.* 2:2129–40
135. Roozendaal R, Mempel TR, Pitcher LA, Gonzalez SF, Verschoor A, et al. 2009. Conduits mediate transport of low-molecular-weight antigen to lymph node follicles. *Immunity* 30:264–76

135. Identifies a follicular conduit system capable of transporting low-molecular-mass antigen to follicular B cells and potentially to FDCs.

136. Gretz J, Norbury C, Anderson A, Proudfoot A, Shaw S. 2000. Lymph-borne chemokines and other low molecular weight molecules reach high endothelial venules via specialized conduits while a functional barrier limits access to the lymphocyte microenvironments in lymph node cortex. *J. Exp. Med.* 192:1425–40
137. Sixt M, Kanazawa N, Selg M, Samson T, Roos G, et al. 2005. The conduit system transports soluble antigens from the afferent lymph to resident dendritic cells in the T cell area of the lymph node. *Immunity* 22:19–29

138–140. Use MPM methods to establish a role for the SCS macrophages in presenting antigen in the form of particulates, viruses, and immune complexes to cognate follicular B cells.

138. Carrasco Y, Batista F. 2007. B cells acquire particulate antigen in a macrophage-rich area at the boundary between the follicle and the subcapsular sinus of the lymph node. *Immunity* 27:160–71

139. Junt T, Moseman E, Iannacone M, Massberg S, Lang P, et al. 2007. Subcapsular sinus macrophages in lymph nodes clear lymph-borne viruses and present them to antiviral B cells. *Nature* 450:110–14

140. Phan T, Grigorova I, Okada T, Cyster J. 2007. Subcapsular encounter and complement-dependent transport of immune complexes by lymph node B cells. *Nat. Immunol.* 8:992–1000

141. Martinez-Pomares L, Gordon S. 2007. Antigen presentation the macrophage way. *Cell* 131:641–43

142. Okada T, Miller M, Parker I, Krummel M, Neighbors M, et al. 2005. Antigen-engaged B cells undergo chemotaxis toward the T zone and form motile conjugates with helper T cells. *PLoS Biol.* 3:e150

143. Qi H, Cannons JL, Klauschen F, Schwartzberg PL, Germain RN. 2008. SAP-controlled T-B cell interactions underlie germinal center formation. *Nature* 455:764–69

144. Qi H, Egen JG, Huang AY, Germain RN. 2006. Extrafollicular activation of lymph node B cells by antigen-bearing dendritic cells. *Science* 312:1672–76

145. Lindquist R, Shakhar G, Dudziak D, Wardemann H, Eisenreich T, et al. 2004. Visualizing dendritic cell networks in vivo. *Nat. Immunol.* 5:1243–50

146. Coffey F, Alabyev B, Manser T. 2009. Initial clonal expansion of germinal center B cells takes place at the perimeter of follicles. *Immunity* 30:599–609

147. Mitchell J, Abbot A. 1965. Ultrastructure of the antigen-retaining reticulum of lymph node follicles as shown by high-resolution autoradiography. *Nature* 208:500–2

148. Nossal G, Abbot A, Mitchell J, Lummus Z. 1968. Antigens in immunity. XV. Ultrastructural features of antigen capture in primary and secondary lymphoid follicles. *J. Exp. Med.* 127:277–90

149. Cinamon G, Zachariah MA, Lam OM, Foss FW Jr, Cyster JG. 2008. Follicular shuttling of marginal zone B cells facilitates antigen transport. *Nat. Immunol.* 9:54–62

150. El Shikh ME, El Sayed RM, Szakal AK, Tew JG. 2009. T-independent antibody responses to T-dependent antigens: a novel follicular dendritic cell-dependent activity. *J. Immunol.* 182:3482–91

151. Suzuki K, Grigorova IL, Phan TG, Kelly LM, Cyster JG. 2009. Visualizing B cell capture of cognate antigen from follicular dendritic cells. *J. Exp. Med.* 206:1485–93

152. Allen C, Okada T, Tang H, Cyster J. 2007. Imaging of germinal center selection events during affinity maturation. *Science* 315:528–31

153. Hauser A, Junt T, Mempel T, Sneddon M, Kleinstein S, et al. 2007. Definition of germinal-center B cell migration in vivo reveals predominant intrazonal circulation patterns. *Immunity* 26:655–67

154. Schwickert T, Lindquist R, Shakhar G, Livshits G, Skokos D, et al. 2007. In vivo imaging of germinal centres reveals a dynamic open structure. *Nature* 446:83–87

From Allergen Genes to Allergy Vaccines

Rudolf Valenta,[1,2] Fatima Ferreira,[4] Margarete Focke-Tejkl,[1,2] Birgit Linhart,[2] Verena Niederberger,[3] Ines Swoboda,[1,2] and Susanne Vrtala[2]

[1]Christian Doppler Laboratory for Allergy Research, [2]Division of Immunopathology, Department of Pathophysiology, Center for Physiology and Pathophysiology, [3]Department of Otorhinolaryngology, Medical University of Vienna, A-1090 Vienna, Austria; email: rudolf.valenta@meduniwien.ac.at

[4]Christian Doppler Laboratory for Allergy Diagnosis and Therapy, University of Salzburg, A-5020 Salzburg, Austria

Annu. Rev. Immunol. 2010. 28:211–41

First published online as a Review in Advance on December 8, 2009

The *Annual Review of Immunology* is online at immunol.annualreviews.org

This article's doi:
10.1146/annurev-immunol-030409-101218

0732-0582/10/0423-0211$20.00

Key Words

allergy, recombinant allergen, specific immunotherapy, IgE, T cell, peptide, diagnosis

Abstract

IgE-mediated allergy is a hypersensitivity disease affecting more than 25% of the population. The structures of the most common allergens have been revealed through molecular cloning technology in the past two decades. On the basis of this knowledge of the sequences and three-dimensional structures of culprit allergens, investigators can now analyze the immune recognition of allergens and the mechanisms of allergic inflammation in allergic patients. Allergy vaccines have been constructed that are able to selectively target the aberrant immune responses in allergic patients via different pathways of the immune system. Here we review various types of allergy vaccines that have been developed based on allergen structures, results from their clinical application in allergic patients, and future strategies for allergen-specific immunotherapy and allergy prophylaxis.

INTRODUCTION

Allergy is a hypersensitivity disease characterized by the production of IgE antibodies against antigens (i.e., allergens) that can enter the body via the respiratory tract, the gastrointestinal tract, the skin, and/or an insect sting or injection of a drug (1). Accordingly, allergic patients can exhibit a variety of allergic manifestations in different target organs, including rhinoconjunctivitis, asthma, food allergy, skin reactions, and severe systemic reactions such as anaphylactic shock, when they encounter the allergens against which they are sensitized. Allergic sensitization occurs early in childhood upon allergen encounter in persons who have an inherited atopic predisposition (2, 3). Environmental factors, route, period, and dose of allergen encounter have an additional influence on the development of the allergic immune response (4–6). In contrast to nonallergic individuals who respond to allergens with production of IgG antibodies and a balanced T cell response, allergic patients produce allergen-specific IgE antibodies and show a preferential allergen-specific Th2 response (7, 8). The class switch to IgE antibody production occurring during primary sensitization in allergic patients is driven by IL-4, which is a product of Th2 cells and other effector cells of the allergic immune response (9, 10).

IgE is the least abundant class of immunoglobulins but can elicit immediate and strong inflammation because it can activate mast cells and basophils via the high-affinity receptor FcεRI (11, 12). Allergens cross-link FcεRI-bound IgE owing to the fact that they contain epitopes able to combine with different IgE paratopes, so that mast cells and basophils become activated and release inflammatory mediators, cytokines, and proteases, leading to immediate allergic inflammation (13). The activation of allergen-specific T cells is achieved by the presentation of allergens via antigen-presenting cells (APCs), a process that may be enhanced by IgE-facilitated allergen presentation (14, 15). Although repeated allergen contact strongly boosts the allergic immune response and enhances the sensitivity to allergens (16, 17), strong evidence also indicates that the allergen and epitope profile recognized by allergic patients after the initial sensitization event remains constant during the natural course of the disease (18).

Almost 100 years ago, long before allergy was understood as an IgE-mediated hypersensitivity toward defined allergenic molecules, the administration of extracts made from allergen sources in the form of subcutaneous vaccines was found to render allergic patients tolerant to allergen exposure (19, 20). This finding was remarkable because it showed that active vaccination with disease-causing allergens can antagonize an already existing hypersensitivity toward the very same allergens. In seminal studies, allergen-specific immunotherapy (SIT) induced allergen-specific IgG antibodies, which compete with IgE antibodies for their binding sites on allergens and hence were termed blocking antibodies (21, 22). Still under investigation is whether the induction of allergen-specific IgG antibodies by SIT is due to alterations in the balance between allergen-specific Th2 and Th1 responses, the induction of regulatory T cell responses, or a de novo induction of an allergen-specific immune response by the vaccine (20, 23).

SIT is clinically effective and, unlike symptomatic antiinflammatory treatment, long-lasting and disease-modifying when it is performed with allergen extracts of acceptable quality (24–26). However, a detailed knowledge of the culprit antigens is a prerequisite for any improvement in treatment, as it is also true for many other areas such as infectious diseases, tumor therapy, autoimmunity, or transplantation for which antigen-targeted therapeutic and prophylactic strategies are being developed. Here we review progress made in the field of allergen characterization during the past two decades and the consequent development of new concepts for allergy vaccination based on the availability of allergen-encoding genes and the structures of their products.

THE IMPACT OF ALLERGEN STRUCTURE

A detailed analysis of the humoral and cellular immune response to a certain antigen requires the availability of the pure antigen and information about its sequence and structure. In the field of allergology, there has always been a strong interest in characterizing the disease-causing allergens because preventive (i.e., allergen avoidance) and therapeutic (i.e., administration of allergy vaccines) measures require the identification of the culprit allergens by diagnostic testing such as in vivo provocation testing or serological detection of allergen-specific IgE antibodies. However, early attempts at allergen characterization were limited to the preparation of crude allergen extracts from the corresponding allergen sources and did not provide pure allergen molecules. The introduction of protein and immunochemical methods enabled certain important allergens to be purified, although the yield and purity were often inadequate. Moreover, it was almost impossible to obtain information about amino acid sequences and three-dimensional structures of allergenic molecules (27–29). This situation changed dramatically with the application of technology of expression cloning to the characterization of allergens in the mid-1980s (30). Allergen expression cloning is based on the isolation of messenger RNA from a given allergen source that is converted into cDNA using reverse transcriptase. The resulting cDNAs coding for allergens are then inserted into expression vector systems so that they can be identified with IgE antibodies from allergic patients. The DNA sequence of the allergen is then determined and the recombinant allergen is expressed in appropriate hosts, enabling a detailed characterization of the allergen's three-dimensional structure (**Figure 1**). Through application of cDNA cloning technologies, the first complete allergen sequences, which became available in the late-1980s (31–33), allowed analysis of the immune recognition of allergens in allergic patients and generation of recombinant allergens for diagnosis, therapy, and prevention (**Figure 1**).

The DNA and amino acid sequences of the most common allergens are now known, and the three-dimensional structures have been elucidated for many important allergens (1, 34, 35). Information about allergen structures with clinical relevance for allergic patients can be obtained via several freely accessible online databases (36) (**Table 1**). In the next section, we discuss the recognition of allergens by T cells and IgE from allergic patients, with an emphasis on some unresolved research questions.

RECOGNITION OF ALLERGENS BY THE IMMUNE SYSTEM

T Cell Recognition of Allergens

When the first allergen sequences became available, several research groups isolated allergen-specific T cell clones from allergic patients and conducted T cell epitope mapping studies using synthetic peptides spanning the allergen sequences (**Figure 2**). Most allergen-specific T cell clones isolated from allergic patients belonged to the $CD4^+$, Th2 subset according to their cytokine secretion profile (37–39). T cell epitopes were spread over the complete allergen sequence in most cases, and allergic patients recognized a variety of different epitopes on a given allergen, showing greatly varying MHCII restrictions (38–43). Frequently recognized and thus dominant T cell epitopes as well as strong HLA associations regarding the recognition of certain T cell epitopes were found only for certain allergens (44–46). Allergen-specific T cells seem to persist in allergic patients over long periods and can be traced via their T cell receptor, indicating the existence of an allergen-specific T cell memory (47, 48).

Studies comparing the T cell recognition of allergens showed that T cells from allergic as well as nonallergic persons recognized similar epitopes and differed only regarding their cytokine secretion profiles, which appeared to

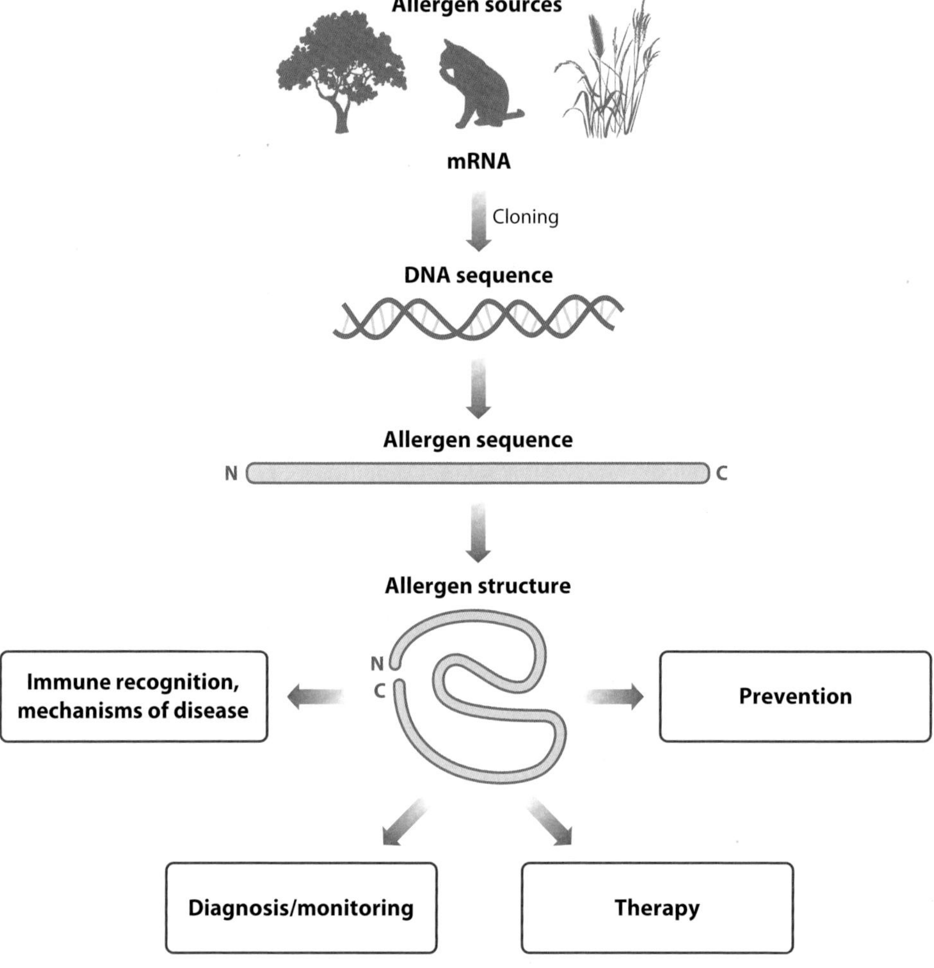

Figure 1

From allergen genes to allergy vaccines. Messenger RNA (mRNA) isolated from allergen sources is converted into cDNA by reverse transcription and is then used as a template to produce the recombinant allergen to determine the three-dimensional allergen structure, and serves as a tool to study immune recognition of allergens and for diagnosis, therapy, and prevention of allergy.

be more Th2 prone in allergic subjects than in nonallergic persons (49–53).

Certain studies analyzing allergen-specific T regulatory (Treg) cells in allergic and nonallergic persons indicated that Treg cells are more frequent in nonallergic persons and in patients who become tolerant to allergens than in allergic patients (54–56). However, other studies demonstrated that Treg cells are present in both allergic and nonallergic persons and can suppress T cell activation as well as cytokine production (57, 58). One study indicated that Treg activity may depend on the nature and concentration of allergen and on the allergic status of individual patients (59). To determine whether a difference between allergen-specific Treg activities in atopic versus nonallergic persons contributes to the manifestation of allergy will require more and larger studies in patients as well as in nonallergic persons to test several different important allergens.

Table 1 Overview of the databases containing allergen sequences and structures

Database	Address	Features
General molecular biology databases		
Entrez Nucleotide Database	**http://www.ncbi.nlm.nih.gov/sites/entrez?db=nucleotide**	All available DNA sequences
Entrez Protein Database	**http://www.ncbi.nlm.nih.gov/sites/entrez?db=protein**	All available protein sequences
Entrez Structure Database	**http://www.ncbi.nlm.nih.gov/sites/entrez?db=structure**	Collection of experimentally determined three-dimensional biomolecular structures
Allergen databases		
IUIS/WHO allergen nomenclature	**http://www.allergen.org**	Summary of allergens submitted to the allergen nomenclature subcommittee
Biotechnology information for food safety (BIFS)	**http://www.iit.edu/~sgendel/fa.htm**	Food and nonfood allergens
Inform All	**http://foodallergens.ifr.ac.uk**	Food allergens, with sequences, biochemical and immunological imformation
Allergen Database (ADB)	**http://allergen.csl.gov.uk/**	Sequences and some information about epitopes
Structural database of allergen proteins (SDAP)	**http://fermi.utmb.edu/SDAP/sdap_src.html**	Sequences, structures, B cell epitopes
AllergenOnline (FARP)	**http://www.allergenonline.com**	Food and nonfood allergens
Allergome	**http://www.allergome.org**	Sequences, biochemical, immunological and clinical information
AllFam	**http://www.meduniwien.ac.at/allergens/allfam**	Allergens grouped into protein families

IgE Recognition of Allergens

Antibodies may recognize continuous epitopes on antigens, which consist of only a few consecutive amino acids within the protein sequence, or may bind to discontinuous, conformational epitopes, which are formed by amino acids located in nonadjacent portions of the protein sequence but that are assembled close to each other through the folding of the protein (60) (**Figure 2**). Through the use of overlapping synthetic peptides and recombinant allergen fragments, continuous IgE epitopes of several important allergens were determined and found to bind only relatively low levels of allergen-specific IgE antibodies (61–64). However, continuous IgE epitopes appear to play a relatively important role in food allergy, because here allergens are digested in the gastrointestinal tract before they sensitize atopic persons. Most respiratory allergens contain primarily conformational IgE epitopes, presumably because they easily elute from allergen-containing particles, intrude, and sensitize as intact proteins via the respiratory mucosa (34). The importance of conformational epitopes is exemplified by calcium-binding allergens that contain IgE epitopes in which conformation depends on protein-bound calcium. Depletion of calcium from these allergens using chelating agents or mutational exchange of those amino acids required for calcium binding leads to a dramatic loss of IgE reactivity (65–67). Another striking example for IgE recognition of conformational epitopes is the major birch pollen allergen, Bet v 1, which binds IgE antibodies only when the protein fold is intact, whereas even two fragments, each representing approximately one-half of the protein, lacked IgE reactivity due to a loss of conformation (68).

The fact that allergens mainly contain conformational IgE epitopes renders epitope mapping of allergens difficult. Thus, sophisticated methods such as mutational analysis, analysis of the three-dimensional structure of antigen-antibody complexes, and use of competitive antibody probes with defined specificity to block IgE binding must be employed.

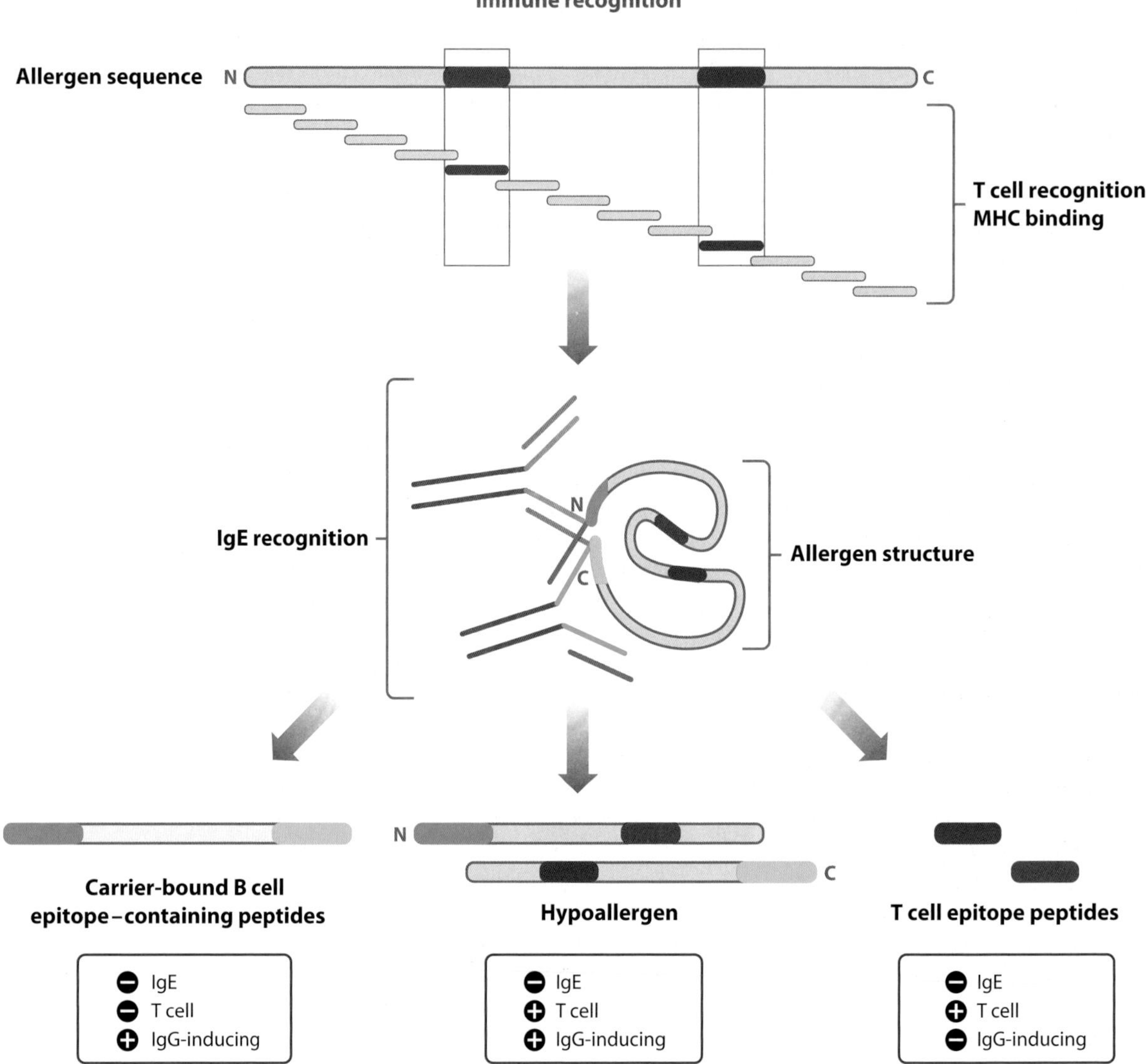

Figure 2

Recognition of allergens by T cells and IgE antibodies. T cell epitopes and MHC-binding sites of allergens can be mapped with overlapping peptides synthesized according to the allergen sequence. IgE antibodies recognize mainly conformational (i.e., discontinuous) epitopes that often cluster on oriented, surface-exposed areas of the allergen. Discontinuous epitopes are assembled by different portions of the allergen that come into spatial proximity in a folded molecule so that they can be recognized by IgE. If the fold of an allergen is disrupted, e.g., when the allergen is fragmented, conformational IgE epitopes are destroyed, resulting in hypoallergenic molecules with no or reduced IgE reactivity, preserved T cell epitopes, and the ability to induce allergen-specific IgG upon immunization. Because of their small size, synthetic peptides containing only T cell epitopes without IgE reactivity generally do not induce allergen-specific IgG antibodies. Peptides derived from conformational IgE epitopes generally lack IgE reactivity owing to the inability of these peptides to reconstitute conformational IgE epitopes. They can be grafted onto nonallergenic carrier proteins to obtain carrier-bound peptides lacking IgE or T cell reactivity but can be used to induce allergen-specific IgG responses upon immunization. IgG antibodies induced with such carrier-bound peptides will bind to the peptides on the folded allergen and thus occupy amino acids within the conformational IgE epitopes and block IgE binding to the allergen.

To cross-link allergen-specific IgE antibodies on effector cells and thereby induce allergic inflammation, allergens must contain several different IgE-binding sites. Monovalent IgE-binding structures (i.e., IgE-reactive haptens) do not cross-link effector cell–bound IgE and thus fail to induce mast cell/basophil degranulation (63, 69). When effector cell–bound IgE is saturated after preincubation with such IgE-reactive haptens, the subsequent degranulation by the complete allergen can be blocked (69). Using the major timothy grass pollen allergen Phl p 1 and the major house dust mite allergen Der p 2, investigators demonstrated that the magnitude of effector cell activation is associated with the number of IgE epitopes and the density of IgE antibodies on the cell surface (69, 70). Also, the affinity of IgE for the given epitopes may be an important factor in efficient effector cell degranulation (70). Recently, three-dimensional structures of complexes consisting of allergen-specific IgE antibodies and the corresponding allergens became available and visualized the conformational IgE recognition of allergens (71, 72). The affinities of the monoclonal human IgE antibodies for their corresponding allergens investigated so far were almost as high as those between IgE and the high-affinity receptor for IgE (71, 72). These findings indicate that high-affinity interactions may be crucial features of the allergen-IgE-effector cell recognition machinery and may explain why allergic inflammation is so strong even though only minute amounts of IgE are present in plasma, in body fluids, and on effector cells and only low allergen amounts intrude into the body.

Several studies provide evidence that IgE epitopes cluster on spatially oriented areas/patches on allergens and thus may become positioned in a manner that facilitates binding to IgE antibodies on effector cells (73–75). Based on these results, IgE epitopes positioned like a defined patch on an allergen are speculated to activate effector cells more efficiently than IgE epitopes that are spread over the complete allergen surface, yet this hypothesis is not proven. A detailed investigation of the influence of epitope geometry and structural constraints on effector cell activation will require sophisticated models based on monoclonal IgE antibodies with known affinities and allergen constructs containing structurally defined epitopes.

The seminal work of Cooke & Loveless clearly demonstrated that allergen-specific IgG antibodies, which block the IgE binding to allergens, can suppress allergen-induced mast cell degranulation and thus immediate allergic inflammation (21, 22). There is also good evidence that allergen-specific IgG antibodies can downregulate the activation of allergen-specific T cells by inhibiting IgE-facilitated antigen presentation (76, 77). Furthermore, the epitope-specificity and titer of allergen-specific IgG antibodies and perhaps also their affinity are critical for their potential to inhibit IgE-mediated pathology (78). In this context, only some of the defined human allergen-specific monoclonal IgG antibodies described to date are able to inhibit IgE binding, whereas others recognize epitopes different from those recognized by IgE and hence fail to inhibit IgE binding (79, 80). It is not yet clear whether the concomitant binding of IgG and IgE antibodies to allergens plays a physiological role in allergic patients by down-modulating effector cell responses via a process termed cocross-linking of receptors for IgE and IgG (81–83). Also unclear is whether supercross-linking of IgE-FcεR-bound allergens or an induction of changes of the IgE-binding capacity of allergens by such IgG antibodies may influence allergic responses in patients because only some paradigmatic, mostly in vitro, data are available to date (80, 84).

Allergen-specific antibodies other than IgE belong mainly to the IgG1, IgG4, and IgG2 subclasses; few allergen-specific IgG3, IgA, and IgM antibodies have been found in allergic and nonallergic persons (8, 85).

Whether the class switch to IgE production during allergic sensitization early in childhood develops through an IgG intermediate or directly is not resolved. However, the fact that allergen-specific IgE has been detected in the blood of children before the occurrence of allergen-specific IgG argues against an exclusively sequential class switch program (3). Studies using defined allergen molecules and IgE-reactive epitopes provided evidence that there is no epitope spreading. The profile of IgE-reactive allergens and epitopes remains stable over the course of allergic disease (18, 86), although the amount of allergen-specific IgE varies depending on allergen contact. In particular, allergen contact via the respiratory and oral mucosa strongly boosts allergen-specific IgE production (18). Allergen-induced boosts of IgE production in already sensitized allergic persons occur a few weeks after allergen exposure and are not associated with detectable increases of allergen-specific IgM responses, suggesting that they result from the stimulation of IgE memory cells without involving de novo class-switch events (18). Still open is whether this allergen-induced boost of IgE production is caused by the stimulation of allergen-specific IgE^+ B cells in the respiratory mucosa and/or in the lymphatic tissues adjacent to the mucosa. Cells producing allergen-specific IgE in the peripheral blood of allergic patients seem to be primarily plasma cells (87). Indeed, functional allergen-specific IgE heavy chain variable sequences have been cloned and expressed from the peripheral blood of allergic patients by combinatorial cloning, demonstrating that the peripheral blood of allergic patients does contain IgE-producing cells (88).

Several studies have indicated that allergen-specific IgE antibodies may exhibit a preferential usage of certain VH regions (89–91), but other studies report a much broader usage of various VH family genes in allergic patients (92–94). Nevertheless, the VH repertoire used by allergen-specific IgE seems to be limited, and certain IgE variable regions specific for a given allergen can be detected even in genetically unrelated patients and in the same patient after several years (95; K. Marth, M. Novatchkova, M. Focke-Tejkl, S. Jenisch, S. Jäger, et al., manuscript in review).

The boost of secondary IgE production is an important process in allergic inflammation because IgE upregulates the expression of its receptors on effector cells and also contributes to survival of these cells (96–99). Allergic patients typically show increased sensitivity to allergens (i.e., small allergen concentrations can elicit strong allergic inflammation) after allergen contact that is associated with increases of IgE levels (18). The immunological mechanisms behind the boosts of secondary IgE production are not fully understood. An experimental animal model for primary allergic sensitization and secondary IgE responses demonstrated that blockade of costimulation prevented allergic sensitization but had no influence on secondary IgE responses or on IgE-induced allergic inflammation (100). This finding indicates that primary sensitization is a T cell–dependent process, whereas the secondary IgE response seems to be T cell independent, at least in this murine model. Important open questions concern the nature of the cell types involved in secondary IgE production and the precise mechanisms of stimulation. Still to be determined are whether and how a secondary IgE response can be controlled, bearing in mind that the secondary IgE response ultimately underlies allergic inflammation in sensitized allergic patients. So far it has only been demonstrated that the boost of secondary IgE production caused by allergen contact is mitigated in allergic patients who have developed allergen-specific IgG antibodies after allergy vaccination (101–103).

Selective Targeting of the Immune System with Allergen Derivatives

Based on allergen sequences and structures, investigators can dissect IgE epitopes and T cell epitopes of clinically relevant allergens (61–64, 104–106) (**Figure 2**). Allergen-specific T cells recognize short, mainly unfolded peptides that generally lack IgE reactivity. Synthetic T cell epitope–containing peptides therefore selectively target T cells but do not induce IgE-mediated allergic inflammation (107). Because of their small size, T cell–reactive peptides do not induce relevant allergen-specific IgG responses when they are administered in animals or in allergic patients (108). The discovery that allergen-derived T cell peptides from the major cat allergen, Fel d 1, induced late-phase allergic symptoms in several patients provided the first evidence for mechanisms of non-IgE-mediated allergic inflammation in allergic patients (109). A similar finding was made with recombinant hypoallergenic allergen derivatives of the major birch pollen allergen, Bet v 1. Two recombinant fragments of Bet v 1, which lacked IgE reactivity but contained the relevant Bet v 1-specific T cell epitopes, induced delayed-type skin inflammation (110), suggesting that allergic persons can also suffer from non-IgE-mediated DTH allergic inflammation. Recombinant hypoallergenic allergen derivatives (so-called hypoallergens) have been made for SIT for many allergen molecules with the aim of reducing IgE-mediated side effects (111). In contrast to T cell epitope–containing synthetic peptides, recombinant hypoallergens can be engineered to preserve most allergen-specific T cell epitopes within one or two molecules. The reduction or abolition of IgE binding is achieved by mutation, fragmentation, or reassembly of fragments so that either the conformational IgE epitopes are destroyed or the amino acids required for IgE binding are mutated. Recombinant hypoallergenic allergen derivatives are proteins that can be engineered to induce robust allergen-specific IgG antibody production upon immunization and therefore are suitable for immunotherapeutic approaches based on the induction of blocking IgG responses as well as for tolerance induction (111).

According to IgE epitope mapping and structural data, it is possible to select peptides from the surface of allergens that are part of or are close to IgE epitopes. Peptides can be selected that either contain only one IgE-binding site (i.e., IgE-reactive hapten) (63) or lack any IgE reactivity due to a lack of a structural fold (105, 106, 112). According to the hapten-carrier principle described by Benacerraf (113), these peptides can be used for active immunization. Such vaccines can induce allergen-specific IgG responses that block IgE binding to the allergen and IgE-dependent allergic inflammation without activating allergen-specific T cells (105, 106, 114) (**Figure 2**).

It is now possible to study the contribution of IgE- versus non-IgE-mediated allergic inflammation in allergic patients by comparing non-IgE-reactive allergen-derived T cell epitope–containing peptides and hypoallergenic allergen derivatives with the corresponding fully IgE-reactive wild-type allergens (**Figure 3**) (110).

IgE-mediated allergic inflammation is typically caused by IgE-mediated mast cell and basophil degranulation, the key mechanism in immediate-type allergic inflammation. Several in vitro studies have demonstrated that IgE-facilitated antigen presentation can activate allergen-specific T cells more strongly than does non-IgE-facilitated allergen presentation

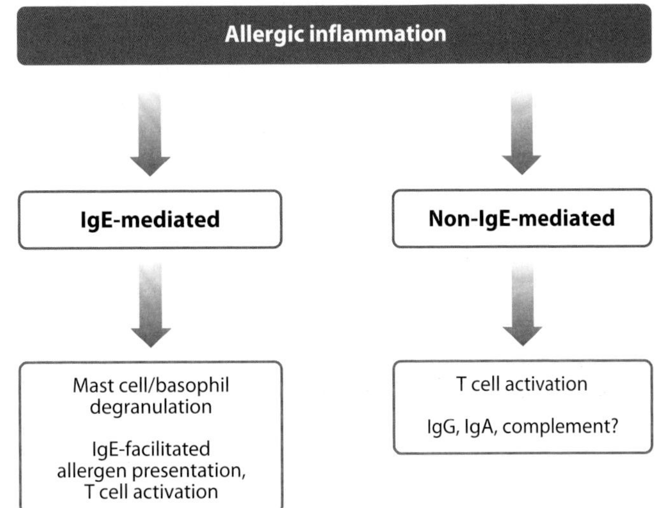

Figure 3

IgE- versus non-IgE-mediated inflammation in allergy. The classical immediate-type symptoms of allergy are caused by the cross-linking of mast cell– and basophil-bound IgE antibodies by allergens and the subsequent release of inflammatory mediators, cytokines, and proteases. IgE-facilitated allergen presentation by APCs containing FcεRI or FcεRII strongly activates allergen-specific T cells and thus late-phase reactions and chronic allergic inflammation. With the availability of defined T cell epitope–containing peptides and hypoallergenic allergen molecules without IgE reactivity, non-IgE-mediated allergic inflammation could also be demonstrated. At present there is no evidence for relevant IgG-, IgA-, or complement-mediated allergic inflammation, although allergic patients may contain allergen-specific antibodies that, in principle, could activate complement.

(14, 15, 115). However, non-IgE-mediated T cell activation can also contribute to allergic inflammation, although the precise mechanisms remain to be elucidated (109, 110). Patients who received non-IgE-reactive T cell peptides or hypoallergens developed late-phase reactions (i.e., after a period of hours). These inflammatory reactions were most likely caused by T cells and/or T cell products, such as IFN-γ, which are secreted by allergen-specific Th1 cells, and/or by $CD8^+$ T cells, which reportedly appear at sites of delayed-type allergic inflammation (116, 117). The contribution of T cell–mediated inflammation to the various manifestations of allergy in patients needs to be determined to understand the extent to which therapeutic strategies targeting either T cells or IgE might be clinically successful.

In principle, allergen-specific IgG and/or IgA responses and associated complement activation may also contribute to non-IgE-mediated allergic inflammation (**Figure 3**). However, there is as yet no evidence that nonallergic persons mounting allergen-specific IgG/IgA responses suffer from IgG/IgA-mediated allergen recognition (8, 85, 118).

DIAGNOSIS AND MONITORING OF IMMUNE RESPONSES WITH RECOMBINANT ALLERGENS

It is now possible to study antibody responses, cell activation, and in vivo responses to defined molecules using purified recombinant allergens (**Figure 4**). Allergen sources typically contain several allergen molecules that are recognized by varying percentages of allergic patients and sometimes exhibit a wide range of allergenic activity (36, 119). Certain allergens are highly specific for a given allergen source and hence allow unambiguous diagnosis of a genuine sensitization toward the corresponding allergen source. Other allergens show extensive cross-reactivity with allergens present in many unrelated allergen sources and hence explain clinical sensitivity of patients to these sources as a result of immunological cross-reactivity (35). Examples of highly cross-reactive allergens include the family of profilin allergens that occur as cytoskeletal proteins in many unrelated allergen sources (120, 121), the muscle protein tropomyosin, which is a cross-reactive allergen in shrimp and mites (122), and the family of calcium-binding allergens that occur in pollen from all plants (123).

The development of diagnostic tests based on microarrayed allergen molecules or use of other multiplex technologies has enabled us to assess antibody responses toward a wide variety of allergen molecules and epitopes with minute amounts of serum samples or other body fluids (124, 125). These diagnostic tests are useful as research tools with which to study the development of allergic immune responses early in childhood, for prescribing SIT, and for monitoring immune responses during the natural course of disease and after various treatment interventions (125).

Comparison of antibody responses with the results from cellular activation tests and in vivo evaluation of the allergenic activity of allergens allows the most relevant allergen molecules to be selected for vaccine cocktails for particular allergen sources (126).

The magnitude of IgE reactivity against a particular allergen does not always predict its ability to activate effector cells and to cause allergic inflammation (127). There seem to be "IgE-reactive antigens," such as carbohydrate epitopes, that bind IgE antibodies but induce only very mild or no degranulation of mast cells. This phenomenon is probably caused by monovalent IgE recognition (128, 129). On the other hand, some allergens, in particular IgE-reactive autoantigens that poorly activate mast cells and basophils, seem to be potent activators of Th1 cells and hence may be involved in inducing delayed-type inflammation in allergy (130). It will be very interesting to investigate in cellular activation tests and by in vivo provocation testing whether allergens vary regarding their ability to induce immediate- and delayed-type inflammatory responses. There is also evidence that certain portions of allergens

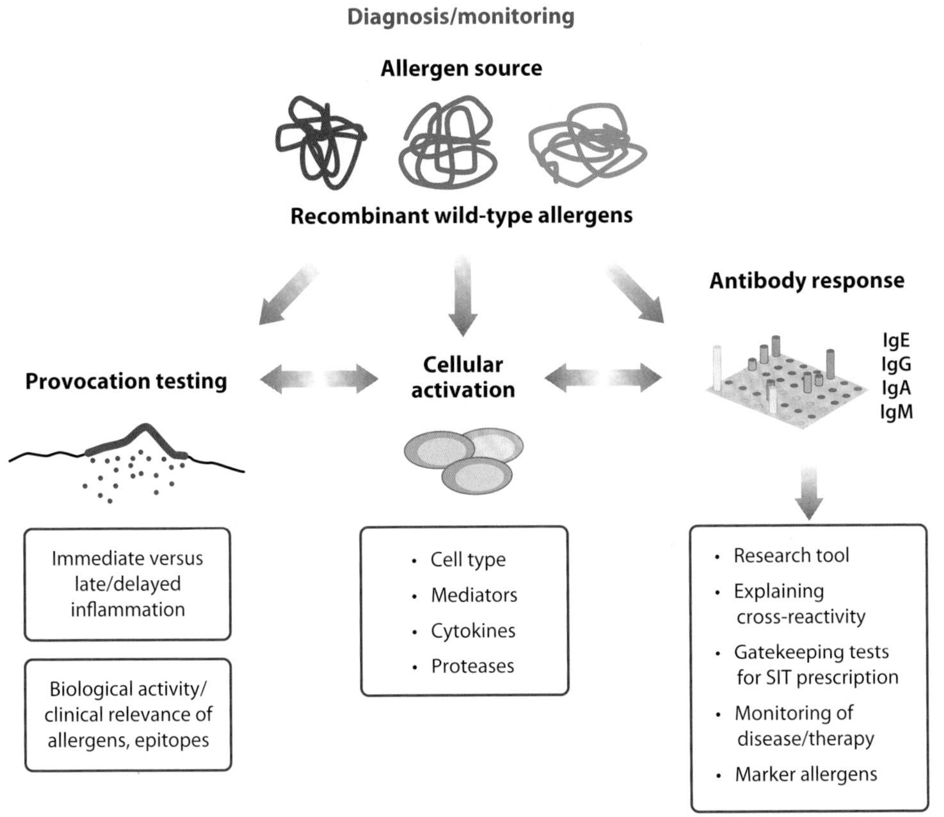

Figure 4

Recombinant allergens for diagnosis and disease monitoring. Recombinant allergens are used to determine whether a patient shows clinically relevant symptoms of allergy upon in vivo provocation testing. In vitro tests based on the activation of allergen-specific cells (e.g., basophils, T cells) can be used to determine the types of cells and proinflammatory cell products. Miniaturized allergen arrays (i.e., allergen chips) allow measurement of allergen-specific antibodies with small serum volumes and are therefore useful research tools. Reactivities against cross-reactive allergens can explain allergies to various allergen sources containing these cross-reactive allergens. Marker allergens allow diagnosis of genuine sensitization to certain allergen sources and can be used to monitor disease and to refine the prescription of allergy vaccines.

(e.g., fragments, peptides) may exhibit different immunological properties such as a preferential activation of certain T cells or other immunomodulatory effects (131–135).

ACTIVE THERAPEUTIC ALLERGY VACCINES

Figure 5 depicts strategies for active allergy vaccination and/or tolerance induction which are based on the knowledge of allergen structures.

T Cell Epitope–Based Vaccines

The concept of using synthetic peptides containing T cell epitopes from allergens for immunotherapy rests on several lines of earlier research (136). Lamb and colleagues (137) demonstrated that antigen-specific T cells can be rendered tolerant in vitro upon exposure to the T cell epitope–containing peptides without APCs and thus without costimulation. The availability of allergen sequences allowed mapping of T cell epitopes of major allergens and induction of peripheral T cell

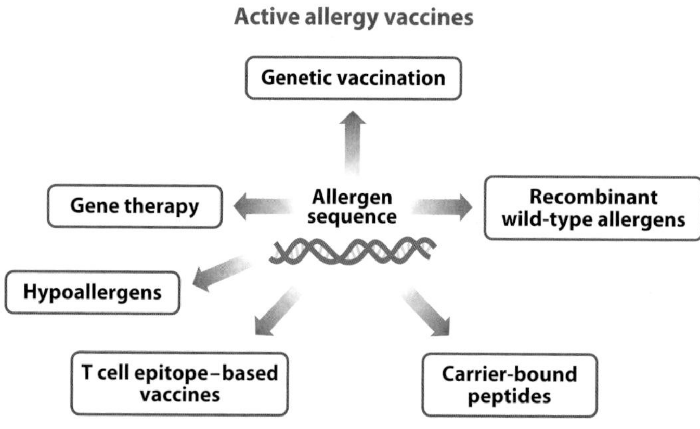

Figure 5

Allergen structures as essential bases for active allergy vaccines. Based on allergen DNA and amino acid sequences, various vaccines can be engineered to target different pathways of the immune system, either in the form of proteins/peptides or via genetic vaccination.

tolerance against the major cat allergen, Fel d 1, in a murine model with Fel d 1-derived T cell epitope–containing peptides (138). Because allergen-derived T cell epitopes represent small peptides, which generally lack IgE reactivity, investigators assumed that the use of allergen-derived T cell epitopes would avoid IgE-mediated side effects during immunotherapy and would, rather, induce allergen-specific T cell tolerance (136). As indicated in **Table 2**, several clinical immunotherapy trials with T cell peptides have been performed over the past ten years, mainly in patients allergic to cat or bee venom (109, 139–153). However, an improvement in clinical symptoms was observed in only a few of the studies (139, 142, 143, 146). No IgE-mediated side effects were reported, but a considerable proportion of patients experienced late-phase side effects (i.e., after several hours), suggesting that they were T cell dependent (109, 139, 140, 144, 145). The side effects may be explained by the fact that, unlike in an in vitro system or in a murine model where APCs can be bypassed during the tolerization step or the T cell receptors and MHC molecules saturated with peptide excess, it is impossible to target selectively T cells avoiding APCs and costimulation in patients. Strategies to avoid costimulation may include sophisticated dosing schedules or the use of altered peptide ligands that would bind only to the T cell receptor or to the MHC (154). However, such altered peptide ligands have not been used in T cell epitope–based therapies to date. It may also prove very difficult to identify appropriate peptide cocktails that can be used to treat allergic patients in light of the diversity of T cell epitope recognition on allergens, the widely varying T cell receptor usage, and MHC diversity in most allergic patients. Moreover, therapy with T cell epitope–containing peptides seems to act primarily on T cells and thus may suppress T cell–mediated allergic inflammation; however, no strong reduction of allergen-specific IgE production and of IgE-mediated allergic inflammation has yet been demonstrated (140, 146).

Recombinant Hypoallergens

Recombinant hypoallergenic allergen derivatives are characterized by a strong reduction or suppression of IgE reactivity and maintenance of T cell epitopes (111). Recombinant hypoallergenic derivatives include molecules in which the IgE-binding residues have been changed by site-directed or random mutagenesis, recombinant fragments, or deletion variants lacking a structural fold and thus conformational IgE epitopes or reassembled molecules in which portions of the allergen have been recombined in the form of mosaic molecules (111, 155–161). Hypoallergenic allergen derivatives have also been obtained by denaturation/modification of the corresponding recombinant wild-type allergen (162). All these molecules possess most T cell epitopes of the wild-type allergen, thus eliminating the need for combining multiple T cell epitope–containing peptides to target the broad T cell repertoire of allergic patients. Recombinant hypoallergenic allergen derivatives exhibit reduced IgE reactivity and hence do not induce IgE-mediated side effects when administered to allergic patients. Higher doses can be administered compared to allergenic wild-type molecules, thereby allowing the number of injections to be reduced and eventually inducing a pronounced

Table 2 Listing of immunotherapy trials performed with synthetic or recombinant allergen peptides

Vaccine	Allergen source/ingredient	Study design	Number of patients	Application mode/ adjuvant	References
T cell epitope–based vaccines	Cat/Fel d 1 peptide	DBPC	95	SC/no adjuvant	139
	Cat/Fel d 1 peptide	DBPC	42	SC/no adjuvant	140
	Cat/Fel d 1 peptide	DBPC	31	SC/no adjuvant	141
	Bee venom/Api m 1 peptide	Open	15	SC/no adjuvant	142
	Cat/Fel d 1 peptide	DBPC	133	SC/no adjuvant	143
	Cat/Fel d 1 peptide	Open	40	ID/no adjuvant	109
	Cat/Fel d 1 peptide	SBPC	34	ID/no adjuvant	144
	Cat/Fel d 1 peptide	Open	24	ID/no adjuvant	145
	Cat/Fel d 1 peptide	DBPC	24	ID/no adjuvant	146
	Bee venom/Api m 1 peptide	DBPC	16	SC/no adjuvant	147
	Cat/Fel d 1 peptide	Open	61	IN/ID/no adjuvant	148
	Cat/Fel d 1 peptide	DBPC	16	ID/no adjuvant	149
	Cat/Fel d 1 peptide	Open	20	ID/no adjuvant	150
	Cat/Fel d 1 peptide	Open	8	ID/no adjuvant	151
	Cat/Fel d 1 peptide	DBPC/open	28	ID/no adjuvant	152
	Bee venom/Api m 1 peptide	Open	12	ID/no adjuvant	153
Hypoallergens	Birch pollen/Bet v 1 fragment/trimer	DBPC	124	SC/alum	102, 166, 168
	Birch pollen/Bet v 1FV	Open	51	SC/alum	164
	Birch pollen/Bet v 1FV	DBPC	211	SC/alum	165
Recombinant wild-type allergens	Grass pollen/Phl p 1/Phl p 2/Phl p 5ab/Phl p 6	DBPC	62	SC/alum	189
	Birch pollen/Bet v 1	DBPC	134	SC/alum	190
Coupled allergens	Ragweed/Amb a 1CpG	DBPC	57	SC/CpG	219
	Ragweed/Amb a 1CpG	DBPC	25	SC/CpG	103
	Mite/Der p 1 virus-like particle	Open	24	SC/IM/virus-like particle	224

FV, folding variant; DBPC, double-blind placebo-controlled; SBPC, single-blind placebo-controlled; SC, subcutaneous; ID, intradermal; IN, intranasal; IM, intramuscular.

Th1-like immune response (111). Furthermore, these derivatives are selected so that upon immunization they will induce blocking IgG antibodies that recognize the corresponding wild-type allergen, block IgE recognition of the wild-type allergen, and block IgE-mediated allergic inflammation (163). Several successful immunotherapy trials have been conducted with hypoallergenic derivatives of the major birch pollen allergen, Bet v 1 (102, 126, 156, 164–166). Patients tolerated high doses of the Bet v 1 derivatives and developed high levels of allergen-specific IgG antibodies that blocked IgE-mediated basophil degranulation as well as allergic symptoms, boosts of allergen-induced IgE increases, and IgE-facilitated allergen presentation to T cells (102, 166). Furthermore, the administration of the hypoallergenic Bet v 1 derivatives did not induce clinically relevant de novo IgE responses against the wild-type allergen, indicating that these derivatives exhibit an allergenicity much lower than that of the wild-type allergen, a potentially significant consideration for prophylactic application (167).

A clinically successful phase III injection immunotherapy trial performed with a hypoallergenic folding variant of Bet v 1 has recently been reported at the Congress of the European Academy of Allergology and Clinical Immunology (165). This vaccine may thus be expected to become available soon for routine immunotherapy of birch pollen allergy. Subsequent analysis indicated that hypoallergenic allergen derivatives do not induce IgE-mediated immediate-type side effects because their IgE reactivity has been reduced. Only delayed-type side effects have been reported; these may have been caused by T cell activation, similar to that for vaccination with the T cell epitope–containing peptides (168). The advantages of recombinant hypoallergenic molecules include reduction/suppression of IgE-mediated side effects and induction of high concentrations of blocking IgG antibodies (i.e., high immunogenicity) that antagonize the broad range of IgE-mediated pathology in patients. Furthermore, these hypoallergenic vaccines can, in principle, also be used for tolerance-induction protocols because most allergen-specific T cell epitopes are preserved (111).

Genetic Vaccination

Genetic vaccination is based on the administration of allergen-encoding nucleic acids, thereby circumventing the need to produce and purify the corresponding antigen (169). The principle of genetic vaccination was developed mainly to promote antiviral immunity by inducing $CD8^+$ and Th1 immunity, but it was soon also considered for allergy vaccines (170). Studies in murine models demonstrated that immunization with allergen-encoding plasmids led to a Th1 immune response and the ability to antagonize allergy (171, 172). Genetic immunization is based on the conversion of the administered nucleic acid by cells of the treated host into proteins and/or peptides that can trigger various forms of immune responses, depending on how the antigens are made, processed, and presented. The responses include $CD8^+$ and Th1, but also Th2 under certain conditions (173). Other important factors influencing the outcome of immunity are the mode and site of nucleic acid administration (173–175).

Concepts for genetic vaccination against allergy have been evaluated mainly in murine models to date. The fact that genetic vaccination may lead to an uncontrolled synthesis of allergens in the vaccinated host has been a major hurdle for application in allergic patients because of the potential risk of inducing severe anaphylactic side effects (176). Research has therefore focused on strategies for nucleic acid delivery that will lead to rapid degradation of the resulting allergen and on the use of nucleic acids coding for hypoallergenic allergen derivatives with strongly reduced allergenic activity (177, 178).

Recombinant Wild-Type Allergens and Hybrid Allergens

The term "recombinant wild-type allergen" defines a recombinant allergen molecule that resembles the structural and immunological properties of the corresponding natural allergen, including IgE reactivity, allergenic activity, T cell epitopes, structural fold, and immunogenicity. When a recombinant wild-type allergen fulfills all the criteria that can be tested by comparing the recombinant with the purified natural allergen in immunological, biochemical, and in vivo tests, it can be used as a reference allergen (179). For certain allergen sources (e.g., birch pollen, cat), one major allergen carries almost the complete epitope spectrum of the source (180, 181), whereas for other sources, several allergens need to be included in a vaccine depending on the frequency of recognition and clinical importance (e.g., grass pollen, house dust mites) (35, 182, 183). For most allergen sources, the spectrum of disease-relevant epitopes can perhaps be represented by only a few molecules, usually less than six, a finding that should greatly facilitate the production of recombinant allergen-based vaccines. Vaccines based on recombinant wild-type allergens have important advantages over the traditional allergen extracts currently used for SIT. The natural allergen extracts often lack important allergens, the amounts of the individual allergens show great variability, and undefined non-allergenic materials are also included (184). As a result, allergen extract-based immunotherapy is often not successful, does not induce protective IgG responses against the culprit allergens, and may also induce unwanted IgE responses. If new IgE reactivities develop against cross-reactive allergens, sensitization to previously unrecognized allergen sources may be induced. Cocktails of recombinant allergens contain well-defined allergens in known concentrations, and their composition may be tailored according to individual patient needs.

Hybrid molecules consisting of several allergens have been developed for allergen sources that contain several important allergens (185–188). Construction of such hybrid molecules allows the disease-relevant allergens of a complex allergen source to be incorporated into one or a few molecules, greatly easing vaccine production. Another important advantage is the increased immunogenicity of allergens that, by themselves, have poor ability to induce protective antibody responses through a fusion to allergens with high immunogenicity (186, 187). However, one important disadvantage of recombinant wild-type allergens is that these molecules are as allergenic as the corresponding natural allergens and hence may induce IgE- as well as T cell–mediated side effects during immunotherapy. Furthermore, they can boost the existing IgE response in patients because they will recombine with IgE antibodies on memory cells as efficiently as the natural allergens. This disadvantage can, however, be overcome by converting the wild-type allergens into recombinant hypoallergenic allergen derivatives (188) (see section on Recombinant Hypoallergens).

Highly successful clinical studies have already been performed with recombinant wild-type allergens. Vaccination with a cocktail of five recombinant timothy grass pollen allergens significantly improved grass pollen–induced immediate-type allergic symptoms and reduced the consumption of medication (189). The mechanism of action seems to be very similar to that reported for the recombinant hypoallergenic allergen derivatives because the recombinant grass pollen vaccine induced high concentrations of grass pollen allergen–specific protective IgG antibodies. Another important study comparing immunotherapy with birch pollen extract, natural purified major birch pollen allergen, the purified recombinant Bet v 1 molecule, and placebo (i.e., adjuvant alone) was recently published (190). The recombinant Bet v 1-based vaccine was as effective in reducing immediate-type allergic symptoms and consumption of medication as the natural allergen and the allergen extract. Again, the amelioration of immediate-type symptoms and skin sensitivity, the latter as determined by objective measurements of wheal sizes in skin prick tests, was associated with induction of high levels of allergen-specific blocking IgG antibodies. This effect was most pronounced in the group treated with recombinant Bet v 1 (190). Furthermore, treatment with recombinant Bet v 1 did not induce any IgE sensitizations to other cross-reactive allergens, whereas sensitizations to the highly cross-reactive Bet v 2 allergen were observed for patients treated with natural allergens (190).

Gene Therapy

Administration of hematopoietic stem cells that had been retrovirally transduced to express xenoantigens or autoantigens can induce robust tolerance in murine models (191–193). This approach has been used recently for robust induction of tolerance in allergy (194). The transfer into mice of hematopoietic stem cells engineered to express the major grass pollen allergen Phl p 5 prevented the development of allergy to Phl p 5, whereas the development of allergy to another unrelated allergen, Bet v 1, was not affected, thus demonstrating the specificity of the protocol. Robust tolerance at the B cell, T cell, and effector cell levels was achieved using this gene therapy approach; no Phl p 5-specific IgE, IgG, or T cell reactivity could be detected in tolerized animals, and there was complete absence of allergic reactions. A comparably complete form of tolerance has not yet been described for other tolerance protocols such as mucosal tolerance induction. Central tolerance most likely plays an important role in the gene therapy approach, but nondeletional mechanisms may also be relevant. Thus, the mechanisms underlying the gene therapy approach to allergy need to be investigated. Also important will be the development of safe protocols to target allergens/epitopes to sites where tolerogenic mechanisms are operative. Whether the gene therapy approach can also be applied for therapy in conjunction with prophylactic application must be clarified. Any therapeutic application will require the use of hypoallergenic allergen derivatives to avoid treatment-induced allergenic side effects. The technical challenge to inducing tolerance against several different allergens simultaneously in a prophylactic scenario may be overcome by using gene constructs capable of expressing several allergens.

Mucosal Tolerance Induction

Early exposure to dietary allergens such as cow's milk may induce food allergy. On the other hand, cow's milk allergy does not persist in some children, indicating that mechanisms of mucosal tolerance may be operative (195). It has been demonstrated in experimental animal models that prefeeding of allergens can better prevent allergic sensitization the earlier in life prefeeding is conducted (196–198). Use of Bet v 1 for prophylactic and therapeutic mucosal administration reduced allergen-specific T cell and B cell responses in a murine model of birch pollen allergy (199, 200).

Allergic sensitization was also prevented when hypoallergenic derivatives of the Bet v 1 allergen were used in nasal treatment (201). The importance of T cell epitopes for mucosal tolerance induction is underscored by studies that demonstrated for several allergen sources (i.e., bee, mite, olive pollen) that mucosal administration of T cell epitope–containing peptides without IgE reactivity induced tolerance in preventive animal studies (202–204). Intranasal tolerance against different immunologically unrelated allergens was induced with immunodominant T cell epitope–containing peptides in a preventive murine allergy model (205).

However, nasal administration of recombinant wild-type allergens to allergic patients resulted in a strong boost of allergen-specific IgE production and increases in skin sensitivity, indicating that mucosal administration of folded wild-type allergens in already sensitized patients tends to aggravate the allergic immune response rather than induce tolerance (18). Strong increases of allergen-specific IgE production were also observed in allergic patients who had received sublingual immunotherapy (206). Approaches for mucosal tolerance induction should therefore focus on the administration of hypoallergenic material such as hydrolyzed allergens, recombinant hypoallergenic allergen derivatives, allergen-derived T cell epitope–containing peptides, and sophisticated delivery strategies such as genetically modified food or engineered bacteria (111, 207–209). Still to be determined is whether mucosal tolerance induction can be used to treat an already established allergic immune response or whether it is better suited to prevent allergic sensitization.

IgE-Reactive Haptens and Mimotopes

The induction of immediate-type allergic inflammation is caused by cross-linking of mast cell and basophil-bound IgE antibodies by allergens (111). This cross-linking can take place only if at least two different epitopes of the allergen combine with the corresponding IgE antibodies (69, 210). By definition, an IgE-reactive hapten contains only one binding site for one IgE antibody and hence will not cross-link effector cell–bound IgE and thus fail to induce allergic inflammation (63, 69). Given a high affinity for the corresponding IgE antibodies, IgE-reactive haptens can be used to saturate effector cell–bound IgE and prevent a subsequent degranulation by the complete allergen (69). Furthermore, such haptenic structures may be useful for active vaccination to focus blocking IgG antibody responses toward the IgE epitopes (211). IgE-reactive haptens have been sought by digestion of allergens or by screening of cDNA libraries expressing allergen fragments. However, that most IgE epitopes belong to the conformational type and hence cannot be obtained by allergen fragmentation presents a major technical hurdle in preparing therapeutic hapten cocktails (63, 211, 212). Furthermore, IgE-reactive haptens, termed mimotopes, have been isolated from synthetic peptide libraries using patients' IgE antibodies (213, 214). Mimotopes are synthetic peptides that combine with the paratopes of the antibodies and that can be isolated from random peptide libraries by panning.

In most cases, mimotopes do not resemble the sequence of the epitope, but they are thought to compete with the epitope by mimicking its binding properties. However, mimotope peptides are small and hence exhibit poor immunogenicity and only modest affinity for IgE. Not yet established is whether mimotope peptides can be used to saturate effector cell–bound IgE and to block allergen-induced effector cell degranulation.

Coupled Allergens/Fusion Proteins

The immunological properties of allergens were demonstrated early on to be profoundly altered by coupling to other compounds. For example, coupling of allergens to polyethylene glycol (mPEG) reduces the allergenic activity of allergens (215). Oligonucleotides containing CpG motifs induce preferential Th1 immune responses (216, 217). In fact, coupling of CpG motifs to allergens reduces their allergenic activity and may favor allergen-specific Th1 immune responses (218). An allergy vaccine based on CpG-coupled major ragweed allergen, Amb a 1, when applied to allergic patients, induced allergen-specific IgG responses and reduced certain clinical symptoms (103, 219). Given that chemical coupling is a process that delivers a product that is difficult to standardize and sometimes has a poor yield, rDNA technology is increasingly used to express defined recombinant fusion proteins for vaccination.

For example, fusion of Bet v 1 with a bacterial surface (S-layer) protein reduced its allergenicity and induced a preferential Th1 immune response (220). A fusion protein consisting of the major cat allergen, Fel d 1, and human IgG was made with the goal of silencing effector cells containing Fel d 1–specific IgE via cocross-linking of receptors for IgE and IgG, whereas others have used a similar construct to target the allergen to APCs for immunomodulation (221, 222). Likewise, a Fel d 1 fusion protein has been made consisting of Fel d 1 fused to a TAT-derived protein translocation domain and to a truncated invariant chain for targeting the MHC class II pathway (223). This fusion protein induced Fel d 1-specific IgG and Th1 responses in mice and showed reduced allergenic activity. Moreover, a peptide derived from the major house dust mite allergen, Der p 1, was incorporated into virus-like particles and induced allergen-specific IgG responses in nonallergic persons (224).

Carrier-Bound B Cell Epitope–Containing Peptide Vaccines

This approach is based on allergen-derived peptides that are subjected to a selection process aimed at fostering several favorable properties for the vaccine. In a first step, those allergens are selected as templates for the peptides that account for the majority of the allergenic activity of a given allergen source. Next, peptides are selected from these allergens that lack IgE as well as allergenic activity and that do not stimulate allergen-specific T cells in order to minimize IgE- and T cell–mediated side effects of the vaccine (106). Peptides are further screened to identify those that, upon immunization, induce strong allergen-specific IgG responses in animal models; such responses can block IgE binding to the allergen and allergen-induced mast cell and basophil degranulation in allergic patients. Following the carrier principle

(60, 113), peptides are bound chemically or by recombinant expression to allergen-unrelated carrier proteins to induce a robust allergen-specific IgG response obtaining T cell help from carrier-derived epitopes. A possible carrier molecule is KLH, which has been used to produce chemically coupled peptide vaccines (105, 106, 112). However, strategies of producing fusion proteins of the allergen-derived peptides with, for example, immunogenic proteins from viruses by recombinant expression offer advantages because these proteins are well defined and can be easily produced by expression in *Escherichia coli* (114). In this context, a grass pollen vaccine based on a peptide from the major grass pollen allergen Phl p 1 fused to the VP1 protein from human rhinovirus has been reported to induce antiallergic responses and a protective immunity against rhinovirus infections in animal models (114). An additional advantage of the carrier-bound peptides is that they can be selected to induce minimal or no allergen-specific IgE responses upon immunization, thus resulting in vaccines that have minimal allergenicity (i.e., sensitization capacity) and hence may well be useful for prophylactic vaccination (105).

Carrier-bound B cell epitope–containing peptide vaccines have been engineered for birch pollen and grass pollen allergy and, according to extensive testing with samples from allergic patients and in animal models, promise to be extremely safe vaccines that could also be used for allergy prevention (105, 106, 114). However, extensive evaluation of the safety of the vaccines is needed by provocation testing in allergic patients and through clinical vaccination trials. It must be demonstrated that this approach can be applied to generate peptide vaccines for the most common allergen sources.

SUMMARY AND FUTURE DIRECTIONS

Table 3 displays a time line of important developments along the way from allergen genes to allergy vaccines. Approximately 20 years ago, the first cDNAs coding for allergens were isolated, including major wasp, house dust mite, and birch pollen allergens (31–33). Soon thereafter it was demonstrated that recombinant allergen molecules could be used for IgE antibody-based diagnosis of birch and grass pollen allergy (225, 226). According to allergen

Table 3 Milestones during the past 20 years on the march from allergen genes to allergy vaccines

Year	Development	References
1988–1989	Allergen cDNAs isolated	31–33
1991–1992	IgE-based diagnosis with recombinant allergens	225, 226
1992–1993	T cell eptitope mapping studies with recombinant allergens/peptides	37, 227, 228
1992–1996	Recombinant allergen-based animal models	229–232
1993–1997	Characterization of recombinant hypoallergens	63, 68, 104, 233–236
1994–1996	Application of recombinant allergens in patients for provocation testing	237–239
1996	SIT with T cell epitope peptides	139–140
1996–1997	3D structures of recombinant allergens	73, 240
1999	Non-IgE-mediated allergic inflammation demonstrated	109
1999–2000	Evaluation of recombinant hypoallergens in patients by provocation testing	241, 242
2002	Microarray based on recombinant allergens for diagnosis	124
2004–2005	SIT with recombinant hypoallergens	102, 166
2005	SIT with recombinant allergens	189
2007–2009	3-D structures of allergen-IgE complexes solved	71, 72
2008	Comparison of extract-, purified allergen–, and recombinant allergen–based SIT	190
2009	Phase III SIT studies with recombinant hypoallergens completed	165

sequences, synthetic peptides were synthesized, and the first reports of mapping of allergen T cell epitopes and a characterization of allergen-specific T cell clones were published (37, 227, 228). Investigators established animal models based on recombinant allergens in mouse and rhesus monkey at almost the same time (229–232), and several groups started to produce and characterize the first hypoallergenic allergen derivatives as candidates for SIT (63, 68, 104, 233–236). From 1994 onward, the first studies in which recombinant allergens were used for provocation testing (i.e., skin testing) in allergic patients were published, demonstrating the usefulness of recombinant proteins for in vivo allergy diagnosis (237–239). In 1996, investigators published the first results from immunotherapy trials with allergen-derived T cell epitope–containing peptides (139, 140) and solved the first three-dimensional structures of allergens by X-ray crystallography and NMR techniques (73, 240). The finding that allergen-derived T cell epitope–containing peptides without IgE reactivity could induce late-phase, T cell–dependent, and MHC-restricted inflammation provided evidence for non-IgE-mediated mechanisms of inflammation in allergy (109). At the same time, investigators conducted the first in vivo provocation tests (i.e., skin tests and nasal provocation tests) with recombinant hypoallergenic allergen derivatives that demonstrated the strongly reduced allergenic activity of these proteins in humans (241, 242). The first study demonstrating that microarrayed allergen molecules can be used for miniaturized allergy testing was published in 2002 (124). The first immunotherapy study with recombinant hypoallergenic allergen molecules was initiated and results from this phase II clinical trial were published in 2004 (102, 166). Soon thereafter, investigators reported the first immunotherapy trial performed with a cocktail of recombinant wild-type grass pollen allergens (189). The first two studies describing the three-dimensional structure of a complex between an allergen-specific human IgE antibody and a milk and grass pollen allergen became available between 2007 and 2009 (71, 72). A pivotal study, based on a double-blind, placebo-controlled multicenter phase II trial, demonstrated that immunotherapy with a single recombinant birch pollen allergen was effective and even showed advantages over allergen extract–based treatment or treatment with a natural purified allergen (190). A successful phase III clinical trial performed with a hypoallergenic recombinant derivative of the major birch pollen allergen Bet v 1 has been reported very recently (165).

So far research has moved from allergen genes to the evaluation of the first successful allergy vaccines in patients. However, the field is now open for further developments, and many important questions remain. Using vaccines based on defined allergens and allergen-derived epitopes should allow us to investigate in greater detail immunological mechanisms underlying SIT, to improve existing therapeutic strategies, and to develop new forms of immunotherapy. At present, SIT can be used only by trained allergologists because of the risk of side effects. A future goal will be to develop effective allergy vaccines that lack IgE- and T cell–mediated side effects and hence may replace antiinflammatory treatment, which ameliorates symptoms but does not modify the course of disease. The biggest challenge will be to develop preventive strategies based on vaccination or tolerance-induction strategies to help in eradicating allergic diseases. An almost complete armamentarium of the disease-relevant allergen molecules is now available, and immunologists may now take up this challenge and start working on prophylactic concepts for allergy.

DISCLOSURE STATEMENT

R.V. is consultant for Phadia, Uppsala, Sweden, and Biomay, Vienna, Austria. F.F. is a consultant for Biomay AG, Vienna, Austria.

ACKNOWLEDGMENTS

The work of the authors was supported by grants F1803, F1815, F1818, L214-B13, and L688-B12 of the Austrian Science Fund, by grants from the Christian Doppler Research Association, Vienna, Austria, and by research grants from Biomay, Vienna, Austria, and Phadia, Uppsala, Sweden.

LITERATURE CITED

1. Kay A. 2008. *Allergy and Allergic Diseases*. Oxford: Blackwell Sci.
2. Kulig M, Bergmann R, Klettke U, Wahn V, Tacke U, Wahn U. 1999. Natural course of sensitization to food and inhalant allergens during the first 6 years of life. *J. Allergy Clin. Immunol.* 103:1173–79
3. Niederberger V, Niggemann B, Kraft D, Spitzauer S, Valenta R. 2002. Evolution of IgM, IgE and IgG(1–4) antibody responses in early childhood monitored with recombinant allergen components: implications for class switch mechanisms. *Eur. J. Immunol.* 32:576–84
4. Sporik R, Holgate ST, Platts-Mills TA, Cogswell JJ. 1990. Exposure to house-dust mite allergen (Der p I) and the development of asthma in childhood. A prospective study. *N. Engl. J. Med.* 323:502–7
5. Platts-Mills T, Vaughan J, Squillace S, Woodfolk J, Sporik R. 2001. Sensitisation, asthma, and a modified Th2 response in children exposed to cat allergen: a population-based cross-sectional study. *Lancet* 357:752–56
6. Braun-Fahrländer C, Riedler J, Herz U, Eder W, Waser M, et al. 2002. Environmental exposure to endotoxin and its relation to asthma in school-age children. *N. Engl. J. Med.* 347:869–77
7. Romagnani S. 1994. Lymphokine production by human T cells in disease states. *Annu. Rev. Immunol.* 12:227–57
8. Stern DA, Riedler J, Nowak D, Braun-Fahrländer C, Swoboda I, et al. 2007. Exposure to a farming environment has allergen-specific protective effects on TH2-dependent isotype switching in response to common inhalants. *J. Allergy Clin. Immunol.* 119:351–58
9. Snapper CM, Paul WE. 1987. Interferon-γ and B cell stimulatory factor-1 reciprocally regulate Ig isotype production. *Science* 236:944–47
10. Brown MA, Pierce JH, Watson CJ, Falco J, Ihle JN, Paul WE. 1987. B cell stimulatory factor-1/interleukin-4 mRNA is expressed by normal and transformed mast cells. *Cell* 50:809–18
11. Ishizaka K, Ishizaka T, Hornbrook MM. 1966. Physico-chemical properties of human reaginic antibody. IV. Presence of a unique immunoglobulin as a carrier of reaginic activity. *J. Immunol.* 97:75–85
12. Gould HJ, Sutton BJ, Beavil AJ, Beavil RL, McCloskey N, et al. 2003. The biology of IGE and the basis of allergic disease. *Annu. Rev. Immunol.* 21:579–628
13. Bischoff SC. 2007. Role of mast cells in allergic and non-allergic immune responses: comparison of human and murine data. *Nat. Rev. Immunol.* 7:93–104
14. Mudde GC, Van Reijsen FC, Boland GJ, de Gast GC, Bruijnzeel PL, Bruijnzeel-Koomen CA. 1990. Allergen presentation by epidermal Langerhans' cells from patients with atopic dermatitis is mediated by IgE. *Immunology* 69:335–41
15. van der Heijden FL, Joost van Neerven RJ, van Katwijk M, Bos JD, Kapsenberg ML. 1993. Serum-IgE-facilitated allergen presentation in atopic disease. *J. Immunol.* 150:3643–50
16. Naclerio RM, Adkinson NF Jr, Moylan B, Baroody FM, Proud D, et al. 1997. Nasal provocation with allergen induces a secondary serum IgE antibody response. *J. Allergy Clin. Immunol.* 100:505–10
17. Chakir J, Laviolette M, Turcotte H, Boutet M, Boulet LP. 2000. Cytokine expression in the lower airways of nonasthmatic subjects with allergic rhinitis: influence of natural allergen exposure. *J. Allergy Clin. Immunol.* 106:904–10
18. Niederberger V, Ring J, Rakoski J, Jager S, Spitzauer S, et al. 2007. Antigens drive memory IgE responses in human allergy via the nasal mucosa. *Int. Arch. Allergy Immunol.* 142:133–44
19. Noon L. 1911. Prophylactic inoculation against hay fever. *Lancet* 1:1572–73
20. Larché M, Akdis CA, Valenta R. 2006. Immunological mechanisms of allergen-specific immunotherapy. *Nat. Rev. Immunol.* 6:761–71
21. Cooke RA, Barnard JH, Hebald S, Stull A. 1935. Serological evidence of immunity with coexisting sensitization in a type of human allergy. *J. Exp. Med.* 62:733–50

22. Loveless MH. 1940. Immunological studies of pollinosis. I. The presence of two antibodies related to the same pollen antigen in the serum of treated hay-fever patients. *J. Immunol.* 38:25–50
23. Valenta R, Ball T, Focke M, Linhart B, Mothes N, et al. 2004. Immunotherapy of allergic disease. *Adv. Immunol.* 82:105–53
24. Bousquet J, Lockey R, Malling HJ. 1998. Allergen immunotherapy: therapeutic vaccines for allergic diseases. A WHO position paper. *J. Allergy Clin. Immunol.* 102:558–62
25. Durham SR, Walker SM, Varga EM, Jacobson MR, O'Brien F, et al. 1999. Long-term clinical efficacy of grass-pollen immunotherapy. *N. Engl. J. Med.* 341:468–75
26. Möller C, Dreborg S, Ferdousi HA, Halken S, Høst A, et al. 2002. Pollen immunotherapy reduces the development of asthma in children with seasonal rhinoconjunctivitis (the PAT-study). *J. Allergy Clin. Immunol.* 109:251–56
27. Johnson P, Marsh DG. 1965. 'Isoallergens' from rye grass pollen. *Nature* 206:935–37
28. Berrens L. 1971. The chemistry of atopic allergens. *Monogr. Allergy* 7:1–298
29. Chapman MD, Platts-Mills TA. 1980. Purification and characterization of the major allergen from Dermatophagoides pteronyssinus-antigen P1. *J. Immunol.* 125:587–92
30. Sehon AH, Kraft D, Kunkel G. 1990. *Epitopes of Atopic Allergens*. Brussels: UCB Inst. Allergy
31. Fang KS, Vitale M, Fehlner P, King TP. 1988. cDNA cloning and primary structure of a white-face hornet venom allergen, antigen 5. *Proc. Natl. Acad. Sci. USA* 85:895–99
32. Chua KY, Stewart GA, Thomas WR, Simpson RJ, Dilworth RJ, et al. 1988. Sequence analysis of cDNA coding for a major house dust mite allergen, Der p 1. Homology with cysteine proteases. *J. Exp. Med.* 167:175–82
33. Breiteneder H, Pettenburger K, Bito A, Valenta R, Kraft D, et al. 1989. The gene coding for the major birch pollen allergen Betv1, is highly homologous to a pea disease resistance response gene. *EMBO J.* 8:1935–38
34. Valenta R, Kraft D. 2001. Recombinant allergen molecules: tools to study effector cell activation. *Immunol. Rev.* 179:119–27
35. Valenta R. 2008. Biochemistry of allergens, recombinant allergens. In *Allergy and Allergic Diseases*, ed. AB Kay, A Kaplan, J Bousquet, P Holt, pp. 898–912. Oxford: Blackwell. 2nd ed.
36. Mari A. 2005. Importance of databases in experimental and clinical allergology. *Int. Arch. Allergy Immunol.* 138:88–96
37. Yssel H, Johnson KE, Schneider PV, Wideman J, Terr A, et al. 1992. T cell activation-inducing epitopes of the house dust mite allergen Der p I. Proliferation and lymphokine production patterns by Der p I-specific $CD4^+$ T cell clones. *J. Immunol.* 148:738–45
38. Ebner C, Schenk S, Szépfalusi Z, Hoffmann K, Ferreira F, et al. 1993. Multiple T cell specificities for Bet v I, the major birch pollen allergen, within single individuals. Studies using specific T cell clones and overlapping peptides. *Eur. J. Immunol.* 23:1523–27
39. van Neerven RJ, van de Pol MM, Wierenga EA, Aalberse RC, Jansen HM, Kapsenberg ML. 1994. Peptide specificity and HLA restriction do not dictate lymphokine production by allergen-specific T-lymphocyte clones. *Immunology* 82:351–56
40. O'Hehir RE, Eckels DD, Frew AJ, Kay AB, Lamb JR. 1988. MHC class II restriction specificity of cloned human T lymphocytes reactive with Dermatophagoides farinae (house dust mite). *Immunology* 64:627–31
41. Sallusto F, Corinti S, Pini C, Biocca MM, Bruno G, Di Felice G. 1996. *Parietaria judaica*-specific T-cell clones from atopic patients: heterogeneity in restriction, V beta usage, and cytokine profile. *J. Allergy Clin. Immunol.* 97:627–37
42. Sone T, Morikubo K, Miyahara M, Komiyama N, Shimizu K, et al. 1998. T cell epitopes in Japanese cedar (*Cryptomeria japonica*) pollen allergens: choice of major T cell epitopes in Cry j 1 and Cry j 2 toward design of the peptide-based immunotherapeutics for the management of Japanese cedar pollinosis. *J. Immunol.* 161:448–57
43. Würtzen P, Wissenbach M, Ipsen H, Bufe A, Arnved J, van Neerven RJ. 1999. Highly heterogeneous Phl p 5-specific T cells from patients with allergic rhinitis differentially recognize recombinant Phl p 5 isoallergens. *J. Allergy Clin. Immunol.* 104:115–22

44. Huang SK, Yi M, Palmer E, Marsh DG. 1995. A dominant T cell receptor beta-chain in response to a short ragweed allergen, Amb a 5. *J. Immunol.* 154:6157–62
45. Huang SK, Zwollo P, Marsh DG. 1991. Class II major histocompatibility complex restriction of human T cell responses to short ragweed allergen, Amb a V. *Eur. J. Immunol.* 21:1469–73
46. Jahn-Schmid B, Fischer GF, Bohle B, Faé I, Gadermaier G, et al. 2005. Antigen presentation of the immunodominant T-cell epitope of the major mugwort pollen allergen, Art v 1, is associated with the expression of HLA-DRB1 *01. *J. Allergy Clin. Immunol.* 115:399–404
47. van Reijsen FC, Bruijnzeel-Koomen CA, de Weger RA, Mudde GC. 1997. Retention of long-lived, allergen-specific T cells in atopic dermatitis skin—letter. *J. Investig. Dermatol.* 108:530
48. Bohle B, Schwihla H, Hu HZ, Friedl-Hajek R, Sowka S, et al. 1998. Long-lived Th2 clones specific for seasonal and perennial allergens can be detected in blood and skin by their TCR-hypervariable regions. *J. Immunol.* 160:2022–27
49. Wierenga EA, Snoek M, Bos JD, Jansen HM, Kapsenberg ML. 1990. Comparison of diversity and function of house dust mite-specific T lymphocyte clones from atopic and non-atopic donors. *Eur. J. Immunol.* 20:1519–26
50. van Neerven RJ, van de Pol MM, van Milligen FJ, Jansen HM, Aalberse RC, Kapsenberg ML. 1994. Characterization of cat dander-specific T lymphocytes from atopic patients. *J. Immunol.* 152:4203–10
51. Ebner C, Schenk S, Najafian N, Siemann U, Steiner R, et al. 1995. Nonallergic individuals recognize the same T cell epitopes of Bet v 1, the major birch pollen allergen, as atopic patients. *J. Immunol.* 154:1932–40
52. Van Overtvelt L, Wambre E, Maillère B, von Hofe E, Louise A, et al. 2008. Assessment of Bet v 1-specific $CD4^+$ T cell responses in allergic and nonallergic individuals using MHC class II peptide tetramers. *J. Immunol.* 180:4514–22
53. Tordesillas L, Cuesta-Herranz J, Gonzalez-Muñoz M, Pacios LF, Compés E, et al. 2009. T-cell epitopes of the major peach allergen, Pru p 3: identification and differential T-cell response of peach-allergic and non-allergic subjects. *Mol. Immunol.* 46:722–28
54. Karlsson MR, Rugtveit J, Brandtzaeg P. 2004. Allergen-responsive $CD4^+CD25^+$ regulatory T cells in children who have outgrown cow's milk allergy. *J. Exp. Med.* 199:1679–88
55. Akdis M, Verhagen J, Taylor A, Karamloo F, Karagiannidis C, et al. 2004. Immune responses in healthy and allergic individuals are characterized by a fine balance between allergen-specific T regulatory 1 and T helper 2 cells. *J. Exp. Med.* 199:1567–75
56. Shreffler WG, Wanich N, Moloney M, Nowak-Wegrzyn A, Sampson HA. 2009. Association of allergen-specific regulatory T cells with the onset of clinical tolerance to milk protein. *J. Allergy Clin. Immunol.* 123:43–52
57. Bellinghausen I, Klostermann B, Knop J, Saloga J. 2003. Human $CD4^+CD25^+$ T cells derived from the majority of atopic donors are able to suppress TH1 and TH2 cytokine production. *J. Allergy Clin. Immunol.* 111:862–68
58. Maggi L, Santarlasci V, Liotta F, Frosali F, Angeli R, et al. 2007. Demonstration of circulating allergen-specific $CD4^+CD25^{high}Foxp3^+$ T-regulatory cells in both nonatopic and atopic individuals. *J. Allergy Clin. Immunol.* 120:429–36
59. Bellinghausen I, König B, Böttcher I, Knop J, Saloga J. 2005. Regulatory activity of human $CD4^+CD25^+$ T cells depends on allergen concentration, type of allergen and atopy status of the donor. *Immunology* 116:103–11
60. Arnon R, van Regenmortel MHV. 1992. Structural basis of antigen specificity and design of new vaccines. *FASEB J.* 6:3265–74
61. Greene WK, Cyster JG, Chua KY, O'Brien RM, Thomas WR. 1991. IgE and IgG binding of peptides expressed from fragments of cDNA encoding the major house dust mite allergen Der p I. *J. Immunol.* 147:3768–73
62. van't Hof W, Driedijk PC, van den Berg M, Beck-Sickinger AG, Jung G, Aalberse RC. 1991. Epitope mapping of the *Dermatophagoides pteronyssinus* house dust mite major allergen Der p II using overlapping synthetic peptides. *Mol. Immunol.* 28:1225–32

63. Ball T, Vrtala S, Sperr WR, Valent P, Susani M, et al. 1994. Isolation of an immunodominant IgE hapten from an epitope expression cDNA library. Dissection of the allergic effector reaction. *J. Biol. Chem.* 269:28323–28
64. van Milligen FJ, van't Hof W, van den Berg M, Aalberse RC. 1994. IgE epitopes on the cat (*Felis domesticus*) major allergen Fel d I: a study with overlapping synthetic peptides. *J. Allergy Clin. Immunol.* 93:34–43
65. Seiberler S, Scheiner O, Kraft D, Lonsdale D, Valenta R. 1994. Characterization of a birch pollen allergen, Bet v III, representing a novel class of Ca^{2+} binding proteins: specific expression in mature pollen and dependence of patients' IgE binding on protein-bound Ca^{2+}. *EMBO J.* 13:3481–86
66. Engel E, Richter K, Obermeyer G, Briza P, Kungl AJ, et al. 1997. Immunological and biological properties of Bet v 4, a novel birch pollen allergen with two EF-hand calcium-binding domains. *J. Biol. Chem.* 272:28630–37
67. Westritschnig K, Focke M, Verdino P, Goessler W, Keller W, et al. 2004. Generation of an allergy vaccine by disruption of the three-dimensional structure of the cross-reactive calcium-binding allergen, Phl p 7. *J. Immunol.* 172:5684–92
68. Vrtala S, Hirtenlehner K, Vangelista L, Pastore A, Eichler HG, et al. 1997. Conversion of the major birch pollen allergen, Bet v 1, into two nonanaphylactic T cell epitope-containing fragments: candidates for a novel form of specific immunotherapy. *J. Clin. Investig.* 99:1673–81
69. Gieras A, Focke-Tejkl M, Ball T, Verdino P, Hartl A, et al. 2007. Molecular determinants of allergen-induced effector cell degranulation. *J. Allergy Clin. Immunol.* 119:384–90
70. Christensen LH, Holm J, Lund G, Riise E, Lund K. 2008. Several distinct properties of the IgE repertoire determine effector cell degranulation in response to allergen challenge. *J. Allergy Clin. Immunol.* 122:298–304
71. Niemi M, Jylhä S, Laukkanen ML, Söderlund H, Mäkinen-Kiljunen S, et al. 2007. Molecular interactions between a recombinant IgE antibody and the beta-lactoglobulin allergen. *Structure* 15:1413–21
72. Padavattan S, Flicker S, Schirmer T, Madritsch C, Randow S, et al. 2009. High-affinity IgE recognition of a conformational epitope of the major respiratory allergen Phl p 2 as revealed by X-ray crystallography. *J. Immunol.* 182:2141–51
73. Fedorov AA, Ball T, Mahoney NM, Valenta R, Almo SC. 1997. The molecular basis for allergen cross-reactivity: crystal structure and IgE-epitope mapping of birch pollen profilin. *Structure* 5:33–45
74. Flicker S, Vrtala S, Steinberger P, Vangelista L, Bufe A, et al. 2000. A human monoclonal IgE antibody defines a highly allergenic fragment of the major timothy grass pollen allergen, Phl p 5: molecular, immunological, and structural characterization of the epitope-containing domain. *J. Immunol.* 165:3849–59
75. Flicker S, Steinberger P, Ball T, Krauth MT, Verdino P, et al. 2006. Spatial clustering of the IgE epitopes on the major timothy grass pollen allergen Phl p 1: importance for allergenic activity. *J. Allergy Clin. Immunol.* 117:1336–43
76. van Neerven RJ, Knol EF, Ejrnaes A, Würtzen PA. 2006. IgE-mediated allergen presentation and blocking antibodies: regulation of T-cell activation in allergy. *Int. Arch. Allergy Immunol.* 141:119–29
77. Wachholz PA, Durham SR. 2004. Mechanisms of immunotherapy: IgG revisited. *Curr. Opin. Allergy Clin. Immunol.* 4:313–18
78. Flicker S, Valenta R. 2003. Renaissance of the blocking antibody concept in type I allergy. *Int. Arch. Allergy Immunol.* 132:13–24
79. Visco V, Dolecek C, Denépoux S, Le Mao J, Guret C, et al. 1996. Human IgG monoclonal antibodies that modulate the binding of specific IgE to birch pollen Bet v 1. *J. Immunol.* 157:956–62
80. Denépoux S, Eibensteiner PB, Steinberger P, Vrtala S, Visco V, et al. 2000. Molecular characterization of human IgG monoclonal antibodies specific for the major birch pollen allergen Bet v 1. Anti-allergen IgG can enhance the anaphylactic reaction. *FEBS Lett.* 465:39–46
81. Daeron M, Malbec O, Latour S, Arock M, Fridman WH. 1995. Regulation of high-affinity IgE receptor-mediated mast cell activation by murine low-affinity IgG receptors. *J. Clin. Investig.* 95:577–85
82. Saxon A, Zhu D, Zhang K, Allen LC, Kepley CL. 2004. Genetically engineered negative signaling molecules in the immunomodulation of allergic diseases. *Curr. Opin. Allergy Clin. Immunol.* 4:563–68

83. Ejrnaes AM, Svenson M, Lund G, Larsen JN, Jacobi H. 2006. Inhibition of rBet v 1-induced basophil histamine release with specific immunotherapy-induced serum immunoglobulin G: no evidence that FcγRIIB signalling is important. *Clin. Exp. Allergy* 36:273–82
84. Sellge G, Laffer S, Mierke C, Vrtala S, Hoffmann MW, et al. 2005. Development of an in vitro system for the study of allergens and allergen-specific immunoglobulin E and immunoglobulin G: Fcε receptor I supercross-linking is a possible new mechanism of immunoglobulin G-dependent enhancement of type I allergic reactions. *Clin. Exp. Allergy* 35:774–81
85. Aghayan-Ugurluoglu R, Ball T, Vrtala S, Schweiger C, Kraft D, Valenta R. 2000. Dissociation of allergen-specific IgE and IgA responses in sera and tears of pollen-allergic patients: a study performed with purified recombinant pollen allergens. *J. Allergy Clin. Immunol.* 105:803–13
86. Ball T, Fuchs T, Sperr WR, Valent P, Vangelista L, et al. 1999. B cell epitopes of the major timothy grass pollen allergen, Phl p 1, revealed by gene fragmentation as candidates for immunotherapy. *FASEB J.* 13:1277–90
87. Horst A, Hunzelmann N, Arce S, Herber M, Manz RA, et al. 2002. Detection and characterization of plasma cells in peripheral blood: correlation of IgE+ plasma cell frequency with IgE serum titre. *Clin. Exp. Immunol.* 130:370–78
88. Steinberger P, Kraft D, Valenta R. 1996. Construction of a combinatorial IgE library from an allergic patient. Isolation and characterization of human IgE Fabs with specificity for the major timothy grass pollen allergen, Phl p 5. *J. Biol. Chem.* 271:10967–72
89. van der Stoep N, van der Linden J, Logtenberg T. 1993. Molecular evolution of the human immunoglobulin E response: high incidence of shared mutations and clonal relatedness among epsilon VH5 transcripts from three unrelated patients with atopic dermatitis. *J. Exp. Med.* 177:99–107
90. Snow RE, Chapman CJ, Frew AJ, Holgate ST, Stevenson FK. 1995. Analysis of Ig VH region genes encoding IgE antibodies in splenic B lymphocytes of a patient with asthma. *J. Immunol.* 154:5576–81
91. Coker HA, Harries HE, Banfield GK, Carr VA, Durham SR, et al. 2005. Biased use of VH5 IgE-positive B cells in the nasal mucosa in allergic rhinitis. *J. Allergy Clin. Immunol.* 116:445–52
92. Eibensteiner P, Spitzauer S, Steinberger P, Kraft D, Valenta R. 2000. Immunoglobulin E antibodies of atopic individuals exhibit a broad usage of VH-gene families. *Immunology* 101:112–19
93. Davies JM, O'Hehir RE. 2004. VH gene usage in immunoglobulin E responses of seasonal rhinitis patients allergic to grass pollen is oligoclonal and antigen driven. *Clin. Exp. Allergy* 34:429–36
94. Lim A, Luderschmidt S, Weidinger A, Schnopp C, Ring J, et al. 2007. The IgE repertoire in PBMCs of atopic patients is characterized by individual rearrangements without variable region of the heavy immunoglobulin chain bias. *J. Allergy Clin. Immunol.* 120:696–706
95. Andréasson U, Flicker S, Lindstedt M, Valenta R, Greiff L, et al. 2006. The human IgE-encoding transcriptome to assess antibody repertoires and repertoire evolution. *J. Mol. Biol.* 362:212–27
96. Yamaguchi M, Sayama K, Yano K, Lantz CS, Noben-Trauth N, et al. 1999. IgE enhances Fcε receptor I expression and IgE-dependent release of histamine and lipid mediators from human umbilical cord blood-derived mast cells: synergistic effect of IL-4 and IgE on human mast cell Fcε receptor I expression and mediator release. *J. Immunol.* 162:5455–65
97. Asai K, Kitaura J, Kawakami Y, Yamagata N, Tsai M, et al. 2001. Regulation of mast cell survival by IgE. *Immunity* 14:791–800
98. Kalesnikoff J, Huber M, Lam V, Damen JE, Zhang J, et al. 2001. Monomeric IgE stimulates signaling pathways in mast cells that lead to cytokine production and cell survival. *Immunity* 14:801–11
99. Katoh N, Kraft S, Wessendorf JH, Bieber T. 2000. The high-affinity IgE receptor (FcεRI) blocks apoptosis in normal human monocytes. *J. Clin. Investig.* 105:183–90
100. Linhart B, Bigenzahn S, Hartl A, Lupinek C, Thalhamer J, et al. 2007. Costimulation blockade inhibits allergic sensitization but does not affect established allergy in a murine model of grass pollen allergy. *J. Immunol.* 178:3924–31
101. Mothes N, Heinzkill M, Drachenberg KJ, Sperr WR, Krauth MT, et al. 2003. Allergen-specific immunotherapy with a monophosphoryl lipid A-adjuvanted vaccine: reduced seasonally boosted immunoglobulin E production and inhibition of basophil histamine release by therapy-induced blocking antibodies. *Clin. Exp. Allergy* 33:1198–208

102. Niederberger V, Horak F, Vrtala S, Spitzauer S, Krauth MT, et al. 2004. Vaccination with genetically engineered allergens prevents progression of allergic disease. *Proc. Natl. Acad. Sci. USA* 101:14677–82
103. Creticos PS, Schroeder JT, Hamilton RG, Balcer-Whaley SL, Khattignavong AP, et al. Immune Tolerance Network Group. 2006. Immunotherapy with a ragweed-Toll-like receptor 9 agonist vaccine for allergic rhinitis. *N. Engl. J. Med.* 355:1445–55
104. Ferreira F, Hirtenlehner K, Jilek A, Godnik-Cvar J, Breiteneder H, et al. 1996. Dissection of immunoglobulin E and T lymphocyte reactivity of isoforms of the major birch pollen allergen Bet v 1: potential use of hypoallergenic isoforms for immunotherapy. *J. Exp. Med.* 183:599–609
105. Focke M, Linhart B, Hartl A, Wiedermann U, Sperr WR, et al. 2004. Non-anaphylactic surface-exposed peptides of the major birch pollen allergen, Bet v 1, for preventive vaccination. *Clin. Exp. Allergy* 34:1525–33
106. Focke M, Mahler V, Ball T, Sperr WR, Majlesi Y, et al. 2001. Nonanaphylactic synthetic peptides derived from B cell epitopes of the major grass pollen allergen, Phl p 1, for allergy vaccination. *FASEB J.* 15:2042–44
107. van Neerven RJ, Ebner C, Yssel H, Kapsenberg ML, Lamb JR. 1996. T-cell responses to allergens: epitope-specificity and clinical relevance. *Immunol. Today* 17:526–32
108. Larché M. 2007. Update on the current status of peptide immunotherapy. *J. Allergy Clin. Immunol.* 119:906–9
109. Haselden BM, Kay AB, Larché M. 1999. Immunoglobulin E-independent major histocompatibility complex-restricted T cell peptide epitope-induced late asthmatic reactions. *J. Exp. Med.* 189:1885–94
110. Campana R, Mothes N, Rauter I, Vrtala S, Reininger R, et al. 2008. Non-IgE-mediated chronic allergic skin inflammation revealed with rBet v 1 fragments. *J. Allergy Clin. Immunol.* 121:528–30
111. Valenta R. 2002. The future of antigen-specific immunotherapy of allergy. *Nat. Rev. Immunol.* 2:446–53
112. Focke M, Swoboda I, Marth K, Valenta R. 2009. Developments in allergen-specific immunotherapy: from allergen extracts to allergy vaccines bypassing allergen-specific IgE and T cell reactivity. *Clin. Exp. Allergy.* In press
113. Siskind GW, Paul WE, Benacerraf B. 1966. Studies on the effect of the carrier molecule on antihapten antibody synthesis. I. Effect of carrier on the nature of the antibody synthesized. *J. Exp. Med.* 123:673–88
114. Edlmayr J, Niespodziana K, Linhart B, Focke-Tejkl M, Westritschnig K, et al. 2009. A combination vaccine for allergy and rhinovirus infections based on rhinovirus-derived surface protein VP1 and a nonallergenic peptide of the major timothy grass pollen allergen Phl p 1. *J. Immunol.* 182:6298–306
115. Maurer D, Fiebiger S, Ebner C, Reininger B, Fischer GF, et al. 1996. Peripheral blood dendritic cells express FcεRI as a complex composed of FcεRIα- and FcεRIγ-chains and can use this receptor for IgE-mediated allergen presentation. *J. Immunol.* 157:607–16
116. Grewe M, Gyufko K, Schöpf E, Krutmann J. 1994. Lesional expression of interferon-γ in atopic eczema. *Lancet* 343:25–26
117. Werfel T, Morita A, Grewe M, Renz H, Wahn U, et al. 1996. Allergen specificity of skin-infiltrating T cells is not restricted to a type-2 cytokine pattern in chronic skin lesions of atopic dermatitis. *J. Investig. Dermatol.* 107:871–76
118. Hoffmann-Sommergruber K, Ferreira ED, Ebner C, Barisani T, Korninger L, et al. 1996. Detection of allergen-specific IgE in tears of grass pollen-allergic patients with allergic rhinoconjunctivitis. *Clin. Exp. Allergy* 26:79–87
119. Westritschnig K, Horak F, Swoboda I, Balic N, Spitzauer S, et al. 2008. Different allergenic activity of grass pollen allergens revealed by skin testing. *Eur. J. Clin. Investig.* 38:260–67
120. Valenta R, Duchene M, Pettenburger K, Sillaber C, Valent P, et al. 1991. Identification of profilin as a novel pollen allergen; IgE autoreactivity in sensitized individuals. *Science* 253:557–60
121. Valenta R, Duchene M, Ebner C, Valent P, Sillaber C, et al. 1992. Profilins constitute a novel family of functional plant pan-allergens. *J. Exp. Med.* 175:377–85
122. Reese G, Ayuso R, Lehrer SB. 1999. Tropomyosin: an invertebrate pan-allergen. *Int. Arch. Allergy Immunol.* 119:247–58
123. Valenta R, Hayek B, Seiberler S, Bugajska-Schretter A, Niederberger V, et al. 1998. Calcium-binding allergens: from plants to man. *Int. Arch. Allergy Immunol.* 117:160–66

124. Hiller R, Laffer S, Harwanegg C, Huber M, Schmidt WM, et al. 2002. Microarrayed allergen molecules: diagnostic gatekeepers for allergy treatment. *FASEB J.* 16:414–16
125. Harwanegg C, Laffer S, Hiller R, Mueller MW, Kraft D, et al. 2003. Microarrayed recombinant allergens for diagnosis of allergy. *Clin. Exp. Allergy* 33:7–13
126. Valenta R, Niederberger V. 2007. Recombinant allergens for immunotherapy. *J. Allergy Clin. Immunol.* 119:826–30
127. Purohit A, Laffer S, Metz-Favre C, Verot A, Kricek F, et al. 2005. Poor association between allergen-specific serum immunoglobulin E levels, skin sensitivity and basophil degranulation: a study with recombinant birch pollen allergen Bet v 1 and an immunoglobulin E detection system measuring immunoglobulin E capable of binding to FceRI. *Clin. Exp. Allergy* 35:186–92
128. van Ree R. 2002. Carbohydrate epitopes and their relevance for the diagnosis and treatment of allergic diseases. *Int. Arch. Allergy Immunol.* 129:189–97
129. Mari A, Ooievaar-de Heer P, Scala E, Giani M, Pirrotta L, Zuidmeer L, et al. 2008. Evaluation by double-blind placebo-controlled oral challenge of the clinical relevance of IgE antibodies against plant glycans. *Allergy* 63:891–96
130. Valenta R, Mittermann I, Werfel T, Garn H, Renz H. 2009. Linking allergy to autoimmune disease. *Trends Immunol.* 30:109–16
131. Hewitt CR, Brown AP, Hart BJ, Pritchard DI. 1995. A major house dust mite allergen disrupts the immunoglobulin E network by selectively cleaving CD23: innate protection by antiproteases. *J. Exp. Med.* 182:1537–44
132. Wan H, Winton HL, Soeller C, Tovey ER, Gruenert DC, et al. 1999. Der p 1 facilitates transepithelial allergen delivery by disruption of tight junctions. *J. Clin. Investig.* 104:123–33
133. Vrtala S, Akdis CA, Budak F, Akdis M, Blaser K, et al. 2000. T cell epitope-containing hypoallergenic recombinant fragments of the major birch pollen allergen, Bet v 1, induce blocking antibodies. *J. Immunol.* 165:6653–59
134. Korematsu S, Tanaka Y, Hosoi S, Koyanagi S, Yokota T, et al. 2000. C8/119S mutation of major mite allergen Derf-2 leads to degenerate secondary structure and molecular polymerization and induces potent and exclusive Th1 cell differentiation. *J. Immunol.* 165:2895–902
135. Shreffler WG, Castro RR, Kucuk ZY, Charlop-Powers Z, Grishina G, et al. 2006. The major glycoprotein allergen from Arachis hypogaea, Ara h 1, is a ligand of dendritic cell-specific ICAM-grabbing nonintegrin and acts as a Th2 adjuvant in vitro. *J. Immunol.* 177:3677–85
136. Wallner BP, Gefter ML. 1996. Peptide therapy for treatment of allergic diseases. *Clin. Immunol. Immunopathol.* 80:105–9
137. Lamb JR, Skidmore BJ, Green N, Chiller JM, Feldmann M. 1983. Induction of tolerance in influenza virus-immune T lymphocyte clones with synthetic peptides of influenza hemagglutinin. *J. Exp. Med.* 157:1434–47
138. Briner TJ, Kuo MC, Keating KM, Rogers BL, Greenstein JL. 1993. Peripheral T-cell tolerance induced in naive and primed mice by subcutaneous injection of peptides from the major cat allergen Fel d I. *Proc. Natl. Acad. Sci. USA* 90:7608–12
139. Norman PS, Ohman JL, Jr, Long AA, Creticos PS, Gefter MA, et al. 1996. Treatment of cat allergy with T-cell reactive peptides. *Am. J. Respir. Crit. Care Med.* 154:1623–28
140. Simons FE, Imada M, Li Y, Watson WT, HayGlass KT. 1996. Fel d 1 peptides: effect on skin tests and cytokine synthesis in cat-allergic human subjects. *Int. Immunol.* 8:1937–45
141. Pene J, Desroches A, Paradis L, Lebel B, Farce M, et al. 1998. Immunotherapy with Fel d 1 peptides decreases IL-4 release by peripheral blood T cells of patients allergic to cats. *J. Allergy Clin. Immunol.* 102:571–78
142. Müller U, Akdis CA, Fricker M, Akdis M, Blesken T, et al. 1998. Successful immunotherapy with T-cell epitope peptides of bee venom phospholipase A2 induces specific T-cell anergy in patients allergic to bee venom. *J. Allergy Clin. Immunol.* 101:747–54
143. Maguire P, Nicodemus C, Robinson D, Aaronson D, Umetsu DT. 1999. The safety and efficacy of ALLERVAX CAT in cat allergic patients. *Clin. Immunol.* 93:222–31

144. Haselden BM, Larche M, Meng Q, Shirley K, Dworski R, et al. 2001. Late asthmatic reactions provoked by intradermal injection of T-cell peptide epitopes are not associated with bronchial mucosal infiltration of eosinophils or T(H)2-type cells or with elevated concentrations of histamine or eicosanoids in bronchoalveolar fluid. *J. Allergy Clin. Immunol.* 108:394–401
145. Oldfield WL, Kay AB, Larche M. 2001. Allergen-derived T cell peptide-induced late asthmatic reactions precede the induction of antigen-specific hyporesponsiveness in atopic allergic asthmatic subjects. *J. Immunol.* 167:1734–39
146. Oldfield WL, Larche M, Kay AB. 2002. Effect of T-cell peptides derived from Fel d 1 on allergic reactions and cytokine production in patients sensitive to cats: a randomised controlled trial. *Lancet* 360:47–53
147. Fellrath JM, Kettner A, Dufour N, Frigerio C, Schneeberger D, et al. 2003. Allergen-specific T-cell tolerance induction with allergen-derived long synthetic peptides: results of a phase I trial. *J. Allergy Clin. Immunol.* 111:854–61
148. Ali FR, Oldfield WL, Higashi N, Larche M, Kay AB. 2004. Late asthmatic reactions induced by inhalation of allergen-derived T cell peptides. *Am. J. Respir. Crit. Care Med.* 169:20–26
149. Smith TR, Alexander C, Kay AB, Larche M, Robinson DS. 2004. Cat allergen peptide immunotherapy reduces $CD4^+$ T cell responses to cat allergen but does not alter suppression by $CD4^+$ $CD25^+$ T cells: a double-blind placebo-controlled study. *Allergy* 59:1097–101
150. Verhoef A, Alexander C, Kay AB, Larché M. 2005. T cell epitope immunotherapy induces a $CD4^+$ T cell population with regulatory activity. *PLoS Med.* 2:e78
151. Alexander C, Ying S, Kay AB, Larché M. 2005. Fel d 1-derived T cell peptide therapy induces recruitment of $CD4^+$ $CD25^+$; $CD4^+$ interferon-γ^+ T helper type 1 cells to sites of allergen-induced late-phase skin reactions in cat-allergic subjects. *Clin. Exp. Allergy* 35:52–58
152. Alexander C, Tarzi M, Larche M, Kay AB. 2005. The effect of Fel d 1-derived T-cell peptides on upper and lower airway outcome measurements in cat-allergic subjects. *Allergy* 60:1269–74
153. Tarzi M, Klunker S, Texier C, Verhoef A, Stapel SO, et al. 2006. Induction of interleukin-10 and suppressor of cytokine signalling-3 gene expression following peptide immunotherapy. *Clin. Exp. Allergy* 36:465–74
154. Faith A, Akdis CA, Akdis M, Joss A, Wymann D, Blaser K. 1999. An altered peptide ligand specifically inhibits Th2 cytokine synthesis by abrogating TCR signaling. *J. Immunol.* 162:1836–42
155. Valenta R, Vrtala S, Focke-Tejkl M, Bugajska S, Ball T, et al. 1999. Genetically engineered and synthetic allergen derivatives: candidates for vaccination against type I allergy. *Biol. Chem.* 380:815–24
156. Linhart B, Valenta R. 2005. Molecular design of allergy vaccines. *Curr. Opin. Immunol.* 17:646–55
157. Ferreira F, Briza P, Infuhr D, Schmidt G, Wallner M, et al. 2006. Modified recombinant allergens for safer immunotherapy. *Inflamm. Allergy Drug Targets* 5:5–14
158. Wallner M, Stocklinger A, Thalhamer T, Bohle B, Vogel L, et al. 2007. Allergy multivaccines created by DNA shuffling of tree pollen allergens. *J. Allergy Clin. Immunol.* 120:374–80
159. Gafvelin G, Parmley S, Neimert-Andersson T, Blank U, Eriksson TL, et al. 2007. Hypoallergens for allergen-specific immunotherapy by directed molecular evolution of mite group 2 allergens. *J. Biol. Chem.* 282:3778–87
160. Westritschnig K, Linhart B, Focke-Tejkl M, Pavkov T, Keller W, et al. 2007. A hypoallergenic vaccine obtained by tail-to-head restructuring of timothy grass pollen profilin, Phl p 12, for the treatment of cross-sensitization to profilin. *J. Immunol.* 179:7624–34
161. Mothes-Luksch N, Stumvoll S, Linhart B, Focke M, Krauth MT, et al. 2008. Disruption of allergenic activity of the major grass pollen allergen Phl p 2 by reassembly as a mosaic protein. *J. Immunol.* 181:4864–73
162. Kahlert H, Suck R, Weber B, Nandy A, Wald M, et al. 2008. Characterization of a hypoallergenic recombinant Bet v 1 variant as a candidate for allergen-specific immunotherapy. *Int. Arch. Allergy Immunol.* 145:193–206
163. Vrtala S, Focke-Tejkl M, Swoboda I, Kraft D, Valenta R. 2004. Strategies for converting allergens into hypoallergenic vaccine candidates. *Methods* 32:313–20
164. Klimek L, Bachert C, Doemer C, Meyer H, Narkus A. 2005. Specific immunotherapy with recombinant birch pollen allergen rBet v 1-FV is clinically efficacious. *Allergy Clin. Immunol. Int.* 2005(Suppl. 1):15

165. Rak S. 2009. *Clinical results with a hypoallergenic recombinant birch pollen allergen derivative*. Presented at 27th Congr., EAACI 2009, Warsaw, June 6–10
166. Reisinger J, Horak F, Pauli G, van Hage M, Cromwell O, et al. 2005. Allergen-specific nasal IgG antibodies induced by vaccination with genetically modified allergens are associated with reduced nasal allergen sensitivity. *J. Allergy Clin. Immunol.* 116:347–54
167. Pree I, Reisinger J, Focke M, Vrtala S, Pauli G, et al. 2007. Analysis of epitope-specific immune responses induced by vaccination with structurally folded and unfolded recombinant Bet v 1 allergen derivatives in man. *J. Immunol.* 179:5309–16
168. Purohit A, Niederberger V, Kronqvist M, Horak F, Gronneberg R, et al. 2008. Clinical effects of immunotherapy with genetically modified recombinant birch pollen Bet v 1 derivatives. *Clin. Exp. Allergy* 38:1514–25
169. Ulmer JB, Donnelly JJ, Parker SE, Rhodes GH, Felgner PL, et al. 1993. Heterologous protection against influenza by injection of DNA encoding a viral protein. *Science* 259:1745–49
170. Weiss R, Scheiblhofer S, Gabler M, Ferreira F, Leitner WW, Thalhamer J. 2006. Is genetic vaccination against allergy possible? *Int. Arch. Allergy Immunol.* 139:332–45
171. Raz E, Tighe H, Sato Y, Corr M, Dudler JA, et al. 1996. Preferential induction of a Th1 immune response and inhibition of specific IgE antibody formation by plasmid DNA immunization. *Proc. Natl. Acad. Sci. USA* 93:5141–45
172. Hsu CH, Chua KY, Tao MH, Lai YL, Wu HD, et al. 1996. Immunoprophylaxis of allergen-induced immunoglobulin E synthesis and airway hyperresponsiveness in vivo by genetic immunization. *Nat. Med.* 2:540–44
173. Weiss R, Scheiblhofer S, Freund J, Ferreira F, Livey I, Thalhamer J. 2002. Gene gun bombardment with gold particles displays a particular Th2-promoting signal that over-rules the Th1-inducing effect of immunostimulatory CpG motifs in DNA vaccines. *Vaccine* 20:3148–54
174. Roy K, Mao HQ, Huang SK, Leong KW. 1999. Oral gene delivery with chitosan–DNA nanoparticles generates immunologic protection in a murine model of peanut allergy. *Nat. Med.* 5:387–91
175. Toda M, Sato H, Takebe Y, Taniguchi Y, Saito S, et al. 2000. Inhibition of immunoglobulin E response to Japanese cedar pollen allergen (Cry j 1) in mice by DNA immunization: different outcomes dependent on the plasmid DNA inoculation method. *Immunology* 99:179–86
176. Slater JE, Paupore E, Zhang YT, Colberg-Poley AM. 1998. The latex allergen Hev b 5 transcript is widely distributed after subcutaneous injection in BALB/c mice of its DNA vaccine. *J. Allergy Clin. Immunol.* 102:469–75
177. Bauer R, Scheiblhofer S, Kern K, Gruber C, Stepanoska T, et al. 2006. Generation of hypoallergenic DNA vaccines by forced ubiquitination: preventive and therapeutic effects in a mouse model of allergy. *J. Allergy Clin. Immunol.* 118:269–76
178. Hochreiter R, Stepanoska T, Ferreira F, Valenta R, Vrtala S, et al. 2003. Prevention of allergen-specific IgE production and suppression of an established Th2-type response by immunization with DNA encoding hypoallergenic allergen derivatives of Bet v 1, the major birch-pollen allergen. *Eur. J. Immunol.* 33:1667–76
179. Chapman MD, Ferreira F, Villalba M, Cromwell O, Bryan D, et al. 2008. The European Union CREATE project: a model for international standardization of allergy diagnostics and vaccines. *J. Allergy Clin. Immunol.* 122:882–89
180. Niederberger V, Pauli G, Gronlund H, Froschl R, Rumpold H, et al. 1998. Recombinant birch pollen allergens (rBet v 1 and rBet v 2) contain most of the IgE epitopes present in birch, alder, hornbeam, hazel, and oak pollen: a quantitative IgE inhibition study with sera from different populations. *J. Allergy Clin. Immunol.* 102:579–91
181. Gronlund H, Bergman T, Sandstrom K, Alvelius G, Reininger R, et al. 2003. Formation of disulfide bonds and homodimers of the major cat allergen Fel d 1 equivalent to the natural allergen by expression in *Escherichia coli*. *J. Biol. Chem.* 278:40144–51
182. Westritschnig K, Horak F, Swoboda I, Balic N, Spitzauer S, et al. 2008. Different allergenic activity of grass pollen allergens revealed by skin testing. *Eur. J. Clin. Investig.* 38:260–67
183. Weghofer M, Thomas WR, Kronqvist M, Mari A, Purohit A, et al. 2008. Variability of IgE reactivity profiles among European mite allergic patients. *Eur. J. Clin. Investig.* 38:959–65

184. Focke M, Marth K, Flicker S, Valenta R. 2008. Heterogeneity of commercial timothy grass pollen extracts. *Clin. Exp. Allergy* 38:1400–8
185. King TP, Jim SY, Monsalve RI, Kagey-Sobotka A, Lichtenstein LM, Spangfort MD. 2001. Recombinant allergens with reduced allergenicity but retaining immunogenicity of the natural allergens: hybrids of yellow jacket and paper wasp venom allergen antigen 5s. *J. Immunol.* 166:6057–65
186. Linhart B, Jahn-Schmid B, Verdino P, Keller W, Ebner C, et al. 2002. Combination vaccines for the treatment of grass pollen allergy consisting of genetically engineered hybrid molecules with increased immunogenicity. *FASEB J.* 16:1301–3
187. Linhart B, Hartl A, Jahn-Schmid B, Verdino P, Keller W, et al. 2005. A hybrid molecule resembling the epitope spectrum of grass pollen for allergy vaccination. *J. Allergy Clin. Immunol.* 115:1010–16
188. Linhart B, Mothes-Luksch N, Vrtala S, Kneidinger M, Valent P, Valenta R. 2008. A hypoallergenic hybrid molecule with increased immunogenicity consisting of derivatives of the major grass pollen allergens, Phl p 2 and Phl p 6. *Biol. Chem.* 389:925–33
189. Jutel M, Jaeger L, Suck R, Meyer H, Fiebig H, Cromwell O. 2005. Allergen-specific immunotherapy with recombinant grass pollen allergens. *J. Allergy Clin. Immunol.* 116:608–13
190. Pauli G, Larsen TH, Rak S, Horak F, Pastorello E, et al. 2008. Efficacy of recombinant birch pollen vaccine for the treatment of birch-allergic rhinoconjunctivitis. *J. Allergy Clin. Immunol.* 122:951–60
191. Bracy JL, Sachs DH, Iacomini J. 1998. Inhibition of xenoreactive natural antibody production by retroviral gene therapy. *Science* 281:1845–47
192. Steptoe RJ, Ritchie JM, Harrison LC. 2003. Transfer of hematopoietic stem cells encoding autoantigen prevents autoimmune diabetes. *J. Clin. Investig.* 111:1357–63
193. Alderuccio F, Murphy K, Toh BH. 2003. Stem cells engineered to express self-antigen to treat autoimmunity. *Trends Immunol.* 24:176–80
194. Baranyi U, Linhart B, Pilat N, Gattringer M, Bagley J, et al. 2008. Tolerization of a type I allergic immune response through transplantation of genetically modified hematopoietic stem cells. *J. Immunol.* 180:8168–75
195. Host A, Jacobsen HP, Halken S, Holmenlund D. 1995. The natural history of cow's milk protein allergy/intolerance. *Eur. J. Clin. Nutr.* 49(Suppl. 1):S13–18
196. David MF. 1977. Prevention of homocytotropic antibody formation and anaphylactic sensitization by prefeeding antigen. *J. Allergy Clin. Immunol.* 60:180–87
197. Holt PG, Vines J, Britten D. 1988. Sublingual allergen administration. I. Selective suppression of IgE production in rats by high allergen doses. *Clin. Allergy* 18:229–34
198. Zemann B, Schwaerzler C, Griot-Wenk M, Nefzger M, Mayer P, et al. 2003. Oral administration of specific antigens to allergy-prone infant dogs induces IL-10 and TGF-β expression and prevents allergy in adult life. *J. Allergy Clin. Immunol.* 111:1069–75
199. Wiedermann U, Jahn-Schmid B, Bohle B, Repa A, Renz H, et al. 1999. Suppression of antigen-specific T- and B-cell responses by intranasal or oral administration of recombinant bet v 1, the major birch pollen allergen, in a murine model of type I allergy. *J. Allergy Clin. Immunol.* 103:1202–10
200. Winkler B, Hufnagl K, Spittler A, Ploder M, Kallay E, et al. 2006. The role of Foxp3$^+$ T cells in long-term efficacy of prophylactic and therapeutic mucosal tolerance induction in mice. *Allergy* 61:173–80
201. Wiedermann U, Herz U, Baier K, Vrtala S, Neuhaus-Steinmetz U, et al. 2001. Intranasal treatment with a recombinant hypoallergenic derivative of the major birch pollen allergen Bet v 1 prevents allergic sensitization and airway inflammation in mice. *Int. Arch. Allergy Immunol.* 126:68–77
202. Astori M, von Garnier C, Kettner A, Dufour N, Corradin G, Spertini F. 2000. Inducing tolerance by intranasal administration of long peptides in naive and primed CBA/J mice. *J. Immunol.* 165:3497–505
203. Jarnicki AG, Tsuji T, Thomas WR. 2001. Inhibition of mucosal and systemic T(h)2-type immune responses by intranasal peptides containing a dominant T cell epitope of the allergen Der p 1. *Int. Immunol.* 13:1223–31
204. Marazuela EG, Rodriguez R, Fernández-García H, García MS, Villalba M, Batanero E. 2008. Intranasal immunization with a dominant T-cell epitope peptide of a major allergen of olive pollen prevents mice from sensitization to the whole allergen. *Mol. Immunol.* 45:438–45

205. Hufnagl K, Winkler B, Focke M, Valenta R, Scheiner O, et al. 2005. Intranasal tolerance induction with polypeptides derived from 3 noncross-reactive major aeroallergens prevents allergic polysensitization in mice. *J. Allergy Clin. Immunol.* 116:370–76
206. Durham SR, Yang WH, Pedersen MR, Johansen N, Rak S. 2006. Sublingual immunotherapy with once-daily grass allergen tablets: a randomized controlled trial in seasonal allergic rhinoconjunctivitis. *J. Allergy Clin. Immunol.* 117:802–9
207. Muraro A, Dreborg S, Halken S, Host A, Niggemann B, et al. 2004. Dietary prevention of allergic diseases in infants and small children. Part I: immunologic background and criteria for hypoallergenicity. *Pediatr. Allergy Immunol.* 15:103–11
208. Takagi H, Hiroi T, Yang L, Takamura K, Ishimitsu R, et al. 2008. Efficient induction of oral tolerance by fusing cholera toxin B subunit with allergen-specific T-cell epitopes accumulated in rice seed. *Vaccine* 26:6027–30
209. Huibregtse IL, Snoeck V, de Creus A, Braat H, De Jong EC, et al. 2007. Induction of ovalbumin-specific tolerance by oral administration of Lactococcus lactis secreting ovalbumin. *Gastroenterology* 133:517–28
210. Segal DM, Taurog JD, Metzger H. 1977. Dimeric immunoglobulin E serves as a unit signal for mast cell degranulation. *Proc. Natl. Acad. Sci. USA* 74:2993–97
211. Malley A, Perlman F. 1970. Timothy pollen fractions in treatment of hay fever. I. Clinical and immunological response to small and higher molecular weight fractions. *J. Allergy* 45:14–29
212. Malley A, Campbell DH, Heimlich EM. 1964. Isolation and immunochemical properties of haptenic material from Timothy Pollen. *J. Immunol.* 93:420–25
213. Ganglberger E, Sponer B, Schöll I, Wiedermann U, Baumann S, et al. 2001. Monovalent fusion proteins of IgE mimotopes are safe for therapy of type I allergy. *FASEB J.* 15:2524–26
214. Suphioglu C, Schäppi G, Kenrick J, Levy D, Davies JM, O'Hehir RE. 2001. A novel grass pollen allergen mimotope identified by phage display peptide library inhibits allergen-human IgE antibody interaction. *FEBS Lett.* 502:46–52
215. Lee WY, Sehon AH. 1977. Abrogation of reaginic antibodies with modified allergens. *Nature* 267:618–19
216. Sato Y, Roman M, Tighe H, Lee D, Corr M, et al. 1996. Immunostimulatory DNA sequences necessary for effective intradermal gene immunization. *Science* 273:352–54
217. Chu RS, Targoni OS, Krieg AM, Lehmann PV, Harding CV. 1997. CpG oligodeoxynucleotides act as adjuvants that switch on T helper 1 (Th1) immunity. *J. Exp. Med.* 186:1623–31
218. Tighe H, Takabayashi K, Schwartz D, Van Nest G, Tuck S, et al. 2000. Conjugation of immunostimulatory DNA to the short ragweed allergen Amb a 1 enhances its immunogenicity and reduces its allergenicity. *J. Allergy Clin. Immunol.* 106:124–34
219. Tulic MK, Fiset PO, Christodoulopoulos P, Vaillancourt P, Desrosiers M, et al. 2004. Amb a 1-immunostimulatory oligodeoxynucleotide conjugate immunotherapy decreases the nasal inflammatory response. *J. Allergy Clin. Immunol.* 113:235–41
220. Bohle B, Breitwieser A, Zwolfer B, Jahn-Schmid B, Sara M, et al. 2004. A novel approach to specific allergy treatment: the recombinant fusion protein of a bacterial cell surface (S-layer) protein and the major birch pollen allergen Bet v 1 (rSbsC-Bet v 1) combines reduced allergenicity with immunomodulating capacity. *J. Immunol.* 172:6642–48
221. Hulse KE, Reefer AJ, Engelhard VH, Satinover SM, Patrie JT, et al. 2008. Targeting Fel d 1 to FcγRI induces a novel variation of the T(H)2 response in subjects with cat allergy. *J. Allergy Clin. Immunol.* 121:756–62
222. Zhu D, Kepley CL, Zhang K, Terada T, Yamada T, Saxon A. 2005. A chimeric human-cat fusion protein blocks cat-induced allergy. *Nat. Med.* 11:446–49
223. Martínez-Gómez JM, Johansen P, Rose H, Steiner M, Senti G, et al. 2009. Targeting the MHC class II pathway of antigen presentation enhances immunogenicity and safety of allergen immunotherapy. *Allergy* 64:172–78
224. Kündig TM, Senti G, Schnetzler G, Wolf C, Prinz Vavricka BM, et al. 2006. Der p 1 peptide on virus-like particles is safe and highly immunogenic in healthy adults. *J. Allergy Clin. Immunol.* 117:1470–76
225. Valenta R, Duchene M, Vrtala S, Birkner T, Ebner C, et al. 1991. Recombinant allergens for immunoblot diagnosis of tree-pollen allergy. *J. Allergy Clin. Immunol.* 88:889–94

226. Valenta R, Vrtala S, Ebner C, Kraft D, Scheiner O. 1992. Diagnosis of grass pollen allergy with recombinant timothy grass (*Phleum pratense*) pollen allergens. *Int. Arch. Allergy Immunol.* 97:287–94
227. Ebner C, Szepfalusi Z, Ferreira F, Jilek A, Valenta R, et al. 1993. Identification of multiple T cell epitopes on Bet v I, the major birch pollen allergen, using specific T cell clones and overlapping peptides. *J. Immunol.* 150:1047–54
228. Joost van Neerven R, van t'Hof W, Ringrose JH, Jansen HM, Aalberse RC, et al. 1993. T cell epitopes of house dust mite major allergen Der p II. *J. Immunol.* 151:2326–35
229. Sehon LZ, Mohapatra SS. 1992. Induction of IgE antibodies in mice with recombinant grass pollen antigens. *Immunology* 76:158–63
230. Zhang L, Mohapatra SS. 1993. Antigen- and isotype-specific immune responses to a recombinant antigen-allergen chimeric (RAAC) protein. *J. Immunol.* 151:791–99
231. Ferreira FD, Mayer P, Sperr WR, Valent P, Seiberler S, et al. 1996. Induction of IgE antibodies with predefined specificity in rhesus monkeys with recombinant birch pollen allergens, Bet v 1 and Bet v 2. *J. Allergy Clin. Immunol.* 97:95–103
232. Vrtala S, Mayer P, Ferreira F, Susani M, Sehon AH, et al. 1996. Induction of IgE antibodies in mice and rhesus monkeys with recombinant birch pollen allergens: different allergenicity of Bet v 1 and Bet v 2. *J. Allergy Clin. Immunol.* 98:913–21
233. Breiteneder H, Ferreira F, Hoffmann-Sommergruber K, Ebner C, Breitenbach M, et al. 1993. Four recombinant isoforms of Cor a I, the major allergen of hazel pollen, show different IgE-binding properties. *Eur. J. Biochem.* 212:355–62
234. Smith AM, Chapman MD. 1996. Reduction in IgE binding to allergen variants generated by site-directed mutagenesis: contribution of disulfide bonds to the antigenic structure of the major house dust mite allergen Der p 2. *Mol. Immunol.* 33:399–405
235. Takai T, Yokota T, Yasue M, Nishiyama C, Yuuki T, et al. 1997. Engineering of the major house dust mite allergen Der f 2 for allergen-specific immunotherapy. *Nat. Biotechnol.* 15:754–58
236. Zeiler T, Taivainen A, Rytkonen M, Rautiainen J, Karjalainen H, et al. 1997. Recombinant allergen fragments as candidate preparations for allergen immunotherapy. *J. Allergy Clin. Immunol.* 100:721–27
237. Moser M, Crameri R, Brust E, Suter M, Menz G. 1994. Diagnostic value of recombinant *Aspergillus fumigatus* allergen I/a for skin testing and serology. *J. Allergy Clin. Immunol.* 93:1–11
238. Menz G, Dolecek C, Schonheit-Kenn U, Ferreira F, Moser M, et al. 1996. Serological and skin-test diagnosis of birch pollen allergy with recombinant Bet v I, the major birch pollen allergen. *Clin. Exp. Allergy* 26:50–60
239. Pauli G, Oster JP, Deviller P, Heiss S, Bessot JC, et al. 1996. Skin testing with recombinant allergens rBet v 1 and birch profilin, rBet v 2: diagnostic value for birch pollen and associated allergies. *J. Allergy Clin. Immunol.* 97:1100–9
240. Gajhede M, Osmark P, Poulsen FM, Ipsen H, Larsen JN, et al. 1996. X-ray and NMR structure of Bet v 1, the origin of birch pollen allergy. *Nat. Struct. Biol.* 3:1040–45
241. van Hage-Hamsten M, Kronqvist M, Zetterstrom O, Johansson E, Niederberger V, et al. 1999. Skin test evaluation of genetically engineered hypoallergenic derivatives of the major birch pollen allergen, Bet v 1: results obtained with a mix of two recombinant Bet v 1 fragments and recombinant Bet v 1 trimer in a Swedish population before the birch pollen season. *J. Allergy Clin. Immunol.* 104:969–77
242. Pauli G, Purohit A, Oster JP, De Blay F, Vrtala S, et al. 2000. Comparison of genetically engineered hypoallergenic rBet v 1 derivatives with rBet v 1 wild-type by skin prick and intradermal testing: results obtained in a French population. *Clin. Exp. Allergy* 30:1076–84

Adaptive Immune Regulation in the Gut: T Cell–Dependent and T Cell–Independent IgA Synthesis

Sidonia Fagarasan,[1] Shimpei Kawamoto,[1,2] Osami Kanagawa,[3] and Keiichiro Suzuki[1]

[1]Laboratory for Mucosal Immunity, [3]Laboratory for Autoimmune Regulation, RIKEN Research Center for Allergy Immunology, Yokohama 230–0045, Japan; email: sidonia-f@rcai.riken.jp

[2]Department of Immunology and Genomic Medicine, Graduate School of Medicine, Kyoto University, Kyoto 606-8501, Japan

Annu. Rev. Immunol. 2010. 28:243–73

First published online as a Review in Advance on December 8, 2009

The *Annual Review of Immunology* is online at immunol.annualreviews.org

This article's doi: 10.1146/annurev-immunol-030409-101314

0732-0582/10/0423-00243$20.00

Key Words

activation-induced cytidine deaminase (AID), bacteria, dendritic cells, follicular T helper cells, Peyer's patches

Abstract

In mammals, the gastrointestinal tract harbors an extraordinarily dense and complex community of microorganisms. The gut microbiota provide strong selective pressure to the host to evolve adaptive immune responses required for the maintenance of local and systemic homeostasis. The continuous antigenic presence in the gut imposes a dynamic remodeling of gut-associated lymphoid tissues (GALT) and the selection of multiple layered strategies for immunoglobulin (Ig) A production. The composite and dynamic gut environment also necessitates heterogeneous, versatile, and convertible T cells, capable of inhibiting (Foxp3$^+$ T cells) or helping (T_{FH} cells) local immune responses. In this review, we describe recent advances in our understanding of dynamic pathways that lead to IgA synthesis, in gut follicular structures and in extrafollicular sites, by T cell–dependent and T cell–independent mechanisms. We discuss the finely tuned regulatory mechanisms for IgA production and emphasize the role of mucosal IgA in the selection and maintenance of the appropriate microbial composition that is necessary for immune homeostasis.

INTRODUCTION

The prokaryotic kingdom represents the largest component of the earth biomass that has undoubtedly functioned as a major selective force for the evolution of eukaryotic organisms (1). Adaptive coevolution between eukaryotic and prokaryotic organisms led to the establishment of commensal and symbiotic relationships that have contributed to the development of the immune system (2). Many bacteria are present in the gut of lower vertebrates as well as invertebrates, and many of these bacteria constitute a commensal flora that is considered beneficial for the host (3). The human gastrointestinal tract harbors a bacterial community containing trillions of members, at present mostly uncultured, comprising thousands of species-level phylogenetic types (4, 5). They are essential to human physiology, as they break down otherwise indigestible dietary components (such as plant polysaccharides), regulate host fat storage (6), stimulate intestinal angiogenesis (7), protect against epithelial injury (8), and serve as a natural defense against colonization with pathogens (9, 10). However, when present outside their physiological niche, some of these so-called friendly bacteria are capable of killing the host. Therefore, an efficient host defense system is likely essential for maintaining the delicate balance in this host-bacteria relationship and for preventing the access of bacteria to the host inner milieu.

The first line of protection against pathogen invasion, and the only one that functions in invertebrates, is innate immune defense (11, 12). Innate immunity relies on cells with germline-encoded receptors called pattern-recognition receptors and molecules such as lysozymes, complement, or antimicrobial peptides (defensins) that, together, trigger inflammatory responses that limit the pathogen invasion (13). Vertebrates, however, have evolved the wondrous machinery of adaptive immunity that relies on lymphocytes with diverse receptors capable of recognizing and removing potential pathogens (14). But what brought the adaptive immune system to vertebrates?

Exciting new findings by Cooper and coworkers (15) revealed that jawless vertebrates possess an adaptive immune system with two distinct lymphocyte populations and highly diverse antigen-recognition receptors, called variable lymphocyte receptor A (VLRA) and VLRB. These receptors apparently assemble through a gene-conversion process mediated by the APOBEC/AID family cytosine deaminase 1 (CDA1) and CDA2 for VLRA and VLRB, respectively (15, 16). Interestingly, VLRA lymphocytes respond to classical T cell mitogens and produce proinflammatory cytokines and chemokines, such as IL-17 and macrophage migration inhibitory factor; whereas VLRB lymphocytes bind microbial antigens, proliferate, and differentiate into VLR antibody-secreting cells. Thus, the compartmentalization of the immune system into T and B cell immunity emerged approximately 500 mya, likely as a need of the host (i.e., modern cyclostomes such as hagfish and lampreys) for efficient defensive strategies against pathogens. However, the key molecular components of the adaptive immune system, such as T cell receptors (TCRs), B cell receptors (BCRs), and their coreceptors, equivalents of major histocompatibility complex (MHC) family members, or the transposable element containing recombination activating gene (RAG-1) and RAG-2, are all absent in jawless vertebrates (12).

The immunoglobulin superfamily-based adaptive immune system may have developed in the gut of primitive jawed fish for protection against the higher rates of injuries and infections inflicted by swallowed prey animals, which often contained bones or scales (17). The new prey-predator relationships likely facilitated the spread of pathogens to other populations across species barriers. Together, these conditions might have provided a strong selective pressure to evolve gut lymphoid tissues in early jawed fish. All primitive jawed fish have macrophages, granulocytes, and lymphocytes in the gut epithelium and lamina propria (LP), as well as lymphoid cell aggregates in the LP similar to cryptopatches

(CPs; see below), which may have been the ancestor of the thymus (18). These gut cells have the capacity to take up antigens and to produce local antibodies. For example, gill cells of rainbow trout can bind and take up particulate antigens. Also, oral immunization in some teleost fish induces antibody responses mostly in intestinal mucus and to a lesser degree in serum, implying the existence of a mucosal immune system (reviewed in Reference 19).

However, efficient immune responses are generated in organized gut-associated lymphoid tissues (GALT), and such structures are found in birds and mammals only. A conspicuous response of the GALT that follows microbial gut colonization is the production of immunoglobulin (Ig) A. In humans, at least 80% of all plasma cells are located in the gut LP, and together they produce more IgA (40–60 mg/kg/day) than any other Ig isotype combined (20, 21). IgA is secreted mainly as dimers or larger polymers after incorporation of the joining (J) chain and association with a transmembrane epithelial protein known as polymeric Ig receptor (pIgR) (22, 23).

The finding that IgA is the most abundant Ig isotype in mucosal secretions led immunologists to search for the origin of IgA plasma cell precursors, the sites and mechanisms of their induction and migration, and the role of IgA at mucosal surfaces.

We begin this review by considering AID-dependent genetic alterations in mature B cells. We then describe the development of sites for generation of gut IgAs and summarize recent advances in understanding of the regulatory pathways for IgA synthesis in the gut. We discuss the role of IgA in the maintenance of mucosal and systemic homeostasis and conclude with new insights into the reciprocal regulation of IgA and bacterial communities in the gut.

AID-DEPENDENT GENETIC ALTERATIONS IN B CELLS

The immune system is known for taking advantage of a series of genetic alterations during lymphocyte differentiation. B cells diversify their antibody repertoire in several developmental stages involving different processes. Developing B cells assemble the variable regions of the Ig heavy (IgH) and light (IgL) chain genes from component variable (V), diversity (D), and joining (J) segments by the process of V(D)J recombination (24). The process is initiated by the RAG-1 and RAG-2 endonuclease complex and completed by the nonhomologous end-joining machinery. Each step of V(D)J recombination is programmed, highly ordered, and tightly controlled by several factors, including cytokines provided by stromal cells (SCs) (24). Mature B lymphocytes that have completed functional V(D)J recombination on H and L chain genes express IgM on the surface and migrate to peripheral lymphoid organs, where they encounter antigens. Appropriately activated B cells proliferate and differentiate into plasma cells or memory B cells. During this process of peripheral differentiation, B cells undergo a second wave of remodeling the Ig loci, namely class switch recombination (CSR) and somatic hypermutation (SHM), which is responsible for isotype switching and affinity maturation, respectively (reviewed in References 25–27).

CSR alters the effector function of antibodies without changing their antigen-binding specificity, by replacing the initial Cμ exon with one of several downstream C_H exons (28). Thus, CSR allows production of different IgH isotypes or Ig classes, such as IgG, IgE, IgA, and in some species even IgD (29, 30). Each isotype and its location or form (surface or secreted, systemic or mucosal, monomeric or polymeric) determine the manner in which captured antigens are eliminated. CSR takes place between two regions comprising repetitive sequences of palindrome-rich motifs, known as S regions, and it results in a looped-out deletion of intervening DNA segments (**Figure 1**) (25, 31). CSR is preceded by the expression of germline transcripts initiated from intronic promoters, which are located 5′ to the S regions and are regulated specifically by various cytokines—i.e., transforming growth factor (TGF)-β1 induces germline α and γ2b transcripts (32).

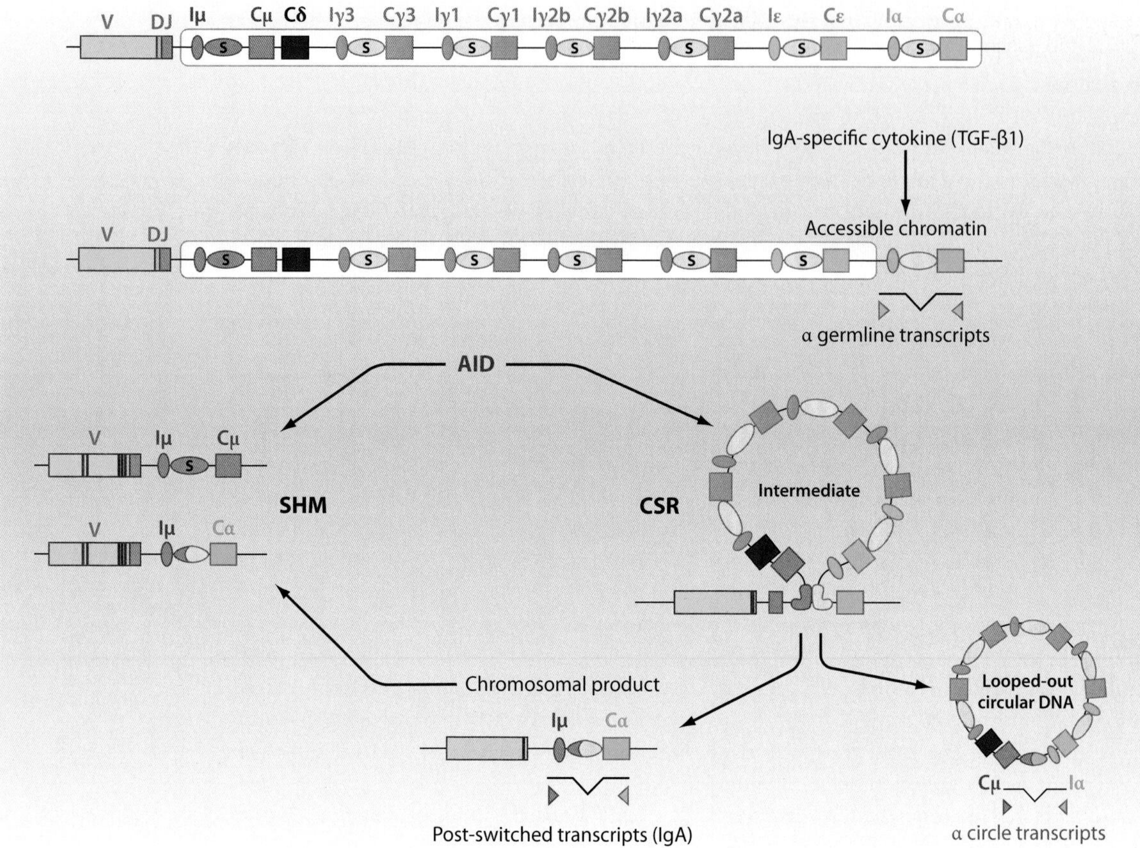

Figure 1

AID-dependent genetic alterations in activated B cells. Events and markers in IgA switch recombination. The organization of the mouse IgH gene locus after the completion of V(D)J recombination is shown. Class switch recombination (CSR) to IgA takes place between the Sμ and downstream Sα regions, and it results in a looped-out deletion of intervening DNA segments. It requires the expression of germline α transcripts (αGT) (initiated from the Iα intronic promoter located upstream of the Sα region upon cytokine stimulation, such as TGF-β1) and the expression of activation-induced cytidine deaminase (AID). CSR to IgA is accompanied by looping-out deletion of the DNA fragment that contains Cμ and other C_H genes located upstream of Cα from the chromosome, and it is followed by repair and ligation of the broken ends by the nonhomologous end-joining repair system. The Iα promoter located on the circular DNA is still active and responsive to cytokines and directs the production of Iα-Cμ transcripts called α circle transcripts (αCT). These αCTs are detected after the induction of AID, simultaneously with expression of IgA on the surface of B cells, and they disappear more quickly than αGTs, AID, or circular DNAs after the removal of switch stimulation. Thus, αCTs are the best available molecular markers for active IgA switch recombination. Antigen-activated B cells that express AID undergo not only CSR, but also somatic hypermutation (SHM). SHM introduces base-pair changes into the V(D)J region of rearranged genes encoding the Ig variable region of the heavy and light chains. Germinal centers are the main, but not the exclusive, sites where CSR and SHM occur.

SHM introduces point mutations in the V region of L and H chain exons, leading to alteration of antibody specificity and affinity maturation (reviewed in Reference 33). Thus, CSR and SHM target different regions and generate quite distinct products. Surprisingly, however, these two genetic alterations—CSR and SHM—are catalyzed by a single enzyme, the activation-induced cytidine deaminase (AID), a molecule belonging to the APOBEC-1-related family of cytidine deaminases (34, 35). AID is also required to initiate the gene conversion process that is involved in the postrearrangement diversification of Ig variable region genes, especially in avian species (36).

AID was discovered by Honjo and colleagues (37, 38) by "cDNA subtraction" utilizing cDNAs derived from the stimulated and nonstimulated murine lymphoma cell line CH12F3-2. AID is present in all jawed vertebrates including shark, teleost fish, and amphibians (39). SHM in hot spot regions similar to that in mammals has been identified in fish (40). Although fish AID can mediate CSR in mammals (i.e., when introduced into AID-deficient mouse B cells), fish do not have S regions and therefore do not undergo CSR (41–43). The ability to modify the effector function of Ig first appears in amphibian, with *Xenopus* B cells able to undergo CSR from IgM to IgY and IgX, the mammalian equivalent of IgG and IgA, respectively (44, 45). *Xenopus* possess not only S regions and AID required for CSR, but also the J chain and a pIgR that can induce efficient polymerization and export of human IgA (46). Although considerable effort has been devoted to the study of the evolution of Ig genes in fish and amphibians, relatively little is known about the molecular origin and physiological function of an IgA equivalent as we know it in mammals.

T CELL–DEPENDENT GENERATION OF IgA IN PEYER'S PATCHES

Development of Peyer's Patches

Peyer's patches (PPs) are large lymphoid structures built on a stromal scaffold, composed of several B cell follicles separated by areas containing T cells and dendritic cells (DCs) that develop before birth. PP organogenesis was originally described by Nishikawa and colleagues (47) as programmed inflammation dependent on interactions between hematopoietic or inducer cells and mesenchymal or organizer cells. The developmental pathway of PPs was extensively reviewed recently (48, 49). Among the key events absolutely necessary for PP formation is the generation of lymphoid tissue–inducer cells (LTi), expressing the inhibitory helix-loop-helix (HLH) transcription factor Id2, the retinoic acid–related orphan receptor (ROR)γt (50, 51), and cytokine and chemokine receptors such as IL-7R, lymphotoxin (LT)$\alpha 1\beta 2$, CXCR4, and CXCR5 (52–54). The expression of IL-7R is required for the survival of LTi cells and for their high levels of expression of LT$\alpha 1\beta 2$, which is critical for LTi clustering with SCs expressing LTβR (55, 56). The LT-LTβR interaction and the downstream activation of the NF-κB pathway through NF-κB-inducing kinase (NIK) result in enhanced expression of chemokines and cytokines by SCs, necessary for the recruitment of lymphocytes and LTi cells to the PP anlagen in a positive feedback loop (57, 58). Finally, the cells recruited and retained into these LTi-SC clusters organize into B cell follicles and T cell areas and induce the development of specialized vasculature.

Germinal Centers: Unique Characteristics in PPs

Most PP lymphocytes are activated cells residing in germinal centers (GCs). GCs are special microenvironments that allow interaction between B cells, antigens, and follicular B helper T cells (T_{FH}) that, through costimulatory molecules and cytokines, facilitate B cell proliferation, induction of AID, and subsequent CSR, SHM, and affinity maturation. All GC cells are brought and kept together by special SCs known as follicular dendritic cells (FDCs), and mice deficient in certain TNF/TNFR family members that fail to develop FDCs do not have GCs (reviewed in Reference 59).

During the past several years, studies on B cells have provided new insights into the migration, proliferation, and interaction dynamics in GCs; the phenotypes of GC B cells; and their specific transcriptional programs. Certainly, the biology of GCs is controlled at multiple levels (reviewed in References 60, 61). Recent studies reveal an important role for specific microRNAs in the development and function of B cells and GCs (62, 63). For example, miR-150 targets c-Myb, a critical transcription factor involved in the control of B cell differentiation (64), whereas miR-155 impacts the regulation of the GC response at two levels: through modulation of cytokine production by T cells (65, 66) and by direct post-transcriptional regulation of AID (67, 68).

Several characteristics distinguish GCs in PPs from GCs in other lymphoid structures such as peripheral lymph nodes. First, GCs are found continuously in PPs but not in peripheral lymph nodes or spleens of conventionally reared mice. The maintenance of PP GCs requires perpetual exposure to diverse bacterial antigens. Indeed, PP GCs are almost absent in germ-free mice (**Figure 2**), and the number and size of PP GCs drastically decrease after reduction and/or elimination of gut bacteria by antibiotics (69). Also, PP GCs attenuate in time in germ-free mice that are colonized with a single bacterium species such as *Morganella morganii* and segmented filamentous bacteria (SFB), in spite of the bacteria persisting in the gut lumen (70). Formation of GCs in PPs was thought to be an antigen-specific reaction, rather than just a polyclonal B cell expansion triggered by stimulation through pattern-recognition receptors, such as Toll-like receptors (TLRs). More recent studies of knock-in mice for latent membrane protein 2A (LMP2A), a membrane protein encoded by Epstein-Barr virus that acts as a BCR surrogate, apparently challenged this view (71). Surprisingly, LMP2A transgenic mice lacking antigen-specific recognition through BCRs, but having constitutive CD40-like signaling in all B cells, developed GCs in PPs but not in spleen. This unexpected result led to a model in which the mucosal B cells are driven into GCs independent of BCR specificity, through the interaction of TLRs on B cells with bacterial components (reviewed in Reference 72). Recent findings that TLR stimulation on B cells enhances myeloid differentiation primary response gene 88 (MyD88)-dependent antibody production supports this model (73). Although the interpretation of these data is still controversial (74, 75), results suggest that mucosal B cells are driven to form GCs through additional signals derived from pattern-recognition receptors.

Second, GC formation in the gut is strictly dependent on T cell help. Apparently, this help can be provided by $\alpha\beta$ and/or $\gamma\delta$ T cells, independent of interactions between antigen-specific B cells and $CD4^+$ T cells through the MHC class II–TCR complex (72, 76, 77) (see also **Figure 2**). How exactly these T cell subsets contribute to GC formation in PPs is currently unknown, although it likely involves the generation of T follicular helper (T_{FH}) cells (reviewed in Reference 78). T_{FH} cells are distinguishable from other effector helper T cells (i.e., Th1, Th2, Th17 cells) by their positioning into B cell follicles (owing to the expression of CXCR5 and possibly other adhesion molecules, such as WUCAM) as well as by the expression of costimulatory molecules (CD40L, inducible costimulator, programmed cell death 1^{hi}, OX40) and cytokines (IL-21, IL-4) associated with regulatory and B helper function (79–88). The development of T_{FH} cells depends on the presence of B cells, B-T interactions modulated by SAP (signaling intracellular adaptor lymphocytic activation molecule–associated protein), and the expression of transcription factor B cell lymphoma 6 (Bcl-6), which was recently proposed to be the master regulator of T_{FH} differentiation (82, 89–93). Bcl-6 binds to the promoters of Th1 and Th17 transcriptional regulators T-bet and RORγt and represses IFN-γ and IL-17 production. In addition, Bcl-6 represses microRNAs, i.e., miR-17–92, which inhibits CXCR5 expression (93). In contrast, the transcription factor B lymphocyte maturation protein-1 (Blimp-1), an antagonist of Bcl-6, inhibits T_{FH} differentiation, thus preventing the formation of GCs and B cell help (91, 94).

Other $CD4^+$ T cells expressing the forkhead-winged helix transcription factor Foxp3, generally known as regulatory T cells

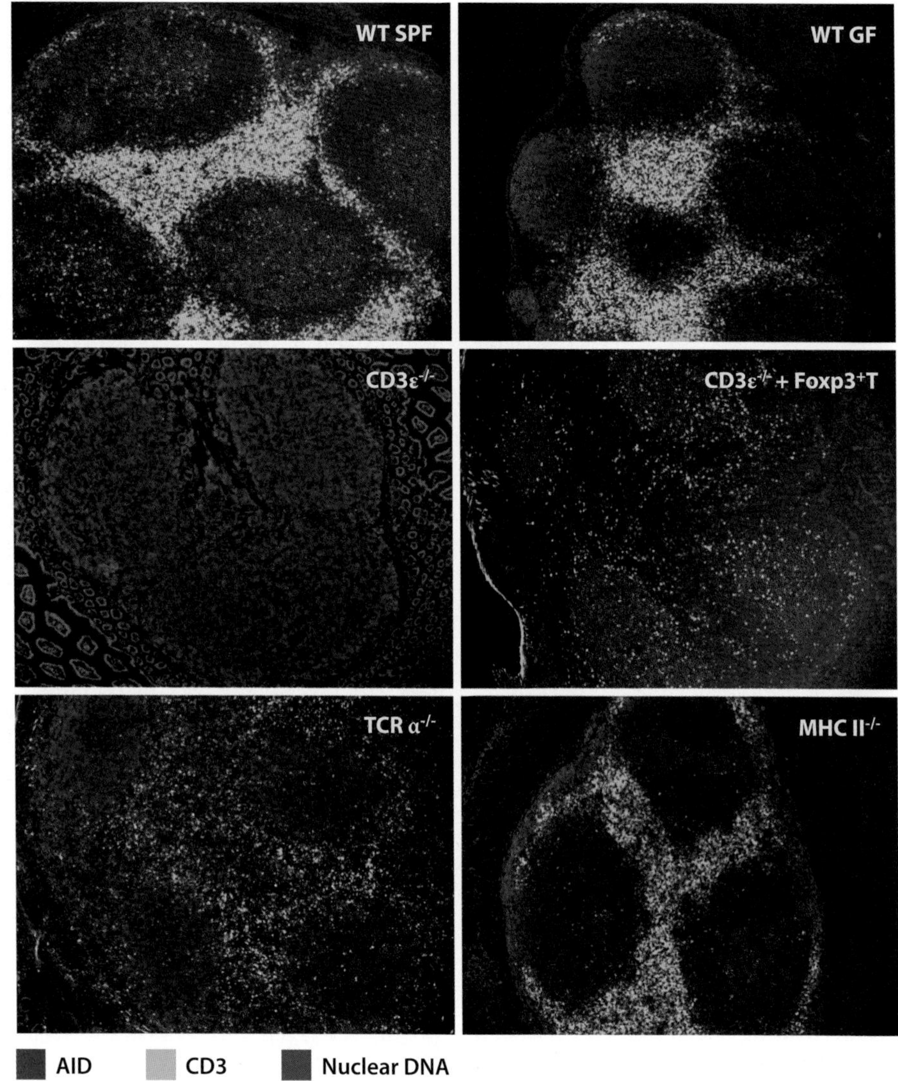

Figure 2

The induction of germinal centers in Peyer's patches depends on bacteria and T cell help. Horizontal sections from Peyer's patches of wild-type mice in specific-pathogen-free conditions (WT SPF), wild-type mice in germ-free conditions (WT GF), T cell–deficient mice (CD3$\varepsilon^{-/-}$ and TCR$\alpha^{-/-}$), CD3$\varepsilon^{-/-}$ mice four weeks after transfer of Foxp3$^+$ T cells, and MHC class II$^{-/-}$ mice, stained for AID (*red*), CD3 (*green*), and nuclear DNA (*blue*). Original magnification: PPx5.

with suppressive functions, may also have inhibitory effects for GC function. Indeed, Foxp3$^+$ T cells expressing CXCR5 are found within the GCs of mucosal lymphoid tissues in mice and humans (95–97). Furthermore, in vitro, the CXCR5$^+$ Foxp3$^+$ T cells isolated from tonsils inhibit the expression of AID and suppress Ig production by B cells, by yet unknown mechanisms (97). Surprisingly, however, some of the T_{FH} cells found in PP GCs derive from Foxp3$^+$ T cells that lose Foxp3 expression and convert into T_{FH} cells

(95). Interestingly, the conversion of Foxp3$^+$ into T_{FH} is apparently restricted to PPs because, even after systemic activation of B and T cells by immunization, Foxp3$^+$ cells cannot generate T_{FH} in spleen or peripheral lymph nodes. This observation raises the possibility that the precursors of T_{FH} in PPs and peripheral lymph nodes might be different. Indeed, T_{FH} cells in lymph nodes can be differentiated from IL-4$^+$ Th2 cells in response to helminth antigens (98, 99). PP T_{FH} cell differentiation is likely controlled by the same upstream signals that promote Foxp3 expression in T cells, namely antigen recognition through the TCR. Consistent with this idea, the transfer of ovalbumin-specific OT-II TCR transgenic RAG-2$^{-/-}$ CD4$^+$ T cells into CD3$\varepsilon^{-/-}$ mice generates Foxp3$^+$ T cells in gut LP and T_{FH} cells in PPs only when fed with ovalbumin (95). Precursors for T_{FH} cells in PPs thus may be enriched in the Foxp3$^+$ T cell population generated in the gut (the so-called inducible Treg) (**Figure 3**). This implies that gut Foxp3$^+$ T cells are different from Foxp3$^+$ T cells generated in the thymus, which are generally known as natural Tregs (100). This idea is supported by recent findings by the groups of Demengeot, Hori, and Bluestone (101–103), namely that some thymus-derived Foxp3$^+$ T cells that lose Foxp3 expression spontaneously differentiate into pathogenic effector cells.

A third characteristic of PP GCs is that only at this site do B cells preferentially switch their isotype from IgM to IgA. Most IgA plasma cells present in the LP are generated in PP GCs. Studies of the cellular basis for IgA production in gut began with the landmark experiments of Craig & Cebra (104, 105), who showed that adoptively transferred PP cells repopulate the recipient animals (rabbits in that case) with IgA plasma cells much more efficiently than do cells isolated from peripheral lymph node. Indeed, PP GCs contain a higher proportion of actively dividing IgA$^+$ B cells than do GCs from peripheral lymph nodes or spleen that are induced after immunization (106).

IgA Switching in Peyer's Patch Germinal Centers

The skewed CSR to IgA is thought to be the result of metabolic products and cytokines generated by activated epithelial cells (ECs), DCs, B cells, and T cells that make the PP GCs a unique milieu (reviewed in References 107, 108) (**Figure 3**). TGF-β1 is the essential cytokine that directs IgA switching because mice rendered deficient for TGF-βRII have extremely few IgA$^+$ B cells in PPs (109, 110). Many cells in PPs (i.e., Foxp3$^+$ T cells, CXCR5$^+$ T_{FH} cells, DCs, or B cells) express TGF-β1 transcripts. Interestingly, independently of bacterial stimulation, in vitro cultured DCs and FDCs isolated from PPs but not from peripheral lymph nodes secrete large amounts of TGF-β1 (111; K. Suzuki & S. Fagarasan, manuscript in preparation). However, this cytokine is embedded in a large latent complex that makes TGF-β1 inactive. Therefore, to function TGF-β1 requires further activation (which involves the liberation of TGF-β1 from the large latent complex), and several molecules, such as matrix metalloproteinase (MMP)9 and MMP13, integrins (αvβ8), or thrombospondin-1, are involved in this process (reviewed in Reference 112). Nevertheless, the cell types and the mechanism through which they generate active TGF-β1 in PP GCs are still unclear.

To generate antigen-specific IgA$^+$ B cells in PPs, TGF-β1 cooperates with CD40 ligand (CD40L), a TNF family member expressed by T_{FH} cells in GCs. The recent findings that Foxp3$^+$ T cells differentiate into T_{FH} cells almost exclusively in PPs raise the possibility that T_{FH} cells derived from Foxp3$^+$ T cells may be superior to other T_{FH} cells for helping IgA switching. How exactly Foxp3$^+$-derived T_{FH} cells help IgA generation in PPs is not known. Interestingly, T_{FH} cells secrete IL-21, and, in humans, IL-21 in synergy with TGF-β1 enhances the proliferation and differentiation of IgA plasma cell precursors (113). These processes appear to be negatively regulated by IL-4, a cytokine produced by CD4$^+$ T cells

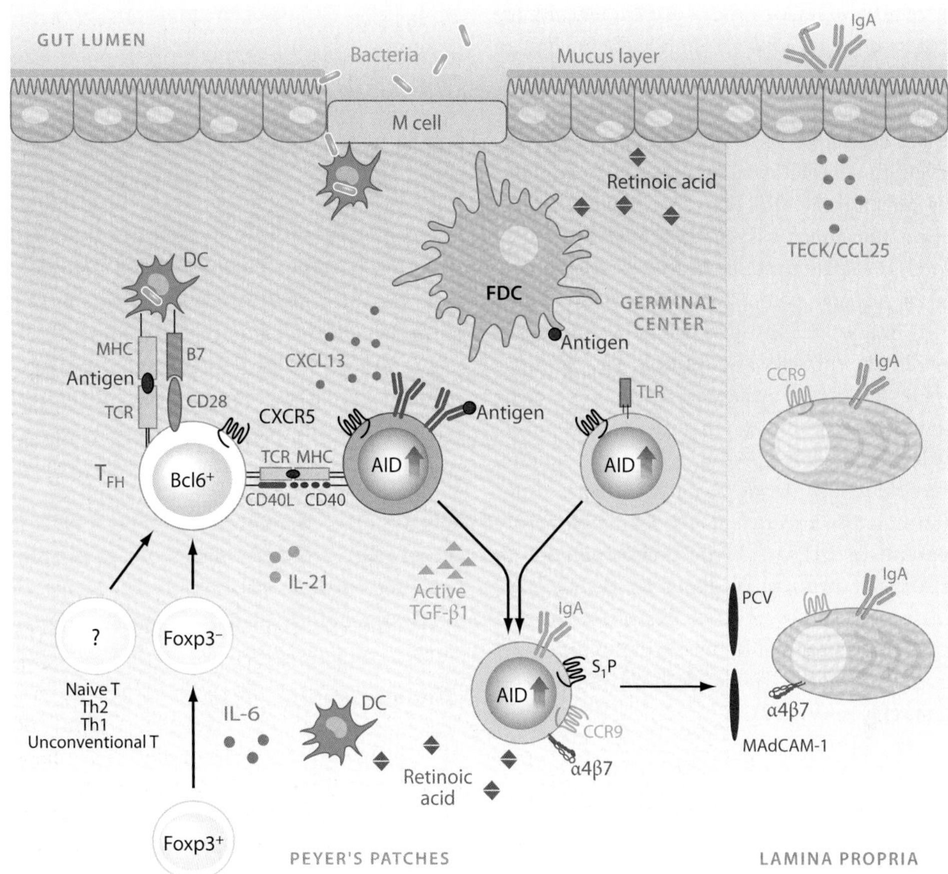

Figure 3

T cell–dependent induction of IgA^+ B cells in the germinal center of Peyer's patches. Dendritic cells (DCs) located beneath specialized M cells take up bacteria and then migrate to the T cell zone, where they activate T cells. Upon induction of the transcription factor Bcl-6, activated $CD4^+$ T cells express CXCR5 and migrate toward CXCL13 into the FDC network, where they provide help for activated B cells (T_{FH} cells). Some T_{FH} cells are derived from $Foxp3^+$ T cell precursors that lose Foxp3 expression in the presence of IL-6 (produced by DCs) and IL-21 (produced by T cells). Conventional B-T interactions through MHC-TCR and CD40-CD40L are critical for the activation of B cells, induction of AID, and CSR/SHM in GCs of PPs. The preferential generation of IgA^+ B cells in PPs is caused by the abundant production of activated TGF-β1, IL-21, and retinoic acid (RA) in this environment. Alternatively, B cells can be activated in the absence of cognate B-T interactions through TLRs and coreceptors (such as CD40). The migration of IgA^+ B cells out of the GCs of PPs involves downregulation of CXCR5 and upregulation of the S1P receptor, whereas their relocalization into the gut LP requires the expression of integrin α4β7 and CCR9, receptors for MAdCAM-1 [expressed by postcapillary venules (PCV)], and TECK/CCL25 (produced by epithelial cells), respectively.

(including some T_{FH} cells) under the influence of local DCs (114). Accumulating evidence indicates that DCs, conditioned by ECs, critically contribute to IgA synthesis in PPs. The unique function of DCs in PPs might be related to their location in the subepithelial dome, where they directly access luminal bacteria, some of them coated by secretory IgA (115, 116). Indeed, the epithelium that covers PPs contains M cells, special cells that are considered to be the major site of antigen entry into the mucosa (117). PP DCs activated by bacteria (especially gram-negative commensals such as *Escherichia coli*) and by ECs through thymic stromal lymphopoietin (TSLP) and retinoic acid, produce TGF-β1 and IL-6 that facilitate CSR and the generation of IgA plasmablasts, respectively (118, 119). After upregulation of gut-homing receptors such as CCR9, the integrin α4β7 (retinoic acid effect), and type 1-sphingosine 1-phosphate (S1P), and after downregulation of CXCR5 expression mediated by IL-21, IgA^+ plasmablasts migrate from PPs to the gut LP, where they further differentiate into IgA plasma cells that secrete IgAs with SHM in their V_H gene (113, 119–122).

T CELL–INDEPENDENT GENERATION OF IgA IN ISOLATED LYMPHOID FOLLICLES

Cryptopatches and Isolated Lymphoid Follicle Formation

CPs were first described as clusters of Lin^-c-kit^+ IL-$7R^+$ Thy1.1^+ lymphoid-like cells and DCs located between intestinal crypts (123). Therefore, their name was derived from their location. More recently, most of these Lin^-c-kit^+ IL-$7R^+$ cells were found to express RORγt and, thus, to resemble embryonic LTi cells (51) (**Figure 4*a***).

CPs have been detected in many strains of mice, including germ-free mice, RAG-deficient mice, athymic nude mice, and severe combined immunodeficiency mice. However, CPs are absent in common γ $chain^{-/-}$ mice and in $LT\alpha^{-/-}$, $LT\beta^{-/-}$, $LT\beta R^{-/-}$, and $Id2^{-/-}$ mice. In $ROR\gamma t^{-/-}$ mice, CPs are absent or very few in number and, as such, are difficult to detect (124, 125). The exact function of CPs is still unknown. Ishikawa and colleagues (126, 127) proposed that CPs are the sites for extrathymic differentiation of intraepithelial T cells (reviewed in Reference 128). Indeed, the transfer of Lin^-c-kit^+ IL-$7R^+$ cells from athymic mice into immunodeficient mice reconstituted the type b intraepithelial compartment (T cells that express either CD8 αα and/or TCR γδ). In contrast, Littman and collaborators (124, 129) proposed that CPs are dynamic structures in which $ROR\gamma t^+$ cells respond to local inflammation by providing sites for T cell maturation into effector cells (i.e., Th17 cells). In addition, CPs are proposed to serve as cradle or anlagen for the formation of isolated lymphoid follicles (ILFs) (reviewed in References 130, 131) (**Figure 4*a***). The development of CPs and subsequent formation of ILFs is blocked by the administration of LTβR-Ig fusion protein during the first two weeks after birth, demonstrating the relationship between the development of CPs and ILFs (132). Along this line, Förster and colleagues (133, 134) proposed the notion of solitary intestinal lymphoid tissue, to include all gut-isolated structures, from tiny lymphoid aggregates almost void of mature lymphocytes (CPs) to large structures dominated by B cells (mature ILFs). In contrast to mice, CPs are not found in humans, probably because they already converted into ILFs. Indeed, ILFs and lymphocyte-filled villi have been described in human small intestine (135).

What are ILFs and how do they develop from the CPs? ILFs are composed of a single cluster of B cells, built on SCs, surrounded by many DCs and a few T cells interspersed between B cells (69, 136). The ILF formation depends on the presence of CPs and $ROR\gamma t^+$ LTi cells and on their interaction with SCs through the LTα1β2-LTβR axis (132, 137–139). Thus, $Id2^{-/-}$, $ROR\gamma t^{-/-}$, $LT\alpha^{-/-}$, $LT\beta^{-/-}$, $LT\beta R^{-/-}$, and *aly/aly* mice [which have impaired signaling through LTβR because of a point mutation in NIK (140)] as well as

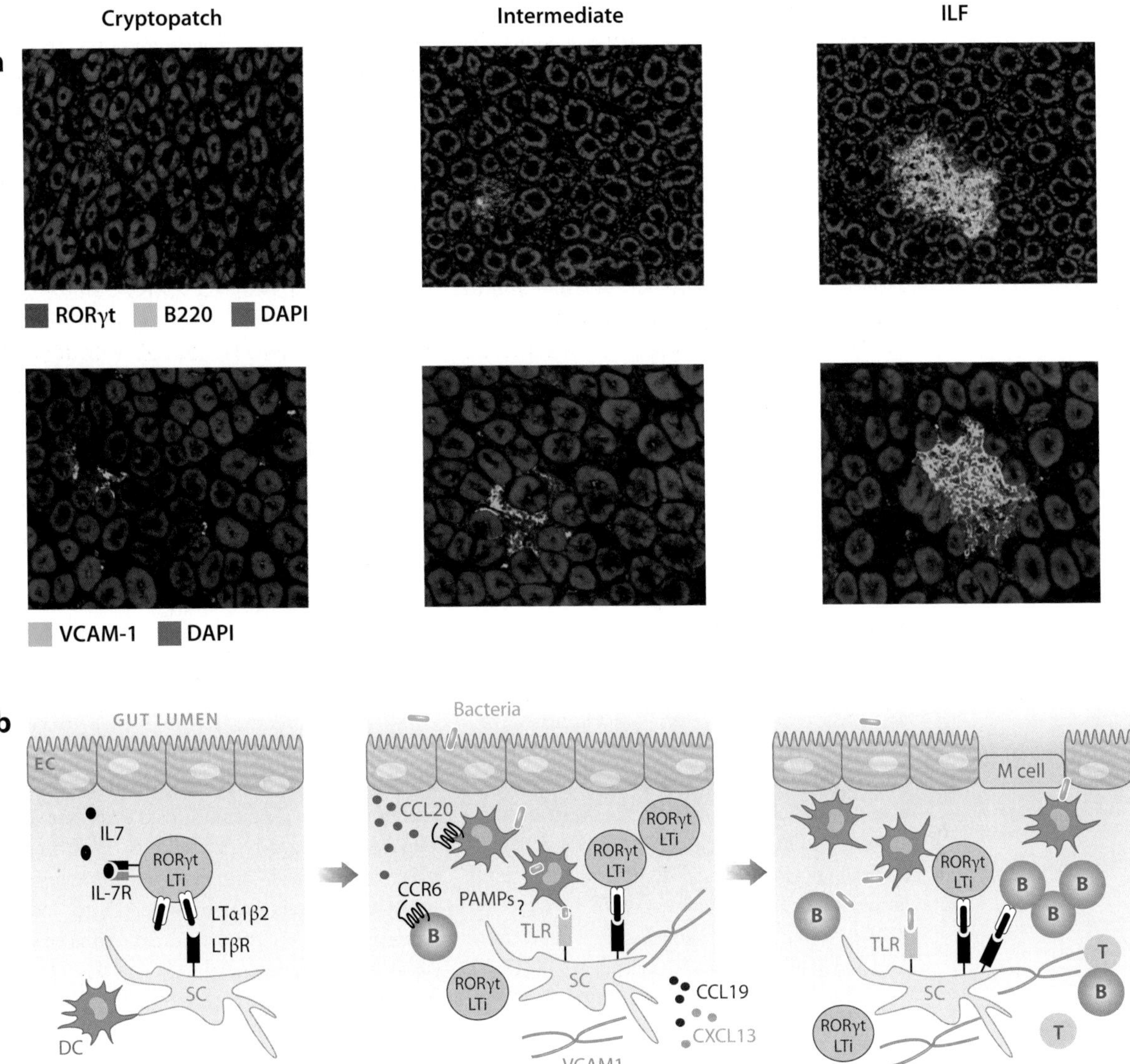

Figure 4

Cryptopatches (CPs) and the formation of isolated lymphoid follicles (ILFs). (*a*) Horizontal sections of the small intestine (cut at the crypt level) from a RORγt$^{-/-}$ mouse at five weeks after reconstitution with RORγt^{+} LTi cells. Upper panels were stained for RORγt (*red*) and B220 (*green*); lower panels were stained for VCAM-1 (*green*). Blue represents nuclear DNA (DAPI) staining. The following structures are shown: small CP with few RORγt^{+} LTi cells (*left panels*), intermediate structure with few B cells (*middle panels*), and typical ILF (*right panels*). Original magnification: ×10. (*b*) Model of CP development into ILFs. CPs are small lymphoid aggregates consisting mainly of RORγt^{+} LTi, DCs, and a few SCs. ILFs are larger aggregates consisting mainly of B cells, surrounded by RORγt^{+} LTi cells, DCs, and a few scattered T cells, all supported by a network of SCs. RORγt^{+} LTi cells and their interactions with SCs through LT-LTβR are required for the formation of CPs. The development of CPs into ILFs requires bacteria, RORγt^{+} LTi cells, and the activation of ECs through innate receptors (TLR, NOD) and of SCs through LTβR and TLRs. CPs receive signals from gut bacteria, most likely through DCs. Concomitant signals from RORγt^{+} LTi cells through LTβR (and possibly other TNF family receptors) and bacteria through TLRs augment the activation of SCs, leading to the expression of adhesion molecules (i.e., VCAM-1, ICAM-1, MadCAM-1) and chemokines (i.e., CCL19, CCL20, CXCL13); the recruitment of B cells, DCs, and T cells; and the organization of ILF.

TNFRI-deficient mice do not develop ILFs (51, 136, 141). The TNF-α/LTα-TNFRI axis may also be involved in the maturation of ILFs by enhancing the recruitment of $CCR6^+$ B cells (142). The interaction between integrin α4β7 and mucosal addressin cell adhesion molecule-1 (MadCAM-1), although nonessential for CP formation, plays a critical role in the recruitment of $ROR\gamma t^+$ LTi cells and other lymphocytes to CPs, and thus in transition of CPs into ILF (143). The development of ILFs is apparently delayed in CXCR5-deficient mice because of the impaired recruitment and/or retention of B cells (144).

In addition to these signals, ILF formation requires stimulation by commensal bacteria (69, 132). Although germ-free mice lack ILFs, they develop CPs (136). Furthermore, the size and cellular composition of ILFs depend on the bacterial load in the intestine (69, 134, 145). For example, hyperplasia of ILFs correlates with the expansion of gram-positive anaerobic bacteria in the small intestine of AID-deficient mice, which lack hypermutated IgA (discussed below). Thus, in sharp contrast to the formation of PPs, $ROR\gamma t^+$ LTi–SC interactions are not sufficient for eliciting robust recruitment of lymphocytes to the gut, which drive the development of CPs into ILFs. This could be explained in part by the lower expression of LTα1β2 by $ROR\gamma t^+$ LTi cells present in adult mice compared with embryonic LTi cells (141, 146).

If ILF formation requires bacteria, $ROR\gamma t^+$ LTi cells, and LTβR-expressing SCs, then how do bacteria influence these cellular interactions? What is the role of bacteria in the activation of immune cells and SCs? Is there any relationship between the activation of ECs and the formation of ILFs?

The coculture of gut $LT\beta R^+$ SCs with $ROR\gamma t^+$ LTi cells induces the expression of gut adhesion molecules and lymphoid chemokines by the SCs (141). This activation of SCs is clearly augmented by bacterial products [such as lipopolysaccharide (LPS)] signaling through TLRs. Consistent with an essential role of LTβR-dependent signaling for the activation of SCs for ILF formation, the expression of MadCAM-1, vascular cell adhesion molecule-1 (VCAM-1), and chemoattractants CCL19 and CXCL13 is extremely reduced or absent in CP SCs of *aly/aly* mice, and, as already mentioned, these mice do not develop ILFs (141, 147).

Besides TLRs, other innate receptors, such as nucleotide-binding oligomerization domain containing 1 (NOD1), are apparently involved in the initial steps of CPs evolving into ILFs (145). Thus, the sensing of peptidoglycan derived from commensal bacteria through NOD1 induces the expression of β-defensin 3 and CCL20 by ECs (especially those from the lower segment of the small intestine). It was proposed that both of these epithelial factors (that activate $CCR6^+$ cells) might be involved in the initial steps of ILF development and that bacterial signals through TLRs are required to sustain the formation of ILFs. However, $ROR\gamma t^+$ LTi cells (i.e., through their secretion of IL-22) may also feed back to the epithelium and enhance the production of lymphoid chemokines (148–150). Moreover, CP DCs likely have an essential role for CP development into ILFs, and $ROR\gamma t^+$ LTi cells are surrounded with a rich ring of DCs in CPs (141) (see also **Figure 5**). These DCs might be sensing signals from alarmed ECs or may be directly sampling the bacteria that reach deep into intestinal crypts. All these possibilities remain to be explored in future studies.

Figure 4*b* schematically represents a model for the development of CPs and ILFs. Thus, bacterial signals that emanate from the lumen are transmitted to immune cells by gut ECs. In addition, simultaneous and direct signals from bacteria and $ROR\gamma t^+$ LTi cells induce the activation of SCs, which causes the high recruitment of DCs and B cells to CPs for ILF formation.

IgA Generation in ILFs

Given that mice that lack or have poorly developed PPs contain an almost normal number of IgA plasma cells in their gut LP, IgA^+ B cells may be generated in lymphoid tissues other

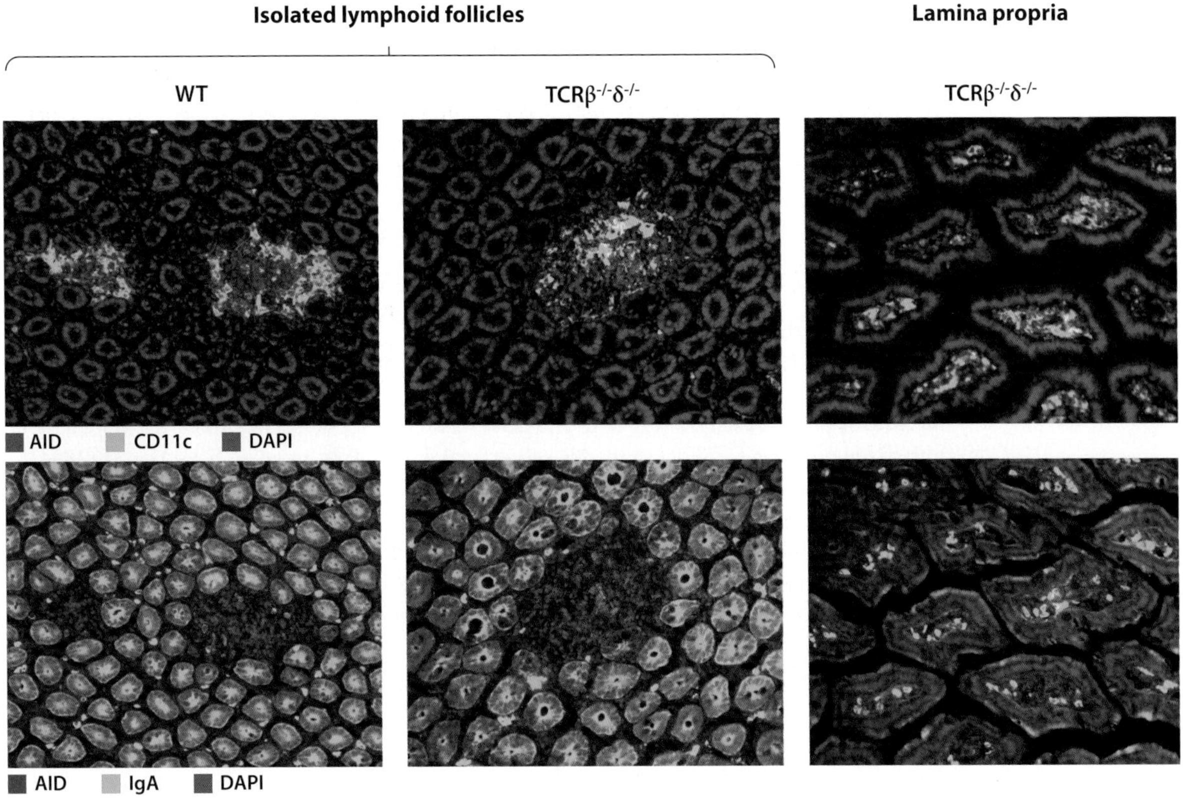

Figure 5

Expression of activation-induced cytidine deaminase (AID) and generation of IgA^+ B cells and plasma cells in isolated lymphoid follicles and lamina propria. Consecutive horizontal sections of ILFs and intestinal villi from the small intestine of mice indicated, stained for AID (*red*) and CD11c (*green*) (*upper panels*) and AID (*red*) and IgA (*green*) (*lower panels*). Blue represents nuclear DNA (DAPI) staining. Original magnification: x20. Note that activated AID-expressing B cells in ILF and LP associate with $CD11c^+$ DCs and also that some AID^+ B cells in intestinal villi are located immediately beneath the epithelium.

than PPs. The notion that ILFs constitute alternative sites to PPs for the induction of mucosal IgA responses was put forward by studies on the progeny of mice treated during gestation with LTβR-Ig fusion protein, which blocks the development of PPs (151). However, the contribution of newly formed ILFs to the generation of IgA in the absence of PPs was only recently demonstrated by studies in $ROR\gamma t^{-/-}$ mice (141). In $ROR\gamma t^{-/-}$ mice (that lack GALT), the frequency of IgA plasma cells increased considerably upon reconstitution with $ROR\gamma t^+$ LTi cells, which induced the formation of CPs and ILFs. Many B cells in newly induced ILFs express AID, as well as surface and/or cytoplasmic IgA, thus providing direct evidence for class switching of B cells to IgA-producing cells in situ in ILFs (**Figure 5**). Interestingly, B cell activation and generation of IgAs within ILFs do not require T cells or the formation of GCs. Most ILFs in specific-pathogen-free mice are B cell aggregates lacking GCs, yet some of the B cells in these GC-free ILFs express AID and IgA (S. Fagarasan & S. Kawamoto, unpublished data). However, when present, T cells contribute to the induction of GCs in ILFs. It remains to be resolved if ILF GCs share characteristics with PP GCs and whether T_{FH} cells or other T cells contribute to GC induction in ILFs.

How are B cells activated in ILFs and what factors direct their switching from IgM to IgA even in the absence of T cells or GCs? Similar to PPs, the epithelium that covers mature ILFs contains M cells, capable of pathogen uptake (i.e., *Salmonella typhimurium*) (136, 152, 153). It is not clear, however, whether all ILFs have a specialized epithelium containing M cells, or whether the M cells are restricted only to mature ILFs that contain larger numbers of B cells. Furthermore, many DCs in mature ILFs are located in a region similar to the subepithelial dome of PPs (69). Interestingly, many subepithelial dome DCs express the fractalkine-receptor CX_3CR1, and this subset of DCs can directly sample bacteria from the intestinal lumen (130, 154). Thus, ILF DCs alone might be sufficient for the activation of B cells. The factors facilitating preferential class switching of ILF B cells to IgA^+ B cells may be derived from DCs, macrophages, and local SCs. Indeed, unlike other DCs from the spleen, peripheral lymph node, or PPs, DCs as well as macrophages isolated from the LP and ILFs express abundant TNF-α following activation with bacteria, and TNF-α/iNOS-producing DCs are required for IgA production in gut (141, 155). TNF-α is one of the strongest physiological inducers of MMPs, and gut but not spleen macrophage-DCs express high levels of MMP9 and MMP13 and can activate TGF-β1 (141, 156). Furthermore, gut macrophage-DCs as well as gut SCs secrete two additional factors, B cell activating factor of the tumor-necrosis factor family (BAFF) and a proliferation-inducing ligand (APRIL), that enhance CSR to IgA, independent of T cell help (141, 155, 157–159).

Figure 6 depicts a proposed model for the possible T-independent IgA generation in ILFs. Thus, ILF B cells that are activated either after antigen presentation by TNF-α-expressing macrophage-DCs or directly by microbial components (LPS, peptidoglycan) undergo preferential class switching to IgA in the absence of T cells, under the influence of TGF-β1, BAFF, and APRIL. The IgA^+ B cells or IgA plasmablasts generated within ILFs undergo differentiation to IgA plasma cells in the LP, with the help of IL-6, IL-10, BAFF, and APRIL secreted by SCs or DCs located at the LP.

T CELL–INDEPENDENT GENERATION OF IgA IN LAMINA PROPRIA

Evidence for In Situ CSR in Lamina Propria

In the absence of PPs or ILFs, IgA can be generated directly in the LP. This is demonstrated by the presence of IgA plasma cells in mutant mice that lack PPs and CP/ILFs (i.e., RORγt$^{-/-}$ or Id2$^{-/-}$ mice) (141, 160). Notably, the frequency of IgA plasma cells in GALT-deficient mice varies depending on the age, mouse strain, and bacterial load in the gut. Id2$^{-/-}$ mice have normal if not more gut IgAs than do wild-type mice, whereas only very few IgA plasma cells can be detected in the LP of Id2$^{-/-}$MyD88$^{-/-}$ mice (160). Thus, the recognition of bacteria through the TLR-MyD88 pathway is essential for IgA generation in the absence of follicular structures.

That B cells undergo CSR in the LP was first suggested following the detection of several molecular markers, such as Cα germline, AID, and α circle transcripts (**Figure 1**) in B cells isolated from the gut after the removal of PPs (161, 162). Other studies, however, failed to detect these markers in the LP (163, 164). These inconsistent results suggest that the efficiency of CSR to IgA^+ cells in the LP might be low and subject to environmental factors. Indeed, in a clean facility it took five months for RORγt$^{-/-}$ mice to reach IgA levels equivalent to those of two-month-old wild-type mice (141), and therefore the interpretation of results may depend on experimental conditions and procedures (i.e., whether sorting of B cells was performed or not). The detection of αCTs seems to be the most problematic, and indeed reliable PCR products of these short-lived transcripts can be obtained only when at minimum 500 cells have completed CSR (162). However, the expression of AID by LP B cells was

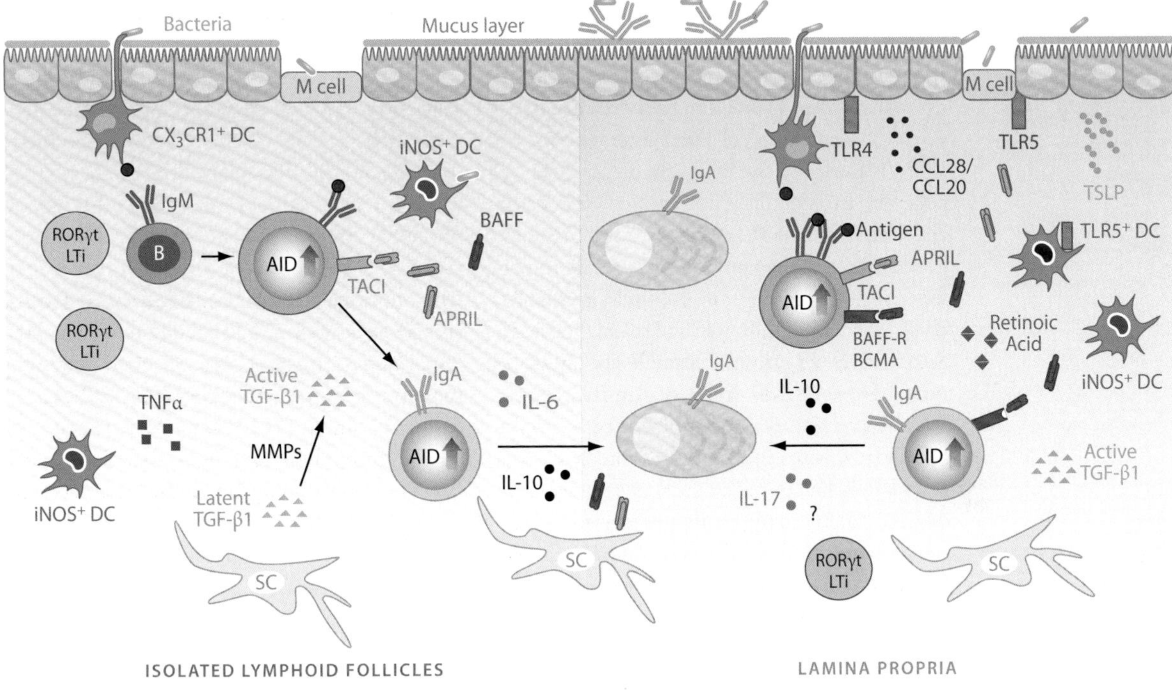

Figure 6

T cell–independent generation of IgAs in isolated lymphoid follicles (ILFs) and lamina propria. (*a*) Unlike in Peyer's patches, the generation of IgA$^+$ cells in ILFs does not require T cells or the formation of GCs. Dendritic cells (DCs), possibly CX$_3$CR1$^+$ DCs, located beneath specialized M cells, take up luminal bacteria and activate ILF B cells as well as local SCs. TNF-α—abundantly produced by activated DCs and also by RORγt$^+$ LTi cells—induces the expression of matrix metalloproteinases (i.e., MMP9 and MMP13 by DCs and MMP2 by SCs). MMPs mediate the conversion of TGF-β1 from inactive to active form. Together with BAFF and APRIL, possibly produced by ILF iNOS$^+$ DCs and SCs, active TGF-β1 facilitates the preferential switching of TLR-activated B cells from IgM to IgA. (*b*) IgM$^+$ B cells (naive B2 or peritoneal B1 cells) attracted to the gut LP by chemokines (i.e., CCL28, CCL20) produced by TLR-stimulated ECs are activated by polyclonal stimuli or by antigens presented by LP DCs, likely CX$_3$CR1$^+$ DCs. Activated DCs, including iNOS$^+$ DCs and TLR5$^+$ DCs, release factors such as TGF-β1, retinoic acid (RA), BAFF, and APRIL (the latter also produced by ECs, upon bacteria/TSLP stimulation). In addition to LP DCs, LP SCs produce and activate TGF-β1, as well as BAFF, APRIL, IL-6, and IL-10. In the presence of all these factors, activated B cells that express AID undergo preferential switching from IgM to IgA. Cytokines such as BAFF, IL-17 (produced not only by Th17 but also by RORγt$^+$ LTi cells in LP), IL-6, and IL-10 facilitate the survival, proliferation, and differentiation of IgA$^+$ B cells into plasma cells.

recently convincingly demonstrated by in situ AID-staining methods or using AID-GFP reporter mice (141, 159, 165). Interestingly, in mice, most AID-expressing cells in the LP are detected directly beneath the epithelium and interact with CD11c$^+$ cells (141) (**Figure 5**), which are most likely DCs expressing CX$_3$CR1 (discussed below). Footprints indicating recent IgA class-switching (αCT) as well as AID were also detected in LP B cells from transgenic mice that express a constitutively active form of TLR4 in the intestinal epithelium (V-TLR4 mice) and in human intestinal LP B cells (166).

Lamina Propria B Cells

What B cells are present in the LP outside follicular structures and how do they reach the LP? Most B cells located in the intestinal villi of the small intestine are reported to be $B220^+IgM^+IgD^+$ conventional B2 cells derived from bone marrow (167, 168). Some B cells located closer to the epithelium have an IgM^-IgD^+ phenotype and also contain intracytoplasmic IgA (168). These B cells are likely the AID-expressing cells that interact with LP DCs (**Figure 5**). Interestingly, $B220^+IgM^+$ B cells are present (and sometimes even more abundant) in the LP of germ-free mice or mice genetically deficient in TLR signaling, implying that the presence of B2 cells in the LP does not require gut microbial sensing (168; K. Suzuki & S. Fagarasan, unpublished observations). However, the frequency of $B220^+IgA^+$ B cells and $B220^-IgA^+$ plasma cells in the LP and the intestinal IgA levels in germ-free or TLR-deficient mice are considerably reduced (155, 160, 169). Together, these observations suggest that the apparent increase in the $B220^+IgM^+IgD^+$ population is not necessarily due to an enhanced recruitment of B2 cells to the LP, but rather is caused by a reduced differentiation of IgM^+ B cells into IgA-producing cells. In fact, TLR signaling in intestinal ECs promotes the recruitment of IgM^+ B cells to the LP and enhances their switching to IgA^+ B cells (107, 159, 166).

A unique B cell population is also detected in the LP of the large intestine (170). Interestingly, colonic LP B cells have low frequency SHM, thus attesting to the ongoing or past expression of AID.

The presence of naive bone marrow–derived B2 cells in the LP strictly depends on LTα expression and activation of NF-κB in gut SCs upon stimulation through LTβR and NIK (167, 171). Indeed, $LT\alpha^{-/-}$, $LT\beta R^{-/-}$, and *aly/aly* mice completely lack B cells in the LP, and as a consequence they have no IgA plasma cells in the gut. Reconstitution of *aly/aly* mice with normal bone marrow cells fails to restore the number of B cells and IgA plasma cells in the gut, unless coinjected with wild-type, NIK-sufficient LP SCs (167). $ROR\gamma t^+$ LTi cells could provide LTα and might initiate LT-LTβR interactions required for direct recruitment of naive B2 cells to the LP in adult intestines. Thus, it remains to be elucidated whether $ROR\gamma t^+$ LTi–SC interactions in the LP are involved in the recruitment of B cells to the LP and formation of lymphocyte-filled villi.

Other than naive B2 cells, LP may also contain some IgM^+ B cells that previously traveled through PPs or ILFs. However, unlike naive IgM^+ B cells, migration of these gut-experienced B cells appears to be independent of NIK-sufficient LP SCs (167). This supposition is supported by the observation that naive bone marrow–derived $B220^+IgM^+$ B cells that experienced a normal gut environment (after short-term parabiosis of bone marrow–reconstituted *aly/aly* mice with RAG-$2^{-/-}$ mice) could migrate to the LP of *aly/aly* mice.

Another subset of B cells that under certain conditions contributes to the generation of intestinal IgA plasma cells is peritoneal B1 cells (169, 172). Peritoneal B1 cells have a $IgM^{hi}IgD^{low}B220^{low}Mac1^{int}$ surface phenotype. Some B1 cells express CD5 on their surface and, based also on their ontogeny, are regarded as a distinct subset of B1 cells, called B1a cells (the rest of the B1 cells constituting the B1b subset) (173, 174). In addition, peritoneal B1 cells express high levels of $\alpha4$, $\alpha6$, and $\beta1$ integrins and CD9, a tetraspanin that associates with other surface molecules, such as integrin $\beta1$ or $\alpha6$, and regulates cell motility (175, 176). These phenotypic properties are likely acquired by B1 cells in the peritoneal environment (177). Intestinal lesions induced by acute gut inflammation (or direct stimulation of peritoneal B1 cells by TLR ligands such as LPS or peptidoglycan) induce the notable egress of B1 cells from the peritoneum, through the omentum and their relocalization to effector tissues, i.e., gut LP (175). The molecular mechanism contributing to TLR-induced mobilization of B1 cells from the peritoneal cavity involves a coordinated downregulation of integrins and tetraspanin CD9 and activation of G protein–coupled receptors (175, 178). Thus, unlike the B1 cell–derived natural IgMs, which are produced even in germ-free mice, the production of intestinal IgA requires the presence of commensal bacteria. Moreover, unlike the

IgA responses that are generated in the GC of PPs, which require T cell help, IgA production by B1 cells seems to be T cell–independent (169). This was shown in lethally irradiated T cell–deficient mice, reconstituted with allotype-marked B1 cells together with host-derived bone marrow cells; most IgA plasma cells were derived from peritoneal B1 cells.

Although the relative contribution and the repertoire specificity of B1 and B2 cell–derived IgA are not known, the IgA production by peritoneal B1 cells may be crucial for preventing or reducing the systemic dissemination of gut bacteria.

Lamina Propria T Cells

The small intestine LP contains several distinct $CD4^+$ T cell subsets, including $Foxp3^+$ T cell and $ROR\gamma t^+$ Th17 T cell populations, which are the most abundant (129, 179–183). Generation and maintenance of $Foxp3^+$ T cells in LP require antigens, not necessarily derived from the gut microbiota, and the presence of TGF-β1 and vitamin A (179–181, 184, 185). In fact, DNA from commensal bacteria apparently limits the generation of $Foxp3^+CD4^+$ T cells in the gut (186). By contrast, specific commensal bacteria and TGF-β1 are required for differentiation or migration of $ROR\gamma t^+$ Th17 cells to gut LP (187). Another T cell subset that preferentially accumulates to the gut LP is the mucosal-associated invariant T (MAIT) cells. Generation and selection or expansion of MAIT cells requires stimulation by commensal bacteria and the presence of B cells (188).

Some $CD4^+$ T cells in the gut can adapt and change their functional programs depending on alterations of the local microenvironment (reviewed in References 183, 189–191). Interestingly, at least one-quarter of $ROR\gamma t^+$ Th17 cells in the LP of the small intestine have apparently expressed Foxp3 during their ontogeny (192). However, all LP T cells are likely involved in the maintenance of intestinal homeostasis and the regulation of gut IgA responses, either directly or indirectly upon the conversion into distinct effector cells (i.e., $Foxp3^+$ T into T_{FH} cells), through the expression of costimulatory molecules and the secretion of cytokines (i.e., CD40L, IL-10, IL-17, IL-21, TGF-β1) (95, 193–195; reviewed in Reference 196). At least in lung, Th17 cells enhance the recruitment of B cells in airways and augment the secretion of IgA into the lung secretion owing to the induction of pIgR expression in the airway epithelium (197). Whether LP Th17 cells exert similar effects on IgA responses in the gut remains to be resolved.

Antigen Recognition, Activation, and CSR of Lamina Propria B Cells

How do LP B cells get activated for in situ IgA switching and how do the immune cells at this site sense bacteria? First, it seems that the epithelium covering the intestinal villi also contains M-like cells that apparently share characteristics with PP M cells but also with intestinal ECs (198). Thus, villus M-like cells are capable of binding, translocating bacteria (i.e., *Salmonella*-, *Yersinia*-, or *E. coli*–expressing invasin), and presenting bacterial antigens to LP cells (199).

Second, LP DCs, especially those expressing CX_3CR1, can project dendrites between ECs and directly sample luminal bacteria, while at the same time preserving EC integrity (154, 200, 201). This bacterial uptake pathway seems to be restricted to the lower segments of the small intestine and may not be present in all mouse strains. Third, there may also be alternative pathways for the entry of noninvasive pathogens into the LP. For example, the access of *Aspergillus* conidia into the LP depends neither on transepithelial dendrite extension by CX_3CR1^+ DCs nor on the presence of $CD11c^+$ cells in the LP (202). Thus, further studies are needed to elucidate the pathways for bacterial or fungal entry into the LP in the absence of GALT structures.

Increasing evidence indicates that T cells are not critical for the class-switching of $B220^+IgM^+$ to $B220^+IgA^+$ B cells and the generation of $B220^-IgA^+$ plasma cells in gut (107, 203) (**Figure 5**). Thus, it seems that local B cells can be activated in the absence of T cells by antigen presentation by CX_3CR1^+ LP DCs, by other macrophage-DCs, or by polyclonal stimulation by microorganisms. Activated AID-expressing B cells are likely switching and differentiating into IgA plasma cells under the influence of factors secreted by ECs, DCs, and LP SCs (**Figure 5**). Gut ECs sensing bacteria not only promote the recruitment of B cells to the LP (i.e., through increased production of CCL20 and CCL28), but also help switching to IgA, through secreting cytokines, i.e., APRIL (141, 157, 159, 166, 204, 205). Furthermore, TLR-activated ECs also secrete TSLP (206, 207), which enhances the production of APRIL and IL-10 from local TNFα and iNOS-producing DCs, thus augmenting CSR (155, 159, 208). The engagement of the receptor transmembrane activator and CALM interactor (TACI) may be sufficient to induce CSR from IgM to IgA of activated AID-expressing LP B cells. Consistent with this, mice that lack APRIL, TACI, or iNOS and humans that express mutant TACI molecules exhibit selective IgA deficiency (155, 209–211).

Not only APRIL, but also BAFF produced by DCs, SCs, and even B cells, especially TLR-stimulated B1 cells, appears to be an important factor for the proliferation and survival of B cells and plasma cells (141, 157, 212). Supporting this notion, the overexpression of BAFF results in B cell hyperplasia and a considerable increase in IgA plasma cells in the gut LP (213). Interestingly, a recent study revealed that BAFF in combination with IL-17 enhances the survival, proliferation, and differentiation of B cells into Ig-secreting cells (214). The effects of BAFF/IL-17 on B cells require induction of NF-κB-regulated transcription factor Twist-1, which, in turn, induces the expression of antiapoptotic proteins (i.e., Twist-2 and Bfl-1) and plasma cell–differentiating factors (i.e., Blimp-1). Thus, in a BAFF-sufficient microenvironment of LP, IL-17 produced by RORγt-expressing cells other than Th17 (i.e., $ROR\gamma t^+$ LTi cells) may also contribute to the generation of IgAs in the gut LP (148; S. Fagarasan, unpublished data).

Recent data indicate that vitamin A plays an important role in IgA synthesis in gut. Gut EC as well as $TLR5^+$ LP DCs express enzymes required for the conversion of vitamin A into its active metabolite—retinoic acid (RA)—and ECs and TLR5+LPDCs contribute to generation of IgAs in situ in the LP (119, 121, 160). However, in vitro, even when abundantly present, it seems that retinoic acid alone does not induce notable IgA class switching in TLR-activated B cells, unless TGF-β1 is present (K. Suzuki & S. Fagarasan, manuscript in preparation). In mice, most of the T cell–independent generation of IgA^+ B cells in the small intestine LP apparently requires the presence of TGF-β1. LP SCs and ECs appear to be the main source of active TGF-β1 in the gut, although the $iNOS^+$ or $CD103^+$ DC subsets may also contribute (155, 161, 180, 206). In humans and in the murine large intestine LP, T cell–independent stimuli, such as BAFF, APRIL, and TLR ligands, might be sufficient to drive CSR to IgA even in the absence of TGF-β1 (107; S. Kawamoto & S. Fagarasan, unpublished observations).

In summary, LP B cells activated either by polyclonal stimulation or after antigen presentation by CX_3CR1-expressing DCs might switch preferentially to IgA under the influence of cytokines secreted by DCs, ECs, and LP SCs, then undergo terminal differentiation into IgA^+ plasma cells (**Figure 6**). Taken together, these observations indicate that the LP might be a site where T-independent IgA responses are generated.

BIOLOGICAL RELEVANCE OF IgA FOR GUT HOMEOSTASIS

The predominance of IgA, as well as the existence of multiple pathways for its generation, suggests that IgA is a constitutive Ig isotype in the gut that represents an evolutionarily primitive form of adaptive immunity. What, then, has led to the evolution of such a system that constitutively generates large amounts of IgA in the intestine under almost any conditions? In other words, what is the physiological importance of IgA secretion in the gut?

Selective IgA deficiency is the most common humoral immunodeficiency in humans, occurring at a frequency of approximately 1 in 400 (in Western populations) to 1 in 2000 (in Japan). The high incidence of IgA deficiency implies that secretory IgA is not essential for survival and that evolution has ensured alternative protective mechanisms at the gut barrier (215). However, IgA-deficient patients as well as some patients with common variable immunodeficiency syndrome (CVID), who have low levels of IgA and IgG and marked reduction of SHM, suffer from frequent respiratory and gastrointestinal infections and develop a lympho-proliferative disorder of the small intestine known as nodular follicular hyperplasia (216).

The biological activities and physiological functions of IgA are still poorly understood. This is partly due to the heterogeneity of clinical manifestations in IgA-deficient patients and to the existence of compensatory mechanisms—such as overproduction of IgM or IgG—that make it very difficult to assess the biological role of IgA. This is also a problem in animal models that have been generated to investigate the physiological role of IgA, such as IgA-, J -chain-, or pIgR-deficient mice. Under specific-pathogen-free conditions, these mice appear to be healthy, although they have more activated B cells in their PPs (IgA$^{-/-}$ mice) (217), impaired intestinal antitoxin protection (J-chain$^{-/-}$ and pIgR$^{-/-}$ mice) (218, 219), or elevated levels of serum IgG that react with intestinal bacteria (pIgR$^{-/-}$ mice) (219).

In neonates, secretory IgAs limit the penetration of commensal bacteria through the intestinal epithelium, and this process does not require the diversification of the natural antibody repertoire (220). For example, the nonmutated nitrophenyl-specific IgAs produced in young quasimonoclonal mice are sufficient to limit penetration of the commensal *Enterobacter cloacae*. Similarly, in adult mice, the presence of secretory IgA limits the translocation of aerobic bacteria from the intestinal lumen to the mesenteric lymph node (221). Accordingly, an increased bacterial translocation to mesenteric lymph node is found in pIgR$^{-/-}$ mice (222). Furthermore, pIgR$^{-/-}$ mice lacking secretory antibodies (IgA and IgM) not only are more susceptible to infection with *Salmonella typhimurium* than are wild-type mice, but also shed more bacteria and thus serve as infection reservoirs (223). Thus, natural secretory IgAs (low-affinity antibodies to redundant surface epitopes of bacteria) protect both the individual host as well as the entire population by preventing the transmission of microbial pathogens.

There is no question about the importance of IgA-mediated protection at mucosal surfaces; however, the role of gut IgA in the regulation of bacterial microflora and how dysregulation of gut bacteria affects the immune system leading to pathological manifestations are controversial subjects.

An animal model that seems to recapitulate the pathology of CVID in humans is AID deficiency in mice. AID-deficient mice develop many protruding follicular structures all along the small intestine, indicating the hypertrophia of ILFs (69). This resembles the nodular follicular hyperplasia found in humans with CVID (203). Furthermore, AID$^{-/-}$ mice have an aberrant expansion of gram-positive anaerobes in all segments of the small intestine (69, 224). Among the expanded anaerobes (evaluated by 16S rRNA sequencing), SFB were predominant. SFB are considered the most potent inducers of IgA synthesis in the gut owing to their capacity for breaking through the mucus layer and anchoring to ECs (70, 225, 226). Interestingly, most of the IgAs induced by SFB are apparently nonspecific, polyclonal IgAs (70). A similar gram-positive anaerobic shift is observed in mice lacking ILFs (NOD1$^{-/-}$, mBD3$^{-/-}$, LTβR-Ig-treated mice) as well as in RAG-2$^{-/-}$ mice, raised under specific-pathogen-free conditions (145, 224). The anaerobic expansion in RAG-2$^{-/-}$ small intestine persists after their reconstitution with bone marrow from AID$^{-/-}$ mice but is abolished by the transfer of bone marrow from normal mice, concomitant with the normalization of IgA levels in intestinal secretions (224). Thus, somatically mutated IgAs seem to play a critical role in regulating bacterial communities in the gut.

In addition to changes of the microbial ecology in the gut, the dysregulation of intestinal antibody responses to commensal bacteria leads to an excessive activation of immune responses. Indeed, a hyperactivated phenotype with nodular lymphoid hyperplasia of the gut and enlarged GCs in all lymphoid tissues is observed in AID-deficient mice and humans as well as in patients with CVID (34, 203, 216, 227, 228). In both mice and humans, an antibiotic treatment that decreases the gut bacterial load, particularly anaerobes, results in the loss of intestinal hyperplasia and in a drastic reduction of mucosal and systemic GC cells (69, 224, 229). The same results are obtained after the reconstitution of normal IgA levels in the intestine, which leads to the normalization of gut microbiota, followed by the disappearance of lymphoid hyperplasia (224).

But how do secretory IgAs limit the inflammatory responses of immune cells? In vitro, dimeric IgA can neutralize *Shigella* LPS located inside ECs and potentially prevent further proinflammatory responses (230). Indeed, IgA colocalizes with LPS in apical recycling endosomes and inhibits the nuclear translocation of NF-κB.

A recent study by Gordon and colleagues (231) provides further clues to how secretory IgA might limit in vivo the inflammatory reactions in the gut. In their system, germ-free mice lacking B and T cells were monoassociated with *Bacteroides thetaiotaomicron* in the presence or absence of specific IgA for a capsular polysaccharide. Clearly, in the presence of specific IgAs, bacteria elicited fewer proinflammatory signals in the host. Interestingly, however, the effect is not restricted to the host. Indeed, bacteria adapted to the presence of specific IgAs by switching the expression of the target epitope to another capsular polysaccharide and by decreasing the expression of genes involved in nitric oxide metabolism. Thus, not only is IgA required to downmodulate or block bacterial-mediated inflammation, but also our adaptive immune system apparently drives the diversification of bacterial surface structures by exposing commensal bacteria to IgA.

Together, these observations establish the relevance of IgA in the gut, which is undoubtedly important for the regulation of the intestinal bacterial community, for the maintenance of an appropriate geographical distribution of bacteria in intestinal segments, and for immune homeostasis generally.

CONCLUSION AND PERSPECTIVE

Recent findings have revealed new complexities in the mechanisms and functions of IgA in the gut. However, more studies are required to understand host-bacterial relationships in the gut. We still know very little about the composition of bacterial communities in the intestine, how these communities adapt to different environmental conditions in distinct segments of the intestine, or their impact on host physiology. We are now just beginning to understand the role of specific versus nonspecific IgA in the gut.

We must acquire more data on IgA generation in organized structures (PP, ILF) as well as in nonorganized tissues (LP), by T-dependent (PP, ILF) as well as T-independent (ILF, LP) mechanisms. In particular, we need to understand more about how commensal bacteria is sensed by the immune system and about requirements for the activation of immune and nonimmune cells in the gut. The answers to these questions will help investigators develop new strategies for mucosal vaccines and novel approaches for the prevention and treatment of gut inflammatory diseases.

DISCLOSURE STATEMENT

The authors are not aware of any affiliations, memberships, funding, or financial holdings that might be perceived as affecting the objectivity of this review.

ACKNOWLEDGMENTS

We are grateful to Tasuku Honjo and Duncan Sutherland for critical reading of the manuscript. This work was supported in part by Grants-in-Aid for Scientific Research in Priority Areas (S.F.).

LITERATURE CITED

1. Ley RE, Lozupone CA, Hamady M, Knight R, Gordon JI. 2008. Worlds within worlds: evolution of the vertebrate gut microbiota. *Nat. Rev. Microbiol.* 6:776–88
2. Hooper LV, Gordon JI. 2001. Commensal host-bacterial relationships in the gut. *Science* 292:1115–18
3. Noverr MC, Huffnagle GB. 2004. Does the microbiota regulate immune responses outside the gut? *Trends Microbiol.* 12:562–68
4. Eckburg PB, Bik EM, Bernstein CN, Purdom E, Dethlefsen L, et al. 2005. Diversity of the human intestinal microbial flora. *Science* 308:1635–38
5. Mahowald MA, Rey FE, Seedorf H, Turnbaugh PJ, Fulton RS, et al. 2009. Characterizing a model human gut microbiota composed of members of its two dominant bacterial phyla. *Proc. Natl. Acad. Sci. USA* 106:5859–64
6. Backhed F, Ley RE, Sonnenburg JL, Peterson DA, Gordon JI. 2005. Host-bacterial mutualism in the human intestine. *Science* 307:1915–20
7. Stappenbeck TS, Hooper LV, Gordon JI. 2002. Developmental regulation of intestinal angiogenesis by indigenous microbes via Paneth cells. *Proc. Natl. Acad. Sci. USA* 99:15451–55
8. Rakoff-Nahoum S, Paglino J, Eslami-Varzaneh F, Edberg S, Medzhitov R. 2004. Recognition of commensal microflora by Toll-like receptors is required for intestinal homeostasis. *Cell* 118:229–41
9. Sonnenburg JL, Angenent LT, Gordon JI. 2004. Getting a grip on things: How do communities of bacterial symbionts become established in our intestine? *Nat. Immunol.* 5:569–73
10. Macpherson AJ, McCoy KD, Johansen FE, Brandtzaeg P. 2008. The immune geography of IgA induction and function. *Mucosal Immunol.* 1:11–22
11. Loker ES, Adema CM, Zhang SM, Kepler TB. 2004. Invertebrate immune systems—not homogeneous, not simple, not well understood. *Immunol. Rev.* 198:10–24
12. Flajnik MF, Du Pasquier L. 2004. Evolution of innate and adaptive immunity: Can we draw a line? *Trends Immunol.* 25:640–44
13. Rakoff-Nahoum S, Medzhitov R. 2008. Innate immune recognition of the indigenous microbial flora. *Mucosal Immunol.* 1(Suppl. 1):S10–14
14. Pancer Z, Cooper MD. 2006. The evolution of adaptive immunity. *Annu. Rev. Immunol.* 24:497–518
15. Guo P, Hirano M, Herrin BR, Li J, Yu C, et al. 2009. Dual nature of the adaptive immune system in lampreys. *Nature* 459:796–801
16. Rogozin IB, Iyer LM, Liang L, Glazko GV, Liston VG, et al. 2007. Evolution and diversification of lamprey antigen receptors: evidence for involvement of an AID-APOBEC family cytosine deaminase. *Nat. Immunol.* 8:647–56
17. Matsunaga T, Rahman A. 1998. What brought the adaptive immune system to vertebrates?—The jaw hypothesis and the seahorse. *Immunol. Rev.* 166:177–86
18. Matsunaga T, Rahman A. 2001. In search of the origin of the thymus: The thymus and GALT may be evolutionarily related. *Scand. J. Immunol.* 53:1–6
19. Peppard JV, Kaetzel CS, Russell MW. 2005. Phylogeny and comparative physiology of IgA. In *Mucosal Immunology*, ed. J Mestecky, M Lamm, J McGhee, J Bienenstock, L Mayer, W Strobel, pp. 195–210. San Diego: Academic

20. Van Der Heijden PJ, Stok W, Bianchi AT. 1987. Contribution of immunoglobulin-secreting cells in the murine small intestine to the total 'background' immunoglobulin production. *Immunology* 62:551–55
21. Van Egmond M, Damen CA, Van Spriel AB, Vidarsson G, Van Garderen E, Van De Winkel JG. 2001. IgA and the IgA Fc receptor. *Trends Immunol.* 22:205–11
22. Mostov KE. 1994. Transepithelial transport of immunoglobulins. *Annu. Rev. Immunol.* 12:63–84
23. Brandtzaeg P, Baekkevold ES, Farstad IN, Jahnsen FL, Johansen FE, et al. 1999. Regional specialization in the mucosal immune system: What happens in the microcompartments? *Immunol. Today* 20:141–51
24. Jung D, Giallourakis C, Mostoslavsky R, Alt FW. 2006. Mechanism and control of V(D)J recombination at the immunoglobulin heavy chain locus. *Annu. Rev. Immunol.* 24:541–70
25. Honjo T, Kinoshita K, Muramatsu M. 2002. Molecular mechanism of class switch recombination: linkage with somatic hypermutation. *Annu. Rev. Immunol.* 20:165–96
26. Chaudhuri J, Basu U, Zarrin A, Yan C, Franco S, et al. 2007. Evolution of the immunoglobulin heavy chain class switch recombination mechanism. *Adv. Immunol.* 94:157–214
27. Muramatsu M, Nagaoka H, Shinkura R, Begum NA, Honjo T. 2007. Discovery of activation-induced cytidine deaminase, the engraver of antibody memory. *Adv. Immunol.* 94:1–36
28. Honjo T, Kataoka T. 1978. Organization of immunoglobulin heavy chain genes and allelic deletion model. *Proc. Natl. Acad. Sci. USA* 75:2140–44
29. Chen K, Xu W, Wilson M, He B, Miller NW, et al. 2009. Immunoglobulin D enhances immune surveillance by activating antimicrobial, proinflammatory and B cell-stimulating programs in basophils. *Nat. Immunol.* 10:889–98
30. Vladutiu AO. 2000. Immunoglobulin D: properties, measurement, and clinical relevance. *Clin. Diagn. Lab. Immunol.* 7:131–40
31. Nikaido T, Nakai S, Honjo T. 1981. Switch region of immunoglobulin Cmu gene is composed of simple tandem repetitive sequences. *Nature* 292:845–48
32. Strobel W, Fagarasan S, Lycke N. 2005. IgA B cell development. In *Mucosal Immunology*, ed. J Mestecky, M Lamm, J McGhee, J Bienenstock, L Mayer, W Strobel, pp. 583–616. San Diego: Academic
33. Goodman MF, Scharff MD, Romesberg FE. 2007. AID-initiated purposeful mutations in immunoglobulin genes. *Adv. Immunol.* 94:127–55
34. Muramatsu M, Kinoshita K, Fagarasan S, Yamada S, Shinkai Y, Honjo T. 2000. Class switch recombination and hypermutation require activation-induced cytidine deaminase (AID), a potential RNA editing enzyme. *Cell* 102:553–63
35. Revy P, Muto T, Levy Y, Geissmann F, Plebani A, et al. 2000. Activation-induced cytidine deaminase (AID) deficiency causes the autosomal recessive form of the Hyper-IgM syndrome (HIGM2). *Cell* 102:565–75
36. Arakawa H, Hauschild J, Buerstedde JM. 2002. Requirement of the activation-induced deaminase (AID) gene for immunoglobulin gene conversion. *Science* 295:1301–6
37. Muramatsu M, Sankaranand VS, Anant S, Sugai M, Kinoshita K, et al. 1999. Specific expression of activation-induced cytidine deaminase (AID), a novel member of the RNA-editing deaminase family in germinal center B cells. *J. Biol. Chem.* 274:18470–76
38. Honjo T. 2008. A memoir of AID, which engraves antibody memory on DNA. *Nat. Immunol.* 9:335–37
39. Conticello SG, Thomas CJ, Petersen-Mahrt SK, Neuberger MS. 2005. Evolution of the AID/APOBEC family of polynucleotide (deoxy)cytidine deaminases. *Mol. Biol. Evol.* 22:367–77
40. Cannon JP, Haire RN, Rast JP, Litman GW. 2004. The phylogenetic origins of the antigen-binding receptors and somatic diversification mechanisms. *Immunol. Rev.* 200:12–22
41. Barreto VM, Pan-Hammarstrom Q, Zhao Y, Hammarstrom L, Misulovin Z, Nussenzweig MC. 2005. AID from bony fish catalyzes class switch recombination. *J. Exp. Med.* 202:733–38
42. Wakae K, Magor BG, Saunders H, Nagaoka H, Kawamura A, et al. 2006. Evolution of class switch recombination function in fish activation-induced cytidine deaminase, AID. *Int. Immunol.* 18:41–47
43. Flajnik MF. 2002. Comparative analyses of immunoglobulin genes: surprises and portents. *Nat. Rev. Immunol.* 2:688–98
44. Mussmann R, Courtet M, Schwager J, Du Pasquier L. 1997. Microsites for immunoglobulin switch recombination breakpoints from *Xenopus* to mammals. *Eur. J. Immunol.* 27:2610–19

45. Marr S, Morales H, Bottaro A, Cooper M, Flajnik M, Robert J. 2007. Localization and differential expression of activation-induced cytidine deaminase in the amphibian *Xenopus* upon antigen stimulation and during early development. *J. Immunol.* 179:6783–89
46. Braathen R, Hohman VS, Brandtzaeg P, Johansen FE. 2007. Secretory antibody formation: conserved binding interactions between J chain and polymeric Ig receptor from humans and amphibians. *J. Immunol.* 178:1589–97
47. Nishikawa SI, Hashi H, Honda K, Fraser S, Yoshida H. 2000. Inflammation, a prototype for organogenesis of the lymphopoietic/hematopoietic system. *Curr. Opin. Immunol.* 12:342–45
48. Mebius RE. 2003. Organogenesis of lymphoid tissues. *Nat. Rev. Immunol.* 3:292–303
49. Finke D, Meier D. 2006. Molecular networks orchestrating GALT development. *Curr. Top. Microbiol. Immunol.* 308:19–57
50. Yokota Y, Mansouri A, Mori S, Sugawara S, Adachi S, et al. 1999. Development of peripheral lymphoid organs and natural killer cells depends on the helix-loop-helix inhibitor Id2. *Nature* 397:702–6
51. Eberl G, Marmon S, Sunshine MJ, Rennert PD, Choi Y, Littman DR. 2004. An essential function for the nuclear receptor RORγ(t) in the generation of fetal lymphoid tissue inducer cells. *Nat. Immunol.* 5:64–73
52. Yoshida H, Honda K, Shinkura R, Adachi S, Nishikawa S, et al. 1999. IL-7 receptor α^+ $CD3^-$ cells in the embryonic intestine induces the organizing center of Peyer's patches. *Int. Immunol.* 11:643–55
53. Mebius RE, Streeter PR, Michie S, Butcher EC, Weissman IL. 1996. A developmental switch in lymphocyte homing receptor and endothelial vascular addressin expression regulates lymphocyte homing and permits $CD4^+$ $CD3^-$ cells to colonize lymph nodes. *Proc. Natl. Acad. Sci. USA* 93:11019–24
54. Finke D, Acha-Orbea H, Mattis A, Lipp M, Kraehenbuhl J. 2002. $CD4^+CD3^-$ cells induce Peyer's patch development: role of $\alpha 4\beta 1$ integrin activation by CXCR5. *Immunity* 17:363–73
55. Yoshida H, Naito A, Inoue J, Satoh M, Santee-Cooper SM, et al. 2002. Different cytokines induce surface lymphotoxin-$\alpha\beta$ on IL-7 receptor-α cells that differentially engender lymph nodes and Peyer's patches. *Immunity* 17:823–33
56. Meier D, Bornmann C, Chappaz S, Schmutz S, Otten LA, et al. 2007. Ectopic lymphoid-organ development occurs through interleukin 7-mediated enhanced survival of lymphoid-tissue-inducer cells. *Immunity* 26:643–54
57. Dejardin E, Droin NM, Delhase M, Haas E, Cao Y, et al. 2002. The lymphotoxin-β receptor induces different patterns of gene expression via two NF-κB pathways. *Immunity* 17:525–35
58. Gommerman JL, Browning JL. 2003. Lymphotoxin/light, lymphoid microenvironments and autoimmune disease. *Nat. Rev. Immunol.* 3:642–55
59. Allen CD, Cyster JG. 2008. Follicular dendritic cell networks of primary follicles and germinal centers: phenotype and function. *Semin. Immunol.* 20:14–25
60. Allen CD, Okada T, Cyster JG. 2007. Germinal-center organization and cellular dynamics. *Immunity* 27:190–202
61. Klein U, Dalla-Favera R. 2008. Germinal centres: role in B-cell physiology and malignancy. *Nat. Rev. Immunol.* 8:22–33
62. Basso K, Sumazin P, Morozov P, Schneider C, Maute RL, et al. 2009. Identification of the human mature B cell miRNome. *Immunity* 30:744–52
63. Xiao C, Rajewsky K. 2009. MicroRNA control in the immune system: basic principles. *Cell* 136:26–36
64. Xiao C, Calado DP, Galler G, Thai TH, Patterson HC, et al. 2007. MiR-150 controls B cell differentiation by targeting the transcription factor c-Myb. *Cell* 131:146–59
65. Rodriguez A, Vigorito E, Clare S, Warren MV, Couttet P, et al. 2007. Requirement of bic/microRNA-155 for normal immune function. *Science* 316:608–11
66. Thai TH, Calado DP, Casola S, Ansel KM, Xiao C, et al. 2007. Regulation of the germinal center response by microRNA-155. *Science* 316:604–8
67. Teng G, Hakimpour P, Landgraf P, Rice A, Tuschl T, et al. 2008. MicroRNA-155 is a negative regulator of activation-induced cytidine deaminase. *Immunity* 28:621–29
68. Dorsett Y, McBride KM, Jankovic M, Gazumyan A, Thai TH, et al. 2008. MicroRNA-155 suppresses activation-induced cytidine deaminase-mediated Myc-Igh translocation. *Immunity* 28:630–38

69. Fagarasan S, Muramatsu M, Suzuki K, Nagaoka H, Hiai H, Honjo T. 2002. Critical roles of activation-induced cytidine deaminase (AID) in the homeostasis of gut flora. *Science* 298:1424–27
70. Cebra JJ. 1999. Influences of microbiota on intestinal immune system development. *Am. J. Clin. Nutr.* 69:S1046–51
71. Casola S, Otipoby KL, Alimzhanov M, Humme S, Uyttersprot N, et al. 2004. B cell receptor signal strength determines B cell fate. *Nat. Immunol.* 5:317–27
72. Casola S, Rajewsky K. 2006. B cell recruitment and selection in mouse GALT germinal centers. *Curr. Top. Microbiol. Immunol.* 308:155–71
73. Pasare C, Medzhitov R. 2005. Control of B-cell responses by Toll-like receptors. *Nature* 438:364–68
74. Gavin AL, Hoebe K, Duong B, Ota T, Martin C, et al. 2006. Adjuvant-enhanced antibody responses in the absence of Toll-like receptor signaling. *Science* 314:1936–38
75. Meyer-Bahlburg A, Khim S, Rawlings DJ. 2007. B cell intrinsic TLR signals amplify but are not required for humoral immunity. *J. Exp. Med.* 204:3095–101
76. Wen L, Pao W, Wong FS, Peng Q, Craft J, et al. 1996. Germinal center formation, immunoglobulin class switching, and autoantibody production driven by "non α/β" T cells. *J. Exp. Med.* 183:2271–82
77. Dianda L, Gulbranson-Judge A, Pao W, Hayday AC, MacLennan IC, Owen MJ. 1996. Germinal center formation in mice lacking αβ T cells. *Eur. J. Immunol.* 26:1603–7
78. Vinuesa CG, Tangye SG, Moser B, Mackay CR. 2005. Follicular B helper T cells in antibody responses and autoimmunity. *Nat. Rev. Immunol.* 5:853–65
79. Walker LS, Gulbranson-Judge A, Flynn S, Brocker T, Raykundalia C, et al. 1999. Compromised OX40 function in CD28-deficient mice is linked with failure to develop CXC chemokine receptor 5-positive CD4 cells and germinal centers. *J. Exp. Med.* 190:1115–22
80. Schaerli P, Willimann K, Lang AB, Lipp M, Loetscher P, Moser B. 2000. CXC chemokine receptor 5 expression defines follicular homing T cells with B cell helper function. *J. Exp. Med.* 192:1553–62
81. Breitfeld D, Ohl L, Kremmer E, Ellwart J, Sallusto F, et al. 2000. Follicular B helper T cells express CXC chemokine receptor 5, localize to B cell follicles, and support immunoglobulin production. *J. Exp. Med.* 192:1545–52
82. Haynes NM, Allen CD, Lesley R, Ansel KM, Killeen N, Cyster JG. 2007. Role of CXCR5 and CCR7 in follicular Th cell positioning and appearance of a programmed cell death gene-1^{high} germinal center-associated subpopulation. *J. Immunol.* 179:5099–108
83. Boles KS, Vermi W, Facchetti F, Fuchs A, Wilson TJ, et al. 2009. A novel molecular interaction for the adhesion of follicular CD4 T cells to follicular DC. *Eur. J. Immunol.* 39:695–703
84. Vinuesa CG, Cook MC, Angelucci C, Athanasopoulos V, Rui L, et al. 2005. A RING-type ubiquitin ligase family member required to repress follicular helper T cells and autoimmunity. *Nature* 435:452–58
85. Reinhardt RL, Liang HE, Locksley RM. 2009. Cytokine-secreting follicular T cells shape the antibody repertoire. *Nat. Immunol.* 10:385–93
86. Hardtke S, Ohl L, Forster R. 2005. Balanced expression of CXCR5 and CCR7 on follicular T helper cells determines their transient positioning to lymph node follicles and is essential for efficient B-cell help. *Blood* 106:1924–31
87. Nurieva RI, Chung Y, Hwang D, Yang XO, Kang HS, et al. 2008. Generation of T follicular helper cells is mediated by interleukin-21 but independent of T helper 1, 2, or 17 cell lineages. *Immunity* 29:138–49
88. Vogelzang A, McGuire HM, Yu D, Sprent J, Mackay CR, King C. 2008. A fundamental role for interleukin-21 in the generation of T follicular helper cells. *Immunity* 29:127–37
89. McCausland MM, Yusuf I, Tran H, Ono N, Yanagi Y, Crotty S. 2007. SAP regulation of follicular helper CD4 T cell development and humoral immunity is independent of SLAM and Fyn kinase. *J. Immunol.* 178:817–28
90. Qi H, Cannons JL, Klauschen F, Schwartzberg PL, Germain RN. 2008. SAP-controlled T-B cell interactions underlie germinal centre formation. *Nature* 455:764–69
91. Johnston RJ, Poholek AC, DiToro D, Yusuf I, Eto D, et al. 2009. Bcl6 and Blimp-1 are reciprocal and antagonistic regulators of T follicular helper cell differentiation. *Science* 325:1006–10
92. Nurieva RI, Chung Y, Martinez GJ, Yang XO, Tanaka S, et al. 2009. Bcl6 mediates the development of T follicular helper cells. *Science* 325:1001–5

93. Yu D, Rao S, Tsai LM, Lee SK, He Y, et al. 2009. The transcriptional repressor Bcl-6 directs T follicular helper cell lineage commitment. *Immunity* 31:457–68
94. Fazilleau N, McHeyzer-Williams LJ, Rosen H, McHeyzer-Williams MG. 2009. The function of follicular helper T cells is regulated by the strength of T cell antigen receptor binding. *Nat. Immunol.* 10:375–84
95. Tsuji M, Komatsu N, Kawamoto S, Suzuki K, Kanagawa O, et al. 2009. Preferential generation of follicular B helper T cells from Foxp3$^+$ T cells in gut Peyer's patches. *Science* 323:1488–92
96. Lim HW, Hillsamer P, Kim CH. 2004. Regulatory T cells can migrate to follicles upon T cell activation and suppress GC-Th cells and GC-Th cell-driven B cell responses. *J. Clin. Invest.* 114:1640–49
97. Lim HW, Hillsamer P, Banham AH, Kim CH. 2005. Cutting edge: direct suppression of B cells by CD4$^+$CD25$^+$ regulatory T cells. *J. Immunol.* 175:4180–83
98. King IL, Mohrs M. 2009. IL-4-producing CD4$^+$ T cells in reactive lymph nodes during helminth infection are T follicular helper cells. *J. Exp. Med.* 206:1001–7
99. Zaretsky AG, Taylor JJ, King IL, Marshall FA, Mohrs M, Pearce EJ. 2009. T follicular helper cells differentiate from Th2 cells in response to helminth antigens. *J. Exp. Med.* 206:991–99
100. Belkaid Y, Tarbell K. 2009. Regulatory T cells in the control of host-microorganism interactions. *Annu. Rev. Immunol.* 27:551–89
101. Duarte JH, Zelenay S, Bergman ML, Martins AC, Demengeot J. 2009. Natural Treg cells spontaneously differentiate into pathogenic helper cells in lymphopenic conditions. *Eur. J. Immunol.* 39:948–55
102. Komatsu N, Mariotti-Ferrandiz ME, Wang Y, Malissen B, Waldmann H, Hori S. 2009. Heterogeneity of natural Foxp3$^+$ T cells: a committed regulatory T-cell lineage and an uncommitted minor population retaining plasticity. *Proc. Natl. Acad. Sci. USA* 106:1903–8
103. Zhou X, Bailey-Bucktrout S, Jeker LT, Penaranda C, Martinez-Llordella M, et al. 2009. Instability of the transcription factor Foxp3 leads to the generation of pathogenic memory T cells in vivo. *Nat. Immunol.* 10:1000–7
104. Craig SW, Cebra JJ. 1971. Peyer's patches: an enriched source of precursors for IgA-producing immunocytes in the rabbit. *J. Exp. Med.* 134:188–200
105. Craig SW, Cebra JJ. 1975. Rabbit Peyer's patches, appendix, and popliteal lymph node B lymphocytes: a comparative analysis of their membrane immunoglobulin components and plasma cell precursor potential. *J. Immunol.* 114:492–502
106. Butcher EC, Rouse RV, Coffman RL, Nottenburg CN, Hardy RR, Weissman IL. 1982. Surface phenotype of Peyer's patch germinal center cells: implications for the role of germinal centers in B cell differentiation. *J. Immunol.* 129:2698–707
107. Cerutti A, Rescigno M. 2008. The biology of intestinal immunoglobulin A responses. *Immunity* 28:740–50
108. Suzuki K, Fagarasan S. 2008. How host-bacterial interactions lead to IgA synthesis in the gut. *Trends Immunol.* 29:523–31
109. Sonoda E, Matsumoto R, Hitoshi Y, Ishii T, Sugimoto M, et al. 1989. Transforming growth factor β induces IgA production and acts additively with interleukin 5 for IgA production. *J. Exp. Med.* 170:1415–20
110. Cazac BB, Roes J. 2000. TGF-β receptor controls B cell responsiveness and induction of IgA in vivo. *Immunity* 13:443–51
111. Fink LN, Frokiaer H. 2008. Dendritic cells from Peyer's patches and mesenteric lymph nodes differ from spleen dendritic cells in their response to commensal gut bacteria. *Scand. J. Immunol.* 68:270–79
112. Annes JP, Munger JS, Rifkin DB. 2003. Making sense of latent TGFβ activation. *J. Cell Sci.* 116:217–24
113. Dullaers M, Li D, Xue Y, Ni L, Gayet I, et al. 2009. A T cell-dependent mechanism for the induction of human mucosal homing immunoglobulin A-secreting plasmablasts. *Immunity* 30:120–29
114. Avery DT, Bryant VL, Ma CS, de Waal Malefyt R, Tangye SG. 2008. IL-21-induced isotype switching to IgG and IgA by human naive B cells is differentially regulated by IL-4. *J. Immunol.* 181:1767–79
115. Kadaoui KA, Corthesy B. 2007. Secretory IgA mediates bacterial translocation to dendritic cells in mouse Peyer's patches with restriction to mucosal compartment. *J. Immunol.* 179:7751–57
116. Rey J, Garin N, Spertini F, Corthesy B. 2004. Targeting of secretory IgA to Peyer's patch dendritic and T cells after transport by intestinal M cells. *J. Immunol.* 172:3026–33

117. Neutra MR, Mantis NJ, Kraehenbuhl JP. 2001. Collaboration of epithelial cells with organized mucosal lymphoid tissues. *Nat. Immunol.* 2:1004–9
118. Sato A, Hashiguchi M, Toda E, Iwasaki A, Hachimura S, Kaminogawa S. 2003. CD11b^{+} Peyer's patch dendritic cells secrete IL-6 and induce IgA secretion from naive B cells. *J. Immunol.* 171:3684–90
119. Mora JR, Iwata M, Eksteen B, Song SY, Junt T, et al. 2006. Generation of gut-homing IgA-secreting B cells by intestinal dendritic cells. *Science* 314:1157–60
120. Pabst O, Ohl L, Wendland M, Wurbel MA, Kremmer E, et al. 2004. Chemokine receptor CCR9 contributes to the localization of plasma cells to the small intestine. *J. Exp. Med.* 199:411–16
121. Iwata M, Hirakiyama A, Eshima Y, Kagechika H, Kato C, Song SY. 2004. Retinoic acid imprints gut-homing specificity on T cells. *Immunity* 21:527–38
122. Gohda M, Kunisawa J, Miura F, Kagiyama Y, Kurashima Y, et al. 2008. Sphingosine 1-phosphate regulates the egress of IgA plasmablasts from Peyer's patches for intestinal IgA responses. *J. Immunol.* 180:5335–43
123. Kanamori Y, Ishimaru K, Nanno M, Maki K, Ikuta K, et al. 1996. Identification of novel lymphoid tissues in murine intestinal mucosa where clusters of c-kit^{+}IL-7R^{+} Thy1^{+} lympho-hemopoietic progenitors develop. *J. Exp. Med.* 184:1449–59
124. Eberl G, Littman DR. 2004. Thymic origin of intestinal $\alpha\beta$ T cells revealed by fate mapping of RORγt^{+} cells. *Science* 305:248–51
125. Naito T, Shiohara T, Hibi T, Suematsu M, Ishikawa H. 2008. RORγt is dispensable for the development of intestinal mucosal T cells. *Mucosal Immunol.* 1:198–207
126. Saito H, Kanamori Y, Takemori T, Nariuchi H, Kubota E, et al. 1998. Generation of intestinal T cells from progenitors residing in gut cryptopatches. *Science* 280:275–78
127. Suzuki K, Oida T, Hamada H, Hitotsumatsu O, Watanabe M, et al. 2000. Gut cryptopatches: direct evidence of extrathymic anatomical sites for intestinal T lymphopoiesis. *Immunity* 13:691–702
128. Hayday A, Gibbons D. 2008. Brokering the peace: the origin of intestinal T cells. *Mucosal Immunol.* 1:172–74
129. Ivanov II, McKenzie BS, Zhou L, Tadokoro CE, Lepelley A, et al. 2006. The orphan nuclear receptor RORγt directs the differentiation program of proinflammatory IL-17^{+} T helper cells. *Cell* 126:1121–33
130. Ivanov, II, Diehl GE, Littman DR. 2006. Lymphoid tissue inducer cells in intestinal immunity. *Curr. Top. Microbiol. Immunol.* 308:59–82
131. Fagarasan S. 2006. Intestinal IgA synthesis: a primitive form of adaptive immunity that regulates microbial communities in the gut. *Curr. Top. Microbiol. Immunol.* 308:137–53
132. Newberry RD, McDonough JS, McDonald KG, Lorenz RG. 2002. Postgestational lymphotoxin/lymphotoxin β receptor interactions are essential for the presence of intestinal B lymphocytes. *J. Immunol.* 168:4988–97
133. Pabst O, Herbrand H, Worbs T, Friedrichsen M, Yan S, et al. 2005. Cryptopatches and isolated lymphoid follicles: dynamic lymphoid tissues dispensable for the generation of intraepithelial lymphocytes. *Eur. J. Immunol.* 35:98–107
134. Pabst O, Herbrand H, Friedrichsen M, Velaga S, Dorsch M, et al. 2006. Adaptation of solitary intestinal lymphoid tissue in response to microbiota and chemokine receptor CCR7 signaling. *J. Immunol.* 177:6824–32
135. Moghaddami M, Cummins A, Mayrhofer G. 1998. Lymphocyte-filled villi: comparison with other lymphoid aggregations in the mucosa of the human small intestine. *Gastroenterology* 115:1414–25
136. Hamada H, Hiroi T, Nishiyama Y, Takahashi H, Masunaga Y, et al. 2002. Identification of multiple isolated lymphoid follicles on the antimesenteric wall of the mouse small intestine. *J. Immunol.* 168:57–64
137. Lorenz RG, Chaplin DD, McDonald KG, McDonough JS, Newberry RD. 2003. Isolated lymphoid follicle formation is inducible and dependent upon lymphotoxin-sufficient B lymphocytes, lymphotoxin β receptor, and TNF receptor I function. *J. Immunol.* 170:5475–82
138. McDonald KG, McDonough JS, Newberry RD. 2005. Adaptive immune responses are dispensable for isolated lymphoid follicle formation: Antigen-naive, lymphotoxin-sufficient B lymphocytes drive the formation of mature isolated lymphoid follicles. *J. Immunol.* 174:5720–28
139. Taylor RT, Lugering A, Newell KA, Williams IR. 2004. Intestinal cryptopatch formation in mice requires lymphotoxin α and the lymphotoxin β receptor. *J. Immunol.* 173:7183–89

140. Shinkura R, Kitada K, Matsuda F, Tashiro K, Ikuta K, et al. 1999. Alymphoplasia is caused by a point mutation in the mouse gene encoding Nf-κb-inducing kinase. *Nat. Genet.* 22:74–77
141. Tsuji M, Suzuki K, Kitamura H, Maruya M, Kinoshita K, et al. 2008. Requirement for lymphoid tissue-inducer cells in isolated follicle formation and T cell-independent immunoglobulin A generation in the gut. *Immunity* 29:261–71
142. McDonald KG, McDonough JS, Wang C, Kucharzik T, Williams IR, Newberry RD. 2007. CC chemokine receptor 6 expression by B lymphocytes is essential for the development of isolated lymphoid follicles. *Am. J. Pathol.* 170:1229–40
143. Wang C, McDonough JS, McDonald KG, Huang C, Newberry RD. 2008. α4β7/MAdCAM-1 interactions play an essential role in transitioning cryptopatches into isolated lymphoid follicles and a nonessential role in cryptopatch formation. *J. Immunol.* 181:4052–61
144. Velaga S, Herbrand H, Friedrichsen M, Jiong T, Dorsch M, et al. 2009. Chemokine receptor CXCR5 supports solitary intestinal lymphoid tissue formation, B cell homing, and induction of intestinal IgA responses. *J. Immunol.* 182:2610–19
145. Bouskra D, Brezillon C, Berard M, Werts C, Varona R, et al. 2008. Lymphoid tissue genesis induced by commensals through NOD1 regulates intestinal homeostasis. *Nature* 456:507–10
146. Kim MY, Toellner KM, White A, McConnell FM, Gaspal FM, et al. 2006. Neonatal and adult $CD4^+CD3^-$ cells share similar gene expression profile, and neonatal cells up-regulate OX40 ligand in response to TL1A (TNFSF15). *J. Immunol.* 177:3074–81
147. Taylor RT, Patel SR, Lin E, Butler BR, Lake JG, et al. 2007. Lymphotoxin-independent expression of TNF-related activation-induced cytokine by stromal cells in cryptopatches, isolated lymphoid follicles, and Peyer's patches. *J. Immunol.* 178:5659–67
148. Takatori H, Kanno Y, Watford WT, Tato CM, Weiss G, et al. 2009. Lymphoid tissue inducer-like cells are an innate source of IL-17 and IL-22. *J. Exp. Med.* 206:35–41
149. Zheng Y, Valdez PA, Danilenko DM, Hu Y, Sa SM, et al. 2008. Interleukin-22 mediates early host defense against attaching and effacing bacterial pathogens. *Nat. Med.* 14:282–89
150. Vivier E, Spits H, Cupedo T. 2009. Interleukin-22-producing innate immune cells: new players in mucosal immunity and tissue repair? *Nat. Rev. Immunol.* 9:229–34
151. Yamamoto M, Rennert P, McGhee JR, Kweon MN, Yamamoto S, et al. 2000. Alternate mucosal immune system: Organized Peyer's patches are not required for IgA responses in the gastrointestinal tract. *J. Immunol.* 164:5184–91
152. Martinoli C, Chiavelli A, Rescigno M. 2007. Entry route of *Salmonella typhimurium* directs the type of induced immune response. *Immunity* 27:975–84
153. Halle S, Bumann D, Herbrand H, Willer Y, Dahne S, et al. 2007. Solitary intestinal lymphoid tissue provides a productive port of entry for *Salmonella enterica* serovar Typhimurium. *Infect. Immun.* 75:1577–85
154. Niess JH, Brand S, Gu X, Landsman L, Jung S, et al. 2005. CX3CR1-mediated dendritic cell access to the intestinal lumen and bacterial clearance. *Science* 307:254–58
155. Tezuka H, Abe Y, Iwata M, Takeuchi H, Ishikawa H, et al. 2007. Regulation of IgA production by naturally occurring TNF/iNOS-producing dendritic cells. *Nature* 448:929–33
156. Heidinger M, Kolb H, Krell HW, Jochum M, Ries C. 2006. Modulation of autocrine TNF-α-stimulated matrix metalloproteinase 9 (MMP-9) expression by mitogen-activated protein kinases in THP-1 monocytic cells. *Biol. Chem.* 387:69–78
157. Litinskiy MB, Nardelli B, Hilbert DM, He B, Schaffer A, et al. 2002. DCs induce CD40-independent immunoglobulin class switching through BLyS and APRIL. *Nat. Immunol.* 3:822–29
158. He B, Raab-Traub N, Casali P, Cerutti A. 2003. EBV-encoded latent membrane protein 1 cooperates with BAFF/BLyS and APRIL to induce T cell-independent Ig heavy chain class switching. *J. Immunol.* 171:5215–24
159. He B, Xu W, Santini PA, Polydorides AD, Chiu A, et al. 2007. Intestinal bacteria trigger T cell-independent immunoglobulin A(2) class switching by inducing epithelial-cell secretion of the cytokine APRIL. *Immunity* 26:812–26
160. Uematsu S, Fujimoto K, Jang MH, Yang BG, Jung YJ, et al. 2008. Regulation of humoral and cellular gut immunity by lamina propria dendritic cells expressing Toll-like receptor 5. *Nat. Immunol.* 9:769–76

161. Fagarasan S, Kinoshita K, Muramatsu M, Ikuta K, Honjo T. 2001. In situ class switching and differentiation to IgA-producing cells in the gut lamina propria. *Nature* 413:639–43
162. Kinoshita K, Harigai M, Fagarasan S, Muramatsu M, Honjo T. 2001. A hallmark of active class switch recombination: transcripts directed by I promoters on looped-out circular DNAs. *Proc. Natl. Acad. Sci. USA* 98:12620–23
163. Shikina T, Hiroi T, Iwatani K, Jang MH, Fukuyama S, et al. 2004. IgA class switch occurs in the organized nasopharynx- and gut-associated lymphoid tissue, but not in the diffuse lamina propria of airways and gut. *J. Immunol.* 172:6259–64
164. Bergqvist P, Gardby E, Stensson A, Bemark M, Lycke NY. 2006. Gut IgA class switch recombination in the absence of CD40 does not occur in the lamina propria and is independent of germinal centers. *J. Immunol.* 177:7772–83
165. Crouch EE, Li Z, Takizawa M, Fichtner-Feigl S, Gourzi P, et al. 2007. Regulation of AID expression in the immune response. *J. Exp. Med.* 204:1145–56
166. Shang L, Fukata M, Thirunarayanan N, Martin AP, Arnaboldi P, et al. 2008. Toll-like receptor signaling in small intestinal epithelium promotes B-cell recruitment and IgA production in lamina propria. *Gastroenterology* 135:529–38
167. Suzuki K, Meek B, Doi Y, Honjo T, Fagarasan S. 2005. Two distinctive pathways for recruitment of naive and primed IgM$^+$ B cells to the gut lamina propria. *Proc. Natl. Acad. Sci. USA* 102:2482–86
168. Velazquez P, Wei B, McPherson M, Mendoza LM, Nguyen SL, et al. 2008. Villous B cells of the small intestine are specialized for invariant NK T cell dependence. *J. Immunol.* 180:4629–38
169. Macpherson AJ, Gatto D, Sainsbury E, Harriman GR, Hengartner H, Zinkernagel RM. 2000. A primitive T cell-independent mechanism of intestinal mucosal IgA responses to commensal bacteria. *Science* 288:2222–26
170. Shimomura Y, Ogawa A, Kawada M, Sugimoto K, Mizoguchi E, et al. 2008. A unique B2 B cell subset in the intestine. *J. Exp. Med.* 205:1343–55
171. Kang HS, Chin RK, Wang Y, Yu P, Wang J, et al. 2002. Signaling via LTβR on the lamina propria stromal cells of the gut is required for IgA production. *Nat. Immunol.* 3:576–82
172. Fagarasan S, Shinkura R, Kamata T, Nogaki F, Ikuta K, et al. 2000. Alymphoplasia (aly)-type nuclear factor κB-inducing kinase (NIK) causes defects in secondary lymphoid tissue chemokine receptor signaling and homing of peritoneal cells to the gut-associated lymphatic tissue system. *J. Exp. Med.* 191:1477–86
173. Martin F, Kearney JF. 2001. B1 cells: similarities and differences with other B cell subsets. *Curr. Opin. Immunol.* 13:195–201
174. Herzenberg LA, Tung JW. 2006. B cell lineages: documented at last! *Nat. Immunol.* 7:225–26
175. Ha SA, Tsuji M, Suzuki K, Meek B, Yasuda N, Kaisho T, Fagarasan S. 2006. Regulation of B1 cell migration by signals through Toll-like receptors. *J. Exp. Med.* 203:2541–50
176. Won WJ, Kearney JF. 2002. CD9 is a unique marker for marginal zone B cells, B1 cells, and plasma cells in mice. *J. Immunol.* 168:5605–11
177. Berberich S, Forster R, Pabst O. 2007. The peritoneal micromilieu commits B cells to home to body cavities and the small intestine. *Blood* 109:4627–34
178. Kunisawa J, Kurashima Y, Gohda M, Higuchi M, Ishikawa I, et al. 2007. Sphingosine 1-phosphate regulates peritoneal B-cell trafficking for subsequent intestinal IgA production. *Blood* 109:3749–56
179. Sun CM, Hall JA, Blank RB, Bouladoux N, Oukka M, et al. 2007. Small intestine lamina propria dendritic cells promote de novo generation of Foxp3 T reg cells via retinoic acid. *J. Exp. Med.* 204:1775–85
180. Coombes JL, Siddiqui KR, Arancibia-Carcamo CV, Hall J, Sun CM, et al. 2007. A functionally specialized population of mucosal CD103$^+$ DCs induces Foxp3$^+$ regulatory T cells via a TGF-β and retinoic acid-dependent mechanism. *J. Exp. Med.* 204:1757–64
181. Benson MJ, Pino-Lagos K, Rosemblatt M, Noelle RJ. 2007. All-trans retinoic acid mediates enhanced T reg cell growth, differentiation, and gut homing in the face of high levels of co-stimulation. *J. Exp. Med.* 204:1765–74
182. Lochner M, Peduto L, Cherrier M, Sawa S, Langa F, et al. 2008. In vivo equilibrium of proinflammatory IL-17$^+$ and regulatory IL-10$^+$ Foxp3$^+$ RORγ t$^+$ T cells. *J. Exp. Med.* 205:1381–93
183. Zhou L, Chong MM, Littman DR. 2009. Plasticity of CD4$^+$ T cell lineage differentiation. *Immunity* 30:646–55

184. Min B, Thornton A, Caucheteux SM, Younes SA, Oh K, et al. 2007. Gut flora antigens are not important in the maintenance of regulatory T cell heterogeneity and homeostasis. *Eur. J. Immunol.* 37:1916–23
185. Mucida D, Park Y, Kim G, Turovskaya O, Scott I, et al. 2007. Reciprocal TH17 and regulatory T cell differentiation mediated by retinoic acid. *Science* 317:256–60
186. Hall JA, Bouladoux N, Sun CM, Wohlfert EA, Blank RB, et al. 2008. Commensal DNA limits regulatory T cell conversion and is a natural adjuvant of intestinal immune responses. *Immunity* 29:637–49
187. Ivanov II, de Lanos Frutos R, Manel N, Yoshinaga K, Rifkin DB, et al. 2008. Specific microbiota direct the differentiation of IL-17-producing T-helper cells in the mucosa of the small intestine. *Cell Host Microbe* 4:337–49
188. Treiner E, Duban L, Bahram S, Radosavljevic M, Wanner V, et al. 2003. Selection of evolutionarily conserved mucosal-associated invariant T cells by MR1. *Nature* 422:164–69
189. Belkaid Y, Oldenhove G. 2008. Tuning microenvironments: induction of regulatory T cells by dendritic cells. *Immunity* 29:362–71
190. Zhou X, Bailey-Bucktrout S, Jeker LT, Bluestone JA. 2009. Plasticity of $CD4^+$ $FoxP3^+$ T cells. *Curr. Opin. Immunol.* 21:281–85
191. Feuerer M, Hill JA, Mathis D, Benoist C. 2009. $Foxp3^+$ regulatory T cells: differentiation, specification, subphenotypes. *Nat. Immunol.* 10:689–95
192. Zhou L, Lopes JE, Chong MM, Ivanov II, Min R, et al. 2008. TGF-β-induced Foxp3 inhibits T(H)17 cell differentiation by antagonizing RORγt function. *Nature* 453:236–40
193. Uhlig HH, Coombes J, Mottet C, Izcue A, Thompson C, et al. 2006. Characterization of $Foxp3^+CD4^+CD25^+$ and IL-10-secreting $CD4^+CD25^+$ T cells during cure of colitis. *J. Immunol.* 177:5852–60
194. Rubtsov YP, Rasmussen JP, Chi EY, Fontenot J, Castelli L, et al. 2008. Regulatory T cell-derived interleukin-10 limits inflammation at environmental interfaces. *Immunity* 28:546–58
195. Li MO, Wan YY, Flavell RA. 2007. T cell-produced transforming growth factor-β1 controls T cell tolerance and regulates Th1- and Th17-cell differentiation. *Immunity* 26:579–91
196. Izcue A, Coombes JL, Powrie F. 2009. Regulatory lymphocytes and intestinal inflammation. *Annu. Rev. Immunol.* 27:313–38
197. Jaffar Z, Ferrini ME, Herritt LA, Roberts K. 2009. Cutting edge: Lung mucosal Th17-mediated responses induce polymeric Ig receptor expression by the airway epithelium and elevate secretory IgA levels. *J. Immunol.* 182:4507–11
198. Terahara K, Yoshida M, Igarashi O, Nochi T, Pontes GS, et al. 2008. Comprehensive gene expression profiling of Peyer's patch M cells, villous M-like cells, and intestinal epithelial cells. *J. Immunol.* 180:7840–46
199. Jang MH, Kweon MN, Iwatani K, Yamamoto M, Terahara K, et al. 2004. Intestinal villous M cells: an antigen entry site in the mucosal epithelium. *Proc. Natl. Acad. Sci. USA* 101:6110–15
200. Rescigno M, Urbano M, Valzasina B, Francolini M, Rotta G, et al. 2001. Dendritic cells express tight junction proteins and penetrate gut epithelial monolayers to sample bacteria. *Nat. Immunol.* 2:361–67
201. Chieppa M, Rescigno M, Huang AY, Germain RN. 2006. Dynamic imaging of dendritic cell extension into the small bowel lumen in response to epithelial cell TLR engagement. *J. Exp. Med.* 203:2841–52
202. Vallon-Eberhard A, Landsman L, Yogev N, Verrier B, Jung S. 2006. Transepithelial pathogen uptake into the small intestinal lamina propria. *J. Immunol.* 176:2465–69
203. Fagarasan S, Honjo T. 2003. Intestinal IgA synthesis: regulation of front-line body defences. *Nat. Rev. Immunol.* 3:63–72
204. Castigli E, Wilson SA, Scott S, Dedeoglu F, Xu S, et al. 2005. TACI and BAFF-R mediate isotype switching in B cells. *J. Exp. Med.* 201:35–39
205. Sakurai D, Hase H, Kanno Y, Kojima H, Okumura K, Kobata T. 2007. TACI regulates IgA production by APRIL in collaboration with HSPG. *Blood* 109:2961–67
206. Iliev ID, Mileti E, Matteoli G, Chieppa M, Rescigno M. 2009. Intestinal epithelial cells promote colitis-protective regulatory T-cell differentiation through dendritic cell conditioning. *Mucosal Immunol.* 2:340–50

207. Taylor BC, Zaph C, Troy AE, Du Y, Guild KJ, et al. 2009. TSLP regulates intestinal immunity and inflammation in mouse models of helminth infection and colitis. *J. Exp. Med.* 206:655–67
208. Xu W, He B, Chiu A, Chadburn A, Shan M, et al. 2007. Epithelial cells trigger frontline immunoglobulin class switching through a pathway regulated by the inhibitor SLPI. *Nat. Immunol.* 8:294–303
209. Castigli E, Scott S, Dedeoglu F, Bryce P, Jabara H, et al. 2004. Impaired IgA class switching in APRIL-deficient mice. *Proc. Natl. Acad. Sci. USA* 101:3903–8
210. Castigli E, Wilson S, Garibyan L, Rachid R, Bonilla F, et al. 2007. Reexamining the role of TACI coding variants in common variable immunodeficiency and selective IgA deficiency. *Nat. Genet.* 39:430–31
211. Salzer U, Chapel HM, Webster AD, Pan-Hammarstrom Q, Schmitt-Graeff A, et al. 2005. Mutations in TNFRSF13B encoding TACI are associated with common variable immunodeficiency in humans. *Nat. Genet.* 37:820–28
212. Chu VT, Enghard P, Riemekasten G, Berek C. 2007. In vitro and in vivo activation induces BAFF and APRIL expression in B cells. *J. Immunol.* 179:5947–57
213. McCarthy DD, Chiu S, Gao Y, Summers-deLuca LE, Gommerman JL. 2006. BAFF induces a hyper-IgA syndrome in the intestinal lamina propria concomitant with IgA deposition in the kidney independent of LIGHT. *Cell. Immunol.* 241:85–94
214. Doreau A, Belot A, Bastid J, Riche B, Trescol-Biemont MC, et al. 2009. Interleukin 17 acts in synergy with B cell-activating factor to influence B cell biology and the pathophysiology of systemic lupus erythematosus. *Nat. Immunol.* 10:778–85
215. Macpherson AJ. 2006. IgA adaptation to the presence of commensal bacteria in the intestine. *Curr. Top. Microbiol. Immunol.* 308:117–36
216. Burt RW, Jacoby RF. 1999. Polyposis syndromes. In *Textbook of Gastroenterology*, ed. T Yamada, D Alpers, L Laine, C Owyang, D Powell, pp. 1995–2022. Philadelphia: Lippincott William & Wilkins
217. Harriman GR, Bogue M, Rogers P, Finegold M, Pacheco S, et al. 1999. Targeted deletion of the IgA constant region in mice leads to IgA deficiency with alterations in expression of other Ig isotypes. *J. Immunol.* 162:2521–29
218. Lycke N, Erlandsson L, Ekman L, Schon K, Leanderson T. 1999. Lack of J chain inhibits the transport of gut IgA and abrogates the development of intestinal antitoxic protection. *J. Immunol.* 163:913–19
219. Johansen FE, Pekna M, Norderhaug IN, Haneberg B, Hietala MA, et al. 1999. Absence of epithelial immunoglobulin A transport, with increased mucosal leakiness, in polymeric immunoglobulin receptor/secretory component-deficient mice. *J. Exp. Med.* 190:915–22
220. Harris NL, Spoerri I, Schopfer JF, Nembrini C, Merky P, et al. 2006. Mechanisms of neonatal mucosal antibody protection. *J. Immunol.* 177:6256–62
221. Macpherson AJ, Uhr T. 2004. Induction of protective IgA by intestinal dendritic cells carrying commensal bacteria. *Science* 303:1662–65
222. Sait LC, Galic M, Price JD, Simpfendorfer KR, Diavatopoulos DA, et al. 2007. Secretory antibodies reduce systemic antibody responses against the gastrointestinal commensal flora. *Int. Immunol.* 19:257–65
223. Wijburg OL, Uren TK, Simpfendorfer K, Johansen FE, Brandtzaeg P, Strugnell RA. 2006. Innate secretory antibodies protect against natural *Salmonella typhimurium* infection. *J. Exp. Med.* 203:21–26
224. Suzuki K, Meek B, Doi Y, Muramatsu M, Chiba T, et al. 2004. Aberrant expansion of segmented filamentous bacteria in IgA-deficient gut. *Proc. Natl. Acad. Sci. USA* 101:1981–86
225. Davis CP, Savage DC. 1974. Habitat, succession, attachment, and morphology of segmented, filamentous microbes indigenous to the murine gastrointestinal tract. *Infect. Immun.* 10:948–56
226. Ohashi Y, Hiraguchi M, Ushida K. 2006. The composition of intestinal bacteria affects the level of luminal IgA. *Biosci. Biotechnol. Biochem.* 70:3031–35
227. Durandy A, Taubenheim N, Peron S, Fischer A. 2007. Pathophysiology of B-cell intrinsic immunoglobulin class switch recombination deficiencies. *Adv. Immunol.* 94:275–306
228. Bastlein C, Burlefinger R, Holzberg E, Voeth C, Garbrecht M, Ottenjann R. 1988. Common variable immunodeficiency syndrome and nodular lymphoid hyperplasia in the small intestine. *Endoscopy* 20:272–75

229. Zaheen A, Boulianne B, Parsa JY, Ramachandran S, Gommerman JL, Martin A. 2009. AID constrains germinal center size by rendering B cells susceptible to apoptosis. *Blood* 114:547–54
230. Fernandez MI, Pedron T, Tournebize R, Olivo-Marin JC, Sansonetti PJ, Phalipon A. 2003. Anti-inflammatory role for intracellular dimeric immunoglobulin A by neutralization of lipopolysaccharide in epithelial cells. *Immunity* 18:739–49
231. Peterson DA, McNulty NP, Guruge JL, Gordon JI. 2007. IgA response to symbiotic bacteria as a mediator of gut homeostasis. *Cell Host Microbe* 2:328–39

On the Composition of the Preimmune Repertoire of T Cells Specific for Peptide–Major Histocompatibility Complex Ligands

Marc K. Jenkins, H. Hamlet Chu, James B. McLachlan, and James J. Moon

Department of Microbiology, Center for Immunology, University of Minnesota Medical School, Minneapolis, Minnesota 55455; email: jenki002@umn.edu, chuxx080@umn.edu, mclac016@umn.edu, jjmoon@umn.edu

Annu. Rev. Immunol. 2010. 28:275–94

The *Annual Review of Immunology* is online at immunol.annualreviews.org

This article's doi:
10.1146/annurev-immunol-030409-101253

0732-0582/10/0423-0275$20.00

Key Words

naive T cell, regulatory T cell, memory T cell, positive selection

Abstract

Millions of T cells are produced in the thymus, each expressing a unique α/β T cell receptor (TCR) capable of binding to a foreign peptide in the binding groove of a host major histocompatibility complex (MHC) molecule. T cell–mediated immunity to infection is due to the proliferation and differentiation of rare clones in the preimmune repertoire that by chance express TCRs specific for peptide-MHC (pMHC) ligands derived from the microorganism. Here we review recent findings that have altered our understanding of how the preimmune repertoire is established. Recent structural studies indicate that a germline-encoded tendency of TCRs to bind MHC molecules contributes to the MHC bias of T cell repertoires. It has also become clear that the preimmune repertoire contains functionally heterogeneous subsets including recent thymic emigrants, mature naive phenotype cells, memory phenotype cells, and natural regulatory T cells. In addition, sensitive new detection methods have revealed that the repertoire of naive phenotype T cells consists of distinct pMHC-specific populations that consistently vary in size in different individuals. The implications of these new findings for the clonal selection theory, self-tolerance, and immunodominance are discussed.

INTRODUCTION

Preimmune: existing before the introduction of foreign antigen into the body

Repertoire: the set of lymphocytes in an individual at a given time

TCR: T cell receptor

MHC: major histocompatibility complex

pMHC: peptide-MHC complex

V: variable segment

D: diversity segment

J: joining segment

The clonal selection theory is one of the cornerstones of immunology (1). It posits that vertebrates produce millions of lymphocytes, each expressing a different randomly generated antigen receptor. Cells that by chance express self-reactive antigen receptors are eliminated during a phase in development when strong antigen receptor engagement causes cell death. The remaining cells pass out of the death-sensitive phase and constitute the preimmune repertoire. Following exposure to a foreign antigen, the rare cells in the preimmune repertoire that by chance express antigen receptors specific for this antigen receive signals that cause proliferation and acquisition of properties that facilitate antigen clearance.

This review focuses on the composition of the preimmune repertoire of T cells that express α/β T cell antigen receptors (TCRs) specific for peptides bound to classical major histocompatibility complex (MHC) molecules (denoted as pMHC) (2). For the purposes of this review, the preimmune repertoire is defined as the set of α/β TCR–expressing lymphocytes that have completed thymic development and entered the secondary lymphoid organs but have never been activated by high-affinity TCR binding to a foreign pMHC. Based on this definition, the preimmune repertoire would be the set of T cells found in the secondary lymphoid organs of a hypothetical germ- and foreign antigen–free individual. Until recently, such an individual might have been expected to contain a functionally homogeneous population of so-called naive T cells. However, as detailed below, recent work indicates that several other types of T cells are contained in this repertoire, some of which are overtly self-reactive or phenotypically similar to memory cells.

THYMIC SELECTION OF THE PREIMMUNE MHC-RESTRICTED T CELL REPERTOIRE

Each pMHC-specific T cell in the preimmune repertoire survived a selection process during development in the thymus. To have a chance to complete development, thymocytes must first produce a TCR by somatic recombination of variable (V), diversity (D), and joining (J) segments at the *Tcrb* locus and V and J segments at the *Tcra* locus (3). These recombination events are completed by the $CD4^+$ $CD8^+$ stage of development. Of the $CD4^+$ $CD8^+$ T cells that produce a TCR, only those with TCRs capable of low-affinity binding to a self-pMHC on radio-resistant thymic epithelial cells receive a signal to survive and are said to have undergone positive selection (4). Any cell that does not express a low-affinity self-pMHC-specific TCR does not receive the survival signal and dies by neglect. Clones that undergo positive selection also commit to either the $CD4^+$ or $CD8^+$ lineage—low-affinity recognition of a self-pMHCI results in loss of CD4 and retention of CD8, producing a $CD8^+$ T cell, whereas higher-affinity recognition of a self-pMHCII results in loss of CD8 and retention of CD4, producing a $CD4^+$ T cell (5). Finally, commitment to the $CD4^+$ or $CD8^+$ lineage is accompanied by commitment to helper or cytotoxic T cell function via differential expression of the ThPOK or Runx3 transcription factors (6).

The T cells that undergo positive selection also express a canonical set of molecules that define the naive phenotype (7) (**Table 1**). Many of these molecules, for example CD62L and CCR7, are required for subsequent trafficking between the secondary lymphoid organs via the blood and lymphatic vessels (8). Naive phenotype cells also express low levels of CD44 in mice and high levels of CD45RA in humans (9). These cells are generally in the G_0 phase of the cell cycle and express molecules such as KLF2, Tob, Nfatc2, and Smad3 (10, 11), which enforce a quiescent state.

Negative selection also shapes the preimmune repertoire (12). Because V(D)J recombination is an essentially random process, some $CD4^+$ $CD8^+$ thymocytes will by chance produce TCRs capable of high-affinity binding to a self-pMHCI or pMHCII. Such cells receive a signal that induces apoptosis, which is beneficial to the host because these cells could cause

Table 1 T cell populations in the pMHC-specific preimmune repertoire

Cell type	Fraction of the repertoire	Function	Markers (mouse)	Self-pMHC affinity
Mature naive phenotype cells	~70%	Precursors of effector cells, iTreg cells, and memory cells	CD62L^{high} CCR7^{high} CD44^{low}	Low
Recent thymic emigrants	~10%	Mature into naive phenotype cells	Lower levels of CD62L, CCR7 than mature naive phenotype cells, CD24^{+}	Low
Memory phenotype cells	~10%	Rapid response in primary generation of effector and memory cells	CD62L^{high} CD44^{high} Ly6C^{high}	Low
nTreg cells	~10%	Maintenance of self-tolerance, prevention of immunopathology	CD62L^{high} CD44^{medium} CCR7^{high} CD25^{high} Foxp3^{+} GITR^{+} CTLA-4^{+}	Medium

autoimmune disease. In addition, some cells that progress to the CD4^{+} stage, perhaps those with TCR affinities for self-pMHC at the high end of the positive selection range, receive signals that induce the Foxp3 transcription factor, which causes the cells to differentiate into regulatory T (Treg) cells (13). These thymus-derived Treg cells are referred to here as natural Treg (nTreg) cells to distinguish them from induced Treg (iTreg) cells that can be generated from naive phenotype cells in the secondary lymphoid organs by certain forms of foreign antigen presentation (14). iTreg cells are not discussed in detail in this review because they are not present in the preimmune repertoire.

The focus of the preimmune T cell repertoire on MHC is in contrast to the preimmune B cell repertoire, which contains clones that display surface antibodies capable of binding to almost any macromolecule. Because TCRs and antibodies are both formed by random V(D)J recombination, it was thought that the MHC bias of the preimmune T cell repertoire related to positive selection of rare clones in the preselection CD4^{+} CD8^{+} population that happened to produce MHC-specific TCRs (4). On the basis of this idea, investigators surmised that the vast majority of preselection CD4^{+} CD8^{+} thymocytes fail positive selection and die by neglect because of a lack of MHC specificity (15). A prediction of this model is that the repertoire of preselection CD4^{+} CD8^{+} thymocytes might contain cells with TCRs specific for non-MHC antigens. Singer and colleagues (16) tested this possibility by producing mice lacking CD4, CD8, MHCI, and MHCII molecules. These investigators reasoned that removal of CD4 and CD8 would free the critical signaling molecule Lck to interact directly with the TCR, allowing positive selection of non-MHC-restricted cells. Remarkably, these mice contained normal numbers of T cells, some of which could be activated by foreign cells lacking MHC molecules. These results suggest that CD4 and CD8 normally bind all of the Lck in thymocytes. Thus, the only way that a thymocyte can normally receive the TCR signal needed for positive selection is to get Lck from a CD4 or CD8 molecule as it interacts with MHC, in effect forcing all selected T cells to have an affinity for MHC.

However, recent work from Kappler, Marrack, and colleagues (17) suggests another explanation for the MHC bias of the T cell repertoire. These investigators studied pMHCII-specific T cell clones from mice in which negative selection was impaired. The TCR α and β chains expressed by these clones contact MHC primarily with complementarity

Treg cell: regulatory T cell

nTreg cell: natural regulatory T cell

iTreg cell: induced regulatory T cell

determining region (CDR) 1 and CDR2 domains (18). CDR1 and CDR2 are located in the germline-encoded V domains and are not created by the random V(D)J joining that creates CDR3, which binds primarily to the peptide. This finding therefore indicates that the CDR1 and CDR2 domains of all TCR V segments are capable of binding to an MHC molecule, probably as the result of evolutionary selection. The implication of this conclusion is that many preselection CD4$^+$ CD8$^+$ thymocytes are deleted because of the inherent MHC specificity of TCRs (**Figure 1**, clones 4 and 5) and that the only cells that are not deleted are those with TCRs containing CDR3s that interfere with CDR1-/CDR2-mediated MHC binding.

CDR: complementarity determining region

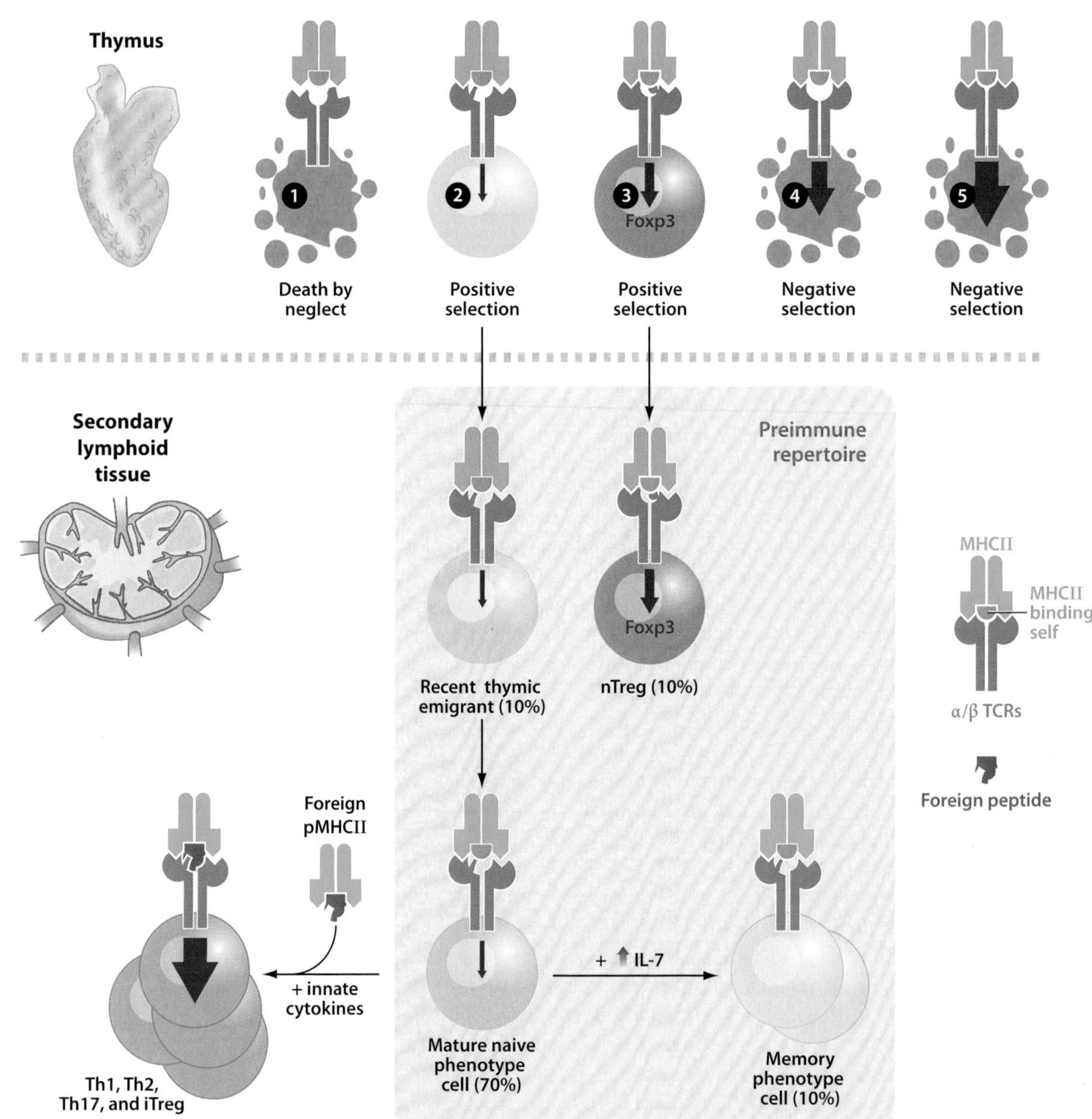

Certain CDR3s could interfere completely, in which case the $CD4^+$ $CD8^+$ T cell would die by neglect (**Figure 1**, clone 1). Other cells might express TCRs with CDR3s that reduce CDR1-/CDR2-mediated MHC binding into the weak range that fosters positive selection and acquisition of the naive phenotype (**Figure 1**, clone 2). Finally, some cells expressing TCRs with CDR3s that reduce MHC binding just enough to prevent deletion might become nTreg cells (**Figure 1**, clone 3). Although most of the preselection $CD4^+$ $CD8^+$ thymocytes may express TCRs specific for MHC, the fact that a huge number of diverse TCRs are in the population raises the possibility that some of them might cross-react on non-MHC antigens, as proposed by Singer and colleagues (16).

The $CD4^+$ and $CD8^+$ thymocytes that survive positive and negative selection undergo changes in the secondary lymphoid organs after leaving the thymus. Although recent thymic emigrants express the molecules that define the naive phenotype, the levels of some of these molecules increase during the first several weeks of recirculation through the secondary lymphoid organs (19) (**Table 1**). The cells also increase their capacity to proliferate and differentiate in response to stimulation by foreign pMHC during this period (19, 20). Thus, the preimmune repertoire of an adult contains a mixture of recent thymic emigrants and fully mature naive phenotype T cells. In adults, most recent thymic emigrants remain in G_0 and retain the set of markers that define the naive phenotype (e.g., $CD44^{low}$) during the maturation process (21). In contrast, recent thymic emigrants that enter secondary lymphoid organs under lymphopenic conditions, for example during the neonatal period (22), undergo lymphopenia-induced proliferation and become $CD44^{high}$. Thus, the preimmune repertoire also contains T cells that never actually responded to a foreign pMHC but lack the naive phenotype (**Table 1**). These cells are referred to here as memory phenotype preimmune cells.

In summary, the preimmune repertoire contains at least four distinct populations (**Figure 1**, **Table 1**). Three of these populations express TCRs with a low affinity for a self-pMHC and contain the precursors of high-affinity foreign pMHC–specific effector and memory T cells. These populations are mature naive phenotype cells, recent thymic emigrants in the process of becoming fully mature naive phenotype cells, and naive phenotype cells that underwent homeostatic proliferation and adopted a memory phenotype. The fourth population consists of $CD4^+$ nTreg cells that likely express TCRs at the high end of the positive selection affinity range and play a critical role in the maintenance of self-tolerance

Figure 1

Cells of the preimmune pMHC-specific T cell repertoire. MHCII molecules are shown in green, α/β TCRs in blue. MHCII-binding self and foreign peptides are shown in orange and brown, respectively. The CDR1/2 domains of the TCR are shown opposed to the tops of the MHCII molecule on either side of the peptide-binding groove. The CDR3 domain of the TCR is shown opposed to the peptide. The juxtaposition of TCR and pMHCII surfaces represents the strength of binding. The red arrows represent the strength of the signal emanating from the TCR when bound to the indicated pMHCII. Cells that form the preimmune repertoire are shown in the box. Five clones expressing TCRs with differing self-pMHCII binding affinities and their fates are shown. Clone 1 has a TCR in which CDR3 prevents both CDR1/2s from interacting with MHCII. This clone receives no TCR signal and dies by neglect. Clone 2 has a TCR in which CDR3 interacts weakly with the peptide but also weakens the interaction of one CDR1/2 with MHCII. This clone receives a weak TCR signal and undergoes positive selection to become a naive phenotype cell. Clone 3 has a TCR in which CDR3 interacts with the peptide better than in the case of clone 2 but still weakens the interaction of one CDR1/2 with MHCII. This clone receives a stronger TCR signal than does clone 2 and undergoes positive selection to become an nTreg cell. Clone 4 has a TCR in which CDR3 does not interact with the peptide and does not interfere with tight interaction of both CDR1/2s with MHCII. This clone receives a strong TCR signal and undergoes negative selection. Clone 5 has a TCR in which CDR3 interacts tightly with the peptide and does not interfere with tight interaction of both CDR1/2s with MHCII. This clone receives the strongest possible TCR signal and undergoes negative selection.

but an uncertain role in the response to foreign pMHCII. The properties of each of these populations are described in more detail below.

NAIVE PHENOTYPE CELLS

Population Size and Diversity

Mature naive phenotype cells account for the majority of the cells in the preimmune repertoire (9). These cells are located in the secondary lymphoid organs because the ligands (PNAd, CCL21, MadCAM) for their trafficking receptors (e.g., CD62L, CCR7, α4/β7 integrin) are only expressed by specialized high endothelial venules in these sites (23). An adult mouse has about 8×10^7 α/β TCR^+ T cells in the secondary lymphoid organs and another 5×10^6 in the blood (J.J. Moon, H.H. Chu & M.K. Jenkins, unpublished data). $CD4^+$ T cells account for about 60% of the cells and $CD8^+$ T cells for about 40%. About 70% of the cells in both subsets are naive phenotype cells, at least in mice housed under specific pathogen-free conditions. Thus, an adult mouse has about 6×10^7 naive phenotype T cells in its body. By extrapolation based on body weight, an adult human has about 3×10^{11} naive phenotype T cells.

The millions of naive phenotype T cells give the host the capacity to respond to a vast number of foreign pMHC. Given that the number of potential TCR amino acid sequences that could be produced by V(D)J recombination ($>10^{15}$) (24) is greater than the number of naive phenotype cells in the body, it is possible that each naive phenotype T cell has a unique TCR. If so, then it is conceivable that each naive phenotype T cell could respond to a different foreign pMHC. This would mean that the naive phenotype repertoire of a mouse has the potential to respond to about 3.5×10^7 different pMHCII and 2.5×10^7 different pMHCI. This would also mean that the naive phenotype repertoires of two otherwise genetically identical mice would contain completely different sets of clones because each would express only 6×10^7 of the 10^{15} possible TCRs.

The actual number of recognizable pMHC is very likely to be lower than the number of naive phenotype T cells in the body. Evidence supporting this possibility comes from Casrouge et al. (25), who used a TCR sequencing approach to estimate that the naive phenotype T cell repertoire of a mouse at any one time consists of about 2×10^6 clones. Because a mouse has about 6×10^7 naive phenotype T cells, this finding leads to the remarkable conclusion that the average T cell clone in the preimmune repertoire exists in 30 copies. The existence of multiple copies of the same naive phenotype clone could come about by cell division at some point after *Tcra* locus rearrangement, either in the thymus or during homeostatic proliferation in the secondary lymphoid organs. Because the set of T cells that respond to a single pMHC is known to consist of at least 5 and as many as 500 different clones (26–28), individual foreign pMHC–specific populations could consist of 150–15,000 cells. If this were true, and assuming that each T cell can only respond to a single pMHC, then the naive phenotype T cell repertoire could respond to as few as 4,000 and as many as 400,000 different foreign pMHC.

Of course, this issue could be resolved by directly measuring the number of cells that are specific for individual foreign pMHC. The way toward this end was paved by the development of fluorochrome-labeled pMHC tetramers (29), which bind specifically to T cells with the relevant pMHC TCRs, marking them for detection in a flow cytometer. The difficulty has been the capacity of the flow cytometer to analyze only about 1% of the cells in the secondary lymphoid organs of a mouse at a time. This inefficiency was crippling when it came to detection of naive phenotype foreign pMHC–specific T cells, which might number only 100 cells spread throughout all the secondary lymphoid organs. The solution to this problem was enrichment of all the pMHC tetramer-binding cells from the secondary lymphoid organs of a mouse using magnetic beads coupled to antibodies specific for the fluorochrome component of the tetramer (30–39).

This approach was used to enumerate $CD4^+$ T cells specific for three different foreign pMHCII in the preimmune repertoires of C57BL/6 (B6) mice (40). The tetramers used in this study contained the I-A^b MHCII molecule bound to the 2W1S variant of peptide 52–68 from the I-E MHCII α chain (41), peptide 427–441 from the FliC protein of *Salmonella typhimurium* (42), or peptide 323–339 from chicken ovalbumin (OVA) (43). The 2W1S:I-A^b-binding $CD4^+$ T cell population consisted of about 200 cells per mouse, whereas the FliC:I-A^b-, and OVA:I-A^b-binding populations contained about 20 cells per mouse. Thus, the frequencies of cells capable of binding to one of these three pMHCII ranged from about 1:200,000 to 1:2,000,000 of the naive phenotype $CD4^+$ T cells in B6 mice that were never exposed to these peptides. The frequency of influenza virus $\text{hemagglutinin}_{306-319}$:HLA-DR4-specific naive phenotype $CD4^+$ T cells in HLA-$DR4^+$ humans is also in this range (44). Similar analyses have been done for 12 different foreign pMHCI-specific $CD8^+$ murine T cell populations by three different laboratories (45–47). The number of naive phenotype $CD8^+$ T cells in B6 mice ranged from 15 lymphocytic choriomeningitis virus (LCMV) $L_{338-346}$:D^b-specific cells at the low end to 1100 vaccinia virus B8R:K^b-specific cells per mouse at the high end. These numbers translate to frequencies of 1:20,000 to 1:1,300,000 of the naive phenotype $CD8^+$ T cells.

These direct measurements can be used to estimate the minimum number of unrelated pMHC that can be recognized by the set of naive phenotype cells in an adult. Although a range of frequencies clearly exists for different pMHC, the results indicate that average pMHCI- and pMHCII-specific naive phenotype populations exist at about 1:100,000 $CD8^+$ and 1:1,000,000 $CD4^+$ T cells. Assuming that each population recognizes a single pMHC, then the naive phenotype $CD8^+$ and $CD4^+$ T cell repertoires could recognize about 100,000 and 1,000,000 different pMHC, respectively. Because humans have at most 10 times more TCR diversity than mice (48), it is reasonable to conclude that the human naive phenotype T cell repertoire would be capable of recognizing 10 times more pMHC.

These estimates are almost certainly on the low side because individual T cell clones are capable of recognizing more than one unrelated pMHC (49). Kappler and colleagues (50) performed an experiment that put limits on the extent of this cross-reactivity. They produced a library containing about 10^5 recombinant baculoviruses, each displaying the same MHCII molecule but each with a different random peptide. The library was screened with a TCR of known pMHCII specificity. Only one pMHC from this library bound this TCR with enough affinity to activate T cells, and the peptide was closely related to the known peptide. This experiment suggests that the number of unrelated pMHC that can be bound with a biologically significant affinity by a given TCR is about 1:100,000. Yewdell and colleagues (51) arrived at a similar number by screening a large library of random peptides for the capacity to activate individual T cell clones. This low level of cross-reactivity indicates that the aforementioned estimate that the naive phenotype $CD8^+$ and $CD4^+$ T cell repertoires recognize about 100,000 and 1,000,000 different pMHC is probably not a gross underestimate.

An important conclusion from the direct measurements is that naive phenotype populations specific for different pMHC vary in size in a predictable fashion, at least in individuals that express the same MHC alleles. It is possible that size differences between pMHC-specific populations in the preimmune repertoire could come about because of negative selection in the preselection repertoire. For example, the $OVA_{323-339}$:I-A^b-specific naive population might be small because $OVA_{323-339}$:I-A^b-specific TCRs are by chance likely to bind with high affinity to a self-pMHCII. Thus, many $OVA_{323-339}$:I-A^b-specific $CD4^+$ $CD8^+$ thymocytes in the preselection repertoire would be deleted and therefore never appear in the preimmune repertoire. A hint of the role of intrathymic negative selection in shaping the repertoire comes from the fact that the

B6: C57BL/6 mouse strain

OVA: chicken ovalbumin

LCMV: lymphocytic choriomeningitis virus

two largest naive phenotype T cell populations identified to date are specific for self-pMHC derived from tissue-restricted extrathymic proteins. Romero and colleagues (52) showed that naive phenotype T cells capable of binding a peptide from the melanocyte-specific protein Melan-A/MART-1 protein complexed with HLA-A2 account for greater than 1:2500 $CD8^+$ T cells in people who express HLA:A2. Similarly, Wucherpfennig and colleagues (34) found that T cells capable of binding a peptide:I-A^{g7} complex that mimics a pancreatic islet cell–derived pMHCII bind to 1:1500 $CD4^+$ thymocytes in NOD (I-A^{g7+}) mice. The large size of these self-pMHC-specific populations may be related to the lack of presentation of these pMHC by the antigen-presenting cells (APCs) that induce clonal deletion in the thymus. Because the Melan-A/MART-1 peptide:HLA-A2-specific population retains the naive phenotype in the blood (52), this pMHCI must also not be presented in the skin draining lymph nodes. In contrast, the population detected with the islet peptide:I-A^{g7} mimic may encounter the relevant pMHCII in the pancreatic lymph node, become activated, and contribute to the diabetes that develops in NOD mice. Although it is not clear why such a large population of naive T cells with high-affinity mimic peptide:I-A^{g7}-specific TCRs is positively selected, it is easy to imagine that this is a predisposing factor for autoimmunity.

Another possibility is that pMHC that are recognized by the larger naive phenotype populations may have structural features that are conducive to recognition by a more diverse set of TCRs. Along these lines, Turner and colleagues (53) showed that peptides containing TCR contact amino acids with prominent side chains stimulated a population of $CD8^+$ T cells with more TCR diversity than did peptides with small side chains. Our study showed that larger pMHCII-specific $CD4^+$ naive phenotype T cell populations contained more TCR diversity than did smaller populations (40). Putting these findings together leads to the conclusion that pMHC with prominent TCR contact residues may be recognized by a larger and more diverse set of naive phenotype T cells than pMHC with small TCR contact residues.

Finally, it is possible that the larger naive phenotype populations use TCRs that are produced more frequently by V(D)J recombination than are other TCRs. This is possible because D segments have very similar sequences that can be made identical by random nucleotide additions or deletions at the ends (54). In addition, several amino acids have more than one codon. Together, these molecular mechanisms create a situation in which as many as 15 different nucleotide sequences can produce the same V(D)J TCR β chain amino acid sequence. It follows that T cell populations that recognize a pMHC with such a TCR would be larger than T cell populations that rely on less frequently produced TCRs.

Functional Consequences of Differences in Naive Phenotype T Cell Population Size

The variable size of the naive phenotype T cell populations specific for different pMHC has functional consequences. Several studies have demonstrated that naive phenotype T cells expand in proportion to their starting frequency following exposure to the relevant pMHC (40, 45). Recent work by Sette and colleagues (46) demonstrated that this finding provides an explanation for the phenomenon of immunodominance. LCMV infection of B6 mice activates $CD8^+$ T cells specific for at least 28 different pMHCI. However, about one-third of the total response is accounted for by three of these pMHCI, whereas 18 others account for a very small fraction. So what makes the top three peptides dominate the response? One possibility is MHCI-binding affinity. The top three peptides were at the high end of the MHCI-binding affinity range, but several of the bottom 18 peptides were also in this range. The best predictor of immunodominance was the size of the naive phenotype population—the populations specific for the top peptides were about 10 times larger than those specific for the bottom peptides. Therefore, although antigen abundance, efficiency of peptide generation by antigen processing, and MHC-binding affinity are important factors in immunodominance (55), so is naive phenotype T cell population size. This importance is likely related to the fact that a large naive phenotype population can generate a fixed number of microbicidal effector cells more quickly than a smaller one. For example, it took 4 days to generate 10,000 effector cells from 200 naive phenotype 2W1S:I-A^b-specific CD4$^+$ T cells, but 8 days from 20 naive phenotype FliC:I-A^b-specific cells (40). Another disadvantage of small population size relates to aging. Blackman and colleagues (56) showed that small influenza virus pMHCI-specific populations could disappear completely as the total preimmune repertoire contracts in aged individuals.

Functional Heterogeneity

The fact that T cells in monoclonal TCR transgenic mice that have never been exposed to the relevant antigen uniformly express CD62L and CCR7 suggests that naive phenotype cells comprise a functionally homogeneous population (7). Indeed, all naive T cells are thought to have the potential to differentiate into diverse types of effector (e.g., Th1, Th2, Th17, iTreg) and memory cells (e.g., central and effector memory cells) depending on the circumstances surrounding initial activation (57). The demonstration of Busch and colleagues (58) that a single naive CD8$^+$ T cell could give rise to central and effector memory cells in an adoptive recipient supports this notion.

However, some phenotypic and functional heterogeneity has been reported for naive phenotype T cells. One source of heterogeneity relates to TCR affinity. A range of TCR affinities for pMHC is likely to exist within any particular naive phenotype population. Using transgenic mice with a fixed TCR β chain, Malherbe et al. (27) showed that the population of pigeon cytochrome C peptide:I-E^k-specific CD4$^+$ T cells present 3 days following immunization with pigeon cytochrome C contains low- and high-affinity cells, whereas the day 7 population contains only high-affinity cells. Similarly, Zehn et al. (59) showed that low-affinity naive phenotype CD8$^+$ T cells begin to expand during microbial infection but are poorly represented later in the response owing to more sustained proliferation by high-affinity cells. In addition, McHeyzer-Williams and colleagues (60) showed that CD4$^+$ T cells with the highest affinities for a foreign pMHCII were most likely to differentiate into follicular helper cells following immunization. Together these results indicate that naive phenotype T cells with TCRs that bind foreign pMHC with low affinity may be capable of proliferating and becoming effector cells, but only cells with high-affinity TCRs receive signals to become memory cells. A possible explanation for this phenomenon was reported by Palmer and colleagues (61), who showed that a mutation of the TCR β chain transmembrane domain that reduced TCR signaling limited memory cell development but had no effect on initial clonal expansion.

McHeyzer-Williams and colleagues (62) described another form of functional heterogeneity. They showed that the naive phenotype CD4$^+$ T cell population (CD44^{low} CD62L$^+$) contains equally abundant subsets that express high or low amounts of the type V glycophosphatidylinositol anchored cell surface protein Ly6C (63). In addition, they showed that the Ly6C^{high} naive phenotype cells were potent helper cells for antigen-specific plasmablasts during a primary immune response, whereas the Ly6C^{low} subset lacked this activity. Remarkably, TCR usage differed between the Ly6C^{high} and Ly6C^{low} subsets. Ly6C is also expressed on naive phenotype CD8$^+$ T cells following lymphopenia-induced proliferation (64, 65). The latter finding suggests that the Ly6C^{high} half of the naive phenotype T cell population is undergoing a process akin to lymphopenia-induced proliferation even in nonlymphopenic adult animals. Cell turnover experiments, however, have shown that most naive phenotype T cells are not cycling (21). Therefore, the reasons why half of all naive phenotype T cells express Ly6C, have a different TCR repertoire, and function differently than naive cells lacking Ly6C are unclear.

Maintenance of Naive Phenotype T Cells

In nonlymphopenic adult mice, mature naive phenotype T cells survive with a half-life of 35–160 days (66–68). Thus, naive phenotype T cells are relatively long-lived, given that mice live for about 900 days. The finding that naive phenotype human T cells have half-lives of 4–6 years supports this contention (69). The survival of naive phenotype T cells depends on exposure to IL-7 produced by the fibroblastic reticular cells of the T cell–rich zones of secondary lymphoid organs (70). Thus, recirculation of naive phenotype T cells through secondary lymphoid organs is critical for their survival by providing access to IL-7.

The survival of naive phenotype $CD8^+$ T cells in nonlymphopenic hosts also depends on TCR-self-pMHCI interactions. The evidence for this contention is that induced TCR ablation (71) or transfer into MHCI-deficient hosts (7, 72, 73) reduces the half-life of naive phenotype $CD8^+$ T cells in adult mice. It is possible that the critical survival signal for each naive T cell emanates from low-affinity TCR binding to the self-pMHCI that caused positive selection in the thymus.

TCR-self-pMHCII interactions are probably also important for the survival of naive phenotype $CD4^+$ T cells. Induced TCR ablation reduced the half-life of naive phenotype $CD4^+$ T cells, although the effect was much smaller than that observed for $CD8^+$ T cells (71). However, this effect may be significant given that several studies showed that $CD4^+$ T cells that were allowed to develop in the thymus in the presence of MHCII survived poorly after entering secondary lymphoid organs lacking MHCII (74, 75). In addition, Lucas and colleagues (76) showed that naive phenotype $CD4^+$ T cells survived less well after transfer into mice lacking all MHCII molecules than after transfer into normal mice. In fact, the magnitude of the reduction in $CD4^+$ T cell survival in MHCII-deficient mice was equal to the reduction observed following induced TCR ablation. Finally, two recent publications showed that self-peptides that cause positive selection of certain $CD4^+$ T cell clones enhanced the survival and function of those clones as mature T cells (77, 78). Together these findings predict that $CD4^+$ T cells that were positively selected and maintained by the same self-pMHCII would be in competition for that ligand. Indeed, Paul and colleagues (79) found that polyclonal naive phenotype $CD4^+$ T cells underwent much less homeostatic proliferation when competing with T cells with a diverse TCR repertoire than when competing with the same number of T cells with a limited repertoire. Similarly, naive monoclonal $CD4^+$ T cells survived better when transferred into normal recipients in small numbers than in very large numbers (68). Therefore, although some controversy exists (67), the bulk of the evidence is in favor of signals downstream from weak TCR-self-pMHCII interactions being important for the survival of naive phenotype $CD4^+$ T cells.

RECENT THYMIC EMIGRANTS

The preimmune repertoire is composed of cells that left the thymus at various times, given that T cell development and thymic output continue for much of adult life. This fact has potential functional significance because T cells undergo phenotypic and functional changes after leaving the thymus. Recent thymic emigrants slightly reduced CD3 and CD24 expression while increasing Qa2, IL-7 receptor α, CD62L, and CD28 expression to the levels of mature naive T cells by about two weeks after leaving the thymus (20). If stimulated by foreign pMHC during this maturation period, recent thymic emigrants produced fewer effector cells and long-lived memory cells than did fully mature naive T cells. Interestingly, given the study mentioned above (62), the memory cells produced from recent thymic emigrants expressed lower amounts of Ly6C than did memory cells produced from mature naive cells. The significance of this phenomenon to immunity is unknown because recent thymic emigrants account for only 10% of the naive phenotype cells in adults (20). However, recent thymic emigrants are likely to account for a larger fraction of the preimmune T cell repertoire in neonates. The reduced responsiveness of these cells may contribute to relative immunodeficiency in newborns.

MEMORY PHENOTYPE T CELLS

Naive T cells in the preimmune repertoire can undergo another post-thymic maturation event that results in phenotypic and functional changes. A recent pMHC tetramer enrichment study noted that 10–20% of the foreign pMHCI-binding $CD8^+$ T cells in mice that were never exposed to the relevant peptide were $CD44^{high}$, as expected for effector/memory cells (47). $CD44^{high}$ T cells also accounted for about 5% of the foreign pMHCII-specific $CD4^+$ T cells in mice that were never exposed to the relevant foreign peptide (40). The $CD8^+$ $CD44^{high}$ T cells in naive mice also responded more quickly than naive phenotype cells following pMHCI stimulation and, unlike naive phenotype cells, produced IFN-γ when exposed to proinflammatory cytokines. The presence of these cells in germ-free mice indicated that they did not adopt these properties by responding to a cross-reactive pMHCI derived from a microorganism.

Rather, the $CD8^+$ $CD44^{high}$ T cells in naive mice are functionally and phenotypically identical to naive phenotype cells that undergo homeostatic proliferation after transfer into lymphopenic hosts (7, 80). This proliferation is driven by low-affinity TCR recognition of self-pMHCI and excess IL-7 that is available because of the lack of T cells that normally consume it. Therefore, the simplest explanation for the existence of memory phenotype cells in the preimmune repertoires of nonlymphopenic adults is that previously unappreciated homeostatic proliferation occurs in these individuals at a low level. Alternatively, it is possible that the memory phenotype cells found in the preimmune repertoires of nonlymphopenic adults underwent homeostatic proliferation during neonatal life, a period of natural lymphopenia, and then survived as memory phenotype cells (22). The presence of memory phenotype cells in the preimmune repertoire suggests that the primary immune response to some pMHC consists of a mixture of rapidly responding memory phenotype cells and more slowly responding naive phenotype cells.

REGULATORY T CELLS

Treg cells are defined by expression of the Foxp3 transcription factor and the capacity to suppress immune responses (13, 81). Two varieties of Treg cells have been identified to date: nTreg cells that develop directly in the thymus (13) and iTreg cells that develop from naive phenotype cells that are stimulated with foreign pMHCII in the secondary lymphoid organs under certain conditions (14, 82, 83). Because nTreg cells develop in germ-free mice (84) presumably in the absence of foreign antigens, they can be considered to be part of the preimmune repertoire. nTreg cells account for about 3% of the $CD4^+$ thymocytes and 10% of the $CD4^+$ T cells in secondary lymphoid organs of a normal mouse (85). Acute ablation of $Foxp3^+$ cells results in T cell–dependent lymphoproliferative disease, demonstrating that the role of nTreg cells in the preimmune repertoire is to suppress immunopathology (86). One interpretation of this finding is that Treg cells continuously suppress self-pMHCII-reactive non-Treg cells that would otherwise cause autoimmunity. It should be noted, however, that the pMHCII specificity of the T cells that cause immunopathology in Treg cell–deficient hosts has yet to be determined.

Factors must exist that determine whether a thymocyte expresses Foxp3 and becomes an nTreg or does not and becomes a naive phenotype T cell. Ninety-five percent of the nTreg cells in the thymus express CD4 and 5% express CD8 (85). $CD4^+$ nTreg cells are absent in MHCII-deficient mice, and the few $CD8^+$ nTreg cells are absent in MHCI-deficient mice, indicating that recognition of MHC is required for nTreg development (85). The fact that most nTreg cells are $CD4^+$ suggests that nTreg development depends on factors such as ThPOK or Tox, which determine $CD4^+$ lineage choice (57, 87). nTreg development is impaired in mice lacking IL-2 (88), the CD25 or common γ chain components of the IL-2 receptor (89), or STAT5, which is part of the common γ chain signal transduction cascade (90). A plausible scenario is that IL-2 receptor signaling induces STAT5 activation in a subset of $CD4^+$ thymocytes, which in combination with ThPOK or Tox cause the cell to become an nTreg. It is possible that the nTreg cells themselves make the IL-2 that drives this process. Indeed, nTreg development depends on CD28 (91), which transduces T cell–intrinsic signals involved in IL-2 production (92). However, it is also possible that the IL-2 comes from other cells, for example thymic dendritic cells (DCs) or other T cells.

Because the pivotal early step in nTreg development appears to be the acquisition of IL-2 sensing capacity via induction of CD25, the question becomes why some $CD4^+$ thymocytes express CD25. CD25 expression in mature naive phenotype T cells is induced by TCR signaling (93). Therefore, it is possible that $CD4^+$ thymocytes that express TCRs with self-pMHCII affinities just below the clonal deletion threshold receive enough TCR signaling to induce CD25. Support for this concept comes from experiments in which a transgene encoding a foreign antigenic peptide was expressed in the thymuses of mice also expressing a transgenic TCR specific for the relevant pMHCII (94, 95, 96). Under these conditions, many cells expressing the transgenic TCR were deleted, and many of the surviving cells developed into nTreg cells. Similarly, Rudensky and colleagues (97) retrovirally transduced TCRα chains from nTreg clones into transgenic T cells expressing a fixed nTreg-permissive TCRβ chain. They found that the cells expressing these nTreg-derived TCRs underwent more pMHCII-dependent homeostatic proliferation after transfer into lymphopenic hosts than did cells expressing non-Treg-derived TCRs and, importantly, induced a wasting autoimmune disease. In addition, T cells that were transduced with nTreg-derived TCRα chains proliferated in vitro in response to APCs displaying a diverse set of self-pMHCII but not in response to APCs displaying a very limited set of self-pMHCII. Together these results make a strong case that expression of a TCR at the high end of the sub deletion self-pMHC-binding affinity range is a necessary condition for nTreg development.

If this contention is correct, then only certain TCRs with the necessary self-pMHCII affinity should be conducive to nTreg development. Several lines of evidence are consistent with this possibility. By sequencing TCRα chains in T cells with an identical TCRβ chain, Rudensky and colleagues (98) found that the nTreg and naive phenotype TCRα chain repertoires were both very diverse but only partially overlapping. This and related studies (99, 100) have estimated this overlap at 10–40%. The fact that at least 60% of nTreg TCRs are never found in naive phenotype T cells indicates that some TCRs preferentially instruct nTreg development.

Recent work from Bautista et al. (101) provided additional evidence for this idea. These investigators made several monoclonal TCR transgenic mouse lines using TCRα chains that were found only in nTreg cells or only in non-nTreg cells. They found that only the transgenic mice produced with TCRs from nTreg cells had the potential to produce nTreg cells. Interestingly, however, the efficiency of nTreg cell development depended on the number of TCR transgenic precursors. Thus, only 10,000 (0.1%) of the 10^7 $CD4^+$ thymocytes that developed in intact nTreg TCR transgenic mice expressed Foxp3. Remarkably, in mixed bone marrow chimeras where 0.1% of the thymocytes were of nTreg TCR transgenic origin, 10,000 (30%) of the ~30,000 $CD4^+$ thymocytes derived from nTreg TCR transgenic bone marrow expressed Foxp3.

These findings indicate that the thymus can only support development of 10,000 nTreg cells with the same pMHCII specificity. The fact that this niche appears to be defined by pMHCII suggests that the self-pMHCII ligands recognized by individual nTreg clones are only displayed on a small subset of thymic APCs. How could that occur? One possibility relates to the autoimmune regulator (AIRE) transcription factor. AIRE regulates the promiscuous expression of extrathymic proteins, for example insulin, in medullary thymic epithelial cells (mTECs) (102). Kyweski and colleagues (103) have shown that AIRE-regulated genes are expressed in a stochastic fashion, creating a situation in which individual mTEC express only a subset of AIRE-regulated proteins. In addition, bone marrow–derived APCs, probably DCs, acquire self-antigens from mTEC (104, 105). If self-pMHCII ligands recognized by individual nTreg clones are derived from AIRE-regulated gene products, then these ligands might be displayed on a small subset of mTEC or DCs, thereby creating the niche-defining resource. An implication of this hypothesis is that AIRE plays an important role in nTreg development. There is evidence on both sides of this issue. On the one hand, Aschenbrenner et al. (106) expressed a model antigen under the control of the AIRE promoter in mice expressing a transgenic TCR specific for a pMHCII derived from the antigen. They found an increase in the fraction of TCR transgenic T cells that became nTreg cells. On the other hand, AIRE-deficient mice have the same number of nTreg cells as normal mice (102). Thus, although AIRE expression may promote nTreg development, it is not essential for this purpose. Another way that small DC populations displaying different pMHCII complexes could be established in the thymus is trafficking from secondary lymphoid organs (107). DCs from the brain would almost certainly display a different set of self-pMHCII complexes than would DCs from the pancreas. If small numbers of each type migrated to the thymus, they could influence distinct populations of nTreg cells.

Although TCR-self-pMHC interactions at the high end of the sub deletion affinity range may favor nTreg development, there may be exceptions to this rule. For example, Mathis and colleagues (108) produced a transgenic system in which a model antigen could be induced in thymic epithelial cells under the control of an inducible promoter in a mouse containing TCR transgenic T cells specific for a pMHCII derived from the antigen. These mice contained about 100,000 TCR transgenic CD4$^+$ nTreg cells in the absence of antigen expression. Remarkably, this number did not change appreciably as antigen expression was induced even though CD25$^-$ TCR transgenic CD4$^+$ T cells underwent clonal deletion. These results lead to two conclusions: nTreg development does not appear to be driven by high-affinity self-pMHCII recognition in this system and nTreg cells are resistant to deletion. If expression of Foxp3 is a TCR-independent event, then one must postulate that CD25 expression is driven by some other signal or is stochastically expressed in 10% of CD4$^+$ thymocytes. However, because this study was done in intact TCR transgenic mice, the role of TCR-self-pMHCII interaction in nTreg differentiation may have been obscured by intraclonal competition between the large numbers of TCR transgenic precursors. Thus, it would be of interest to perform the inducible antigen experiment under conditions in which the TCR transgenic precursors were only a small fraction of the total T cell pool as described by Bautista et al. (101).

AIRE: autoimmune regulator

mTEC: medullary thymic epithelial cell

The results of Bautista et al. (101) also point to the need to complement studies of monoclonal TCR transgenic mice with analyses of the normal polyclonal nTreg cell repertoire. pMHCII tetramer enrichment is a useful tool in this regard. As mentioned above, B6 mice contain 200 polyclonal 2W1S:I-A^b-binding CD4$^+$ T cells in the spleen and lymph nodes (40). Burchill et al. (109) found that less than 5% of these cells expressed Foxp3, which were presumed to be nTreg cells because the mice had never been exposed to the 2W1S peptide. This percentage was lower than the 10% value for the total CD4$^+$ T cell population but clearly higher than background. Thus, nTreg

GITR: glucocorticoid-inducible tumor necrosis factor receptor

cells were underrepresented but present in this foreign pMHCII-specific population. Conventional wisdom suggests that these cells became nTreg cells because their 2W1S:I-A^b-specific TCRs had a higher affinity for a positively selecting self-pMHCII than the 2W1S:I-A^b-specific cells that became naive phenotype cells.

The existence of the Foxp3- and $Foxp3^+$ 2W1S:I-A^b-specific cells in B6 mice provided an opportunity to study the behavior of polyclonal naive and nTreg cells with the identical pMHCII specificity during an immune response. Way and colleagues (110) produced an attenuated strain of *Listeria monocytogenes* expressing the 2W1S peptide. The $Foxp3^-$ but not the $Foxp3^+$ 2W1S:I-A^b-binding T cells underwent a dramatic clonal expansion in B6 mice infected with these bacteria. Therefore, although $Foxp3^+$ nTreg cells were present in the 2W1S:I-A^b-specific preimmune repertoire, these cells did not undergo clonal expansion like the naive phenotype cells with this TCR specificity. In contrast, McLachlan et al. (111) found that $Foxp3^+$ cells accounted for 20% of the total 2W1S:I-A^b-binding population in the draining lymph nodes of B6 mice two weeks after subcutaneous injection of 2W1S peptide in emulsified incomplete Freund's adjuvant. However, other evidence indicated that these cells were naive phenotype cells that became iTreg cells. Because of the potential for iTreg conversion from naive phenotype cells, it is not clear if and how foreign pMHCII-specific nTreg cells from the preimmune repertoire participate in the immune responses to foreign antigens. Investigators have suggested that nTreg cells specific for *Leishmania major*–derived pMHCII limit clearance of the parasite (112). These cells were identified as nTreg cells based on expression of CD25, which is expressed at higher levels on nTreg cells than on iTreg cells. Because phenotypic distinctions are not absolute, the involvement of *L. major* pMHCII-specific nTreg cells in immunity to this infection must await demonstration that $Foxp3^+$ *L. major* pMHCII-specific T cells exist in the preimmune repertoire and change their behavior in a *L. major* pMHCII-specific fashion following infection with this parasite.

If nTreg cells are capable of responding to foreign pMHCII, then we are left with the perplexing reality that 10% of the preimmune $CD4^+$ T cell repertoire is poised to suppress rather than initiate immunity. At face value this appears to run counter to the goal of eliminating infections and tumors. However, the coexistence of suppressive and antimicrobial T cells may allow for the fine-tuning of immunity. The induction of iTreg cells from naive phenotype T cells with the same pMHCII specificity during a chronic infection is thought to represent a form of negative feedback control on the intensity of an immune response needed to protect the host from damage caused by excessive inflammation (14). The existence of foreign pMHCII-specific nTreg cells takes this idea one step further in that nTreg cells could provide immediate negative regulation to adjust the speed and intensity of the conventional T cell response.

CONCLUSION

The clonal selection theory is still the foundation of current understanding of adaptive immunity and self-tolerance. However, some of the recent developments described in this review point to the need for subtle modifications of this theory. The original theory posited that the repertoire is formed by the production of millions of clones with random receptors (1). However, it is now becoming clear that TCRs produced by the repertoire of immature preselection thymocytes do not have random specificities for different macromolecules. Rather, TCRs appear to have evolved to recognize MHC via germline-encoded CDR1 and CDR2 domains (18). Thus, the critical function of V(D)J recombination is not only receptor diversification but also disruption of the germline-encoded interactions to prevent excessive clonal deletion. The original theory posited that self-reactive lymphocytes are eliminated from the repertoire (1). It is now clear that not all overtly self-pMHC-reactive T cells undergo clonal deletion. Indeed, self-pMHCII-specific nTreg cells appear to be purposefully retained in the repertoire to suppress autoimmunity (13). The original clonal selection theory posited activation of foreign-specific lymphocytes to become effector cells and memory cells (1). This strategy could be compared to controlling the speed of a car by pressing on the accelerator. Current evidence points to simultaneous activation of microorganism-specific suppressor and effector lymphocytes to clear the infection while limiting immunopathology (13). This is like driving a car with one foot on the accelerator and the other on the brake. A small change in pressure by either foot will cause a rapid jump forward or quick stop. Perhaps this is the nimbleness that the host needs to stay one step ahead of the microorganisms.

SUMMARY POINTS

1. The preimmune repertoire of α/β TCR$^+$, pMHC-specific T cells contains functionally heterogeneous subsets, including recent thymic emigrants, mature naive phenotype cells, memory phenotype cells, and nTreg cells.
2. A germline-encoded tendency of TCR V segments to bind MHC molecules contributes to the MHC bias of the preimmune repertoire.
3. The repertoire of naive phenotype T cells consists of distinct pMHC-specific populations that consistently vary in size in different individuals.
4. Variation in the size of naive phenotype pMHC-specific populations is a factor in immunodominance.

FUTURE ISSUES

1. How is the variation in the size of naive phenotype pMHC-specific populations determined?
2. Can all foreign pMHCs be recognized by clones in the preimmune repertoire or are repertoire holes common?
3. Do recent thymic emigrants and the memory phenotype T cells in the preimmune repertoire play special roles in the primary immune response?
4. Which factors account for the niches that support only small numbers of pMHCII-specific naive phenotype cells and nTreg cells?
5. Which peptides, self and/or foreign, are recognized by nTreg cells?
6. What is the source of IL-2 that is needed for nTreg development?

DISCLOSURE STATEMENT

The authors are not aware of any affiliations, memberships, funding, or financial holdings that might be perceived as affecting the objectivity of this review.

ACKNOWLEDGMENTS

The authors acknowledge Stephen Jameson and Kris Hogquist for critical reviews of the manuscript.

LITERATURE CITED

1. Burnet FM. 1959. *The Clonal Selection Theory of Acquired Immunity*. Cambridge, UK: Cambridge Univ. Press
2. Rudolph MG, Stanfield RL, Wilson IA. 2006. How TCRs bind MHCs, peptides, and coreceptors. *Annu. Rev. Immunol.* 24:419–66
3. Taghon T, Rothenberg EV. 2008. Molecular mechanisms that control mouse and human TCR-$\alpha\beta$ and TCR-$\gamma\delta$ T cell development. *Semin. Immunopathol.* 30:383–98
4. Starr TK, Jameson SC, Hogquist KA. 2003. Positive and negative selection of T cells. *Annu. Rev. Immunol.* 21:139–76
5. Singer A, Adoro S, Park JH. 2008. Lineage fate and intense debate: myths, models and mechanisms of CD4- versus CD8-lineage choice. *Nat. Rev. Immunol.* 8:788–801
6. Collins A, Littman DR, Taniuchi I. 2009. RUNX proteins in transcription factor networks that regulate T-cell lineage choice. *Nat. Rev. Immunol.* 9:106–15
7. Surh CD, Sprent J. 2008. Homeostasis of naive and memory T cells. *Immunity* 29:848–62
8. Weinreich MA, Hogquist KA. 2008. Thymic emigration: when and how T cells leave home. *J. Immunol.* 181:2265–70
9. Dutton RW, Bradley LM, Swain SL. 1998. T cell memory. *Annu. Rev. Immunol.* 16:201–23
10. Kuo CT, Veselits ML, Leiden JM. 1997. LKLF: A transcriptional regulator of single-positive T cell quiescence and survival. *Science* 277:1986–90
11. Modiano JF, Johnson LD, Bellgrau D. 2008. Negative regulators in homeostasis of naive peripheral T cells. *Immunol. Res.* 41:137–53
12. Hogquist KA, Baldwin TA, Jameson SC. 2005. Central tolerance: learning self-control in the thymus. *Nat. Rev. Immunol.* 5:772–82
13. Josefowicz SZ, Rudensky A. 2009. Control of regulatory T cell lineage commitment and maintenance. *Immunity* 30:616–25
14. Curotto de Lafaille MA, Lafaille JJ. 2009. Natural and adaptive Foxp3^{+} regulatory T cells: more of the same or a division of labor? *Immunity* 30:626–35
15. Surh CD, Sprent J. 1994. T-cell apoptosis detected in situ during positive and negative selection in the thymus. *Nature* 372:100–3
16. Van Laethem F, Sarafova SD, Park JH, Tai X, Pobezinsky L, et al. 2007. Deletion of CD4 and CD8 coreceptors permits generation of $\alpha\beta$ T cells that recognize antigens independently of the MHC. *Immunity* 27:735–50
17. Huseby ES, White J, Crawford F, Vass T, Becker D, et al. 2005. How the T cell repertoire becomes peptide and MHC specific. *Cell* 122:247–60
18. Dai S, Huseby ES, Rubtsova K, Scott-Browne J, Crawford F, et al. 2008. Crossreactive T cells spotlight the germline rules for $\alpha\beta$ T cell-receptor interactions with MHC molecules. *Immunity* 28:324–34
19. Makaroff LE, Hendricks DW, Niec RE, Fink PJ. 2009. Postthymic maturation influences the CD8 T cell response to antigen. *Proc. Natl. Acad. Sci. USA* 106:4799–804
20. Boursalian TE, Golob J, Soper DM, Cooper CJ, Fink PJ. 2004. Continued maturation of thymic emigrants in the periphery. *Nat. Immunol.* 5:418–25
21. Tough DF, Sprent J. 1994. Turnover of naive- and memory-phenotype T cells. *J. Exp. Med.* 179:1127–35
22. Min B, McHugh R, Sempowski GD, Mackall C, Foucras G, Paul WE. 2003. Neonates support lymphopenia-induced proliferation. *Immunity* 18:131–40
23. von Andrian UH, Mackay CR. 2000. T-cell function and migration. *N. Engl. J. Med.* 343:1020–34
24. Davis MM, Bjorkman PJ. 1988. T-cell antigen receptor genes and T-cell recognition. *Nature* 334:395–402

25. Casrouge A, Beaudoing E, Dalle S, Pannetier C, Kanellopoulos J, Kourilsky P. 2000. Size estimate of the αβ TCR repertoire of naive mouse splenocytes. *J. Immunol.* 164:5782–87
26. Maryanski JL, Jongeneel CV, Bucher P, Casanova JL, Walker PR. 1996. Single-cell PCR analysis of TCR repertoires selected by antigen in vivo: a high magnitude CD8 response is comprised of very few clones. *Immunity* 4:47–55
27. Malherbe L, Hausl C, Teyton L, McHeyzer-Williams MG. 2004. Clonal selection of helper T cells is determined by an affinity threshold with no further skewing of TCR binding properties. *Immunity* 21:669–79
28. Kedzierska K, Day EB, Pi J, Heard SB, Doherty PC, et al. 2006. Quantification of repertoire diversity of influenza-specific epitopes with predominant public or private TCR usage. *J. Immunol.* 177:6705–12
29. Altman JD, Moss PAH, Goulder JR, Barouch DH, McHeyzer-Williams MG, et al. 1996. Phenotypic analysis of antigen-specific T lymphocytes. *Science* 274:94–96
30. Bodinier M, Peyrat MA, Tournay C, Davodeau F, Romagne F, et al. 2000. Efficient detection and immunomagnetic sorting of specific T cells using multimers of MHC class I and peptide with reduced CD8 binding. *Nat. Med.* 6:707–10
31. McDermott AB, Spiegel HM, Irsch J, Ogg GS, Nixon DF. 2001. A simple and rapid magnetic bead separation technique for the isolation of tetramer-positive virus-specific CD8 T cells. *AIDS* 15:810–12
32. Keenan RD, Ainsworth J, Khan N, Bruton R, Cobbold M, et al. 2001. Purification of cytomegalovirus-specific CD8 T cells from peripheral blood using HLA-peptide tetramers. *Br. J. Haematol.* 115:428–34
33. Jager E, Hohn H, Necker A, Forster R, Karbach J, et al. 2002. Peptide-specific $CD8^+$ T-cell evolution in vivo: response to peptide vaccination with Melan-A/MART-1. *Int. J. Cancer.* 98:376–88
34. Jang MH, Seth NP, Wucherpfennig KW. 2003. Ex vivo analysis of thymic CD4 T cells in nonobese diabetic mice with tetramers generated from I-A(g7)/class II-associated invariant chain peptide precursors. *J. Immunol.* 171:4175–86
35. Day CL, Seth NP, Lucas M, Appel H, Gauthier L, et al. 2003. Ex vivo analysis of human memory CD4 T cells specific for hepatitis C virus using MHC class II tetramers. *J. Clin. Invest.* 112:831–42
36. Lemaitre F, Viguier M, Cho MS, Fourneau JM, Maillere B, et al. 2004. Detection of low-frequency human antigen-specific $CD4^+$ T cells using MHC class II multimer bead sorting and immunoscope analysis. *Eur. J. Immunol.* 34:2941–49
37. Barnes E, Ward SM, Kasprowicz VO, Dusheiko G, Klenerman P, Lucas M. 2004. Ultra-sensitive class I tetramer analysis reveals previously undetectable populations of antiviral $CD8^+$ T cells. *Eur. J. Immunol.* 34:1570–77
38. Lucas M, Day CL, Wyer JR, Cunliffe SL, Loughry A, et al. 2004. Ex vivo phenotype and frequency of influenza virus-specific CD4 memory T cells. *J. Virol.* 78:7284–87
39. Scriba TJ, Purbhoo M, Day CL, Robinson N, Fidler S, et al. 2005. Ultrasensitive detection and phenotyping of $CD4^+$ T cells with optimized HLA class II tetramer staining. *J. Immunol.* 175:6334–43
40. Moon JJ, Chu HH, Pepper M, McSorley SJ, Jameson SC, et al. 2007. Naive $CD4^+$ T cell frequency varies for different epitopes and predicts repertoire diversity and response magnitude. *Immunity* 27:203–13
41. Rees W, Bender J, Teague TK, Kedl RM, Crawford F, et al. 1999. An inverse relationship between T cell receptor affinity and antigen dose during $CD4^+$ T cell responses in vivo and in vitro. *Proc. Natl. Acad. Sci. USA* 96:9781–86
42. McSorley SJ, Cookson BT, Jenkins MK. 2000. Characterization of $CD4^+$ T cell responses during natural infection with *Salmonella typhimurium*. *J. Immunol.* 164:986–93
43. Barnden MJ, Allison J, Heath WR, Carbone FR. 1998. Defective TCR expression in transgenic mice constructed using cDNA-based α- and β-chain genes under the control of heterologous regulatory elements. *Immunol. Cell Biol.* 76:34–40
44. Chu HH, Moon JJ, Takada K, Pepper M, Molitor JA, et al. 2009. Positive selection optimizes the number and function of MHCII-restricted $CD4^+$ T cell clones in the naive polyclonal repertoire. *Proc. Natl. Acad. Sci. USA* 106:11241–45
45. Obar JJ, Khanna KM, Lefrancois L. 2008. Endogenous naive $CD8^+$ T cell precursor frequency regulates primary and memory responses to infection. *Immunity* 28:859–69

46. Kotturi MF, Scott I, Wolfe T, Peters B, Sidney J, et al. 2008. Naive precursor frequencies and MHC binding rather than the degree of epitope diversity shape $CD8^+$ T cell immunodominance. *J. Immunol.* 181:2124–33
47. Haluszczak C, Akue AD, Hamilton SE, Johnson LD, Pujanauski L, et al. 2009. The antigen-specific $CD8^+$ T cell repertoire in unimmunized mice includes memory phenotype cells bearing markers of homeostatic expansion. *J. Exp. Med.* 206:435–48
48. Arstila TP, Casrouge A, Baron V, Even J, Kanellopoulos J, Kourilsky P. 1999. A direct estimate of the human $\alpha\beta$ T cell receptor diversity. *Science* 286:958–61
49. Evavold BD, Sloan-Lancaster J, Wilson KJ, Rothbard JB, Allen PM. 1995. Specific T cell recognition of minimally homologous peptides: evidence for multiple endogenous ligands. *Immunity* 2:655–63
50. Crawford F, Huseby E, White J, Marrack P, Kappler JW. 2004. Mimotopes for alloreactive and conventional T cells in a peptide-MHC display library. *PLoS Biol.* 2:E90
51. Ishizuka J, Grebe K, Shenderov E, Peters B, Chen Q, et al. 2009. Quantitating T cell cross-reactivity for unrelated peptide antigens. *J. Immunol.* 183:4337–45
52. Pittet MJ, Valmori D, Dunbar PR, Speiser DE, Lienard D, et al. 1999. High frequencies of naive Melan-A/MART-1-specific $CD8^+$ T cells in a large proportion of human histocompatibility leukocyte antigen (HLA)-A2 individuals. *J. Exp. Med.* 190:705–15
53. Turner SJ, Kedzierska K, Komodromou H, La Gruta NL, Dunstone MA, et al. 2005. Lack of prominent peptide-major histocompatibility complex features limits repertoire diversity in virus-specific $CD8^+$ T cell populations. *Nat. Immunol.* 6:382–89
54. Venturi V, Price DA, Douek DC, Davenport MP. 2008. The molecular basis for public T-cell responses? *Nat. Rev. Immunol.* 8:231–38
55. Yewdell JW. 2006. Confronting complexity: real-world immunodominance in antiviral $CD8^+$ T cell responses. *Immunity* 25:533–43
56. Yager EJ, Ahmed M, Lanzer K, Randall TD, Woodland DL, Blackman MA. 2008. Age-associated decline in T cell repertoire diversity leads to holes in the repertoire and impaired immunity to influenza virus. *J. Exp. Med.* 205:711–23
57. Zhou L, Chong MM, Littman DR. 2009. Plasticity of $CD4^+$ T cell lineage differentiation. *Immunity* 30:646–55
58. Stemberger C, Huster KM, Koffler M, Anderl F, Schiemann M, et al. 2007. A single naive $CD8^+$ T cell precursor can develop into diverse effector and memory subsets. *Immunity* 27:985–97
59. Zehn D, Lee SY, Bevan MJ. 2009. Complete but curtailed T-cell response to very low-affinity antigen. *Nature* 458:211–14
60. Fazilleau N, McHeyzer-Williams LJ, Rosen H, McHeyzer-Williams MG. 2009. The function of follicular helper T cells is regulated by the strength of T cell antigen receptor binding. *Nat. Immunol.* 10:375–84
61. Teixeiro E, Daniels MA, Hamilton SE, Schrum AG, Bragado R, et al. 2009. Different T cell receptor signals determine $CD8^+$ memory versus effector development. *Science* 323:502–5
62. McHeyzer-Williams LJ, McHeyzer-Williams MG. 2004. Developmentally distinct Th cells control plasma cell production in vivo. *Immunity* 20:231–42
63. Rock KL, Reiser H, Bamezai A, McGrew J, Benacerraf B. 1989. The LY-6 locus: a multigene family encoding phosphatidylinositol-anchored membrane proteins concerned with T-cell activation. *Immunol. Rev.* 111:195–224
64. Ge Q, Hu H, Eisen HN, Chen J. 2002. Different contributions of thymopoiesis and homeostasis-driven proliferation to the reconstitution of naive and memory T cell compartments. *Proc. Natl. Acad. Sci. USA* 99:2989–94
65. Tanchot C, Le Campion A, Martin B, Leaument S, Dautigny N, Lucas B. 2002. Conversion of naive T cells to a memory-like phenotype in lymphopenic hosts is not related to a homeostatic mechanism that fills the peripheral naive T cell pool. *J. Immunol.* 168:5042–46
66. Clarke SR, Rudensky AY. 2000. Survival and homeostatic proliferation of naive peripheral $CD4^+$ T cells in the absence of self peptide:MHC complexes. *J. Immunol.* 165:2458–64
67. Dorfman JR, Stefanova I, Yasutomo K, Germain RN. 2000. $CD4^+$ T cell survival is not directly linked to self-MHC-induced TCR signaling. *Nat. Immunol.* 1:329–35

68. Hataye J, Moon JJ, Khoruts A, Reilly C, Jenkins MK. 2006. Naive and memory CD4$^+$ T cell survival controlled by clonal abundance. *Science* 312:114–16
69. Vrisekoop N, den Braber I, de Boer AB, Ruiter AF, Ackermans MT, et al. 2008. Sparse production but preferential incorporation of recently produced naive T cells in the human peripheral pool. *Proc. Natl. Acad. Sci. USA* 105:6115–20
70. Link A, Vogt TK, Favre S, Britschgi MR, Acha-Orbea H, et al. 2007. Fibroblastic reticular cells in lymph nodes regulate the homeostasis of naive T cells. *Nat. Immunol.* 8:1255–65
71. Polic B, Kunkel D, Scheffold A, Rajewsky K. 2001. How αβ T cells deal with induced TCR α ablation. *Proc. Natl. Acad. Sci. USA* 98:8744–49
72. Tanchot C, Lemonnier FA, Perarnau B, Freitas AA, Rocha B. 1997. Differential requirements for survival and proliferation of CD8 memory T cells. *Science* 276:2057–62
73. Takada K, Jameson SC. 2009. Self-class I MHC molecules support survival of naive CD8 T cells, but depress their functional sensitivity through regulation of CD8 expression levels. *J. Exp. Med.* 206:2253–69
74. Brocker T. 1997. Survival of mature CD4 T lymphocytes is dependent on major histocompatibility complex class II-expressing dendritic cells. *J. Exp. Med.* 186:1223–32
75. Witherden D, van Oers N, Waltzinger C, Weiss A, Benoist C, Mathis D. 2000. Tetracycline-controllable selection of CD4$^+$ T cells: half-life and survival signals in the absence of major histocompatibility complex class II molecules. *J. Exp. Med.* 191:355–64
76. Martin B, Becourt C, Bienvenu B, Lucas B. 2006. Self-recognition is crucial for maintaining the peripheral CD4$^+$ T-cell pool in a nonlymphopenic environment. *Blood* 108:270–77
77. Lo WL, Felix NJ, Walters JJ, Rohrs H, Gross ML, Allen PM. 2009. An endogenous peptide positively selects and augments the activation and survival of peripheral CD4$^+$ T cells. *Nat. Immunol.* 10:1155–61
78. Ebert PJ, Jiang S, Xie J, Li QJ, Davis MM. 2009. An endogenous positively selecting peptide enhances mature T cell responses and becomes an autoantigen in the absence of microRNA miR-181a. *Nat. Immunol.* 10:1162–69
79. Min B, Foucras G, Meier-Schellersheim M, Paul WE. 2004. Spontaneous proliferation, a response of naive CD4 T cells determined by the diversity of the memory cell repertoire. *Proc. Natl. Acad. Sci. USA* 101:3874–79
80. Jameson SC. 2002. Maintaining the norm: T-cell homeostasis. *Nat. Rev. Immunol.* 2:547–56
81. Shevach EM. 2009. Mechanisms of Foxp3$^+$ T regulatory cell-mediated suppression. *Immunity* 30:636–45
82. Thorstenson KM, Khoruts A. 2001. Generation of anergic and potentially immunoregulatory CD25$^+$CD4 T cells in vivo after induction of peripheral tolerance with intravenous or oral antigen. *J. Immunol.* 167:188–95
83. Apostolou I, Verginis P, Kretschmer K, Polansky J, Huhn J, von Boehmer H. 2008. Peripherally induced Treg: mode, stability, and role in specific tolerance. *J. Clin. Immunol.* 28:619–24
84. Hrncir T, Stepankova R, Kozakova H, Hudcovic T, Tlaskalova-Hogenova H. 2008. Gut microbiota and lipopolysaccharide content of the diet influence development of regulatory T cells: studies in germ-free mice. *BMC Immunol.* 9:65
85. Fontenot JD, Rasmussen JP, Williams LM, Dooley JL, Farr AG, Rudensky AY. 2005. Regulatory T cell lineage specification by the forkhead transcription factor Foxp3. *Immunity* 22:329–41
86. Kim JM, Rasmussen JP, Rudensky AY. 2007. Regulatory T cells prevent catastrophic autoimmunity throughout the lifespan of mice. *Nat. Immunol.* 8:191–97
87. Aliahmad P, Kaye J. 2008. Development of all CD4 T lineages requires nuclear factor TOX. *J. Exp. Med.* 205:245–56
88. Malek TR. 2008. The biology of interleukin-2. *Annu. Rev. Immunol.* 26:453–79
89. Fontenot JD, Rasmussen JP, Gavin MA, Rudensky AY. 2005. A function for interleukin 2 in Foxp3-expressing regulatory T cells. *Nat. Immunol.* 6:1142–51
90. Burchill MA, Yang J, Vogtenhuber C, Blazar BR, Farrar MA. 2007. IL-2 receptor β-dependent STAT5 activation is required for the development of Foxp3$^+$ regulatory T cells. *J. Immunol.* 178:280–90
91. Salomon B, Lenschow DJ, Rhee L, Ashourian N, Singh B, et al. 2000. B7/CD28 costimulation is essential for the homeostasis of the CD4$^+$CD25$^+$ immunoregulatory T cells that control autoimmune diabetes. *Immunity* 12:431–40

92. Jenkins MK, Taylor PS, Norton SD, Urdahl KB. 1991. CD28 delivers a costimulatory signal involved in antigen-specific IL-2 production by human T cells. *J. Immunol.* 147:2461–66
93. Kim HP, Imbert J, Leonard WJ. 2006. Both integrated and differential regulation of components of the IL-2/IL-2 receptor system. *Cytokine Growth Factor Rev.* 17:349–66
94. Jordan MS, Boesteanu A, Reed AJ, Petrone AL, Holenbeck AE, et al. 2001. Thymic selection of $CD4^{+}CD25^{+}$ regulatory T cells induced by an agonist self-peptide. *Nat. Immunol.* 2:301–6
95. Apostolou I, Sarukhan A, Klein L, von Boehmer H. 2002. Origin of regulatory T cells with known specificity for antigen. *Nat. Immunol.* 3:756–63
96. DiPaolo RJ, Shevach EM. 2009. $CD4^{+}$ T-cell development in a mouse expressing a transgenic TCR derived from a Treg. *Eur. J. Immunol.* 39:234–40
97. Hsieh CS, Liang Y, Tyznik AJ, Self SG, Liggitt D, Rudensky AY. 2004. Recognition of the peripheral self by naturally arising $CD25^{+}$ $CD4^{+}$ T cell receptors. *Immunity* 21:267–77
98. Hsieh CS, Zheng Y, Liang Y, Fontenot JD, Rudensky AY. 2006. An intersection between the self-reactive regulatory and nonregulatory T cell receptor repertoires. *Nat. Immunol.* 7:401–10
99. Pacholczyk R, Ignatowicz H, Kraj P, Ignatowicz L. 2006. Origin and T cell receptor diversity of $Foxp3^{+}CD4^{+}CD25^{+}$ T cells. *Immunity* 25:249–59
100. Wong J, Obst R, Correia-Neves M, Losyev G, Mathis D, Benoist C. 2007. Adaptation of TCR repertoires to self-peptides in regulatory and nonregulatory $CD4^{+}$ T cells. *J. Immunol.* 178:7032–41
101. Bautista JL, Lio CW, Lathrop SK, Forbush K, Liang Y, et al. 2009. Intraclonal competition limits the fate determination of regulatory T cells in the thymus. *Nat. Immunol.* 10:610–17
102. Mathis D, Benoist C. 2009. Aire. *Annu. Rev. Immunol.* 27:287–312
103. Derbinski J, Pinto S, Rosch S, Hexel K, Kyewski B. 2008. Promiscuous gene expression patterns in single medullary thymic epithelial cells argue for a stochastic mechanism. *Proc. Natl. Acad. Sci. USA* 105:657–62
104. Gallegos AM, Bevan MJ. 2004. Central tolerance to tissue-specific antigens mediated by direct and indirect antigen presentation. *J. Exp. Med.* 200:1039–49
105. Koble C, Kyewski B. 2009. The thymic medulla: a unique microenvironment for intercellular self-antigen transfer. *J. Exp. Med.* 206:1505–13
106. Aschenbrenner K, D'Cruz LM, Vollmann EH, Hinterberger M, Emmerich J, et al. 2007. Selection of $Foxp3^{+}$ regulatory T cells specific for self antigen expressed and presented by $Aire^{+}$ medullary thymic epithelial cells. *Nat. Immunol.* 8:351–58
107. Bonasio R, Scimone ML, Schaerli P, Grabie N, Lichtman AH, von Andrian UH. 2006. Clonal deletion of thymocytes by circulating dendritic cells homing to the thymus. *Nat. Immunol.* 7:1092–100
108. van Santen HM, Benoist C, Mathis D. 2004. Number of T reg cells that differentiate does not increase upon encounter of agonist ligand on thymic epithelial cells. *J. Exp. Med.* 200:1221–30
109. Burchill MA, Yang J, Vang KB, Moon JJ, Chu HH, et al. 2008. Linked T cell receptor and cytokine signaling govern the development of the regulatory T cell repertoire. *Immunity* 28:112–21
110. Ertelt JM, Rowe JH, Johanns TM, Lai JC, McLachlan JB, Way SS. 2009. Selective priming and expansion of antigen-specific $Foxp3^{-}$ $CD4^{+}$ T cells during *Listeria monocytogenes* infection. *J. Immunol.* 182:3032–38
111. McLachlan JB, Catron DM, Moon JJ, Jenkins MK. 2009. Dendritic cell antigen presentation drives simultaneous cytokine production by effector and regulatory T cells in inflamed skin. *Immunity* 30:277–88
112. Suffia IJ, Reckling SK, Piccirillo CA, Goldszmid RS, Belkaid Y. 2006. Infected site-restricted $Foxp3^{+}$ natural regulatory T cells are specific for microbial antigens. *J. Exp. Med.* 203:777–88

The Role of ThPOK in Control of CD4/CD8 Lineage Commitment

Xi He, Kyewon Park, and Dietmar J. Kappes

Fox Chase Cancer Center, Philadelphia, Pennsylvania 19111; email: DJ_Kappes@fccc.edu

Annu. Rev. Immunol. 2010. 28:295–320

The *Annual Review of Immunology* is online at immunol.annualreviews.org

This article's doi:
10.1146/annurev.immunol.25.022106.141715

0732-0582/10/0423-0295$20.00

Key Words

thymus, development, T lymphocyte, helper T cell

Abstract

During $\alpha\beta$ T cell development, cells diverge into alternate CD4 helper and $CD8^+$ cytotoxic T cell lineages. The precise correlation between a T cell's CD8 and CD4 choice and its TCR specificity to class I or class II MHC was noted more than 20 years ago, and establishing the underlying mechanism has remained a focus of intense study since then. This review deals with three formerly discrete topics that are gradually becoming interconnected: the role of TCR signaling in lineage commitment, the regulation of expression of the CD4 and CD8 genes, and transcriptional regulation of lineage commitment. It is widely accepted that TCR signaling exerts a decisive influence on lineage choice, although the underlying mechanism remains intensely debated. Current evidence suggests that both duration and intensity of TCR signaling may control lineage choice, as proposed by the kinetic signaling and quantitative instructive models, respectively. Alternate expression of the CD4 and CD8 genes is the most visible manifestation of lineage choice, and much progress has been made in defining the responsible *cis* elements and transcription factors. Finally, important clues to the molecular basis of lineage commitment have been provided by the recent identification of the transcription factor ThPOK as a key regulator of lineage choice. ThPOK is selectively expressed in class II–restricted cells at the $CD4^+8^{lo}$ stage and is necessary and sufficient for development to the CD4 lineage. Given the central role of ThPOK in lineage commitment, understanding its upstream regulation and downstream gene targets is expected to reveal further important aspects of the molecular machinery underlying lineage commitment.

INTRODUCTION

Development of αβ T cells in the thymus proceeds through three major stages, defined according to their expression pattern of the coreceptor molecules CD4 and CD8, in order of maturity: $CD4^-CD8^-$ (double negative or DN), $CD4^+CD8^+$ (double positive or DP), and $CD4^+CD8^-$ or $CD4^-CD8^+$ (single positive or SP). The complete αβ TCR complex is first expressed at the DP stage, allowing engagement by intrathymic peptide/MHC ligands. CD4 and CD8 molecules interact respectively with class II and class I MHC molecules, thereby critically stabilizing or enhancing the interaction of TCRs with their MHC ligands. Coexpression of CD4 and CD8 at the DP stage allows thymocytes to receive optimal signals through either MHC class I– or class II–specific TCRs. Negative selection leads to death by apoptosis, whereas positive selection leads to thymocyte activation (as evidenced by the upmodulation of activation markers such as CD5 and CD69) and to differentiation into SP T cells. Coincident with positive selection, thymocytes diverge into SP CD4 and CD8 subsets.

Detailed analysis of development from the DP to SP CD4 and CD8 stages has revealed that positively selected thymocytes undergo intricate changes in coreceptor expression pattern during this transition and that there is a striking asymmetry in the phenotypic changes undergone by cells developing to the CD4 and CD8 lineages (1–7). In particular, rather than alternately downregulating CD4 and CD8, as might have been expected, most thymocytes regardless of their final coreceptor expression pattern initially downmodulate CD8, giving rise to a common $CD4^+8^{lo}$ intermediate stage. Subsequent to the $CD4^+8^{lo}$ stage, class II–restricted cells progress directly to the SP CD4 stage, whereas class I–restricted cells pass through two more intermediate stages, $CD4^{lo}8^{lo}$ (TCR^{hi}) and $CD4^{lo}8^+$, before becoming SP CD8 (4, 6). Mature T cells show an almost perfect correlation between specificity for MHC class I or II molecules and expression of the CD8 or CD4 molecules. Seminal early studies using TCR transgenic mice demonstrated that this correlation was achieved during thymocyte development, a process referred to as lineage commitment (8, 9). Since those early studies, a major focus of the field has been on elucidating the mechanism by which this process is regulated.

Models of CD4/8 Lineage Commitment

Initially, investigators proposed two competing models in which lineage commitment is determined either (*a*) randomly, followed by a selection step that eliminates thymocytes that express the inappropriate coreceptor (stochastic/selective model) (10, 11), or (*b*) instructively, i.e., by qualitatively distinct signals initiated upon TCR engagement by MHC class I or class II ligands (instructive model) (12). Because the former model proposes that thymocytes are eliminated if they fail to express the appropriate coreceptor, i.e., the one that matches their TCR specificity, it predicts that such mismatched cells should be rescued by ectopic expression of the correct coreceptor. This hypothesis was directly tested by several groups using transgenic mouse lines that constitutively expressed either CD4 or CD8. Although some mismatched cells developed in these systems, their generation was notably inefficient, which seemed inconsistent with a stochastic model, although it did not definitively disprove it (10–17). A substantial ambiguity in these studies arose from the fact that the coreceptor transgenes employed were expressed throughout T cell development so that investigators could not distinguish whether generation of some mismatched cells reflected rescue of cells that had already undergone lineage commitment, consistent with the stochastic/selective model, or perturbation of lineage commitment itself. This issue was recently addressed using transgenic mice in which ectopic CD4 expression was limited to CD8-committed thymocytes by placing CD4 under the control of the CD8 E8I enhancer, which is only functional after CD8 commitment (18–20). Significantly, this transgene failed to reveal any mismatched thymocytes, i.e., class II–restricted cells that had adopted the CD8 lineage, suggesting that mismatched cells observed in earlier studies actually resulted from effects of the coreceptor transgenes on lineage commitment itself. In particular, the authors suggested that transgenic vectors used in previous studies underwent downregulation during positive selection and that the resulting decrease in TCR signaling perturbed normal lineage commitment. Given the lack of compelling data in its support, as well as more attractive competing models (see below), the stochastic/selective model of lineage commitment has largely fallen out of favor.

The instructive model, as originally conceived, proposed that lineage choice was determined by qualitatively distinct signals that arose upon coengagement of MHC ligands by class I– or class II–restricted TCRs and their matching CD8 or CD4 coreceptors (21). Implicit in this model was the assumption that the CD4 and CD8 coreceptors were essential for mediating signals that direct CD4 and CD8 commitment, respectively. Indeed, CD4 molecules expressed ectopically at the DN stage of thymocyte development can mediate development to the DP stage in RAG-deficient mice, indicating that coreceptors can even mediate signals independently of the TCR (22). However, several studies using CD4-deficient mice have demonstrated that coreceptor involvement is not essential for lineage commitment. Thus, thymocytes expressing the class II–restricted AND TCR transgene are efficiently redirected to the CD8 lineage in the absence of CD4, indicating that CD8 commitment does not require coengagement of TCR and CD8 by MHC class I ligand (23). Similarly, in CD4-deficient mice that do not express a particular class II–restricted TCR transgene, it appears that most CD8 T cells are class II restricted (24). Conversely, another study has shown that thymocytes expressing the class II–restricted N3.L2 TCR transgene on a CD4-deficient background continue to develop to the CD4 lineage if stimulated by strong antagonist peptide, indicating that CD4 is dispensable for CD4 commitment (25). Taken together, these studies demonstrate that coreceptors do not play an obligatory role in directing lineage choice, contradicting a central premise of the original instructive model.

Instead, these data suggested that lineage might be determined by relative TCR signal strength. According to this quantitative instructive model, stronger and weaker TCR signals would lead to CD4 or CD8 lineage commitment, respectively (23). Coreceptors in this model play a key role in regulating TCR signal strength by recruiting p56Lck to the TCR/CD3 complex, but coreceptor involvement is not obligatory. Providing the logical underpinning for this model, the cytoplasmic tail of CD4 binds Lck with higher affinity than that of CD8α (26, 27), so that coengagement of TCR and CD4 by class II ligands will lead to greater recruitment of Lck to the TCR and greater phosphorylation of downstream signaling components. Consistent with such a model, replacing the cytoplasmic tail of CD8α with that of CD4 transfers capacity for high-affinity Lck interaction to the CD8 coreceptor and engenders a marked shift in development of class I–restricted cells to the CD4 lineage (28). Further studies in which the TCR signal is modulated quantitatively by limiting availability or function of key downstream mediators of TCR signaling such as Lck or Zap70 have also lent considerable support to this model (29–32). In particular, it was shown that reducing Lck activity redirected class II–restricted thymocytes to the CD8 lineage, while increasing Lck activity redirected class I–restricted thymocytes to the CD4 lineage (29). It remains unclear, however, how such quantitative differences in TCR signaling are translated into alternate lineage–determining signals. Thus, the signaling pathway(s) downstream of Lck and ZAP that regulate alternate lineage commitment remains largely undefined. Although studies using pharmacological inhibitors initially indicated a preferential role for the Ras>Mek>Erk pathway in CD4 development (33, 34), genetic approaches have shown that this reflects a selective requirement for Erk during CD4 differentiation rather than lineage determination (35, 36). In addition to the requirement for TCR signaling, an important role for cytokine signaling has been suggested in maturation of CD8 lineage cells (37). Indeed, ablation of the gene for Socs1, a negative regulator of cytokine signaling, favors development to the CD8 lineage, in part by redirection of class II–restricted cells (38, 39). Hence, heightened susceptibility to cytokine signaling seems to promote CD8 development, although the precise mechanism remains to be established.

An implicit early presumption in the field was that lineage commitment was determined at the DP stage of thymocyte development because this was believed to be the last common intermediate before divergence of the CD4 and CD8 lineages. Thus, the discovery that there is, in fact, a later common intermediate, the $CD4^+8^{lo}$ subset (1–7), was a surprise, with important potential implications for the lineage commitment mechanism. Of particular interest, many $CD4^+8^{lo}$ cells are not yet irreversibly committed to either lineage, indicating that commitment may occur at the $CD4^+8^{lo}$ stage or later, at least for some thymocytes (37, 40). The possibility that lineage commitment occurs at the transitional $CD4^+8^{lo}$ stage rather than at the DP stage has led to another model of lineage commitment, the kinetic signaling model (37). This postulates that selective downmodulation of CD8 at the $CD4^+8^{lo}$ stage specifically impairs TCR signaling in class I– but not in class II–restricted cells and that interruption or persistence of TCR signaling promotes CD8 and CD4 commitment, respectively (31, 37, 41). This may be because the cumulative duration of TCR signaling determines lineage choice (42) or because lineage choice remains reversible until the $CD4^+8^{lo}$ stage, so that only signals received at this stage are relevant for final lineage choice.

In contrast to the quantitative instructive model, inherent differences in signaling capacity between class I– and class II–restricted TCRs are, in principle, irrelevant for lineage commitment according to the kinetic signaling model. The most compelling support for this model comes from recent experiments that use another CD8 enhancer, E8III (43), to terminate CD4 expression after the DP stage, which results in a complete shift in commitment of class II–restricted cells to the CD8 lineage (41). One caveat to this result is that it is not clear how closely regulation of transgene expression by the E8III enhancer recapitulates normal regulation of CD8 during the DP-to-$CD4^+8^{lo}$ transition, as E8III is only one of several CD8 enhancers active at this stage (44). If CD4 expression under the sole control of the E8III enhancer is terminated too early, i.e., in cells that would normally still exhibit a DP phenotype, the observed redirection of class II–restricted cells to the CD8 lineage could reflect a reduction in TCR signal strength at the DP stage rather than shortened duration of signaling. Furthermore, certain other results are difficult to reconcile with the kinetic signaling model, in particular the facts that some class I–restricted cells omit the $CD4^+8^{lo}$ stage, (7, 45), that constitutive $CD8\alpha/\beta$ expression fails to redirect most class I–restricted cells to the CD4 lineage (46), and that some class II–restricted cells can mature to the CD4 lineage in the absence of CD4 (25, 47). In principle, signal strength and kinetic signaling models need not be mutually exclusive and instead could complement one another. In such a combined instructive/kinetic model, intrinsic differences in signaling capacity between class I– and class II–restricted TCRs may be sufficient to determine lineage at the DP stage for low-affinity class I–restricted cells, which could progress directly to the SP CD8 stage. Class II–restricted and high-affinity class I–restricted thymocytes, on the other hand, may both be directed to the $CD4^+8^{lo}$ stage, at which point downmodulation of CD8 would act as a quality-control mechanism to selectively diminish TCR signaling by class I–restricted cells and prevent their development to the CD4 lineage (**Figure 1**).

Developmental Control of CD4 and CD8 Expression

Much effort has been devoted to elucidating the regulation of CD4 and CD8 expression, the most obvious genes to be regulated in a lineage-specific manner, in the expectation that this would lead to identification of upstream signaling factors important for lineage specification. Nuclear run-on experiments have shown that CD4 and CD8 expression in thymocytes is regulated primarily at the level of transcription, focusing attention on the responsible *cis* elements (48). Initial studies indicated that the stage- and lineage-specific expression of coreceptor genes is not regulated primarily by their promoters but rather by a combination of enhancer and/or silencer elements. A fundamental difference likely exists between regulation of CD4, which is controlled by a lineage-specific silencer, and of CD8, which seems to be controlled by multiple enhancers with differing stage and lineage specificities. Positive regulation of CD4 transcription depends on a proximal enhancer located 13 kb upstream of the CD4 promoter (49). The minimal 339-bp CD4 proximal enhancer contains binding sites for TCF-1 and for E box factors HEB (HeLa E-box binding protein) and E2A (49, 50). Knockout mice with deficiencies in expression of these factors show reduced CD4 levels at the DP stage, consistent with an important role for these factors in CD4 transcription (51–53). CD4 proximal enhancer activity also requires the chromatin remodeling factor Mi-2b, presumably to mediate an open chromatin conformation (54). Significantly, the CD4 proximal enhancer lacks lineage specificity and so mediates reporter expression in both CD4 and CD8 T cells, suggesting that an additional repressive element is required to enforce lineage specificity (55).

Indeed, several studies identified an element within the first CD4 intron that selectively represses CD4 transcription in SP CD8 T cells, but not in SP CD4 T cells, in a position- and orientation-independent manner, consistent with a lineage-specific silencer (48, 55, 56). Using transgenic reporter mice, CD4 silencer activity has been narrowed down to a minimal 300-bp fragment in mice (57) and a 190-bp fragment in humans (56). Targeted deletion of the CD4 silencer in mice results in derepression of CD4 on all CD8 T cells, demonstrating the physiological role of this element (57). Conditional deletion of the CD4 silencer in mature CD8 T cells, i.e., after completion of lineage commitment, does not relieve CD4 silencing, thus defining two stages in silencing: initiation, which is silencer-dependent, followed by permanent heritable silencing, which is not (58). Permanent lineage-specific silencing appears to involve repositioning of both CD4 and CD8 loci to heterochromatin (59, 60) and requires the mammalian chromatin remodeling BAF (BRG1/brm-associated factors) complex (61, 62). In vivo dissection of the CD4 silencer has led to the identification of functionally critical motifs, including consensus Runx-binding sites, which are indispensable for CD4 silencing (57, 63) (see below).

In contrast to silencer-mediated control of CD4 transcription, lineage-specific CD8 expression is controlled by a complex array of stage-specific enhancers, E8I–E8IV, located 5′ to the CD8α promoter (19, 20, 43, 64–66). The first enhancer to be characterized, E8I, is specifically activated in CD8 lineage cells upon positive selection, i.e., in SP CD8$^+$ but not in DP thymocytes (19, 20). In addition, E8I activity is detected in CD8αα$^+$ intraepithelial lymphocytes (19). Interestingly, the E8I enhancer does not seem to drive expression of reporter constructs in transient transfection assays, suggesting a dependency on chromatin conformation (67). Nor does targeted deletion of E8I affect expression of CD8α and CD8β in thymus-derived T cells (43, 65), indicating that CD8 expression in mature CD8 cells is regulated redundantly by multiple *cis* elements that can compensate for one another. Further transgenic reporter assays were used to define additional enhancer elements, E8II–E8IV. Each element shows a different developmental expression pattern, i.e., the E8II enhancer functions in both DP and SP CD8 thymocytes; the E8III enhancer functions only in DP thymocytes; and the E8IV enhancer, in conjunction with E8II, functions in DP, CD8, and CD4 thymocytes (43). Finally, a DNAse hypersensitive (DHS) element near the CD8α

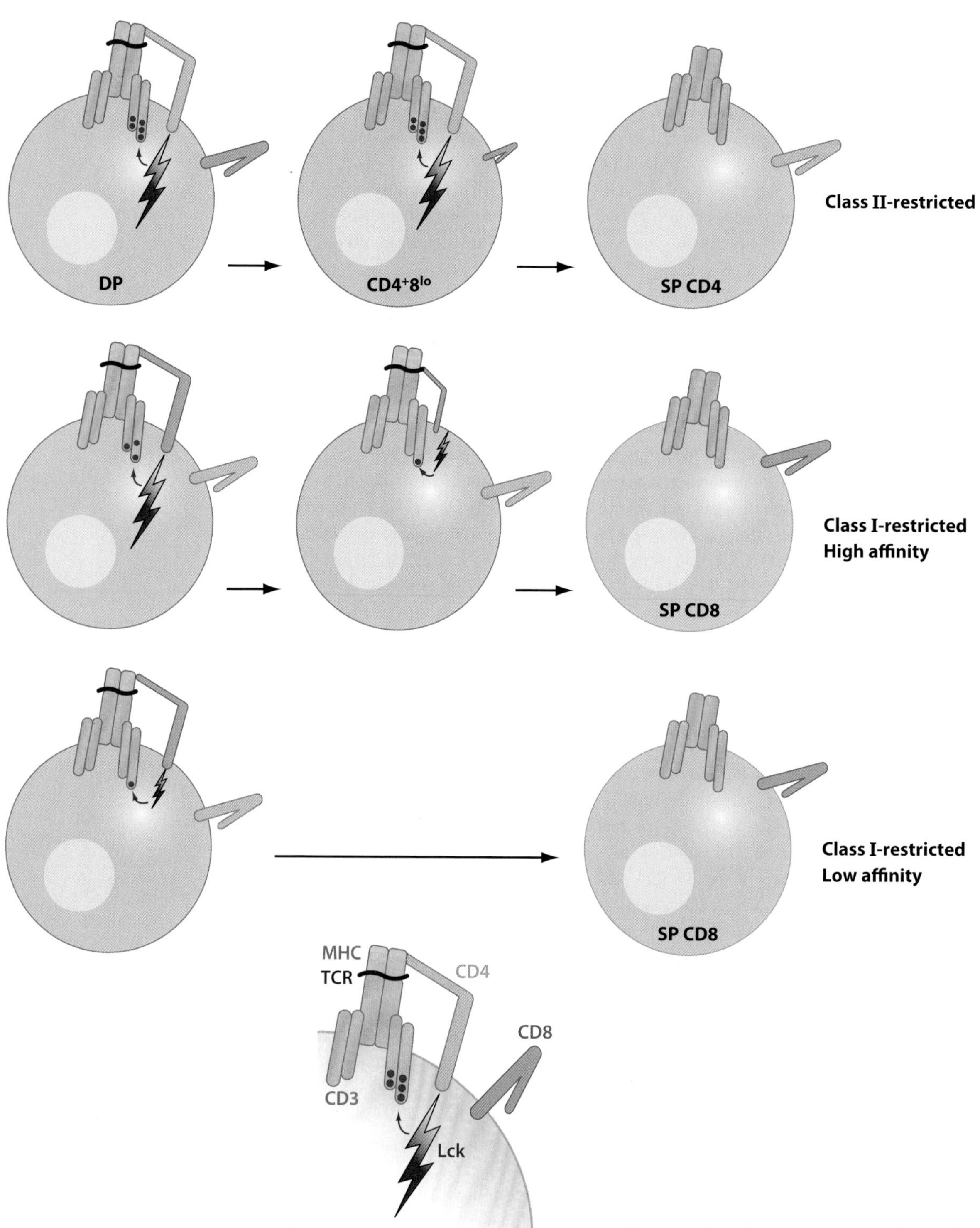
DP
CD4+8lo
SP CD4
Class II-restricted
SP CD8
Class I-restricted
High affinity
SP CD8
Class I-restricted
Low affinity
MHC
TCR
CD4
CD8
CD3
Lck

promoter (cluster II), although lacking inherent enhancer activity, can collaborate with the E8I enhancer to additionally direct reporter expression in DP thymocytes (65). Although the ability of the E8IV enhancer to drive transcription in both CD8 and CD4 T cells suggests the requirement for a negative element to restrict E8IV activity to the CD8 lineage, no such CD8 silencer has yet been identified.

Studies summarized above have led to a broad consensus that alternate lineage choices are triggered by the relative strength or length of TCR signaling. However, a complete understanding of the process awaits elucidation of the underlying intracellular pathways. In this regard, recent studies have made important progress in defining transcription factors involved in CD4/CD8 lineage commitment, in particular ThPOK, Runx3, and Gata3. In the following sections, we review the evidence implicating each of these factors, as well as the possible mechanisms involved and functional interactions between factors.

Identification of the HD Mutation, a Genetic Defect that Prevents CD4 Development

Progress in understanding lineage commitment has been hampered for a long time by the fact that the underlying molecular pathways remained unknown. Hence, the identification of so-called helper deficient, or HD, mice, a mutant mouse strain that seemed to be specifically impaired in CD4 lineage commitment but not in positive selection of class II–restricted thymocytes, was of considerable interest. The striking feature of these mice that led to their identification was the almost complete absence of CD4 T cells in peripheral blood samples as well as in other peripheral lymphoid organs (68). Although HD mice arose from an intercross between multiple knockout and transgenic models, selective breeding demonstrated that none of these induced modifications cosegregated with the HD defect, indicating that the responsible mutation mapped elsewhere. Indeed, when the HD mutation was eventually pinpointed, it turned out to be a de novo point mutation, i.e., an A>G transversion (69). Furthermore, the mutation was linked to BALB/c genetic markers, indicating that it did not arise during the generation of any of the knockout or transgenic alleles, which were produced on different genetic backgrounds. Selective breeding experiments showed that the HD phenotype was caused by a single recessive mutation. Only homozygous ($HD^{-/-}$) mice exhibited CD4 deficiency, whereas heterozygous ($HD^{+/-}$) animals lacked any detectable phenotype, supporting the argument that the HD mutation resulted in loss of function of the affected gene. The CD4-deficient phenotype was highly consistent between $HD^{-/-}$ mice and was unchanged after backcrossing for 10 generations to different genetic backgrounds, i.e., C57BL/6 and BALB/c, indicating that penetrance of the mutation was unaffected by genetic background. The decrease in peripheral CD4 T cells in $HD^{-/-}$ mice was accompanied by an equivalent increase in the proportion of CD8 T cells, so that the total number of T cells remained unchanged. Nonconventional CD4 T cell subsets, including both CD4 iNKT and CD4 Treg cells, are also severely diminished in $HD^{-/-}$ mice (I. Engel, M. Kronenberg, and D.J. Kappes, unpublished data). Aside from these T cell defects, $HD^{-/-}$

Figure 1

Combined quantitative/kinetic model of lineage commitment. This model combines key aspects of the quantitative instructive and kinetic signaling models. Class I–restricted cells receive a relatively weak TCR signal at the DP stage owing to the weaker interaction of Lck with CD8α than with CD4, as postulated by the quantitative instructive model. Low-affinity class I–restricted cells, which would receive the weakest signal of all thymocytes, would be directed immediately to the CD8 stage, without traversing the $CD4^{+}8^{lo}$ intermediate stage. High-affinity class I–restricted cells, like all class II–restricted cells, would receive a stronger signal that drives development to the $CD4^{+}8^{lo}$ stage. Downmodulation of CD8 at the $CD4^{+}8^{lo}$ stage would specifically impair signaling by high-affinity class I–restricted cells and thus prevent their development to the CD4 lineage.

but not $HD^{+/-}$ mice exhibit severely reduced female fecundity, such that $HD^{-/-}$ female mice produce very few offspring, whether mated to wild-type or to $HD^{-/-}$ males. However, male fertility is unaffected, as $HD^{-/-}$ males produce normal numbers of offspring when mated to wild-type females. In addition, an uncharacterized developmental defect leads to loss of 75% of $HD^{-/-}$ embryos before birth (70). Breeding experiments demonstrate that these defects cosegregate with CD4 deficiency, indicating that they are caused either by the same or by a closely linked mutation and that they persist in the absence of T cells, i.e., in $HD^{-/-}$ $Rag^{-/-}$ mice, further indicating that they do not depend on potentially aberrant T cell populations generated on the $HD^{-/-}$ background.

Identification of the HD Gene as the Transcription Factor ThPOK

The above results indicated that the HD mutation specifically prevented development of CD4 T cells. The most obvious possible explanations for such a phenotype were defects in CD4 expression by thymocytes or in MHC class II expression by antigen-presenting cells. Even though $HD^{-/-}$ mice exhibited normal CD4 expression on DP thymocytes, a subtle defect in CD4 regulation that terminated CD4 expression after this stage could still be imagined. However, constitutive CD4 expression in $HD^{-/-}$ thymocytes failed to restore CD4 development, excluding such a possibility (69). Furthermore, a defect in class II MHC antigen expression was unlikely because MHC class II expression in $HD^{-/-}$ mice seemed grossly normal by flow cytometry, and backcross analysis showed that the HD defect was genetically unlinked to the MHC locus. A defect in antigen presentation was formally excluded by adoptive transfer of $HD^{-/-}$ bone marrow into normal hosts, which failed to restore CD4 development (68). Cotransfer experiments in which $HD^{-/-}$ and wild-type bone marrow were introduced into the same host revealed that they developed autonomously, i.e., $HD^{-/-}$ cells still gave rise only to CD8 cells, whereas wild-type cells gave rise to both CD4 and CD8 cells. Thus, the defect in CD4 development in $HD^{-/-}$ mice is intrinsic to class II–restricted thymocytes themselves, i.e., it is not mediated in *trans* by some other hematopoietic lineage (69). These experiments established that the HD phenotype reflected a thymocyte-intrinsic defect of unknown molecular basis.

A genetic mapping approach was adopted to identify the relevant gene, which involved intercrossing $HD^{-/-}$ mutant animals with genetically distant wild mouse subspecies *Mus musculus castaneus* and *M. m. molossinus*. Because of the complex genetic background of the HD line, the strain of origin of the mutant allele was not precisely known, although it must have originated on either C57BL/6, 129/Sv, BALB/C, or C3H/He backgrounds. Importantly, wild mouse subspecies differ from these strains at a large proportion of SSLP (simple sequence length polymorphism) markers, so that it was not necessary a priori to know the precise haplotype on which the HD mutation arose. Mapping of the mutant allele was accomplished by a two-step outcross and backcross strategy, involving outcrossing of $HD^{-/-}$ males to wild females to yield $HD^{+/-}$ N1 progeny, followed by backcrossing of N1 females to $HD^{-/-}$ males to yield a mixture of $HD^{-/-}$, $HD^{+/-}$, and $HD^{+/+}$ N2 progeny. Homologous crossover events could occur between HD and wild chromosomes during meiosis in $HD^{+/-}$ mice. Genetic mapping depends on the fact that closely linked markers will recombine at much lower frequency than more distant ones. PCR-based linkage analysis was carried out on a pool of about 600 $HD^{-/-}$ N2 progeny, in which one mutant allele was derived from $HD^{+/-}$ N1 parents and thus located on a potentially recombinant chromosome.

Linkage of the HD mutation was detected with polymorphic markers on chromosome 3, eventually allowing mapping of the gene to a small region between markers D3Mit49 and D3Mit341. Further mapping of the HD mutation was accomplished by transgenic complementation of $HD^{-/-}$ mice with bacterial artificial chromosome (BAC) clones spanning this region. Eventually this narrowed the relevant region to a 30-kb segment containing the gene for the zinc-finger transcription factor ThPOK (T helper–inducing POZ/Krüppel factor, also known as Zbtb7b, Zfp67, or cKrox) (69). Confirmation of the genetic identification was obtained by the following approaches: (*a*) Sequencing of the ThPOK cDNA from $HD^{-/-}$ mice identified a point mutation in one of its zinc-finger domains, i.e., an A>G transversion. This mutation results in a R>G amino acid substitution that is predicted to interfere with DNA binding, consistent with a loss-of-function mutation. Importantly, this substitution is not observed in any normal mouse strain, indicating that it is not an allelic polymorphism. Furthermore, the wild-type arginine amino acid is strictly conserved in all mammalian species and even in fish, consistent with a critical function. (*b*) CD4 development could be restored in $HD^{-/-}$ mice by ectopic expression in thymocytes of a wild-type ThPOK cDNA. (*c*) Knockout mice in which expression of ThPOK is precluded exhibit a similar CD4-deficient phenotype (71–73). The latter observation provides confirmation that the HD defect reflects a loss- rather than gain-of-function mutation. Since identification of the HD locus as ThPOK, homozygous HD mutant mice have been referred to as $ThPOK^{HD/HD}$ mice.

ThPOK belongs to the POK family of transcription factors, defined by a Krüppel-like zinc-finger domain responsible for DNA binding and a regulatory POZ/BTB domain that mediates interactions with other factors (74). Several members of the POK family have recently been implicated as important mediators of hematopoietic development, e.g., Plzf in iNKT development (75, 76), Bcl6 in germinal center formation (77–79), and LRF (leukemia/lymphoma-related factor)/Pokemon in B lineage choice (80). Consistent with their key roles in regulating developmental transitions, dysregulated expression of several POK family members has been linked to various cancers, including Plzf in acute myeloid leukemia (81), Bcl6 in B cell lymphoma (82, 83), and LRF/Pokemon in T cell lymphoma and lung cancer (80). The ThPOK gene is highly conserved within the vertebrate lineage including in teleost fish, implying an important evolutionarily conserved function. Two close relatives of ThPOK in vertebrates, LRF/Pokemon and Apm-1, may overlap functionally with ThPOK and thus compensate for ThPOK deficiency in some tissues (but not in thymocytes, where expression of these two factors is low or undetectable). Little is known about nonimmunological functions of ThPOK, beyond its original identification as a negative regulator of collagen gene transcription (84–87). Interestingly, the amphibian ThPOK homolog, champignon, has been implicated in gastrulation (88), which may relate to the apparent high embryonic lethality suffered by $HD^{-/-}$ mice (70).

The DNA target sequences recognized by ThPOK are not well defined, beyond a general preference for guanine-rich sequences (85). A broad capacity to recognize guanine-rich elements implies that these factors recognize many targets throughout the genome. Alternately, additional unknown mechanisms may confer greater target specificity. The remarkable conservation of the ThPOK zinc-finger domain, including most residues not predicted to interact with DNA, suggests that this region performs additional critical functions, for instance, binding to other transcription factors that may confer additional target specificity. Although ThPOK was originally cloned by screening of a fibroblast cDNA expression library with a negative *cis*-acting element from the collagen a1(I) promoter and can repress collagen promoter activity in vitro (84, 86, 87), it remains to be established whether it functions exclusively or predominantly as a transcriptional repressor in the control of lineage commitment. Although the best-characterized function of POK factors lies in gene silencing via POZ-mediated recruitment of corepressor molecules, such as N-CoR and Smrt (89), in some cases the POZ domain seems instead to be required for transcriptional activation (90, 91). Identifying the target genes of ThPOK in thymocytes and deciphering which ones are relevant to lineage commitment are important goals for the field.

Class II–Restricted Cells Are Redirected to the CD8 Lineage in ThPOK$^{HD/HD}$ Mice

In principle, class II–restricted cells in ThPOK$^{HD/HD}$ mice might be arrested in development or might adopt an alternate developmental fate. Indeed, the high proportion of SP CD8 peripheral T cells in ThPOK$^{HD/HD}$ mice suggested the intriguing possibility that class II–restricted thymocytes might be developing aberrantly into CD8 cells. This was assessed by limiting positive selection in ThPOK$^{HD/HD}$ mice to class II–restricted cells, allowing their fate to be specifically tracked in the absence of class I–restricted cells, e.g., by preventing expression of class I MHC by crossing to a β2m$^{-/-}$ background. Strikingly, this revealed that class II–restricted cells developed efficiently and exclusively into peripheral CD8 T cells on the ThPOK$^{HD/HD}$ background (92). Similar experiments demonstrated that class I–restricted cells still developed normally into CD8 T cells in these mice. Hence, the mature SP CD8 compartment in ThPOK$^{HD/HD}$ mice consists of both class I– and class II–restricted cells. Consistent with this conclusion, TCR Vα and Vβ region usage by mature peripheral CD8$^+$ cells in ThPOK$^{HD/HD}$ mice reflects the combined V repertoire of wild-type CD4$^+$ and CD8$^+$ T cells (70). Detailed analysis of class II–restricted thymocyte development in ThPOK$^{HD/HD}$ β2m$^{-/-}$ mice reveals that mature SP CD4 CD69$^-$ cells are almost completely absent, whereas SP CD8 cells are considerably expanded. In addition, large populations of immature CD4$^+$8^{lo} and SP CD4 CD69$^+$ cells are observed. When cultured in the absence of TCR stimulation, the latter cells give rise exclusively to SP CD8 cells, indicating that they are not arrested in development but rather represent intermediates in development to the CD8 lineage (93). Importantly, the frequency of CD69$^+$ thymocytes, an indicator of the efficiency of positive selection, is similar in ThPOK$^{HD/HD}$ and wild-type mice, indicating that positive selection is relatively unaffected by the HD mutation. Hence, ThPOK$^{HD/HD}$ mice provided the first evidence that lineage commitment is mechanistically distinct from positive selection.

Interestingly, these immature CD4$^+$8^{lo} and SP CD4 CD69$^+$ cells are greatly reduced in ThPOK$^{HD/HD}$ IAb$^{-/-}$ mice, in which only class I–restricted cells can be positively selected, indicating that their appearance is mainly mediated by class II–restricted TCR signals. This suggests that unknown genes selectively induced by class II–restricted ligands drive development to these stages and that this process does not require ThPOK. Gata3 may be an important effector of this process, as Gata3 deficiency severely impairs the generation of CD4$^+$8^{lo} cells (see below). Constitutive ThPOK expression in thymocytes causes all cells to develop into CD4 cells, including class I–restricted cells (69, 94). Importantly, redirected class I–restricted CD4 cells exhibit other changes in gene expression consistent with adoption of the CD4 fate, such as Gata3 upregulation (94). Similarly, in mice expressing ThPOK constitutively owing to Runx deficiency, redirected class I–restricted CD4 cells exhibit typical characteristics of CD4 cells, including induction of CD40L and IL-4 production in response to TCR stimulation (72). Conversely, redirected class II–restricted CD8 T cells in ThPOK$^{HD/HD}$ mice exhibit upmodulation of Perforin, consistent with adoption of the CD8 fate (69). Redirected class II–restricted CD8 cells in these mice also show repression of reporter transgenes controlled by the CD4 silencer, directly demonstrating normal CD8 lineage–specific control of CD4 transcription (70). Hence, ThPOK is necessary and sufficient for adoption of the CD4 lineage–specific program of gene expression and for repressing the CD8 lineage–specific program of gene expression.

ThPOK Expression Levels in Developing Thymocytes Correlate with Relative TCR Signal

Although widely expressed in other tissues, ThPOK shows a tightly regulated and highly lineage- and stage-specific expression pattern during thymic development. Importantly, ThPOK RNA is not expressed in αβ lineage T cells at the DN or DP stages, implying that it is not required for β selection or positive selection. This is confirmed by the fact that neither the proportions nor the absolute numbers of DP and total SP thymocytes are affected in $HD^{-/-}$ mice (although all positively selected thymocytes become SP CD8). Very low ThPOK levels are first detected in $CD4^{lo}8^{lo}$ thymocytes, and substantial induction is first detected at the $CD4^{+}8^{lo}$ stage. Importantly, although ThPOK expression is detected in both class I– and class II–restricted $CD4^{+}8^{lo}$ thymocytes, levels are considerably higher in class II–restricted cells and increase further during the transition of class II–restricted cells to the SP CD4 stage, while diminishing to background levels during the transition of class I–restricted cells to the SP CD8 stage (69, 94). The correlation between ThPOK expression levels and MHC specificity at the $CD4^{+}8^{lo}$ stage, i.e., before lineage commitment, suggests that ThPOK expression is determined instructively by relative TCR signal strength at this stage. In contrast, at the earlier DP stage, the ThPOK locus seems insensitive to TCR stimulation. Thus, ThPOK expression is induced neither in DP thymocytes that have upmodulated CD69 in response to a class II–restricted positive selection signal in vivo nor in DP thymocytes subjected to a strong antibody-mediated TCR stimulus in vitro (93).

Intraperitoneal administration of anti-TCRβ antibody to MHC class II–deficient mice leads to high-level ThPOK induction in thymocytes after two days, providing strong evidence of a causal link between TCR engagement and ThPOK expression. However, ThPOK is detected only in $CD4^{+}8^{lo}$ and SP CD4 cells, and not in DP thymocytes, even though the latter are activated, as evidenced by their elevated CD69 surface expression (93). Together, these observations suggest either that DP (in contrast to $CD4^{+}8^{lo}$) thymocytes are not susceptible to TCR-mediated induction of ThPOK or that there is a delay in ThPOK induction until cells reach the $CD4^{+}8^{lo}$ stage. In principle, ThPOK expression in SP thymocytes and mature T cells could also be regulated by differences in TCR stimulation or might be determined by lineage-specific mechanisms. To distinguish these possibilities, a constitutive CD4 transgene was introduced into $HD^{-/-}$ $\beta 2m^{-/-}$ mice, so that effective signaling by class II–restricted TCRs would be maintained even after commitment to the CD8 lineage. Notably, ThPOK expression is severely reduced in class II–restricted CD8 cells that develop in these mice, compared with normal CD4 T cells, suggesting that the ThPOK locus undergoes a switch in regulation during development, from a TCR-dependent mode at the DP>$CD4^{+}8^{lo}$ transition to a predominantly TCR-independent lineage-specific mode after commitment. The continued expression of ThPOK in peripheral CD4 T cells suggests that it may be required for maintenance of the CD4 phenotype and/or for T helper function. Indeed, peripheral CD4 T cells from mice expressing a hypomorphic ThPOK allele or mice in which ThPOK is conditionally deleted after maturation fail to appropriately repress genes associated with the CD8 lineage (73) (see below).

Transcriptional Control of ThPOK

A tight correlation between ThPOK protein and mRNA expression in thymocytes indicates that the main method of controlling ThPOK during development is at the level of transcription (71, 94). Consequently, elucidating the transcriptional regulation of ThPOK should eventually lead to identification of upstream pathways that control lineage choice, a so-called bottoms-up approach. BAC transgene complementation of $ThPOK^{HD/HD}$ mice demonstrated that normal regulation of lineage commitment could be achieved by a 20-kb genomic fragment extending from 17 kb upstream to 500 bp downstream of the ThPOK coding exons. Specifically, this fragment restored development of class II–restricted thymocytes to the CD4 lineage without perturbing development

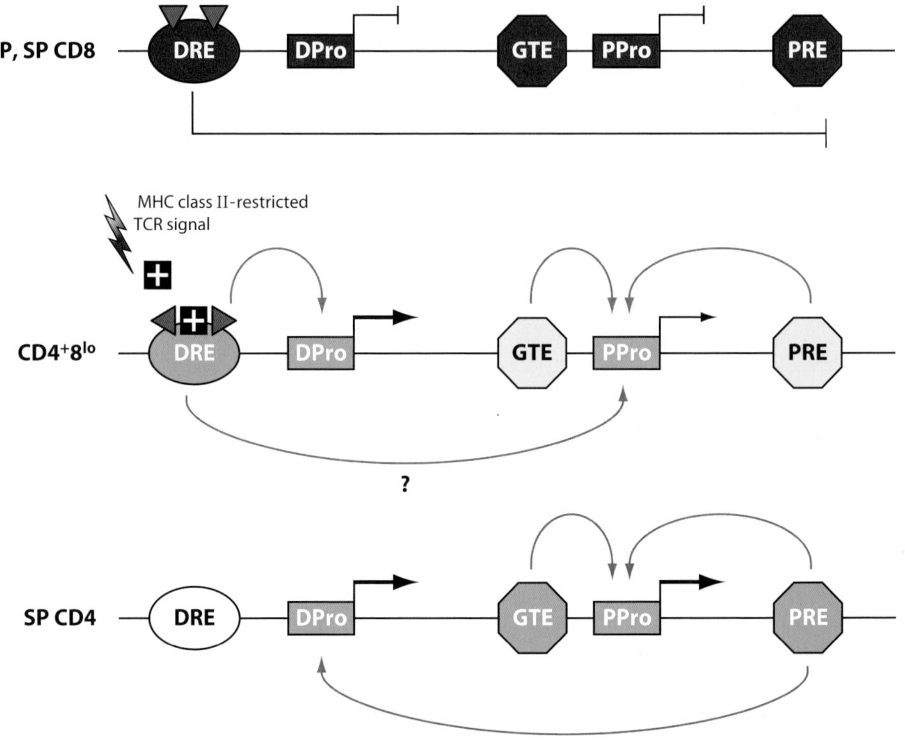

Figure 2

Transcriptional control of ThPOK. Schematic representation of the relative position and activity of transcriptional control elements at the ThPOK locus. Distal and proximal promoters (DPro, PPro) are indicated by rectangles, general T lymphoid and proximal regulatory enhancers (GTE, PRE) by octagons, and the DRE dual silencer/enhancer element by an oval. Elements engaged in active transcription or repression are shaded in green or red, respectively. The capacity to exert positive or negative transcriptional control over other elements is indicated by arrows or straight bars, respectively.

of class I–restricted cells to the CD8 lineage, demonstrating that it contains all elements required for normal regulation of ThPOK expression (93).

The ThPOK locus contains two promoters, located 6 kb apart and conserved between human and mouse (72, 93) (**Figure 2**). Although transcripts produced from these promoters differ in their first noncoding exons, they nevertheless encode the same protein product, as the first in-frame start codon is located within a common downstream exon. Both promoters are used in thymocytes, but they exhibit distinct developmental expression patterns, with the distal promoter preferentially active earlier at the $CD4^{+}8^{lo}$ stage. Comparison of ThPOK genes from different species reveals a striking conservation of noncoding sequences near the ThPOK gene, consistent with the presence of important regulatory elements. Analysis of DHS sites, which often mark regulatory elements associated with DNA-binding factors, identified six discrete sites or clusters of sites within the minimal functional 20-kb ThPOK gene. Two of these DHS sites coincide with the distal and proximal promoters, whereas the others could represent potential enhancers or other types of control elements. Functional analysis of these putative regulatory elements was carried out in transgenic mice using a series of GFP reporter constructs containing different fragments of the 20-kb minimal ThPOK locus (72, 93). Strikingly, deletion of a 500-bp segment spanning DHS site A led to promiscuous reporter expression in both CD4 and CD8 lineages, indicating that this distal regulatory element (DRE) functions as a lineage-specific silencer. Deletion of the ThPOK silencer in mice, either through targeting of the endogenous ThPOK locus or by introduction of a mutant BAC transgene lacking this region, resulted in derepression of ThPOK in class I–restricted cells and severe reduction of CD8 T cells, indicating an essential physiological role for this element in lineage-specific transcriptional control of ThPOK (72, 93). By linking the 500-bp DRE to a minimal human CD2 promoter that lacks inherent transcriptional activity, investigators further showed that the DRE also encodes enhancer activity. Importantly, expression of the DRE-pCD2 reporter transgene was still restricted to the CD4 lineage, indicating that the 500-bp DRE element is sufficient to mediate silencer activity and is capable of repressing a heterologous promoter (93).

Reporter constructs containing the DRE element in the context of the distal promoter show highest expression in $CD4^+8^{lo}$ cells, when lineage is probably determined, suggesting that regulation of DRE function is critical for lineage commitment. It remains to be established whether enhancer and silencer functions of the DRE are encoded by overlapping or separable regions of the DRE. The 500-bp ThPOK silencer contains transcription factor consensus sites with potential relevance to lineage commitment, in particular two consensus Runx sites. However, the precise importance of these sites for lineage-specific ThPOK expression is somewhat unclear. In one study, mutation of both Runx sites led to partial derepression of a reporter transgene in the CD8 lineage (72), whereas deletion of both sites in another study did not impair repression in CD8 cells (93). This discrepancy may reflect differences in transgene copy number and/or integration site. Of note, even in the former study the proportion of GFP^+ cells was much lower in CD8 than in CD4 cells, indicating that Runx factors cannot be the only regulators of DRE-mediated silencing activity.

The observation that the ThPOK silencer is necessary to suppress ThPOK expression in the CD8 lineage implies that the ThPOK locus encodes another *cis* element with promiscuous enhancer activity. This could be the enhancer activity encoded by the DRE element or another enhancer located elsewhere. Indeed, further reporter gene assays have identified a strong enhancer near DHS site C (located downstream of the distal promoter) that exhibits activity in both CD4 and CD8 lineages (referred to as the general T lymphoid element, or GTE) (93). Deletion of DHS site C, within the context of a 6-kb reporter construct that lacks the DRE, abolishes this promiscuous expression, indicating that this region is necessary for GTE activity, although additional downstream regions may be required. Importantly, inserting the DRE into a reporter construct containing an intact GTE restricts reporter expression to the CD4 lineage, directly demonstrating that the DRE silencer controls GTE activity. A distinct CD4 lineage–specific enhancer maps near DHS site E (1-kb downstream of the proximal promoter), i.e., the ThPOK proximal regulatory element (PRE) (93, 95). The PRE is incapable of suppressing activity of the GTE in the CD8 lineage and thus seems to function only as an enhancer and not as a silencer (93). Furthermore, it appears to function predominantly late in development, as reporter transgenes controlled exclusively by the PRE show highest expression in peripheral CD4 T cells, and targeted deletion of the PRE causes a severe 20-fold reduction in ThPOK expression in peripheral CD4 T cells (but only a fivefold reduction in SP CD4 thymocytes) (93, 95). Importantly, targeted deletion of the PRE element causes only a mild decrease in the generation of SP CD4 thymocytes, suggesting that it does not play a major role in CD4 lineage commitment (95).

Taken together, these results support a model in which the DRE silencer functions as the primary regulator of ThPOK induction in class I– versus class II–restricted $CD4^+8^{lo}$ thymocytes and thus is the most likely target of TCR-dependent signaling factors that determine lineage choice. We suggest that the DRE acts as a constitutive silencer, unless bound by factors induced/activated by strong TCR signals. When DRE silencer activity is overcome by these factors, the DRE- and GTE-encoded enhancers drive ThPOK transcription, leading to CD4 commitment. It remains to be established which one of these enhancers plays the predominant role in this process, or whether both are essential.

What Is the Mechanism by which ThPOK Promotes CD4 Commitment?

ThPOK may regulate lineage choice by two general mechanisms: (*a*) by controlling lineage-specifying genes, i.e., by activating CD4-specifying genes and/or repressing CD8-specifying genes, or (*b*) indirectly by controlling genes involved in TCR signaling, i.e., by activating genes that amplify TCR signaling and/or repressing negative regulators of TCR signaling. Analysis of ThPOK$^{HD/HD}$ mice provides two compelling arguments against the latter possibility: (*a*) Biochemical readouts of TCR signaling pathways seem unaffected in cells from these mice, as judged by normal TCR-mediated Ca^{2+} flux and normal phosphorylation of CD3ζ, ZAP70, Lck, and mitogen-associated protein kinases (Erk/JNK/p38), and (*b*) functional readouts of TCR signaling, including TCR-mediated proliferation as well as positive and negative selection, also appear normal (69, 92). The efficiency of positive selection, as measured by the steady-state proportions of CD4^{+}8^{lo} and SP CD8 thymocytes, is unaltered for class I–restricted cells, as demonstrated in mice expressing particular class I–restricted TCR transgenes (92). Although mature class II–restricted CD8 cells are reduced by about 50% compared with the normal number of CD4 T cells, this deficit is corrected by introduction of a constitutive CD4 transgene, suggesting that it reflected a secondary consequence of CD4 downregulation rather than an intrinsic defect in TCR signaling (X. He, Y. Zhang & D.J. Kappes, unpublished data). ThPOK deficiency could also impair TCR signaling by causing downmodulation of CD4 or TCR at the CD4^{+}8^{lo} stage (23, 24, 41). However, FACS analysis of ThPOK$^{HD/HD}$ thymocytes shows that TCR expression increases normally during the DP-to-SP CD8 transition, and introduction of a constitutive CD4 transgene fails to rescue development of SP CD4 T cells, indicating that redirection of class II–restricted cells is not a secondary consequence of aberrant CD4 downmodulation. The possibility that ThPOK deficiency promotes development to the CD8 compartment independent of TCR signaling was excluded using ThPOK$^{HD/HD}$ mice that either lack MHC expression entirely or express a class II–restricted TCR transgene in the absence of the MHC class II ligand recognized by that TCR. In both cases, no SP CD8 thymocytes are generated (70, 92). Thus, ThPOK$^{HD/HD}$ thymocytes appear to possess normal TCR signaling capacity, exhibit normal developmental regulation of TCR and CD4, and are normally dependent on TCR signaling for positive selection and development to the CD8 lineage. Collectively, these data strongly support the argument that ThPOK does not influence lineage commitment indirectly by controlling TCR signaling, but more likely does so directly by controlling lineage-specific gene expression.

Several recent reports provide compelling support for ThPOK as a major regulator of lineage-specific gene expression, including of the CD4 and CD8 genes. Transduction of ThPOK into a CD8^{+}CD4^{-} T cell line and constitutive expression of a ThPOK transgene in DN thymocytes both mediate derepression of CD4 (95; X. He, Y. Zhang & D.J. Kappes, unpublished data). Given the importance of Runx factors in CD4 silencing, the functional interaction of ThPOK and Runx factors was specifically examined using an in vitro cotransfection assay. These experiments showed that expression of ThPOK impairs Runx-mediated repression of a reporter gene linked to the CD4 silencer (96). Interestingly, the antagonistic effect of ThPOK on Runx-mediated silencing was impaired by addition of the histone deacetylase inhibitor TsA, suggesting that antagonism depends on transcriptional repression by ThPOK of an unknown factor that acts in conjunction with Runx, a repressor-of-repressor model.

A role for ThPOK in CD4 regulation is further supported by the observation that peripheral class II–restricted cells from genetically altered mice that express low ThPOK levels are susceptible to loss of CD4 expression, indicating that high ThPOK levels are important for maintaining CD4 expression in mature CD4 T cells (73, 95). CD4 expression in these cells is fully restored by deletion of the CD4 silencer, indicating that ThPOK antagonizes silencer function. ChIP-on-chip analysis further demonstrated that wild-type ThPOK, but not the HD mutant form, could bind near the CD4 silencer in SP CD4 thymocytes (95). Nevertheless, it remains to be formally demonstrated that binding of ThPOK to the CD4 silencer is actually necessary for antagonism, so that an indirect repressor-of-repressor model cannot currently be excluded. Mice lacking expression of both ThPOK and Runx factors still generate SP CD4 cells, indicating that ThPOK is not absolutely required for CD4 expression (71). This is perhaps not surprising given that Runx factors are essential for activity of the CD4 silencer. Inactivation of the CD4 silencer in the absence of Runx should then allow promiscuous CD4 expression under the control of other non-lineage-specific *cis* elements, i.e., the CD4 promoter and CD4 proximal enhancer. Activity of these elements is expected to be independent of ThPOK because ablation of the CD4 silencer causes CD4 derepression in CD8 cells that lack ThPOK.

SP CD4 cells from mice expressing reduced levels of ThPOK show additional defects in the CD4 lineage–specific gene expression program, including impaired TCR-dependent CD40L and IL-4 production, while gaining expression of some CD8 lineage genes, including *Runx3* and *Eomes* (95). A similar phenotype was observed in mice carrying a hypomorphic ThPOK allele owing to insertion of a Neo cassette into the ThPOK locus. Thus, SP CD4 cells from these mice showed impaired TCR-dependent CD40L induction and exhibited upmodulation of CD8 lineage markers, including CD8, Perforin, GranzymeB, Eomes, and Runx3, upon adoptive transfer into Rag-deficient hosts (73). Derepression of a Runx3 reporter in a large proportion of class II–restricted $CD4^{+}8^{lo}$ and SP CD4 thymocytes in ThPOK-deficient mice provides additional evidence for a role of ThPOK in repressing Runx3 (71). To distinguish whether induction of CD8 genes in ThPOK hypomorphic CD4 cells reflects a continued requirement for ThPOK in mature CD4 T cells or whether it reflects an earlier developmental requirement, ThPOK was specifically ablated in mature CD4 T cells. This still resulted in acquisition of CD8 expression and CD8 effector functions by adoptively transferred CD4 T cells, indicating that ThPOK is permanently required to repress these features of CD8 cells in peripheral CD4 cells (73). Conversely, ectopic expression of ThPOK in mature CD8 T cells perturbs the normal CD8-specific gene expression program, causing reduced expression of CD8, Perforin, GranzymeB, and Eomes, as well as impaired IFN-γ production, while activating certain aspects of the CD4-specific gene expression program, such as increased Gata3 expression and enhanced IL-2 production (although CD4 expression remains repressed) (97). Mice expressing ThPOK constitutively exhibit partial derepression of ThPOK in DP thymocytes, and ChIP-on-chip analysis shows binding of ThPOK near the ThPOK DRE element, suggesting a role for ThPOK in antagonizing its own silencer (95). However, the degree of derepression observed is much lower than that achieved by deleting the DRE element, so the physiological significance of this observation is unclear. Casting further doubt on a notable role for ThPOK in regulating its silencer is the fact that ThPOK is induced at normal levels in class II–restricted $CD4^{+}8^{lo}$ thymocytes from $ThPOK^{HD/HD}$ mice, i.e., even in the absence of functional ThPOK (93).

These observations indicate an important role for ThPOK in repressing genes involved in CD8 differentiation and activating genes involved in CD4 differentiation. However, the extent to which these effects reflect direct control of these genes by ThPOK or indirect control by as yet unknown intermediary factors remains to be determined.

Selective Requirement for Gata3 and TOX in Development of Class II–Restricted Thymocytes

The zinc-finger transcription factor Gata3 is preferentially upregulated in class II–restricted thymocytes beginning early in positive selection at the $CD4^{lo}8^{lo}$ stage, and its induction is controlled by relative TCR signal strength, suggesting a specific role for Gata3 in commitment and/or development of class II–restricted thymocytes (98). Indeed, when Gata3 is conditionally knocked out beginning at the DP stage (by CD4-Cre), development of SP CD4 cells is blocked. In addition, the number of $CD4^{+}8^{lo}$ thymocytes is drastically reduced, similar to class II–deficient mice, suggesting that the block in development of class II–restricted thymocytes occurs before this stage (73, 99). In contrast, development of class I–restricted thymocytes is relatively normal in Gata3-deficient mice (99). Significantly, class II–restricted cells are mainly blocked in development rather than redirected to the CD8 lineage in $Gata3^{-/-}$ mice (73, 99). Although redirection of class II–restricted thymocytes to the CD8 lineage is observed in some experimental systems, the efficiency is very low (5–10% of the normal number of SP CD4 thymocytes) (73).

Two observations suggest that the requirement for Gata3 in development of class II–restricted thymocytes precedes that for ThPOK: (*a*) Gata3 but not ThPOK is induced in DP thymocytes upon TCR stimulation (94, 98), and (*b*) ThPOK-deficient mice, in contrast to Gata3-deficient mice, show abundant generation of $CD4^{+}8^{lo}$ thymocytes (68). These observations are consistent with a direct role for Gata3 in inducing ThPOK and hence in promoting CD4 commitment. Interestingly, consensus Gata3 sites have been identified upstream of the ThPOK coding exons, and this region appears essential for ThPOK expression (73). Hence, Gata3 binding to this region may be necessary for ThPOK transcription. However, Gata3 clearly must play an additional role in the development of class II–restricted cells that is independent of ThPOK, for two reasons: (*a*) Class II–restricted cells are efficiently redirected to the CD8 lineage in ThPOK-deficient mice, but not in Gata3-deficient mice, suggesting that Gata3 deficiency blocks development of class II–restricted thymocytes before they are competent to undergo differentiation to the SP CD8 stage, and (*b*) a constitutive ThPOK transgene does not restore development of class II–restricted cells to the CD4 lineage in $Gata3^{-/-}$ mice (73). However, constitutive ThPOK expression still prevents development of class I–restricted cells to the CD8 lineage, indicating that ThPOK-mediated blockade of CD8 development does not require Gata3. Hence, the functions of Gata3 and ThPOK in promoting the development of class II–restricted thymocytes are at least partly nonoverlapping. The severe depletion of $CD4^{+}8^{lo}$ thymocytes in $Gata3^{-/-}$ mice suggests that the key function of Gata3 may lie in promoting development to this stage rather than in directing lineage commitment per se.

Gata3 deficiency also blocks the development of $CD4^{+}8^{lo}$ cells in mice expressing the class I–restricted OT-1 TCR transgene, indicating a general role in development of this subset that is independent of MHC specificity (99). The high proportion of $CD4^{+}8^{lo}$ cells in OT-1 TCR transgenic mice may reflect the relatively high affinity of the OT-1 TCR for its intrathymic ligand, as other lower affinity class I–restricted TCR transgenes exhibit far fewer of these cells (7). These considerations suggest a model in which Gata3 is specifically required to promote differentiation of high-affinity thymocytes to the $CD4^{+}8^{lo}$ stage. Upmodulation of CD4 at the $CD4^{+}8^{lo}$ stage is probably critical for completion of TCR-mediated positive selection of class II–restricted cells, so that failure to reach this stage would explain the block in development of these cells in Gata3-deficient mice. It would also explain the lack of ThPOK induction in Gata3$^{-/-}$ thymocytes because ThPOK is first induced at this stage. The mechanism by which Gata3 promotes development to the CD4^{+}8^{lo} stage remains to be elucidated. It may act indirectly to enhance/amplify TCR signaling, a suggestion based on reduced surface expression of TCR and CD69 exhibited by Gata3-deficient thymocytes (73, 99).

The high-mobility group family factor TOX is transiently induced during positive selection at the DP-to-SP transition in both CD4 and CD8 lineages (100, 101). The finding that constitutive TOX expression leads to increased generation of SP CD8 thymocytes suggested that TOX might function to promote CD8 lineage commitment (101). Increased SP CD8 generation was observed even in the absence of TCRα or MHC and thus does not require any TCR stimulus (100). Interestingly, mice in which the bHLH transcription factors HEB and E2A are deleted at the DP stage exhibit similar exclusive development of SP CD8 T cells in the absence of TCR expression (52). This suggests that both types of factors may be involved in amplifying TCR signal intensity, rather than directly controlling lineage commitment. Consistent with such a view, TOX knockout mice show a selective block in development of SP CD4 thymocytes, which are postulated to require a stronger/longer TCR signal than do SP CD8 thymocytes (102). Interestingly, class II–restricted cells are blocked in these mice prior to the CD4^{+}8^{lo} stage and do not undergo redirection to the CD8 lineage. In contrast, development of class I–restricted cells is only mildly impaired in TOX$^{-/-}$ mice. Given that TCR signal initiation, as assessed by Ca^{2+} flux and Erk phosphorylation, is normal in TOX$^{-/-}$ mice, more distal aspects of TCR signaling may be affected. The inability of class II–restricted thymocytes to progress to the CD4^{+}8^{lo} stage in TOX$^{-/-}$ could explain the defects in ThPOK upmodulation and CD4 commitment in these mice, as suggested above for Gata3$^{-/-}$ mice. CD4^{lo}8^{lo} cells still develop in TOX$^{-/-}$ mice and show normal expression of Gata3, suggesting that the effect of TOX deficiency is independent of Gata3.

The Role of Runx Factors in CD8 Development and Lineage Commitment

As outlined above, the transcriptional regulation of CD4 and CD8 has been extensively studied, leading to the important insight that Runx factors are indispensable for CD4 silencing (57, 63). Both Runx1 and Runx3 are expressed during thymopoiesis. Of particular interest, Runx3 protein is selectively expressed in the CD8 lineage, whereas Runx1 shows no such selectivity, suggesting that Runx3 is the main factor responsible for CD8 lineage–specific CD4 silencing (57, 103, 104). Indeed, blocking Runx3 expression in developing thymocytes, either by a conditional knockout approach (71) or by using chimeric mice reconstituted with Runx3-deficient fetal liver cells (105), causes notable derepression of CD4 in CD8 cells. Most Runx3 protein in thymocytes appears to derive from transcripts produced by the distal promoter (71, 106), and selectively blocking production of functional Runx3 transcripts by this promoter similarly leads to partial derepression of CD4 in CD8 cells (106). It has subsequently become clear that the role of Runx factors in development of CD8 T cells extends beyond control of coreceptor transcription. Thus, in both conditional Runx3 and Cbfβ knockout mice (Cbfβ is a common subunit of all Runx heterodimers), the efficiency of generation of CD8 cells is markedly diminished, and the remaining CD8 cells fail to upregulate the CD8 lineage marker CD103 (106, 107).

Repression of ThPOK transcription has recently been identified as an additional important function of Runx factors. This was established using mice that lacked expression of both Runx3 and Runx1, either by targeting both genes simultaneously or targeting their common Cbfβ subunit (57). Strikingly, in both kinds of mice, ThPOK is expressed constitutively, beginning at the DP stage, resulting in substantial redirection of class I–restricted thymocytes to the CD4 lineage. Furthermore, Runx-mediated repression of ThPOK activity requires direct binding to the ThPOK silencer element. An earlier study had reported that expression of dominant-negative Runx1 in a thymocyte reaggregate culture system caused immature thymocytes to adopt the SP CD4 rather than the SP CD8 phenotype, which in retrospect may also have reflected ThPOK derepression (103). Because only Runx3 is regulated in a lineage-specific fashion during thymic development, whereas Runx1 is expressed in both lineages, eliminating all Runx creates a rather nonphysiological situation that is not observed during normal CD4 development. Indeed, Runx1 is necessary for normal selection and survival of CD4 thymocytes (106). Hence,

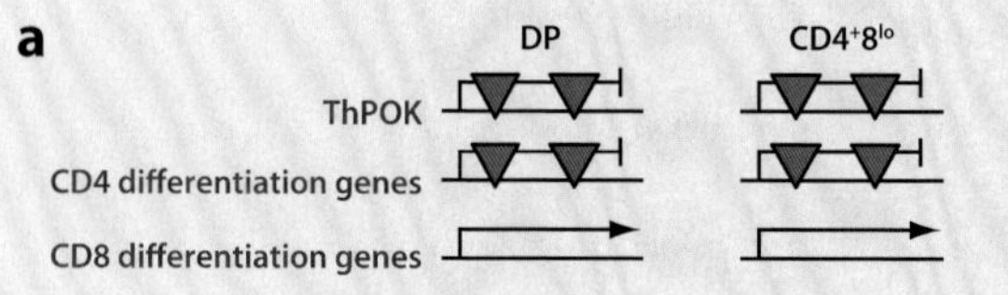

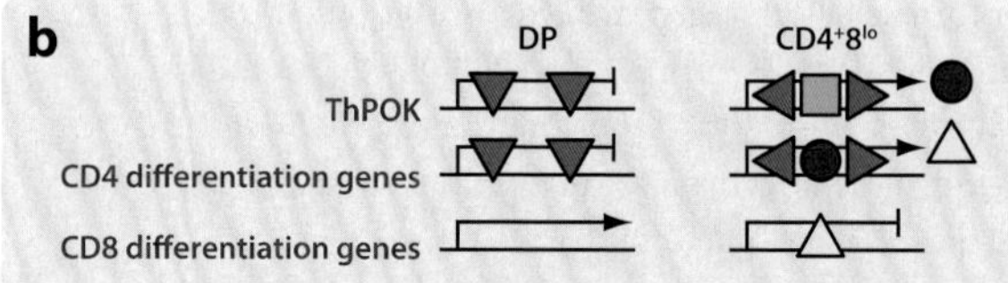

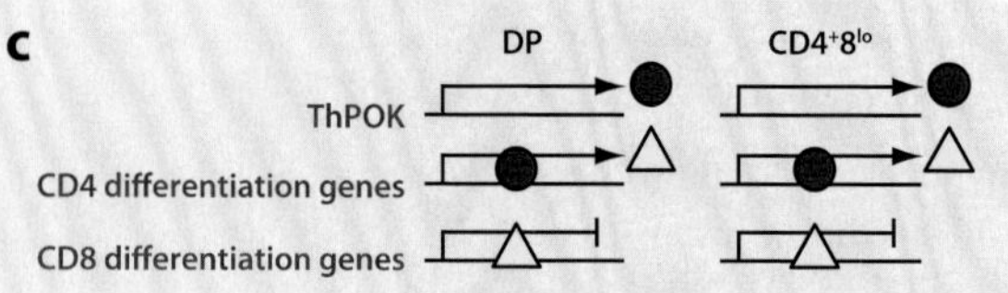

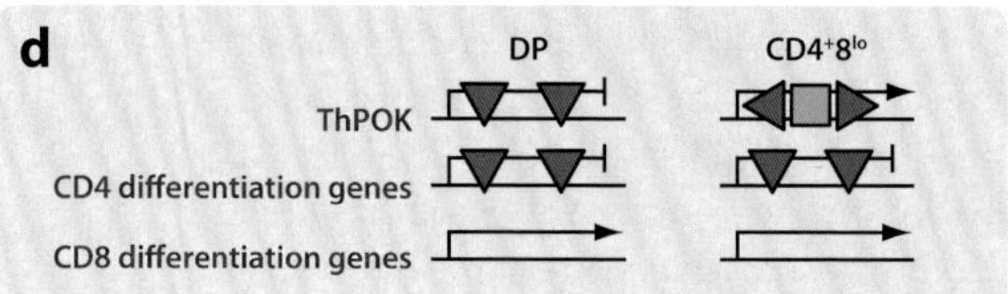

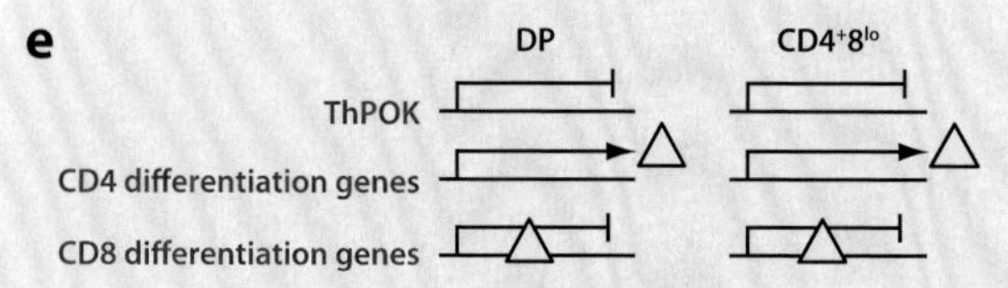

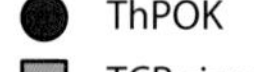

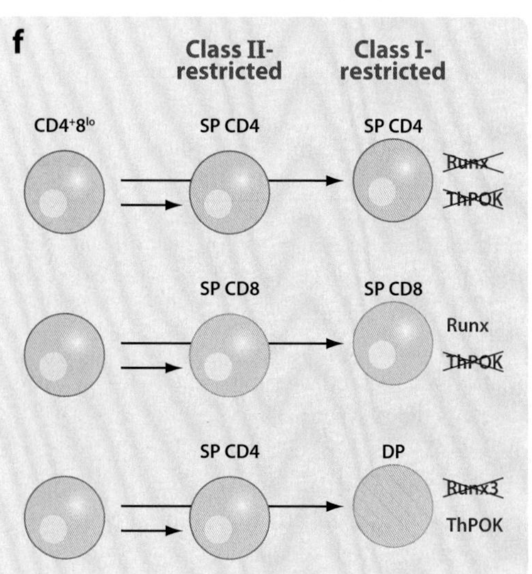

although ThPOK derepression in mice lacking functional Runx clearly shows that Runx factors are collectively necessary for DRE silencer function, the mechanistic implications for lineage commitment are unclear. In principle, there are two possible interpretations: (*a*) Runx factors may function upstream of ThPOK during the lineage commitment process, and hence directly control lineage commitment, or (*b*) Runx factors may function as constitutive repressors of ThPOK transcription that block ThPOK induction unless counteracted by unknown CD4-specifying factors (which in turn are presumably induced/activated by strong TCR signals).

Several considerations support the latter hypothesis. First, the expression pattern of Runx3, the only Runx factor to be regulated in a lineage-specific fashion, seems inconsistent with a lineage-specifying function. In particular, Runx3 induction occurs mainly after the $CD4^{+}8^{lo}$ stage, i.e., after the peak of ThPOK induction and after lineage commitment is believed to be determined (69, 71, 106). Second, as mentioned above, targeted ablation of Runx3 by itself does not cause redirection of class I–restricted cells to the CD4 lineage (106). Interestingly, Runx1 levels are significantly increased in Runx3-deficient peripheral blood CD8 T cells, compared with normal CD8 T cells, indicating some type of feedback mechanism that may partly compensate for Runx3 deficiency and hence might obscure the full physiological role of Runx3 (71). However, it remains to be established whether such compensatory Runx1 induction also occurs in Runx3-deficient thymocytes, where it might mask a defect in lineage commitment. Third, Runx factors appear to bind the ThPOK silencer constitutively, i.e., even in ThPOK-expressing cells (72), suggesting that lineage-specific silencer derepression is controlled by positive factors that counteract Runx function, not by the presence/absence of Runx factors. Fourth, and most notably, constitutive Runx3 expression does not prevent CD4 commitment of class II–restricted thymocytes. Although Runx3 overexpression results in redirection of class II–restricted cells to the CD8 lineage (105, 108), this effect is corrected by ectopic CD4 expression (105). This reflects the previously established fact that interruption of CD4 expression during lineage commitment causes redirection of class II–restricted cells to the CD8 lineage, presumably by impairing TCR signaling (23, 41). Hence, redirection of class II–restricted cells in Runx3 transgenic mice reflects a secondary consequence of Runx-mediated CD4 downregulation, rather than a direct role for Runx factors in CD8 lineage specification. Consistent with this interpretation, transgenic overexpression of Runx3 does not impair ThPOK induction by class II–restricted thymocytes (71).

Figure 3

Hypothetical model of transcriptional control of CD4/CD8 lineage commitment. Based on current evidence, ThPOK (*red circles*) is the primary physiological regulator of lineage commitment. In wild-type mice, ThPOK is selectively expressed in class II–restricted thymocytes, where it relieves Runx-mediated repression of unknown CD4 differentiation genes, including ones that function as repressors of CD8 differentiation (*yellow triangles*) (panel *b*). In the absence of ThPOK, CD4 differentiation genes remain repressed, and class II–restricted thymocytes undergo default development to the CD8 lineage (panel *d*), similar to class I–restricted thymocytes (panel *a*). ThPOK expression by class II–restricted thymocytes is hypothesized to be induced by unknown upstream factors (*green squares*) induced by strong TCR signals. Runx factors (*blue triangles*) appear to act as constitutive repressors of ThPOK, keeping ThPOK silenced until strong TCR signals are received. Such strong TCR stimuli lead to recruitment of unknown positive factors (*green squares*) to the DRE silencer, counteracting the effect of Runx and potentially other negative regulatory factors, thereby leading to ThPOK induction. Other unknown factors that promote CD4 differentiation (*yellow triangles*) may also be derepressed in the absence of Runx (panel *c*). In the absence of both Runx and ThPOK factors, these unknown CD4 differentiation genes (*yellow triangles*) are sufficient to promote CD4 commitment (panel *e*). Note that ThPOK-independent CD4 commitment is not observed under physiological circumstances, because no wild-type thymocytes ever lack Runx factors and ThPOK is indispensable for CD4 commitment by Runx-sufficient cells. The demonstrated or predicted lineage fates, according to this model, are indicated in panel *f* for class I– and II–restricted thymocytes. In panels *a–f*, actively transcribed or silent loci are indicated by arrows or by lines ending with vertical bars, respectively.

Overall, therefore, current data suggest a model in which Runx factors play an essential but not necessarily exclusive role in suppressing ThPOK transcription during early thymopoiesis via the DRE silencer. Upon receipt of a strong class II–restricted TCR stimulus, other unknown factors are induced/activated that bind to the DRE element and disable its silencer function. Because selective induction of Runx3 in class I–restricted thymocytes occurs predominantly after CD8 commitment, it may be important to cement the CD8 lineage choice and prevent reversion to the CD4 lineage by repressing genes involved in CD4 specification, in particular ThPOK.

As discussed above, in mice lacking functional ThPOK, class II–restricted cells are redirected efficiently to the CD8 lineage. Interestingly, in compound knockout mice, lacking both ThPOK and Cbfβ, development of all cells to the CD8 lineage is prevented, and some cells instead develop to the CD4 lineage, although with reduced efficiency (about 20% of the number of CD4 thymocytes found in wild-type mice) (71). These cells also express CD40L, another marker of CD4 commitment. Generation of CD4 cells in double ThPOK/Cbfβ knockout mice is a striking outcome that demonstrates that ThPOK is not absolutely required for CD4 commitment and/or for CD4 expression by mature thymocytes. This result could be interpreted in at least two ways: (*a*) There may be another factor besides ThPOK that is specifically induced in class II–restricted thymocytes and that can direct their development to the CD4 lineage even in the absence of ThPOK. This interpretation requires that this factor be active only when Runx is lacking because it cannot restore CD4 development in mice lacking ThPOK alone. (*b*) CD4 commitment may be a default pathway that is adopted when normal regulators of lineage choice and differentiation, i.e., ThPOK and Runx, are absent (**Figure 3**). In this model, Runx factors act as constitutive inhibitors of CD4 development by repressing genes involved in CD4 commitment and differentiation. This negative regulation is released either when Runx expression is genetically blocked or under physiological circumstances by countervailing activity of ThPOK. When Runx factors are absent, CD4 commitment is no longer blocked, and thus ThPOK is no longer required to overcome Runx activity. Notably, this interpretation does not require another CD4-specifying factor besides ThPOK.

To distinguish these possibilities, investigators might determine whether CD4 thymocytes generated in double ThPOK/CBFβ knockout mice consist only of class II–restricted cells or of both class I– and class II–restricted cells. If, on the one hand, CD4 commitment occurs by default, it should by definition be independent of TCR specificity, so that SP CD4 cells in double knockout mice should consist of class I– and class II–restricted cells. If, on the other hand, a CD4-specifying factor induced by class II–restricted TCR signals is required, SP CD4 cells in double knockout mice should consist only of class II–restricted cells, as class I–restricted cells should lack this factor.

CONCLUSIONS

Considerable evidence now supports the view that alternate CD4/CD8 lineage choice is controlled by the relative strength or length of TCR signaling. Hence, further progress in the field will involve defining the molecular pathways by which these alternate TCR signals are translated into different programs of gene expression. Several transcription factors have been implicated in this process, including in particular Runx3, Gata3, and ThPOK. Each of these factors appears to play an essential stage-specific role in lineage commitment. Runx factors, in addition to their key role in post-CD8-commitment control of coreceptor expression, appear important to prevent premature ThPOK expression at the DP stage. In this role, they seem to constitutively preclude CD4 commitment unless counteracted by class II–restricted TCR signals. Next, Gata3 appears to promote the DP-to-$CD4^{+}8^{lo}$ transition in response to strong TCR signals, although possibly not discriminating between class I– and class II–restricted TCR signals. Finally, the differential induction of ThPOK at the CD4^{+}8^{lo} stage in response to class I– or class II–restricted TCR signals determines entry to the CD8 or CD4 lineages, respectively. Key unresolved issues regarding the role of ThPOK include determining which upstream pathways control its expression and which functionally relevant downstream targets it regulates. Hence, defining the DNA target specificity of ThPOK and the cofactors with which it interacts represents a major future goal of the field.

DISCLOSURE STATEMENT

The authors are not aware of any affiliations, memberships, funding, or financial holdings that might be perceived as affecting the objectivity of this review.

ACKNOWLEDGMENTS

This research was supported by grants from the NIH to D.J.K. (AI068907, AI079247) and Fox Chase Cancer Center (CA06927) and by an appropriation from the Commonwealth of Pennsylvania.

LITERATURE CITED

1. Barthlott T, Kohler H, Pircher H, Eichmann K. 1997. Differentiation of CD4^{high}CD8^{low} coreceptor-skewed thymocytes into mature CD8 single-positive cells independent of MHC class I recognition. *Eur. J. Immunol.* 27:2024–32
2. Guidos CJ, Danska JS, Fathman CG, Weissman IL. 1990. T cell receptor-mediated negative selection of autoreactive T lymphocyte precursors occurs after commitment to the CD4 or CD8 lineages. *J. Exp. Med.* 172:835–45
3. Kydd R, Lundberg K, Vremec D, Harris AW, Shortman K. 1995. Intermediate steps in thymic positive selection. Generation of CD4^{-}8^{+} T cells in culture from CD4^{+}8^{+}, CD4^{int}8^{+}, and CD4^{+}8^{int} thymocytes with up-regulated levels of TCR-CD3. *J. Immunol.* 155:3806–14
4. Lucas B, Germain RN. 1996. Unexpectedly complex regulation of CD4/CD8 coreceptor expression supports a revised model for CD4^{+}CD8^{+} thymocyte differentiation. *Immunity* 5:461–77
5. Lundberg K, Heath W, Kontgen F, Carbone FR, Shortman K. 1995. Intermediate steps in positive selection: differentiation of CD4^{+}8^{int} TCR^{int} thymocytes into CD4^{-}8^{+}TCR^{hi} thymocytes. *J. Exp. Med.* 181:1643–51
6. Suzuki H, Punt JA, Granger LG, Singer A. 1995. Asymmetric signaling requirements for thymocyte commitment to the CD4^{+} versus CD8^{+} T cell lineages: a new perspective on thymic commitment and selection. *Immunity* 2:413–25
7. Chan S, Correia-Neves M, Dierich A, Benoist C, Mathis D. 1998. Visualization of CD4/CD8 T cell commitment. *J. Exp. Med.* 188:2321–33
8. Kisielow P, Teh HS, Bluthmann H, von Boehmer H. 1988. Positive selection of antigen-specific T cells in thymus by restricting MHC molecules. *Nature* 335:730–33
9. Kaye J, Vasquez NJ, Hedrick SM. 1992. Involvement of the same region of the T cell antigen receptor in thymic selection and foreign peptide recognition. *J. Immunol.* 148:3342–53
10. Chan SH, Cosgrove D, Waltzinger C, Benoist C, Mathis D. 1993. Another view of the selective model of thymocyte selection. *Cell* 73:225–36
11. Davis CB, Killeen N, Crooks ME, Raulet D, Littman DR. 1993. Evidence for a stochastic mechanism in the differentiation of mature subsets of T lymphocytes. *Cell* 73:237–47
12. Robey EA, Fowlkes BJ, Gordon JW, Kioussis D, von Boehmer H, Ramsdell F. 1991. Axel R thymic selection in CD8 transgenic mice supports an instructive model for commitment to a CD4 or CD8 lineage. *Cell* 64:99–107

13. Borgulya P, Kishi H, Muller U, Kirberg J, von Boehmer H. 1991. Development of the CD4 and CD8 lineage of T cells: instruction versus selection. *EMBO J.* 10:913–18
14. Itano A, Kioussis D, Robey E. 1994. Stochastic component to development of class I major histocompatibility complex-specific T cells. *Proc. Natl. Acad. Sci. USA* 91:220–24
15. van Meerwijk JP, Germain RN. 1993. Development of mature CD8$^+$ thymocytes: selection rather than instruction? *Science* 261:911–15
16. Chan SH, Waltzinger C, Baron A, Benoist C, Mathis D 1994. Role of coreceptors in positive selection and lineage commitment. *EMBO J.* 13:4482–89
17. Baron A, Hafen K, von Boehmer H. 1994. A human CD4 transgene rescues CD4$^-$CD8$^+$ cells in beta 2-microglobulin-deficient mice. *Eur. J. Immunol.* 24:1933–36
18. Adoro S, Erman B, Sarafova SD, Van Laethem F, Park JH, et al. 2008. Targeting CD4 coreceptor expression to postselection thymocytes reveals that CD4/CD8 lineage choice is neither error-prone nor stochastic. *J. Immunol.* 181:6975–83
19. Ellmeier W, Sunshine MJ, Losos K, Hatam F, Littman DR. 1997. An enhancer that directs lineage-specific expression of CD8 in positively selected thymocytes and mature T cells. *Immunity* 7:537–47
20. Hostert A, Tolaini M, Roderick K, Harker N, Norton T, Kioussis D. 1997. A region in the CD8 gene locus that directs expression to the mature CD8 T cell subset in transgenic mice. *Immunity* 7:525–36
21. von Boehmer H. 1986. The selection of the α,β heterodimeric T-cell receptor for antigen. *Immunol. Today* 7:333–36
22. Norment AM, Forbush KA, Nguyen N, Malissen M, Perlmutter RM. 1997. Replacement of pre-T cell receptor signaling functions by the CD4 coreceptor. *J. Exp. Med.* 185:121–30
23. Matechak EO, Killeen N, Hedrick SM, Fowlkes BJ. 1996. MHC class II-specific T cells can develop in the CD8 lineage when CD4 is absent. *Immunity* 4:337–47
24. Tyznik AJ, Sun JC, Bevan MJ. 2004. The CD8 population in CD4-deficient mice is heavily contaminated with MHC class II-restricted T cells. *J. Exp. Med.* 199:559–65
25. Kao H, Allen PM. 2005. An antagonist peptide mediates positive selection and CD4 lineage commitment of MHC class II-restricted T cells in the absence of CD4. *J. Exp. Med.* 201:149–58
26. Ravichandran KS, Burakoff SJ. 1994. Evidence for differential intracellular signaling via CD4 and CD8 molecules. *J. Exp. Med.* 179:727–32
27. Veillette A, Bookman MA, Horak EM, Bolen JB. 1988. The CD4 and CD8 T cell surface antigens are associated with the internal membrane tyrosine-protein kinase p56^{lck}. *Cell* 55:301–8
28. Itano A, Salmon P, Kioussis D, Tolaini M, Corbella P, Robey EA. 1996. The cytoplasmic domain of CD4 promotes the development of CD4 lineage T cells. *J. Exp. Med.* 183:731–41
29. Hernandez-Hoyos G, Sohn SJ, Rothenberg EV, Alberola-Ila J. 2000. Lck activity controls CD4/CD8 T cell lineage commitment. *Immunity* 12:313–22
30. Legname G, Seddon B, Lovatt M, Tomlinson P, Sarner N, et al. 2000. Inducible expression of a p56Lck transgene reveals a central role for Lck in the differentiation of CD4 SP thymocytes. *Immunity* 12:537–46
31. Liu X, Bosselut R. 2004. Duration of TCR signaling controls CD4-CD8 lineage differentiation in vivo. *Nat. Immunol.* 5:280–88
32. Liu X, Taylor BJ, Sun G, Bosselut R. 2005. Analyzing expression of perforin, Runx3, and Thpok genes during positive selection reveals activation of CD8-differentiation programs by MHC II-signaled thymocytes. *J. Immunol.* 175:4465–74
33. Bommhardt U, Basson MA, Krummrei U, Zamoyska R. 1999. Activation of the extracellular signal-related kinase/mitogen-activated protein kinase pathway discriminates CD4 versus CD8 lineage commitment in the thymus. *J. Immunol.* 163:715–22
34. Sharp LL, Schwarz DA, Bott CM, Marshall CJ, Hedrick SM. 1997. The influence of the MAPK pathway on T cell lineage commitment. *Immunity* 7:609–18
35. Alberola-Ila J, Hernandez-Hoyos G. 2003. The Ras/MAPK cascade and the control of positive selection. *Immunol. Rev.* 191:79–96
36. Fischer AM, Katayama CD, Pages G, Pouyssegur J, Hedrick SM. 2005. The role of erk1 and erk2 in multiple stages of T cell development. *Immunity* 23:431–43

37. Brugnera E, Bhandoola A, Cibotti R, Yu Q, Guinter TI, et al. 2000. Coreceptor reversal in the thymus: signaled CD4$^+$8$^+$ thymocytes initially terminate CD8 transcription even when differentiating into CD8$^+$ T cells. *Immunity* 13:59–71
38. Catlett IM, Hedrick SM. 2005. Suppressor of cytokine signaling 1 is required for the differentiation of CD4$^+$ T cells. *Nat. Immunol.* 6:715–21
39. Chong MM, Cornish AL, Darwiche R, Stanley EG, Purton JF, et al. 2003. Suppressor of cytokine signaling-1 is a critical regulator of interleukin-7-dependent CD8$^+$ T cell differentiation. *Immunity* 18:475–87
40. Bosselut R, Guinter TI, Sharrow SO, Singer A. 2003. Unraveling a revealing paradox: Why major histocompatibility complex I-signaled thymocytes "paradoxically" appear as CD4$^+$8^{lo} transitional cells during positive selection of CD8$^+$ T cells. *J. Exp. Med.* 197:1709–19
41. Sarafova SD, Erman B, Yu Q, Van Laethem F, Guinter T, et al. 2005. Modulation of coreceptor transcription during positive selection dictates lineage fate independently of TCR/coreceptor specificity. *Immunity* 23:75–87
42. Yasutomo K, Doyle C, Miele L, Fuchs C, Germain RN. 2000. The duration of antigen receptor signaling determines CD4$^+$ versus CD8$^+$ T-cell lineage fate. *Nature* 404:506–10
43. Ellmeier W, Sunshine MJ, Losos K, Littman DR. 1998. Multiple developmental stage-specific enhancers regulate CD8 expression in developing thymocytes and in thymus-independent T cells. *Immunity* 9:485–96
44. Feik N, Bilic I, Tinhofer J, Unger B, Littman DR, et al. 2005. Functional and molecular analysis of the double-positive stage-specific CD8 enhancer E8III during thymocyte development. *J. Immunol.* 174:1513–24
45. Correia-Neves M, Mathis D, Benoist C. 2001. A molecular chart of thymocyte positive selection. *Eur. J. Immunol.* 31:2583–92
46. Bosselut R, Feigenbaum L, Sharrow SO, Singer A. 2001. Strength of signaling by CD4 and CD8 coreceptor tails determines the number but not the lineage direction of positively selected thymocytes. *Immunity* 14:483–94
47. Locksley RM, Reiner SL Hatam F, Littman DR, Killeen N. 1993. Helper T cells without CD4: control of leishmaniasis in CD4-deficient mice. *Science* 261:1448–51
48. Siu G, Wurster AL, Duncan DD, Soliman TM, Hedrick SM. 1994. A transcriptional silencer controls the developmental expression of the CD4 gene. *EMBO J.* 13:3570–79
49. Sawada S, Littman DR. 1991. Identification and characterization of a T-cell-specific enhancer adjacent to the murine CD4 gene. *Mol. Cell. Biol.* 11:5506–15
50. Sawada S, Littman DR. 1993. A heterodimer of HEB and an E12-related protein interacts with the CD4 enhancer and regulates its activity in T-cell lines. *Mol. Cell. Biol.* 13:5620–28
51. Zhuang Y, Cheng P, Weintraub H. 1996. B-lymphocyte development is regulated by the combined dosage of three basic helix-loop-helix genes, E2A, E2-2, and HEB. *Mol. Cell. Biol.* 16:2898–905
52. Jones ME, Zhuang Y. 2007. Acquisition of a functional T cell receptor during T lymphocyte development is enforced by HEB and E2A transcription factors. *Immunity* 27:860–70
53. Huang Z, Xie H, Ioannidis V, Held W, Clevers H, et al. 2006. Transcriptional regulation of CD4 gene expression by T cell factor-1/beta-catenin pathway. *J. Immunol.* 176:4880–87
54. Williams CJ, Naito T, Arco PG, Seavitt JR, Cashman SM, et al. 2004. The chromatin remodeler Mi-2beta is required for CD4 expression and T cell development. *Immunity* 20:719–33
55. Sawada S, Scarborough JD, Killeen N, Littman DR. 1994. A lineage-specific transcriptional silencer regulates CD4 gene expression during T lymphocyte development. *Cell* 77:917–29
56. Donda A, Schulz M, Burki K, De Libero G, Uematsu Y. 1996. Identification and characterization of a human CD4 silencer. *Eur. J. Immunol.* 26:493–500
57. Taniuchi I, Osato M, Egawa T, Sunshine MJ, Bae SC, et al. 2002. Differential requirements for Runx proteins in CD4 repression and epigenetic silencing during T lymphocyte development. *Cell* 111:621–33
58. Zou YR, Sunshine MJ, Taniuchi I, Hatam F, Killeen N, Littman DR. 2001. Epigenetic silencing of CD4 in T cells committed to the cytotoxic lineage. *Nat. Genet.* 29:332–36

59. Merkenschlager M, Amoils S, Roldan E, Rahemtulla A, O'Connor E, et al. 2004. Centromeric repositioning of coreceptor loci predicts their stable silencing and the CD4/CD8 lineage choice. *J. Exp. Med.* 200:1437–44
60. Delaire S, Huang YH, Chan SW, Robey EA. 2004. Dynamic repositioning of CD4 and CD8 genes during T cell development. *J. Exp. Med.* 200:1427–35
61. Chi TH, Wan M, Zhao K, Taniuchi I, Chen L, et al. 2002. Reciprocal regulation of CD4/CD8 expression by SWI/SNF-like BAF complexes. *Nature* 418:195–99
62. Chi TH, Wan M, Lee PP, Akashi K, Metzger D, et al. 2003. Sequential roles of Brg, the ATPase subunit of BAF chromatin remodeling complexes, in thymocyte development. *Immunity* 19:169–82
63. Woolf E, Xiao C, Fainaru O, Lotem J, Rosen D, et al. 2003. Runx3 and Runx1 are required for CD8 T cell development during thymopoiesis. *Proc. Natl. Acad. Sci. USA* 100:7731–36
64. Hostert A, Tolaini M, Festenstein R, McNeill L, Malissen B, et al. 1997. A CD8 genomic fragment that directs subset-specific expression of CD8 in transgenic mice. *J. Immunol.* 158:4270–81
65. Hostert A, Garefalaki A, Mavria G, Tolaini M, Roderick K, et al. 1998. Hierarchical interactions of control elements determine CD8α gene expression in subsets of thymocytes and peripheral T cells. *Immunity* 9:497–508
66. Zhang W, Trible RP, Samelson LE. 1998. LAT palmitoylation: its essential role in membrane microdomain targeting and tyrosine phosphorylation during T cell activation. *Immunity* 9:239–46
67. Ellmeier W, Sawada M, Littman DR. 1999. The regulation of CD4 and CD8 coreceptor gene expression during T cell development. *Annu. Rev. Immunol.* 17:523–54
68. Davé VP, Allman D, Keefe R, Hardy RR, Kappes DJ. 1998. HD mice: a novel mouse mutant with a specific defect in the generation of $CD4^+$ T cells. *Proc. Natl. Acad. Sci. USA* 95:8187–92
69. He X, Dave VP, Zhang Y, Hua X, Nicolas E, et al. 2005. The zinc finger transcription factor Th-POK regulates CD4 versus CD8 T-cell lineage commitment. *Nature* 433:826–33
70. Kappes DJ, He X, He X. 2006. Role of the transcription factor Th-POK in CD4:CD8 lineage commitment. *Immunol. Rev.* 209:237–52
71. Egawa T, Littman DR. 2008. ThPOK acts late in specification of the helper T cell lineage and suppresses Runx-mediated commitment to the cytotoxic T cell lineage. *Nat. Immunol.* 9:1131–39
72. Setoguchi R, Tachibana M, Naoe Y, Muroi S, Akiyama K, et al. 2008. Repression of the transcription factor Th-POK by Runx complexes in cytotoxic T cell development. *Science* 319:822–25
73. Wang L, Wildt KF, Zhu J, Zhang X, Feigenbaum L, et al. 2008. Distinct functions for the transcription factors GATA-3 and ThPOK during intrathymic differentiation of $CD4^+$ T cells. *Nat. Immunol.* 9:1122–30
74. Kelly KF, Daniel JM. 2006. POZ for effect—POZ-ZF transcription factors in cancer and development. *Trends Cell Biol.* 16:578–87
75. Kovalovsky D, Uche OU, Eladad S, Hobbs RM, Yi W, et al. 2008. The BTB-zinc finger transcriptional regulator PLZF controls the development of invariant natural killer T cell effector functions. *Nat. Immunol.* 9:1055–64
76. Savage AK, Constantinides MG, Han J, Picard D, Martin E, et al. 2008. The transcription factor PLZF directs the effector program of the NKT cell lineage. *Immunity* 29:391–403
77. Dent AL, Shaffer AL, Yu X, Allman D, Staudt LM. 1997. Control of inflammation, cytokine expression, and germinal center formation by BCL-6. *Science* 276:589–92
78. Fukuda T, Yoshida T, Okada S, Hatano M, Miki T, et al. 1997. Disruption of the *Bcl6* gene results in an impaired germinal center formation. *J. Exp. Med.* 186:439–48
79. Ye BH, Cattoretti G, Shen Q, Zhang J, Hawe N, et al. 1997. The BCL-6 proto-oncogene controls germinal-center formation and Th2-type inflammation. *Nat. Genet.* 16:161–70
80. Maeda T, Hobbs RM, Merghoub T, Guernah I, Zelent A, et al. 2005. Role of the proto-oncogene *Pokemon* in cellular transformation and *ARF* repression. *Nature* 433:278–85
81. Chen Z, Brand NJ, Chen A, Chen SJ, Tong JH, et al. 1993. Fusion between a novel *Krüppel*-like zinc finger gene and the retinoic acid receptor-alpha locus due to a variant t(11;17) translocation associated with acute promyelocytic leukaemia. *EMBO J.* 12:1161–67

82. Kerckaert JP, Deweindt C, Tilly H, Quief S, Lecocq G, Bastard C. 1993. *LAZ3*, a novel zinc-finger encoding gene, is disrupted by recurring chromosome 3q27 translocations in human lymphomas. *Nat. Genet.* 5:66–70
83. Ye BH, Lista F, Lo Coco F, Knowles DM, Offit K, et al. 1993. Alterations of a zinc finger-encoding gene, *BCL6*, in diffuse large-cell lymphoma. *Science* 262:747–50
84. Widom RL, Lee JY, Joseph C, Gordon-Froome I, Korn JH. 2001. The hcKrox gene family regulates multiple extracellular matrix genes. *Matrix Biol.* 20:451–62
85. Galera P, Park RW, Ducy P, Mattei MG, Karsenty G 1996. c-Krox binds to several sites in the promoter of both mouse type I collagen genes. Structure/function study and developmental expression analysis. *J. Biol. Chem.* 271:21331–39
86. Galera P, Musso M, Ducy P, Karsenty G. 1994. c-Krox, a transcriptional regulator of type I collagen gene expression, is preferentially expressed in skin. *Proc. Natl. Acad. Sci. USA* 91:9372–76
87. Widom RL, Culic I, Lee JY, Korn JH. 1997. Cloning and characterization of hcKrox, a transcriptional regulator of extracellular matrix gene expression. *Gene* 198:407–20
88. Goto T, Hasegawa K, Kinoshita T, Kubota HY. 2001. A novel POZ/zinc finger protein, *champignon*, interferes with gastrulation movements in *Xenopus*. *Dev. Dyn.* 221:14–25
89. Melnick A, Carlile G, Ahmad KF, Kiang CL, Corcoran C, et al. 2002. Critical residues within the BTB domain of PLZF and Bcl-6 modulate interaction with corepressors. *Mol. Cell. Biol.* 22:1804–18
90. Kobayashi A, Yamagiwa H, Hoshino H, Muto A, Sato K, et al. 2000. A combinatorial code for gene expression generated by transcription factor Bach2 and MAZR (MAZ-related factor) through the BTB/POZ domain. *Mol. Cell. Biol.* 20:1733–46
91. Peukert K, Staller P, Schneider A, Carmichael G, Hanel F, Eilers M. 1997. An alternative pathway for gene regulation by Myc. *EMBO J.* 16:5672–86
92. Keefe R, Dave V, Allman D, Wiest D, Kappes DJ. 1999. Regulation of lineage commitment distinct from positive selection. *Science* 286:1149–53
93. He X, Park K, Wang H, Zhang Y, Hua X, et al. 2008. CD4-CD8 lineage commitment is regulated by a silencer element at the ThPOK transcription-factor locus. *Immunity* 28:346–58
94. Sun G, Liu X, Mercado P, Jenkinson SR, Kypriotou M, et al. 2005. The zinc finger protein cKrox directs CD4 lineage differentiation during intrathymic T cell positive selection. *Nat. Immunol.* 6:373–81
95. Muroi S, Naoe Y, Miyamoto C, Akiyama K, Ikawa T, et al. 2008. Cascading suppression of transcriptional silencers by ThPOK seals helper T cell fate. *Nat. Immunol.* 9:1113–21
96. Wildt KF, Sun G, Grueter B, Fischer M, Zamisch M, et al. 2007. The transcription factor Zbtb7b promotes CD4 expression by antagonizing Runx-mediated activation of the CD4 silencer. *J. Immunol.* 179:4405–14
97. Jenkinson SR, Intlekofer AM, Sun G, Feigenbaum L, Reiner SL, Bosselut R. 2007. Expression of the transcription factor cKrox in peripheral CD8 T cells reveals substantial postthymic plasticity in CD4-CD8 lineage differentiation. *J. Exp. Med.* 204:267–72
98. Hernandez-Hoyos G, Anderson MK, Wang C, Rothenberg EV, Alberola-Ila J 2003. GATA-3 expression is controlled by TCR signals and regulates CD4/CD8 differentiation. *Immunity* 19:83–94
99. Pai SY, Truitt ML, Ting CN, Leiden JM, Glimcher LH, Ho IC. 2003. Critical roles for transcription factor GATA-3 in thymocyte development. *Immunity* 19:863–75
100. Aliahmad P, O'Flaherty E, Han P, Goularte OD, Wilkinson B, et al. 2004. TOX provides a link between calcineurin activation and CD8 lineage commitment. *J. Exp. Med.* 199:1089–99
101. Wilkinson B, Chen JY, Han P, Rufner KM, Goularte OD, Kaye J. 2002. TOX: an HMG box protein implicated in the regulation of thymocyte selection. *Nat. Immunol.* 3:272–80
102. Aliahmad P, Kaye J. 2008. Development of all CD4 T lineages requires nuclear factor TOX. *J. Exp. Med.* 205:245–56
103. Sato T, Ohno S, Hayashi T, Sato C, Kohu K, et al. 2005. Dual functions of Runx proteins for reactivating CD8 and silencing CD4 at the commitment process into CD8 thymocytes. *Immunity* 22:317–28
104. Ehlers M, Laule-Kilian K, Petter M, Aldrian CJ, Grueter B, et al. 2003. Morpholino antisense oligonucleotide-mediated gene knockdown during thymocyte development reveals role for Runx3 transcription factor in CD4 silencing during development of $CD4^{-}/CD8^{+}$thymocytes. *J. Immunol.* 171:3594–604

105. Grueter B, Petter M, Egawa T, Laule-Kilian K, Aldrian CJ, et al. 2005. Runx3 regulates integrin alpha E/CD103 and CD4 expression during development of $CD4^{-}/CD8^{+}$ T cells. *J. Immunol.* 175:1694–705
106. Egawa T, Tillman RE, Naoe Y, Taniuchi I, Littman DR. 2007. The role of the Runx transcription factors in thymocyte differentiation and in homeostasis of naive T cells. *J. Exp. Med.* 204:1945–57
107. Naoe Y, Setoguchi R, Akiyama K, Muroi S, Kuroda M, et al. 2007. Repression of interleukin-4 in T helper type 1 cells by Runx/Cbfβ binding to the *Il4* silencer. *J. Exp. Med.* 204:1749–55
108. Kohu K, Sato T, Ohno S, Hayashi K, Uchino R, et al. 2005. Overexpression of the Runx3 transcription factor increases the proportion of mature thymocytes of the CD8 single-positive lineage. *J. Immunol.* 174:2627–36

The Sterile Inflammatory Response

Kenneth L. Rock,[1] Eicke Latz,[2] Fernando Ontiveros,[1] and Hajime Kono[1]

[1]Department of Pathology and [2]Infectious Diseases and Immunology, University of Massachusetts Medical School, Worcester, Massachusetts 01655; email: kenneth.rock@umassmed.edu

Annu. Rev. Immunol. 2010. 28:321–42

The *Annual Review of Immunology* is online at immunol.annualreviews.org

This article's doi:
10.1146/annurev-immunol-030409-101311

0732-0582/10/0423-0321$20.00

Key Words

sterile particulates, inflammasome, danger signal, IL-1, NLRP3

Abstract

The acute inflammatory response is a double-edged sword. On the one hand, it plays a key role in initial host defense, particularly against many infections. On the other hand, its aim is imprecise, and as a consequence, when it is drawn into battle, it can cause collateral damage in tissues. In situations where the inciting stimulus is sterile, the cost-benefit ratio may be high; because of this, sterile inflammation underlies the pathogenesis of a number of diseases. Although there have been major advances in our understanding of how microbes trigger inflammation, much less has been learned about this process in sterile situations. This review focuses on a subset of the many sterile stimuli that can induce inflammation—specifically dead cells and a variety of irritant particles, including crystals, minerals, and protein aggregates. Although this subset of stimuli is structurally very diverse and might appear to be unrelated, there is accumulating evidence that the innate immune system may recognize them in similar ways and stimulate the sterile inflammatory response via common pathways. Here we review established and emerging data about these responses.

INTRODUCTION

Inflammation is one of the oldest recorded medical conditions, presumably because in ancient times, as now, it was experienced by humans frequently and its signs and symptoms were not subtle. Written symbols for inflammation have been identified in Sumerian hieroglyphics dating back to 2700 BCE, and what we recognize today as the essential signs and symptoms of inflammation—redness, heat, swelling, and pain—were described by the Roman academician Aulus Cornelius Celsus in the first century CE (1–3). Pus, which is another sign of inflammation primarily seen in certain infections, has also been described since ancient times (4).

We now know that most of the signs and symptoms of inflammation are caused by changes in the local vasculature of an affected tissue (5–7). The smooth muscle of arterioles relaxes, leading to vasodilation and the signs of erythema and heat. This also increases hydrostatic pressure across the vascular bed, which in combination with changes in the permeability of the vascular endothelial barrier leads to the leakage of protein-rich fluid into the tissue, thereby causing edema. Endothelial cells in venules express adhesion molecules that allow neutrophils and subsequently monocytes to adhere and migrate between endothelial cells into the tissue. If the recruitment of neutrophils into the tissue is sufficiently robust, it becomes visible to the naked eye as pus (7).

Once triggered, the inflammatory response can develop very rapidly. Vasodilation can occur within seconds, and fluid leakage and leukocyte extravasation can occur within minutes to hours (8). The net result is rapid delivery of many of the body's innate defenses to the offending site. This includes soluble defenses, such as antibody, complement, and collectins, and cellular defenses, such as granulocytes and monocytes. Once in the tissue, these various components attempt to neutralize, sequester, and/or otherwise contain the inciting stimulus. If this is successful, then the innate defenses help clear debris and stimulate tissue repair. Once the inciting stimulus is gone, then the inflammatory response resolves.

One of the major triggers of inflammation is infection, with the inciting stimulus being certain proinflammatory molecules of the invading microbe (9–11). However, a potpourri of sterile stimuli including mechanical trauma, ischemia, toxins, minerals, crystals, chemicals, and antigens also triggers inflammation. Most of these sterile stimuli can be broadly categorized into ones that are injurious, irritant, or antigenic.

All of the various triggers of inflammation, whether they are infectious or sterile, ultimately lead to the same downstream vascular and cellular manifestations of inflammation. However, although the final inflammatory response is similar in all these situations, the initial events that elicit and control the response can be very different. This review focuses on inflammation that is triggered in sterile situations and, in particular, on a subset of sterile proinflammatory stimuli: dead cells and irritant particles. The rationale for this focus is recent and emerging data that suggest that this diverse subset of proinflammatory stimuli may in fact stimulate responses through common mechanisms.

THE MEDICAL SIGNIFICANCE OF INFECTIOUS AND STERILE INFLAMMATION

The inflammatory response plays an important role in host defense. It is one of the first lines of defense recruited to combat a potential threat. In the case of microbial invasion it often plays a critical role in clearing, containing, and/or slowing the infection. Consequently, animals or patients that have defects in mounting adequate inflammatory responses suffer from recurrent infections and, if the defects are profound, increased mortality (12). Because of this, infections are believed to have been one of the major forces driving the evolution of the inflammatory response.

Although the inflammatory response is essential for host defense, it is very much a double-edged sword. The effector mechanisms used by the innate immune system to kill microbes are extremely potent and can (and in fact do) also damage and kill mammalian cells. The recruited leukocytes kill microbes by producing highly reactive chemical species, such as reactive oxygen species (ROS), sodium hypochlorite (bleach), and other destructive molecules such as proteases. Although these molecules are generally effective in destroying microbes, some of them leak from living and dying leukocytes and, in so doing, damage adjacent normal cells in the tissue. One of the major culprits in causing this collateral damage is the neutrophil, a cell type that is one of the focuses of this review. In infections, tissue damage is a small price to pay to contain potentially life-threatening situations. Moreover, because infections are often rapidly cleared by immune mechanisms, the duration of the neutrophilic inflammatory response (and hence its attendant damage) is often limited.

However, the cost-benefit ratio may be very different in situations of sterile inflammation. Here the inciting stimulus may not be injurious to the host, and in any case, the innate immune mechanisms that are mobilized may do little or no good. As a result, the dominant effect of the inflammation in these situations may be collateral damage inflicted by the inflammatory response on otherwise healthy cells in the tissue. This process, if sufficiently robust, can cause acute disease and/or exacerbate damage from other etiologies. Moreover, if the sterile stimulus is not resolved, this can lead to chronic inflammation and ongoing tissue damage that can also lead to and/or exacerbate disease. A number of these acute and chronic conditions are described below.

INFLAMMATION AND DISEASE CAUSED BY STERILE PARTICULATES

A diverse set of sterile particles can stimulate inflammation, in some cases associated with prominent fibrosis. These particles include ones whose composition is inorganic [e.g., silica dioxide (13), iron oxide (14), calcium pyrophosphate (15), asbestos (13)] and organic [e.g., monosodium urate (16), amyloid-β (17), cholesterol (18)] and whose structure can be crystalline (e.g., silicates, monosodium urate) or amorphous (e.g., alum and iron oxide) (**Table 1**).

For many of these particles it is not actually clear whether the inflammatory response is subserving a useful role such as host defense. This is because the particles may not themselves be injurious, and in any case the inflammatory response certainly fails to clear them, although it may help to collect and compartmentalize them. However, the damage caused by the sterile inflammatory response and its attendant fibrosis can lead to disease.

One of the classic crystal-based diseases, and the oldest to be recognized, is gout (16, 19). This condition occurs in a fraction of patients with hyperuricemia who nucleate crystals of monosodium urate (MSU) in their joints (20). The crystals incite an intense acute inflammatory response that can be exceedingly painful. These acute episodes wax and wane, but over time the recurrent inflammatory responses can damage the affected joint leading to chronic arthritis with associated dysfunction. Other crystals that deposit in joints can similarly lead to acute arthritis. This is seen, for example, with crystals of calcium pyrophosphate, which can form spontaneously in joints and cause the disease of pseudogout (21). In addition to affecting the joint, all of these particles can and do incite inflammation when they are deposited in other tissues, either spontaneously or experimentally by injection (22, 23).

Environmental and other exogenous particles can cause disease if they deposit in tissues. This most often occurs when certain particles are inhaled during respiration and accumulate in sufficient amounts in the lung. This is typically seen in occupational exposure, e.g., after inhalation of silicate particles (silica dioxide crystals and asbestos) (13). In the lung these particles cause inflammation and can lead to extensive pulmonary fibrosis and other complications. Particles that enter the body in other ways, e.g., through a wound or injection, can also cause inflammation. This is seen, for example, with injection of alum (an adjuvant

Table 1 Sterile stimulus and consequences

Sterile stimulus	Diseases	Organs	Symptoms or consequences	IL-1 dependency	Inflammasome dependency	References
Cell death	Many (ischemia, toxic damage, etc.)	Many	Increased damage, fibrosis	Yes (in vivo and vitro)	Yes (in vivo and vitro)	27, 28, 30–34
Monosodium urate crystal	Gout	Joint	Inflammation, chronic arthritis	Yes (in vivo and vitro)	Yes (in vivo and vitro)	16, 19, 20, 22, 23; H. Kono, unpublished data
Calcium pyrophosphate	Pseudogout	Joint	Inflammation, chronic arthritis	Yes (in vivo and vitro)	Yes (in vivo and vitro)	15, 21, 23
Silica	Silicosis	Lung	Inflammation, fibrosis	Yes (in vivo and vitro)	Yes (in vivo and vitro)	13, 56, 89
Iron oxide	Siderosis	Lung	Inflammation, fibrosis	ND[a]	ND[a]	120
Metal wear particulates	Joint loosening	Joint (implanted)	Periprosthetic osteolysis, revision surgery	Yes (in vivo and vitro)	Yes (in vitro)	121, 122
Asbestos	Asbestosis	Lung	Inflammation, fibrosis, mesothelioma, lung cancer	Yes (in vivo and vitro)	Yes (in vivo and vitro)	13, 57
Cholesterol crystal	Atherosclerosis	Arteries	Inflammation, occlusion of arteries to ischemia	Yes (in vivo and vitro)	Yes (in vivo and vitro)	18; Duewell, unpublished data
Amyloid-β	Alzheimer's disease	Brain	Neuronal degeneration	Yes (in vivo and vitro)	Yes (in vivo and vitro)	17, 26
Aluminum salts		Skin, peritoneal cavity	Inflammation, adjuvant activity	Yes (in vivo and vitro)	Yes (in vivo and vitro)	24, 58, 59, 98, 123
Talcum powder		Pleural cavity	Inflammation, pleurodesis	ND[a]	ND[a]	25

[a]ND, no data.

composed of particles of aluminum salt) (24) or the introduction of talcum powder (25).

There are other conditions that are not traditionally thought of as particle-based diseases but in which particle-stimulated inflammation might play a role. Examples include the diseases of atherosclerosis and Alzheimer's disease. In atherosclerosis, chronic inflammation in arteries leads to intimal thickening that narrows the vascular lumen and compromises blood flow (18). In this condition cholesterol crystals develop in the artery wall, and recent data suggest that this may be one of the stimulants of sterile inflammation (P. Duewell, H. Kono, F.G. Bauernfeind, C.M. Sirois, K.L. Rock, et al., unpublished manuscript). In Alzheimer's disease, neurodegeneration occurs in the cortex of the brain and leads to dementia (17). This disease is associated with the deposition of amyloid peptide aggregates, and recent data suggest that these aggregates may stimulate microglial cells to make proinflammatory mediators that may contribute to neural damage and disease pathogenesis (26).

Thus, a wide range of sterile particulates can provoke inflammation and, in so doing, cause disease. Because of this, the sterile inflammatory response is medically important; consequently, this process and these particular stimuli are the focus of this review.

INFLAMMATION TO STERILE CELL DEATH

Other kinds of proinflammatory particles, albeit more complicated ones than those discussed above, are necrotic cells and their debris. When cells die by necrosis, they stimulate a robust acute inflammatory response in vivo (27, 28). In fact, the occurrence and progression of the ensuing inflammation is so stereotypical that it can be used forensically to date the time of a tissue insult, e.g., in a heart attack (29). This inflammatory response is seen irrespective of the specific cause of cell injury and, of importance to this review, is seen in situations where cell death is caused by sterile insults, e.g., from ischemia or toxins.

If cells are dying from infection, the acute inflammatory response may be beneficial in containing this process, as discussed above. However, in situations of sterile cell death, the inflammatory response, and particularly the infiltration of tissues with neutrophils, can increase the amount of injury, similar to what was discussed above for diseases caused by sterile particles. This has been shown in ischemic or toxic damage to the heart (30), lung (31), liver (32), brain (33), and kidney (34). In all these situations, depleting neutrophils with antibodies (30–32) or blocking the signals that lead to their recruitment (33, 34) reduces the amount of tissue injury.

How does a cell that is not inflammatory when alive become proinflammatory after death? This is incompletely understood, and there may be multiple different mechanisms. One of the presently favored models is that after dying, cells release or expose proinflammatory molecules (also called proinflammatory damage-associated molecular patterns, or DAMPs) that are normally intracellular and hidden by the plasma membrane (35, 36). Indeed, one of the common events when cells undergo necrosis from whatever cause is a loss of integrity of the plasma membrane. Consistent with this idea, simply rupturing the plasma membrane by freeze-thawing or mechanical stress makes cells proinflammatory in vivo (28). Similarly, injecting cytoplasm from healthy cells into mice induces inflammation (37). Such findings have led to the hypothesis that the innate immune system has evolved mechanisms to sense cell injury by detecting the presence of a subset of molecules that are only exposed after death.

The identities of only a few proinflammatory DAMPs are known, and it is likely that there are others yet to be discovered. Interestingly, there is emerging evidence that one of these is uric acid (H. Kono, C-J. Chen, F. Ontiveros, K.L. Rock, unpublished manuscript)—the same molecule responsible for the inflammatory disease of gout (see above)—and this may in part account for some of the similarities between inflammation elicited by sterile particles and by dead cells. Cells contain very high levels of uric acid from purine catabolism and can even continue to generate it after death (H. Kono, C-J. Chen, F. Ontiveros, K.L. Rock, unpublished manuscript). In addition to uric acid, there are other known DAMPs. DNA and probably more specifically unmethylated CpG-rich DNA regions may also contribute to death-induced inflammation (38). In addition, a few intracellular molecules also have intrinsic proinflammatory activity including HMGB1 (39), SAP130 (40), IL-1α (37), IL-33 (41), DNA (42, 43), S100 proteins (44), heat shock proteins (45, 46), and others (47). HMGB1 is normally a chromatin-associated protein that is released from necrotic cells and sometimes from living cells by a nonclassical secretion mechanism (48). SAP130 is a protein found in the U2 small nuclear ribonucleoprotein–associated protein complex, which is associated with the spliceosome (49). Other intracellular proteins may not be proinflammatory directly but may work by generating other bioactive mediators. This has been reported for a nonmuscle myosin heavy chain that, when released into the extracellular fluids, binds a natural (preexisting) antimyosin IgM antibody that leads to the activation of complement and the production of proinflammatory complement split products (50, 51). Similarly, released cellular proteases can cleave extracellular matrix components into bioactive fragments (52). It is also possible that the particulate nature of dead cells contributes to triggering inflammation (see below). For a more complete discussion of proinflammatory DAMPs, interested readers are referred to recent reviews (47, 53).

THE ROLE OF IL-1 IN THE NEUTROPHILIC INFLAMMATORY RESPONSE TO STERILE PARTICULATES AND CELL DEATH

Until recently, much more was known about how innate immunity senses infection than about sterile particles and dead cells. In infections, the innate immune system uses Toll-like receptors (TLRs) and other receptors to sense many extracellular microbes and their products and trigger an inflammatory response. Although TLRs typically recognize unique microbial (nonself) molecules (that is, pathogen-associated molecular patterns, or PAMPs), there are also examples where these receptors recognize mammalian molecules. Given this and the fact that microbes and sterile particles/dead cells both trigger the same acute inflammatory response, it was investigated whether TLRs might be involved in detecting and responding to sterile proinflammatory particulates such as MSU and dead cells. Although initial experiments suggested a potential role for TLR2 and TLR4 in the responses to MSU (54), subsequent studies found no role for these or other individual TLRs (22). Similarly, mice deficient in TLR2+4 showed only a minor reduction in the inflammatory response to sterile dead cells, and animals deficient in other individual TLRs had normal responses (although not all individual or combinations of TLRs were examined) (28). There is also some evidence for a role of TLR3 or TLR9 in sensing cell injury in gut ischemia (55) or in liver toxicity (38), respectively.

Although it currently appears that TLRs do not play a major role in triggering the inflammatory responses to at least some sterile particles and dead cells, the investigations into this issue led to an important insight into these responses. It was found that mice that lacked the adaptor protein MyD88, which is needed for signal transduction by most TLRs, generated almost no neutrophilic inflammation to either MSU or dead cells (22, 28). This led to an evaluation of the two other MyD88-dependent cellular receptors, the IL-1 and IL-18 receptors. These studies revealed that mice deficient in the IL-1 receptor (IL-1R) were similar to those lacking MyD88 and generated almost no neutrophilic inflammation to MSU (22) or dead cells (28). Thus, investigations into the requirement for MyD88 led to the recognition of a key role for the IL-1 pathway in the neutrophilic inflammatory response to dead cells and MSU.

Subsequent studies have found a similar requirement for the IL-1 pathway in the generation of neutrophilic inflammation to a diverse set of sterile particulate stimuli. This is seen in vivo for silica dioxide crystals (56, 57), alum (24, 58–60), asbestos (57), and cholesterol crystals (P. Duewell, H. Kono, F.G. Bauernfeind, C.M. Sirois, K.L. Rock, et al., unpublished manuscript). In contrast, IL-1 is not required for neutrophilic inflammation to at least some microbial stimuli. Thus, IL-1R-deficient mice respond normally to the yeast cell wall preparation zymosan (28) or muramyl dipeptide (61). Interestingly, although IL-1R mutant mice had little neutrophilic inflammation to sterile stimuli, the subsequent recruitment of monocytes was less reduced or unaffected (28). This difference in IL-1 dependency suggests that different signals were involved in the recruitment of the two different leukocytes. Together these results demonstrated that the IL-1 pathway plays a key role in the neutrophilic inflammation to diverse sterile stimuli including a variety of irritant particles and dead cells.

A BRIEF PRIMER ON THE IL-1 PATHWAY

Because the IL-1 pathway plays a critical role in the sterile neutrophilic inflammatory response (discussed in further detail below), it is important to briefly review some of the essential features of this cytokine and its receptor. There are three major forms of IL-1: IL-1α, IL-1β, and IL-1ra, each of which is encoded by a separate but related gene. The mature forms of IL-1α and IL-1β both bind to and stimulate the same receptor, IL-1R1 (referred to here as the IL-1R), whereas IL-1ra is a competitive antagonist for this receptor. There are also other IL-1-related cytokine genes that utilize other receptors (e.g., IL-18, IL-33), but as yet few studies have investigated whether they are involved in the sterile inflammatory response (41, 62, 63).

IL-1β is a potent multifunctional proinflammatory cytokine, whose activity is controlled at the transcriptional, translational, maturation, and secretion levels (64). There are many cell stimuli [including TLR activators, TNF-α, and IL-1 or IL18 (65, 66)] that activate the transcription of the IL-1β gene. Although most inflammatory cytokines are mainly transcriptionally regulated and contain a leader sequence resulting in their release via the secretory pathway after translation and transport into the endoplasmic reticulum, the regulation and release of IL-1β is more complex. IL-1β is first produced in the cytosol as a biologically inactive proform (pro-IL-1β), which requires proteolytic cleavage for its activation and release from cells. The cleavage of pro-IL-1β to mature IL-1β is catalyzed by the cysteine protease caspase-1 (formerly known as IL-1β converting enzyme, ICE) (67). While intracellular cleavage of pro-IL-1β is under the control of caspase-1, pro-IL-1β can also be released from cells and cleaved extracellularly by other proteases into mature IL-1 (68, 69).

In resting cells, caspase-1 itself is present as a zymogen, procaspase-1, and its conversion to mature and active caspase-1 is under the control of members of the Nod-like receptor (NLR) family. In 2002, an NLR-containing multiprotein complex was isolated that controls the cleavage of procaspase-1 into the catalytically active form (70). In analogy to the apoptosome, which controls the activation of apoptosis-inducing caspases, the NLR protein complex that controls the activity of the inflammatory caspase-1 was termed the inflammasome (70). Activation of inflammasomes cleaves caspase-1, which then hydrolyzes pro-IL-1β into its mature and active form.

Since the original description of the inflammasome, many more of these complexes have been identified, and these all differ from one another in their NLR subunits. There are inflammasomes containing the NLRP1, NLRP3, NLRC4, and AIM-2 NLR proteins, and because there are many more NLR proteins, there may be other complexes yet to be discovered (71). NLRP1, NLRC4, and AIM-2 inflammasomes are thought to be mainly involved in recognizing microbial products, whereas, as discussed below, the NLRP3 complex is the one implicated in responses to a number of sterile stimuli. The NLRP3 protein contains a C-terminal leucine-rich repeat (LRR)-rich domain, followed by a central nucleotide-binding NACHT oligomerization domain, and an N-terminal protein–protein interaction pyrin domain (PYD) (72). Upon activation, NLRP3 interacts with the adaptor molecule called apoptosis-associated speck-like protein (ASC; also termed pycard or TMS1) and induces changes in its aggregation status (73). ASC serves as an adaptor protein, linking NLRP3 to caspase-1. After ASC interacts with NLRP3 via PYD domain interactions, it associates via its C-terminal CARD domain with the CARD domain of procaspase-1. Induced close association of procaspase-1 is believed to provoke its self-cleavage into active caspase-1. Active caspase-1, in turn, can cleave pro-IL-1β into mature IL-1β (74). ASC also interacts with other NLR proteins and is similarly critical for caspase-1 activation in response to a broad range of stimuli, although there are some differences in the nature of the intermolecular interactions. NLRC4 (also called IPAF) recognizes bacterial flagellin and, with ASC, forms an inflammasome (75). In contrast to NRLP3, NLRC4 lacks a PYD domain and instead contains an N-terminal CARD domain, which can directly associate with the CARD domain of procaspase-1. NALP1 is the only NALP family member that contains both a PYD domain and a CARD domain, the latter of which can recruit caspase-5 (76). Another inflammasome-forming protein, AIM-2, is a bipartite protein consisting of a DNA-binding domain (HIN200 domain) and a pyrin domain, which upon activation by intracellular double-stranded DNA forms an inflammasome with ASC to activate procaspase-1 (77–79).

The molecular mechanisms that control the inflammasome protein assembly are not fully understood. It is believed that the sensor NLR, for example NALP3, is held in an inactive conformation in the absence of stimuli. In this conformation, self-interaction via the NACHT domains is prevented. However, stimulation of the NLR is thought to induce a change in its conformation, leading to homoassociation and inflammasome assembly with subsequent caspase-1 activation. Indeed, several activating mutations in NLRs have been identified as the cause for a number of autoinflammatory hereditary periodic fever syndromes, which are diseases characterized by spontaneous attacks of systemic inflammation, severe local inflammation, and episodes of fever (80). Many mutations within NALP3 have been described in patients with the autoinflammatory diseases Muckle-Wells syndrome (MWS), familial cold autoinflammatory syndrome (FCAS), and chronic neurologic cutaneous and articular syndrome (CINCA) (80). These mutations can induce the spontaneous assembly of the NALP3 inflammasome with concomitant constitutive release of IL-1β, or these mutations influence NALP3 to respond to stimuli with a lower threshold than the wild-type protein (81). The stimuli that lead to the activation of NLRP3 and potential mechanisms of how NLRP3 stimuli induce inflammasome assembly are discussed below.

The production of IL-1α has both similarities as well as differences from that of IL-1β. IL-1α can be produced by a broader range of cells, and low levels may be expressed in some tissues without overt stimulation. Stimulation of these cells activates transcription of the IL-1α gene. Like IL-1β, the IL-1α protein is initially synthesized as a longer proform, which can be cleaved by intracellular proteases into the mature cytokine, and is also released from cells by a nonclassical secretion mechanism. However, in contrast to IL-1β, this proform is biologically active, and a portion of it is also expressed on the plasma membrane (82, 83). Furthermore, the proteases involved in cleaving pro-IL-1α into IL-1α may be different from those for the processing of pro-IL-1β, although this is less well understood (84, 85). This step may not require the inflammasome, although reduced IL-1α production has been reported from caspase-1-deficient cells (74), and physical interactions between pro- IL-1α and caspase-1 have been reported (86).

IL-1 has long been known to be a proinflammatory cytokine. In fact, it was discovered based on its bioactivity in promoting fever

(65, 87). Investigators soon appreciated that, in addition to inducing fever, IL-1 had a spectrum of other proinflammatory effects that were largely similar to those induced by TNF. Injection of IL-1 by itself is sufficient to induce inflammation, and patients with mutations in inflammasome components that lead to overproduction of IL-1β develop autoinflammatory diseases (80). However, in many settings of inflammation, IL-1 is just one of the many cytokines produced and probably often not the dominant one driving the responses; presumably because of this, neutralizing IL-1 (e.g., with IL-1ra), has incomplete or limited efficacy in reducing inflammation in many situations (often less effect than blocking other cytokines such as TNF). In contrast, it appears to play a much more central role in driving the neutrophilic inflammation to cell death and sterile irritant particles, and this had not been appreciated before the studies described above (28, 37).

THE FORM AND SOURCES OF IL-1 IN STERILE INFLAMMATION

Although a role for the IL-1R has been shown in the sterile neutrophilic inflammatory response in vivo to a large group of sterile particulates and dead cells (see above), reciprocal experiments to examine the role of IL-1 in animals have been reported for only a few of these stimuli. Antibody neutralization of IL-1 inhibits the neutrophilic inflammatory response in mice to dead cells (28) and MSU (22). Similarly, the IL-1R antagonist IL-1ra was reported to ameliorate MSU-induced inflammatory symptoms in a small study of human patients with gout (88). Given these findings and the observations that other sterile particulates induce IL-1 (56, 57), it is almost certain that IL-1 is driving the neutrophilic inflammation to all of the IL-1R-dependent, sterile proinflammatory particulates.

Information about the contribution of the different forms of IL-1 (i.e., IL-1α versus IL-1β) in these sterile inflammatory responses is even more limited. For dead cells, neutralizing anti-IL-1α antibodies significantly inhibited the neutrophilic inflammatory response, indicating an important role for IL-1α. In contrast, anti-IL-1β antibodies did not inhibit responses (28); however, this negative result does not rule out a role for IL-1β because complete blockade with antibodies is difficult to achieve, and small amounts of residual IL-1β can be sufficient to cause biological effects. In fact, more recent studies using IL-1-mutant mice have shown a role for both IL-1α and IL-1β (H. Kono, D. Karmarkar, Y. Iwakura, K.L. Rock, unpublished manuscript). Studies have not yet been performed to evaluate the relative roles of IL-1α and IL-1β in the inflammatory response to the other sterile particulates. However, in responses to MSU (23), cholesterol crystal (P. Duewell, H. Kono, F.G. Bauernfeind, C.M. Sirois, K.L. Rock, et al., unpublished manuscript), silica (89), and amyloid-β (26), mice lacking components of the inflammasome show decreased inflammation in vivo, which suggests a role for IL-1β (although these results do not rule out a contribution from IL-1α). There may also be caspase-1-independent pathways of inflammation (28, 90–93) (H. Kono and K.L. Rock, unpublished data).

Given that IL-1 is critical in these responses, where is it coming from (**Figure 1**)? This is an important question because it gets at the fundamental issue of how cell death is sensed by the innate immune system. In the case of dead cells, this cytokine could, on the one hand, be generated by host cells. On the other hand, because cells can contain an intracellular pool of IL-1 molecules, the IL-1 could come from the dead cell itself, released when the cells become necrotic. Supporting this latter idea, injection of necrotic (wild-type) dendritic cells stimulated inflammation in vivo, whereas necrotic IL-1α-deficient dendritic cells did not (37). However, this is unlikely to be the whole story. Necrotic IL-1-deficient and wild-type cells of other tissues (e.g., brain, liver) stimulate equivalent inflammation (H. Kono, D. Karmarkar, Y. Iwakura, and K.L. Rock, unpublished data). In addition, for sterile particles other than dead cells, the IL-1 must obviously come from cells in the host. Newly emerging data

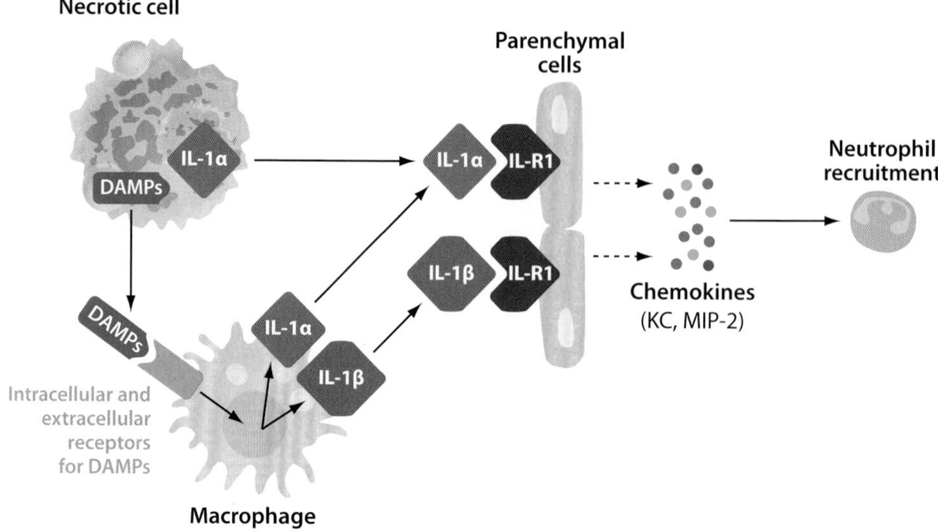

Figure 1

Source and role of IL-1 in recruiting neutrophils to sterile cell death. IL-1α in necrotic cells can be released and directly activate parenchymal (radioresistant) cells. In addition, necrotic cells release DAMPs (damage-associated molecular patterns) that are recognized by macrophages, which in turn produce IL-1α and IL-1β to stimulate parenchymal cells. IL-1-stimulated parenchymal cells secrete chemokines to recruit neutrophils.

suggest that the innate immune system of the host also recognizes dead cells and in response produces IL-1. In these experiments (H. Kono and K.L. Rock, unpublished data), inflammation to necrotic wild-type cells is markedly decreased in IL-1-deficient mice. Therefore, the contribution of IL-1 from the dead cell versus the host may depend on the particular kind or state of the cell that is dying or on other factors.

In situations where the host is making IL-1, what is the cellular source of this cytokine? For dead cells, depletion of CD11b^{+} cells (which include macrophages) in vivo inhibits the inflammatory response, and, importantly, the response can be reconstituted by transfer of wild-type but not of IL-1-deficient macrophages (H. Kono and K.L. Rock, unpublished data). Therefore, macrophages are at least one important cell in producing IL-1 in response to dead cells. The source of IL-1 that drives the acute neutrophilic inflammatory response to sterile particulates in vivo has not been elucidated. However, in vitro LPS-primed macrophages have been shown to produce IL-1β in response to MSU, silica, alum, cholesterol crystals, and asbestos (56; P. Duewell, H. Kono, F.G. Bauernfeind, C.M. Sirois, K.L. Rock, et al., unpublished manuscript). Another cell type of the macrophage lineage, microglia, produces IL-1β when stimulated with amyloid-β aggregates (26). MSU also stimulates IL-1 production from neutrophils (94, 95), synovial exudate cells, and human monocytes (96, 97); therefore, it is likely that macrophages will be an important source of IL-1 that drives neutrophilic inflammation to many of the irritant particles.

THE ROLE OF NLRP3 IN THE GENERATION OF IL-1β TO STERILE PARTICLES

How do the various sterile proinflammatory particles stimulate the production of IL-1 that drives the acute neutrophilic inflammatory response? A key observation in understanding this problem was the discovery by Tschopp

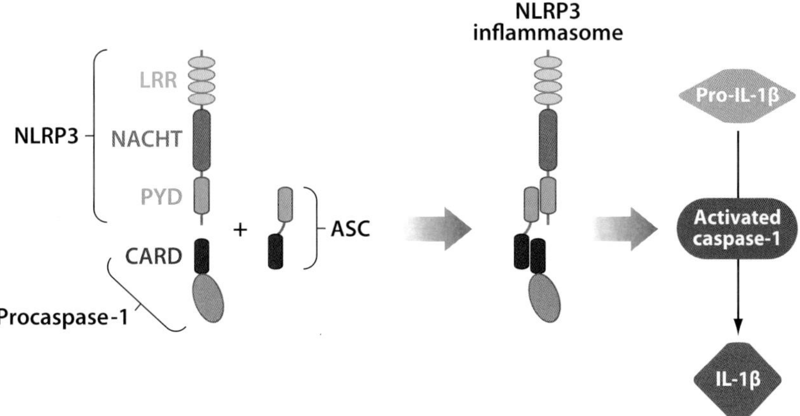

Figure 2

The NLRP3 inflammasome. The NLRP3 inflammasome is a heterotrimeric protein complex composed of NLRP3, the apoptosis-associated speck-like protein (ASC), and procaspase-1. Its NLRP3 subunit is composed of three distinct domains. One of these is a leucine-rich repeat region (LRR) that is thought to be involved in ligand recognition. The two other domains, NACHT and Pyrin-domain (PYD), are involved in protein-protein interactions. The PYD domain of NLRP3 binds to the PYD domain in ASC. Using its CARD domain, ASC recruits procaspase-1. This complex assembles in the cytosol of cells. Upon activation it cleaves and releases activated caspase-1, which then cleaves pro-IL-1β into its mature and active form.

and colleagues that NLRP3 (NALP3) and its associated inflammasome components were required for LPS-primed macrophages to produce mature IL-1β when stimulated by MSU crystals (23) (**Figure 2**). Subsequent studies by a number of groups found that NLRP3-deficient macrophages failed to produce mature IL-1β after stimulation with a variety of sterile particles including silica (56, 57), alum (24, 56, 58, 59, 98), asbestos (57), and cholesterol crystals (P. Duewell, H. Kono, F.G. Bauernfeind, C.M. Sirois, K.L. Rock, et al., unpublished manuscript). Similarly, NLRP3 was required for microglia to produce mature IL-1β when stimulated with amyloid-β aggregates (26). Therefore, NLRP3 is a key component in the pathway by which IL-1 is generated in response to these various sterile particles.

These findings led to the question of how NLRP3 was actually working in this pathway. Because it is a leucine-rich repeat (LRR) protein and other LRR repeat proteins (such as TLRs) are involved in ligand recognition, it seemed likely that NLRP3 somehow sensed the presence of the sterile particulates. However, it was unclear how this might be occurring because NLRP3 and the sterile particles are present, at least initially, in distinct locations—the cytosol versus the extracellular fluids. Moreover, the particles that stimulated the NLRP3-dependent response were chemically quite diverse, making it unclear how they might all bind to the same receptor. Insights into this problem came from a series of studies that examined the interaction of particles with macrophages.

It had long been known that particles are avidly internalized into macrophages by phagocytosis, and it was found that blocking this process with cytochalasin inhibited the NLRP3-dependent generation of mature IL-1β. Importantly, blocking phagocytosis inhibited IL-1β production stimulated by sterile particles but not by ATP, a soluble stimulator of the NLRP3 pathway (56). These findings did not themselves solve the problem of how NLRP3 might sense the particles because particles in phagosomes are still segregated from NLRP3 in the cytosol. However, the results pointed to a potentially important role of internalization of particles in NLRP3 stimulation of macrophages and led to further studies of the events occurring in the particle-containing phagosomes.

One of the events that occurs after particles are internalized into phagosomes is the activation of NADPH-oxidase and the generation of ROS. Tschopp found that NLRP3-dependent IL-1β production was blocked in cells that were unable to produce ROS or in which ROS were eliminated with chemical scavengers (57), although this was not seen in another system (56). This raises the possibility that NLRP3 senses ROS or a ROS-dependent event. However, the precise connection between ROS and NLRP3 stimulation is not presently known.

Another study followed the fate of particles after internalization into phagosomes. Surprisingly, some of the internalized particles were not in membrane-bound vesicles but instead were free in the cytosol, presumably due to the rupture of phagosomes. This finding raised the possibility that NLRP3 might be able to recognize the free particles directly. However, an alternative possibility was that NLRP3 might somehow sense the rupture of the phagosomes. In support of this latter mechanism, it was found that experimentally rupturing endocytic vesicles that did not contain particles, e.g., by hypertonic lysis of pinosomes, stimulated the generation of mature IL-1β, and importantly this was dependent on NLRP3 (56). Thus, sterile particles cause a rupture of vesicles, and such a rupture can be sufficient to trigger the NLRP3 inflammasome. Whether the role of ROS generation in NLRP3 activation (see above) is through this mechanism (i.e., by damaging the phagosomal membrane and promoting rupture) or independent of it remains to be determined. In any case, these findings have led to the hypothesis that one of the things that NLRP3 senses is internal cell damage and specifically the rupture of endocytic vesicles. This model is attractive because it can easily explain how structurally dissimilar particles can all stimulate NLRP3.

How might NLRP3 sense vesicular rupture? Another event that occurs after phagosomes form is that these vesicles acidify. Blocking this acidification inhibits NLRP3 activation by particles but not by a soluble stimulus such as ATP (56, 99). Why might acidification be required for this process? One of the effects of vesicular acidification is to activate acid optimal proteases in the vacuole. Therefore, one possibility is that activated vacuolar proteases might be involved in NLRP3 activation. Consistent with this hypothesis, macrophages in which cathepsin B was inhibited or genetically absent showed a partial but significant reduction in IL-1β production in response to particles but not to ATP (56, 99). There is emerging data that cathepsin L may also contribute to this response (P. Duewell, H. Kono, F.G. Bauernfeind, C.M. Sirois, K.L. Rock, et al., unpublished manuscript). These findings suggest a model (**Figure 3**) wherein activated cathepsins cleave a substrate, either in the vacuole or the cytosol, and in so doing generate a ligand for NLRP3. Proving this model will require identification of the putative cathepsin substrate(s) that activates NLRP3.

The experiments described in this section have all been performed with macrophages in cell culture. Do these same mechanisms operate in animals during a sterile inflammatory response? There is limited data that sterile inflammation stimulated by MSU (23), silica (89), cholesterol crystals (P. Duewell, H. Kono, F.G. Bauernfeind, C.M. Sirois, K.L. Rock, et al., unpublished manuscript), and dead cells (38) is reduced in NLRP3-mutant mice. However, in the NLRP3-negative animals, responses are often only partially reduced and in some cases seem largely independent of the inflammasome components (C-J. Chen, H. Kono, and K.L. Rock, unpublished data). Other cellular processes such as autophagy may also be involved in IL-1 responses. Mice deficient in the autophagy protein Atg16L1 are susceptible to dextran sulfate sodium–induced colitis that is at least partially dependent on IL-1β. In this system, enhanced secretion of IL-1β is dependent on endotoxin priming (100). Therefore, the mechanisms operating in vivo may be more complicated and may involve redundant pathways.

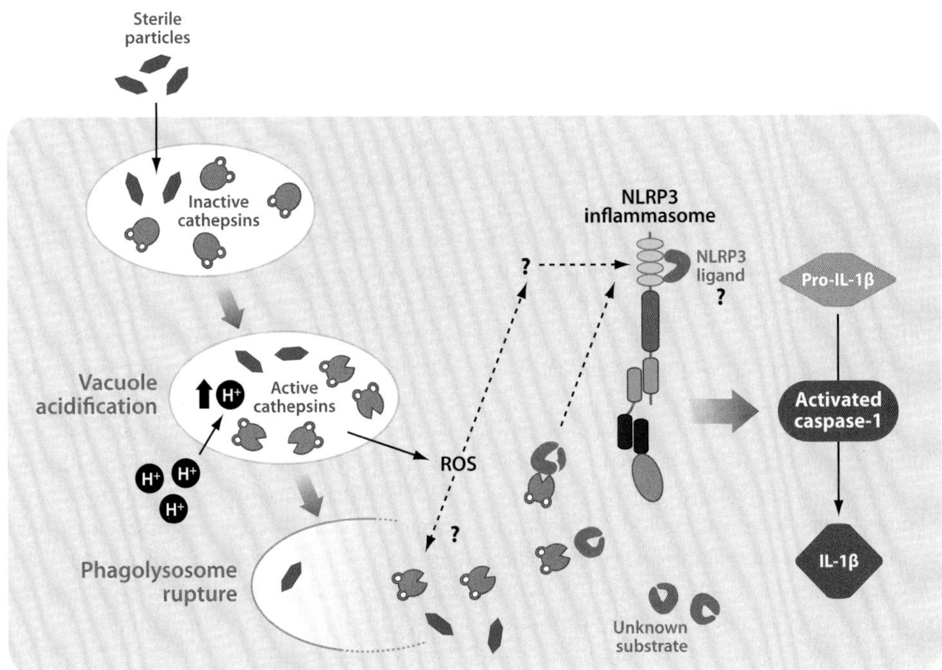

Figure 3

Phagolysosome disruption and activation of the inflammasome. Phagosomes containing sterile particles acidify and generate reactive oxygen species (ROS), and then some of these vesicles rupture. The ROS that are produced have been implicated in the activation of NLRP3 inflammasomes through an unknown mechanism, possibly involving phagosomal destabilization or direct stimulation of NLRP3. The rupture of phagosomes releases activated cathepsins that trigger the NLRP3 inflammasome, possibly by cleaving an endogenous NLRP3 ligand into an active form. Dashed lines and question marks are hypothetical steps in this pathway.

PRIMING REGULATES THE NLRP3 INFLAMMASOME ACTIVITY

There are other interesting differences between the conditions needed to stimulate NLRP3-dependent responses in vivo compared with that in cell culture. In intact animals, NLRP3 stimuli (e.g., crystals, ATP, or pore-forming toxins) will elicit a response by themselves but are insufficient to stimulate macrophages in culture unless these cells have first received a distinct priming stimulus. Of note, this priming is required not only for the induction of pro-IL-1 (as mentioned above), but also for the activation of caspase-1 (101). This indicates that priming induces factors upstream of caspase-1 that are limiting for NLRP3 activation in macrophages. One of these factors may be NLRP3 itself, as a recent study revealed that NLRP3 is present at very low levels in resting macrophages and that priming stimuli leads to significant upregulation of NLRP3 in an NF-κB-dependent pathway (101). Importantly, heterologous expression of NLRP3 in macrophages was sufficient for caspase-1 activation in response to crystals, ATP, or pore-forming toxins in the absence of prior priming (101).

A key role for NLRP3 levels in regulating the activity of the inflammasome pathway is also suggested by clinical data. Certain patients with autoinflammatory syndromes (cryopyrinopathies) have mutations in the coding sequence of NLRP3, and these mutations may lead to overly active NLRP3, resulting in the inflammatory phenotype. However, a substantial fraction (~40%) of cryopyrinopathy patients have classical clinical symptoms in the absence of any mutations in the coding region of NLRP3 (80). A recent promoter analysis of NLRP3 identified various unique sequence variants in the promoter region of NLRP3 of cryopyrinopathy patients, suggesting that promoter SNPs could lead to dysregulated NLRP3 expression (102). Indeed, a unique SNP (−1064T) in the NLRP3 promoter led to increased promoter activity, and therefore dysregulation of NLRP3 expression levels could be the cause for the clinical inflammatory symptoms found in these patients.

These data suggest that, in normal individuals, macrophages only commit to NLRP3 inflammasome activation and concomitant caspase-1-dependent (pyroptotic) cell death after they are primed by molecules present during infection (i.e., activator of PRRs), or by encountering potent proinflammatory cytokines such as TNF-α (66). These findings further imply that many of the reported NLRP3 inflammasome activators (such as LPS, lipopeptides, or imiquimod/resiquimod, etc.) that act together with ATP to induce NLRP3 inflammasome activation are not inflammasome activators per se. Instead, these proinflammatory pattern-recognition receptor ligands are necessary for priming and assembly of the NLRP3 inflammasome rather than being bona fide inflammasome activators.

The requirement of two or more independent signals for triggering cellular responses is a recurrent theme in immune cell activation. In macrophages, these mechanisms may operate to prevent uncontrolled NLRP3 activation. Unrestricted NLRP3 inflammasome activation could lead to the excessive production of proinflammatory IL-1β cytokine family members and could additionally induce pyroptotic cell death and the release of a range of additional caspase-1 regulated factors other than IL-1β (103). The regulation of the NLRP3 inflammasome via NF-κB activity provides a secure mechanism of control because the activity of NF-κB itself is controlled by an elaborate set of molecules and by finely regulated feedback mechanisms (104).

How the inflammasome is primed in vivo remains to be fully determined. Recent reports (38, 105), however, support the hypothesis that priming via a pattern-recognition receptor might also play a fundamental role for the recognition of danger signals in vivo. It was demonstrated that induction of sterile inflammation by pharmacologically induced liver damage was dependent on both TLR9 and NLRP3. Studies with TLR9 inhibitors as well as with TLR9-deficient mice suggested that TLR9 activation by excessively released host DNA provides a priming step for pro-IL-1β synthesis (38). Thus, TLR9 likely also plays a role in NLRP3 priming in vivo, allowing NLRP3 inflammasome activation by released danger signals, at least in some situations. Similar mechanisms could operate during crystal-induced NLRP3 activation in vivo; however, these hypotheses have yet to be tested.

OTHER SIGNALING PATHWAYS STIMULATED BY STERILE STIMULI

Particles and dead cells also stimulate macrophages in other ways besides the NLRP3 pathway described above, although the precise receptors and pathways are poorly understood overall. Most of the information on these processes is in relation to MSU crystals because these are the most studied sterile proinflammatory particles. The activation of a number of kinases has been described in different cell types. Stimulation of macrophages and neutrophils with MSU leads to the activation of ERK1/2 (106) and of TEC (107), respectively. Exactly how MSU leads to the activation of these kinases is not clear. This may be mediated by membrane receptors. MSU has been reported to stimulate TLR2 and 4 (54), although the inflammatory response is not diminished in TLR2 and 4 double mutant animals (28). It has also been suggested that blockade of the surface markers CD16 and CD11b (108) or deficiency in CD14 (109) can reduce or prevent MSU from inducing an inflammatory response. More recently, a receptor-independent pathway of kinase activation has been described (110). MSU crystals bind with high affinity to cholesterol in the plasma membrane and in so doing cause aggregation of lipid rafts. This clustering of lipid rafts, which contain a number of kinases, led to the activation of the syk kinase.

The precise role of these additional signaling events in the generation of the sterile inflammatory response is not clear. They may contribute to some of the events reviewed above such as stimulating phagocytosis, triggering the oxidative burst, or priming macrophages to produce pro-IL-1β. Alternatively, there might be many other inflammatory mediators that are generated in response to the sterile particulates, and these involve signaling pathways distinct from the ones needed to generate IL-1. Unfortunately, at this time there is insufficient information available to understand all the various signaling pathways and their roles in the sterile inflammatory response.

THE TARGET OF IL-1 IN THE NEUTROPHILIC INFLAMMATORY RESPONSE TO STERILE PARTICLES AND DEAD CELLS

Because IL-1 is required for the neutrophilic inflammatory response to sterile particulates and dead cells, where is it acting? The IL-1R is expressed broadly on many tissues (111), and therefore IL-1 could affect a large number of cell types. There is at present very limited information about which of these cells is the key target(s) in IL-1-stimulated neutrophil recruitment. Experiments have been performed with radiation bone marrow chimeras to address whether the IL-1R is needed on cells of hematopoietic origin, such as leukocytes, and/or on ones of nonhematopoietic origin (referred to herein as parenchymal cells). Chimeric mice in which the IL-1R is lacking from all bone marrow-derived elements, but not other cells, showed no impairment in their neutrophilic inflammatory responses to either sterile particles (MSU) (22) or dead cells (28). In contrast, chimeras that expressed the IL-1R on bone marrow elements, but lacked it on all other cells, showed reduced sterile neutrophilic inflammation to both particles (22) and dead cells (28). Therefore, a key target(s) of IL-1 in the sterile inflammatory response to both MSU and dead cells is a radioresistant parenchymal cell(s). Presumably, these same mechanisms are also operative in the response to other sterile particulates, but this has not yet been formally tested.

The identity of the key parenchymal target of IL-1 in sterile inflammation in vivo is not known. However, an in vitro study found that IL-1α stimulated cultured peritoneal mesothelial cells to produce the neutrophil chemotactic chemokines KC and MIP-2 (37, 112). Based on these findings, it was proposed that when dead cells are injected into the peritoneum, IL-1α is released and acts on peritoneal mesothelial cells to produce chemokines that then recruit neutrophils. We do not yet know whether these mesothelial cell responses actually occur and/or are required in vivo and, if so, whether they are the only target of IL-1 that is required. However, in other settings there must be other essential cellular targets because necrosis-induced neutrophilic inflammation is seen in tissue sites where mesothelium is not present, e.g., in the parenchyma of organs.

THERAPEUTIC IMPLICATIONS

Because the inflammation stimulated by sterile particles and dead cells contributes to the pathogenesis of a number of diseases, it would be medically useful to develop therapeutics to inhibit this process. Ideally, this could be done in ways that block the damaging component of the sterile inflammation without compromising host defense to, e.g., infection. The findings reviewed in this article raise the possibility that such selective inhibition could be obtained and point to some potential molecular targets that might allow this to be achieved.

Blocking IL-1 production or action is a potential therapeutic target to inhibit sterile inflammation because IL-1 is required for the neutrophil recruitment in this setting, and this cell type is the most damaging component of the response. One such inhibitor is already available clinically (IL-1ra) (113), and others are under development (64). There are at least two reasons why these targets might give some relative selectivity. First, animals that lack the IL-1 pathway clearly can still mount neutrophilic inflammation to at least some microbial components (22, 28). Second, the monocyte-macrophage component of the acute inflammatory response is much less dependent on IL-1 (28). Therefore, important components of the innate immune response to infection may still be intact after the IL-1 pathway is blocked. Supporting this idea, patients who are treated with IL-1ra have only a very small increase in the incidence of infections (88, 113, 114), although it remains to be seen if this becomes a greater problem with agents that may block IL-1 responses more effectively than IL-1ra. However, blocking IL-1 itself will affect many responses other than those stimulated by dead cells and sterile particulates.

Further selectivity might be achieved by blocking steps in the pathway that are more restricted or unique to the production of IL-1 in response to sterile particles and dead cells. NLRP3 might be one such target. Moreover, the upstream mechanisms by which sterile particles trigger NLRP3 may be even more selective ones. Based on the emerging data about this process, such targets might include phagosomal rupture, specific cathepsins, and/or the putative endogenous ligand of NLRP3; as far as is known, these steps function uniquely in the sterile inflammatory response and not in host defense to microbes.

It is presently unclear whether the overall concept and the specific molecular targets considered above would truly be efficacious in treating many of the sterile inflammatory diseases. Similarly, it is not known whether and/or how much selectivity these targets would provide and whether they would be tractable for drug design. It is nevertheless intriguing that limited data support the idea that inhibition of the IL-1 pathway may be effective in blocking sterile inflammation in gout (88). If this is found to be true in other sterile inflammatory diseases, then there would be a strong rationale to develop additional and selective inhibitors of this pathway.

OTHER STERILE INFLAMMATION

This review focuses on a small subset of the sterile stimuli that can cause inflammation: cell death and irritant particles. Sterile inflammation also occurs in response to trauma, immunogenic antigens, and autoimmune conditions, to name just a few other examples. Under these conditions, whether and to what extent the inflammation is stimulated by similar IL-1-inflammasome-dependent mechanisms is mostly unknown at this time. However, in a number of situations where the IL-1 pathway is lacking genetically or has been neutralized, sterile inflammatory responses still occur (28, 115–119). It is also clear that molecules like zymosan that engage scavenger receptors and TLRs can stimulate acute neutrophilic inflammation in the absence of the IL-1 pathway. Therefore, although there may be a common molecular pathway underlying the inflammation triggered by dead cells and particles, it seems likely that for many other sterile stimuli there will be additional and/or distinct molecular mechanisms that underlie the sterile inflammatory response.

CONCLUSION

There has been major progress in understanding the mechanisms underlying the generation of the neutrophilic inflammatory response to sterile irritant particles and dead cells. An important advance was the finding that all of these diverse stimuli elicit this response through the same key mediator, IL-1. Surprisingly, emerging data further suggest that there might be common mechanisms through which these diverse stimuli lead to IL-1 production. The sterile particulates all stimulate the NLRP3 inflammasome, which processes pro-IL-1β to the mature and bioactive form. Moreover, these particles may all stimulate NLRP3 via the same mechanisms that operate in the phagosomes of macrophages. New potential players that function in this process have been identified, including ROS and cathepsins (56, 57, 99). These findings are opening up avenues to developing new therapies and therapeutics to treat diseases that are caused by sterile inflammation.

Nevertheless, many of these new insights need further validation, particularly in vivo, and there are many missing pieces to the puzzle. For example, in the IL-1 pathway it is unclear how phagocytes are primed to make pro-IL-1β, how ROS and cathepsins function, what causes phagosomal rupture, what the roles and regulators are of IL-1α versus IL-1β, what the potential redundancy is of mechanisms, and what the key targets are of IL-1, to name but a few of the unresolved issues. Beyond this, we do not understand what controls other aspects of the sterile inflammatory response, such as monocyte recruitment, and the role of other receptors and signaling pathways. Given the medical importance of the sterile inflammatory response, these are key issues that must be addressed. Solving these issues and developing a comprehensive understanding of the mechanisms controlling the sterile inflammatory responses is important to understanding disease pathogenesis and in devising novel rational methods for treatment.

DISCLOSURE STATEMENT

H.K. receives partial support from sanofi-aventis. The other authors are not aware of any affiliations, memberships, funding, or financial holdings that might be perceived as affecting the objectivity of this review.

ACKNOWLEDGMENTS

This work was supported by grants to E.L. and K.L.R. from the NIH and to K.L.R. from the American Asthma Foundation. Core resources supported by the Diabetes Endocrinology Research Center grant DK32520 were also used.

LITERATURE CITED

1. Celsus AC. circa 30 A.D. De Medicina
2. Rocha e Silva M. 1978. A brief survey of the history of inflammation. *Agents Actions* 8:45–49
3. Majno G, Joris I. 1995. Apoptosis, oncosis, and necrosis. An overview of cell death. *Am. J. Pathol.* 146:3–15
4. Majno G. 1991. *The Healing Hand: Man and Wound in the Ancient World*. Cambridge, MA: Harvard Univ. Press, 600 pp.
5. Waller A. 1846. Microscopical observation on the perforation of capillaries by the corpuscles of the blood and on the origin of mucus and pus-globules. *Philos. Mag. (3rd Series)* 29:397–405
6. Cohnheim J. 1867. Ueber Entzündung und Eiterung. *Virchows Arch.* 40:1–79
7. Majno G, Joris I. 2004. *Cells, Tissues and Diseases: Principles of General Pathology*. Cambridge, MA: Oxford Univ. Press, 1040 pp.
8. Peters NC, Egen JG, Secundino N, Debrabant A, Kimblin N, et al. 2008. In vivo imaging reveals an essential role for neutrophils in leishmaniasis transmitted by sand flies. *Science* 321:970–74
9. Medzhitov R. 2008. Origin and physiological roles of inflammation. *Nature* 454:428–35
10. Akira S, Uematsu S, Takeuchi O. 2006. Pathogen recognition and innate immunity. *Cell* 124:783–801
11. Inohara C, McDonald C, Nunez G. 2005. NOD-LRR proteins: role in host-microbial interactions and inflammatory disease. *Annu. Rev. Biochem.* 74:355–83
12. Boxer L, Dale DC. 2002. Neutropenia: causes and consequences. *Semin. Hematol.* 39:75–81
13. Mossman BT, Churg A. 1998. Mechanisms in the pathogenesis of asbestosis and silicosis. *Am. J. Respir. Crit. Care Med.* 157:1666–80

14. Billings CG, Howard P. 1993. Occupational siderosis and welders' lung: a review. *Monaldi Arch. Chest. Dis.* 48:304–14
15. Ea HK, Liote F. 2004. Calcium pyrophosphate dihydrate and basic calcium phosphate crystal-induced arthropathies: update on pathogenesis, clinical features, and therapy. *Curr. Rheumatol. Rep.* 6:221–27
16. Nuki G, Simkin PA. 2006. A concise history of gout and hyperuricemia and their treatment. *Arthritis Res. Ther.* 8(Suppl. 1):S1
17. Weiner HL, Frenkel D. 2006. Immunology and immunotherapy of Alzheimer's disease. *Nat. Rev. Immunol.* 6:404–16
18. Galkina E, Ley K. 2009. Immune and inflammatory mechanisms of atherosclerosis. *Annu. Rev. Immunol.* 27:165–97
19. Hippocrates. 1886. *The Genuine Works of Hippocrates. Volumes I and II.* New York: William Wood
20. McCarty DJ, Hollander JL. 1961. Identification of urate crystals in gouty synovial fluid. *Ann. Int. Med.* 54:452–60
21. Beck C, Morbach H, Richl P, Stenzel M, Girschick HJ. 2009. How can calcium pyrophosphate crystals induce inflammation in hypophosphatasia or chronic inflammatory joint diseases? *Rheumatol. Int.* 29:229–38
22. Chen CJ, Shi Y, Hearn A, Fitzgerald K, Golenbock D, et al. 2006. MyD88-dependent IL-1 receptor signaling is essential for gouty inflammation stimulated by monosodium urate crystals. *J. Clin. Invest.* 116:2262–71
23. Martinon F, Petrilli V, Mayor A, Tardivel A, Tschopp J. 2006. Gout-associated uric acid crystals activate the NALP3 inflammasome. *Nature* 440:237–41
24. Eisenbarth SC, Colegio OR, O'Connor W, Sutterwala FS, Flavell RA. 2008. Crucial role for the Nalp3 inflammasome in the immunostimulatory properties of aluminum adjuvants. *Nature* 453:1122–26
25. Van Den Heuvel MM, Smit HJ, Barbierato SB, Havenith CE, Beelen RH, Postmus PE. 1998. Talc-induced inflammation in the pleural cavity. *Eur. Respir. J.* 12:1419–23
26. Halle A, Hornung V, Petzold GC, Stewart CR, Monks BG, et al. 2008. The NALP3 inflammasome is involved in the innate immune response to amyloid-β. *Nat. Immunol.* 9:857–65
27. Majno G, La Gattuta M, Thompson TE. 1960. Cellular death and necrosis: chemical, physical and morphologic changes in rat liver. *Virchows Arch.* 333:421–65
28. Chen CJ, Kono H, Golenbock D, Reed G, Akira S, Rock KL. 2007. Identification of a key pathway required for the sterile inflammatory response triggered by dying cells. *Nat. Med.* 13:851–56
29. Antman EM, Braunwald E. 2007. ST-elevation myocardial infarction: pathology, pathophysiology, and clinical features. In *Braunwald's Heart Disease: A Textbook of Cardiovascular Medicine*, ed. P Libby, RO Bonow, DL Mann, DP Zipes, pp. 1207–30. Philadelphia, PA: Saunders Elsevier. 8th ed.
30. Romson JL, Hook BG, Kunkel SL, Abrams GD, Schork MA, Lucchesi BR. 1983. Reduction of the extent of ischemic myocardial injury by neutrophil depletion in the dog. *Circulation* 67:1016–23
31. Kishi M, Richard LF, Webster RO, Dahms TE. 1999. Role of neutrophils in xanthine/xanthine oxidase-induced oxidant injury in isolated rabbit lungs. *J. Appl. Physiol.* 87:2319–25
32. Liu ZX, Han D, Gunawan B, Kaplowitz N. 2006. Neutrophil depletion protects against murine acetaminophen hepatotoxicity. *Hepatology* 43:1220–30
33. Abulafia DP, de Rivero Vaccari JP, Lozano JD, Lotocki G, Keane RW, Dietrich WD. 2009. Inhibition of the inflammasome complex reduces the inflammatory response after thromboembolic stroke in mice. *J. Cereb. Blood Flow Metab.* 29:534–44
34. Kelly KJ, Williams WW Jr, Colvin RB, Meehan SM, Springer TA, et al. 1996. Intercellular adhesion molecule-1-deficient mice are protected against ischemic renal injury. *J. Clin. Invest.* 97:1056–63
35. Matzinger P. 1994. Tolerance, danger, and the extended family. *Annu. Rev. Immunol.* 12:991–1045
36. Matzinger P. 2002. The danger model: a renewed sense of self. *Science* 296:301–5
37. Eigenbrod T, Park JH, Harder J, Iwakura Y, Nunez G. 2008. Cutting edge: critical role for mesothelial cells in necrosis-induced inflammation through the recognition of IL-1α released from dying cells. *J. Immunol.* 181:8194–98
38. Imaeda AB, Watanabe A, Sohail MA, Mahmood S, Mohamadnejad M, et al. 2009. Acetaminophen-induced hepatotoxicity in mice is dependent on Tlr9 and the Nalp3 inflammasome. *J. Clin. Invest.* 119:305–14

39. Scaffidi P, Misteli T, Bianchi ME. 2002. Release of chromatin protein HMGB1 by necrotic cells triggers inflammation. *Nature* 418:191–95
40. Yamasaki S, Ishikawa E, Sakuma M, Hara H, Ogata K, Saito T. 2008. Mincle is an ITAM-coupled activating receptor that senses damaged cells. *Nat. Immunol.* 9:1179–88
41. Moussion C, Ortega N, Girard JP. 2008. The IL-1-like cytokine IL-33 is constitutively expressed in the nucleus of endothelial cells and epithelial cells in vivo: a novel 'alarmin'? *PLoS ONE* 3:e3331
42. Ishii KJ, Suzuki K, Coban C, Takeshita F, Itoh Y, et al. 2001. Genomic DNA released by dying cells induces the maturation of APCs. *J. Immunol.* 167:2602–7
43. Barrat FJ, Meeker T, Gregorio J, Chan JH, Uematsu S, et al. 2005. Nucleic acids of mammalian origin can act as endogenous ligands for Toll-like receptors and may promote systemic lupus erythematosus. *J. Exp. Med.* 202:1131–39
44. Foell D, Wittkowski H, Vogl T, Roth J. 2007. S100 proteins expressed in phagocytes: a novel group of damage-associated molecular pattern molecules. *J. Leukoc. Biol.* 81:28–37
45. Osterloh A, Veit A, Gessner A, Fleischer B, Breloer M. 2008. Hsp60-mediated T cell stimulation is independent of TLR4 and IL-12. *Int. Immunol.* 20:433–43
46. Basu S, Binder RJ, Ramalingam T, Srivastava PK. 2001. CD91 is a common receptor for heat shock proteins gp96, hsp90, hsp70, and calreticulin. *Immunity* 14:303–13
47. Rock KL, Kono H. 2008. The inflammatory response to cell death. *Annu. Rev. Pathol. Mech. Dis.* 3:99–126
48. Landsman D, Bustin M. 1993. A signature for the HMG-1 box DNA-binding proteins. *BioEssays* 15:539–46
49. Das BK, Xia L, Palandjian L, Gozani O, Chyung Y, Reed R. 1999. Characterization of a protein complex containing spliceosomal proteins SAPs 49, 130, 145, and 155. *Mol. Cell. Biol.* 19:6796–802
50. Weiser MR, Williams JP, Moore FD Jr, Kibzik L, Ma M, et al. 1996. Reperfusion injury of ischemic skeletal muscle is mediated by natural antibody and complement. *J. Exp. Med.* 183:2343–48
51. Zhang M, Alicot EM, Chiu I, Li J, Verna N, et al. 2006. Identification of the target self-antigens in reperfusion injury. *J. Exp. Med.* 203:141–52
52. Jiang D, Liang J, Fan J, Yu S, Chen S, et al. 2005. Regulation of lung injury and repair by Toll-like receptors and hyaluronan. *Nat. Med.* 11:1173–79
53. Kono H, Rock KL. 2008. How dying cells alert the immune system to danger. *Nat. Rev. Immunol.* 8:279–89
54. Liu-Bryan R, Scott P, Sydlaske A, Rose DM, Terkeltaub R. 2005. Innate immunity conferred by Toll-like receptors 2 and 4 and myeloid differentiation factor 88 expression is pivotal to monosodium urate monohydrate crystal-induced inflammation. *Arthritis Rheum.* 52:2936–46
55. Cavassani KA, Ishii M, Wen H, Schaller MA, Lincoln PM, et al. 2008. TLR3 is an endogenous sensor of tissue necrosis during acute inflammatory events. *J. Exp. Med.* 205:2609–21
56. Hornung V, Bauernfeind F, Halle A, Samstad EO, Kono H, et al. 2008. Silica crystals and aluminum salts activate the NALP3 inflammasome through phagosomal destabilization. *Nat. Immunol.* 9:847–56
57. Dostert C, Petrilli V, Van Bruggen R, Steele C, Mossman BT, Tschopp J. 2008. Innate immune activation through Nalp3 inflammasome sensing of asbestos and silica. *Science* 320:674–77
58. Kool M, Petrilli V, De Smedt T, Rolaz A, Hammad H, et al. 2008. Cutting edge: alum adjuvant stimulates inflammatory dendritic cells through activation of the NALP3 inflammasome. *J. Immunol.* 181:3755–59
59. Franchi L, Nunez G. 2008. The Nlrp3 inflammasome is critical for aluminum hydroxide-mediated IL-1β secretion but dispensable for adjuvant activity. *Eur. J. Immunol.* 38:2085–89
60. Li H, Nookala S, Re F. 2007. Aluminum hydroxide adjuvants activate caspase-1 and induce IL-1β and IL-18 release. *J. Immunol.* 178:5271–76
61. Rosenzweig HL, Martin TM, Planck SR, Galster K, Jann MM, et al. 2008. Activation of NOD2 in vivo induces IL-1β production in the eye via caspase-1 but results in ocular inflammation independently of IL-1 signaling. *J. Leukoc. Biol.* 84:529–36
62. Leung BP, Culshaw S, Gracie JA, Hunter D, Canetti CA, et al. 2001. A role for IL-18 in neutrophil activation. *J. Immunol.* 167:2879–86
63. Li X, Kovacs EJ, Schwacha MG, Chaudry IH, Choudhry MA. 2007. Acute alcohol intoxication increases interleukin-18-mediated neutrophil infiltration and lung inflammation following burn injury in rats. *Am. J. Physiol. Lung Cell. Mol. Physiol.* 292:L1193–201

64. Dinarello CA. 2009. Immunological and inflammatory functions of the interleukin-1 family. *Annu. Rev. Immunol.* 27:519–50
65. Dinarello CA, Ikejima T, Warner SJ, Orencole SF, Lonnemann G, et al. 1987. Interleukin 1 induces interleukin 1. I. Induction of circulating interleukin 1 in rabbits in vivo and in human mononuclear cells in vitro. *J. Immunol.* 139:1902–10
66. Franchi L, Eigenbrod T, Nunez G. 2009. TNF-α mediates sensitization to ATP and silica via the NLRP3 inflammasome in the absence of microbial stimulation. *J. Immunol.* 183:792–96
67. Thornberry NA, Bull HG, Calaycay JR, Chapman KT, Howard AD, et al. 1992. A novel heterodimeric cysteine protease is required for interleukin-1β processing in monocytes. *Nature* 356:768–74
68. Fantuzzi G, Ku G, Harding MW, Livingston DJ, Sipe JD, et al. 1997. Response to local inflammation of IL-1 β-converting enzyme- deficient mice. *J. Immunol.* 158:1818–24
69. Coeshott C, Ohnemus C, Pilyavskaya A, Ross S, Wieczorek M, et al. 1999. Converting enzyme-independent release of tumor necrosis factor α and IL-1β from a stimulated human monocytic cell line in the presence of activated neutrophils or purified proteinase 3. *Proc. Natl. Acad. Sci. USA* 96:6261–66
70. Martinon F, Burns K, Tschopp J. 2002. The inflammasome: a molecular platform triggering activation of inflammatory caspases and processing of proIL-β. *Mol. Cell* 10:417–26
71. Franchi L, Warner N, Viani K, Nunez G. 2009. Function of Nod-like receptors in microbial recognition and host defense. *Immunol. Rev.* 227:106–28
72. Hoffman HM, Mueller JL, Broide DH, Wanderer AA, Kolodner RD. 2001. Mutation of a new gene encoding a putative pyrin-like protein causes familial cold autoinflammatory syndrome and Muckle-Wells syndrome. *Nat. Genet.* 29:301–5
73. Masumoto J, Taniguchi S, Ayukawa K, Sarvotham H, Kishino T, et al. 1999. ASC, a novel 22-kDa protein, aggregates during apoptosis of human promyelocytic leukemia HL-60 cells. *J. Biol. Chem.* 274:33835–38
74. Kuida K, Lippke JA, Ku G, Harding MW, Livingston DJ, et al. 1995. Altered cytokine export and apoptosis in mice deficient in interleukin-1β converting enzyme. *Science* 267:2000–3
75. Franchi L, Amer A, Body-Malapel M, Kanneganti TD, Özören N, et al. 2006. Cytosolic flagellin requires Ipaf for activation of caspase-1 and interleukin 1β in salmonella-infected macrophages. *Nat. Immunol.* 7:576–82
76. Martinon F, Mayor A, Tschopp J. 2009. The inflammasomes: guardians of the body. *Annu. Rev. Immunol.* 27:229–65
77. Burckstummer T, Baumann C, Bluml S, Dixit E, Durnberger G, et al. 2009. An orthogonal proteomic-genomic screen identifies AIM2 as a cytoplasmic DNA sensor for the inflammasome. *Nat. Immunol.* 10:266–72
78. Fernandes-Alnemri T, Yu JW, Datta P, Wu J, Alnemri ES. 2009. AIM2 activates the inflammasome and cell death in response to cytoplasmic DNA. *Nature* 458:509–13
79. Hornung V, Ablasser A, Charrel-Dennis M, Bauernfeind F, Horvath G, et al. 2009. AIM2 recognizes cytosolic dsDNA and forms a caspase-1-activating inflammasome with ASC. *Nature* 458:514–18
80. Masters SL, Simon A, Aksentijevich I, Kastner DL. 2009. *Horror autoinflammaticus*: the molecular pathophysiology of autoinflammatory disease. *Annu. Rev. Immunol.* 27:621–68
81. Agostini L, Martinon F, Burns K, McDermott MF, Hawkins PN, Tschopp J. 2004. NALP3 forms an IL-1β-processing inflammasome with increased activity in Muckle-Wells autoinflammatory disorder. *Immunity* 20:319–25
82. Kurt-Jones EA, Beller DI, Mizel SB, Unanue ER. 1985. Identification of a membrane-associated interleukin 1 in macrophages. *Proc. Natl. Acad. Sci. USA* 82:1204–8
83. Brody DT, Durum SK. 1989. Membrane IL-1: IL-1α precursor binds to the plasma membrane via a lectin-like interaction. *J. Immunol.* 143:1183–87
84. Black RA, Kronheim SR, Cantrell M, Deeley MC, March CJ, et al. 1988. Generation of biologically active interleukin-1β by proteolytic cleavage of the inactive precursor. *J. Biol. Chem.* 263:9437–42
85. Hazuda DJ, Strickler J, Kueppers F, Simon PL, Young PR. 1990. Processing of precursor interleukin 1β and inflammatory disease. *J. Biol. Chem.* 265:6318–22
86. Keller M, Ruegg A, Werner S, Beer HD. 2008. Active caspase-1 is a regulator of unconventional protein secretion. *Cell* 132:818–31

87. King MK, Wood WB Jr. 1958. Studies on the pathogenesis of fever. IV. The site of action of leukocytic and circulating endogenous pyrogen. *J. Exp. Med.* 107:291–303
88. So A, De Smedt T, Revaz S, Tschopp J. 2007. A pilot study of IL-1 inhibition by anakinra in acute gout. *Arthritis Res. Ther.* 9:R28
89. Cassel SL, Eisenbarth SC, Iyer SS, Sadler JJ, Colegio OR, et al. 2008. The Nalp3 inflammasome is essential for the development of silicosis. *Proc. Natl. Acad. Sci. USA* 105:9035–40
90. Miwa K, Asano M, Horai R, Iwakura Y, Nagata S, Suda T. 1998. Caspase 1-independent IL-1β release and inflammation induced by the apoptosis inducer Fas ligand. *Nat. Med.* 4:1287–92
91. Maelfait J, Vercammen E, Janssens S, Schotte P, Haegman M, et al. 2008. Stimulation of Toll-like receptor 3 and 4 induces interleukin-1β maturation by caspase-8. *J. Exp. Med.* 205:1967–73
92. Schonbeck U, Mach F, Libby P. 1998. Generation of biologically active IL-1β by matrix metalloproteinases: a novel caspase-1-independent pathway of IL-1β processing. *J. Immunol.* 161:3340–46
93. Mehta VB, Hart J, Wewers MD. 2001. ATP-stimulated release of interleukin (IL)-1β and IL-18 requires priming by lipopolysaccharide and is independent of caspase-1 cleavage. *J. Biol. Chem.* 276:3820–26
94. Roberge CJ, Grassi J, De Medicis R, Frobert Y, Lussier A, et al. 1991. Crystal-neutrophil interactions lead to interleukin-1 synthesis. *Agents Actions* 34:38–41
95. Roberge CJ, de Médicis R, Dayer JM, Rola-Pleszczynski M, Naccache PH, Poubelle PE. 1994. Crystal-induced neutrophil activation. V. Differential production of biologically active IL-1 and IL-1 receptor antagonist. *J. Immunol.* 152:5485–94
96. Di Giovine FS, Malawista SE, Nuki G, Duff GW. 1987. Interleukin 1 (IL 1) as a mediator of crystal arthritis. Stimulation of T cell and synovial fibroblast mitogenesis by urate crystal-induced IL 1. *J. Immunol.* 138:3213–18
97. di Giovine FS, Malawista SE, Thornton E, Duff GW. 1991. Urate crystals stimulate production of tumor necrosis factor α from human blood monocytes and synovial cells. Cytokine mRNA and protein kinetics, and cellular distribution. *J. Clin. Invest.* 87:1375–81
98. Li H, Willingham SB, Ting JP, Re F. 2008. Cutting edge: inflammasome activation by alum and alum's adjuvant effect are mediated by NLRP3. *J. Immunol.* 181:17–21
99. Sharp FA, Ruane D, Claass B, Creagh E, Harris J, et al. 2009. Uptake of particulate vaccine adjuvants by dendritic cells activates the NALP3 inflammasome. *Proc. Natl. Acad. Sci. USA* 106:870–75
100. Saitoh T, Fujita N, Jang MH, Uematsu S, Yang BG, et al. 2008. Loss of the autophagy protein Atg16L1 enhances endotoxin-induced IL-1β production. *Nature* 456:264–68
101. Bauernfeind F, Horvath G, Stutz A, Alnemri ES, MacDonald K, et al. 2009. NF-κB activating pattern recognition and cytokine receptors license NLRP3 inflammasome activation by regulating NLRP3 expression. *J. Immunol.* 183:787–91
102. Anderson JP, Mueller JL, Misaghi A, Anderson S, Sivagnanam M, et al. 2008. Initial description of the human NLRP3 promoter. *Genes Immun.* 9:721–26
103. Gurcel L, Abrami L, Girardin S, Tschopp J, Van Der Goot FG. 2006. Caspase-1 activation of lipid metabolic pathways in response to bacterial pore-forming toxins promotes cell survival. *Cell* 126:1135–45
104. Hayden MS, Ghosh S. 2008. Shared principles in NF-κB signaling. *Cell* 132:344–62
105. Giamarellos-Bourboulis EJ, Mouktaroudi M, Bodar E, Van Der Ven J, Kullberg BJ, et al. 2009. Crystals of monosodium urate monohydrate enhance lipopolysaccharide-induced release of interleukin 1β by mononuclear cells through a caspase 1-mediated process. *Ann. Rheum. Dis.* 68:273–78
106. Jaramillo M, Godbout M, Naccache PH, Olivier M. 2004. Signaling events involved in macrophage chemokine expression in response to monosodium urate crystals. *J. Biol. Chem.* 279:52797–805
107. Popa-Nita O, Marois L, Pare G, Naccache PH. 2008. Crystal-induced neutrophil activation: X. Proinflammatory role of the tyrosine kinase Tec. *Arthritis Rheum.* 58:1866–76
108. Barabe F, Gilbert C, Liao N, Bourgoin SG, Naccache PH. 1998. Crystal-induced neutrophil activation VI. Involvement of FcγRIIIB (CD16) and CD11b in response to inflammatory microcrystals. *FASEB J.* 12:209–20
109. Scott P, Ma H, Viriyakosol S, Terkeltaub R, Liu-Bryan R. 2006. Engagement of CD14 mediates the inflammatory potential of monosodium urate crystals. *J. Immunol.* 177:6370–78

110. Ng G, Sharma K, Ward SM, Desrosiers MD, Stephens LA, et al. 2008. Receptor-independent, direct membrane binding leads to cell-surface lipid sorting and Syk kinase activation in dendritic cells. *Immunity* 29:807–18
111. Deyerle KL, Sims JE, Dower SK, Bothwell MA. 1992. Pattern of IL-1 receptor gene expression suggests role in noninflammatory processes. *J. Immunol.* 149:1657–65
112. Armstrong DA, Major JA, Chudyk A, Hamilton TA. 2004. Neutrophil chemoattractant genes KC and MIP-2 are expressed in different cell populations at sites of surgical injury. *J. Leukoc. Biol.* 75:641–48
113. Fleischmann R, Stern R, Iqbal I. 2004. Anakinra: an inhibitor of IL-1 for the treatment of rheumatoid arthritis. *Expert. Opin. Biol. Ther.* 4:1333–44
114. Goldbach-Mansky R, Dailey NJ, Canna SW, Gelabert A, Jones J, et al. 2006. Neonatal-onset multisystem inflammatory disease responsive to interleukin-1β inhibition. *N. Engl. J. Med.* 355:581–92
115. Kokkola R, Andersson A, Mullins G, Ostberg T, Treutiger CJ, et al. 2005. RAGE is the major receptor for the proinflammatory activity of HMGB1 in rodent macrophages. *Scand. J. Immunol.* 61:1–9
116. Lubberts E, Joosten LA, Oppers B, Van Den Bersselaar L, Coenen-de Roo CJ, et al. 2001. IL-1-independent role of IL-17 in synovial inflammation and joint destruction during collagen-induced arthritis. *J. Immunol.* 167:1004–13
117. Lin HW, Basu A, Druckman C, Cicchese M, Krady JK, Levison SW. 2006. Astrogliosis is delayed in type 1 interleukin-1 receptor-null mice following a penetrating brain injury. *J. Neuroinflamm.* 3:15
118. Bertini R, Howard OM, Dong HF, Oppenheim JJ, Bizzarri C, et al. 1999. Thioredoxin, a redox enzyme released in infection and inflammation, is a unique chemoattractant for neutrophils, monocytes, and T cells. *J. Exp. Med.* 189:1783–89
119. Altemeier WA, Zhu X, Berrington WR, Harlan JM, Liles WC. 2007. Fas (CD95) induces macrophage proinflammatory chemokine production via a MyD88-dependent, caspase-independent pathway. *J. Leukoc. Biol.* 82:721–28
120. Pauluhn J. 2009. Retrospective analysis of 4-week inhalation studies in rats with focus on fate and pulmonary toxicity of two nanosized aluminum oxyhydroxides (boehmite) and pigment-grade iron oxide (magnetite): the key metric of dose is particle mass and not particle surface area. *Toxicology* 259:140–48
121. Epstein NJ, Warme BA, Spanogle J, Ma T, Bragg B, et al. 2005. Interleukin-1 modulates periprosthetic tissue formation in an intramedullary model of particle-induced inflammation. *J. Orthop. Res.* 23:501–10
122. Caicedo MS, Desai R, McAllister K, Reddy A, Jacobs JJ, Hallab NJ. 2009. Soluble and particulate Co-Cr-Mo alloy implant metals activate the inflammasome danger signaling pathway in human macrophages: a novel mechanism for implant debris reactivity. *J. Orthop. Res.* 27:847–54
123. Kool M, Soullie T, van Nimwegen M, Willart MA, Muskens F, et al. 2008. Alum adjuvant boosts adaptive immunity by inducing uric acid and activating inflammatory dendritic cells. *J. Exp. Med.* 205:869–82

Functions of Notch Signaling in the Immune System: Consensus and Controversies

Julie S. Yuan, Philaretos C. Kousis, Sara Suliman, Ioana Visan, and Cynthia J. Guidos

Program in Stem Cell and Developmental Biology, Hospital for Sick Children Research Institute, and Department of Immunology, Faculty of Medicine, University of Toronto, Toronto, Ontario M5G 1L7, Canada; email: Cynthia.guidos@sickkids.ca

Annu. Rev. Immunol. 2010. 28:343–65

First published online as a Review in Advance on January 4, 2010

The *Annual Review of Immunology* is online at immunol.annualreviews.org

This article's doi:
10.1146/annurev.immunol.021908.132719

0732-0582/10/0423-0343$20.00

Key Words

hematopoiesis, lymphopoiesis, lineage commitment

Abstract

Mammalian genomes encode up to four Notch receptors (Notch1–4) and five Notch ligands of the DSL (Delta/Serrate/Lag-2) family, and Notch signaling controls a wide spectrum of developmental processes. Intrathymic Notch1 signaling is essential for several distinct aspects of early T cell development. Notch signaling has also been implicated as a key regulator of peripheral T cell activation and effector cell differentiation, but its functions in these processes remain poorly understood. Notch signaling is dispensable for B cell development in the bone marrow, but it is required to generate the innate-like marginal zone B cell subset in the spleen and may also regulate plasma cell functions. Modification of Notch receptors by fringe glycosyltransferases influences many Notch-dependent aspects of hematopoiesis by altering Notch responsiveness to Delta-like versus Jagged DSL ligands. Here we review recent advances in general aspects of Notch signaling, as well as studies probing Notch functions in these immunological processes.

EGF: epidermal growth factor

Dll: Delta-like

DSL: Delta/Serrate/Lag-2

NOTCH RECEPTORS AND LIGANDS

Notch receptors are type I transmembrane heterodimeric receptors that directly activate transcription of gene targets upon productive interactions with Notch ligands belonging to several related families (1, 2). Notch extracellular (N^{EC}) domains are composed of tandem 29–36 epidermal growth factor (EGF)-like repeats, followed by three Lin-12/Notch (LNR) repeats and a heterodimerization (HD) domain that together comprise a negative regulatory region (NRR) (3). After synthesis and transit to the Golgi, most Notch receptors are cleaved within the extracellular juxtamembrane HD region by a furin-like protease to generate two fragments containing the N-terminal N^{EC} and C-terminal transmembrane/intracellular domains (N^{TMIC}), respectively. These fragments remain associated via noncovalent interactions between the N- and C-terminal halves of the HD domain to form the mature Notch heterodimer, but the N^{EC} domain undergoes extensive N-linked and O-linked glycosylation (described in more detail below) before Notch heterodimers transit from the Golgi to the cell surface.

Canonical Notch ligands are also type I transmembrane proteins belonging to two related families, Delta-like (Dll) and Jagged (Delta and Serrate in *Drosophila*) (4). Both families contain highly conserved N-terminal DSL domains and varying numbers of EGF repeats in their extracellular domains. Genetic and biochemical studies have implicated the DSL domain and EGF repeats 1, 2, 11, 12, and 24–29 in binding to Notch ligands (2, 5–8). However, Dll3 appears unable to activate Notch in vitro (9) or to bind Notch receptors on hematopoietic cells (10). Under some conditions (9), Dll3 could antagonize Notch activation by other DSL ligands, but this was not observed in vivo (11). Several molecules lacking DSL domains (DNER, EGFL7) or both DSL and EGF repeats (F3/contactin, microfibril-associated glycoprotein-1 and -2) appear to function as Notch ligands in some contexts (2, 12).

Recent studies identified a novel family of *Caenorhabditis elegans* proteins lacking DSL domains but containing a novel DOS (Delta and OSM-11) domain at the N terminus, composed of two variant EGF repeats, in addition to several classical EGF repeats (13). Interestingly, all worm DSL ligands lack the DOS domain, and genetic evidence suggests that the OSM-11 protein functions as a coligand to enhance Notch activation by DSL ligands in some developmental contexts. Phylogenetic comparisons suggest that EGF-1 and EGF-2 in some (Jagged1, Jagged2, and Dll1) but not all (Dll3 and Dll4) mammalian DSL ligands contain a DOS domain. Interestingly, mice and humans express a DOS-EGF protein known as Delta-like-1 homolog (Dlk1), which can bind Notch1 EGF repeats and inhibit (14) or enhance (13) Notch signaling when ectopically expressed in flies or worms, respectively. Similarly, EGFL7 can bind all four mammalian Notch receptors and antagonize Jagged1-induced Notch activation (12). Dlk-deficient mice show some abnormalities in B cell development and function, but the role of dysregulated Notch signaling in this phenotype was not determined (15). Future studies must examine the potential for DOS-EGF or noncanonical Notch ligands to modulate Notch activation by DSL ligands in cells of the immune system.

MECHANISM OF NOTCH ACTIVATION

Notch receptor-ligand interactions trigger sequential proteolytic cleavages of the N^{TMIC} fragment, first by ADAM (a disintegrin and metalloprotease) proteases at the S2 site in the juxtamembrane extracellular region, followed by γ-secretase at the S3 site within the transmembrane region (reviewed in 1, 2, 8). The latter cleavage releases the Notch intracellular (N^{IC}) domain as the final step of Notch activation. Crystallographic and biochemical analyses of the NRR support a model in which the LNR folds around the HD domain, occluding the S2 site to autoinhibit Notch activation (16).

Accumulating evidence suggests that ligand-induced endocytosis of both Notch (into the signal-receiving cell) and Delta or Serrate/Jagged (into the signal-sending cell) is critical to conformationally disrupt the NRR (reviewed in 1, 2, 8), allowing cleavage at the S2 site, which then facilitates γ-secretase cleavage at the S3 site to release N^{IC} from the inner face of the plasma membrane.

The N^{IC} contains several protein motifs that regulate protein-protein interactions (RAM and ANK domains), nuclear localization, and protein stability (PEST domain), all of which are critical for regulating transcription of Notch target genes. Transcriptional repressors of the *Hairy/enhancer of split* (*Hes*) family are directly induced by Notch activation in most cells (17) together with tissue-specific Notch targets. N^{IC} does not bind DNA directly. Rather, N^{IC} interacts via its RAM and ANK domains with CSL (CBF-1/Su(H)/Lag-1) proteins (also known as RBPJk) bound to *cis*-acting elements in promoters and enhancers, displacing corepressor molecules and recruiting transcriptional coactivators belonging to the Mastermind-like (MAML) family (3). This interaction is now understood in elegant molecular detail from crystallographic studies (18–20). CSL-dependent Notch activation is referred to as canonical Notch signaling to distinguish it from non-canonical CSL-independent Notch signaling that has been detected in some settings but remains poorly understood. The C-terminal N^{IC} PEST domain contains several phosphorylation sites, including a WSSSSP motif and a Cdc4 phospho-degron that critically regulate N^{IC} half-life (21, 22). Serines and threonines within these motifs are phosphorylated by Cdk8 and GSK-3β (and probably other kinases) to tag N^{IC} for proteasomal degradation by the FBW7 E3 ubiquitin ligase. This degradation critically limits the duration of Notch-mediated transcriptional activation and explains why PEST domain truncations promote Notch-induced T cell acute lymphoblastic leukemia (23–28).

REGULATION OF NOTCH FUNCTION BY O-LINKED GLYCANS

Notch expression and function are critically regulated by two types of O-linked glycosylation of the N^{EC}. In flies, the Rumi glycosyltransferase adds glucose moieties to Ser residues in certain EGF repeats (29). Notch that lacks O-glucose can reach the cell surface and bind Delta but cannot signal. Pofut1 (O-fucosyltransferase-1) is an endoplasmic reticulum–localized glycosyltransferase that adds O-fucose moieties to Ser or Thr residues to Notch EGF repeats with the consensus sequence $C^2X_{4-5}(S/T)C^3$, where X is any amino acid (30). In flies and mammals, many (but not all) O-fucose-modified EGF repeats on Notch receptors are further extended by Fringe glycosyltransferases, which add N-acetylglucosamine moieties (30, 31). In flies, Fringe enhances Notch activation by Delta family ligands and decreases Serrate/Jagged-mediated Notch activation within a discrete subset of cells at the dorsal/ventral boundary of the developing wing to regulate a key patterning event in wing morphogenesis. Three vertebrate Fringe proteins have been identified: Lunatic, Manic, and Radical. Lunatic Fringe (Lfng) is essential for temporal and spatial coordination of Notch1 activation during somitogenesis in vertebrate embryos (32) and also regulates vertebrate neurogenesis (33, 34). To date, essential functions for Manic Fringe (Mfng) and Radical Fringe (Rfng) in embryonic development have not been identified (35, 36). By contrast, Lfng plays an important role in modulating Notch signaling during T cell development, and Lfng and Mfng cooperatively regulate marginal zone (MZ) B cell development in the spleen, as further discussed below.

CSL: CBF-1/Su(H)/Lag-1

MAML: Mastermind-like

Lfng: Lunatic Fringe

Mfng: Manic Fringe

Rfng: Radical Fringe

EXPERIMENTAL MANIPULATION OF NOTCH SIGNALING

Investigators have used various experimental approaches to probe the functions of Notch signaling in hematopoiesis and lymphocyte

GSI: γ-secretase inhibitor

activation, including genetic disruption of Notch receptors, ligands, and signaling molecules (reviewed in 37, 38, 39). The utility of constitutive knockouts is somewhat limited because embryonic lethality often results when a key Notch component is knocked out. Because many Notch receptors and ligands exhibit haploinsufficiency (40–45), mice heterozygous for a null mutation in these genes provide another genetic approach to weaken but not completely ablate Notch activation (41, 45–47). Conditional knockouts that specifically disrupt Notch activation in discrete cells or tissues are particularly important for probing Notch functions in specific cells or tissues (37–39). However, cell nonautonomous effects of dysregulated signaling can sometimes confound interpretations (48). Nonetheless, these genetic strategies provide the most rigorous approach for testing the requirement for a particular Notch receptor, ligand, or signaling molecule in the development or functions of immune cell types.

Gain-of-function genetic approaches, such as retroviral or transgenic expression of constitutively active N^{IC}, can also be useful, but this approach typically results in a very strong Notch signal that may not be physiologically attainable, especially when the PEST domain is also truncated. Misexpression of Notch regulators and targets such as Lfng (41, 45, 49), Deltex (50), Numb (51), Nrarp (52), or dominant-negative MAML (53–55) is another useful experimental approach for altering Notch signaling in vivo. However, many of these regulators are not absolutely specific for the Notch pathway (56–58). Ideally, results from loss-of-function experiments should mirror those from gain-of-function experiments, but as described below, this is not always the case, perhaps reflecting subtle but important differences in the timing or degree of regulator expression versus genetic deletion.

In vitro approaches have also been devised to elucidate functions of Notch signaling. These include overexpression of Notch ligands in stromal (59, 60) or antigen-presenting cells (61) and culture with Notch ligand fusion proteins (62, 63) that contain a DSL ligand extracellular domain fused to an Ig Fc region. These can be very powerful approaches, but the high amount of ligand presented is probably not reflective of normal physiology. Furthermore, even though a particular ligand may induce a strong outcome in vitro (64–66), that ligand may not be physiologically relevant for inducing the same outcome in vivo (47) owing to extensive redundancies, particularly among ligands belonging to the same Delta or Jagged family. Furthermore, Notch receptors and ligands are widely expressed in cells of the immune system, and Notch activation may influence many cell types in a culture, even though only one cell type is being assayed. Finally, γ-secretase inhibitors (GSI) can be added to cell or organ cultures to block Notch ligand–induced proteolysis (67), but γ-secretase activity also regulates other signaling pathways (68), so this approach may also alter outcomes in a Notch-independent fashion.

In summary, a wide array of genetic and biochemical approaches can be used to probe Notch functions in vivo and in vitro. As we point out in this review, each approach has strengths and liabilities that must be considered when interpreting the data. Ideally, a combination of these approaches should be used to rigorously evaluate the role of Notch signaling in a particular hematopoietic or immunological process.

NOTCH SIGNALING IN MULTIPOTENT HEMATOPOIETIC CELLS

The first definitive hematopoietic stem cells (HSCs) capable of generating adult-type erythrocytes and myeloid and lymphoid cells arise in murine embryos at around embryonic day 9.5 and express Notch1, Notch2, and Notch 4 (69). However, Notch1 but not Notch2 is required to generate definitive HSCs during embryonic development. The *Scl*, *Gata2*, and *Runx1* genes, which encode transcription factors required for definitive hematopoiesis, are downregulated in *Notch1*$^{-/-}$ (69) and *CSL*$^{-/-}$ (70) embryonic HSCs, suggesting that

Notch1/CSL-dependent signaling regulates their induction. Indeed, data from *Drosophila* (71) and zebrafish (72) have identified a highly conserved Notch-Runx pathway regulating HSC specification. Interestingly, however, neither Runx1 (73) nor SCL (74) is required for HSC maintenance in adults, indicating that distinct transcription factors are needed for HSC generation during embryogenesis versus HSC maintenance in the adult.

Functions of Notch signaling in postnatal HSC self-renewal and maintenance have been less clear. Gain-of-function experiments, involving exposure of progenitors to Dll (75, 76) or Jagged1 (77, 78) Notch ligands in vitro, overexpression of constitutively active Notch alleles (79–81), and Notch downstream targets such as *Hes1* (82, 83) have suggested that Notch increases self-renewal and decreases differentiation of hematopoietic progenitors. Genetic manipulations that appear to increase Jagged1 expression in bone marrow stem cell niches can enhance self-renewal of adult HSCs (84). However, the notion that Notch signaling critically regulates HSC self-renewal in vivo has not been clearly supported by loss-of-function data. For example, conditional ablation of *Notch1* or *Jagged1* did not reveal defects in HSC maintenance even in competitive reconstitution assays (85), but potential functional redundancy with other Notch ligands and receptors could not be excluded. Nonetheless, HSCs lacking CSL, which therefore lack all canonical Notch signaling, generate normal numbers of short-lived myeloid cells (86), suggesting that HSC maintenance is not compromised by loss of Notch signaling.

Recently, Pear and colleagues (87) globally inactivated canonical Notch signaling in HSCs by expressing a mutant version of the coactivator MAML, which binds N^{IC} to dominantly inhibit CSL-dependent Notch activation. Rigorous in vivo self-renewal assays revealed that canonical Notch signaling is dispensable in maintaining adult HSCs, contradicting an earlier study that concluded that CSL-dependent Notch activation enhances adult HSC differentiation at the expense of self-renewal (88). Reasons for these disparate conclusions have yet to be elucidated but likely relate to the experimental approaches employed. For example, the retroviral overexpression strategies used may not have achieved similar levels of expression or have targeted long-term HSCs to the same degree. Similarly, Cre transgenes may delete floxed alleles of Notch receptors, ligands, or signaling components with varying efficiencies in different HSC subsets (89). Because long-term HSCs, which consist of a relatively small subset within the total HSC compartment, can now be prospectively isolated (90, 91), it should be feasible to resolve this question definitively by efficiently inactivating Notch signaling specifically in these cells.

Although dispensable for HSC maintenance, recent in vitro and in vivo data strongly implicate Notch signaling in early stages of myeloerythroid differentiation. HSCs cultured with OP9 bone marrow stromal cells expressing Dll1 underwent CSL-dependent megakaryocyte specification (92). Fresh ex vivo megakaryocyte-erythrocyte precursors expressed Notch4 and several direct Notch target genes, implicating Notch4 as a possible mediator of Notch-induced megakaryocyte development. However, neither the Notch receptor(s) nor ligand(s) that drives this hematopoietic outcome in vivo was identified. Interestingly, recent evidence implicates dysregulated activation of CSL-dependent Notch signaling in acute megakaryoblastic leukemia (93).

In multipotent progenitors that have lost erythro-megakaryocytic potential, maintenance of Notch1 expression is part of a lymphoid specification program induced by transcription factors such as Ikaros, PU.1, E2A, and Mef2c (94–97). Notch1 expression in such lymphoid-primed multipotent progenitors (LMPPs) specifically depends on E2A (96, 98) and perhaps also Ikaros (99). Current evidence indicates that thymus-seeding progenitors reside within a $Flt3^+$ and $CCR9^+$ subset of early lymphoid-biased progenitors in the bone marrow (100, 101). As discussed further below, Notch1 is specifically required to generate intrathymic T cell precursors but is dispensable for B lymphoid and myeloid cell development in the bone marrow. Therefore, Notch1 expression in prethymic T cell progenitors such as LMPPs likely represents one of the earliest events in specification of the T cell lineage.

Given that several Notch ligands are expressed in the bone marrow (102), mechanisms likely exist to prevent LMPPs from activating Notch1 and generating T cells prior to thymic seeding. Indeed, Notch1 activation and T cell development in bone marrow progenitors are actively repressed by the lymphoma-related factor transcriptional repressor (103). This repression can apparently be overcome by retroviral expression of Dll4 in bone marrow cells, which induces ectopic T cell development up to the CD4/CD8 double-positive (DP) stage in the bone marrow (104, 105). Importantly, these and previous studies (49, 106, 107) demonstrate that with the exception of failing to promote robust Notch1 activation, the bone marrow provides a suitable microenvironment for supporting T lymphopoiesis. Interestingly, Notch/CSL signaling promotes T cell development up to the DP stage in the spleen and lymph nodes of irradiated mice, but this process appears to be suppressed in the absence of lymphopenia (55). This extrathymic T cell development may have therapeutic relevance in a bone marrow transplantation setting. Additional studies are needed to identify the Notch receptors and ligands involved in this process and will likely identify additional regulatory mechanisms that prevent Notch-induced extrathymic T cell development.

NOTCH SIGNALING IN MYELOID DEVELOPMENT

There have been conflicting reports on the role of Notch signaling in granulocyte-macrophage differentiation. Retroviral transduction of N^{IC} or Hes1 into hematopoietic progenitors did not affect this process in vivo in one study (108), but it impaired myelopoiesis in others (80, 109). More recent studies show that coculture of HSCs or early hematopoietic progenitors with OP9 stromal cells overexpressing Notch ligands profoundly impairs granulocyte generation, with some disagreement about the developmental stage at which this block occurs (110, 111). Nonetheless, mice harboring a mutation that globally impairs protein fucosylation exhibit excessive granulopoiesis in vivo, which was linked to defective Notch activation (111). These data therefore suggest that Notch signaling under physiological circumstances may indeed inhibit at least some aspects of myelopoiesis. Notch-induced expression of GATA2, a direct Notch target (70), is critical for suppressing myelopoiesis in OP9-Dll1 cocultures (110). Notch2 is highly expressed in early myeloid progenitors (K. Cretegny and C.J. Guidos, unpublished observations), but further studies will need to characterize the Notch receptor and ligands that physiologically regulate these effects in vivo.

Many in vitro studies have implicated Notch signaling at various stages of dendritic cell (DC) generation and maturation, but no clear consensus has emerged. Typically, Notch ligand–expressing stromal cells or fusion proteins are added to cultures of precursors with cytokines that favor DC development. Investigators have suggested that Dll1 promotes (112–114) or inhibits (115) DC development from hematopoietic precursors. Discrepant results were also reported concerning the role of Dll1-induced Notch signaling in plasmacytoid DC generation (116, 117), highlighting the complexity of interpreting these experiments. Several issues contribute to this complexity. The amount of ligand expressed likely does not correspond to physiologically attainable levels and may be quite different among the studies. In addition, few studies have used defined subtypes of early hematopoietic or DC progenitors, but rather have employed heterogeneous progenitor mixes that were enriched using different approaches and thus were likely different in each study. Finally, because each study employed distinct cytokine cocktails and culture conditions, the relevance of the conclusions for DC development in vivo remains to be demonstrated.

In contrast to some in vitro experiments, genetic loss-of-function studies have failed to identify an essential role for Notch signaling in DC development from bone marrow precursors. Notch1 is dispensable for generation of all DC subsets from bone marrow precursors after adoptive transfer (118). Furthermore, CSL deficiency does not compromise DC generation from bone marrow precursors under various culture conditions in vitro (119). However, DCs can also develop intrathymically from early T cell precursors (ETPs) (reviewed in 120). Because ETP generation is Notch1 dependent (41, 121), the development of at least some thymic DCs can be said to be Notch dependent. However, as discussed further below, Notch signaling restrains ETPs from adopting a DC fate in the thymus (122–124). Thus, generation of thymic DCs requires that Notch signaling first be active (to generate ETPs) and then attenuated so that these ETPs do not mature into T cells.

Interestingly, conditional disruption of all CSL-dependent Notch signaling using CD11c-Cre impairs homeostasis of $CD8^-$ DCs in the spleen (119). Furthermore, CSL deficiency decreased the frequency of cytokine-secreting DCs after challenge with Toll-like receptor (TLR) ligands. A more recent study by Hu and colleagues (125) may explain this finding; they identified an unusual Notch-independent synergism between TLR signaling and CSL for induction of certain inflammatory cytokines. Collectively, these genetic studies suggest that Notch signaling critically regulates development, homeostasis, and function of some DC subsets. Further progress in this area will require genetic approaches combined with prospective isolation of defined early myeloid and DC progenitors to study the requirement for Notch activation at discrete stages of DC development.

NOTCH SIGNALING IN EARLY T LYMPHOCYTE DEVELOPMENT

Within the hematopoietic system, Notch signaling is best characterized for its role in promoting T lineage commitment and maturation. Several Notch receptors are expressed during thymopoiesis, and they display distinct and overlapping expression patterns, suggesting that they may serve redundant as well as nonredundant functions. Notch2 is expressed throughout the earliest CD4/CD8 double-negative (DN) stages of T cell development; however, the only essential hematopoietic function of Notch2 is to elicit development of MZ B cells (46). Notch3 is also highly expressed in thymocytes beginning at the DN3 stage (107), but genetic deletion of Notch3 only marginally affects thymocyte number in older mice (126). Interestingly, ectopic activation of Notch2 or Notch3 can disrupt intrathymic T cell development (127, 128), but this could reflect functional overlap with the Notch1 intracellular domain, rather than specific functions for Notch2 or Notch3. Genetic studies to address potential synergies of Notch2 or Notch3 with Notch1 in T cell development have yet to be reported. Forced expression of the intracellular domain of Notch4 in human cord blood cells results in ectopic immature T cell development in the bone marrow and spleen and a block in B cell differentiation after adoptive transfer into mice (129). However, Notch4-deficient mice do not display any hematopoietic defects (130).

ETP: early thymocyte progenitor

In contrast to the lack of an essential T lymphopoietic function for Notch2, Notch3, or Notch4, Notch1 is absolutely necessary and sufficient for the development of T cells. Mice transplanted with HSCs conditionally lacking Notch1 have large numbers of immature B cells in the thymus but no T cell precursors (106, 131). Conversely, constitutive Notch1 activation in bone marrow HSCs results in the ectopic development of immature T cells in the bone marrow at the expense of B cell development (108). Thus, Notch1 signals are critical to promote T cell fate, but also to suppress B cell fate in the thymus. Although investigators have suggested that fetal thymus-seeding progenitors lose B cell potential prethymically (132), recent studies show that immature B cells predominate in adult and fetal thymi when Dll4 is conditionally deleted from thymic epithelial cells (133, 134). This finding strongly suggests that fetal thymus-seeding progenitors do not lose B cell potential prethymically.

The most immature intrathymic progenitors are found within the ETP ($CD117^+CD44^+CD25^-$) subset of DN1 cells. About 15% express Flt3 and CCR9, and a small fraction of these display clonogenic T, B, and myeloid lineage potential (10, 100, 121), likely reflecting their recent generation from thymus-seeding LMPPs. In contrast, $CCR9^-$ $Flt3^-$ ETPs lack B cell potential and express high levels of *Hes1* (10, 121), suggesting that they have activated Notch1 signaling and suppressed the B cell fate. Indeed, ETPs require Notch signals for their generation and therefore are likely downstream progeny of thymus-seeding progenitors (41, 121). Notch1 deletion beginning in $Flt3^-$ ETPs (using Cpa3-Cre) resulted in minimal intrathymic B cell development (124), confirming other studies showing that B cell potential has been largely suppressed by the late ETP stage.

Even though B cell potential has been suppressed in most ETPs, Notch1 signals are continuously required through the DN2 ($CD117^+CD44^+CD25^+$) stage to suppress other non–T cell potentials, because they adopt natural killer (NK), macrophage-granulocyte, and DC fates when Notch activation is prevented (122, 123, 135, 136). Dll-mediated Notch activation can also suppress myeloid development from DN thymocytes engineered to ectopically express transcriptional regulators of the myeloid cell fate (137–139). Although it remains unclear how Notch1 activation immediately silences B cell but not myeloid potential of thymus-seeding progenitors, it may have to do with differential ability of Notch-CSL signaling to repress genes involved in B lymphoid versus myeloid specification. However, because ETPs and DN2 thymocytes also express Notch2 (107), the involvement of different Notch receptor-ligand pairs in suppressing B versus myeloid potential cannot be ruled out.

Studies of intrathymic T cell development from *Notch1*$^{+/-}$ HSCs revealed that weak Notch signals can inhibit the B cell fate, whereas stronger Notch signals are needed to promote T cell development in vivo (45). This notion is also supported by in vitro studies in which Notch signaling was attenuated by varying doses of GSI (135, 136). These findings strongly suggest that low amounts of activated N^{IC} will regulate different sets of genes from those induced by intermediate or high levels of activated N^{IC}. Which genes will be activated by a given dose of N^{IC} will likely be determined by the nature of the CSL-binding sites as well as by the spectrum of adjacent *cis*-acting transcriptional elements in the promoters or enhancers of direct Notch target genes (140). The direct Notch targets Hes1 or Hes5 can suppress B cell development downstream of Notch activation in the thymus, but neither gene is sufficient to promote T lymphopoiesis in the absence of Notch-CSL signaling (109, 141, 142). Thus, different Notch-regulated genes are involved in lineage commitment versus specification.

NOTCH SIGNALING IN SELECTION OF αβ VERSUS γδ T CELLS

By the time T cell progenitors reach the early DN3a ($CD27^{lo}CD5^{lo}CD117^-CD44^-CD25^+$) stage, all non–T cell lineage potentials have been effectively suppressed, and they are undergoing *TCR* gene rearrangements. DN3a progenitors that successfully rearrange both *TCRG* and *TCRD* will express γδ TCRs and be selected to mature into γδ T cells. In contrast, successful *TCRB* rearrangement allows expression of pre-TCR complexes, consisting of pre-TCRα (Ptcra), TCRβ, and CD3 proteins, which signal in a ligand-independent fashion (143) to induce β-selection. This process entails survival and maturation of preselection DN3a cells into $CD27^{hi}CD5^{hi}$ DN3b blasts. Their DN4 ($CD44^-CD117^-CD25^-$) progeny proliferate extensively before differentiating to the DP stage.

Early evidence indicated that Notch signals might direct the αβ/γδ T cell lineage decision because weakening or ablating Notch1 activation (through heterozygosity or conditional deletion of *CSL*) appeared to favor production of $\gamma\delta$ T cells over $\alpha\beta$ T cells (40, 144). However, using the OP9-Dll1 coculture approach, data from Zúñiga-Pflücker and colleagues (66) suggested that TCR rather than Notch signals determine the $\alpha\beta$ versus $\gamma\delta$ lineage decision. Notch signaling is required to maintain glucose metabolism and viability of preselection DN2 or DN3a thymocytes (65). Investigators have also suggested that Notch signaling regulates IL-7 receptor expression on early thymocytes, but diversion of T cell progenitors to other cell fates may also explain the data (145).

Downstream of TCR expression, only $\alpha\beta$ T cell progenitors require continued Notch signals to drive maturation (66). Indeed, Notch1/CSL signals are essential downstream of pre-TCR expression in β-selection in vivo (54). Although pre-TCR-expressing DN3b thymocytes can generate DP thymocytes in the absence of Notch signals in vitro (146), many more DP cells are produced when Notch activation is sustained through the DN4 stage in mice (147) and humans (148). One key function of Notch signaling in this context is to sustain or enhance signaling through the phosphoinositide 3-kinase pathway, which elevates expression of nutrient receptors to support the metabolic demands of this proliferative burst (149). However, mechanisms by which Notch activation regulates phosphoinositide 3-kinase signaling have not been defined.

TCR complexes lacking Ptcra can also promote the DN3-DP transition in a Notch-dependent fashion, and it has been suggested that Ptcra-deficient DN3 progenitors are inefficient competitors for Notch ligands (147). Although Lfng overexpression in *Ptcra*$^{-/-}$ DN3 thymocytes improved the capacity of Ptcra-deficient DN3s to bind and compete for Dll ligands, this modification compensated only slightly for the intrinsically poor efficiency with which Ptcra-deficient TCRs promote the DN3-DP transition (I. Visan, J.S. Yuan, Y. Liu, P. Stanley, and C.J. Guidos, unpublished observations). These data argue against a role for the pre-TCR in regulating Notch1 activation by modulating ligand accessibility. Rather, they strongly suggest that pre-TCR and Notch signaling have largely nonoverlapping functions in β-selection, a conclusion supported by recent studies of human T cell development (148). However, it remains unclear why Notch signaling, which is clearly active from the ETP to the DN3a stages, only promotes robust proliferation after pre-TCR expression. A clear understanding of this issue will require a detailed molecular dissection of the mechanisms by which pre-TCR and Notch signaling are integrated during β-selection.

NOTCH SIGNALING IN THE DP-TO-SP TRANSITION

Several lines of evidence suggest that Notch signaling must be minimally active in DP thymocytes for proper differentiation of SP (single-positive) thymocytes expressing $\alpha\beta$ TCRs. Indeed, ectopic Notch activation in DP thymocytes disrupts the DP-to-SP transition (108, 150, 151). Whether this disruption reflects premalignant changes that interfere with normal developmental cues or more specifically reflects a role for Notch in positive selection has not been resolved. DP thymocytes express very little Notch1, although Notch2 and Notch3 are expressed (107). This implies that Notch1 expression as well as Notch2 or Notch3 signaling must be strictly regulated in a stage-specific manner. DP thymocytes express very little Lfng, which likely contributes to limiting Dll4-induced Notch activation in these cells (45, 107). Furthermore, pre-TCR signaling induces expression of Id3, which interferes with E2A-dependent Notch1 transcription in DP thymocytes (152).

Early gain-of-function studies suggested that Notch may direct DP thymocytes toward the CD8 lineage or promote both CD4 and CD8 T cell development, but loss-of-function studies indicated that Notch activation is not essential for the DP-to-SP transition (reviewed in 39, 153). Moreover, analyses of mice expressing the hypomorphic *Notch1*^{12f} allele suggested that Notch1 signaling may delay the DP-to-SP transition (154). However, a more recent study has suggested a role for presenilin, a component of the γ-secretase complex, in positive selection (155). Conditional deletion of *presenilin1* and *presenilin2* in DP thymocytes dramatically reduced DP thymocyte numbers and impaired CD4 SP thymocyte generation. The latter defect correlated with impaired TCR signaling as evidenced by a reduced Ca^{2+} flux upon TCR stimulation in vitro and in vivo. Transgenic N^{IC} expression restored thymic cellularity and TCR signaling, suggesting that presenilin-mediated Notch signals modulate TCR signals to influence positive selection. Notably, however, a CSL-independent role for presenilins in mature T cell activation has also been described (156). Thus, further experiments are required to clarify the role of Notch signaling and presenilins in TCR signaling in DP thymocytes and mature T cells.

NOTCH SIGNALING IN T CELL ACTIVATION AND DIFFERENTIATION

Several studies have implicated Notch signaling in TCR-mediated activation and proliferation of peripheral T cells. In keeping with this notion, naive CD4 T cells express Notch1 and Notch2 (but not Notch3 or Notch4) mRNA (61). Furthermore, TCR stimulation considerably increases expression of all four Notch receptors within 24 h (157). Finally, several studies detected N^{IC} within 24 h of TCR stimulation in the absence of antigen-presenting cells (61, 158). Because CD4 T cells do not express appreciable amounts of DSL Notch ligands, this may represent a novel mode of Notch receptor activation. Although these data imply that Notch signaling may regulate CD4 T cell activation or differentiation, investigators disagree about whether Notch plays a potentiating or inhibitory role. In contrast, genetic evidence strongly supports a role for Notch2 activation in promoting the acquisition of cytolytic effector function in CD8 T cells through direct regulation of granzyme B and perforin expression (159, 160).

A potentiating role for Notch signaling in T cell activation was supported by studies of CD4 T cells transduced with N^{IC} (157) or cultured with Dll1-Fc fusion protein (62). Other studies reached this conclusion by showing that a Notch1 antisense transgene, GSI, or antagonistic Notch1 antibody inhibited anti-TCR-induced proliferation of CD4 T cells in vitro (63, 158). In other studies, Notch receptor engagement with immobilized Jagged1 protein or agonistic Notch1 antibody inhibited TCR-induced activation and proliferation of naive CD4 T cells, suggesting that Notch signaling negatively regulates T cell activation (63). This finding was reproduced by another group that attributed the Notch inhibitory effect to Jagged1-induced expression of GRAIL (gene related to anergy in lymphocytes) (161). Another study showed that intramuscular delivery of a plasmid encoding soluble Jagged1 inhibited CD8 T cell proliferation, although in vitro studies suggested that this effect was indirect (162). Several other studies employing complex methods have also examined functions of Notch signaling in CD4 T cell activation, but the variety of experimental approaches employed has not allowed a consensus conclusion to be drawn.

Many studies have reported that Notch signaling critically influences differentiation of activated T cells into Th1 versus Th2 cells that control cellular versus humoral immunity, respectively. However, once again there is debate about the exact role of Notch signaling in this process. Several in vitro studies implicated Notch1 in promoting Tbet expression during Th1 differentiation (62, 163, 164). However, CD4 T cells lacking Notch1 or expressing dominant-negative MAML show normal Th1-mediated clearance of *Leishmania* in vivo (165, 166). In one study, no role for CSL-dependent Notch signaling could be detected during Th1 or Th2 differentiation in vitro (156). In contrast, other groups reported that conditional inactivation of all CSL-dependent Notch signaling reduced or ablated production of Th2 cytokines and allowed Th1 differentiation under Th2 polarizing conditions in vitro (61, 144, 166). Furthermore, CD4 T cells lacking Notch1 and Notch2 (167) or expressing dominant-negative MAML (166) could not undergo Th2 differentiation in response to parasite antigens in vivo. Interestingly, CD4 T cells lacking only Notch1 or Notch2 showed no defect in Th2 differentiation in this study, demonstrating that these Notch receptors are redundant in this context. The ability of Notch signaling to promote Th2 differentiation has been linked to its direct regulating expression of *Gata3*, a key transcriptional regulator of Th2 differentiation (167, 168), as well as to *IL4* transcription (169).

In summary, accumulating genetic evidence suggests that Notch activation regulates Th1 and Th2 differentiation. However, many factors, including the convenient but nonphysiological practice of using cytokines to polarize Th differentiation in vitro, have contributed to the disparate conclusions about how Notch signaling influences this critical aspect of CD4 T cell differentiation (170). Notch signaling has also been implicated in inducing regulatory T cell differentiation (171) and function (172, 173), but this role for Notch has not yet been evaluated using genetic approaches. A clearer understanding of Notch functions in T cell activation and differentiation awaits further studies using genetic methods to modulate Notch signaling in specific cell populations during immune responses in vivo.

NOTCH SIGNALING IN B CELL DEVELOPMENT AND DIFFERENTIATION

In contrast to T cell development, B cell development in the bone marrow does not require CSL-dependent Notch activation. However, CSL-dependent Notch2 activation is selectively required to generate MZ B cell precursors and mature MZ B cells after newly formed B cells migrate from bone marrow to spleen (reviewed in 31). MZ B cells have unique functional properties and provide crucial T-independent protection against bacterial sepsis. Conditional deletion of *Dll1* in postnatal mice also prevents MZ B cell generation, identifying Dll1 as a nonredundant Notch2 ligand for MZ B cell precursors (47). Most current models suggest that Notch2 signaling regulates the ability of a common progenitor to choose the MZ B cell over the follicular B cell fate. However, several observations are not easily reconciled with this simple binary cell fate model. First, follicular B cells are generated early in ontogeny, whereas MZ B cells do not arise until a few weeks after birth and continue to increase postnatally for several months (174). Second, MZ B cells are selectively maintained when B cell production in the bone marrow is abrogated postnatally, suggesting that they may undergo homeostatic expansion in response to lymphopenia. Indeed, highly purified follicular B cells can convert into MZ B cells in lymphopenic hosts (175), and this homeostatic conversion is Notch2 dependent (J. Tan and C.J. Guidos, unpublished observations).

Using Notch2-LacZ reporter mice, we have shown that Notch2 is heterogeneously expressed in fresh ex vivo follicular and MZ B cells (176). Furthermore, Notch2 expression is dramatically increased after B cells are activated by lipopolysaccharide or B cell receptor (BCR) cross-linking (J. Tan and C.J. Guidos, unpublished observations), suggesting that Notch signaling may regulate B cell activation or differentiation. Several in vitro studies support this notion. OP9-Dll1 stromal cells enhanced B cell proliferation as well as secretion of IgG1 in response to BCR or CD40 stimulation (177). Inhibitor studies suggested that this enhanced proliferation required MEK1/2 activity. Another study reported that OP9-Dll1 enhanced spontaneous Ig secretion by MZ and B1 cells, and also enhanced plasma cell differentiation in response to BCR cross-linking (178). Furthermore, genetic approaches implicated CSL-dependent Notch1 signaling in lipopolysaccharide-induced Ig secretion. Interestingly, this group reported that OP9-Jagged1 stromal cells inhibited, rather than enhanced Ig secretion, suggesting that different Notch ligands could have opposing effects on activated B cells. Notably, disruption of CSL-dependent Notch activation in B lineage cells does not impair antibody responses or plasma cell generation in vivo (179). Thus, Notch signaling may modulate B cell antibody production only in certain circumstances.

NOTCH LIGANDS IN LYMPHOCYTE DEVELOPMENT AND DIFFERENTIATION

Constitutive deletion of *Dll1*, *Dll4*, or *Jagged1* causes embryonic lethality in mice (reviewed in 107), making the requirement for particular Notch ligands in the immune system difficult to assess. However, in some contexts, a clear picture is emerging from conditional knockouts and in vitro culture systems in which stromal cells are engineered to ectopically express a DSL ligand. Initial studies with S17 stromal cells suggested Dll1, but not Jagged1, could inhibit B cell development and promote emergence of T/NK cell progenitors from human hematopoietic progenitors (59). Subsequent studies using OP9 stroma confirmed that Dll1 or Dll4, but not Jagged1, could suppress B cell development and drive T lineage development from fetal HSCs and various other hematolymphoid progenitors (180, 181). However, OP9-Jagged1 supported T cell development from human hematopoietic progenitors in another study (116).

This discrepancy highlights a disadvantage of using Notch ligand–expressing stromal cell lines to identify roles for Notch signaling in hematopoiesis. These immortalized lines have been in culture for many years and display tremendous karyotypic instability (J.S. Yuan and C.J. Guidos, unpublished observations). Thus, the genome of a given stromal cell line will likely evolve distinctly over time in different labs, which may explain why different results are sometimes reported with a particular Notch ligand–expressing stromal cell line. Furthermore, it should not be assumed that expression of the transfected Notch ligand is the only difference from the untransfected control cell line. We have observed a surprisingly large number of differences in the genome-wide transcriptomes of OP9 versus OP9-Dll1 stromal cells (J.S. Yuan and C.J. Guidos, unpublished observations). Nonetheless, these stromal cell lines provide a valuable experimental tool, as long as extreme caution is observed in data interpretation.

Lehar, Bevan, and colleagues (181) observed that although OP9-Jagged1 cells do not impair B cell development from HSCs, they could prevent B cell emergence from DN1 thymocytes. Similarly, Bleul's group (10) found that oligomerized Jagged1-Fc could suppress B cell development from the multipotent subset of DN1 thymocytes. Collectively, these data suggest that multipotent DN1 thymocytes are more sensitive to Jagged1 than are bone marrow–derived HSCs or LMPPs. Because a higher threshold of Notch signals is needed to promote T cell development than to suppress the B cell fate (41, 135, 136), these data suggest that Jagged1 only weakly activates Notch in developing thymocytes. This notion is also supported by studies showing that HSCs, thymocytes (DN and SP), and mature T cells bind Fc fusion proteins containing the extracellular domains of Dll1 or Dll4 but not Jagged1 or Jagged2 (10, 45, 182, 183). Thus, HSCs, T cell precursors, and CD4 T cells show a strong preference for Dll over Jagged ligands.

Unfortunately, these in vitro approaches do not reveal whether a ligand physiologically regulates a Notch-dependent process in vivo. Unexpectedly, OP9-Dll1 promoted T cell development from Notch1-deficient HSCs, despite the well-established Notch1 dependency of T lymphopoiesis in vivo (182). Dll1-induced T cell development in vitro is Notch2 dependent when Notch1 is absent, but for reasons yet to be elucidated Dll1-Notch2 signaling only promotes T cell maturation up to the DN3 stage. Therefore, OP9-Dll1 stimulates T cell development via Notch1 and Notch2 activation in vitro. In contrast, Notch2 binding to Dll4-Fc is not detectable, and OP9-Dll4 does not promote T cell development from Notch1-deficient HSCs in vitro. Thus, in vivo T lymphopoiesis occurs only via Dll4-induced Notch1 activation. Of interest is whether T cell progenitors develop identically in response to Notch1 versus Notch2 activation.

Conditional knockout studies are thus needed to identify the DSL ligand(s) that physiologically regulate(s) a given process. T lymphopoiesis is unaffected in mice conditionally deleted for Jagged1 (85), and Jagged2-deficient mice exhibit only a marginal reduction in $\gamma\delta$ T cells in the perinatal thymus (184), suggesting that Jagged ligands play no essential role in T cell generation. Despite the robust ability of Dll1 to promote T cell development in vitro, Dll1 is dispensable for T cell development, although it is required for MZ B cell generation in vivo (47). Several reports (using nonquantitative RT-PCR or polyclonal antisera) suggested that Dll1 is highly expressed by thymic epithelium, but recent studies clearly demonstrate that Dll4 is the most abundant Delta family DSL ligand expressed in this tissue (133, 134). Indeed, conditional deletion experiments recently demonstrated an absolute requirement for Dll4 expressed in thymic epithelium to drive T lymphopoiesis (133, 134).

To identify Dll1-expressing splenic cells that drive MZ B cell development, we used mice harboring *LacZ* knocked into the *Dll1* locus (176). Using a histochemical technique to identify and localize Dll1-expressing cells, we showed that red pulp endothelium within the MZ expresses the highest levels of Dll1 (185). Parallel analyses of Jagged1 and Dll4 LacZ reporter mice revealed that these DSL Notch ligands are expressed in largely nonoverlapping vascular compartments of the spleen. Thus, only Dll1 is highly expressed within the MZ. Previous studies showed that fewer MZ B cells develop in mice heterozygous for *Notch2* or *Dll1*, so we analyzed MZ B cell production in bone marrow chimeras in which *Notch2*$^{+/-}$ progenitors developed in *Dll1*$^{+/LacZ}$ hosts and vice versa. Our study revealed that Notch2 activation in MZ precursors requires interaction with Dll1 on radio-resistant stromal cells to drive MZ B cell production in the spleen. An independent study reached a similar conclusion (186). Mature MZ B cells can be depleted by treating mice with anti-Dll1 antibody, suggesting that Dll1-Notch2 interactions may also be important in homeostatic maintenance of the MZ B cell pool (187).

Studies of mice conditionally deficient in *mindbomb*, an E3 ubiquitin ligase that critically regulates endocytosis of DSL ligands, demonstrate that endocytosis of Dll1 and Dll4 is needed for them to induce Notch-dependent MZ B cell and T cell development in the spleen and thymus, respectively (188). The pulling force generated as Dll ligands are endocytosed into the signal-sending cell may be important for conformationally disrupting the NRR to allow proteolytic activation of Notch1 and Notch2. Alternatively, prior to receptor engagement, Dll ligands may need to transit through the recycling endosome pathway to render them capable of high-affinity binding to Notch receptors.

Interestingly, the ability of different innate stimuli to selectively induce Dll versus Jagged Notch ligands on DCs may influence Th1 versus Th2 differentiation (61, 189–191). Further experiments using Dll fusion proteins or artificial antigen-presenting cells engineered to express Dll or Jagged ligands suggest that Dll1 or Dll4 instructs Th1 differentiation (61, 62, 190), whereas Jagged1 (61) or Jagged2 (190) instructs Th2 differentiation in response to antigen in vitro. Another group showed that *Jagged2*$^{-/-}$ DCs cannot polarize Th2 differentiation in vitro, but they can direct normal Th2 responses in vivo (191), once again revealing dichotomous conclusions from in vitro and in vivo experimental approaches. This group suggests that Dll ligands promote Th1 differentiation by inhibiting IL-4 signal transduction, rather than by inducing Tbet or other Th1-promoting transcription factors (164).

THE IMPORTANCE OF O-GLYCANS IN NOTCH-DEPENDENT ASPECTS OF HEMATOPOIESIS

As described throughout this review, cells of the immune system often show differential responsiveness to Dll versus Jagged DSL ligands. Fringe expression accounts for this bias in HSCs, at least in part, by altering the strength of Notch activation by Dll versus Jagged Notch ligands (J.S. Yuan, J.B. Tan, K. Xue, Y. Liu, P. Stanley, S.E. Egan, and C.J. Guidos, manuscript in preparation). Using Notch ligand Fc fusion proteins, OP9 stromal cell lines, and mice lacking Lfng, Mfng, and/or Rfng, we demonstrated that Dll and Jagged family members have intrinsically different Fringe-independent affinities for Notch receptors. HSCs lacking all Fringe modifications bind Dll1 and Dll4, and OP9 stromal cells expressing either ligand can promote robust T cell development in vitro. Thus, Fringe modification of O-fucose is not required for Notch receptors to respond to Dll ligands during T cell development. Nonetheless, Fringes greatly enhance Notch receptor binding and strength of Notch signaling by Dll1 and Dll4. In contrast, deletion of Lfng and Mfng from HSCs is required for them to generate T cell progenitors in response to OP9-Jagged1. Thus, Lfng and Mfng cooperate to suppress Jagged1-Notch-induced T cell development (J.S. Yuan, J.B. Tan, K. Xue, Y. Liu, P. Stanley, S.E. Egan, and C.J. Guidos, manuscript in preparation). Our data suggest that by modulating the strength of Notch receptor-ligand interactions, Fringe proteins play key roles in determining whether strong or weak Notch signals are transduced and, ultimately, which cell fates are chosen.

Lfng is also highly expressed in DN and SP thymocytes but is dramatically downregulated in DP thymocytes (45). Lfng strengthens Notch binding and activation by Dll1 or Dll4 to augment Dll-dependent Notch1 activation in thymus-seeding progenitors, enhancing their ability to compete for limiting thymic niches (45, 49). Lfng continues to be highly expressed from the ETP to DN4 stages, but it is precipitously downregulated upon transition to the DP stage. This decline is accompanied by reduced binding capacity for Dll1 and Dll4 (10, 45, 182), but DP thymocyte binding of both ligands is greatly enhanced by transgenic misexpression of Lfng using the *Lck*-proximal promoter. Indeed, Lfng misexpression allows DP thymocytes to block Dll4-induced Notch1 signaling in thymus-seeding progenitors, diverting them from the T cell fate toward the B cell fate (45, 49). Thus, Lfng downregulation ensures that Notch receptors expressed by the much more abundant DP population do not prevent thymus-seeding progenitors from interacting with Dll4 in the thymus. Using genetic approaches we have also demonstrated that Lfng critically enhances DN3b precursor competition for intrathymic Dll ligands (likely Dll4) to maximize Notch-induced clonal expansion during the earliest stage of β-selection in vivo (I. Visan, J.S. Yuan, Y. Liu, P. Stanley, C.J. Guidos, unpublished observations).

There are 21 consensus sites for O-fucose modification of Notch1 EGF repeats by Pofut1, generating many potential sites for Fringe modification (31). In mice, Pofut1 is not required for surface expression of Notch, but O-fucose modification is required for Notch to signal optimally, and this is likely Fringe independent (192). One of the most conserved O-fucose sites in all Notch receptors is EGF repeat 12 (31), which lies within the ligand-binding domain, defined in *Drosophila* Notch as consisting of EGF repeats 11 and 12. Mutation of this site to Ala precludes O-fucose addition and removes the substrate for Lfng in the Notch1 ligand–binding domain. Cells overexpressing this mutant Notch1^{12f} receptor cannot undergo ligand-dependent Notch activation in coculture assays (192), but analyses of mice knocked in for this *Notch1*^{12f} mutation reveal that it is a hypomorphic allele because *Notch1*$^{-/-}$ mice die in utero, but *Notch1*$^{12f/12f}$ mice are viable and fertile (154). Interestingly, signaling through this mutant Notch1 receptor is strong enough to suppress intrathymic B cell development but not to promote normal T cell development. These findings demonstrate that O-fucosylation of EGF12 is important for Notch1 activation in vivo.

Notch2 interacts with Dll1 weakly (182), but there have been conflicting reports on the ability of Fringes to enhance Dll1-dependent Notch2 activation in vitro (reviewed in 31). Lfng and Mfng are expressed in newly formed B cells and MZ B cell precursors in the spleen, and we showed that Lfng and Mfng cooperatively enhance Dll1-Notch2 interaction to promote MZ B cell development (176). Thus, this study defines a biological function for Mfng in vivo and suggests that red pulp vasculature provides a microenvironmental niche in which MZ B cell precursors compete for limiting Dll1, homeostatically regulating the size of the MZ B cell pool.

As described above, different kinds of innate stimuli appear to differentially induce Dll versus Jagged ligands, and there are data suggesting that these families have different capacities to induce Th1 versus Th2 differentiation. The differential responsiveness of CD4 T cells to Dll versus Jagged ligands may be due to Notch receptor glycosylation by Fringe proteins, although this remains to be demonstrated. CD4 T cells express Lfng (45), which should make them preferentially responsive to activation by Dll ligands. Indeed, a recent study demonstrated that Dll1 but not Jagged1 could induce biochemically detectable levels of activated Notch (N^{IC}) in CD4 T cells (156). Thus, the preferential ability of Dll ligands to promote the Th1 fate (at least in some contexts) may reflect a requirement for stronger Notch activation in Th1 relative to Th2 differentiation. Manipulating Lfng expression in CD4 T cells should provide insight into this issue.

CONCLUDING REMARKS

Notch signaling clearly plays many fundamental roles in the development and function of the immune system. Our understanding of these roles is well developed in some cases, but many questions remain about the important targets of Notch signaling and how Notch signals are integrated with other critical signaling pathways. In other immune system contexts, more experiments are needed to clarify the importance and functions of Notch signaling. Genetic approaches that allow disruption of Notch signaling in discrete cell types will be particularly important for this purpose. Although in vitro assays have been and will continue to be highly valuable, their capacity to accurately recapitulate normal physiological processes must be always evaluated. Finally, altering Notch modification by O-glycans in specific cell types will enhance our understanding of how changes in the strength and specificity of Notch signaling affect Notch-dependent immunological processes.

DISCLOSURE STATEMENT

The authors are not aware of any affiliations, memberships, funding, or financial holdings that might be perceived as affecting the objectivity of this review.

ACKNOWLEDGMENTS

This work was supported by the Canadian Institutes of Health Research with a postdoctoral fellowship award to I.V. and operating grants to C.J.G. (FRN 81300 and 11530), as well as studentship awards from the Hospital for Sick Children RESTRACOMP to S.S. and J.S.Y.

LITERATURE CITED

1. Fortini ME. 2009. Notch signaling: the core pathway and its posttranslational regulation. *Dev. Cell* 16:633–47
2. Kopan R, Ilagan MX. 2009. The canonical Notch signaling pathway: unfolding the activation mechanism. *Cell* 137:216–33
3. Gordon WR, Arnett KL, Blacklow SC. 2008. The molecular logic of Notch signaling—a structural and biochemical perspective. *J. Cell Sci.* 121:3109–19
4. D'Souza B, Miyamoto A, Weinmaster G. 2008. The many facets of Notch ligands. *Oncogene* 27:5148–67

5. Cordle J, Johnson S, Tay JZ, Roversi P, Wilkin MB, et al. 2008. A conserved face of the Jagged/Serrate DSL domain is involved in Notch trans-activation and *cis*-inhibition. *Nat. Struct. Mol. Biol.* 15:849–57
6. Cordle J, Redfieldz C, Stacey M, Van Der Merwe PA, Willis AC, et al. 2008. Localization of the Delta-like-1-binding site in human Notch-1 and its modulation by calcium affinity. *J. Biol. Chem.* 283:11785–93
7. Shimizu K, Chiba S, Kumano K, Hosoya N, Takahashi T, et al. 1999. Mouse Jagged1 physically interacts with Notch2 and other Notch receptors. Assessment by quantitative methods. *J. Biol. Chem.* 274:32961–69
8. Tien AC, Rajan A, Bellen HJ. 2009. A Notch updated. *J. Cell Biol.* 184:621–29
9. Ladi E, Nichols JT, Ge W, Miyamoto A, Yao C, et al. 2005. The divergent DSL ligand Dll3 does not activate Notch signaling but cell autonomously attenuates signaling induced by other DSL ligands. *J. Cell Biol.* 170:983–92
10. Heinzel K, Benz C, Martins VC, Haidl ID, Bleul CC. 2007. Bone marrow-derived hemopoietic precursors commit to the T cell lineage only after arrival in the thymic microenvironment. *J. Immunol.* 178:858–68
11. Geffers I, Serth K, Chapman G, Jaekel R, Schuster-Gossler K, et al. 2007. Divergent functions and distinct localization of the Notch ligands DLL1 and DLL3 in vivo. *J. Cell Biol.* 178:465–76
12. Schmidt MH, Bicker F, Nikolic I, Meister J, Babuke T, et al. 2009. Epidermal growth factor-like domain 7 (EGFL7) modulates Notch signaling and affects neural stem cell renewal. *Nat. Cell Biol.* 11:873–80
13. Komatsu H, Chao MY, Larkins-Ford J, Corkins ME, Somers GA, et al. 2008. OSM-11 facilitates LIN-12 Notch signaling during *Caenorhabditis elegans* vulval development. *PLoS Biol.* 6:e196
14. Bray SJ, Takada S, Harrison E, Shen SC, Ferguson-Smith AC. 2008. The atypical mammalian ligand Delta-like homologue 1 (Dlk1) can regulate Notch signaling in *Drosophila*. *BMC Dev. Biol.* 8:11
15. Raghunandan R, Ruiz-Hidalgo M, Jia Y, Ettinger R, Rudikoff E, et al. 2008. Dlk1 influences differentiation and function of B lymphocytes. *Stem Cells Dev.* 17:495–507
16. Gordon WR, Vardar-Ulu D, Histen G, Sanchez-Irizarry C, Aster JC, Blacklow SC. 2007. Structural basis for autoinhibition of Notch. *Nat. Struct. Mol. Biol.* 14:295–300
17. Kageyama R, Ohtsuka T, Kobayashi T. 2007. The Hes gene family: repressors and oscillators that orchestrate embryogenesis. *Development* 134:1243–51
18. Nam Y, Sliz P, Song L, Aster JC, Blacklow SC. 2006. Structural basis for cooperativity in recruitment of MAML coactivators to Notch transcription complexes. *Cell* 124:973–83
19. Wilson JJ, Kovall RA. 2006. Crystal structure of the CSL-Notch-Mastermind ternary complex bound to DNA. *Cell* 124:985–96
20. Nam Y, Sliz P, Pear WS, Aster JC, Blacklow SC. 2007. Cooperative assembly of higher-order Notch complexes functions as a switch to induce transcription. *Proc. Natl. Acad. Sci. USA* 104:2103–8
21. Chiang MY, Xu ML, Histen G, Shestova O, Roy M, et al. 2006. Identification of a conserved negative regulatory sequence that influences the leukemogenic activity of NOTCH1. *Mol. Cell. Biol.* 26:6261–71
22. Welcker M, Clurman BE. 2008. FBW7 ubiquitin ligase: a tumor suppressor at the crossroads of cell division, growth and differentiation. *Nat. Rev. Cancer* 8:83–93
23. Pear WS, Aster JC, Scott ML, Hasserjian RP, Soffer B, et al. 1996. Exclusive development of T cell neoplasms in mice transplanted with bone marrow expressing activated Notch alleles. *J. Exp. Med.* 183:2283–91
24. Weng AP, Ferrando AA, Lee W, Morris JP IV, Silverman LB, et al. 2004. Activating mutations of NOTCH1 in human T cell acute lymphoblastic leukemia. *Science* 306:269–71
25. Lin YW, Nichols RA, Letterio JJ, Aplan PD. 2006. Notch1 mutations are important for leukemic transformation in murine models of precursor-T leukemia/lymphoma. *Blood* 107:2540–43
26. O'Neil J, Calvo J, McKenna K, Krishnamoorthy V, Aster JC, et al. 2006. Activating Notch1 mutations in mouse models of T-ALL. *Blood* 107:781–85
27. O'Neil J, Grim J, Strack P, Rao S, Tibbitts D, et al. 2007. FBW7 mutations in leukemic cells mediate NOTCH pathway activation and resistance to γ-secretase inhibitors. *J. Exp. Med.* 204:1813–24
28. Thompson BJ, Buonamici S, Sulis ML, Palomero T, Vilimas T, et al. 2007. The SCFFBW7 ubiquitin ligase complex as a tumor suppressor in T cell leukemia. *J. Exp. Med.* 204:1825–35
29. Acar M, Jafar-Nejad H, Takeuchi H, Rajan A, Ibrani D, et al. 2008. Rumi is a CAP10 domain glycosyltransferase that modifies Notch and is required for Notch signaling. *Cell* 132:247–58

30. Stanley P. 2007. Regulation of Notch signaling by glycosylation. *Curr. Opin. Struct. Biol.* 17:530–35
31. Stanley P, Guidos CJ. 2009. Regulation of Notch signaling during T- and B-cell development by O-fucose glycans. *Immunol. Rev.* 230:201–15
32. Kageyama R, Masamizu Y, Niwa Y. 2007. Oscillator mechanism of Notch pathway in the segmentation clock. *Dev. Dyn.* 236:1403–9
33. de Bellard ME, Barembaum M, Arman O, Bronner-Fraser M. 2007. Lunatic fringe causes expansion and increased neurogenesis of trunk neural tube and neural crest populations. *Neuron Glia Biol.* 3:93–103
34. Nikolaou N, Watanabe-Asaka T, Gerety S, Distel M, Koster RW, Wilkinson DG. 2009. Lunatic fringe promotes the lateral inhibition of neurogenesis. *Development* 136:2523–33
35. Moran JL, Shifley ET, Levorse JM, Mani S, Ostmann K, et al. 2009. Manic fringe is not required for embryonic development, and fringe family members do not exhibit redundant functions in the axial skeleton, limb, or hindbrain. *Dev. Dyn.* 238:1803–12
36. Svensson P, Bergqvist I, Norlin S, Edlund H. 2009. *MFng* is dispensable for mouse pancreas development and function. *Mol. Cell. Biol.* 29:2129–38
37. Maillard I, Fang T, Pear WS. 2005. Regulation of lymphoid development, differentiation, and function by the Notch pathway. *Annu. Rev. Immunol.* 23:945–74
38. Radtke F, Wilson A, Mancini SJ, MacDonald HR. 2004. Notch regulation of lymphocyte development and function. *Nat. Immunol.* 5:247–53
39. Tanigaki K, Honjo T. 2007. Regulation of lymphocyte development by Notch signaling. *Nat. Immunol.* 8:451–56
40. Washburn T, Schweighoffer E, Gridley T, Chang D, Fowlkes BJ, et al. 1997. Notch activity influences the αβ versus γδ T cell lineage decision. *Cell* 88:833–43
41. Tan JB, Visan I, Yuan JS, Guidos CJ. 2005. Requirement for Notch1 signals at sequential early stages of intrathymic T cell development. *Nat. Immunol.* 6:671–79
42. Harper JA, Yuan JS, Tan JB, Visan I, Guidos CJ. 2003. Notch signaling in development and disease. *Clin. Genet.* 64:461–72
43. Krebs LT, Shutter JR, Tanigaki K, Honjo T, Stark KL, Gridley T. 2004. Haploinsufficient lethality and formation of arteriovenous malformations in Notch pathway mutants. *Genes Dev.* 18:2469–73
44. Gale NW, Dominguez MG, Noguera I, Pan L, Hughes V, et al. 2004. Haploinsufficiency of Delta-like 4 ligand results in embryonic lethality due to major defects in arterial and vascular development. *Proc. Natl. Acad. Sci. USA* 101:15949–54
45. Visan I, Tan JB, Yuan JS, Harper JA, Koch U, Guidos CJ. 2006. Regulation of T lymphopoiesis by Notch1 and Lunatic fringe-mediated competition for intrathymic niches. *Nat. Immunol.* 7:634–43
46. Saito T, Chiba S, Ichikawa M, Kunisato A, Asai T, et al. 2003. Notch2 is preferentially expressed in mature B cells and indispensable for marginal zone B lineage development. *Immunity* 18:675–85
47. Hozumi K, Negishi N, Suzuki D, Abe N, Sotomaru Y, et al. 2004. Delta-like 1 is necessary for the generation of marginal zone B cells but not T cells in vivo. *Nat. Immunol.* 5:638–44
48. Demehri S, Turkoz A, Kopan R. 2009. Epidermal Notch1 loss promotes skin tumorigenesis by impacting the stromal microenvironment. *Cancer Cell* 16:55–66
49. Koch U, Lacombe TA, Holland D, Bowman JL, Cohen BL, et al. 2001. Subversion of the T/B lineage decision in the thymus by Lunatic Fringe-mediated inhibition of Notch-1. *Immunity* 15:225–36
50. Izon DJ, Aster JC, He Y, Weng A, Karnell FG, et al. 2002. Deltex1 redirects lymphoid progenitors to the B cell lineage by antagonizing Notch1. *Immunity* 16:231–43
51. French MB, Koch U, Shaye RE, McGill MA, Dho SE, et al. 2002. Transgenic expression of numb inhibits Notch signaling in immature thymocytes but does not alter T cell fate specification. *J. Immunol.* 168:3173–80
52. Yun TJ, Bevan MJ. 2003. Notch-regulated ankyrin-repeat protein inhibits Notch1 signaling: multiple Notch1 signaling pathways involved in T cell development. *J. Immunol.* 170:5834–41
53. Maillard I, Weng AP, Carpenter AC, Rodriguez CG, Sai H, et al. 2004. Mastermind critically regulates Notch-mediated lymphoid cell fate decisions. *Blood* 104:1696–702
54. Maillard I, Tu L, Sambandam A, Yashiro-Ohtani Y, Millholland J, et al. 2006. The requirement for Notch signaling at the β selection checkpoint in vivo is absolute and independent of the pre-T cell receptor. *J. Exp. Med.* 203:2239–45

55. Maillard I, Schwarz BA, Sambandam A, Fang T, Shestova O, et al. 2006. Notch-dependent T-lineage commitment occurs at extrathymic sites following bone marrow transplantation. *Blood* 107:3511–19
56. Barolo S, Walker RG, Polyanovsky AD, Freschi G, Keil T, Posakony JW. 2000. A Notch-independent activity of suppressor of hairless is required for normal mechanoreceptor physiology. *Cell* 103:957–69
57. McElhinny AS, Li JL, Wu L. 2008. Mastermind-like transcriptional coactivators: emerging roles in regulating cross talk among multiple signaling pathways. *Oncogene* 27:5138–47
58. Shen H, McElhinny AS, Cao Y, Gao P, Liu J, et al. 2006. The Notch coactivator, MAML1, functions as a novel coactivator for MEF2C-mediated transcription and is required for normal myogenesis. *Genes Dev.* 20:675–88
59. Jaleco AC, Neves H, Hooijberg E, Gameiro P, Clode N, et al. 2001. Differential effects of Notch ligands Delta-1 and Jagged-1 in human lymphoid differentiation. *J. Exp. Med.* 194:991–1002
60. Schmitt TM, Zúñiga-Pflücker JC. 2002. Induction of T cell development from hematopoietic progenitor cells by Delta-like-1 in vitro. *Immunity* 17:749–56
61. Amsen D, Blander JM, Lee GR, Tanigaki K, Honjo T, Flavell RA. 2004. Instruction of distinct CD4 T helper cell fates by different Notch ligands on antigen-presenting cells. *Cell* 117:515–26
62. Maekawa Y, Tsukumo S, Chiba S, Hirai H, Hayashi Y, et al. 2003. Delta1-Notch3 interactions bias the functional differentiation of activated $CD4^+$ T cells. *Immunity* 19:549–59
63. Eagar TN, Tang Q, Wolfe M, He Y, Pear WS, Bluestone JA. 2004. Notch 1 signaling regulates peripheral T cell activation. *Immunity* 20:407–15
64. Schmitt N, Chene L, Boutolleau D, Nugeyre MT, Guillemard E, et al. 2003. Positive regulation of CXCR4 expression and signaling by interleukin-7 in $CD4^+$ mature thymocytes correlates with their capacity to favor human immunodeficiency X4 virus replication. *J. Virol.* 77:5784–93
65. Ciofani M, Zúñiga-Pflücker JC. 2005. Notch promotes survival of pre-T cells at the β-selection checkpoint by regulating cellular metabolism. *Nat. Immunol.* 6:881–88
66. Ciofani M, Knowles GC, Wiest DL, von Boehmer H, Zúñiga-Pflücker JC. 2006. Stage-specific and differential Notch dependency at the αβ and γδ T lineage bifurcation. *Immunity* 25:105–16
67. Hadland BK, Manley NR, Su D, Longmore GD, Moore CL, et al. 2001. γ-secretase inhibitors repress thymocyte development. *Proc. Natl. Acad. Sci. USA* 98:7487–91
68. Hass MR, Sato C, Kopan R, Zhao G. 2009. Presenilin: RIP and beyond. *Semin. Cell Dev. Biol.* 20:201–10
69. Kumano K, Chiba S, Kunisato A, Sata M, Saito T, et al. 2003. Notch1 but not Notch2 is essential for generating hematopoietic stem cells from endothelial cells. *Immunity* 18:699–711
70. Robert-Moreno A, Espinosa L, de la Pompa JL, Bigas A. 2005. RBPjκ-dependent Notch function regulates Gata2 and is essential for the formation of intraembryonic hematopoietic cells. *Development* 132:1117–26
71. Lebestky T, Jung SH, Banerjee U. 2003. A Serrate-expressing signaling center controls *Drosophila* hematopoiesis. *Genes Dev.* 17:348–53
72. Burns CE, Traver D, Mayhall E, Shepard JL, Zon LI. 2005. Hematopoietic stem cell fate is established by the Notch-Runx pathway. *Genes Dev.* 19:2331–42
73. Ichikawa M, Asai T, Saito T, Seo S, Yamazaki I, et al. 2004. AML-1 is required for megakaryocytic maturation and lymphocytic differentiation, but not for maintenance of hematopoietic stem cells in adult hematopoiesis. *Nat. Med.* 10:299–304
74. Mikkola HK, Klintman J, Yang H, Hock H, Schlaeger TM, et al. 2003. Haematopoietic stem cells retain long-term repopulating activity and multipotency in the absence of stem-cell leukaemia *SCL/tal-1* gene. *Nature* 421:547–51
75. Karanu FN, Murdoch B, Miyabayashi T, Ohno M, Koremoto M, et al. 2001. Human homologues of Delta-1 and Delta-4 function as mitogenic regulators of primitive human hematopoietic cells. *Blood* 97:1960–67
76. Suzuki T, Yokoyama Y, Kumano K, Takanashi M, Kozuma S, et al. 2006. Highly efficient ex vivo expansion of human hematopoietic stem cells using Delta1-Fc chimeric protein. *Stem Cells* 24:2456–65
77. Varnum-Finney B, Purton LE, Yu M, Brashem-Stein C, Flowers D, et al. 1998. The Notch ligand, Jagged-1, influences the development of primitive hematopoietic precursor cells. *Blood* 91:4084–91
78. Karanu FN, Murdoch B, Gallacher L, Wu DM, Koremoto M, et al. 2000. The Notch ligand jagged-1 represents a novel growth factor of human hematopoietic stem cells. *J. Exp. Med.* 192:1365–72

79. Varnum-Finney B, Xu L, Brashem-Stein C, Nourigat C, Flowers D, et al. 2000. Pluripotent, cytokine-dependent, hematopoietic stem cells are immortalized by constitutive Notch1 signaling. *Nat. Med.* 6:1278–81
80. Stier S, Cheng T, Dombkowski D, Carlesso N, Scadden DT. 2002. Notch1 activation increases hematopoietic stem cell self-renewal in vivo and favors lymphoid over myeloid lineage outcome. *Blood* 99:2369–78
81. Varnum-Finney B, Brashem-Stein C, Bernstein ID. 2003. Combined effects of Notch signaling and cytokines induce a multiple log increase in precursors with lymphoid and myeloid reconstituting ability. *Blood* 101:1784–89
82. Kunisato A, Chiba S, Nakagami-Yamaguchi E, Kumano K, Saito T, et al. 2003. HES-1 preserves purified hematopoietic stem cells ex vivo and accumulates side population cells in vivo. *Blood* 101:1777–83
83. Shojaei F, Trowbridge J, Gallacher L, Yuefei L, Goodale D, et al. 2005. Hierarchical and ontogenic positions serve to define the molecular basis of human hematopoietic stem cell behavior. *Dev. Cell* 8:651–63
84. Calvi LM, Adams GB, Weibrecht KW, Weber JM, Olson DP, et al. 2003. Osteoblastic cells regulate the haematopoietic stem cell niche. *Nature* 425:841–46
85. Mancini SJ, Mantei N, Dumortier A, Suter U, MacDonald HR, Radtke F. 2005. Jagged1-dependent Notch signaling is dispensable for hematopoietic stem cell self-renewal and differentiation. *Blood* 105:2340–42
86. Han H, Tanigaki K, Yamamoto N, Kuroda K, Yoshimoto M, et al. 2002. Inducible gene knockout of transcription factor recombination signal binding protein-J reveals its essential role in T versus B lineage decision. *Int. Immunol.* 14:637–45
87. Maillard I, Koch U, Dumortier A, Shestova O, Xu L, et al. 2008. Canonical Notch signaling is dispensable for the maintenance of adult hematopoietic stem cells. *Cell Stem Cell* 2:356–66
88. Duncan AW, Rattis FM, DiMascio LN, Congdon KL, Pazianos G, et al. 2005. Integration of Notch and Wnt signaling in hematopoietic stem cell maintenance. *Nat. Immunol.* 6:314–22
89. Schmidt-Supprian M, Rajewsky K. 2007. Vagaries of conditional gene targeting. *Nat. Immunol.* 8:665–68
90. Kiel MJ, Yilmaz OH, Iwashita T, Terhorst C, Morrison SJ. 2005. SLAM family receptors distinguish hematopoietic stem and progenitor cells and reveal endothelial niches for stem cells. *Cell* 121:1109–21
91. Papathanasiou P, Attema JL, Karsunky H, Xu J, Smale ST, Weissman IL. 2009. Evaluation of the long-term reconstituting subset of hematopoietic stem cells with CD150. *Stem Cells* 27:2498–508
92. Mercher T, Cornejo MG, Sears C, Kindler T, Moore SA, et al. 2008. Notch signaling specifies megakaryocyte development from hematopoietic stem cells. *Cell Stem Cell* 3:314–26
93. Mercher T, Raffel GD, Moore SA, Cornejo MG, Baudry-Bluteau D, et al. 2009. The OTT-MAL fusion oncogene activates RBPJ-mediated transcription and induces acute megakaryoblastic leukemia in a knockin mouse model. *J. Clin. Investig.* 119:852–64
94. Yoshida T, Ng SY, Zúñiga-Pflücker JC, Georgopoulos K. 2006. Early hematopoietic lineage restrictions directed by Ikaros. *Nat. Immunol.* 7:382–91
95. Arinobu Y, Mizuno S, Chong Y, Shigematsu H, Iino T, et al. 2007. Reciprocal activation of GATA-1 and PU.1 marks initial specification of hematopoietic stem cells into myeloerythroid and myelolymphoid lineages. *Cell Stem Cell* 1:416–27
96. Dias S, Mansson R, Gurbuxani S, Sigvardsson M, Kee BL. 2008. E2A proteins promote development of lymphoid-primed multipotent progenitors. *Immunity* 29:217–27
97. Stehling-Sun S, Dade J, Nutt SL, DeKoter RP, Camargo FD. 2009. Regulation of lymphoid versus myeloid fate 'choice' by the transcription factor Mef2c. *Nat. Immunol.* 10:289–96
98. Ikawa T, Kawamoto H, Goldrath AW, Murre C. 2006. E proteins and Notch signaling cooperate to promote T cell lineage specification and commitment. *J. Exp. Med.* 203:1329–42
99. Ng SY, Yoshida T, Zhang J, Georgopoulos K. 2009. Genome-wide lineage-specific transcriptional networks underscore Ikaros-dependent lymphoid priming in hematopoietic stem cells. *Immunity* 30:493–507
100. Benz C, Bleul CC. 2005. A multipotent precursor in the thymus maps to the branching point of the T versus B lineage decision. *J. Exp. Med.* 202:21–31
101. Schwarz BA, Sambandam A, Maillard I, Harman BC, Love PE, Bhandoola A. 2007. Selective thymus settling regulated by cytokine and chemokine receptors. *J. Immunol.* 178:2008–17

102. Singh N, Phillips RA, Iscove NN, Egan SE. 2000. Expression of Notch receptors, Notch ligands, and fringe genes in hematopoiesis. *Exp. Hematol.* 28:527–34
103. Maeda T, Merghoub T, Hobbs RM, Dong L, Maeda M, et al. 2007. Regulation of B versus T lymphoid lineage fate decision by the proto-oncogene LRF. *Science* 316:860–66
104. Yan XQ, Sarmiento U, Sun Y, Huang G, Guo J, et al. 2001. A novel Notch ligand, Dll4, induces T-cell leukemia/lymphoma when overexpressed in mice by retroviral-mediated gene transfer. *Blood* 98:3793–99
105. Dorsch M, Zheng G, Yowe D, Rao P, Wang Y, et al. 2002. Ectopic expression of Delta4 impairs hematopoietic development and leads to lymphoproliferative disease. *Blood* 100:2046–55
106. Wilson A, MacDonald HR, Radtke F. 2001. Notch 1-deficient common lymphoid precursors adopt a B cell fate in the thymus. *J. Exp. Med.* 194:1003–12
107. Visan I, Yuan JS, Tan JB, Cretegny K, Guidos CJ. 2006. Regulation of intrathymic T-cell development by Lunatic Fringe-Notch1 interactions. *Immunol. Rev.* 209:76–94
108. Pui JC, Allman D, Xu L, DeRocco S, Karnell FG, et al. 1999. Notch1 expression in early lymphopoiesis influences B versus T lineage determination. *Immunity* 11:299–308
109. Kawamata S, Du C, Li K, Lavau C. 2002. Overexpression of the Notch target genes Hes in vivo induces lymphoid and myeloid alterations. *Oncogene* 21:3855–63
110. de Pooter RF, Schmitt TM, de la Pompa JL, Fujiwara Y, Orkin SH, Zúñiga-Pflücker JC. 2006. Notch signaling requires GATA-2 to inhibit myelopoiesis from embryonic stem cells and primary hemopoietic progenitors. *J. Immunol.* 176:5267–75
111. Zhou L, Li LW, Yan Q, Petryniak B, Man Y, et al. 2008. Notch-dependent control of myelopoiesis is regulated by fucosylation. *Blood* 112:308–19
112. Ohishi K, Varnum-Finney B, Serda RE, Anasetti C, Bernstein ID. 2001. The Notch ligand, Delta-1, inhibits the differentiation of monocytes into macrophages but permits their differentiation into dendritic cells. *Blood* 98:1402–7
113. Cheng P, Nefedova Y, Corzo CA, Gabrilovich DI. 2007. Regulation of dendritic-cell differentiation by bone marrow stroma via different Notch ligands. *Blood* 109:507–15
114. Zhou J, Cheng P, Youn JI, Cotter MJ, Gabrilovich DI. 2009. Notch and wingless signaling cooperate in regulation of dendritic cell differentiation. *Immunity* 30:845–59
115. Cheng P, Nefedova Y, Miele L, Osborne BA, Gabrilovich D. 2003. Notch signaling is necessary but not sufficient for differentiation of dendritic cells. *Blood* 102:3980–88
116. Dontje W, Schotte R, Cupedo T, Nagasawa M, Scheeren F, et al. 2006. Delta-like1-induced Notch1 signaling regulates the human plasmacytoid dendritic cell versus T-cell lineage decision through control of GATA-3 and Spi-B. *Blood* 107:2446–52
117. Olivier A, Lauret E, Gonin P, Galy A. 2006. The Notch ligand Delta-1 is a hematopoietic development cofactor for plasmacytoid dendritic cells. *Blood* 107:2694–701
118. Radtke F, Ferrero I, Wilson A, Lees R, Aguet M, MacDonald HR. 2000. Notch1 deficiency dissociates the intrathymic development of dendritic cells and T cells. *J. Exp. Med.* 191:1085–94
119. Caton ML, Smith-Raska MR, Reizis B. 2007. Notch-RBP-J signaling controls the homeostasis of $CD8^-$ dendritic cells in the spleen. *J. Exp. Med.* 204:1653–64
120. Shortman K, Naik SH. 2007. Steady-state and inflammatory dendritic-cell development. *Nat. Rev. Immunol.* 7:19–30
121. Sambandam A, Maillard I, Zediak VP, Xu L, Gerstein RM, et al. 2005. Notch signaling controls the generation and differentiation of early T lineage progenitors. *Nat. Immunol.* 6:663–70
122. Bell JJ, Bhandoola A. 2008. The earliest thymic progenitors for T cells possess myeloid lineage potential. *Nature* 452:764–67
123. Wada H, Masuda K, Satoh R, Kakugawa K, Ikawa T, et al. 2008. Adult T-cell progenitors retain myeloid potential. *Nature* 452:768–72
124. Feyerabend TB, Terszowski G, Tietz A, Blum C, Luche H, et al. 2009. Deletion of Notch1 converts pro-T cells to dendritic cells and promotes thymic B cells by cell-extrinsic and cell-intrinsic mechanisms. *Immunity* 30:67–79
125. Hu X, Chung AY, Wu I, Foldi J, Chen J, et al. 2008. Integrated regulation of Toll-like receptor responses by Notch and interferon-γ pathways. *Immunity* 29:691–703

126. Kitamoto T, Takahashi K, Takimoto H, Tomizuka K, Hayasaka M, et al. 2005. Functional redundancy of the Notch gene family during mouse embryogenesis: analysis of Notch gene expression in Notch3-deficient mice. *Biochem. Biophys. Res. Commun.* 331:1154–62
127. Bellavia D, Campese AF, Alesse E, Vacca A, Felli MP, et al. 2000. Constitutive activation of NF-κB and T-cell leukemia/lymphoma in Notch3 transgenic mice. *EMBO J.* 19:3337–48
128. Witt CM, Hurez V, Swindle CS, Hamada Y, Klug CA. 2003. Activated Notch2 potentiates CD8 lineage maturation and promotes the selective development of B1 B cells. *Mol. Cell. Biol.* 23:8637–50
129. Vercauteren SM, Sutherland HJ. 2004. Constitutively active Notch4 promotes early human hematopoietic progenitor cell maintenance while inhibiting differentiation and causes lymphoid abnormalities in vivo. *Blood* 104:2315–22
130. Krebs LT, Xue Y, Norton CR, Shutter JR, Maguire M, et al. 2000. Notch signaling is essential for vascular morphogenesis in mice. *Genes Dev.* 14:1343–52
131. Radtke F, Wilson A, Stark G, Bauer M, van Meerwijk J, et al. 1999. Deficient T cell fate specification in mice with an induced inactivation of Notch1. *Immunity* 10:547–58
132. Jenkinson EJ, Jenkinson WE, Rossi SW, Anderson G. 2006. The thymus and T-cell commitment: the right niche for Notch? *Nat. Rev. Immunol.* 6:551–55
133. Hozumi K, Mailhos C, Negishi N, Hirano K, Yahata T, et al. 2008. Delta-like 4 is indispensable in thymic environment specific for T cell development. *J. Exp. Med.* 205:2507–13
134. Koch U, Fiorini E, Benedito R, Besseyrias V, Schuster-Gossler K, et al. 2008. Delta-like 4 is the essential, nonredundant ligand for Notch1 during thymic T cell lineage commitment. *J. Exp. Med.* 205:2515–23
135. Schmitt TM, Ciofani M, Petrie HT, Zúñiga-Pflücker JC. 2004. Maintenance of T cell specification and differentiation requires recurrent Notch receptor-ligand interactions. *J. Exp. Med.* 200:469–79
136. De Smedt M, Hoebeke I, Reynvoet K, Leclercq G, Plum J. 2005. Different thresholds of Notch signaling bias human precursor cells toward B-, NK-, monocytic/dendritic-, or T-cell lineage in thymus microenvironment. *Blood* 106:3498–506
137. Franco CB, Scripture-Adams DD, Proekt I, Taghon T, Weiss AH, et al. 2006. Notch/Delta signaling constrains reengineering of pro-T cells by PU.1. *Proc. Natl. Acad. Sci. USA* 103:11993–98
138. Laiosa CV, Stadtfeld M, Xie H, de Andres-Aguayo L, Graf T. 2006. Reprogramming of committed T cell progenitors to macrophages and dendritic cells by C/EBPα and PU.1 transcription factors. *Immunity* 25:731–44
139. Taghon T, Yui MA, Rothenberg EV. 2007. Mast cell lineage diversion of T lineage precursors by the essential T cell transcription factor GATA-3. *Nat. Immunol.* 8:845–55
140. Ong CT, Cheng HT, Chang LW, Ohtsuka T, Kageyama R, et al. 2006. Target selectivity of vertebrate Notch proteins. Collaboration between discrete domains and CSL-binding site architecture determines activation probability. *J. Biol. Chem.* 281:5106–19
141. Hoebeke I, De Smedt M, Van de Walle I, Reynvoet K, De Smet G, et al. 2006. Overexpression of HES-1 is not sufficient to impose T-cell differentiation on human hematopoietic stem cells. *Blood* 107:2879–81
142. Varnum-Finney B, Dallas MH, Kato K, Bernstein ID. 2008. Notch target Hes5 ensures appropriate Notch induced T- versus B-cell choices in the thymus. *Blood* 111:2615–20
143. Yamasaki S, Ishikawa E, Sakuma M, Ogata K, Sakata-Sogawa K, et al. 2006. Mechanistic basis of pre-T cell receptor-mediated autonomous signaling critical for thymocyte development. *Nat. Immunol.* 7:67–75
144. Tanigaki K, Tsuji M, Yamamoto N, Han H, Tsukada J, et al. 2004. Regulation of αβ/γδ T cell lineage commitment and peripheral T cell responses by Notch/RBP-J signaling. *Immunity* 20:611–22
145. Gonzalez-Garcia S, Garcia-Peydro M, Martin-Gayo E, Ballestar E, Esteller M, et al. 2009. CSL-MAML-dependent Notch1 signaling controls T lineage-specific IL-7Rα gene expression in early human thymopoiesis and leukemia. *J. Exp. Med.* 206:779–91
146. Taghon T, Yui MA, Pant R, Diamond RA, Rothenberg EV. 2006. Developmental and molecular characterization of emerging β- and γδ-selected pre-T cells in the adult mouse thymus. *Immunity* 24:53–64
147. Garbe AI, Krueger A, Gounari F, Zúñiga-Pflücker JC, von Boehmer H. 2006. Differential synergy of Notch and T cell receptor signaling determines αβ versus γδ lineage fate. *J. Exp. Med.* 203:1579–90
148. Taghon T, Van de Walle I, De Smet G, De Smedt M, Leclercq G, et al. 2009. Notch signaling is required for proliferation but not for differentiation at a well-defined β-selection checkpoint during human T-cell development. *Blood* 113:3254–63

149. Kelly AP, Finlay DK, Hinton HJ, Clarke RG, Fiorini E, et al. 2007. Notch-induced T cell development requires phosphoinositide-dependent kinase 1. *EMBO J.* 26:3441–50
150. Deftos ML, Huang E, Ojala EW, Forbush KA, Bevan MJ. 2000. Notch1 signaling promotes the maturation of CD4 and CD8 SP thymocytes. *Immunity* 13:73–84
151. Fowlkes BJ, Robey EA. 2002. A reassessment of the effect of activated Notch1 on CD4 and CD8 T cell development. *J. Immunol.* 169:1817–21
152. Yashiro-Ohtani Y, He Y, Ohtani T, Jones ME, Shestova O, et al. 2009. Pre-TCR signaling inactivates Notch1 transcription by antagonizing E2A. *Genes Dev.* 23:1665–76
153. Laky K, Fowlkes BJ. 2008. Notch signaling in CD4 and CD8 T cell development. *Curr. Opin. Immunol.* 20:197–202
154. Ge C, Stanley P. 2008. The O-fucose glycan in the ligand-binding domain of Notch1 regulates embryogenesis and T cell development. *Proc. Natl. Acad. Sci. USA* 105:1539–44
155. Laky K, Fowlkes BJ. 2007. Presenilins regulate $\alpha\beta$ T cell development by modulating TCR signaling. *J. Exp. Med.* 204:2115–29
156. Ong CT, Sedy JR, Murphy KM, Kopan R. 2008. Notch and presenilin regulate cellular expansion and cytokine secretion but cannot instruct Th1/Th2 fate acquisition. *PLoS One* 3:e2823
157. Adler SH, Chiffoleau E, Xu L, Dalton NM, Burg JM, et al. 2003. Notch signaling augments T cell responsiveness by enhancing CD25 expression. *J. Immunol.* 171:2896–903
158. Palaga T, Miele L, Golde TE, Osborne BA. 2003. TCR-mediated Notch signaling regulates proliferation and IFN-γ production in peripheral T cells. *J. Immunol.* 171:3019–24
159. Cho OH, Shin HM, Miele L, Golde TE, Fauq A, et al. 2009. Notch regulates cytolytic effector function in $CD8^+$ T cells. *J. Immunol.* 182:3380–89
160. Maekawa Y, Minato Y, Ishifune C, Kurihara T, Kitamura A, et al. 2008. Notch2 integrates signaling by the transcription factors RBP-J and CREB1 to promote T cell cytotoxicity. *Nat. Immunol.* 9:1140–47
161. Kostianovsky AM, Maier LM, Baecher-Allan C, Anderson AC, Anderson DE. 2007. Up-regulation of gene related to anergy in lymphocytes is associated with Notch-mediated human T cell suppression. *J. Immunol.* 178:6158–63
162. Kijima M, Iwata A, Maekawa Y, Uehara H, Izumi K, et al. 2009. Jagged1 suppresses collagen-induced arthritis by indirectly providing a negative signal in $CD8^+$ T cells. *J. Immunol.* 182:3566–72
163. Minter LM, Turley DM, Das P, Shin HM, Joshi I, et al. 2005. Inhibitors of γ-secretase block in vivo and in vitro T helper type 1 polarization by preventing Notch upregulation of Tbx21. *Nat. Immunol.* 6:680–88
164. Sun J, Krawczyk CJ, Pearce EJ. 2008. Suppression of Th2 cell development by Notch ligands Delta1 and Delta4. *J. Immunol.* 180:1655–61
165. Tacchini-Cottier F, Allenbach C, Otten LA, Radtke F. 2004. Notch1 expression on T cells is not required for $CD4^+$ T helper differentiation. *Eur. J. Immunol.* 34:1588–96
166. Tu L, Fang TC, Artis D, Shestova O, Pross SE, et al. 2005. Notch signaling is an important regulator of type 2 immunity. *J. Exp. Med.* 202:1037–42
167. Amsen D, Antov A, Jankovic D, Sher A, Radtke F, et al. 2007. Direct regulation of Gata3 expression determines the T helper differentiation potential of Notch. *Immunity* 27:89–99
168. Fang TC, Yashiro-Ohtani Y, Del Bianco C, Knoblock DM, Blacklow SC, Pear WS. 2007. Notch directly regulates Gata3 expression during T helper 2 cell differentiation. *Immunity* 27:100–10
169. Tanaka S, Tsukada J, Suzuki W, Hayashi K, Tanigaki K, et al. 2006. The interleukin-4 enhancer CNS-2 is regulated by Notch signals and controls initial expression in NKT cells and memory-type CD4 T cells. *Immunity* 24:689–701
170. Amsen D, Antov A, Flavell RA. 2009. The different faces of Notch in T-helper-cell differentiation. *Nat. Rev. Immunol.* 9:116–24
171. Hoyne GF, Dallman MJ, Lamb JR. 2000. T-cell regulation of peripheral tolerance and immunity: the potential role for Notch signaling. *Immunology* 100:281–88
172. Asano N, Watanabe T, Kitani A, Fuss IJ, Strober W. 2008. Notch1 signaling and regulatory T cell function. *J. Immunol.* 180:2796–804

173. Ostroukhova M, Qi Z, Oriss TB, Dixon-McCarthy B, Ray P, Ray A. 2006. Treg-mediated immunosuppression involves activation of the Notch-HES1 axis by membrane-bound TGF-β. *J. Clin. Investig.* 116:996–1004
174. Pillai S, Cariappa A, Moran ST. 2005. Marginal zone B cells. *Annu. Rev. Immunol.* 23:161–96
175. Srivastava B, Quinn WJ 3rd, Hazard K, Erikson J, Allman D. 2005. Characterization of marginal zone B cell precursors. *J. Exp. Med.* 202:1225–34
176. Tan JB, Xu K, Cretegny K, Visan I, Yuan JS, et al. 2009. Lunatic and manic fringe cooperatively enhance marginal zone B cell precursor competition for Delta-like 1 in splenic endothelial niches. *Immunity* 30:254–63
177. Thomas M, Calamito M, Srivastava B, Maillard I, Pear WS, Allman D. 2007. Notch activity synergizes with B-cell-receptor and CD40 signaling to enhance B-cell activation. *Blood* 109:3342–50
178. Santos MA, Sarmento LM, Rebelo M, Doce AA, Maillard I, et al. 2007. Notch1 engagement by Delta-like-1 promotes differentiation of B lymphocytes to antibody-secreting cells. *Proc. Natl. Acad. Sci. USA* 104:15454–59
179. Tanigaki K, Han H, Yamamoto N, Tashiro K, Ikegawa M, et al. 2002. Notch-RBP-J signaling is involved in cell fate determination of marginal zone B cells. *Nat. Immunol.* 3:443–50
180. Schmitt TM, Zúñiga-Pflücker JC. 2006. T-cell development, doing it in a dish. *Immunol. Rev.* 209:95–102
181. Lehar SM, Dooley J, Farr AG, Bevan MJ. 2005. Notch ligands Delta1 and Jagged1 transmit distinct signals to T-cell precursors. *Blood* 105:1440–47
182. Besseyrias V, Fiorini E, Strobl LJ, Zimber-Strobl U, Dumortier A, et al. 2007. Hierarchy of Notch-Delta interactions promoting T cell lineage commitment and maturation. *J. Exp. Med.* 204:331–43
183. Rutz S, Mordmuller B, Sakano S, Scheffold A. 2005. Notch ligands Delta-like1, Delta-like4 and Jagged1 differentially regulate activation of peripheral T helper cells. *Eur. J. Immunol.* 35:2443–51
184. Jiang R, Lan Y, Chapman HD, Shawber C, Norton CR, et al. 1998. Defects in limb, craniofacial, and thymic development in Jagged2 mutant mice. *Genes Dev.* 12:1046–57
185. Tan JB, Xu K, Cretegny K, Visan I, Yuan JS, et al. 2009. Lunatic and manic fringe cooperatively enhance marginal zone B cell precursor competition for Delta-like 1 in splenic endothelial niches. *Immunity* 30:254–63
186. Sheng Y, Yahata T, Negishi N, Nakano Y, Habu S, et al. 2008. Expression of Delta-like 1 in the splenic nonhematopoietic cells is essential for marginal zone B cell development. *Immunol. Lett.* 121:33–37
187. Moriyama Y, Sekine C, Koyanagi A, Koyama N, Ogata H, et al. 2008. Delta-like 1 is essential for the maintenance of marginal zone B cells in normal mice but not in autoimmune mice. *Int. Immunol.* 20:763–73
188. Song R, Kim YW, Koo BK, Jeong HW, Yoon MJ, et al. 2008. Mind bomb 1 in the lymphopoietic niches is essential for T and marginal zone B cell development. *J. Exp. Med.* 205:2525–36
189. Napolitani G, Rinaldi A, Bertoni F, Sallusto F, Lanzavecchia A. 2005. Selected Toll-like receptor agonist combinations synergistically trigger a T helper type 1-polarizing program in dendritic cells. *Nat. Immunol.* 6:769–76
190. Krawczyk CM, Sun J, Pearce EJ. 2008. Th2 differentiation is unaffected by Jagged2 expression on dendritic cells. *J. Immunol.* 180:7931–37
191. Worsley AG, LeibundGut-Landmann S, Slack E, Phng LK, Gerhardt H, et al. 2008. Dendritic cell expression of the Notch ligand jagged2 is not essential for Th2 response induction in vivo. *Eur. J. Immunol.* 38:1043–49
192. Stahl M, Uemura K, Ge C, Shi S, Tashima Y, Stanley P. 2008. Roles of Pofut1 and O-fucose in mammalian Notch signaling. *J. Biol. Chem.* 283:13638–51

HMGB1 and RAGE in Inflammation and Cancer

Gary P. Sims,[1] Daniel C. Rowe,[1] Svend T. Rietdijk,[2] Ronald Herbst,[1] and Anthony J. Coyle[1]

[1]Department of Respiratory, Inflammation and Autoimmune Disease, MedImmune, One Medimmune Way, Gaithersburg, Maryland 20878; email: CoyleA@Medimmune.com

[2]Department of Gastroenterology and Hepatology, Academic Medical Center, Amsterdam, NL-1105 AZ, The Netherlands

Annu. Rev. Immunol. 2010. 28:367–88

First published online as a Review in Advance on January 4, 2010

The *Annual Review of Immunology* is online at immunol.annualreviews.org

This article's doi:
10.1146/annurev.immunol.021908.132603

0732-0582/10/0423-0367$20.00

Key Words

high mobility group box 1, necrosis, S100 proteins, Toll-like receptors, tolerance, autoimmune disease

Abstract

The immune system has evolved to respond not only to pathogens, but also to signals released from dying cells. Cell death through necrosis induces inflammation, whereas apoptotic cell death provides an important signal for tolerance induction. High mobility group box 1 (HMGB1) is a DNA-binding nuclear protein, released actively following cytokine stimulation as well as passively during cell death; it is the prototypic damage-associated molecular pattern (DAMP) molecule and has been implicated in several inflammatory disorders. HMGB1 can associate with other molecules, including TLR ligands and cytokines, and activates cells through the differential engagement of multiple surface receptors including TLR2, TLR4, and RAGE. RAGE is a multiligand receptor that binds structurally diverse molecules, including not only HMGB1, but also S100 family members and amyloid-β. RAGE activation has been implicated in sterile inflammation as well as in cancer, diabetes, and Alzheimer's disease. While HMGB1 through interactions with TLRs may also be important, this review focuses on the role of the HMGB1-RAGE axis in inflammation and cancer.

PAMP: pathogen-associated molecular pattern

DAMP: damage-associated molecular pattern

HMGB1: high mobility group box 1

RAGE: receptor for advanced glycation end products

AGEs: advanced glycation end products

INTRODUCTION

Sensing the presence of a pathogen is the first step for the immune system to mount an effective response to eliminate an invading organism and establish protective immunity. Over the last decade, the molecular and cellular mechanisms required for efficient microbial detection have begun to be appreciated following the identification of a number of pattern-recognition receptors that detect components of microbes though pathogen-associated molecular patterns (PAMPs). The best studied of these pattern detectors are the Toll-like receptors (TLRs). TLRs are, however, not alone in this function; other molecules, including the cytoplasmic sensing molecules, the helicases, and the nucleotide-binding oligomerization domain (NOD)- or caspase recruitment domain (CARD)-containing proteins, also play critical roles as pathogen sensors. Furthermore, we now know that, in addition to recognizing PAMPs, the immune system has evolved to recognize endogenous danger signals or, by analogy, damage-associated molecular patterns (DAMPs), many of which are released by dying or necrotic cells and contribute to inflammation in a noninfectious sterile setting. In this regard, liberation of the nuclear DNA-binding molecule high mobility group box 1 (HMGB1) may play a critical role in mediating the immune responses to damage.

DANGER SIGNALS, DAMPs, AND STERILE INFLAMMATION

How cells die has profound effects on the immune system. Our current understanding is that when cells undergo necrosis, necrotic debris leads to inflammation and priming for adaptive T cell responses, whereas cell death by apoptosis leads primarily to tolerogenic responses (**Figure 1**). The recognition of necrotic cell death is mediated by DAMPs, a structurally and sequence-diverse family of endogenous molecules, generally intracellular, often released from necrotic cells, that activate the innate immune system (1, 2). Our understanding of the DAMP superfamily is growing, such that known members now include breakdown products of the extracellular matrix such as hyaluronan fragments (3), heat shock proteins (HSPs), S100 family of proteins (4), fibrils of amyloid-β (5), uric acid (6, 7), cytokines including IL-1α and IL-33 (8, 9), and nuclear-associated proteins such as HMGB1.

Unlike the PAMPs, the molecules that detect DAMPs are less fully understood, although recently an important role for the NALP3 inflammasome has been implicated in mediating the response to uric acid and fibrils of amyloid-β (5, 10). Some of the responses to DAMPs are also through TLRs; for example, TLR4 not only responds to LPS, but also is activated by hyaluronan (11) and S100A8/9 (4). There is emerging interest in the role of the multiligand receptor RAGE, or receptor for advanced glycation end products. As the name suggests, RAGE binds advanced glycation end products (AGEs), but more recently it has been described to bind to a diverse array of DAMPs, including HMGB1. RAGE activation plays a role in various diseases, including sepsis, rheumatoid arthritis, diabetic nephropathy, atherosclerosis,

Figure 1

HMGB1 and immune homeostasis during cell death. How cells die has important consequences for the host and immune homeostasis. Cell death through necrosis is highly proinflammatory (*a*); cell death through apoptosis is tolerogenic (*b*); and cell death in situations of impaired recognition of apoptotic cells can lead to secondary necrosis (*c*). All these mechanisms can contribute to disease pathology, but in different ways. In necrotic cell death, molecules that include HMGB1 are released, associate with other molecules (including DNA or immune complexes), and activate plasmacytoid DCs, myeloid DCs, and macrophages to induce IFN-α and TNF-α, upregulate costimulatory molecules such as CD80 and CD86, and expand effector T cells (*a*). In contrast, during apoptosis, through the generation of reactive oxygen species, molecules including HMGB1 are oxidized and deliver tolerogenic signals to dampen immune activation (*b*). If, however, professional phagocytes have an impaired ability to remove apoptotic cells, cells undergo secondary necrosis and release nucleosomes associated with HMGB1 that can induce inflammatory cytokine production from macrophages and potentially represent an alternative pathway to immune complex–mediated diseases (*c*).

and neurological diseases. The focus of this review is the role of HMGB1 and the multiligand receptor RAGE in inflammation and cancer, although HMGB1-TLR4 may also be important. Recent reviews on the importance of RAGE in diabetes (12), cardiovascular disease (13), and Alzheimer's disease (14) are highlighted elsewhere.

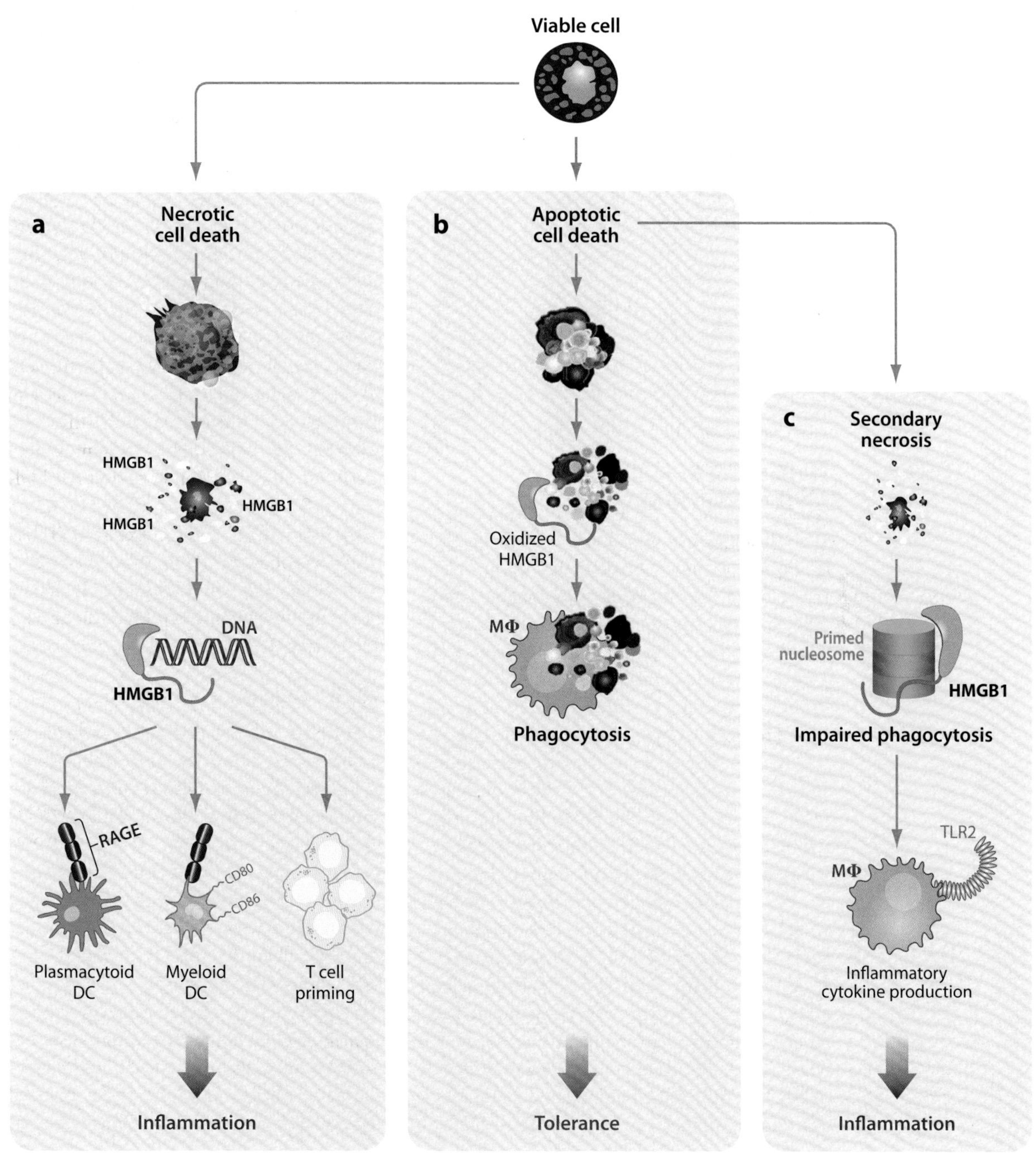

DANGER SIGNALS AND THE INFLAMMASOME

Recently, interest has focused on mechanisms that lead to caspase-1-dependent activation of IL-1β, and the term inflammasome is now used to describe the assembly of the high-molecular-weight complex that integrates several extracellular and intracellular signals required for IL-1β processing. Although the diversity of the inflammasome has yet to be fully appreciated, the NALP3 inflammasome is the best characterized. This system is activated by danger signals that include monosodium urate crystals, alum, and silica, as well as ATP and UV exposure, bacterial toxins such as *Staphylococcus aureus*, viral DNA, and NOD2 ligands. The Pyrin domain of NALP3 interacts with the adaptor molecule ASC (apoptosis-associated speck-like protein), which contains a caspase recruitment domain and in turn recruits caspase-1 to the complex. Manipulation of the inflammasome has implications in vaccine therapy, given that NALP3 deficiency impairs primary antibody responses. In addition, in diseases such as gout, therapeutic approaches to inhibit the inflammasome may be of benefit.

HMGB1 STRUCTURE AND CONFORMATION

HMGB1 is a relatively small protein of 215 amino acid residues. Structurally, the protein is organized into three distinct domains: two tandem HMG box domains (A box and B box), which are spaced by a short flexible linker, and a 30 amino acid–long acidic C-terminal tail. As structural units, HMG boxes are well conserved throughout evolution and are characterized by three α-helices, which are arranged in an L-shaped configuration (15). In the nucleus, HMGB1 is a nonhistone DNA-binding protein and serves as a structural component to facilitate the assembly of nucleoprotein complexes (16). The unique conformation of the A and B box domains likely plays an important role in the way HMG box proteins interact with chromatin (17). The HMGB proteins bind DNA in a conformation-dependent but sequence-independent manner. The A and B box domains of HMGB1 bind the minor groove of DNA. HMGB1 also binds four-way Holliday junctions as well as platinum-modified DNA. The ability of nuclear, chromatin-associated HMGB1 to bend DNA is likely related to the function of HMGB1 as a transcriptional regulator (17). The nuclear localization of HMGB1 is facilitated by two nuclear localization signal sequences, one embedded within the A box and the other located just before the acidic tail sequence.

Whereas the HMG box domains of HMGB1 have been studied in detail, much less is known about the function of the unusual acidic C-terminal tail. Early studies suggested that the C-terminal tail regulates the interaction of HMGB1 with DNA (18). Further analysis demonstrated that the acidic tail region can bind both HMG boxes of HMGB1, although the affinity for the A box appears to be higher than the affinity for the B box (19). This intramolecular interaction of the acidic tail provides the basis for the regulation of HMGB1 binding to DNA. The intra- as well as extracellular function of HMGB1 is further regulated by post-translational modification of the protein. More recently, HMGB1 has been shown to undergo oxidation (20) that may have the potential to modulate various aspects of HMGB1 function, including subcellular localization, interaction with DNA, cytokine activity, and proinflammatory activity.

HMGB1 Release from Cells

For HMGB1 to function as a cytokine, it must be released into the extracellular milieu. This can be accomplished either by active secretion or by passive release from damaged or necrotic cells. In 1999, Wang and colleagues first reported that HMGB1 was liberated from cells stimulated with cytokines and that HMGB1 played an important role in mediating experimental sepsis (21). Subsequently, it was demonstrated by Scaffidi and colleagues (22) that HMGB1 is released from cells undergoing necrosis, but not from apoptotic cells, because HMGB1 is tightly bound to chromatin. Importantly, the form of HMGB1 released from necrotic mouse embryonic fibroblasts has cytokine activity and can stimulate monocytes to produce tumor necrosis factor (TNF)-α (22). Recent reports demonstrate that HMGB1 can also be released by apoptotic cells (23, 24). HMGB1 released from such cells appears to be tolerogenic rather than proinflammatory (25) (**Figure 2**). During apoptosis, HMGB1 is oxidized on Cys106 in a process that requires

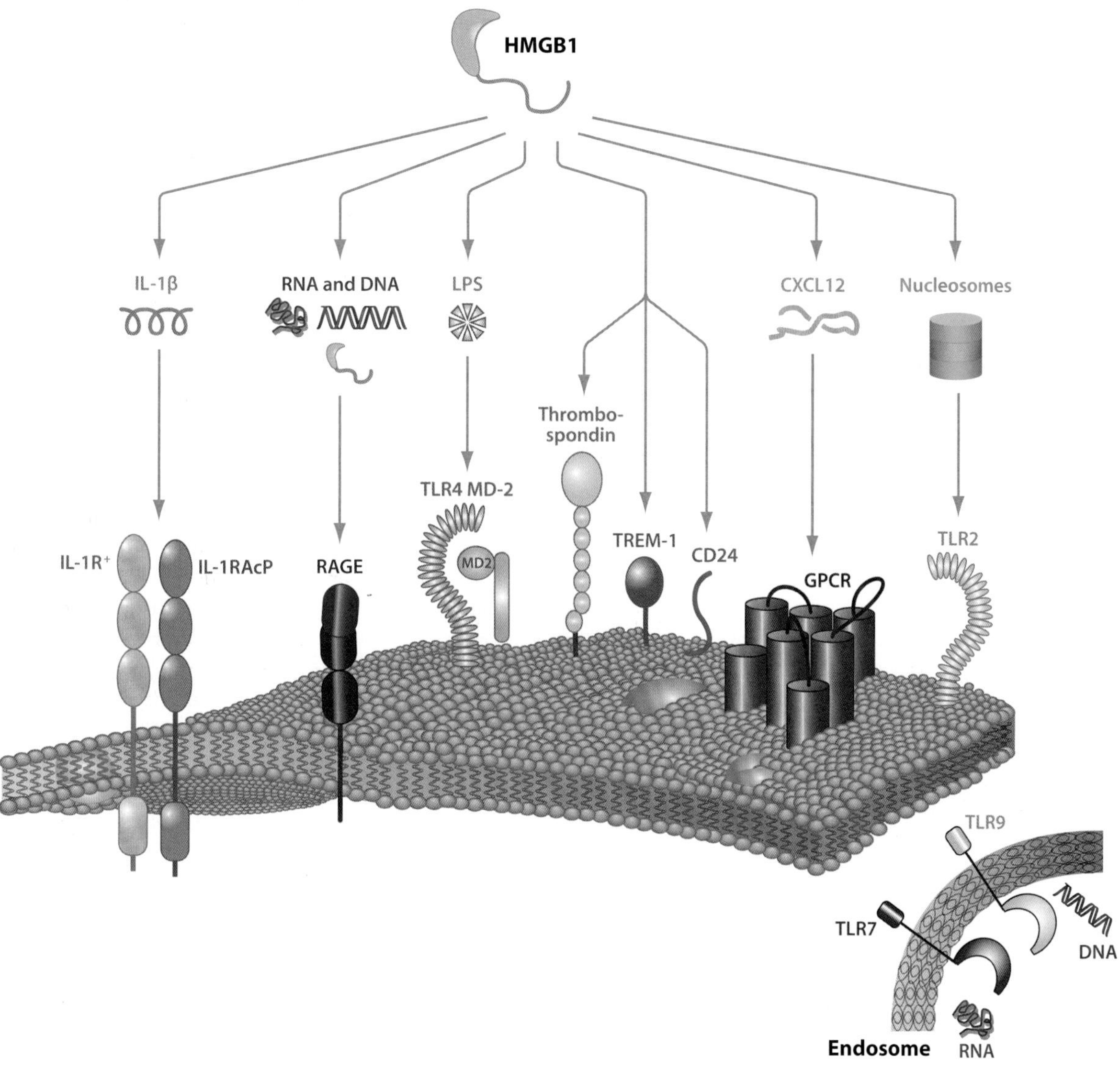

Figure 2

HMGB1-associated molecules and differential interaction with cell-surface molecules. Whether HMGB1 is released from either necrotic cells or apoptotic cells or is actively induced by cytokines, HMGB1 can potentially bind to and associate with other molecules. HMGB1 can bind to DNA and RNA and signal through RAGE. HMGB1 can also bind to IL-1β and signal through the IL-1R/IL-1RAcP complex or associate with lipopolysaccharide and activate TLR4. When HMGB1 is associated with the nucleosome, released during secondary necrosis, TLR2 is preferentially engaged. HMGB1 has also been reported to bind to TREM-1 (triggering receptor expressed on myeloid cells-1). Thrombospondin and CD24 also bind to HMGB1 and may provide important negative regulatory signals to inhibit HMGB1-mediated coagulation and inflammation.

iDC: immature dendritic cell

pDC: plasmacytoid dendritic cell

caspase activity and mitochondrial reactive oxygen species (ROS). Interestingly, Cys106 lies within the B box, which could explain the lack of inflammatory activity of oxidized HMGB1 from apoptotic cells (25), although whether Cys106 HMGB1 interacts with different binding partners and/or receptors remains to be determined.

Active secretion of HMGB1 requires shuttling of the protein from the nucleus into the cytosol or prevention of nuclear import of newly synthesized HMGB1. Several forms of post-translational modifications, such as phosphorylation, methylation, and acetylation, result in the accumulation of HMGB1 in the cytosol (26–28). Because HMGB1 does not contain a leader sequence, the protein is released via a nonclassical secretory pathway that may involve specialized vesicles of the endolysosomal compartment (29). The secretion of HMGB1 can be triggered by different stimuli. For example, IFN-γ can induce HMGB1 release from macrophages that, at least in part, requires induction and signaling through TNF-α (30). HMGB1 secretion can also be triggered by endotoxin [lipopolysaccharide (LPS)] and IL-1β (21). HMGB1 release in response to LPS and TNF-α appears to depend on the NF-κB pathway and can be blocked by compounds that prevent NF-κB activation (21, 31). In addition, molecules such as ethyl pyruvate, a lipophilic pyruvate derivative, and cholinergic agonists prevent HMGB1 release and improve survival in experimental mouse models of sepsis (31–33). In contrast, LPS-induced release of HMGB1 from macrophages may require IFN-β signaling via JAK kinases and Stat-1, but not via NF-κB (34). Differences between this and previous studies may be, at least in part, due to differences in the experimental systems and the pharmacological inhibitors used to interrogate signaling pathways. Given the different mechanisms of HMGB1 release and the variety of post-translational modifications (and combinations thereof) involved, caution must be exercised when comparing soluble forms of HMGB1 generated under different conditions.

In Vitro Functions of HMGB1

HMGB1 can promote inflammatory responses by numerous mechanisms. Comparisons of the necrotic cell debris from HMGB1-deficient and wild-type cells demonstrate that HMGB1-deficient cells have a profoundly reduced capacity to induce cytokines (22). Recombinant HMGB1 also induces cytokine production from human monocytes but not from lymphocytes (35). However, several groups have more recently shown that highly purified HMGB1 does not induce significant amounts of proinflammatory cytokines (36–39). Indeed, the capacity of HMGB1 to bind other molecules (see below) may be the underlying basis for these observations. However, it should also be noted that recombinant HMGB1 may be different from the native protein, with changes in the oxidative status having a profound impact on its biological activity (25). HMGB1 induces the phenotypic maturation of immature DCs (iDCs) with upregulation of costimulatory molecules and MHC class II and the secretion of proinflammatory cytokines, including IL-12 and IFN-γ, that together potently stimulate allogeneic T cells, polarizing them toward a Th1 phenotype (40, 41). HMGB1 is also implicated in the maturation of plasmacytoid DCs (pDCs) (42, 43). As DCs mature, they switch their function from antigen uptake to antigen presentation. During this process, they reorganize their cytoskeleton and become more responsive to chemokines in draining lymph nodes. HMGB1 induces the migration of iDCs but not of mature DCs; furthermore, RAGE expressed on iDCs is necessary for homing to lymph nodes (44, 45).

Stimulation of neutrophils and monocytes with HMGB1 induces cytokine release and increases the interaction between Mac-1 and RAGE that enables these cells to adhere to activated vascular endothelium and migrate into inflamed tissue (46, 47). HMGB1 also primes the vascular endothelium by upregulating TNF-α and monocyte chemotactic protein (MCP)-1, as well as upregulating intercellular adhesion molecule (ICAM)-1 and vascular cell adhesion molecule (VCAM)-1 to facilitate the adhesion of inflammatory cells (48). An additional mechanism by which HMGB1 may promote inflammation is by interfering with phagocytosis. If apoptotic cells are not efficiently removed by phagocytosis, cells become necrotic, and their contents fuel an inflammatory response. Interestingly, HMGB1 binds to phosphatidylserine and blocks phosphatidylserine-mediated phagocytosis of apoptotic neutrophils (49).

HMGB1 Interactions and Receptors

Although the role of HMGB1 inside the nucleus is beyond the scope of this review (for a recent review, see Reference 50), it is important to highlight the vital contribution HMGB1 makes to nuclear function. DNA was the first molecule to be described that interacts with HMGB1. Subsequent work revealed that HMGB1 preferentially binds to altered DNA structures and can bend DNA upon binding to confer transcriptional stability (51). These traits are central to the notion that HMGB1 acts as a molecular linchpin facilitating the arrangement of complex nucleoprotein structures (52).

One emerging concept in HMGB1 biology is its ability to interact with other molecules, including DNA, RNA, IL-1β, and LPS, and also with nucleosomes that augment or modify the function of HMGB1 itself (**Figure 2**). Recognition of self-DNA is normally kept in check by extracellular nucleases and by the endosomal localization of TLR9. Breakdown of this mechanism can occur either when extracellular DNA is protected from nucleases and/or when DNA has a means to enter the endosomal pathway where it can encounter TLR9. A well-studied example of this mechanism is with pathogenic DNA-containing immune complexes. These complexes contain DNA bound to a protein component (nucleosomes, HMGB1) and can enter the endosomal pathway of pDCs or B cells via CD32-mediated uptake (53). Because HMGB1 can directly bind DNA, we hypothesize that extracellular HMGB1-DNA complexes, alone or bound to autoantibodies, may activate the immune system via RAGE and TLR9. Indeed, HMGB1-CpG-A complexes stimulate greater IFN-α production from mouse bone marrow–derived pDCs than does either component alone. In addition, not only was HMGB1 present in DNA-containing immune complexes, it was also essential for inducing cytokine production in a TLR9-mediated manner (37). Ivanov et al. (39) similarly reported that HMGB1-deficient immortalized fetal liver DCs (iFLDCs) produce less IFN-α/β in response to CpG-DNA than do wild-type iFLDCs. Interestingly, HMGB1 can also interact with TLR9 independently of DNA (37, 39).

iFLDC: immortalized fetal liver dendritic cell

Autoantibodies, particularly autoantibodies to nuclear antigens, are a common feature in many systemic autoimmune diseases, especially systemic lupus erythematosus (SLE), and impairment of apoptotic cell clearance likely contributes to disease pathogenesis (55–57). Recently, Urbonaviciute et al. (58) implicated HMGB1-containing nucleosomes derived from secondary necrotic cells as potent proinflammatory activators of macrophages and DCs (**Figure 1**). To elucidate the mechanism of action, a series of activation experiments were performed on macrophages defective in RAGE and several TLR pathways. Surprisingly, the deletion of *MyD88* or *TLR2* inhibited activation (58). Thus, if HMGB1 is associated with DNA, then the complex signals through RAGE/TLR9, whereas if HMGB1 is associated with the nucleosome, signaling is strictly TLR2 dependent (**Figure 2**).

HMGB1 also has the potential to bind to other PAMPs, including LPS (59). HMGB1, like LPS-binding protein, can actively destabilize LPS aggregates and present LPS monomers to CD14, thus increasing the overall sensitivity of the TLR4/MD-2 receptor complex. As with HMGB1-DNA complexes, HMGB1 and LPS synergize for optimal cytokine production (59). Whether this is due to the LPS transfer properties of HMGB1 or is a direct result of HMGB1 signaling remains to be determined.

HMGB1 administration to LPS-resistant C3H/HeJ mice can induce lethality, suggesting a TLR4-independent pathway (21). A clue to this outcome came in 2007 with the identification of TREM-1 (triggering receptor expressed on myeloid cells-1) as a potential detector of HMGB1-mediated cytokine induction (60). In this case, investigators employed neutralizing antibodies to identify HMGB1 and HSP70 as key danger signals present in necrotic cell lysates and to implicate TREM-1 as their receptor on exposed cells. However, no direct binding of HMGB1 to TREM-1 has been demonstrated thus far. More recently, investigators have explored the interaction of HMGB1 with various cytokines and chemokines. First, purified HMGB1 from cells treated with doxycycline and either TNF-α, IFN-γ, or IL-1β acquired enhanced proinflammatory activity (38). Biochemical studies uncovered the ability of HMGB1 and IL-1β to form a reversible complex. Furthermore, studies with blocking antibodies to IL-1β or using IL-1RA completely abrogated this newly acquired activity of HMGB1. Interestingly, a common theme emerged in this study as well: the capacity of HMGB1 to synergize with normally inert amounts of a compound and, by doing so, exert proinflammatory effects (**Figure 2**).

Yet another binding partner of HMGB1 is CXCL12 (also known as stromal cell-derived factor-1). As described by Campana et al. (61), HMGB1 secretion is required for CXCL12-dependent migration of DCs and to a lesser extent migration of macrophages. In addition, HMGB1 protects the conformation of CXCL12 in a reducing environment, a state existing in the draining lymph node. However, experiments using the HMGB1 specific inhibitor HMGB1 A box and a CXCL12 inhibitor only partially inhibited DC migration, suggesting that multiple receptors are responsible for mediating the response to the HMGB1/CXCL12 complex.

Several negative regulators of HMGB1 have also been identified. CD24-deficient mice exhibit increased responsiveness to acetaminophen-mediated liver necrosis. Using a series of biochemical approaches, investigators demonstrated that CD24 is associated with HMGB1 (62). Anti-HMGB1 antibody reversed the increased lethality seen in CD24-deficient mice, leading to the hypothesis that CD24 recognition of HMGB1 suppresses its proinflammatory effects. Further experiments identified Siglec-10 as the signal transducer of the CD24-HMGB1 interaction, and similar results were obtained for endogenous danger signals HSP70 and HSP90. Thus, the CD24 and Siglec-10 receptor complex appears to provide a molecular break for endogenous danger signals without compromising responses to infectious agents (62). This mechanism would provide the host a unique way of sensing damage to inflamed tissues during sterile inflammation, but it would also allow an appropriate response to invading organisms.

Lastly, thrombospondin also inhibits HMGB1. Thrombospondin is a cell-surface glycoprotein, predominately expressed on vascular endothelial cells, that mediates thrombin-dependent activation of protein C, which has critical anticoagulant activity (63). The N-terminal lectin-binding domain of thrombospondin binds HMGB1 and blocks its interaction with RAGE (64). Binding promotes the cleavage of the N-terminal domain of HMGB1, thereby reducing its proinflammatory potential (65). Thrombospondin may therefore act as a natural negative regulator of HMGB1 and modulate vascular inflammatory responses (**Figure 2**).

HMGB1 AND DISEASE

HMGB1 and Sepsis

Sepsis is induced by infectious organisms that enter the blood stream and disseminate throughout the body. Despite advances in antibiotics and supportive care, the incidence of sepsis syndromes is increasing and is responsible for over 200,000 deaths in the United States annually (66). Sepsis syndromes result from an exaggerated systemic inflammatory response characterized by a massive release of mediators such as TNF-α and IL-1β that drives a largely uncontrolled proinflammatory response.

In a model of murine sepsis, systemic administration of LPS induces a lethal proinflammatory response. Within the first few hours, LPS triggers TNF-α and IL-1β production followed by the delayed release of HMGB1, all of which induces cellular damage. HMGB1 antibodies inhibit endotoxin lethality in mice (67, 68) and also inhibit lung inflammation following airway LPS exposure (69). RAGE-deficient mice are also protected from endotoxemia, suggesting that HMGB1-induced lethality is mediated through RAGE signaling (64). RAGE expression on the endothelium appears to be essential and sufficient to mediate lethality (70). The important roles of HMGB1 and RAGE in mediating pathological innate responses in sepsis have been confirmed in the cecal ligation and puncture (CLP) model, a lethal polymicrobial insult (70–72). The C5a-HMGB1 axis is important in the development of sepsis, and C5L2, rather than C5AR, appears to play a key role in HMGB1 release (73). TLR9-deficient mice are also protected in the CLP model, which is associated with increased numbers of peritoneal DCs and neutrophils, reduced bacterial dissemination, and reduced circulating proinflammatory cytokines. Transfer of TLR9-deficient DCs to wild-type mice conveys protection (74) and suggests that HMGB1-DNA complexes released from dying cells may reduce phagocytic activity and cellular recruitment in a TLR9-dependent manner. HMGB1 also mediates the secretion of plasminogen activator inhibitor-1 and tissue plasminogen activator from endothelial cells (48). This finding, in conjunction with the release of tissue factor from monocytes, suggests that HMGB1 plays a key role in the microvasculature and in the initiation of the coagulation cascade in the pathophysiology of sepsis.

HMGB1, Trauma, and Sterile Inflammation

In the absence of pathogens, severe trauma and hemorrhagic shock can also induce systemic autoinflammatory reactions with clinical manifestations similar to those in sepsis syndrome, indicating commonality in the pathophysiology. HMGB1 levels are elevated in patients with mechanical trauma, strokes, acute myocardial infarction, acute respiratory distress, and liver transplantation (75–79). In a model of hepatic ischemia-reperfusion injury, HMGB1 levels are increased as early as 1 h after reperfusion and are sustained for at least 24 h (79). Administration of soluble RAGE or neutralizing anti-HMGB1 antibody decreased liver damage (79, 80). TLR4-deficient mice are also protected during hepatic ischemia-reperfusion injury. Compelling evidence using TLR4-defective mice also supports a role for a HMGB1-TLR4 axis in hemorrhagic shock/resuscitation-induced injury, systemic inflammation, and end-organ damage induced by bilateral femur fractures (81, 82).

Improved survival and liver regeneration in RAGE-deficient mice following partial hepectomy is associated with reduced apoptosis and IL-6 production (83). RAGE-deficient mice also exhibit less damage following ischemia-reperfusion injury in the heart (84). Interestingly, in addition to being one of the potential receptors for triggering HMGB1-mediated inflammation, TLR4 is also responsible for the secretion of HMGB1. Early after ischemia-reperfusion, hypoxia induces the active release of HMGB1 from hepatocytes, a process regulated by TLR4-dependent ROS production and downstream calcium-dependent kinase signaling (80). In marked contrast to these studies, investigators have also shown that preconditioning with HMGB1 prior to hepatic insult protects mice from injury in a TLR4-dependent manner (85). Which cells are responsible for mediating this effect and whether this phenomenon occurs in other ischemia-reperfusion models are still unclear. Nevertheless, outcome of HMGB1-TLR signaling likely depends on other signaling events and may be context dependent.

Accommodating all these findings into a simple unifying hypothesis is challenging. Most probably, multiple receptors mediate HMGB1 responses, and their relative importance may depend on the levels of HMGB1, the expression of the receptors in the target organ, and the ability of HMGB1 to interact with other molecules, as shown in **Figure 2**. Potentially, there is significant cross-talk between receptors, and the deficient or defective receptor may influence the function of other receptors. The use of specific ligand-blocking antibodies may help clarify the roles of the individual receptors.

IPF: idiopathic pulmonary fibrosis

HMGB1 in Chronic Inflammatory and Autoimmune Diseases

HMGB1 may also play a role in chronic autoimmune disorders (86). In this regard, increased levels of HMGB1 and increased numbers of HMGB1-secreting cells have been identified at specific sites of inflammation, including in the inflamed synovium of patients with rheumatoid arthritis. Anti-HMGB1 antibodies inhibit the development of synovial inflammation and joint swelling in experimental models of arthritis (87, 88), and this appears to be independent of the TNF-α pathway (88). Moreover, anti-TNF-α monoclonal antibody therapy in patients with rheumatoid arthritis had no notable effect on HMGB1 expression (89). Thus, TNF-α may not be the main inducer of extranuclear HMGB1. Rather, HMGB1 may represent a TNF-α-independent pathway for possible future therapeutic intervention in arthritis.

Elevated levels of HMGB1 have also been reported in patients with SLE. The autoantibodies that form against double-stranded DNA and nucleosomes are characteristic of SLE. Evidence suggests that impaired phagocytosis of apoptotic cells and subsequent secondary necrosis may contribute to disease pathogenesis (90). As discussed above, HMGB1, when released from apoptotic cells, remains bound to nucleosomes and can be detected in the plasma of SLE patients (58, 91). Notably, HMGB1 is also part of immunostimulatory complexes that bind to and activate autoreactive B cells (37). Finally, HMGB1-DNA complexes induce cytokine secretion from mesangial cells in vitro (92). Serum HMGB1 levels are higher in patients with scleroderma and correlate with skin fibrosis and impaired lung function (93). The association with fibrosis is not restricted to autoimmune disorders, given that elevated levels of HMGB1 occur in patients with idiopathic pulmonary fibrosis (IPF) (94). The potential pathogenic role of HMGB1 in IPF is supported by experimental animal model studies demonstrating that anti-HMGB1 antibodies prevent bleomycin-induced lung fibrosis (94).

HMGB1 and Cancer

The involvement of HMGB1 in cancer is complex, and intracellular/nuclear and extracellular forms of HMGB1 have been implicated in tumor formation, progression, and metastasis and in the response to chemotherapeutics. Elevated expression of HMGB1 occurs in several solid tumors, including melanoma, colon cancer, prostate cancer, pancreatic cancer, and breast cancer (20, 95, 96). In gastrointestinal stromal tumors, the overexpression of HMGB1 is closely associated with gain-of-function mutations in c-kit (97). Importantly, HMGB1 in cancer is associated with invasion and metastasis (95, 98). HMGB1 may be directly involved in tumor cell metastasis through its ability to promote cell migration, to modulate the adhesive properties of cells, and to modify components of the extracellular matrix. In certain cases, however, the effect may be indirect, and, by enhancing the activity of NF-κB p65, HMGB1 leads to the induction of melanoma inhibitory activity (MIA) (99, 100), an 11-kDa secreted protein, which binds to fibronectin as well as to certain integrins and enhances migration and invasion of tumor cells (99). Thus, HMGB1 does not necessarily have to be secreted by tumor cells to enhance their invasive and metastatic potential.

One rate-limiting step in tumor growth and progression is neoangiogenesis. As the growing tumor exceeds the capacity of the existing vasculature, hypoxia results in necrotic cell death within the tumor. As a cytokine, HMGB1 not only stimulates inflammatory cells, but also can activate vascular endothelial cells. HMGB1 can stimulate endothelial cell proliferation and sprouting in vitro and neovascularization in vivo (101). The importance of this pathway in vivo is suggested by the observation that blockade of HMGB1 and RAGE suppresses tumor growth and metastasis in a murine model of lung cancer (102). Van Beijnum and colleagues (103) analyzed the gene expression profile of tumor-associated endothelium compared with normal tissue endothelium. HMGB1 was one of several genes specifically overexpressed in tumor endothelium. Furthermore, an anti-HMGB1 antibody inhibited angiogenesis in the chick chorioallantoic membrane assay (103). Together, these data suggest that HMGB1 is a proangiogenic cytokine that may contribute to tumor growth and progression by promoting neoangiogenesis. Whether HMGB1 needs to be associated with other cellular components to mediate the proangiogenic effect is currently unknown.

Dying tumor cells can, in some circumstances, induce an effective antitumor response if cells die in such a manner as to induce maturation of DCs that can promote a cytotoxic T lymphocyte response through cross-presentation of tumor antigens. HMGB1 has been shown to be released from both irradiated and doxorubicin treated tumor cells (104). In this context, HMGB1 plays an important role in activation of DCs through TLR4 for the efficient presentation of tumor antigens liberated by dying cells (104). Notably, the role of HMGB1 in this process appears to be independent of the contribution of HMGB1 to DCs' maturation and migration, which primarily involves RAGE activation (41), but appears to modulate processing and cross-presentation of tumors through TLR4 (104).

THE RECEPTOR FOR ADVANCED GLYCATION END PRODUCTS (RAGE)

The loci (*AGER*) encoding RAGE is located on chromosome 6 near MHC class III in humans and mice, close to the genes encoding TNF-α, lymphotoxin, and HOX12 (105). RAGE is a type I transmembrane protein composed of three extracellular immunoglobulin-like domains (V, C1, and C2), a single transmembrane domain, and a short cytoplasmic tail (106). A combination of biochemical approaches revealed that the V and C1 domains form an integrated structural unit, separated from a fully independent C2 domain by a flexible linker (107). Interactions between RAGE and its ligands are mapped to the V/C1 domain, with the amino-terminal V domain providing the major contribution (107, 108).

RAGE has two potential N-glycosylation sites, both located in the V domain. Carboxylation of these N-glycans enhances the binding of HMGB1 and AGEs and subsequent signal transduction (109). Because the carbohydrate groups are easily removed from the native protein by PNGase F (109), they are not predicted to alter the conformation of the protein. The surface exposure of the carboxylated glycan groups may influence ligand binding directly.

Numerous human RAGE mRNA species have been isolated from different cell types (110). Most mRNA species, including the N-truncated isoform, are likely to be targeted to the nonsense-mediated mRNA decay pathway or to otherwise fail to generate the protein. Some rare mRNA species with alterations in the V/C1 domain could be interesting because they could differentially bind ligands; however, their roles remain speculative in the absence of extensive functional characterization. Only two functionally relevant spliced isoforms are currently known: the abundant full-length transmembrane form, which can initiate signaling through its intracellular tail, and a soluble isoform (known as esRAGE, C-truncated RAGE, and RAGE_v1), which can act as a decoy receptor. The transmembrane form of RAGE may also be proteolytically cleaved proximal to the membrane to generate a soluble form of RAGE that will have the same decoy capacity as esRAGE (111).

RAGE is constitutively expressed at high levels in the lung. Expression is localized to alveolar type II cells (112) and on the basolateral membranes of the alveolar type I epithelial cells (113). The physiological relevance of the high expression in these cells is unknown. Elsewhere, there is widespread but relatively low expression of RAGE on vascular endothelial cells, neutrophils, monocytes/macrophages, lymphocytes, DCs, cardiomyocytes, and neurons (114, 115). RAGE expression increases in circumstances when ligands, such as AGEs, and inflammatory mediators accumulate (106, 116). Because the RAGE promoter contains multiple functional NF-κB and SP-1 transcription factor–binding sites (117, 118), ligands and proinflammatory cytokines can promote the expression of RAGE, potentially triggering a receptor-dependent autoinflammatory loop.

RAGE AS A MULTILIGAND RECEPTOR

As its name suggests, the receptor for advanced glycation end products was initially identified as a receptor for AGEs (106). Since then, we have learned that this receptor has various binding partners. Rather than binding to a single specific ligand or even a group of closely related ligands, RAGE binds to several classes of molecules that lack sequence similarities (**Figure 3**). These ligands include HMGB1, several members of the calcium-binding S100 family of proteins, some species of AGEs, and β-sheet fibrillar material such as amyloid-β, serum amyloid A, immunoglobulin light chains, transthyretin, and prions, among others (**Figure 3**). Consequently, RAGE can be considered a pattern-recognition receptor that

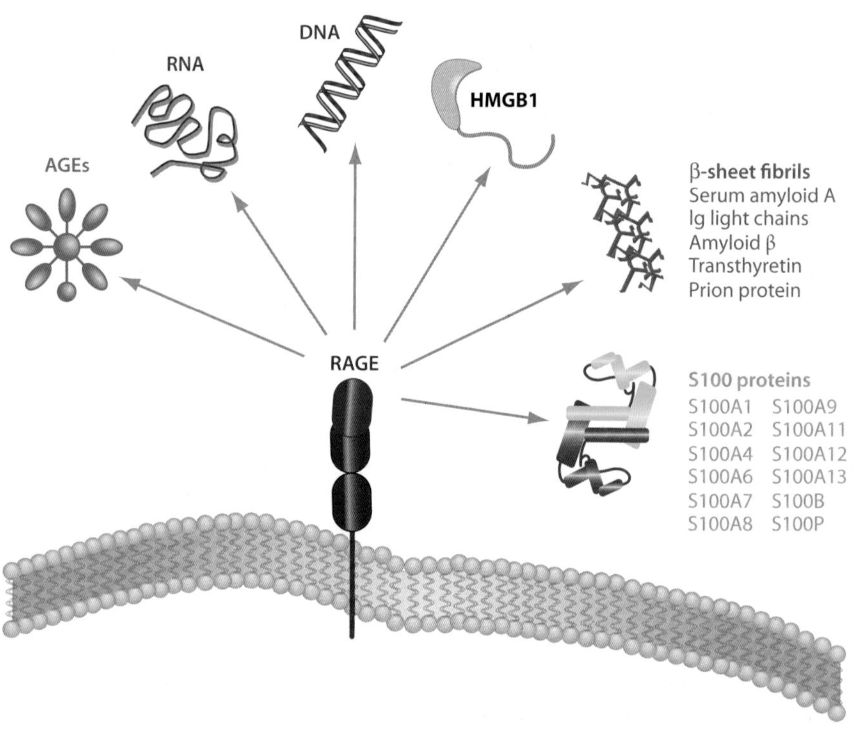

Figure 3

RAGE is a multiligand receptor and the prototypic DAMP receptor. RAGE can bind to structurally diverse molecules that include not only AGEs, but also DNA and RNA that bind in a sequence-independent manner, HMGB1, an array of S100 family member proteins, and fibrillar proteins that include amyloid-β. The association of ligands with RAGE results in a complex signal transduction cascade leading to cell activation.

binds predominately endogenous molecules that are either generated or released during cellular or physiological stresses.

RAGE SIGNALING

Although there are compelling data to support the hypothesis that RAGE is central to many inflammatory disorders, the structural features (or lack thereof) at the C terminus of RAGE raise questions as to whether RAGE is a signal transducer. Insight into this question was gleaned through the use of a RAGE construct lacking the intracellular tail. In these studies, this RAGE construct behaved like a dominant negative, supporting the notion that RAGE can indeed function as a bona fide signaling molecule (102, 116, 119). RAGE engagement by a myriad ligands is linked to an array of signaling pathways. These include the activation of NF-κB (120–122), MAPKs (122–124), PI3K/Akt (125), Rho GTPases (126), Jak/STAT (127), and Src family kinases (128), among others. This variety of reported RAGE signal transduction pathways is quite extraordinary. However, the diverse nature of the RAGE ligands, and possibly their contaminating elements, coupled with the broad expression pattern of RAGE may account for such an assortment of signals.

The predicted cytoplasmic domain of RAGE consists of a short 43 amino acid tail with no obvious signaling domains or motifs. Hence, a major question in the field was how RAGE transduces signals from the cell surface to the nucleus. Several papers have tried to address this question by searching for direct binding partners using the cytoplasmic tail of RAGE as bait. Ishihara et al. (129) identified both extracellular signal-related kinase-1 and -2 (ERK1/2) as direct RAGE-binding partners. Further truncation of the cytoplasmic domain unveiled a putative ERK docking site at the membrane-proximal region. HMGB1 stimulation of RAGE-transfected HT1080 cells induced the interaction of RAGE and ERK1/2. Hudson et al. (126) employed a yeast two-hybrid system to explore possible cytoplasmic-binding partners of RAGE. Results from this study indicate that the FH1 domain of mammalian Diaphanous-1 (mDia-1) interacts with RAGE. A functional link between the relationship of mDia-1 and RAGE was illustrated in mDia-1 siRNA knockdown assays that impaired the GTPase activity of Rac-1 and Cdc42, two Rho GTPases involved in cellular migration (130, 131). Interestingly, mDia-1 had previously been implicated in cytokinesis and Src signal transduction (132).

OTHER RAGE LIGANDS

Advanced Glycation End Products (AGEs)

AGEs result from the nonenzymatic reaction between reducing sugars and cellular components, including proteins, lipids, and nucleic acids. Glycation of proteins usually occurs at the N terminus and at particular amino acid side chains (133). The reaction, also known as the Maillard reaction, is initiated by the interaction between the sugar carbonyl moiety and the primary amino group of the protein (in the case of N-terminally modified proteins). The resulting Schiff base is transformed into a more stable Amadori product. Next, a series of lesser understood oxidation and dehydration reactions lead to the formation of AGEs. Furthermore, AGEs can cause extensive cross-linking of proteins, leading to their deposition. Recently, alternative pathways leading to AGE formation have been uncovered (134, 135).

Overall, the accumulation of AGEs in the body increases with time and in certain disease states such as diabetes and Alzheimer's, with disease progression linked to higher AGE levels (136, 137). AGEs can also bind to other receptors, including AGE-R1 and lysozyme, that facilitate the degradation and clearance of AGEs (138). The binding of AGEs to RAGE appears to be proinflammatory, however, and upregulates TNF-α, IL-6, and nitric oxide (124). Thus, the stimulation of RAGE through AGEs may contribute to several pathological conditions and diseases.

S100 Family Members

The S100s are a family of over 20 related calcium-binding proteins that are exclusively expressed in vertebrates, where their expression patterns are tissue- and cell-type specific (139). These small, acidic proteins (10–12 kDa) are characterized by two calcium EF-hand motifs: a C-terminal canonical EF-hand, common to all EF-hand proteins, and an N-terminal pseudo EF-hand, characteristic of S100 proteins, connected by a central hinge (140). Calcium binding to the EF-hand motif occurs in response to increased intracellular calcium concentrations and triggers conformational changes that expose a wide hydrophobic cleft that interacts with target proteins. The structural homology of the S100s permits the formation of active heterodimers, such as S100A1/A4 and S100A8/A9 (141). S100A4, S100A8/9, S100A12, and S100B can generate tetramers, hexamers, and higher-order multimeric structures that alter binding properties and physiological responses (108, 142). S100s modulate an array of intracellular functions, including calcium homeostasis, cytoskeletal organization, cell cycle progression, and cell growth and differentiation (139, 140). Besides their intracellular functions, S100s released from different cell types during inflammation serve as useful markers of disease activity (143, 144).

S100A12 [also known as extracellular newly identified RAGE-binding protein (EN-RAGE) or Calgranulin C] and S100B were the first identified S100 RAGE ligands (120, 121). Subsequently, S100A1, S100A2, S100A4, S100A5, S100A6, S100A7, S100A8 (MRP8, Calgranulin A), S100A9 (MRP14, Calgranulin B), S100A11, S100A13, and S100P have also been shown to bind to RAGE (145). The extracellular functions of all the S100 proteins have not been completely delineated. Some S100s, such as S100A1, S100A7, and S100B, are primarily associated with inflammation in the heart, skin, and brain, respectively, whereas a subset of the S100s known as the calgranulins, S100A8 (Calgranulin A, MRP8), S100A9 (Calgranulin B, MRP14), and S100A12 (Calgranulin C, EN-RAGE), are predominately expressed by granulocytes and monocytes and have a broad role in inflammatory responses (4). The S100A8/A9 heterodimer and S100A12, released from activated phagocytes, mediate the recruitment of leukocytes (146, 147). The importance of S100 proteins in inflammation is also demonstrated by the fact that migration of neutrophils and monocytes during monosodium crystal–mediated gouty arthritis is inhibited by anti-S100 antibodies (147).

S100A12 and S100A8/A9 also increase the expression of the proinflammatory cytokines IL-1β and TNF-α (120, 148). Using anti-RAGE antibodies and a DN-RAGE signaling–deficient construct, investigators observed that the S100A12-induced response is mediated by RAGE. However, despite the sequence similarity of S100A12 with S100A8 and S100A9, S100A8-mediated cytokine induction was mediated by TLR4, not by RAGE (148). Interestingly, S100A9 and the S100A8/A9 heterodimer failed to activate macrophages in the absence of LPS, suggesting that S100A9 modulates the activity of its partner (148).

Much remains to be understood regarding the role of S100s in inflammation. These proinflammatory S100 proteins are almost always upregulated at inflammatory lesions and in the blood of patients with a range of inflammatory and autoimmune disorders (4, 144). Whether they are molecular patterns that may be useful diagnostic markers or whether they actively contribute to disease pathogenesis remains to be determined. Recently, investigators reported that a quinoline-3-carboxamide derivative that inhibits S100A9 interaction with RAGE and TLR4 suppresses inflammation in an experimental model of autoimmune encephalomyelitis. This finding provides a proof of concept in early clinical evaluation in multiple sclerosis and type 1 diabetes, suggesting that S100A9 may indeed be an important mediator of inflammatory disorders (149).

CONCLUSIONS AND FUTURE PERSPECTIVES

HMGB1 is undoubtedly an important effector molecule and plays an important role in many pathological settings from acute sepsis to sterile inflammation during trauma, as well as in chronic inflammatory diseases from rheumatoid arthritis to SLE. In addition, HMGB1 is implicated in other diseases characterized by cell death and damage including diabetes and Alzheimer's disease. Despite this key role, many questions remain to be addressed. Given that highly purified recombinant HMGB1 possesses little if any inflammatory properties, what is the true nature of the pathological form of HMGB1 in disease? Do post-translational modifications of HMGB1 influence biological activity? Indeed, given the growing number of HMGB1-binding partners, are there different types of HMGB1 complexes that are formed in the context of different pathological situations, as has been reported in SLE, where HMGB1 nucleosomes are believed to be pathogenic? Oxidative stress of the cell also has important implications for the role of HMGB1 and presumably switches the ability of HMGB1 to activate DCs and prime T cells to a molecule that promotes tolerance. Whether the oxidized form of HMGB1 mediates tolerance through RAGE is unknown. Recently, HMGB2 has also been shown to be liberated from necrotic cells and to exert proinflammatory effects (150), raising the possibility that effective therapies will require inhibition of both HMGB1 and HMGB2. In this respect, not only HMGB1 (151), but also HMGB2 and HMGB3 have been reported to function as universal sentinels for nucleic acid–mediated activation of innate immune responses (151). The relative contribution of intracellular and extracellular HMGBs in this response remains to be determined, however. The role of RAGE as the principal receptor for HMGB1 is also unresolved, as studies also support a role for TLR2 and TLR4. The molecular basis for differential receptor engagement may be related to the nature of the HMGB1 complex. In this respect, most studies performed to date have relied on inhibition of HMGB1 with polyclonal antibodies. To target this complex protein successfully with monoclonal antibodies, careful characterization of the biological activities specifically associated with particular diseases will be necessary.

DISCLOSURE STATEMENT

A.J.C., R.H., G.S., S.T.R., and D.R. are all employees of Medimmune LLC. The authors are not aware of any affiliations, memberships, funding, or financial holdings that might be perceived as affecting the objectivity of this review.

LITERATURE CITED

1. Foell D, Wittkowski H, Roth J. 2007. Mechanisms of disease: a 'DAMP' view of inflammatory arthritis. *Nat. Clin. Pract. Rheumatol.* 3:382–90
2. Rubartelli A, Lotze MT. 2007. Inside, outside, upside down: damage-associated molecular-pattern molecules (DAMPs) and redox. *Trends Immunol.* 28:429–36
3. Taylor KR, Trowbridge JM, Rudisill JA, Termeer CC, Simon JC, Gallo RL. 2004. Hyaluronan fragments stimulate endothelial recognition of injury through TLR4. *J. Biol. Chem.* 279:17079–84
4. Foell D, Wittkowski H, Vogl T, Roth J. 2007. S100 proteins expressed in phagocytes: a novel group of damage-associated molecular pattern molecules. *J. Leukoc. Biol.* 81:28–37
5. **Halle A, Hornung V, Petzold GC, Stewart CR, Monks BG, et al. 2008. The NALP3 inflammasome is involved in the innate immune response to amyloid-beta. *Nat. Immunol.* 9:857–65**

5. Demonstration that amyloid-β induces IL-1β secretion, dependent on NALP3.

6. Martinon F, Petrilli V, Mayor A, Tardivel A, Tschopp J. 2006. Gout-associated uric acid crystals activate the NALP3 inflammasome. *Nature* 440:237–41
7. Martinon F, Mayor A, Tschopp J. 2009. The inflammasomes: guardians of the body. *Annu. Rev. Immunol.* 27:229–65
8. Cayrol C, Girard JP. 2009. The IL-1-like cytokine IL-33 is inactivated after maturation by caspase-1. *Proc. Natl. Acad. Sci. USA* 106:9021–26

9. Haraldsen G, Balogh J, Pollheimer J, Sponheim J, Kuchler AM. 2009. Interleukin-33—cytokine of dual function or novel alarmin? *Trends Immunol.* 30:227–33
10. Gasse P, Riteau N, Charron S, Girre S, Fick L, et al. 2009. Uric acid is a danger signal activating NALP3 inflammasome in lung injury inflammation and fibrosis. *Am. J. Respir. Crit. Care Med.* 179:903–13
11. Taylor KR, Yamasaki K, Radek KA, Di Nardo A, Goodarzi H, et al. 2007. Recognition of hyaluronan released in sterile injury involves a unique receptor complex dependent on Toll-like receptor 4, CD44, and MD-2. *J. Biol. Chem.* 282:18265–75
12. Yan SF, Ramasamy R, Schmidt AM. 2008. Mechanisms of disease: advanced glycation end-products and their receptor in inflammation and diabetes complications. *Nat. Clin. Pract. Endocrinol. Metab.* 4:285–93
13. Yan SF, Ramasamy R, Schmidt AM. 2009. The receptor for advanced glycation endproducts (RAGE) and cardiovascular disease. *Expert Rev. Mol. Med.* 11:e9
14. Chen X, Walker DG, Schmidt AM, Arancio O, Lue LF, Yan SD. 2007. RAGE: a potential target for Aβ-mediated cellular perturbation in Alzheimer's disease. *Curr. Mol. Med.* 7:735–42
15. Read CM, Cary PD, Crane-Robinson C, Driscoll PC, Norman DG. 1993. Solution structure of a DNA-binding domain from HMG1. *Nucleic Acids Res.* 21:3427–36
16. Thomas JO. 2001. HMG1 and 2: architectural DNA-binding proteins. *Biochem. Soc. Trans.* 29:395–401
17. Thomas JO, Travers AA. 2001. HMG1 and 2, and related 'architectural' DNA-binding proteins. *Trends Biochem. Sci.* 26:167–74
18. Stros M, Stokrova J, Thomas JO. 1994. DNA looping by the HMG-box domains of HMG1 and modulation of DNA binding by the acidic C-terminal domain. *Nucleic Acids Res.* 22:1044–51
19. Watson M, Stott K, Thomas JO. 2007. Mapping intramolecular interactions between domains in HMGB1 using a tail-truncation approach. *J. Mol. Biol.* 374:1286–97
20. Sparvero LJ, Asafu-Adjei D, Kang R, Tang D, Amin N, et al. 2009. RAGE (receptor for advanced glycation endproducts), RAGE ligands, and their role in cancer and inflammation. *J. Transl. Med.* 7:17
21. **Wang H, Bloom O, Zhang M, Vishnubhakat JM, Ombrellino M, et al. 1999. HMG-1 as a late mediator of endotoxin lethality in mice. *Science* 285:248–51**
22. **Scaffidi P, Misteli T, Bianchi ME. 2002. Release of chromatin protein HMGB1 by necrotic cells triggers inflammation. *Nature* 418:191–95**
23. Bell CW, Jiang W, Reich CF 3rd, Pisetsky DS. 2006. The extracellular release of HMGB1 during apoptotic cell death. *Am. J. Physiol. Cell Physiol.* 291:C1318–25
24. Jiang W, Bell CW, Pisetsky DS. 2007. The relationship between apoptosis and high-mobility group protein 1 release from murine macrophages stimulated with lipopolysaccharide or polyinosinic-polycytidylic acid. *J. Immunol.* 178:6495–503
25. **Kazama H, Ricci JE, Herndon JM, Hoppe G, Green DR, Ferguson TA. 2008. Induction of immunological tolerance by apoptotic cells requires caspase-dependent oxidation of high-mobility group box-1 protein. *Immunity* 29:21–32**
26. Ito I, Fukazawa J, Yoshida M. 2007. Post-translational methylation of high mobility group box 1 (HMGB1) causes its cytoplasmic localization in neutrophils. *J. Biol. Chem.* 282:16336–44
27. Bonaldi T, Talamo F, Scaffidi P, Ferrera D, Porto A, et al. 2003. Monocytic cells hyperacetylate chromatin protein HMGB1 to redirect it towards secretion. *EMBO J.* 22:5551–60
28. Youn JH, Shin JS. 2006. Nucleocytoplasmic shuttling of HMGB1 is regulated by phosphorylation that redirects it toward secretion. *J. Immunol.* 177:7889–97
29. Gardella S, Andrei C, Ferrera D, Lotti LV, Torrisi MR, et al. 2002. The nuclear protein HMGB1 is secreted by monocytes via a non-classical, vesicle-mediated secretory pathway. *EMBO Rep.* 3:995–1001
30. Rendon-Mitchell B, Ochani M, Li J, Han J, Wang H, et al. 2003. IFN-γ induces high mobility group box 1 protein release partly through a TNF-dependent mechanism. *J. Immunol.* 170:3890–97
31. Ulloa L, Ochani M, Yang H, Tanovic M, Halperin D, et al. 2002. Ethyl pyruvate prevents lethality in mice with established lethal sepsis and systemic inflammation. *Proc. Natl. Acad. Sci. USA* 99:12351–56
32. Wang H, Liao H, Ochani M, Justiniani M, Lin X, et al. 2004. Cholinergic agonists inhibit HMGB1 release and improve survival in experimental sepsis. *Nat. Med.* 10:1216–21
33. Ulloa L, Messmer D. 2006. High-mobility group box 1 (HMGB1) protein: friend and foe. *Cytokine Growth Factor Rev.* 17:189–201

21. HMGB1 is released following cytokine stimulation and is important in sepsis.

22. First report describing that for necrotic cell death to induce inflammation HMGB1 is required.

25. Demonstration that oxidation of HMGB1 is important in tolerance induction mediated by apoptotic cells.

34. Kim JH, Kim SJ, Lee IS, Lee MS, Uematsu S, et al. 2009. Bacterial endotoxin induces the release of high mobility group box 1 via the IFN-β signaling pathway. *J. Immunol.* 182:2458–66
35. Andersson U, Erlandsson-Harris H. 2004. HMGB1 is a potent trigger of arthritis. *J. Intern. Med.* 255:344–50
36. Rouhiainen A, Tumova S, Valmu L, Kalkkinen N, Rauvala H. 2007. Pivotal advance: analysis of proinflammatory activity of highly purified eukaryotic recombinant HMGB1 (amphoterin). *J. Leukoc. Biol.* 81:49–58
37. **Tian J, Avalos AM, Mao SY, Chen B, Senthil K, et al. 2007. Toll-like receptor 9-dependent activation by DNA-containing immune complexes is mediated by HMGB1 and RAGE. *Nat. Immunol.* 8:487–96**

37. HMGB1 is a component of DNA immune complexes and signals though TLR9 and RAGE.

38. Sha Y, Zmijewski J, Xu Z, Abraham E. 2008. HMGB1 develops enhanced proinflammatory activity by binding to cytokines. *J. Immunol.* 180:2531–37
39. Ivanov S, Dragoi AM, Wang X, Dallacosta C, Louten J, et al. 2007. A novel role for HMGB1 in TLR9-mediated inflammatory responses to CpG-DNA. *Blood* 110:1970–81
40. Messmer D, Yang H, Telusma G, Knoll F, Li J, et al. 2004. High mobility group box protein 1: an endogenous signal for dendritic cell maturation and Th1 polarization. *J. Immunol.* 173:307–13
41. Dumitriu IE, Baruah P, Valentinis B, Voll RE, Herrmann M, et al. 2005. Release of high mobility group box 1 by dendritic cells controls T cell activation via the receptor for advanced glycation end products. *J. Immunol.* 174:7506–15
42. Dumitriu IE, Baruah P, Bianchi ME, Manfredi AA, Rovere-Querini P. 2005. Requirement of HMGB1 and RAGE for the maturation of human plasmacytoid dendritic cells. *Eur. J. Immunol.* 35:2184–90
43. Dumitriu IE, Baruah P, Valentinis B, Voll RE, Herrmann M, et al. 2005. Release of high mobility group box 1 by dendritic cells controls T cell activation via the receptor for advanced glycation end products. *J. Immunol.* 174:7506–15
44. Yang D, Chen Q, Yang H, Tracey KJ, Bustin M, Oppenheim JJ. 2007. High mobility group box-1 protein induces the migration and activation of human dendritic cells and acts as an alarmin. *J. Leukoc. Biol.* 81:59–66
45. Manfredi AA, Capobianco A, Esposito A, De Cobelli F, Canu T, et al. 2008. Maturing dendritic cells depend on RAGE for in vivo homing to lymph nodes. *J. Immunol.* 180:2270–75
46. Rouhiainen A, Imai S, Rauvala H, Parkkinen J. 2000. Occurrence of amphoterin (HMG1) as an endogenous protein of human platelets that is exported to the cell surface upon platelet activation. *Thromb. Haemost.* 84:1087–94
47. Orlova VV, Choi EY, Xie C, Chavakis E, Bierhaus A, et al. 2007. A novel pathway of HMGB1-mediated inflammatory cell recruitment that requires Mac-1-integrin. *EMBO J.* 26:1129–39
48. Fiuza C, Bustin M, Talwar S, Tropea M, Gerstenberger E, et al. 2003. Inflammation-promoting activity of HMGB1 on human microvascular endothelial cells. *Blood* 101:2652–60
49. Liu JH, Li ZJ, Tang J, Liu YW, Zhao L, et al. 2006. High mobility group box-1 protein activates endothelial cells to produce cytokines and has synergistic effect with lipopolysaccharide in inducing interleukin-6 release. *Zhonghua Yi Xue Za Zhi* 86:1191–95
50. Agresti A, Bianchi ME. 2003. HMGB proteins and gene expression. *Curr. Opin. Genet. Dev.* 13:170–78
51. Paull TT, Haykinson MJ, Johnson RC. 1993. The nonspecific DNA-binding and -bending proteins HMG1 and HMG2 promote the assembly of complex nucleoprotein structures. *Genes Dev.* 7:1521–34
52. Grosschedl R, Giese K, Pagel J. 1994. HMG domain proteins: architectural elements in the assembly of nucleoprotein structures. *Trends Genet.* 10:94–100
53. Means TK, Latz E, Hayashi F, Murali MR, Golenbock DT, Luster AD. 2005. Human lupus autoantibody-DNA complexes activate DCs through cooperation of CD32 and TLR9. *J. Clin. Invest.* 115:407–17
54. Deleted in proof
55. Lovgren T, Eloranta ML, Bave U, Alm GV, Ronnblom L. 2004. Induction of interferon-α production in plasmacytoid dendritic cells by immune complexes containing nucleic acid released by necrotic or late apoptotic cells and lupus IgG. *Arthritis Rheum.* 50:1861–72

56. Bave U, Magnusson M, Eloranta ML, Perers A, Alm GV, Ronnblom L. 2003. FcγRIIa is expressed on natural IFN-α-producing cells (plasmacytoid dendritic cells) and is required for the IFN-α production induced by apoptotic cells combined with lupus IgG. *J. Immunol.* 171:3296–302
57. Baumann I, Kolowos W, Voll RE, Manger B, Gaipl U, et al. 2002. Impaired uptake of apoptotic cells into tingible body macrophages in germinal centers of patients with systemic lupus erythematosus. *Arthritis Rheum.* 46:191–201
58. Urbonaviciute V, Furnrohr BG, Meister S, Munoz L, Heyder P, et al. 2008. Induction of inflammatory and immune responses by HMGB1-nucleosome complexes: implications for the pathogenesis of SLE. *J. Exp. Med.* 205:3007–18
59. Youn JH, Oh YJ, Kim ES, Choi JE, Shin JS. 2008. High mobility group box 1 protein binding to lipopolysaccharide facilitates transfer of lipopolysaccharide to CD14 and enhances lipopolysaccharide-mediated TNF-α production in human monocytes. *J. Immunol.* 180:5067–74
60. El Mezayen R, El Gazzar M, Seeds MC, McCall CE, Dreskin SC, Nicolls MR. 2007. Endogenous signals released from necrotic cells augment inflammatory responses to bacterial endotoxin. *Immunol. Lett.* 111:36–44
61. Campana L, Bosurgi L, Bianchi ME, Manfredi AA, Rovere-Querini P. 2009. Requirement of HMGB1 for stromal cell-derived factor-1/CXCL12-dependent migration of macrophages and dendritic cells. *J. Leukoc. Biol.* 86:609–15
62. Chen GY, Tang J, Zheng P, Liu Y. 2009. CD24 and Siglec-10 selectively repress tissue damage-induced immune responses. *Science* 323:1722–25
63. Van de Wouwer M, Collen D, Conway EM. 2004. Thrombomodulin-protein C-EPCR system: integrated to regulate coagulation and inflammation. *Arterioscler. Thromb. Vasc. Biol.* 24:1374–83
64. Abeyama K, Stern DM, Ito Y, Kawahara K, Yoshimoto Y, et al. 2005. The N-terminal domain of thrombomodulin sequesters high-mobility group-B1 protein, a novel antiinflammatory mechanism. *J. Clin. Invest.* 115:1267–74
65. Ito T, Kawahara K, Nakamura T, Yamada S, Nakamura T, et al. 2007. High-mobility group box 1 protein promotes development of microvascular thrombosis in rats. *J. Thromb. Haemost.* 5:109–16
66. Angus DC, Wax RS. 2001. Epidemiology of sepsis: an update. *Crit. Care Med.* 29:S109–16
67. Wang H, Yang H, Tracey KJ. 2004. Extracellular role of HMGB1 in inflammation and sepsis. *J. Intern. Med.* 255:320–31
68. Wang H, Bloom O, Zhang M, Vishnubhakat JM, Ombrellino M, et al. 1999. HMG-1 as a late mediator of endotoxin lethality in mice. *Science* 285:248–51
69. Abraham E, Arcaroli J, Carmody A, Wang H, Tracey KJ. 2000. HMG-1 as a mediator of acute lung inflammation. *J. Immunol.* 165:2950–54
70. Liliensiek B, Weigand MA, Bierhaus A, Nicklas W, Kasper M, et al. 2004. Receptor for advanced glycation end products (RAGE) regulates sepsis but not the adaptive immune response. *J. Clin. Invest.* 113:1641–50
71. Yang H, Ochani M, Li J, Qiang X, Tanovic M, et al. 2004. Reversing established sepsis with antagonists of endogenous high-mobility group box 1. *Proc. Natl. Acad. Sci. USA* 101:296–301
72. Lutterloh EC, Opal SM, Pittman DD, Keith JC Jr, Tan XY, et al. 2007. Inhibition of the RAGE products increases survival in experimental models of severe sepsis and systemic infection. *Crit. Care* 11:R122
73. Rittirsch D, Flierl MA, Nadeau BA, Day DE, Huber-Lang M, et al. 2008. Functional roles for C5a receptors in sepsis. *Nat. Med.* 14:551–57
74. Plitas G, Burt BM, Nguyen HM, Bamboat ZM, DeMatteo RP. 2008. Toll-like receptor 9 inhibition reduces mortality in polymicrobial sepsis. *J. Exp. Med.* 205:1277–83
75. Peltz ED, Moore EE, Eckels PC, Damle SS, Tsuruta Y, et al. 2009. HMGB1 is markedly elevated within 6 hours of mechanical trauma in humans. *Shock* 32:17–22
76. Kohno T, Anzai T, Naito K, Miyasho T, Okamoto M, et al. 2009. Role of high-mobility group box 1 protein in post-infarction healing process and left ventricular remodelling. *Cardiovasc. Res.* 81:565–73
77. Goldstein RS, Gallowitsch-Puerta M, Yang L, Rosas-Ballina M, Huston JM, et al. 2006. Elevated high-mobility group box 1 levels in patients with cerebral and myocardial ischemia. *Shock* 25:571–74

58. HMGB1-associated nucleosomes signal though TLR2 and induce cytokine secretion.

62. Demonstrated a novel role for CD24-HMGB1 in distinguishing between microbial- and injury-associated inflammation during sterile inflammation.

78. Nakamura T, Fujiwara N, Sato E, Kawagoe Y, Ueda Y, et al. 2009. Effect of polymyxin B-immobilized fiber hemoperfusion on serum high mobility group box-1 protein levels and oxidative stress in patients with acute respiratory distress syndrome. *ASAIO J.* 55:395–99
79. Tsung A, Sahai R, Tanaka H, Nakao A, Fink MP, et al. 2005. The nuclear factor HMGB1 mediates hepatic injury after murine liver ischemia-reperfusion. *J. Exp. Med.* 201:1135–43
80. Tsung A, Klune JR, Zhang X, Jeyabalan G, Cao Z, et al. 2007. HMGB1 release induced by liver ischemia involves Toll-like receptor 4 dependent reactive oxygen species production and calcium-mediated signaling. *J. Exp. Med.* 204:2913–23
81. Levy RM, Mollen KP, Prince JM, Kaczorowski DJ, Vallabhaneni R, et al. 2007. Systemic inflammation and remote organ injury following trauma require HMGB1. *Am. J. Physiol. Regul. Integr. Comp. Physiol.* 293:R1538–44
82. Kaczorowski DJ, Nakao A, Vallabhaneni R, Mollen KP, Sugimoto R, et al. 2009. Mechanisms of Toll-like receptor 4 (TLR4)-mediated inflammation after cold ischemia/reperfusion in the heart. *Transplantation* 87:1455–63
83. Cataldegirmen G, Zeng S, Feirt N, Ippagunta N, Dun H, et al. 2005. RAGE limits regeneration after massive liver injury by coordinated suppression of TNF-α and NF-κB. *J. Exp. Med.* 201:473–84
84. Bucciarelli LG, Kaneko M, Ananthakrishnan R, Harja E, Lee LK, et al. 2006. Receptor for advanced-glycation end products: key modulator of myocardial ischemic injury. *Circulation* 113:1226–34
85. Izuishi K, Tsung A, Jeyabalan G, Critchlow ND, Li J, et al. 2006. Cutting edge: High-mobility group box 1 preconditioning protects against liver ischemia-reperfusion injury. *J. Immunol.* 176:7154–58
86. Pisetsky DS, Erlandsson-Harris H, Andersson U. 2008. High-mobility group box protein 1 (HMGB1): an alarmin mediating the pathogenesis of rheumatic disease. *Arthritis Res. Ther.* 10:209
87. Kokkola R, Li J, Sundberg E, Aveberger AC, Palmblad K, et al. 2003. Successful treatment of collagen-induced arthritis in mice and rats by targeting extracellular high mobility group box chromosomal protein 1 activity. *Arthritis Rheum.* 48:2052–58
88. Pullerits R, Jonsson IM, Kollias G, Tarkowski A. 2008. Induction of arthritis by high mobility group box chromosomal protein 1 is independent of tumour necrosis factor signalling. *Arthritis Res. Ther.* 10:R72
89. Sundberg E, Grundtman C, Af Klint E, Lindberg J, Ernestam S, et al. 2008. Systemic TNF blockade does not modulate synovial expression of the pro-inflammatory mediator HMGB1 in rheumatoid arthritis patients—a prospective clinical study. *Arthritis Res. Ther.* 10:R33
90. Herrmann M, Voll RE, Zoller OM, Hagenhofer M, Ponner BB, Kalden JR. 1998. Impaired phagocytosis of apoptotic cell material by monocyte-derived macrophages from patients with systemic lupus erythematosus. *Arthritis Rheum.* 41:1241–50
91. Sanford AN, Dietzmann K, Sullivan KE. 2005. Apoptotic cells, autoantibodies, and the role of HMGB1 in the subcellular localization of an autoantigen. *J. Autoimmun.* 25:264–71
92. Qing X, Pitashny M, Thomas DB, Barrat FJ, Hogarth MP, Putterman C. 2008. Pathogenic anti-DNA antibodies modulate gene expression in mesangial cells: involvement of HMGB1 in anti-DNA antibody-induced renal injury. *Immunol. Lett.* 121:61–73
93. Yoshizaki A, Komura K, Iwata Y, Ogawa F, Hara T, et al. 2009. Clinical significance of serum HMGB-1 and sRAGE levels in systemic sclerosis: association with disease severity. *J. Clin. Immunol.* 29:180–89
94. Hamada N, Maeyama T, Kawaguchi T, Yoshimi M, Fukumoto J, et al. 2008. The role of high mobility group box1 in pulmonary fibrosis. *Am. J. Respir. Cell Mol. Biol.* 39:440–47
95. Ellerman JE, Brown CK, de Vera M, Zeh HJ, Billiar T, et al. 2007. Masquerader: high mobility group box-1 and cancer. *Clin. Cancer Res.* 13:2836–48
96. Brezniceanu ML, Volp K, Bosser S, Solbach C, Lichter P, et al. 2003. HMGB1 inhibits cell death in yeast and mammalian cells and is abundantly expressed in human breast carcinoma. *FASEB J.* 17:1295–97
97. Choi YR, Kim H, Kang HJ, Kim NG, Kim JJ, et al. 2003. Overexpression of high mobility group box 1 in gastrointestinal stromal tumors with KIT mutation. *Cancer Res.* 63:2188–93
98. Chung HW, Lee SG, Kim H, Hong DJ, Chung JB, et al. 2009. Serum high mobility group box-1 (HMGB1) is closely associated with the clinical and pathologic features of gastric cancer. *J. Transl. Med.* 7:38

99. Poser I, Golob M, Buettner R, Bosserhoff AK. 2003. Upregulation of HMG1 leads to melanoma inhibitory activity expression in malignant melanoma cells and contributes to their malignancy phenotype. *Mol. Cell. Biol.* 23:2991–98
100. Sasahira T, Kirita T, Oue N, Bhawal UK, Yamamoto K, et al. 2008. High mobility group box-1-inducible melanoma inhibitory activity is associated with nodal metastasis and lymphangiogenesis in oral squamous cell carcinoma. *Cancer Sci.* 99:1806–12
101. Schlueter C, Weber H, Meyer B, Rogalla P, Roser K, et al. 2005. Angiogenetic signaling through hypoxia: HMGB1: an angiogenetic switch molecule. *Am. J. Pathol.* 166:1259–63
102. Taguchi A, Blood DC, del Toro G, Canet A, Lee DC, et al. 2000. Blockade of RAGE-amphoterin signalling suppresses tumour growth and metastases. *Nature* 405:354–60
103. van Beijnum JR, Petersen K, Griffioen AW. 2009. Tumor endothelium is characterized by a matrix remodeling signature. *Front. Biosci.* 1:216–25
104. Apetoh L, Ghiringhelli F, Tesniere A, Obeid M, Ortiz C, et al. 2007. Toll-like receptor 4-dependent contribution of the immune system to anticancer chemotherapy and radiotherapy. *Nat. Med.* 13:1050–59
105. Malherbe P, Richards JG, Gaillard H, Thompson A, Diener C, et al. 1999. cDNA cloning of a novel secreted isoform of the human receptor for advanced glycation end products and characterization of cells co-expressing cell-surface scavenger receptors and Swedish mutant amyloid precursor protein. *Brain Res. Mol. Brain Res.* 71:159–70
106. Schmidt AM, Yan SD, Yan SF, Stern DM. 2001. The multiligand receptor RAGE as a progression factor amplifying immune and inflammatory responses. *J. Clin. Invest.* 108:949–55
107. Dattilo BM, Fritz G, Leclerc E, Kooi CW, Heizmann CW, Chazin WJ. 2007. The extracellular region of the receptor for advanced glycation end products is composed of two independent structural units. *Biochemistry* 46:6957–70
108. Ostendorp T, Leclerc E, Galichet A, Koch M, Demling N, et al. 2007. Structural and functional insights into RAGE activation by multimeric S100B. *EMBO J.* 26:3868–78
109. Wilton R, Yousef MA, Saxena P, Szpunar M, Stevens FJ. 2006. Expression and purification of recombinant human receptor for advanced glycation endproducts in *Escherichia coli*. *Protein Expr. Purif.* 47:25–35
110. Hudson BI, Carter AM, Harja E, Kalea AZ, Arriero M, et al. 2008. Identification, classification, and expression of RAGE gene splice variants. *FASEB J.* 22:1572–80
111. Raucci A, Cugusi S, Antonelli A, Barabino SM, Monti L, et al. 2008. A soluble form of the receptor for advanced glycation endproducts (RAGE) is produced by proteolytic cleavage of the membrane-bound form by the sheddase a disintegrin and metalloprotease 10 (ADAM10). *FASEB J.* 22:3716–27
112. Katsuoka F, Kawakami Y, Arai T, Imuta H, Fujiwara M, et al. 1997. Type II alveolar epithelial cells in lung express receptor for advanced glycation end products (RAGE) gene. *Biochem. Biophys. Res. Commun.* 238:512–16
113. Fehrenbach H, Kasper M, Tschernig T, Shearman MS, Schuh D, Muller M. 1998. Receptor for advanced glycation endproducts (RAGE) exhibits highly differential cellular and subcellular localisation in rat and human lung. *Cell. Mol. Biol. (Noisy-le-grand)* 44:1147–57
114. Schmidt AM, Yan SD, Brett J, Mora R, Nowygrod R, Stern D. 1993. Regulation of human mononuclear phagocyte migration by cell surface-binding proteins for advanced glycation end products. *J. Clin. Invest.* 91:2155–68
115. Brett J, Schmidt AM, Yan SD, Zou YS, Weidman E, et al. 1993. Survey of the distribution of a newly characterized receptor for advanced glycation end products in tissues. *Am. J. Pathol.* 143:1699–712
116. Huttunen HJ, Fages C, Rauvala H. 1999. Receptor for advanced glycation end products (RAGE)-mediated neurite outgrowth and activation of NF-κB require the cytoplasmic domain of the receptor but different downstream signaling pathways. *J. Biol. Chem.* 274:19919–24
117. Li J, Qu X, Schmidt AM. 1998. Sp1-binding elements in the promoter of RAGE are essential for amphoterin-mediated gene expression in cultured neuroblastoma cells. *J. Biol. Chem.* 273:30870–78
118. Li J, Schmidt AM. 1997. Characterization and functional analysis of the promoter of RAGE, the receptor for advanced glycation end products. *J. Biol. Chem.* 272:16498–506
119. Sakaguchi T, Yan SF, Yan SD, Belov D, Rong LL, et al. 2003. Central role of RAGE-dependent neointimal expansion in arterial restenosis. *J. Clin. Invest.* 111:959–72

120. Hofmann MA, Drury S, Fu C, Qu W, Taguchi A, et al. 1999. RAGE mediates a novel proinflammatory axis: a central cell surface receptor for S100/calgranulin polypeptides. *Cell* 97:889–901

121. Huttunen HJ, Kuja-Panula J, Sorci G, Agneletti AL, Donato R, Rauvala H. 2000. Coregulation of neurite outgrowth and cell survival by amphoterin and S100 proteins through receptor for advanced glycation end products (RAGE) activation. *J. Biol. Chem.* 275:40096–105

122. Palumbo R, De Marchis F, Pusterla T, Conti A, Alessio M, Bianchi ME. 2009. Src family kinases are necessary for cell migration induced by extracellular HMGB1. *J. Leukoc. Biol.* 86:617–23

123. Bassi R, Giussani P, Anelli V, Colleoni T, Pedrazzi M, et al. 2008. HMGB1 as an autocrine stimulus in human T98G glioblastoma cells: role in cell growth and migration. *J. Neurooncol.* 87:23–33

124. Dukic-Stefanovic S, Gasic-Milenkovic J, Deuther-Conrad W, Munch G. 2003. Signal transduction pathways in mouse microglia N-11 cells activated by advanced glycation endproducts (AGEs). *J. Neurochem.* 87:44–55

125. Toure F, Zahm JM, Garnotel R, Lambert E, Bonnet N, et al. 2008. Receptor for advanced glycation end-products (RAGE) modulates neutrophil adhesion and migration on glycoxidated extracellular matrix. *Biochem. J.* 416:255–61

126. Hudson BI, Kalea AZ, Del Mar Arriero M, Harja E, Boulanger E, et al. 2008. Interaction of the RAGE cytoplasmic domain with diaphanous-1 is required for ligand-stimulated cellular migration through activation of Rac1 and Cdc42. *J. Biol. Chem.* 283:34457–68

127. Kim JY, Park HK, Yoon JS, Kim SJ, Kim ES, et al. 2008. Advanced glycation end product (AGE)-induced proliferation of HEL cells via receptor for AGE-related signal pathways. *Int. J. Oncol.* 33:493–501

128. Reddy MA, Li SL, Sahar S, Kim YS, Xu ZG, et al. 2006. Key role of src kinase in S100B-induced activation of the receptor for advanced glycation end products in vascular smooth muscle cells. *J. Biol. Chem.* 281:13685–93

129. Ishihara K, Tsutsumi K, Kawane S, Nakajima M, Kasaoka T. 2003. The receptor for advanced glycation end-products (RAGE) directly binds to ERK by a D-domain-like docking site. *FEBS Lett.* 550:107–13

130. Allen WE, Zicha D, Ridley AJ, Jones GE. 1998. A role for Cdc42 in macrophage chemotaxis. *J. Cell Biol.* 141:1147–57

131. Ridley AJ, Allen WE, Peppelenbosch M, Jones GE. 1999. Rho family proteins and cell migration. *Biochem. Soc. Symp.* 65:111–23

132. Tominaga T, Sahai E, Chardin P, McCormick F, Courtneidge SA, Alberts AS. 2000. Diaphanous-related formins bridge Rho GTPase and Src tyrosine kinase signaling. *Mol. Cell* 5:13–25

133. Munch G, Schicktanz D, Behme A, Gerlach M, Riederer P, et al. 1999. Amino acid specificity of glycation and protein-AGE crosslinking reactivities determined with a dipeptide SPOT library. *Nat. Biotechnol.* 17:1006–10

134. Kaneko M, Bucciarelli L, Hwang YC, Lee L, Yan SF, et al. 2005. Aldose reductase and AGE-RAGE pathways: key players in myocardial ischemic injury. *Ann. N. Y. Acad. Sci.* 1043:702–9

135. Miyata T, Ueda Y, Yamada Y, Izuhara Y, Wada T, et al. 1998. Accumulation of carbonyls accelerates the formation of pentosidine, an advanced glycation end product: carbonyl stress in uremia. *J. Am. Soc. Nephrol.* 9:2349–56

136. Huebschmann AG, Regensteiner JG, Vlassara H, Reusch JE. 2006. Diabetes and advanced glycoxidation end products. *Diabetes Care* 29:1420–32

137. Srikanth V, Maczurek A, Phan T, Steele M, Westcott B, et al. 2009. Advanced glycation endproducts and their receptor RAGE in Alzheimer's disease. *Neurobiol. Aging.* In press

138. Li YM, Tan AX, Vlassara H. 1995. Antibacterial activity of lysozyme and lactoferrin is inhibited by binding of advanced glycation-modified proteins to a conserved motif. *Nat. Med.* 1:1057–61

139. Heizmann CW, Fritz G, Schafer BW. 2002. S100 proteins: structure, functions and pathology. *Front. Biosci.* 7:d1356–68

140. Donato R. 2001. S100: a multigenic family of calcium-modulated proteins of the EF-hand type with intracellular and extracellular functional roles. *Int. J. Biochem. Cell Biol.* 33:637–68

141. Tarabykina S, Kriajevska M, Scott DJ, Hill TJ, Lafitte D, et al. 2000. Heterocomplex formation between metastasis-related protein S100A4 (Mts1) and S100A1 as revealed by the yeast two-hybrid system. *FEBS Lett.* 475:187–91

142. Kiryushko D, Novitskaya V, Soroka V, Klingelhofer J, Lukanidin E, et al. 2006. Molecular mechanisms of Ca^{2+} signaling in neurons induced by the S100A4 protein. *Mol. Cell. Biol.* 26:3625–38
143. Frosch M, Strey A, Vogl T, Wulffraat NM, Kuis W, et al. 2000. Myeloid-related proteins 8 and 14 are specifically secreted during interaction of phagocytes and activated endothelium and are useful markers for monitoring disease activity in pauciarticular-onset juvenile rheumatoid arthritis. *Arthritis Rheum.* 43:628–37
144. Foell D, Roth J. 2004. Proinflammatory S100 proteins in arthritis and autoimmune disease. *Arthritis Rheum.* 50:3762–71
145. Leclerc E, Fritz G, Vetter SW, Heizmann CW. 2009. Binding of S100 proteins to RAGE: an update. *Biochim. Biophys. Acta* 1793:993–1007
146. Wolf R, Howard OM, Dong HF, Voscopoulos C, Boeshans K, et al. 2008. Chemotactic activity of S100A7 (psoriasin) is mediated by the receptor for advanced glycation end products and potentiates inflammation with highly homologous but functionally distinct S100A15. *J. Immunol.* 181:1499–506
147. Ryckman C, Vandal K, Rouleau P, Talbot M, Tessier PA. 2003. Proinflammatory activities of S100: proteins S100A8, S100A9, and S100A8/A9 induce neutrophil chemotaxis and adhesion. *J. Immunol.* 170:3233–42
148. Vogl T, Tenbrock K, Ludwig S, Leukert N, Ehrhardt C, et al. 2007. Mrp8 and Mrp14 are endogenous activators of Toll-like receptor 4, promoting lethal, endotoxin-induced shock. *Nat. Med.* 13:1042–49
149. Bjork P, Bjork A, Vogl T, Stenstrom M, Liberg D, et al. 2009. Identification of human S100A9 as a novel target for treatment of autoimmune disease via binding to quinoline-3-carboxamides. *PLoS Biol.* 7:e97
150. Pusterla T, de Marchis F, Palumbo R, Bianchi ME. 2009. High mobility group B2 is secreted by myeloid cells and has mitogenic and chemoattractant activities similar to high mobility group B1. *Autoimmunity* 42:308–10
151. Yanai H, Ban T, Wang Z, Choi MK, Kawamura T, et al. 2009. HMGB proteins function as universal sentinels for nucleic-acid-mediated innate immune responses. *Nature* 462(7269):99–103

Slow Down and Survive: Enigmatic Immunoregulation by BTLA and HVEM

Theresa L. Murphy[1] and Kenneth M. Murphy[1,2]

[1]Department of Pathology and Immunology, [2]Howard Hughes Medical Institute, Washington University School of Medicine, St. Louis, Missouri 63110; email: tmurphy@wustl.edu, kmurphy@wustl.edu

Annu. Rev. Immunol. 2010. 28:389–411

The *Annual Review of Immunology* is online at immunol.annualreviews.org

This article's doi:
10.1146/annurev-immunol-030409-101202

0732-0582/10/0423-0389$20.00

Key Words

inhibitory receptor, costimulation, autoimmunity, immunoglobulin superfamily, TNF receptor superfamily

Abstract

B and T lymphocyte associated (BTLA) is an Ig domain superfamily protein with cytoplasmic immunoreceptor tyrosine-based inhibitory motifs. Its ligand, herpesvirus entry mediator (HVEM), is a tumor necrosis factor receptor superfamily member. The unique interaction between BTLA and HVEM allows for a system of bidirectional signaling that must be appropriately regulated to balance the outcome of the immune response. HVEM engagement of BTLA produces inhibitory signals through SH2 domain–containing protein tyrosine phosphatase 1 (Shp-1) and Shp-2 association, whereas BTLA engagement of HVEM produces proinflammatory signals via activation of NF-κB. The BTLA-HVEM interaction is intriguing and quite complex given that HVEM has four other ligands that also influence immune responses, the conventional TNF ligand LIGHT and lymphotoxin α, as well as herpes simplex virus glycoprotein D and the glycosylphosphatidylinositol-linked Ig domain protein CD160. BTLA-HVEM interactions have been shown to regulate responses in several pathogen and autoimmune settings, but our understanding of this complex system of interactions is certainly incomplete. Recent findings of spontaneous inflammation in BTLA-deficient mice may provide an important clue.

INTRODUCTION

Lymphocyte receptor signaling upon antigen encounter with either the T cell receptor or the B cell receptor can be modulated by a second signal delivered by either costimulators or coinhibitors (1–5). Costimulation of lymphocyte receptor signaling affects the duration and quality of the signal, leading to increased proliferation and lymphocyte survival. Engagement of coinhibitors leads to dampening or complete lack of lymphocyte receptor signaling and may be involved in suppression or termination of the response to antigen.

The focus of this review is the coinhibitory molecule B and T lymphocyte associated (BTLA, also known as CD272) (6, 7). Because of its unique interaction with the costimulatory molecule herpesvirus entry mediator (HVEM, also known as Tnfrsf14, ATAR, HVEA, LIGHTR, and TR2), BTLA is part of a bidirectional signaling complex that balances activation and inhibition during an immune response (8, 9). HVEM interacts with four other molecules in addition to BTLA. CD160 and glycoprotein D (gD), as well as BTLA, bind to the membrane distal cysteine-rich domain 1 (CRD1) of HVEM (8, 10). In contrast, LIGHT (lymphotoxin-like, inducible expression, competes with herpes simplex virus glycoprotein D for HVEM, a receptor expressed by T lymphocytes) and lymphotoxin α ($LT\alpha_3$) bind to CRD2 and CRD3 of HVEM (11). HVEM is referred to as a "molecular switch" (12) because of its capacity to deliver costimulatory signals when bound to LIGHT or LTα and to produce inhibitory signals when bound to BTLA or CD160.

T cell costimulators and coinhibitors belong to two structural families of surface proteins, either the immunoglobulin (Ig) superfamily or the tumor necrosis factor receptor (TNFR) superfamily. There are two Ig domain–containing costimulators whose counterreceptors also contain Ig domains, including CD28, which binds to CD80 and CD86, and ICOS (inducible T cell costimulator), which binds to ICOSL (1, 2). Costimulatory members of the TNFR superfamily include 4-1BB, OX40, CD27, CD30, CD40, and HVEM (3, 4). Each of these receptor molecules has a ligand that is a member of the TNF superfamily, namely 4-1BBL, OX40L, CD70, CD30L, CD40L, and LIGHT or LTα, respectively.

There are three inhibitory receptors for T cells that are members of the Ig superfamily: CTLA-4 (cytotoxic T lymphocyte antigen 4), which binds to CD80 and CD86 (13); PD-1 (programmed death 1), which has two ligands, PD-L1 and PD-L2, both of which are Ig domain–containing proteins (14); and BTLA. BTLA is unique among the Ig domain–containing inhibitory receptors because it binds to HVEM, a TNFR superfamily member, rather than to an Ig domain–containing protein (8, 15). Most studies of BTLA have focused on BTLA's regulation of T cells, but BTLA is also expressed on other cells such as B cells, dendritic cells (DCs), and other myeloid cells, where its function is less well understood.

DISCOVERY OF BTLA AND ITS INTERACTION WITH HVEM

BTLA was first discovered as being expressed more highly in Th1 cells than in Th2 cells (6) [later confirmed by proteomic analysis of surface proteins on Th1 and Th2 cells (16)] and as being an early marker of thymocyte positive selection (7). BTLA is a type I membrane glycoprotein with a single C-type Ig domain and three conserved tyrosine motifs in its cytoplasmic tail. Two of these tyrosine motifs are found within immunoreceptor tyrosine-based inhibition motifs (ITIMs). Thus, BTLA was predicted and then confirmed to have an inhibitory function in lymphocytes (6, 7).

BTLA has at least two splice variants. In addition to the major isoform containing the Ig domain, transmembrane region, and cytoplasmic domain, an isoform lacking the Ig domain and one lacking the transmembrane region have been observed (6, 7). The expression and function of the alternatively spliced isoforms have not been investigated. BTLA exists as three alleles in the mouse. The Balb/c and MRL/lpr alleles differ at one amino acid in the Ig domain, but C57BL/6 has nine additional differences in the Ig domain. These differences alter the predicted cysteine bonding pattern (17), although there is no difference in the binding of the various alleles to HVEM (8). A panel of antibodies has been prepared that can distinguish these alleles in mouse strains (17).

Because of its extracellular Ig domain, BTLA was expected to bind to a counterreceptor or ligand within the Ig domain superfamily, as do other costimulatory molecules. Early studies suggested that such a ligand might be the orphan B7 molecule B7x (B7H4) (6). However, using a BTLA tetramer to screen a retroviral spleen cDNA expression library, the ligand for BTLA was instead discovered to be HVEM (8). The interaction between BTLA and HVEM is conserved between mouse and human and was independently verified in a Biacore assay screening a panel of purified proteins for BTLA binding (15). The interaction between the inhibitory molecule BTLA and the costimulatory molecule HVEM provides an unexpected opportunity for cross-talk between the signaling by receptors of the Ig and TNFR superfamilies.

HVEM HAS CANONICAL TNF LIGANDS AND Ig DOMAIN LIGANDS

HVEM was originally discovered because of its role in allowing herpes simplex virus 1 (HSV1) entry into Chinese hamster ovary cells (18). This was later shown to be mediated by the HSV viral gD binding to HVEM (19). Three other groups identified mouse and human cDNAs for HVEM using homology-based searches for novel TNFRs (20–22). Subsequently, the TNF ligand LTα was identified as a ligand for HVEM using an HVEM-Fc fusion protein. A second TNF ligand, LIGHT, was identified as a binding partner for HVEM in a candidate-based search for new TNF ligands (23).

Investigators recently identified another HVEM ligand, CD160 (10, 24). Antibodies to CD160 strongly inhibit CD4$^+$ T cell proliferation and cytokine production, prompting a search for a binding partner other than MHC class I molecules with which natural killer (NK) cell–expressed CD160 binds with low affinity (25). A CD160-Fc fusion protein identified HVEM as a binding partner using a library from human B lymphocytes (10).

CD160 has an IgV domain and a glycosylphosphatidylinositol (GPI) anchor (26). Four isoforms of human CD160 have been observed, which result in proteins either with or without transmembrane and cytoplasmic domains and with or without the Ig domain (27). The transmembrane transcripts appeared to have restricted expression only in peripheral blood mononuclear cells and IL-15-activated NK cells (27). There is a single tyrosine within the cytoplasmic domain in human; however, in mouse, an isoform containing a transmembrane and cytoplasmic domain has not been observed. If the same splicing event that produces a transmembrane and cytoplasmic domain in human were to occur in mouse, the predicted cytoplasmic domain would contain only eight amino acids and would not contain a tyrosine residue (24), presumably reducing its potential for signaling in a manner similar to BTLA. This would mean that the transmembrane form only of human CD160 would have the intrinsic potential for tyrosine-based signaling.

HVEM is part of a network of shared ligand-receptor interactions within the TNF superfamily (**Figure 1**) (28, 29). LTα_3 is a homotrimeric soluble protein (30) and binds to TNFR1 and TNFR2 in addition to HVEM. LIGHT, a homotrimeric type II membrane protein (31), binds to LTβR and decoy receptor 3 (DcR3) as well as to HVEM (23, 32). This signaling network also includes TNF binding to TNFR1 and TNFR2 and LTα1β2 binding to LTβR. Thus, even without considering the role of BTLA in this interactome, the TNF-TNFR and LT$\alpha\beta$-LTβR systems control multiple physiological processes, including T cell homeostasis, inflammation, differentiation, and maintenance of lymphoid organs (28, 33, 34).

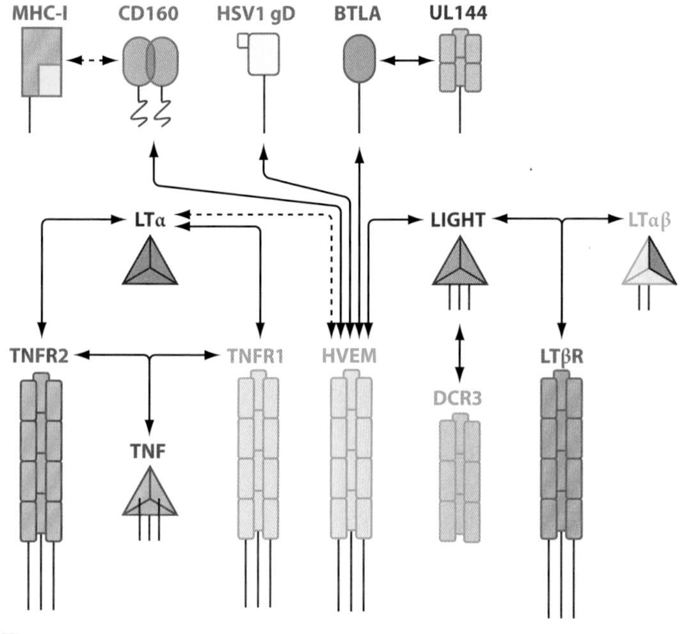

Figure 1

BTLA is part of a shared receptor-ligand network. BTLA binds to the TNF receptor superfamily member HVEM and the herpes virus protein UL144, which has homology to HVEM. HVEM also binds to herpes simplex virus protein glycoprotein D (HSV1 gD) and to the canonical TNF ligands LIGHT and LTα. LIGHT binds to LTβR and to decoy receptor 3 (DcR3), in addition to HVEM. LTα binds to TNFR1 and TNFR2 in addition to HVEM. The newest member of this network is CD160, a GPI-linked protein that binds to both HVEM and MHC class I molecules.

BROAD CELLULAR DISTRIBUTION OF PROTEINS ALLOWS FOR VARIED INTERACTIONS

Analysis of the functional outcome of BTLA engagement is complicated by the widespread and regulated expression of BTLA, CD160, and HVEM, and the latter's TNF ligands LIGHT and LTα. Most cells in the lymphoid compartment, including T cells, DCs, and B cells, express BTLA, CD160, HVEM, LIGHT, and LTα at some time, in either their resting or activated state. BTLA is expressed almost exclusively in cells of the immune system (6). BTLA is expressed at a low level by B cells in the bone marrow during the pro- and pre-B cell stages of development and at somewhat higher levels in immature B cells, and it is highly expressed on resting peripheral B cells (17). A low level of BTLA expression on bone marrow–derived CD11c$^+$ DCs is increased following lipopolysaccharide (LPS) stimulation (7). Interestingly, in vitro stimulation by LPS of B cells from C57BL/6 but not from BALB/c mice decreased BTLA expression, and BTLA was expressed on CD11b$^+$ macrophages and NK cells in C57BL/6 but not in BALB/c mice. However, the causes and consequences of these variations in expression have not been investigated.

BTLA is expressed by thymic T cells during positive selection (7). BTLA expression on naive CD4$^+$ T cells is low and is rapidly increased following antigen-specific activation with peak surface expression on day 2 (17). After multiple rounds of TCR activation in vitro, BTLA becomes preferentially expressed on Th1 cells, compared with Th2 cells, in mouse and human systems (6, 16). However, a separate study reported a loss of BTLA expression in both Th1 and Th2 clones, with heterogeneous but equivalent expression in Th1 and Th2 cultures (35). The basis for the difference between these findings and the initial cloning of BTLA by its selective expression in Th1 cells has not been resolved. In contrast to the inhibitory receptors PD-1 and CTLA-4, BTLA is not highly expressed on regulatory T cells (Tregs) (17). However, BTLA may have a role in maintaining tolerance or in anergy, given that it is highly expressed on anergic T cells generated by chronic exposure to antigen (17). A potential role for BTLA in T cell anergy is reminiscent of the function of PD-1 during chronic viral responses, where PD-1 is crucial for inducing CD8$^+$ T cell exhaustion (36). BTLA has recently been shown to be highly expressed on T follicular helper (Tfh) cells, which also express PD-1 (37, 38). These observations remain descriptive, and explanations for BTLA expression by Tfh are speculative (38). In summary, the widespread cellular distribution of BTLA on T cells, B cells, and DCs suggests that BTLA can deliver an inhibitory signal to many cells in the immune system.

HVEM shows a reciprocal expression pattern to that of BTLA during T cell activation. HVEM is highly expressed on naive T cells, but its expression decreases during T cell activation and is restored to high levels as cells become quiescent (39). HVEM downregulation may be mediated by interaction with LIGHT during T cell activation, given that blocking this interaction with HVEM-Fc fusion proteins or HVEM-specific antibodies prevents HVEM downregulation. HVEM expression is increased by activation of FoxP3$^+$ CD4$^+$ Tregs with αCD3 and αCD28 activation (40). Mouse B cells express low levels of HVEM, but this level is slightly increased following LPS activation. In contrast, naive and memory human B cells express high levels of HVEM, which are reduced following LIGHT stimulation and are undetectable on germinal center B cells. Similarly, LIGHT engagement leads to decreased HVEM expression on immature DCs (41). The dynamic regulation of HVEM is part of the mechanism for controlling HVEM's interactions with BTLA, CD160, and LIGHT.

CD160 was recently found to be a ligand for HVEM (10), similar to BTLA. CD160 is highly expressed on human CD56^{dim} CD16$^+$ NK cells, NKT cells, γδ T cells, and CD8$^+$ T cells and on all intestinal intraepithelial T lymphocytes (IELs) (CD8$^+$CD28$^-$CD101$^+$), but not on B or myeloid cells. In the mouse immune system, CD160 is expressed on most NKT cells and CD8$^+$ IELs and on 50% of CD4$^+$ IELs. In murine spleen, CD160 is expressed on memory CD8$^+$ T cells (CD44^{high}) and on 20% of NK cells, but only on a few CD4$^+$ T cells. CD160$^+$ CD4$^+$ T cells in skin may contribute to skin inflammation (42). Antigen activation of human CD8$^+$ CD28$^+$ T cells increases CD160 expression only after long periods, whereas in mouse CD8$^+$ T cells, CD160 is upregulated more rapidly (43, 44). In vivo activation of human CD4$^+$ T cells with αCD3 and αCD28 induced CD160 expression by day 3 following treatment (10). Because CD160 is a GPI-linked protein, it may be located predominantly in lipid rafts (10), and in NK cells it appears to colocalize with CD2 (45). IL-15 treatment of human NK lymphocytes induces metalloprotease-mediated shedding of a soluble form of CD160 (46). Thus, BTLA and CD160 have mostly nonoverlapping expression patterns, suggesting that their inhibitory actions may be distinct as well.

LIGHT is expressed on monocytes and granulocytes as well as on immature DCs from the spleen and lymph nodes (47, 48). Expression on DCs decreases during DC maturation (48), implying a possible role in early T cell activation. Development is normal in LIGHT$^{-/-}$ mice; however, LIGHT is involved neonatally in mesenteric lymph node formation (49, 50). In humans, TCR signals induce LIGHT expression in peripheral blood lymphocytes, but in mucosal tissues CD4$^+$ T cells and NK cells constitutively express LIGHT (51). LIGHT is a type II transmembrane protein with a C-terminal TNF homology domain that assembles into a homotrimer (23, 31), a structure that allows LIGHT to cluster its cell surface receptors HVEM and LTβR. However, biophysical analysis showed that the LIGHT homotrimer has only two high-affinity binding sites for the LTβR (52). Because the LTβR is not expressed in T or B cells, LIGHT's role in regulating these cells is presumably mediated primarily through interactions with HVEM (53).

LIGHT binding to HVEM may interact and influence BTLA's ability to bind HVEM. LIGHT can be proteolytically shed into a soluble form (39, 54), indicating that cell-cell contact may not be required for LIGHT-HVEM interaction. Overexpression of LIGHT on T cells is strongly activating, suggesting that the membrane form of LIGHT is a costimulatory molecule that may operate through signaling mechanisms that involve increased mitogen-activated protein (MAP) kinase activity (55–58). However, LIGHT itself does not have obvious signaling motifs (23). The bioavailability of LIGHT may be affected by the presence of DcR3 in humans, but the gene for DcR3 is not present in mice (32).

LTα lacks a transmembrane domain, unlike most TNF superfamily members. On its own, LTα is secreted as a homotrimer, $LT\alpha_3$, which is the form that interacts with HVEM as well as with TNFR1 and TNFR2 (23). LTα can also be found in heterotrimers with the type

II transmembrane protein LTβ. LTαβ heterotrimers bind to the LTβR. LTα has not been extensively studied in the context of the BTLA-HVEM interaction, but it could potentially behave similarly to the shed form of LIGHT.

STRUCTURAL STUDIES OF BTLA BOUND TO HVEM

The TNFR superfamily is characterized by multiple pseudorepeats of extracellular cysteine-rich domains (CRDs) (30). The extracellular domain of HVEM consists of four CRDs. Deletion mutation analysis showed that the N-terminal CRD (CRD1) is required for binding to a BTLA tetramer or to a Fc fusion protein (8). In contrast, LIGHT is predicted to contact HVEM using an elongated surface spanning CRD2 and 3 (31, 59) (**Figure 2**).

The crystal structure of the human BTLA-HVEM complex is in agreement with the deletion mutation analysis of HVEM binding to BTLA (60, 61). BTLA recognizes an extended β-strand in HVEM's CRD1 (residues 35–39, TVCEP), forming an intramolecular antiparallel β-sheet with residues 122–128 (NLIESHS) of human BTLA. BTLA and gD bind to an overlapping site on HVEM using a similar β-sheet motif (12). Although no crystal structure is available for CD160 bound to HVEM, deletion of CRD1 of HVEM abolished binding of CD160-Fc fusion protein and allowed binding of LIGHT-Fc fusion protein (10). This indicates that CD160 interacts with HVEM in the same region that BTLA interacts with HVEM. However, whereas BTLA-Ig could completely inhibit binding of CD160-Ig to HVEM, CD160-Ig only partially blocked binding of BTLA-Ig to HVEM, suggesting that the binding sites for BTLA and CD160 on HVEM might not completely overlap.

Because BTLA and LIGHT bind to regions on opposite sides of HVEM, a ternary complex between BTLA and LIGHT on one cell binding to HVEM on the opposing cell is physically possible (**Figure 2**). Soluble LIGHT enhances both the binding of BTLA-Fc to HVEM as well as the ability of membrane-bound BTLA to activate NF-κB through HVEM (12, 62). This indicates cooperativity in the formation of the ternary LIGHT-BTLA-HVEM complex when LIGHT is soluble. However, membrane-bound LIGHT noncompetitively disrupts the binding between HVEM and BTLA (12). Thus, regulation of protease cleavage of LIGHT may be essential for determining whether an inhibitory signal is provided by BTLA when engaging HVEM.

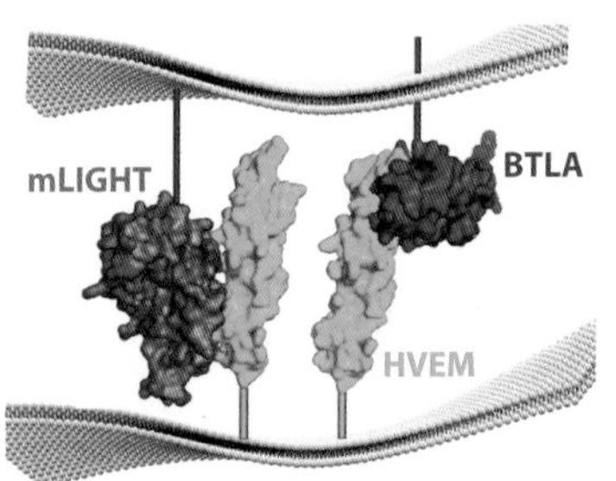

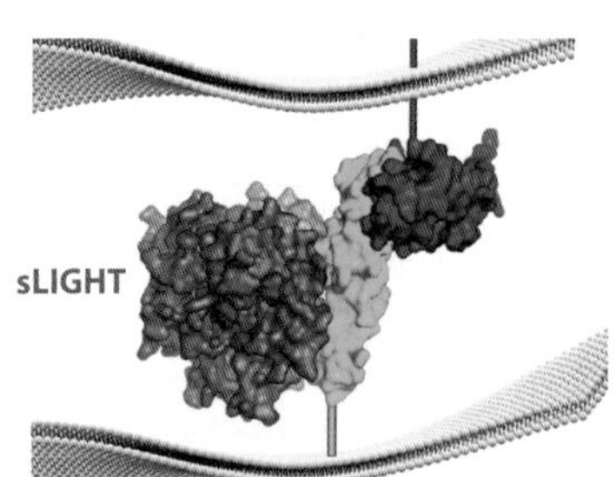

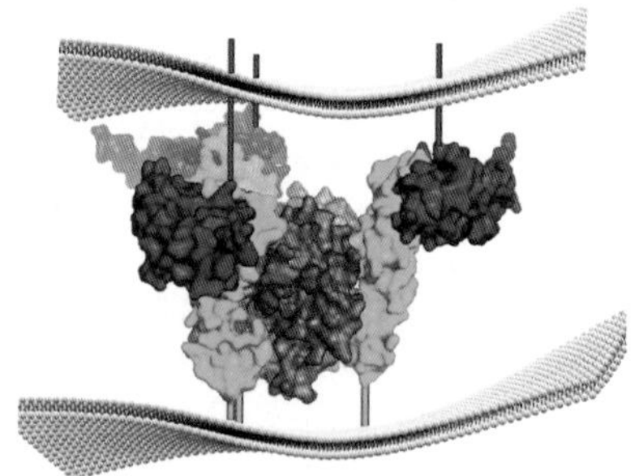

mLIGHT and BTLA bind opposite surfaces of HVEM, but mLIGHT may conformationally impede BTLA binding

sLIGHT may bind HVEM without impeding BTLA binding, allowing inhibition of cells that shed mLIGHT

Figure 2

Modeling the HVEM-LIGHT-BTLA ternary complex. Binding of LIGHT to HVEM was based on threading of HVEM through DR5 in the complex of DR5 with human TRAIL (PDB 1DU3), followed by superimposition of LIGHT onto TRAIL in the same structure. HVEM and BTLA binding was modeled as presented in 2AW2 structure (60). (mLIGHT, membrane-bound LIGHT; sLIGHT, soluble LIGHT.)

Binding of membrane LIGHT that is induced on activated T cells could displace HVEM from BTLA, decreasing inhibition through BTLA and increasing NF-κB activation through HVEM. Subsequent LIGHT cleavage would reestablish inhibition by enhancing the HVEM-BTLA interaction (28) (**Figure 2**). Further studies are needed to determine the nature of the ternary complex in vivo.

BTLA could interact with HVEM in *cis* (15, 28) on cells in which both BTLA and HVEM are expressed, such as T and B cells and DCs (**Figure 3**). Interactions in *trans* and *cis* are not mutually exclusive. *Trans* interactions do occur and result in transmission of inhibitory signals from cells expressing HVEM to cells expressing BTLA (8). However, this fact does not exclude the possibility that *cis* interactions may occur, act in a signaling capacity, or regulate the extent or quality of *trans* interactions. Instead, there could be dynamic interplay of *cis* and *trans* interactions, allowing for several routes of regulation. Conceivably, cells expressing BTLA and HVEM may not be stimulated by LIGHT as effectively as cells expressing HVEM alone because of *cis*-binding interactions (15, 28). Understanding the consequences of *cis* HVEM-BTLA interactions is currently an active area of research.

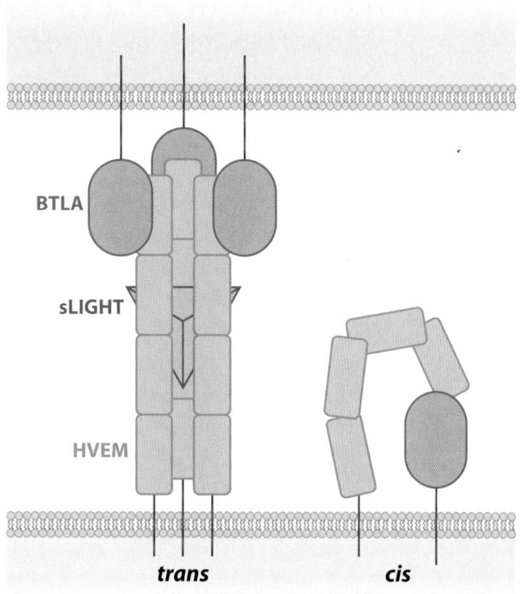

Figure 3

Trans versus *cis* interactions of HVEM and BTLA. *Trans* interactions occur between BTLA expressed on the surface of one cell and HVEM expressed on the surface of a separate cell. Expression of BTLA and HVEM on the surface of the same cell provides the possibility of *cis* interactions. *Cis* interactions could interfere with the ability of HVEM to be activated by LIGHT expressed by other cells, as recently proposed (15, 28).

SIGNALING THROUGH BTLA AND HVEM IS BIDIRECTIONAL

BTLA contains three tyrosine motifs in its cytoplasmic domain that are conserved from zebrafish to human (63). The membrane-proximal tyrosine is contained within a Grb-2 association motif, and the two membrane-distal tyrosines are each contained within ITIMs, similar to those in PD-1 and CTLA-4. All three tyrosines are phosphorylated upon treatment with pervanadate in T and B cells and by TCR cross-linking in a T cell hybridoma. SH2 domain–containing protein tyrosine phosphatase (Shp)-1 and Shp-2 are each recruited to the ITIMs of BTLA (8, 64, 65). For both mouse and human BTLA, Shp-1 and Shp-2 recruitment requires both ITIMs, in contrast to other inhibitory receptors such as PD-1 that require a single ITIM for Shp-1/2 recruitment. Recruitment of Shp-1 and Shp-2 is consistent with an inhibitory function for BTLA (66).

The membrane-proximal tyrosine is contained within the motif YDND. Using biotinylated peptides and mass spectrometry, investigators showed that this motif binds to Grb-2 as predicted and interacts with the p85 subunit of phosphatidylinositol 3-kinase (PI3K), although a direct interaction between BTLA and these proteins was not confirmed (67). The in vivo significance of these interactions is not known, but they do not seem congruent with the function of BTLA as an inhibitor. Inhibitory actions of BTLA may be provided within the context of a prosurvival signal as well. In some physiological settings, BTLA exerts what appear to be prosurvival effects, although investigators did not test whether that effect involved Grb-2 and PI3K (68). The direct downstream consequence of Grb-2 association and the targets of the Shp-1/2 phosphatases have not been clearly identified. One study suggests that BTLA and CD3ζ might interact within the lipid raft fraction of activated T cells, leading to a decrease in phosphorylation of some lipid raft components (69). Another study analyzed the consequence of BTLA signaling in B cells that were stimulated with αIgM with or without HVEM (70). BTLA was not present in lipid rafts of activated B cells but did coimmunoprecipitate with the BCR and CD79a/b. Although phosphorylation of CD79a/b is unaltered by HVEM activation, the levels of phosphorylation of signaling molecules downstream of the BCR, including Syk, Blink, and phospholipase C-γ1, are decreased by HVEM stimulation of BTLA. Decreased nuclear localization of NF-κB after HVEM treatment results from reduced Syk and Blink phosphorylation (70). These results support the role of BTLA as a suppressor of B cell activation via interaction with HVEM. Distinguishing these various possibilities will require the generation of selective mutants of BTLA in mice that could separate inhibitory from prosurvival activity, followed by examination in various experimental settings in vivo.

As a TNFR member, HVEM signals in a canonical manner in response to its TNF family ligands. HVEM can directly recruit TNF receptor–associated factors (TRAFs) to its cytoplasmic domain and does not contain a death domain (71). HVEM overexpression induces NF-κB activation, association with TRAF1, 2, 3, and 5, and activation of JNK and AP-1 (20, 21). Both membrane-bound and soluble LIGHT can induce NF-κB through HVEM (**Figure 4**), with membrane-bound LIGHT having a more robust activity than soluble LIGHT (55, 62).

A recent study analyzed signaling through HVEM using the non-TNF family binding partners of HVEM, namely BTLA, CD160, and gD (62). Membrane-bound and Fc fusions of BTLA activated an NF-κB reporter in HVEM-expressing cells (62). BTLA and HVEM extracellular domains may interact as monomers in a 1:1 stoichiometry (60, 61); however, FRET (fluorescent resonance energy transfer) occurred between molecules of BTLA cytoplasmically tagged with cyan fluorescent protein and DsRed (62). This observation indicated that BTLA may exist in cells as oligomers that are capable of clustering HVEM, which is required for activation of TNFRs by conventional trimeric TNF ligands (72, 73). There may be cooperativity between LIGHT and BTLA for activation of NF-κB because soluble LIGHT augments NF-κB activity induced by membrane-bound BTLA (62) (**Figure 5**). Membrane-bound CD160 and gD-Fc fusion protein also activate an NF-κB reporter in HVEM-expressing cells (62). Ligation of HVEM with BTLA-Fc or membrane-bound CD160 results in TRAF2 recruitment and RelA nuclear translocation (62). BTLA-Fc treatment of wild-type and BTLA$^{-/-}$ T cells appears to increase the survival of activated T cells (62). Thus, bidirectional signaling between BTLA and HVEM can occur and needs to be considered when interpreting outcomes in disease models in either BTLA- or HVEM-deficient mice.

Because CD160 is predominantly GPI linked, its signaling pathway is not yet understood. In NK cells and CD8$^+$ T cells, interaction of CD160 with aggregated MHC class I molecules increases cytolytic activity and cytokine production (44). However, in human CD4$^+$ T cells, cross-linking CD160 with a high-affinity antibody inhibits proliferation and cytokine production in vitro and decreases phosphorylation of some proteins downstream of CD3 signaling (10). Cross-linking of CD160 in human NK cells induces AKT phosphorylation and PI3K/CD160 colocalization and increases ERK phosphorylation (74). The transmembrane form of CD160 (CD160-TM) does not associate with the signaling adaptor proteins DAP10, DAP12, CD3ζ, or FcεRIγ in COS cells (27). Cross-linking CD8 using a CD8-CD160-TM fusion protein increases proliferation and ERK phosphorylation in Jurkat cells in a manner dependent on Lck and

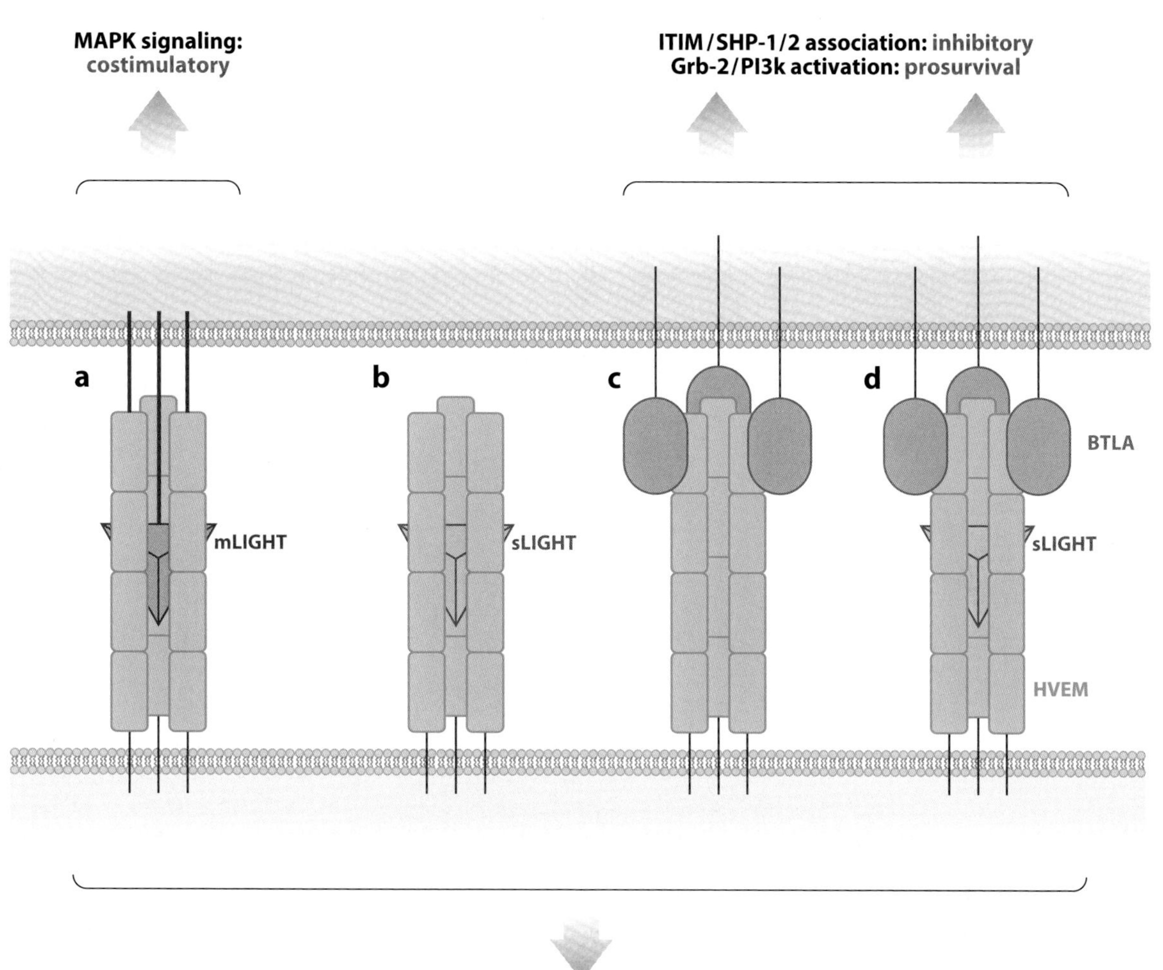

Figure 4

Bidirectional signaling between HVEM, BTLA, and LIGHT. (*a*) mLIGHT may provide direct costimulatory signals via MAPK pathways (55–58). (*a–d*) mLIGHT and sLIGHT (55, 62, 71) and BTLA (62) can activate NF-κB through HVEM. (*c–d*) Both inhibitory and prosurvival actions could be mediated by BTLA, via ITIM motifs or through the recruitment of Grb-2/PI3K (8, 64, 67).

mediated through [225]Tyrosine of CD160-TM (27). However, this tyrosine is not predicted to be present in mouse CD160-TM (24), and these results do not explain inhibitory actions of CD160 in human T cells.

BTLA AND HVEM HAVE NEGATIVE REGULATORY ROLES

$BTLA^{-/-}$ mice are viable and fertile (6, 75, 76). BTLA contains two tyrosine-based ITIMs in its cytoplasmic domain; thus, investigators initially proposed that it is an inhibitory molecule. Consistent with this, $BTLA^{-/-}$ lymphocytes show enhanced ^{3}H incorporation following αCD3 treatment and αIgM treatment (6, 7), and $BTLA^{-/-}$ mice show enhanced susceptibility to experimental autoimmune encephalitis (EAE) (6).

One function of BTLA in a noninflammatory situation may be to control homeostasis of T cells. Krieg et al. (75) have proposed that

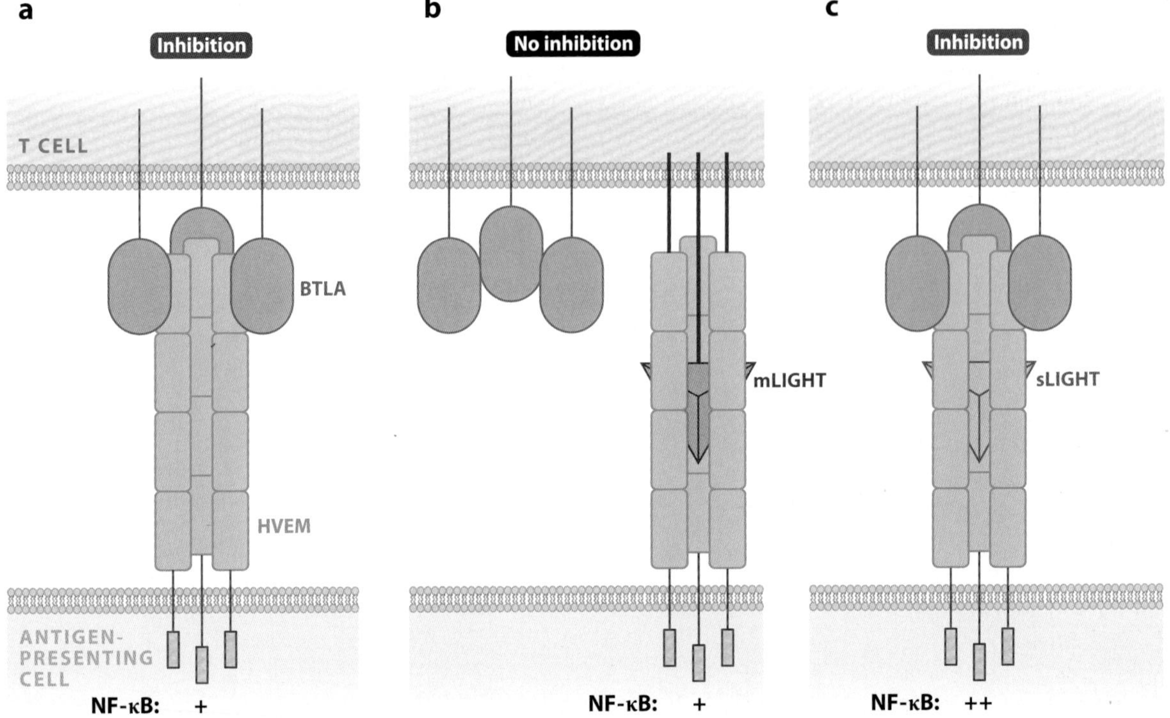

Figure 5

Potential regulation by mLIGHT of BTLA-dependent inhibition. (*a*) In the absence of LIGHT, HVEM induces BTLA to deliver inhibitory signals to the T cell. (*b*) Expression of mLIGHT by the T cell, for example during T cell activation, may prevent efficient engagement of BTLA by HVEM, reducing inhibition by BTLA during T cell activation. (*c*) After cleavage of mLIGHT to sLIGHT, HVEM may once again engage BTLA and deliver inhibitory signals. Furthermore, in this condition, BTLA and sLIGHT may more strongly activate NF-κB through HVEM on the antigen-presenting cell, providing a form of synergy in the costimulatory actions of these ligands.

the observed increase in T cell proliferation in vitro is due to an increased number of memory-phenotype $CD8^+$ T cells ex vivo. In addition, $BTLA^{-/-}$ $CD4^+$ and $CD8^+$ T cells show a competitive advantage in homeostatic proliferation compared with wild-type cells. BTLA may also be important in regulating homeostasis of DCs (77). In particular, the increase in the number of $CD8^-$ conventional DCs was observed in the spleens of $BTLA^{-/-}$ mice. In contrast, mice deficient in LTα, LTβ, and LTβR have decreased $CD8^-$ conventional DCs (78). These data suggest that BTLA and the LTαβ-LTβR pathway influence the same DC subset but in opposite directions and by different pathways (77), and that inhibition through BTLA expressed on DCs may counterbalance LTβR-mediated DC expansion (79). A lack of homeostasis of B cells in $BTLA^{-/-}$ mice has not been reported so far. Interestingly, $HVEM^{-/-}$ mice show a similar loss of homeostasis in T cell subpopulations (75) and in $CD8^-$ DCs (77), consistent with HVEM's function as the ligand for BTLA.

Spontaneous autoimmunity was not seen in the original reports of the three published BTLA knockouts (7, 76, 80). However, some evidence suggests that BTLA is important in the maintenance of tolerance and prevention of autoimmune disease. In one study, $BTLA^{-/-}$ mice on the pure 129SvEv background developed autoimmune hepatitis by 12 months of age, which was accompanied by hypergammaglobulinemia, antinuclear antibodies, anti-SSA antibodies, anti–double stranded DNA antibodies, and increased activated $CD4^+$ T cells in the periphery (81). This development was interpreted as indicating that BTLA is important in the maintenance of tolerance and prevention of autoimmune disease. An alternative interpretation is that an unidentified environmental condition specific to that study exists that differs from the setting of other studies. In this setting, there would be a more severe phenotype with BTLA deficiency than seen in other environmental settings. One possibility, for example, could be differences in the commensal biome (82), which might influence the immune system and be affected differently by the absence of BTLA. For example, a specific gut commensal organism, or perhaps even a pathogen, unique to this study may require BTLA for immune regulation to avoid inappropriate collateral tissue damage during the immune response. The follow-up regarding this finding should shed light on the raison d'être of BTLA's evolutionary conservation. In a separate study, roles for BTLA in oral tolerance induction, peptide-induced tolerance induction, and $CD8^+$ T cell–mediated autoimmunity were also observed (76).

The finding that HVEM is the ligand for BTLA provided insight into the phenotype of the HVEM knockout (83). The TNF ligand LIGHT had been characterized as a potent costimulatory molecule on T cells through its interaction with HVEM. Consistent with this characterization, T cell–expressed LIGHT enhances T cell–mediated immunity and promotes autoimmunity and inflammation, and $LIGHT^{-/-}$ mice have impaired T cell responses (48, 56, 84, 85). At the time, the prediction was that HVEM deficiency should phenocopy LIGHT deficiency. Unexpectedly, $HVEM^{-/-}$ mice have characteristics implying an inhibitory rather than an activating role for HVEM, including enhanced T cell proliferation in vitro, increased susceptibility to EAE, and enhanced systemic inflammatory responses to Concanavalin A (ConA) administration (83). These experiments can now be reinterpreted in the context of the BTLA-HVEM interaction. HVEM deficiency not only removes activatory LIGHT signaling through HVEM, but also removes inhibitory HVEM signaling through BTLA, with a net result of enhanced T cell activation. This suggests that the inhibitory role of BTLA, at least in some situations, dominates the activating role of LIGHT during immune responses. However, more extensive examination and comparison of additional immune situations are needed.

BTLA AS AN INHIBITOR IN DISEASE MODELS

The role of BTLA, LIGHT, and HVEM in vivo has been analyzed in several disease models using BTLA-, HVEM-, and LIGHT-deficient animals, antibodies against BTLA, and LIGHT transgenic mice (**Table 1**) (28). Infection of mice with *Plasmodium berghei ANKA* is a model for human cerebral malaria characterized by sequestration of leukocytes in brain capillaries. Using this model, investigators observed that BTLA and HVEM were inducted in the brain during infection, along with accumulated $CD8^+$ and $CD4^+$ T cells (86). Treatment with a presumably agonistic anti-BTLA antibody (17) before infection led to decreased cerebral malaria and fewer T cells in the brains of infected mice (86).

Inflammatory bowel disease in humans can be modeled by transferring $CD4^+$ $CD45RB^{high}$ T cells into $Rag^{-/-}$ mice. Colitis was accelerated when wild-type T cells were transferred into $HVEM^{-/-}$ $Rag^{-/-}$ mice compared with $HVEM^{+/+}$ $Rag^{-/-}$ mice (87). Surprisingly, however, transfer of $BTLA^{-/-}$ T cells into $Rag^{-/-}$ mice did not accelerate colitis, in comparison with the transfer of wild-type T cells. This was attributed to the failure of the $BTLA^{-/-}$ T cells to accumulate, as was observed in a nonirradiated model of graft-versus-host disease (GVHD) (68). However, treatment of $HVEM^{-/-}$ $Rag^{-/-}$ recipients with an antibody to BTLA reversed colitis, perhaps by acting as an agonist of BTLA. Thus, this is

Table 1 Blockade of BTLA and HVEM in experimental immune models[a]

Model	Result	References
BTLA		
MOG-induced EAE	Enhanced susceptibility in $BTLA^{-/-}$ mice	6
Partially mismatched cardiac allografts	Prolonged survival in $BTLA^{-/-}$ recipients	91
Fully mismatched cardiac allografts	Faster rejection in $BTLA^{-/-}$ recipients	91
Nonirradiated parent-into-F1 GVHD	Decreased survival of $BTLA^{-/-}$ donor cells	68
Airway inflammation	Prolonged inflammation in $BTLA^{-/-}$ mice	88–90
ConA-induced hepatitis	Increased inflammation/death in $BTLA^{-/-}$ mice	95
Inflammatory bowel disease model	Anti-BTLA decreased T cell–induced colitis in $Rag^{-/-}$ mice	87
Spontaneous disease	Autoimmune hepatitis in $BTLA^{-/-}$ mice	81
Islet allografts	Anti-BTLA with CTLA-4-Ig prolonged allograft survival	94, 139
Diabetes in NOD	Depleting BTLA antibody delayed diabetes	93
Experimental cerebral malaria	Agonist BTLA antibody decreased disease	86
Collagen-induced arthritis	HVEM-Ig aggravated autoimmunity	98
HVEM		
Inflammatory bowel disease model	$HVEM^{-/-}$ $Rag^{-/-}$ mice have increased T cell–induced colitis	87
GVHD	Less severe disease using $HVEM^{-/-}$ donor T cells or antagonist anti-HVEM	100
ConA-induced hepatitis	Increased inflammation/death in $HVEM^{-/-}$ mice	83
MOG-induced EAE	Enhanced susceptibility in $HVEM^{-/-}$ mice	83

[a]Abbreviations: BTLA, B and T lymphocyte associated; EAE, experimental autoimmune encephalomyelitis; GVHD, graft-versus-host disease; HVEM, herpesvirus entry mediator; MOG, myelin oligodendrocyte glycoprotein; NOD, nonobese diabetic.

an example of the relative contribution of the HVEM-BTLA interaction to inhibition of T cell responses compared with the contribution of the LIGHT-HVEM interaction to activating T cell responses.

In a model of airway inflammation induced by inhaled antigen, BTLA was not required for the initiation of the immune response, but it was required for the termination of the response as reflected by prolonged inflammation in $BTLA^{-/-}$ mice (88), perhaps owing to increased survival of $BTLA^{-/-}$ T cells (89). Prolonged T cell persistence in lungs correlated with induction of HVEM in the airway epithelium at late time points during the disease. $BTLA^{-/-}$ mice had increased neutrophil and eosinophil recruitment into the lungs. The increased eosinophil recruitment may be due to increased production of IL-5 by $BTLA^{-/-}$ T cells (90).

BTLA has also been evaluated in transplantation models. Cardiac allografts into partially MHC-mismatched recipients survive long term compared with transplants into fully MHC-mismatched recipients (91). Partially MHC-mismatched heart transplants (class I– or class II–mismatched) into $BTLA^{-/-}$ recipients are rapidly rejected, whereas the same transplants into wild-type or $PD\text{-}1^{-/-}$ recipients survive long term. This finding indicates that BTLA, unlike PD-1, can inhibit a functional allogeneic immune response in the context of a partial, but not complete, MHC mismatch. Fully MHC-mismatched cardiac transplants survive slightly longer in $BTLA^{-/-}$ recipients compared with wild-type recipients. This phenomenon is attributed to increased expression of PD-1 in the $BTLA^{-/-}$ recipients in the setting of fully mismatched transplants, but it could also be explained by lack of a BTLA-mediated survival signal, normally provided either through BTLA itself or through HVEM-mediated NF-κB activation (91).

Survival of fully MHC-mismatched cardiac allografts can be prolonged by enhanced Treg function in recipients treated with trichostatin A and rapamycin (92). However, such allografts do not survive in $BTLA^{-/-}$ or $HVEM^{-/-}$ recipients (40). This model supports a role for HVEM that is expressed on Tregs as a functional feature of Treg activity. BTLA may provide an inhibitory signal for effector T cells via HVEM on both effector T cells and Tregs. However, this pathway cannot be a major mechanism of Treg activity because HVEM-deficient mice do not display the spontaneous autoimmunity seen in mice lacking Tregs.

In a model of mouse islet allografts (fully MHC-mismatched), islet survival is greatly enhanced by concurrent treatment with CTLA-4-Ig and a depleting antibody to BTLA (93) or an agonistic antibody to BTLA (94). This suggests that allograft survival could be affected either by depletion of $BTLA^{+}$ alloreactive T cells or by triggering the BTLA coinhibitory signal. The effect of the anti-BTLA antibodies requires concurrent inhibition of the costimulatory signal using CTLA-4-Ig in this model, suggesting a potential strategy for preventing allograft rejection in humans.

$HVEM^{-/-}$ mice are extremely susceptible to ConA-induced hepatitis (83). Similarly, $BTLA^{-/-}$ mice succumb to ConA-induced hepatitis within 12 h of administration of 20 mg/kg of ConA and show increased proinflammatory cytokines (95). BTLA also inhibits early cytokine release from NKT cells in this model. Thus, BTLA acts to control T cells early in the immune response as well as in later adaptive responses.

BTLA CAN HAVE PROSURVIVAL EFFECTS

Activation of BTLA with agonistic antibodies appears to have an anti-inflammatory effect (35, 94, 96, 97). However, treatment with HVEM-Ig, which could potentially also activate BTLA, has the opposite effect in the collagen-induced arthritis model and results in increased disease (98). This might occur either by inhibiting HVEM-BTLA signaling or by promoting a prosurvival signal through either BTLA or LIGHT.

A prosurvival function for BTLA was revealed using a nonirradiated parent-into-F1 model of GVHD (68). In this model, transfer of C57BL/6 donor cells into C57BL/6 × BALB/c F_1 causes acute disease with donor cell expansion and antihost CTL activity (99). $BTLA^{-/-}$ splenocytes initially expand but are unable to sustain the GVHD response compared with wild-type counterparts. Blocking BTLA-HVEM interactions using an antibody to the C57BL/6 (donor) BTLA allele recapitulates the effect of BTLA deficiency, suggesting that the interaction of BTLA with HVEM is necessary to support the survival of donor lymphocytes in this model. Whether the prosurvival function of BTLA is mediated through BTLA signaling motifs such as the Grb-2 domain or through HVEM-mediated NF-κB signaling remains an open question.

In a related study, HVEM and LIGHT were each required on donor T cells to produce antihost CTL activity and survival of donor cells in the nonirradiated parent-into-F1 model of GVHD (100). This prosurvival role of LIGHT and HVEM was also observed in GVHD using transfers into lethally irradiated hosts. GVHD is ameliorated by both LIGHT and HVEM deficiency on transferred bone marrow cells or by treatment with an antagonistic antibody to HVEM that blocks both HVEM-LIGHT and HVEM-BTLA interactions (100). Blocking the HVEM-BTLA interaction may have resulted in increased GVHD owing to the removal of BTLA-mediated inhibition. Because this did not occur, the results suggest that antibody treatment removed an important HVEM-LIGHT costimulatory signal or removed a survival signal delivered through BTLA. Nevertheless, these results suggest that modulation of the LIGHT-HVEM-BTLA triumvirate could be therapeutic in GVHD.

IN VIVO ACTIONS OF LIGHT ENGAGE HVEM AND LTβR

Studies using LIGHT transgenic animals and LIGHT$^{-/-}$ mice suggest that LIGHT plays a costimulatory role in the immune system. Transgenic expression of LIGHT in thymocytes and mature T cells causes thymocyte deletion and expansion of T cells in the periphery (101, 102). LIGHT deficiency reduces CD3-induced T cell activation but does not affect ConA-induced activation (49, 83, 103). Fully MHC-mismatched cardiac allografts survive longer in LIGHT$^{-/-}$ recipients (104). Hosts that are deficient in both LIGHT and CD28 tolerate allogeneic skin grafts longer than controls (49). Similarly, blocking both LIGHT-HVEM and B7-CD28 interactions facilitates long-term islet graft survival (105). A separate study suggests that LIGHT signaling through HVEM on NK cells increases IFN-γ, contributing to antitumor response. LIGHT activation of HVEM on tumor cells increases Fas expression, increasing susceptibility of tumors to apoptosis (106). These studies all suggest that LIGHT costimulates T cells through HVEM. However, LIGHT transmits costimulatory signals to T cells upon cross-linking with DCR3-Fc or antibody, which potentially mimics HVEM activation of LIGHT. This suggests that HVEM also costimulates T cells through LIGHT (57, 58).

LIGHT also clearly has effects that occur via LTβR signaling. LIGHT$^{-/-}$ mice show less IL-12 being produced from DCs during *Leishmania* infection. This results in increased susceptibility, probably because of loss of LTβR activation on DCs by LIGHT, leading to inefficient T cell priming (107). LIGHT expressed on tumor cells in a noncleavable form enhances antitumor activity, possibly through binding of LIGHT to LTβR (108).

Most studies of LIGHT overexpression and deficiency were performed before the identification of BTLA and CD160 as ligands for HVEM. Recent studies on HVEM signaling reveal that soluble LIGHT can enhance the interaction of BTLA with HVEM and activation of NF-κB through HVEM (62). Thus, the concept of LIGHT modulating the BTLA-HVEM interaction has not yet been thoroughly addressed in vivo.

HERPESVIRUS TARGETS HVEM FOR VIRAL ENTRY AND BINDING TO BTLA

The HVEM-BTLA interaction is mimicked by two separate viral proteins. The original name for HVEM, herpesvirus entry mediator, arose because it is a cellular protein used by gD of HSV1 (α herpesvirus) to gain entry into the cell (18). Crystallography (109) and mutation analysis (110) showed that gD contains an Ig-like fold with an extended loop through which it contacts HVEM. The contact region, which in an intentional pun is referred to as the DARC (gD and BTLA-binding site on the TNFR HVEM in CRD1) side, is on the opposite side of the LIGHT contact region on HVEM. gD competes for BTLA binding to HVEM, but their binding sites are not completely overlapping. gD binding to HVEM activates NF-κB (111) and may produce the antiapoptotic effect seen for HSV1 (112).

UL144 is an open reading frame of the cytomegalovirus, a β herpesvirus evolutionarily distinct from HSV1 (113). It has high homology to the first two CRDs of HVEM but lacks CRD3 and so cannot bind TNF ligands, including LIGHT (12). UL144 binds to human but not to mouse BTLA, and UL144-Fc fusion protein inhibits T cell proliferation even more efficiently than does HVEM-Fc fusion, suggesting viral subversion of the immune system using BTLA-mediated inhibition (12, 114).

ROLE OF BTLA IN HUMANS

In humans, there is a reported association between a C(+800)T single nucleotide polymorphism (SNP) in BTLA with rheumatoid arthritis susceptibility in the Taiwanese population (115). This SNP converts leucine to proline in the region between the two ITIMs in the BTLA cytoplasmic tail. Because both ITIMs are required for BTLA to bind SHP-2, this mutation could conceivably alter conformation between the ITIMs to prevent or alter the nature of engagement of these tyrosines with the two SH2 domains of the SHP phosphatase. Interestingly, this region of mouse and rat BTLA contains a proline residue, but it is located several residues toward the carboxy terminus of BTLA and is not in the same location as the human SNP. The functional consequence of this human SNP has not been evaluated. Interestingly, there appear to be no associations of three separate SNPs in the *BTLA* gene with the development of type 1 diabetes or systemic lupus erythematosus in the Japanese population (116, 117).

BTLA may be involved in altering antigen-specific T cell responses following allergen-specific immunotherapy. A cohort of patients allergic to Japanese cedar pollen was examined (118). BTLA expression was reduced in untreated patients but was maintained after allergen-specific immunotherapy, and this correlated with reduced IL-5 expression. Investigators suggested that BTLA-mediated inhibition of IL-5 production may be a beneficial outcome of allergen immunotherapy.

Studies in mouse models suggest that it may be possible to use antibodies to BTLA to deliver an inhibitory signal to T cells, especially at the outset of T cell activation. The HVEM-BTLA-gD system has been used as a strategy to enhance vaccines in mice (119). Antigen fused to gD enhances antigen-specific T and B cell responses by binding to HVEM, which inhibits the HVEM-BTLA interaction. These approaches might be useful for human bone marrow transplantation, in which the timing of initial allo-immunization is well defined. This strategy might be applicable to human vaccines as well.

MECHANISMS FOR INHIBITION BY BTLA, PD-1, AND CTLA-4

Thus far, three major inhibitory receptors have been identified in T cells: BTLA, PD-1, and CTLA-4. The signaling pathways and pattern of expression of these receptors differ, reflecting their role in T cells during different stages of the immune response. CTLA-4$^{-/-}$ mice develop multiorgan lymphoproliferative disease and die within 3–4 weeks of birth (120, 121), indicating that CTLA-4 has a critical role in regulating naive T cell activation. PD-1, expressed on activated T and B lymphocytes, also inhibits autoimmunity, but the autoimmune disease seen in PD-1$^{-/-}$ mice evolves more slowly and is more tissue specific and dependent on genetic background than that in CTLA-4$^{-/-}$ mice (122–124). BTLA is expressed on naive and activated T and B lymphocytes and potentially regulates all phases of T cell activation. However, BTLA$^{-/-}$ mice show very little sign of spontaneous autoimmunity. Thus, CTLA-4 seems the most important for establishing and maintaining self-tolerance. By contrast, PD-1 and BTLA exert regulation by inhibition but operate on a finer scale than CTLA-4 in terms of the magnitude of responses that are regulated.

These inhibitory receptors have been reported to signal through ITIM-mediated Shp recruitment after interaction with their respective ligands, although this report is controversial. Shp-1 and Shp-2 recruitment has been clearly documented for PD-1 and BTLA (6, 64, 65, 125). Both cytoplasmic tyrosine residues of CTLA-4 are phosphorylated after interaction with CD80 or CD86, but demonstrating the association between CTLA-4 and Shp-2 has been difficult (126–128). In T cells, investigators have proposed that the targets of the protein tyrosine phosphatases following PD-1 and CTLA-4 engagement include signaling proteins in the TCR signaling complex such as

TCRζ, LAT, and Zap70 (129–133). However, downstream targets following BTLA engagement have not been clearly identified (69).

Other mechanisms have been proposed for CTLA-4 and PD-1. These include sequestration of CD80 and CD86 from CD28, preventing CD28-mediated costimulation (134). PD-1 may also inhibit CD28-mediated cell survival signals by Shp-1/2 targeting of the PI3K/protein kinase B pathway (135), which investigators also suggest operates for CTLA-4 (136). The mechanism of inhibition by CTLA-4, PD-1, and BTLA involves the blockade of proximal TCR signals. However, more recent studies have also indicated that CTLA-4 may exert significant effects via noncell intrinsic actions (137, 138), but this issue is currently unresolved.

CONCLUDING REMARKS

The importance of molecules is sometimes measured by the severity of their knockout phenotype. The lack of spontaneous autoimmunity in BTLA$^{-/-}$ mice that we initially reported (6) might suggest that BTLA simply fine tunes the immune response. Alternatively, the lack of a spontaneous phenotype could indicate that its actions are so important that the genome carries a spare, such as CD160, to provide fault-tolerant redundancy. However, in the absence of a clear signaling mechanism for CD160, and with no data yet on the phenotype of CD160$^{-/-}$ BTLA$^{-/-}$ double-knockout mice, this issue remains unsettled.

However, it is now not so clear whether BTLA$^{-/-}$ mice lack a spontaneous autoinflammatory phenotype (81). The cause of the new results from Oya et al. (81) is still unclear and unexpected, given the number of studies so far on BTLA$^{-/-}$ mice. Pathogen studies have revealed alteration of immune responses upon manipulation of BTLA (86), and clearly BTLA has undergone evolutionary conservation (63). It is tempting to speculate that Oya et al. (81) have identified an environmental condition in which BTLA plays an important, and selectable, regulatory role, perhaps dampening damaging autoaggressive reactions that take place in response to very specific yet common environmental agents. Analysis of the nature of this spontaneous inflammatory condition will help to identify the natural role of BTLA in the immune response, but in the meantime, its presence might be of some use as a therapeutic target or as a point of intervention in immune responses that prove undesirable.

DISCLOSURE STATEMENT

T.L.M. and K.M.M. have patents and grants on BTLA and HVEM.

LITERATURE CITED

1. Sharpe AH, Freeman GJ. 2002. The B7-CD28 superfamily. *Nat. Rev. Immunol.* 2:116–26
2. Greenwald RJ, Freeman GJ, Sharpe AH. 2005. The B7 family revisited. *Annu. Rev. Immunol.* 23:515–48
3. Croft M. 2003. Co-stimulatory members of the TNFR family: keys to effective T-cell immunity? *Nat. Rev. Immunol.* 3:609–20
4. Watts TH. 2005. TNF/TNFR family members in costimulation of T cell responses. *Annu. Rev. Immunol.* 23:23–68
5. Chen L. 2004. Co-inhibitory molecules of the B7-CD28 family in the control of T-cell immunity. *Nat. Rev. Immunol.* 4:336–47
6. Watanabe N, Gavrieli M, Sedy JR, Yang J, Fallarino F, et al. 2003. BTLA is a lymphocyte inhibitory receptor with similarities to CTLA-4 and PD-1. *Nat. Immunol.* 4:670–79
7. Han P, Goularte OD, Rufner K, Wilkinson B, Kaye J. 2004. An inhibitory Ig superfamily protein expressed by lymphocytes and APCs is also an early marker of thymocyte positive selection. *J. Immunol.* 172:5931–39

8. Sedy JR, Gavrieli M, Potter KG, Hurchla MA, Lindsley RC, et al. 2005. B and T lymphocyte attenuator regulates T cell activation through interaction with herpesvirus entry mediator. *Nat. Immunol.* 6:90–98
9. Murphy KM, Nelson CA, Sedy JR. 2006. Balancing co-stimulation and inhibition with BTLA and HVEM. *Nat. Rev. Immunol.* 6:671–81
10. Cai G, Anumanthan A, Brown JA, Greenfield EA, Zhu B, Freeman GJ. 2008. CD160 inhibits activation of human CD4$^+$ T cells through interaction with herpesvirus entry mediator. *Nat. Immunol.* 9:176–85
11. Sarrias MR, Whitbeck JC, Rooney I, Ware CF, Eisenberg RJ, et al. 2000. The three HveA receptor ligands, gD, LT-α and LIGHT bind to distinct sites on HveA. *Mol. Immunol.* 37:665–73
12. Cheung TC, Humphreys IR, Potter KG, Norris PS, Shumway HM, et al. 2005. Evolutionarily divergent herpesviruses modulate T cell activation by targeting the herpesvirus entry mediator cosignaling pathway. *Proc. Natl. Acad. Sci. USA* 102:13218–23
13. Egen JG, Kuhns MS, Allison JP. 2002. CTLA-4: new insights into its biological function and use in tumor immunotherapy. *Nat. Immunol.* 3:611–18
14. Keir ME, Butte MJ, Freeman GJ, Sharpe AH. 2008. PD-1 and its ligands in tolerance and immunity. *Annu. Rev. Immunol.* 26:677–704
15. Gonzalez LC, Loyet KM, Calemine-Fenaux J, Chauhan V, Wranik B, et al. 2005. A coreceptor interaction between the CD28 and TNF receptor family members B and T lymphocyte attenuator and herpesvirus entry mediator. *Proc. Natl. Acad. Sci. USA* 102:1116–21
16. Loyet KM, Ouyang W, Eaton DL, Stults JT. 2005. Proteomic profiling of surface proteins on Th1 and Th2 cells. *J. Proteome Res.* 4:400–9
17. Hurchla MA, Sedy JR, Gavrielli M, Drake CG, Murphy TL, Murphy KM. 2005. B and T lymphocyte attenuator exhibits structural and expression polymorphisms and is highly induced in anergic CD4$^+$ T cells. *J. Immunol.* 174:3377–85
18. Montgomery RI, Warner MS, Lum BJ, Spear PG. 1996. Herpes simplex virus-1 entry into cells mediated by a novel member of the TNF/NGF receptor family. *Cell* 87:427–36
19. Spear PG. 2004. Herpes simplex virus: receptors and ligands for cell entry. *Cell. Microbiol.* 6:401–10
20. Hsu H, Solovyev I, Colombero A, Elliott R, Kelley M, Boyle WJ. 1997. ATAR, a novel tumor necrosis factor receptor family member, signals through TRAF2 and TRAF5. *J. Biol. Chem.* 272:13471–74
21. Marsters SA, Ayres TM, Skubatch M, Gray CL, Rothe M, Ashkenazi A. 1997. Herpesvirus entry mediator, a member of the tumor necrosis factor receptor (TNFR) family, interacts with members of the TNFR-associated factor family and activates the transcription factors NF-κB and AP-1. *J. Biol. Chem.* 272:14029–32
22. Kwon BS, Tan KB, Ni J, Oh KO, Lee ZH, et al. 1997. A newly identified member of the tumor necrosis factor receptor superfamily with a wide tissue distribution and involvement in lymphocyte activation. *J. Biol. Chem.* 272:14272–76
23. Mauri DN, Ebner R, Montgomery RI, Kochel KD, Cheung TC, et al. 1998. LIGHT, a new member of the TNF superfamily, and lymphotoxin α are ligands for herpesvirus entry mediator. *Immunity* 8:21–30
24. Cai G, Freeman GJ. 2009. The CD160, BTLA, LIGHT/HVEM pathway: a bidirectional switch regulating T-cell activation. *Immunol. Rev.* 229:244–58
25. Agrawal S, Marquet J, Freeman GJ, Tawab A, Bouteiller PL, et al. 1999. Cutting edge: MHC class I triggering by a novel cell surface ligand costimulates proliferation of activated human T cells. *J. Immunol.* 162:1223–26
26. Anumanthan A, Bensussan A, Boumsell L, Christ AD, Blumberg RS, et al. 1998. Cloning of BY55, a novel Ig superfamily member expressed on NK cells, CTL, and intestinal intraepithelial lymphocytes. *J. Immunol.* 161:2780–90
27. Giustiniani J, Bensussan A, Marie-Cardine A. 2009. Identification and characterization of a transmembrane isoform of CD160 (CD160-TM), a unique activating receptor selectively expressed upon human NK cell activation. *J. Immunol.* 182:63–71
28. Ware CF. 2008. Targeting lymphocyte activation through the lymphotoxin and LIGHT pathways. *Immunol. Rev.* 223:186–201
29. Schneider K, Potter KG, Ware CF. 2004. Lymphotoxin and LIGHT signaling pathways and target genes. *Immunol. Rev.* 202:49–66

30. Smith CA, Farrah T, Goodwin RG. 1994. The TNF receptor superfamily of cellular and viral proteins: activation, costimulation, and death. *Cell* 76:959–62
31. Rooney IA, Butrovich KD, Glass AA, Borboroglu S, Benedict CA, et al. 2000. The lymphotoxin-β receptor is necessary and sufficient for LIGHT-mediated apoptosis of tumor cells. *J. Biol. Chem.* 275:14307–15
32. Yu KY, Kwon B, Ni J, Zhai Y, Ebner R, Kwon BS. 1999. A newly identified member of tumor necrosis factor receptor superfamily (TR6) suppresses LIGHT-mediated apoptosis. *J. Biol. Chem.* 274:13733–36
33. Locksley RM, Killeen N, Lenardo MJ. 2001. The TNF and TNF receptor superfamilies: integrating mammalian biology. *Cell* 104:487–501
34. Fu YX, Chaplin DD. 1999. Development and maturation of secondary lymphoid tissues. *Annu. Rev. Immunol.* 17:399–433
35. Otsuki N, Kamimura Y, Hashiguchi M, Azuma M. 2006. Expression and function of the B and T lymphocyte attenuator (BTLA/CD272) on human T cells. *Biochem. Biophys. Res. Commun.* 344:1121–27
36. Blackburn SD, Shin H, Haining WN, Zou T, Workman CJ, et al. 2009. Coregulation of CD8$^+$ T cell exhaustion by multiple inhibitory receptors during chronic viral infection. *Nat. Immunol.* 10:29–37
37. Nurieva RI, Chung Y, Hwang D, Yang XO, Kang HS, et al. 2008. Generation of T follicular helper cells is mediated by interleukin-21 but independent of T helper 1, 2, or 17 cell lineage. *Immunity* 29:138–49
38. M'Hidi H, Thibult M-L, Chetaille B, Rey F, Bouadallah R, et al. 2009. High expression of the inhibitory receptor BTLA in T-follicular helper cells and in B-cell small lymphocytic lymphoma/chronic lymphocytic leukemia. *Am. J. Clin. Pathol.* 132:589–96
39. Morel Y, Schiano de Colella JM, Harrop J, Deen KC, Holmes SD, et al. 2000. Reciprocal expression of the TNF family receptor herpes virus entry mediator and its ligand LIGHT on activated T cells: LIGHT down-regulates its own receptor. *J. Immunol.* 165:4397–404
40. Tao R, Wang L, Murphy KM, Fraser CC, Hancock WW. 2008. Regulatory T cell expression of herpesvirus entry mediator suppresses the function of B and T lymphocyte attenuator-positive effector T cells. *J. Immunol.* 180:6649–55
41. Morel Y, Truneh A, Sweet RW, Olive D, Costello RT. 2001. The TNF superfamily members LIGHT and CD154 (CD40 ligand) costimulate induction of dendritic cell maturation and elicit specific CTL activity. *J. Immunol.* 167:2479–86
42. Abecassis S, Giustiniani J, Meyer N, Schiavon V, Ortonne N, et al. 2007. Identification of a novel CD160$^+$ CD4$^+$ T-lymphocyte subset in the skin: a possible role for CD160 in skin inflammation. *J. Invest. Dermatol.* 127:1161–66
43. Merino J, Ramirez N, Moreno C, Toledo E, Fernandez M, Sanchez-Ibarrola A. 2007. BY55/CD160 cannot be considered a cytotoxic marker in cytomegalovirus-specific human CD8$^+$ T cells. *Clin. Exp. Immunol.* 149:87–96
44. Maeda M, Carpenito C, Russell RC, Dasanjh J, Veinotte LL, et al. 2005. Murine CD160, Ig-like receptor on NK cells and NKT cells, recognizes classical and nonclassical MHC class I and regulates NK cell activation. *J. Immunol.* 175:4426–32
45. Rabot M, Bensussan A, Le Bouteiller P. 2006. Engagement of the CD160 activating NK cell receptor leads to its association with CD2 in circulating human NK cells. *Transpl. Immunol.* 17:36–38
46. Giustiniani J, Marie-Cardine A, Bensussan A. 2007. A soluble form of the MHC class I-specific CD160 receptor is released from human activated NK lymphocytes and inhibits cell-mediated cytotoxicity. *J. Immunol.* 178:1293–300
47. Zhai Y, Guo R, Hsu TL, Yu GL, Ni J, et al. 1998. LIGHT, a novel ligand for lymphotoxin β receptor and TR2/HVEM induces apoptosis and suppresses in vivo tumor formation via gene transfer. *J. Clin. Invest.* 102:1142–51
48. Tamada K, Shimozaki K, Chapoval AI, Zhai Y, Su J, et al. 2000. LIGHT, a TNF-like molecule, costimulates T cell proliferation and is required for dendritic cell-mediated allogeneic T cell response. *J. Immunol.* 164:4105–10
49. Scheu S, Alferink J, Potzel T, Barchet W, Kalinke U, Pfeffer K. 2002. Targeted disruption of LIGHT causes defects in costimulatory T cell activation and reveals cooperation with lymphotoxin β in mesenteric lymph node genesis. *J. Exp. Med.* 195:1613–24
50. Tamada K, Ni J, Zhu G, Fiscella M, Teng B, et al. 2002. Cutting edge: selective impairment of CD8$^+$ T cell function in mice lacking the TNF superfamily member LIGHT. *J. Immunol.* 168:4832–35

51. Cohavy O, Zhou J, Ware CF, Targan SR. 2005. LIGHT is constitutively expressed on T and NK cells in the human gut and can be induced by CD2-mediated signaling. *J. Immunol.* 174:646–53
52. Eldredge J, Berkowitz S, Corin AF, Day ES, Hayes D, et al. 2006. Stoichiometry of LTβR binding to LIGHT. *Biochemistry* 45:10117–28
53. Wang J, Anders RA, Wang Y, Turner JR, Abraham C, et al. 2005. The critical role of LIGHT in promoting intestinal inflammation and Crohn's disease. *J. Immunol.* 174:8173–82
54. Granger SW, Butrovich KD, Houshmand P, Edwards WR, Ware CF. 2001. Genomic characterization of LIGHT reveals linkage to an immune response locus on chromosome 19p13.3 and distinct isoforms generated by alternate splicing or proteolysis. *J. Immunol.* 167:5122–28
55. Harrop JA, McDonnell PC, Brigham-Burke M, Lyn SD, Minton J, et al. 1998. Herpesvirus entry mediator ligand (HVEM-L), a novel ligand for HVEM/TR2, stimulates proliferation of T cells and inhibits HT29 cell growth. *J. Biol. Chem.* 273:27548–56
56. Tamada K, Shimozaki K, Chapoval AI, Zhu G, Sica G, et al. 2000. Modulation of T-cell-mediated immunity in tumor and graft-versus-host disease models through the LIGHT co-stimulatory pathway. *Nat. Med.* 6:283–89
57. Wan X, Zhang J, Luo H, Shi G, Kapnik E, et al. 2002. A TNF family member LIGHT transduces costimulatory signals into human T cells. *J. Immunol.* 169:6813–21
58. Shi G, Luo H, Wan X, Salcedo TW, Zhang J, Wu J. 2002. Mouse T cells receive costimulatory signals from LIGHT, a TNF family member. *Blood* 100:3279–86
59. Banner DW, D'Arcy A, Janes W, Gentz R, Schoenfeld HJ, et al. 1993. Crystal structure of the soluble human 55 kd TNF receptor-human TNFβ complex: implications for TNF receptor activation. *Cell* 73:431–45
60. Compaan DM, Gonzalez LC, Tom I, Loyet KM, Eaton D, Hymowitz SG. 2005. Attenuating lymphocyte activity: the crystal structure of the BTLA-HVEM complex. *J. Biol. Chem.* 280:39553–61
61. Nelson CA, Fremont MD, Sedy JR, Norris PS, Ware CF, et al. 2008. Structural determinants of herpesvirus entry mediator recognition by murine B and T lymphocyte attenuator. *J. Immunol.* 180:940–47
62. Cheung TC, Steinberg MW, Oborne LM, Macauley MG, Fukuyama S, et al. 2009. Unconventional ligand activation of herpesvirus entry mediator signals cell survival. *Proc. Natl. Acad. Sci. USA* 106:6244–49
63. Bernard D, Hansen JD, Du Pasquier L, Lefranc MP, Benmansour A, Boudinot P. 2007. Costimulatory receptors in jawed vertebrates: conserved CD28, odd CTLA4 and multiple BTLAs. *Dev. Comp. Immunol.* 31:255–71
64. Gavrieli M, Watanabe N, Loftin SK, Murphy TL, Murphy KM. 2003. Characterization of phosphotyrosine binding motifs in the cytoplasmic domain of B and T lymphocyte attenuator required for association with protein tyrosine phosphatases SHP-1 and SHP-2. *Biochem. Biophys. Res. Commun.* 312:1236–43
65. Chemnitz JM, Lanfranco AR, Braunstein I, Riley JL. 2006. B and T lymphocyte attenuator-mediated signal transduction provides a potent inhibitory signal to primary human CD4 T cells that can be initiated by multiple phosphotyrosine motifs. *J. Immunol.* 176:6603–14
66. Plas DR, Thomas ML. 1998. Negative regulation of antigen receptor signaling in lymphocytes. *J. Mol. Med.* 76:589–95
67. Gavrieli M, Murphy KM. 2006. Association of Grb-2 and PI3K p85 with phosphotyrosile peptides derived from BTLA. *Biochem. Biophys. Res. Commun.* 345:1440–45
68. Hurchla MA, Sedy JR, Murphy KM. 2007. Unexpected role of B and T lymphocyte attenuator in sustaining cell survival during chronic allostimulation. *J. Immunol.* 178:6073–82
69. Wu TH, Zhen Y, Zeng C, Yi HF, Zhao Y. 2007. B and T lymphocyte attenuator interacts with CD3ζ and inhibits tyrosine phosphorylation of TCRζ complex during T-cell activation. *Immunol. Cell Biol.* 85:590–95
70. Vendel AC, Calemine-Fenaux J, Izrael-Tomasevic A, Chauhan V, Arnott D, Eaton DL. 2009. B and T lymphocyte attenuator regulates B cell receptor signaling by targeting Syk and BLNK. *J. Immunol.* 182:1509–17
71. Dempsey PW, Doyle SE, He JQ, Cheng G. 2003. The signaling adaptors and pathways activated by TNF superfamily. *Cytokine Growth Factor Rev.* 14:193–209

72. Bossen C, Ingold K, Tardivel A, Bodmer JL, Gaide O, et al. 2006. Interactions of tumor necrosis factor (TNF) and TNF receptor family members in the mouse and human. *J. Biol. Chem.* 281:13964–71
73. Bodmer JL, Schneider P, Tschopp J. 2002. The molecular architecture of the TNF superfamily. *Trends Biochem. Sci.* 27:19–26
74. Rabot M, El Costa H, Polgar B, Marie-Cardine A, Aguerre-Girr M, et al. 2007. CD160-activating NK cell effector functions depend on the phosphatidylinositol 3-kinase recruitment. *Int. Immunol.* 19:401–9
75. Krieg C, Boyman O, Fu YX, Kaye J. 2007. B and T lymphocyte attenuator regulates $CD8^+$ T cell-intrinsic homeostasis and memory cell generation. *Nat. Immunol.* 8:162–71
76. Liu XK, Alexiou M, Martin-Orozco N, Chung Y, Nurieva RI, et al. 2009. Cutting edge: a critical role of B and T lymphocyte attenuator in peripheral T cell tolerance induction. *J. Immunol.* 182:4516–20
77. De Trez C, Schneider K, Potter K, Droin N, Fulton J, et al. 2008. The inhibitory HVEM-BTLA pathway counter regulates lymphotoxin receptor signaling to achieve homeostasis of dendritic cells. *J. Immunol.* 180:238–48
78. Kabashima KTA, Banks KM, Ansel TT, Lu TT, Ware CF, Cyster JG. 2005. Intrinsic lymphotoxin-β receptor requirement for homeostasis of lymphoid tissue dendritic cells. *Immunity* 22:439–50
79. De Trez C, Ware CF. 2008. The TNF receptor and Ig superfamily members form an integrated signaling circuit controlling dendritic cell homeostasis. *Cytokine Growth Factor Rev.* 19:277–84
80. Adams TE, Hansen JA, Starr R, Nicola NA, Hilton DJ, Billestrup N. 1998. Growth hormone preferentially induces the rapid, transient expression of SOCS-3, a novel inhibitor of cytokine receptor signaling. *J. Biol. Chem.* 273:1285–87
81. Oya Y, Watanabe N, Owada T, Oki M, Hirose K, et al. 2008. Development of autoimmune hepatitis-like disease and production of autoantibodies to nuclear antigens in mice lacking B and T lymphocyte attenuator. *Arthritis Rheum.* 58:2498–510
82. Hooper LV. 2009. Do symbiotic bacteria subvert host immunity? *Nat. Rev. Microbiol.* 7:367–74
83. Wang Y, Subudhi SK, Anders RA, Lo J, Sun Y, et al. 2005. The role of herpesvirus entry mediator as a negative regulator of T cell-mediated responses. *J. Clin. Invest.* 115:711–17
84. Gommerman JL, Browning JL. 2003. Lymphotoxin/LIGHT, lymphoid microenvironments and autoimmune disease. *Nat. Rev. Immunol.* 3:642–55
85. Shaikh RB, Santee S, Granger SW, Butrovich K, Cheung T, et al. 2001. Constitutive expression of LIGHT on T cells leads to lymphocyte activation, inflammation, and tissue destruction. *J. Immunol.* 167:6330–37
86. Lepenies B, Pfeffer K, Hurchla MA, Murphy TL, Murphy KM, et al. 2007. Ligation of B and T lymphocyte attenuator prevents the genesis of experimental cerebral malaria. *J. Immunol.* 179:4093–100
87. Steinberg MW, Turovskaya O, Shaikh RB, Kim G, McCole DF, et al. 2008. A crucial role for HVEM and BTLA in preventing intestinal inflammation. *J. Exp. Med.* 205:1463–76
88. Deppong C, Juehne TI, Hurchla M, Friend LD, Shah DD, et al. 2006. Cutting edge: B and T lymphocyte attenuator and programmed death receptor-1 inhibitory receptors are required for termination of acute allergic airway inflammation. *J. Immunol.* 176:3909–13
89. Deppong C, Degnan JM, Murphy TL, Murphy KM, Green JM. 2008. B and T lymphocyte attenuator regulates T cell survival in the lung. *J. Immunol.* 181:2973–79
90. Tamachi T, Watanabe N, Oya Y, Kagami S, Hirose K, et al. 2007. B and T lymphocyte attenuator inhibits antigen-induced eosinophil recruitment into the airways. *Int. Arch. Allergy Immunol.* 143(Suppl. 1):50–55
91. Tao R, Wang L, Han R, Wang T, Ye Q, et al. 2005. Differential effects of B and T lymphocyte attenuator and programmed death-1 on acceptance of partially versus fully MHC-mismatched cardiac allografts. *J. Immunol.* 175:5774–82
92. Tao R, de Zoeten EF, Ozkaynak E, Chen C, Wang L, et al. 2007. Deacetylase inhibition promotes the generation and function of regulatory T cells. *Nat. Med.* 13:1299–307

93. Truong W, Hancock WW, Plester JC, Merani S, Rayner DC, et al. 2009. BTLA targeting modulates lymphocyte phenotype, function, and numbers and attenuates disease in nonobese diabetic mice. *J. Leukoc. Biol.* 86:41–51
94. Truong W, Plester JC, Hancock WW, Kaye J, Merani S, et al. 2007. Negative and positive co-signaling with anti-BTLA (PJ196) and CTLA4Ig prolongs islet allograft survival. *Transplantation* 84:1368–72
95. Miller ML, Sun Y, Fu YX. 2009. Cutting edge: B and T lymphocyte attenuator signaling on NKT cells inhibits cytokine release and tissue injury in early immune responses. *J. Immunol.* 183:32–36
96. Krieg C, Han P, Stone R, Goularte OD, Kaye J. 2005. Functional analysis of B and T lymphocyte attenuator engagement on $CD4^+$ and $CD8^+$ T cells. *J. Immunol.* 175:6420–27
97. Wang XF, Chen YJ, Wang Q, Ge Y, Dai Q, et al. 2007. Distinct expression and inhibitory function of B and T lymphocyte attenuator on human T cells. *Tissue Antigens* 69:145–53
98. Pierer M, Schulz A, Rossol M, Kendzia E, Kyburz D, et al. 2009. Herpesvirus entry mediator-Ig treatment during immunization aggravates rheumatoid arthritis in the collagen-induced arthritis model. *J. Immunol.* 182:3139–45
99. Tschetter JR, Mozes E, Shearer GM. 2000. Progression from acute to chronic disease in a murine parent-into-F1 model of graft-versus-host disease. *J. Immunol.* 165:5987–94
100. Xu Y, Flies AS, Flies DB, Zhu G, Anand S, et al. 2007. Selective targeting of the LIGHT-HVEM costimulatory system for the treatment of graft-versus-host disease. *Blood* 109:4097–104
101. Wang J, Lo JC, Foster A, Yu P, Chen HM, et al. 2001. The regulation of T cell homeostasis and autoimmunity by T cell-derived LIGHT. *J. Clin. Invest.* 108:1771–80
102. Wang J, Chun T, Lo JC, Wu Q, Wang Y, et al. 2001. The critical role of LIGHT, a TNF family member, in T cell development. *J. Immunol.* 167:5099–105
103. Liu J, Schmidt CS, Zhao F, Okragly AJ, Glasebrook A, et al. 2003. LIGHT-deficiency impairs $CD8^+$ T cell expansion, but not effector function. *Int. Immunol.* 15:861–70
104. Ye Q, Fraser CC, Gao W, Wang L, Busfield SJ, et al. 2002. Modulation of LIGHT-HVEM costimulation prolongs cardiac allograft survival. *J. Exp. Med.* 195:795–800
105. Fan K, Wang H, Wei H, Zhou Q, Kou G, et al. 2007. Blockade of LIGHT/HVEM and B7/CD28 signaling facilitates long-term islet graft survival with development of allospecific tolerance. *Transplantation* 84:746–54
106. Costello RT, Mallet F, Barbarat B, Schiano de Colella JM, Sainty D, et al. 2003. Stimulation of non-Hodgkin's lymphoma via HVEM: an alternate and safe way to increase Fas-induced apoptosis and improve tumor immunogenicity. *Leukemia* 17:2500–7
107. Xu G, Liu D, Okwor I, Wang Y, Korner H, et al. 2007. LIGHT is critical for IL-12 production by dendritic cells, optimal $CD4^+$ Th1 cell response, and resistance to *Leishmania major*. *J. Immunol.* 179:6901–9
108. Yu P, Lee Y, Liu W, Chin RK, Wang J, et al. 2004. Priming of naive T cells inside tumors leads to eradication of established tumors. *Nat. Immunol.* 5:141–49
109. Carfi A, Willis SH, Whitbeck JC, Krummenacher C, Cohen GH, et al. 2001. Herpes simplex virus glycoprotein D bound to the human receptor HveA. *Mol. Cell* 8:169–79
110. Whitbeck JC, Connolly SA, Willis SH, Hou W, Krummenacher C, et al. 2001. Localization of the gD-binding region of the human herpes simplex virus receptor, HveA. *J. Virol.* 75:171–80
111. Sciortino MT, Medici MA, Marino-Merlo F, Zaccaria D, Giuffre-Cuculletto M, et al. 2008. Involvement of HVEM receptor in activation of nuclear factor κB by herpes simplex virus 1 glycoprotein D. *Cell. Microbiol.* 10:2297–311
112. Sciortino MT, Medici MA, Marino-Merlo F, Zaccaria D, Giuffre-Cuculletto M, et al. 2008. Involvement of gD/HVEM interaction in NF-κB-dependent inhibition of apoptosis by HSV-1 gD. *Biochem. Pharmacol.* 76:1522–32
113. Benedict CA, Butrovich KD, Lurain NS, Corbeil J, Rooney I, et al. 1999. Cutting edge: a novel viral TNF receptor superfamily member in virulent strains of human cytomegalovirus. *J. Immunol.* 162:6967–70

114. Sedy JR, Spear PG, Ware CF. 2008. Cross-regulation between herpesviruses and the TNF superfamily members. *Nat. Rev. Immunol.* 8:861–73

115. Lin SC, Kuo CC, Chan CH. 2006. Association of a BTLA gene polymorphism with the risk of rheumatoid arthritis. *J. Biomed. Sci.* 13:853–60

116. Inuo M, Ihara K, Matsuo T, Kohno H, Hara T. 2009. Association study between B- and T-lymphocyte attenuator gene and type 1 diabetes mellitus or systemic lupus erythematosus in the Japanese population. *Int. J. Immunogenet.* 36:65–68

117. Tsutsumi Y, Jie X, Ihara K, Nomura A, Kanemitsu S, et al. 2006. Phenotypic and genetic analyses of T-cell-mediated immunoregulation in patients with type 1 diabetes. *Diabet. Med.* 23:1145–50

118. Okano M, Otsuki N, Azuma M, Fujiwara T, Kariya S, et al. 2008. Allergen-specific immunotherapy alters the expression of B and T lymphocyte attenuator, a co-inhibitory molecule, in allergic rhinitis. *Clin. Exp. Allergy* 38:1891–900

119. Lasaro MO, Tatsis N, Hensley SE, Whitbeck JC, Lin SW, et al. 2008. Targeting of antigen to the herpesvirus entry mediator augments primary adaptive immune responses. *Nat. Med.* 14:205–12

120. Waterhouse P, Penninger JM, Timms E, Wakeham A, Shahinian A, et al. 1995. Lymphoproliferative disorders with early lethality in mice deficient in *Ctla-4*. *Science* 270:985–88

121. Tivol EA, Borriello F, Schweitzer AN, Lynch WP, Bluestone JA, Sharpe AH. 1995. Loss of CTLA-4 leads to massive lymphoproliferation and fatal multiorgan tissue destruction, revealing a critical negative regulatory role of CTLA-4. *Immunity* 3:541–47

122. Nishimura H, Okazaki T, Tanaka Y, Nakatani K, Hara M, et al. 2001. Autoimmune dilated cardiomyopathy in PD-1 receptor-deficient mice. *Science* 291:319–22

123. Nishimura H, Nose M, Hiai H, Minato N, Honjo T. 1999. Development of lupus-like autoimmune diseases by disruption of the PD-1 gene encoding an ITIM motif-carrying immunoreceptor. *Immunity* 11:141–51

124. Wang J, Yoshida T, Nakaki F, Hiai H, Okazaki T, Honjo T. 2005. Establishment of NOD-*Pdcd1*$^{-/-}$ mice as an efficient animal model of type I diabetes. *Proc. Natl. Acad. Sci. USA* 102:11823–28

125. Chemnitz JM, Parry RV, Nichols KE, June CH, Riley JL. 2004. SHP-1 and SHP-2 associate with immunoreceptor tyrosine-based switch motif of programmed death 1 upon primary human T cell stimulation, but only receptor ligation prevents T cell activation. *J. Immunol.* 173:945–54

126. Nakaseko C, Miyatake S, Iida T, Hara S, Abe R, et al. 1999. Cytotoxic T lymphocyte antigen 4 (CTLA-4) engagement delivers an inhibitory signal through the membrane-proximal region in the absence of the tyrosine motif in the cytoplasmic tail. *J. Exp. Med.* 190:765–74

127. Schneider H, da Rocha DS, Hu H, Rudd CE. 2001. A regulatory role for cytoplasmic YVKM motif in CTLA-4 inhibition of TCR signaling. *Eur. J. Immunol.* 31:2042–50

128. Schneider H, Rudd CE. 2000. Tyrosine phosphatase SHP-2 binding to CTLA-4: absence of direct YVKM/YFIP motif recognition. *Biochem. Biophys. Res. Commun.* 269:279–83

129. Guntermann C, Alexander DR. 2002. CTLA-4 suppresses proximal TCR signaling in resting human $CD4^{+}$ T cells by inhibiting ZAP-70 Tyr(319) phosphorylation: a potential role for tyrosine phosphatases. *J. Immunol.* 168:4420–29

130. Lee KM, Chuang E, Griffin M, Khattri R, Hong DK, et al. 1998. Molecular basis of T cell inactivation by CTLA-4. *Science* 282:2263–66

131. Marengere LE, Waterhouse P, Duncan GS, Mittrucker HW, Feng GS, Mak TW. 1996. Regulation of T cell receptor signaling by tyrosine phosphatase SYP association with CTLA-4. *Science* 272:1170–73

132. Sheppard KA, Fitz LJ, Lee JM, Benander C, George JA, et al. 2004. PD-1 inhibits T-cell receptor induced phosphorylation of the ZAP70/CD3ζ signalosome and downstream signaling to PKCθ. *FEBS Lett.* 574:37–41

133. Okazaki T, Maeda A, Nishimura H, Kurosaki T, Honjo T. 2001. PD-1 immunoreceptor inhibits B cell receptor-mediated signaling by recruiting src homology 2-domain-containing tyrosine phosphatase 2 to phosphotyrosine. *Proc. Natl. Acad. Sci. USA* 98:13866–71

134. Teft WA, Kirchhof MG, Madrenas J. 2006. A molecular perspective of CTLA-4 function. *Annu. Rev. Immunol.* 24:65–97

135. Alegre ML, Frauwirth KA, Thompson CB. 2001. T-cell regulation by CD28 and CTLA-4. *Nat. Rev. Immunol.* 1:220–28
136. Frauwirth KA, Thompson CB. 2004. Regulation of T lymphocyte metabolism. *J. Immunol.* 172:4661–65
137. Bachmann MF, Kohler G, Ecabert B, Mak TW, Kopf M. 1999. Cutting edge: lymphoproliferative disease in the absence of CTLA-4 is not T cell autonomous. *J. Immunol.* 163:1128–31
138. Friedline RH, Brown DS, Nguyen H, Kornfeld H, Lee J, et al. 2009. $CD4^+$ regulatory T cells require CTLA-4 for the maintenance of systemic tolerance. *J. Exp. Med.* 206:421–34
139. Truong W, Plester JC, Hancock WW, Merani S, Murphy TL, et al. 2007. Combined coinhibitory and costimulatory modulation with anti-BTLA and CTLA4Ig facilitates tolerance in murine islet allografts. *Am. J. Transplant.* 7:2663–74

The Role of Antibodies in HIV Vaccines

John R. Mascola[1] and David C. Montefiori[2]

[1]Vaccine Research Center, National Institute of Allergy and Infectious Diseases, National Institutes of Health, Bethesda, Maryland 20892; email: jmascola@nih.gov

[2]Department of Surgery, Duke University Medical Center, Durham, North Carolina 27710; email: monte@duke.edu

Annu. Rev. Immunol. 2010. 28:413–44

First published online as a Review in Advance on January 4, 2010

The *Annual Review of Immunology* is online at immunol.annualreviews.org

This article's doi:
10.1146/annurev-immunol-030409-101256

0732-0582/10/0423-0413$20.00

Key Words

envelope glycoprotein, neutralizing antibodies, vaccine design

Abstract

Licensed vaccines against viral diseases generate antibodies that neutralize the infecting virus and protect against infection or disease. Similarly, an effective vaccine against HIV-1 will likely need to induce antibodies that prevent initial infection of host cells or that limit early events of viral dissemination. Such antibodies must target the surface envelope glycoproteins of HIV-1, which are highly variable in sequence and structure. The first subunit vaccines to enter clinical trails were safe and immunogenic but unable to elicit antibodies that neutralized most circulating strains of HIV-1. However, potent virus neutralizing antibodies (NAbs) can develop during the course of HIV-1 infection, and this is the type of antibody response that researchers seek to generate with a vaccine. Thus, current vaccine design efforts have focused on a more detailed understanding of these broadly neutralizing antibodies and their epitopes to inform the design of improved vaccines.

HIV-1: human immunodeficiency virus type-1

Env: envelope glycoprotein

Neutralizing antibodies (NAbs): antibodies that block viral infection of host cells

Viral envelope: the membrane surrounding a virus particle; it usually contains host cell lipids and proteins as well as the virus-encoded glycoproteins

INTRODUCTION

Functional antibodies are necessary for the protection afforded by most successful vaccines and are thought to be a critical component of an effective human immunodeficiency virus type-1 (HIV-1) vaccine (1–5). The T and B cell compartments of the immune system generally work in concert to provide protective immunity against viral pathogens. Although the interplay between the cellular and humoral immunity is complex, $CD8^+$ T cells are considered necessary to control viral replication, whereas antibodies can block viral entry into host cells. This paradigm is thought to be applicable to HIV-1 infection, which is a chronic progressive lentiviral infection (2, 6–8). Upon breaching the mucosal surface, HIV-1 infects submucosal $CD4^+$ T cells and rapidly disseminates to produce widespread systemic infection. Viral escape from adaptive antibody and T cell immune responses allows persistent viral replication and the progressive destruction of $CD4^+$ T cells, which eventually leads to the development of acquired immunodeficiency syndrome (AIDS) (8, 9).

Soon after the discovery of HIV-1 and the appreciation that the viral genome encodes a surface-exposed envelope glycoprotein (Env) (10), researchers focused on developing a vaccine that could elicit antibodies that bind the viral Env and block initial infection of target cells (2, 3, 11). Nonhuman primate studies confirmed the likely importance of such antibodies, as passive immunization with neutralizing antibodies (NAbs) could prevent the acquisition of infection (4, 12). Unfortunately, the generation of viral NAbs has turned out to be a complex and difficult task (2, 3). Initial recombinant protein vaccines, which were based on the surface gp120 component of Env, induced high levels of antigen-specific antibody responses. However, these antibodies did not neutralize most circulating strains of HIV-1 (13, 14), and a well-conducted human efficacy trial showed that the gp120 vaccine did not prevent infection or impact plasma viral load (15–17). Our understanding of the atomic-level structure of several regions of HIV-1 Env has facilitated the design of newer vaccine immunogens (18), but current vaccines still elicit NAbs of limited breadth (2, 3, 18). An improved knowledge of Env structure and neutralization epitopes as well as B cell biology will likely be required to design an effective antibody-based vaccine (11, 18–21). This review summarizes our current understanding of the role of antibodies in HIV-1 infection and explores the difficult problem of generating virus NAbs via immunization. We highlight recent novel approaches to immunization and studies of the natural NAb responses to HIV-1 that can inform our approach to improved immunogen design.

NEUTRALIZATION EPITOPES ON THE HIV-1 ENV

Infection with HIV-1 results in an antibody response to most viral proteins, but only antibodies to the surface Env are capable of mediating virus neutralization (22, 23). The HIV-1 Env is a heavily glycosylated trimeric protein composed of three identical surface gp120 molecules, each noncovalently associated with a transmembrane gp41 molecule (22, 24). This trimeric structure, called the Env spike, is responsible for interacting with the host cell to initiate viral entry. Upon initial binding of gp120 to its primary host cell receptor CD4, the viral Env undergoes a conformational change that exposes an adjacent region of gp120 to bind a secondary receptor, usually the chemokine receptor CCR5 or CXCR4. The final steps of viral envelope fusion to the host cell membrane are mediated by gp41 (24). Despite these functionally conserved requirements for viral entry, the gene encoding the viral Env displays an enormous amount of diversity. HIV-1 genes, including *env*, can be divided into genetic subtypes A–K, also called clades (25). Although these genetic subtypes of Env do not directly represent distinct antigenic serotypes of the virus, Env does manifest a broad range of antigenic diversity that impacts antibody reactivity (26–28). Each Env clade differs from the others by about 30% based on amino acid sequence. Moreover, amino acid sequence diversity within a single clade can be as high as 20% (25, 29). HIV-1 clades also differ in prevalence by geographic region. Clades A, C, and D viruses predominate on the African continent, whereas most infections in India and China derive from clade C viruses (30). Subtype B, which comprises most infections in the United States and Western Europe, is uncommon in most other parts of the world. Because HIV-1 was first isolated from individuals infected with subtype B viruses, most of what is known about Env structure and antibody reactivity has been derived from studies of clade B HIV-1 infection. For example, most monoclonal antibodies (mAbs) against HIV-1 Env have been derived from clade B–infected patients (19, 31).

Numerous mAbs to the HIV-1 Env have been isolated from humans, but only a few of these can effectively neutralize most strains of the virus (2, 5, 23, 28, 31–37). This highlights one of the central features of the humoral immune response against HIV-1: Most of the anti-Env antibodies generated during natural infection are directed to regions of gp120 or gp41 that are not exposed on the mature functional virus spike. This may arise because gp120 readily dissociates from gp41 and because certain epitopes on monomeric forms of gp120 and exposed regions of gp41 are highly immunogenic (2, 3, 22). This results in a large proportion of antibodies that can be detected by gp120 or gp140 enzyme-linked immunosorbent assay (ELISA) but are unable to bind the native virus spike and neutralize the virus. However, sera from some HIV-1-infected subjects are able to potently neutralize diverse isolates of HIV-1 (38–45), which demonstrates that there are vulnerable regions on the functional Env trimer. Until recently, little was known about how such HIV-1-positive sera were able to neutralize the virus, and much of what we know about neutralization epitopes of HIV-1 has been derived from the crystal structures of the few known neutralizing mAbs bound to their epitopes on gp120 or gp41.

The first broadly reactive, neutralizing human mAb against HIV-1, b12, was isolated from a clade B–infected patient in 1992 by phage techniques. The phage technique combines random heavy and light chains, and, therefore, this antibody may or may not be a naturally occurring anti-HIV antibody. Nevertheless, it was subsequently shown to bind to the CD4-binding site (CD4bs) region of gp120 (33). mAb b12 can neutralize more than 50% of clade B viral isolates and about 30% of non–clade B viruses (28, 46). This is an impressive breadth of reactivity for a single mAb, but the lack of complete breadth suggests that the virus is able to tolerate some degree of antigenic variation, even in the functionally conserved CD4bs region (47). Interestingly, numerous other human anti-CD4bs mAbs have been isolated, but most of these are considered to be non-neutralizing or are only able to neutralize a limited subset of highly sensitive strains of HIV-1 (28, 48). Though we do not completely understand the structural basis that distinguishes b12 from other anti-CD4bs mAbs, the recent atomic-level crystal structure of b12 bound to the core of gp120 and the analogous structures of two non-neutralizing mAbs have shed some light on this issue (49, 50). Although most anti-CD4bs mAbs can bind monomeric gp120, the potent neutralization by b12 results from a rather unique ability to access the recessed CD4bs that is shielded by variable loops of gp120 and by numerous surface glycans that can restrict antibody access. Thus, slight differences in antibody recognition of the CD4bs can impact actual access to this region on the native trimeric viral spike. If an antibody does not bind the native viral spike, it will not neutralize HIV-1. The other conserved vulnerable site on gp120 is formed by a complex set of glycans on the surface of the molecule. Only one mAb, 2G12, is known to bind to this glycan epitope (51). This antibody has a highly unusual domain swap structure that produces a single combining site (52). mAb 2G12 can neutralize many primary isolates from clade B, but its breadth of reactivity again falls off on non–clade B viruses (28, 37, 46,

mAb: monoclonal antibody

CD4bs: CD4-binding site

Glycan: a carbohydrate chain covalently linked to a specific amino acid of a protein

53). Whether there are additional NAbs against glycan-dependent sites on gp120 remains to be defined. One other well-characterized epitope on gp120 is the coreceptor binding region, often called the CD4-induced (CD4i) region because it is most highly exposed after the virus engages CD4 (10, 54–56). Antibodies to this region, defined by the prototype mAb 17b, have increased binding affinity when soluble CD4 triggers gp120. Although this CD4-induced epitope is highly conserved across HIV-1 clades (57), mAb 17b and related mAbs have only weak neutralization activity against most primary isolates of HIV-1, presumably because this epitope is exposed only briefly after viral attachment, when steric hindrance severely limits antibody access (58). Thus, the anti-CD4i mAbs studied to date are unable to effectively access the binding site efficiently enough to block viral entry.

In addition to the two known conserved neutralization epitopes on gp120, one region on gp41 is vulnerable to NAbs. This region, called the membrane proximal external region (MPER), is formed by a linear sequence of approximately 30 amino acids and is the target of three distinct neutralizing antibodies, 2F5, 4E10, and Z13 (34–36). Binding to the MPER is thought to interfere with viral fusion to the host cell, thereby blocking viral entry (59). Although these anti-MPER mAbs display an impressive breadth of reactivity, particularly mAb 4E10, they also appear to be uncommon during natural infection (40, 60–62). Interestingly, the MPER may share homology to self proteins, and data suggest that mechanisms of self tolerance select against MPER-reactive antibody B cell clones (63). Overall, despite many years of study, our structural knowledge of HIV-1 neutralization epitopes is limited to two defined epitopes on gp120 and one region of gp41. And with some very recent exceptions, all mAbs isolated and studied to date were derived from clade B–infected individuals. Finally, none of these broadly neutralizing antibodies has been elicited by immunization. This highlights the importance of isolating additional mAbs to increase our understanding of neutralization epitopes on the HIV-1 Env.

THE NATURAL NAb RESPONSE TO HIV-1

The initial NAb response to HIV-1 is slow to develop. Although binding antibodies to gp41 and variable regions of gp120 can be detected as early as three weeks after infection (64, 65), detectable NAbs against the viral Env are generated only after several months of infection. Importantly, this early NAb response is complicated by successive waves of viral escape from autologous virus NAbs (38, 66–74), as is the case for several animal lentiviruses. NAbs do appear to exert immune pressure on the virus, but escape occurs rapidly enough to ensure continued high-level viral replication (38, 66–76). The result is that the serum from a specific time point during HIV-1 infection usually neutralizes autologous viruses from months earlier in infection, but not concurrent circulating viruses.

Recent evidence suggests that autologous NAbs are directed to variable regions of gp120 and may be influenced by the pattern of surface Env glycosylation that varies widely among viruses (73, 74, 77–85). Such NAbs to rapidly changing Env regions may explain the observation that sera from the early months of HIV-1 infection are able to potently neutralize the patient's autologous virus but have limited neutralization activity toward the patient's own escape mutants or against heterologous viruses derived from other patients. Interestingly, viruses that escape the autologous serum NAb response generally remain sensitive to neutralization mediated by known mAbs such as b12, 2G12, and the MPER-directed mAbs described above. This is consistent with our understanding that the initial NAb response is not directed to these more conserved epitopes on gp120. In addition, neutralization escape mutants of HIV-1 generally remain sensitive to neutralization by heterologous sera, suggesting that fitness constraints preclude complete virus escape from the spectrum of NAbs in most sera.

Broadly Reactive NAb in Some HIV-1-Positive Sera

In contrast to the early autologous NAb response described above, the NAb response that arises after several years of infection can be remarkably potent and cross-reactive. Serum from some HIV-1-infected individuals (HIV-1$^+$ sera) contains antibodies that can neutralize diverse HIV-1 strains including viruses from different clades (38–45, 61). This broadly reactive NAb response was initially thought to be quite uncommon, but recent cross-sectional studies show that approximately 25% of HIV-1$^+$ sera can neutralize many circulating virus strains, and a subset of these sera, perhaps 10%, contains NAbs that can neutralize most known HIV-1 strains (39, 41, 45, 61). This NAb response is of interest because it provides proof of concept that the natural B cell response can generate broadly reactive NAbs against HIV-1 and because it is this type of antibody response that we would like to elicit with a preventative vaccine. As is reviewed below, nonhuman primate studies using a chimeric simian-human immunodeficiency virus (SHIV) show that potent NAbs directed to the HIV-1 Env can prevent acquisition of viral infection (4, 12). Because prior efforts to elicit NAbs by Env immunization have met with limited success, it becomes important to understand which viral epitopes are targeted by the NAbs present in these HIV-1$^+$ sera (2, 11, 21). There appear to be two possibilities that are not mutually exclusive. Broad serum neutralization may be mediated by a polyclonal set of NAbs that accrue over time during HIV-1 infection and that target several independent Env epitopes (91). Alternatively, neutralization breadth may arise from a maturation of the B cell response that results in a high-affinity NAb to one or two highly conserved sites on the viral Env, such as the CD4 or coreceptor binding regions. Several recent studies have begun to shed light on this question. Highly selected, broadly neutralizing sera have been shown to contain antibodies directed to the CD4bs of gp120 (40, 41, 43, 44, 61). This has been demonstrated for both clade B and clade C sera, and the anti-CD4bs NAbs are clearly different in specificity to mAb12, which is the only known broadly neutralizing mAb directed to the CD4bs. There is also a suggestion that some serum NAbs target the coreceptor binding region of gp120 (44), though this finding requires further confirmation. Sera that contain anti-MPER NAbs appear to be uncommon, but several broadly neutralizing sera contain NAbs directed to MPER epitopes (40, 61, 62). Importantly, many of the HIV-1$^+$ sera studied can neutralize HIV-1 by targeting epitopes that have not yet been well defined. In some cases, serum neutralization can be mapped to regions of gp120 that are not cross-reactive with the CD4bs or coreceptor binding site. In other cases, the neutralizing IgG fraction of sera cannot be attributed to either gp120 or gp41, suggesting that NAbs may be directed to trimer-specific regions of the viral Env spike (40, 41, 44, 61, 86). Further investigation and improved epitope mapping technologies will be required to understand the full spectrum of the NAb response against HIV-1.

Isolation of Novel Neutralizing mAbs

In addition to further serum mapping studies, the B cells of HIV-infected patients with high levels of broadly reactive NAbs may be a rich source of novel neutralizing mAbs. A great deal of structural knowledge has been derived from the few available neutralizing mAbs. Crystallographic analysis of these mAbs while complexed to their cognate regions of gp120 or gp41 has provided atomic-level detail of the structure of several viral neutralization epitopes (19, 34, 49, 87, 88). The translation of such structural information to the design of improved immunogens has been termed "structure-assisted vaccine design," and this is currently a major focus of antibody-based vaccine efforts (18, 20, 21, 31, 89). However, these design efforts are limited by the small set of available neutralizing mAbs and by the fact that most known mAbs were derived from clade B–infected subjects. Hence, there is little or no structural data on non–clade

B viral epitopes from which to design vaccine immunogens. As previously noted, mAb b12 was isolated more than 15 years ago, and no additional broadly neutralizing anti-CD4bs mAb has been isolated since that time. Fortunately, new technologies may allow for much more efficient isolation of mAbs from B cells of HIV-1-infected subjects. Single Env-specific B cells can now be identified by flow cytometry (39, 90) and sorted at the single cell level. In one recent study, single cell polymerase chain reaction (PCR) augmented this methodology to recover IgG heavy and light chains and to express the matched pairs as full IgG molecules. Among six HIV-1-infected patients, between 10 and 50 independent mAbs were derived per patient, many of these with some level of neutralization activity (91). This technology and related methods (92) should produce large numbers of novel mAbs in the next few years. One recent example is the isolation of two novel neutralizing antibodies from a patient whose sera contained broadly reactive NAbs. mAbs PG9 and PG16 were derived from the culture and from the screening of thousands of single memory B cells that were stimulated in vitro to divide and secrete IgG. The use of a high-throughput microneutralization assay facilitated the identification of HIV-1-specific B cells that secrete NAbs, and the IgG heavy and light chain genes from these cells were amplified by PCR (93). mAbs PG9 and PG16 are closely related somatic mutants that bind to a novel epitope on the HIV-1 Env that is composed of variable regions V2 and V3. These two mAbs potently neutralize approximately 75% of diverse strains of HIV-1. Hence, they are the most broadly reactive NAbs isolated to date (94). These novel mAbs can be used for crystal structure analysis to augment our understanding of the structural basis of neutralization and to improve vaccine design efforts.

One area of some confusion relates to the observation that the presence of broadly reactive NAbs in a patient's plasma does not necessarily lead to low levels of viral replication. Hence, it is important to distinguish between the potential protective role of preexisting NAbs that could act on the low viral inocula at the mucosal surface and the apparent lack of clinical benefit of NAbs during the chronic phase of HIV-1 infection. The study of the natural NAb response to HIV-1 can provide insights for the design of improved antibody-based HIV-1 vaccines.

WHAT ANTIBODY LEVEL IS NEEDED TO PROTECT?

Studies of the antibody response that evolves during HIV-1 infection provide proof of concept that B cells can generate cross-reactive NAbs, even in the setting of the massive ongoing destruction of $CD4^+$ T cells. It is therefore reasonable to ask if the NAb levels found in HIV-1^+ sera would be high enough to mediate protection if they were present prior to viral exposure. Except for the early phase III gp120 vaccine trials in humans, which showed that non-neutralizing antibodies did not protect against HIV-1 infection, human data on the role and level of NAbs in protection are limited and indirect. Several research groups have studied autologous NAb responses in HIV-1-infected mothers and their newborn infants in an attempt to discern if NAbs play a role in preventing mother-to-child transmission of HIV-1 (95–98). Such studies are difficult to perform, and many have suffered from small sample size; results among studies have thus been inconsistent. However, the data from several recent studies using well-established genetic analyses and autologous NAb assays do suggest an association between maternal autologous NAb and lower rates of HIV-1 transmission to the child (99–101). These data support the hypothesis that NAbs have a protective role in acquisition of HIV-1 infection but do not give us quantitative data on the NAb level that a vaccine would need to elicit. Similarly, one recent report suggested that a lack of NAbs to HIV-1 predisposed to HIV-1 superinfection (102), but larger clinical studies will be needed to confirm this finding.

The most quantitative data on the level of NAbs needed to protect against acquisition of infection come from nonhuman primate models of SHIV infection. The simian backbone of the SHIV permits effective viral replication in the macaque host, whereas the HIV-1 Env allows the study of HIV-1 Env–specific antibodies (103, 104). Numerous passive immunization studies have been performed using both polyclonal IgG and single or combinations of mAbs (4, 105–111). Importantly, SHIV challenge studies demonstrated that passive transfer of non-neutralizing antibodies had little or no protective effect (105, 107), confirming the premise that a vaccine should induce NAbs. Initial studies used high doses of challenge virus, delivered intravenously or mucosally, to infect all control animals. In this setting, high levels of passively infused NAbs were often required to protect against infection. The in vitro NAb titer needed to protect animals varied depending on the assay format and antibodies used, but several studies found that sterile protection was seen when the serum dilution providing 90% neutralization (serum ID90) of the challenge virus was in the range of 1:40–1:400 (108, 111); one group calculated a 99% serum neutralization titer in the range of 1:40 (112). This led to some pessimism about the ability of HIV-1 vaccines ever to elicit such high NAb levels (111, 112). However, the level of NAbs required to protect also depends on the specific antibody used. In contrast to mAb b12, passive transfer studies with mAb 2G12 have shown that a serum ID90 of 1:10 or less can mediate sterile protection (113, 114).

The most recent passive antibody transfer study employed a low-dose mucosal challenge model that requires multiple exposures to infect all control animals (115). Using this model, investigators again studied mAb b12 and demonstrated a 21-fold decrease in the risk of SHIV infection compared to control animals with no antibody. Among protected animals, the serum ID90 was approximately 1:5. This contrasted to the serum dilution value of 1:80 or greater that the same researchers observed using mAb b12 with a high-dose mucosal challenge. Although there are limitations inherent in any animal model, the low-dose mucosal challenge model may be closer to the natural route of infection of humans than prior animal models. Hence, it may provide a better approximation of the level of NAbs needed to protect against human acquisition of HIV-1. A review of the existing passive transfer data suggests that antibody levels sufficient to mediate a 90% (tenfold) decrease in virus levels in vitro can impact the rate of experimental SHIV infection. To compare these values with the neutralization titers measured in chronic HIV-1 infection, HIV-1$^+$ human sera and passive immune monkey sera can be tested in the same standardized Env-pseudovirus neutralization assays. In this assay, the sera from protected monkeys have a serum ID50 of between 1:125 and 1:300 (115), which is similar to the levels found in many HIV-1$^+$ sera. Thus, until actual vaccine efficacy trials in humans provide further guidance, these ID50 values appear to be a reasonable approximation of the level of serum NAb that we would like to generate with Env vaccines.

Serum ID: serum inhibitory dilution mediating a 50% or 90% inhibition of viral infectivity

One interesting aspect of the passive immunization studies has been the focus on IgG antibodies and virus neutralization rather than on other Fc-mediated effector functions of antibodies. The carboxy-terminal region of the IgG heavy chains contains the Fc region that binds both to proteins of the complement system and to Fc receptors on host immune cells. Engagement of the complement can lead to viral lysis, whereas antibody engagement of the Fc receptor on natural killer cells can mediate antibody-dependent cellular cytotoxicity (ADCC) of HIV-1-infected cells. One group of investigators recently used two mutated versions of mAb b12 to study the role of such Fc effector functions (116). Two mutant versions of mAb b12 were created, one that could not bind complement and one that could bind neither complement nor the Fc receptor. These two mutants were compared to the wild-type b12 for protection against SHIV challenge. Interestingly, the wild-type and complement binding–defective mutant b12 produced equal levels of protection, but the version of b12 that was unable to bind the Fc receptor protected only about half the animals. This strongly suggested that ADCC plays a role in the protection afforded by mAb b12. Thus, there was some level of protection against infection even in the complete absence of complement or ADCC, but the data do strongly suggest that ADCC can augment the direct virus neutralization function of antibodies.

VACCINE-ELICITED NAb RESPONSES IN HUMAN CLINICAL TRIALS

Human clinical trials have evaluated various candidate HIV-1 Env-containing vaccines with the goal of eliciting NAbs (**Table 1**). Some vaccines incorporated additional immunogens, such as Gag, Pol, and Nef, for the elicitation of virus-specific $CD8^+$ T cell responses in addition to NAbs. Most Env-containing vaccines were well tolerated and generated NAbs, and three were evaluated for efficacy in high-risk populations. Vaccine immunogens for NAb responses have been administered either as Env protein or as Env-expressing DNA and viral vectors. Highly attenuated versions of vaccinia virus [HIVAC, modified vaccinia Ankara (MVA)], canarypox virus (ALVAC), adenovirus serotype 5 (Ad5), and Venezuelan equine encephalitis virus (VEE) have been used as vectors for Env immunogens in human trials. The vaccines have been tested as single agents and as heterologous "prime-boost" vaccines, where subjects were first administered an Env-encoding DNA or viral vector and were later boosted with Env protein or heterologous viral vectors. Because of concerns regarding the safety of live-attenuated virus (117) and a lack of efficacy of whole-inactivated virus in nonhuman primates (118), HIV-1 vaccines based on conventional approaches that yielded successful vaccines for other viral pathogens have not advanced to human clinical trials. Thus, efforts to develop an HIV-1 vaccine have emphasized subunit immunogens because they pose no risk of generating infectious virus and because effective subunit vaccines for other viruses, such as hepatitis B and papilloma virus, have been licensed.

With few options available at the time, most early Env vaccine immunogens were monomeric, monovalent gp120, and uncleaved forms of gp160 derived from T cell line adapted (TCLA) strains of subtype B HIV-1 that were the first strains isolated in the epidemic (e.g., IIIB, MN, SF2). Many recipients of these early vaccines developed a NAb response against the vaccine strain and other TCLA virus strains (119–125), but the antibodies exhibited little or no neutralizing activity against primary patient isolates (13, 126, 161). Failure to neutralize primary isolates was an early indication that these antibodies would afford little or no protection. This concern was reinforced when two bivalent gp120 protein vaccines failed to either prevent infection or impact plasma viral load in efficacy trials (15, 16, 127). Both vaccines were designed and tested on the basis of eliciting NAbs. One vaccine (AIDSVAX B/B, Vax004 trial) consisted of a high dose of gp120 from two subtype B viruses (300 μg each of $gp120_{MN}$ and $gp120_{GNE8}$ in alum) and was tested in men who have sex with men and among women at high risk of heterosexual HIV-1 transmission in North America and the Netherlands (15, 16). The second vaccine (AIDSVAX B/E, Vax003 trial) contained $gp120_{MN}$ and $gp120_{A244}$ (CRF01-AE) and was tested in injection drug users in Bangkok, Thailand (127). Both vaccines elicited high titers of NAbs against the sensitive HIV-1 strain MN (mean titer >1000). A more extensive investigation of NAbs was conducted for the Vax004 trial, in which moderate titers of NAb were often detected against other highly neutralization-sensitive strains of virus (e.g., SF162 and BaL), and weak neutralizing activity was occasionally detected against primary isolates (D.C. Montefiori, M. Wang, T. Wrin, C. Petropoulos, M.Gurwith, et al., manuscript submitted). Moreover, there was no measurable impact on the de novo NAb response that evolved in vaccine recipients who later acquired infection (128). These findings are a strong indication that a different quality of NAbs will be required for vaccine protection.

Many Env immunogens in human clinical trials were derived from viruses that are classified as tier 1 because the virus is highly susceptibility to neutralization (129). Although a common feature of TCLA strains, a small fraction of primary isolates also possess a tier 1 neutralization phenotype. This unusual phenotype is often associated with epitopes in the variable loops and CD4i region of gp120 that tend to be strongly immunogenic and exhibit spontaneous exposure for easy antibody access to the virus (57, 80). In contrast, most primary isolates have evolved under immune pressure to evade these NAbs by masking their cognate epitopes with N-linked glycans and other structurally imposed constraints (22, 24, 130). Epitope masking contributes to an overall lower level of neutralization sensitivity for most primary isolates—a phenotype that is classified as tier 2 (129). New immunogens that elicit broadly reactive NAbs against tier 2 viruses are now being sought because these viruses are thought to more closely approximate the relevant targets of a protective vaccine-elicited antibody response. For improved immune monitoring efforts, multisubtype panels of well-characterized tier 1 and tier 2 reference strains have been created for standardized assessments of NAbs (53, 131, 132).

Little progress has been made in eliciting stronger NAb responses against these panels of tier 2 reference strains in recent clinical trials. Poor neutralization of tier 2 viruses was seen even though some immunogens elicited high titers of NAbs against tier 1 viruses (133–139). Despite this lack of progress, considerable information has been gained on how to optimize the dose, schedule, adjuvant, and vector (e.g., choice of insert, expression, mode of delivery) for HIV-1 NAb responses in humans. Although not formally proven, these insights could be valuable for optimizing future vaccines that aim to elicit NAbs against tier 2 viruses. Two of the best immunogens for NAb responses against tier 1 viruses in human clinical trials have been $gp120_{W61D}$ in AS02A adjuvant (134) and V2-deleted $ogp140_{SF162}$ in MF59 adjuvant (P. Spearman, M. Lally, M. Elizaga, D.C. Montefiori, M.J. McElrath, et al., manuscript in preparation). Potent responses against tier 1 viruses also were achieved with high doses of bivalent gp120 in alum (15, 16, 127). Other reasonably potent immunogens include (*a*) priming with a canarypox vaccine (vCP1452) expressing membrane-anchored $gp120_{MN}$ and boosting with $gp120_{MN}$ or $gp120_{MN+GNE8}$ in alum (133, 136) and (*b*) priming with a mixture of DNA vectors expressing polyvalent gp120 (subtypes A, B, C, and E) and boosting with the corresponding gp120 proteins in QS-21 adjuvant (135). AS02A, MF59, and QS-21 have been superior to alum as adjuvants for Env protein immunogens (134, 135), although a higher dose of immunogen might compensate for the weaker alum adjuvant effect (119, 140). QS-21 was effective even at the very low dose of 3 μg of gp120 (140). Marginal effects on the NAb response were observed by varying the dose (approximate range 40–800 μg) (119, 120, 122, 124, 125, 134) and schedule (120, 121, 140, 141) of Env protein administration. In some cases, gender, race, and risk of acquiring HIV-1 infection appeared to affect the magnitude of NAb responses in clinical trials of gp120 immunogens formulated with alum (16, 141, 142). These latter observations suggest a need to enroll diverse populations of subjects to fully evaluate immunogenicity.

In contrast to the strong NAb response against tier 1 viruses that some Env proteins elicit in humans, NAb responses have been weak or undetectable for Env-encoding DNA (143–145), vaccinia virus (146–149), MVA (150), ALVAC (133, 136, 151–157), and Ad5 (158) vaccines as single agents. In addition to eliciting virus-specific T cell responses (159, 160), these DNA and viral vectors have the potential to prime B cells for a rapid high-titer NAb response after boosting with either Env protein or heterologous viral vectors. Efficient priming by recombinant ALVAC vaccines has resulted in high-titer NAb responses after only one or two Env protein boosts (133, 136, 152, 154, 161). This is a substantial dose-sparing effect compared to the three or four inoculations that are required for high-titer NAb induction with Env protein alone (119, 120, 134, 140, 141). Moreover, peak titers of NAbs were

Table 1 Phase I and II clinical trials with HIV-1 Env immunogens

Env immunogen[a]	HIV-1 strain	Clade	Tier	Source[b]	Adjuvant[c]	Tier 1 NAb (GMT)[d]	References
Subunit protein							
gp160	IIIB	B	1	Insect	Alum	±	122, 123, 125
gp160	MN	B	1	Vero	Alum-DOC	+	120
gp120	IIIB	B	1	CHO	Alum	+	124
gp120	MN	B	1	CHO	Alum	++	119, 140, 141
gp120	MN	B	1	CHO	QS-21	++	140
gp120	MN	B	1	CHO	QS-21+Alum	++	140
gp120	SF2	B	1	CHO	MF59	+	137, 141, 154
gp120	CM235	CRF01_AE	2	CHO	MF59	+	137
bivalent gp120	SF2 + CM235	B, CRF01-AE	1, 2	CHO	MF59	+	138
gp160, gp120	MN, MN	B	1	Vero, CHO	Alum-DOC/Alum	++	121
gp120	W61D	B	1	CHO	AS02A	+++	134
ogp140ΔV2	SF162	B	1	CHO	MF59	+++	
Single vaccine vector							
VAC-gp160	IIIB	B	1	NA	NA	–	146, 148, 149
ALVAC-gp160	MN	B	1	NA	NA	±	153, 157
ALVAC-gp120	MN	B	1	NA	NA	+	133, 151, 152, 155, 156, 161
DNA-gp140	ADA	B	2	NA	NA	–	143
DNA-polyvalent gp140	Bal/IIIB chimera	B	1	NA	NA	–	144, 145
	92RW020	A	2				
	97ZA012	C	2				
Ad5-polyvalent gp140	Bal/IIIB chimera	B	1	NA	NA	–	158
	92RW020	A	2				
	97ZA012	C	2				
Prime-boost							
VAC-gp160 prime/gp160 boost	IIIB	B	1	Insect	Alum	+	147, 148, 162
ALVAC-gp160 prime/gp160 boost	MN	B	1	BHK-21	Alum	+	157
ALVAC-gp160 prime/gp160 boost	MN	B	1	BHK-21	ISA-51	+	157
ALVAC-gp160 prime/gp120 boost	MN, SF2	B, B	1, 1	CHO	MF59	++	153
ALVAC-gp120 prime/gp120 boost	MN, SF2	B, B	1	CHO	MF59	++	152, 154–156, 161

ALVAC-gp120 prime/gp120 boost	MN, MN	B	1	CHO	Alum	+++	136
ALVAC-gp120 prime/bivalent gp120 boost	MN, MN+GNE8	B, B	1, ?	CHO	Alum	+++	133
ALVAC-gp120 prime/bivalent gp120 boost	92TH023, MN+A244	E, E+B	2, 1	CHO	Alum	++	139
DNA-gp120 + NYVAC-gp120	97CN54	CRF07_BC'	?	NA	NA	–	150
Polyvalent DNA-gp120 prime/matched polyvalent gp120 boost	92UG037.8	A	2	All CHO-derived	All in QS-21	+++	135
	92US715.6	B	2				
	Bal	B	1				
	96ZM651	C	2				
	93TH976.17	E	2				
Ongoing and planned							
VEEgp120	Du151	C	2	NA	NA		
DNA-polyvalent gp140ΔCFI prime/Ad5-polyvalent gp140ΔCFI boost	Bal/IIIB chimera	B	1	NA	NA		
	92RW020	A	2				
	97ZA012	C	2				
DNA-gp140 prime, MVA-gp140 boost	ADA	B	2	NA	NA		
DNA-gp140 prime, MVA-gp140 boost	Du151	C	2	NA	NA		
DNA-gp140, DNA-IL-12 or DNA-IL-15	Consensus sequence	B	?				
Ad35-gp140 prime/Ad5-gp140 boost	92RW020	A	2	NA	NA		
Ad5-gp140 prime/Ad35-gp140 boost	92RW020	A	2	NA	NA		

[a]Unless indicated otherwise (e.g., delivery via recombinant DNA or viral vector), Env immunogens were recombinant proteins. VAC, vaccinia virus; NYVAC, New York strain of vaccinia virus; MVA, modified vaccina Ankara (attenuated strain of vaccinia virus); ALVAC, recombinant canarypox virus; Ad5 and Ad35, adenovirus serotypes 5 and 35, respectively; VEE, Venezuelan equine encephalitis virus. Some vaccines contained additional HIV-1 immunogens that are not shown because they are not targets for NAbs; these immunogens were incorporated into vaccines for the elicitation of virus-specific T cell responses.

[b]Source is for Env proteins only. Insect cells, baculovirus-derived immunogen made in *Spodoptera frugiperda* cells; CHO, Chinese hamster ovary cells; BHK-21, baby hamster kidney cells; NA, not applicable.

[c]Alum, aluminum hydroxide; DOC, deoxycholate; MF59, microfluidized oil-in-water emulsion; MTE-PE, muramyl tripeptide covalently linked with dipalmitoyl phosphatidylethanolamine; QS-21, saponin extract from the bark of Quillaja saponaria; AS02A, QS-21 plus 3-deacylated monophosphoryl lipid A (MPL) in an oil-in-water emulsion; ISA-51, Freund's incomplete adjuvant as one part mannid monooleate (Montanide 80) for nine parts mineral oil; NA, not applicable.

[d]Values are relative magnitudes of the NAb response at peak immunity (2–4 weeks post final boosting) for the optimal vaccine dose, formulation, and vector design and as measured against either the vaccine strain (when the vaccine strain is a tier 1 virus) or against HIV-1_{MN} (when the vaccine strain is a tier 2 virus). Each "+" indicates an approximate three- to fivefold incremental increase in NAb titer. A "±" indicates a weak response in a minor subset of individuals. These approximations are used because of differences in assay systems and data reporting in various clinical trials. The NAb response in chronic HIV-1 infection would be equivalent to ++++.

significantly elevated after ALVAC prime/Env protein boost as compared to immunizing with Env protein alone (147, 154, 155, 162). Strong priming was also evident in a clinical trial that evaluated a DNA prime/gp120 protein boost (135). Other viral vectors probably prime B cells, but this has not yet been tested in humans. Also, some viral vectors might be used as an alternative to Env protein for heterologous prime-boost immunization. A study in macaques showed that a gp140 immunogen delivered by DNA prime/Ad5 boost elicits much higher titers of NAbs than either vaccine alone (163). A similar DNA prime/Ad5 boost vaccine is now in human trials.

Several clinical trials have addressed the optimal delivery of heterologous prime-boost vaccines. Vector priming before Env protein boosting was shown to be superior to simultaneous administration of both vaccines (155, 156). Also, longer intervals between vector priming and Env protein boosting (152, 164) and between Env protein boosts (141) appeared advantageous. Further optimization of DNA and viral vector vaccines for T and B cell responses might be possible by coexpressing immunomodulatory cytokines—a concept that is now in a human clinical trial of a multicomponent DNA vaccine (**Table 1**).

MODEST SUCCESS WITH A PRIME-BOOST VACCINE IN AN EFFICACY TRIAL

Only one heterologous prime-boost vaccine has been tested in an efficacy trial. This trial (RV144), which was conducted in Thailand and completed in October 2009, mainly enrolled heterosexuals at risk of HIV-1 infection (165). The prime consisted of a recombinant canarypox vaccine (vCP1521) encoding Gag, Pol, Nef and membrane-anchored $gp120_{92TH023}$, administered at months 0, 1, 3, and 6. The boost consisted of bivalent $gp120_{MN}/gp120_{A244}$ in alum, administered at months 3 and 6. Vaccination appeared to reduce the rate of acquisition of HIV-1 infection but had no significant effect on early viral loads or on $CD4^+$ T cell counts in vaccine recipients who later acquired infection. Vaccine efficacy was estimated to be 31.2% ($p = 0.04$) in a modified intent-to-treat analysis that excluded subjects who were found in retrospective testing to be HIV-1 infected at the time of randomization. Vaccine efficacy in intent-to-treat and per-protocol analyses was 26.4% ($p = 0.08$) and 26.2% ($p = 0.16$), respectively. Although neither of these latter analyses was statistically significant, both continued to show a trend toward modest protection against infection. This modest efficacy, though not deemed adequate for licensure, is the first indication that effective vaccination against HIV-1 is within reach. The outcome also suggests that prevention of HIV-1 infection is an achievable goal for vaccines. As emphasized by the scientists who conducted this trial (165) and in a recent editorial (166), critical next steps are to seek an immune correlate of protection, to determine the relative contribution of the prime and boost vaccine components in eliciting protective immunity, and to study the impact of risk factors and routes of HIV-1 exposure on vaccine efficacy.

Another small efficacy trial that recently opened to enrollment is evaluating a DNA prime/rAd5 boost vaccine (HVTN 505). The DNA prime for this vaccine encodes proteins for Gag, Pol, Nef, and subtype A, B, and C gp140s, whereas the rAd5 boost encodes the same proteins with the exception of Nef. This vaccine regimen elicits robust T cell responses and moderate antibody levels, but it is not expected to elicit a substantial NAb response against tier 2 viruses. Nonetheless, in the absence of a known correlate of immunity against HIV-1, this trial may address important questions about NAbs and other antibody effector mechanisms should this vaccine prove to be at least partially protective.

NOVEL IMMUNOGEN APPROACHES

The data from human clinical trials demonstrate that the first generation of soluble protein and vectored Env immunogens was safe and immunogenic, but that the NAbs elicited were reactive with only a small subset of highly sensitive strains of HIV-1. Thus, the design of improved Env vaccine immunogens remains one of the most important challenges facing HIV-1 vaccine researchers. The explanation for the poor cross-reactivity of vaccine-elicited NAbs appears to relate to the restricted repertoire of induced antibodies and to the complex conformational structure of the native viral spike, which consists of a trimeric complex of noncovalently linked gp120 and gp41 molecules (24, 130). Fully functional Env requires post-translational proteolytic cleavage of gp120 and gp41, and the viral spike is heavily shielded by variable loop regions of Env and by numerous glycans that make up approximately half of the Env molecular weight (22, 24, 130). Several lines of evidence show that antibodies induced by subunit gp120 or gp41 immunogens are able to bind monomeric forms of the Env gp120 but are generally unable to access their epitope on the native trimer (18, 130, 167–170). Some highly sensitive HIV-1 strains have a more flexible or open configuration that allows antibody access, but most circulating HIV-1 strains are not neutralized by vaccine-elicited antibodies (2, 13, 14, 126). In addition, the surface-exposed variable regions of HIV-1 Env are immunodominant and often lead to the induction of antibodies that react with a highly limited set of viral isolates (18, 171–174). In total, these features of Env help explain the observation that vaccine-elicited antibodies may neutralize a virus homologous to the vaccine strain or some highly sensitive HIV-1 strains, but will not neutralize most primary isolates of HIV-1. This failure of initial antibody-based vaccine strategies has led to numerous novel approaches to generate more broadly reactive NAbs. Several major categories of immunogen design can be described: (*a*) mimics of the structure of the native viral spike, (*b*) removal or masking of immunodominant regions of Env, (*c*) polyvalent and consensus Env immunogens to enhance coverage of circulating strains of the virus, (*d*) Env stabilization to improve the immunogenicity of conserved epitopes, and (*e*) structure-assisted vaccine design to generate immunogens that mimic specific known neutralization epitopes. Several excellent reviews of this subject have recently been published (2, 18, 20, 22, 29, 170); we discuss several examples of novel immunogen approaches here.

Because monomeric gp120 does not elicit broadly NAbs and because antibodies must bind the native viral spike to neutralize the virus, there has been a great deal of focus on vector-based and soluble protein immunogens that can mimic the viral Env trimer. Conceptually, an intact inactivated virus particle or a genetically engineered virus-like particle (VLP) could present native Env. Unfortunately, the low Env content per virion, approximately 10 spikes per virus, appears to limit the immunogenicity of both inactivated virus and VLP products (175, 176). Newer strategies to increase the Env content on VLP may allow for improved immunogenicity of this approach in the future (177). An alternate approach is to produce soluble trimeric Env proteins. Most attempts to generate such immunogens have used gp140 versions of Env that are truncated in the transmembrane region of gp41 to allow secretion of the soluble protein. A major challenge is that expression of fully cleaved, soluble Env protein will result in the dissociation of the gp120 and gp41 subunits. Hence, investigators have modified the gp120-gp41 cleavage site to prevent subunit dissociation and produce stable protein immunogens (178–181) (**Figure 1**). These trimeric proteins appear to be more immunogenic than monomeric gp120 and to elicit a slightly more cross-reactive NAb response (171, 172, 178, 180, 182–184), but the protein is still a suboptimal mimic of the native viral spike. Evidence suggests that virus NAbs bind preferentially to functional cleaved Env trimers compared to noncleaved versions of Env (168, 169, 185). In an attempt to produce a more native fully cleaved trimer protein, investigators have introduced disulfide bonds that hold the gp120 and gp41 subunits in place after cleavage (186–188). Various forms of the cleavage-defective and disulfide-bonded gp140 trimer proteins have been tested in animal immunogenicity studies with rather disappointing

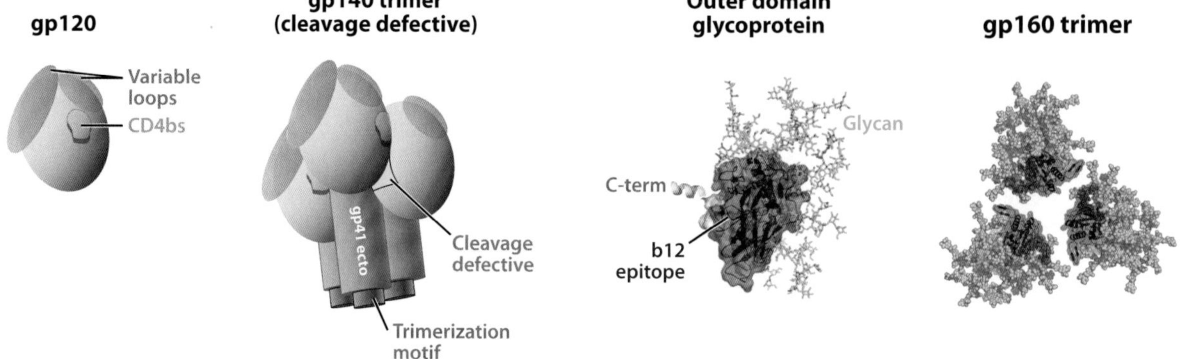

Figure 1

Env-based vaccine immunogens. The phase III VaxGen trial was conducted with a recombinant monomeric gp120 vaccine, depicted in the left-most diagram. The second Env immunogen is a soluble recombinant trimeric gp140 with an engineered defective cleavage site such that gp120 remains linked to gp41. A trimerization motif is added to the gp41 ectodomain region to stabilize the protein in a trimeric configuration. The third immunogen is an outer domain portion of gp120, which contains the neutralization epitope bound by mAb b12. Furthest to the right is a depiction of a full Env spike composed of a tri-molecular complex of gp120-gp41 heterodimers (viewed from an angle seen by CD4 and its coreceptor). The inner and outer domains of the core of gp120 are shown as the red and gray shaded regions, respectively. The green circles depict complex carbohydrate molecules (N-linked glycans) that cover much of the Env surface. Such a trimeric immunogen, if it could be designed, could present the native form of the HIV-1 Env to the immune system.

results. For reasons that are not well understood, these modified trimer proteins still elicit high levels of antibodies that are reactive with dominant regions of Env, such as variable loops, and low levels of cross-reactive NAbs (171, 172, 178, 180, 182–184, 186–189). Trimeric Env immunogens may also be delivered via gene-based vectors such as plasmid DNA or various viral vectors. DNA is often used to prime CD4 helper immune responses prior to boosting with a soluble protein or viral vector. These prime-boost delivery platforms induce high-titer Env-specific antibody responses in small animals and nonhuman primates, but the resulting NAb response is currently no more cross-reactive than that achieved by soluble protein alone (163, 181, 188–191).

Other immunogen design approaches focus on the antigenic diversity of Env and aim to overcome this by immunizing with polyvalent immunogens (multiple Envs in a combined mixture), or with artificial Envs consisting of an amino acid sequence that is a consensus of a large number of HIV-1 variants. Although initial studies with both types of immunogens in small animals have shown some improvement over prototypic Env (192, 193), the NAb response is still quite limited in titer and breadth. A strategic combination of both approaches is also worth considering (194).

The relatively poor induction of NAbs by gp120 and gp140 immunogens presents an interesting incongruity between the antigenic properties of the protein and the resulting immune response (42, 43, 195). For example, gp120 can adsorb the neutralizing activity from some HIV-1^+ sera (41–43, 195). In addition, the anti-CD4bs neutralizing mAb b12 will bind with high affinity to gp120 and gp140 soluble proteins, yet these proteins are unable to reelicit antibodies similar to b12. The poor immunogenic properties of some regions of Env are not well understood, but possible explanations include the conformational flexibility of the gp120 molecule and the gp120-gp41 trimer complex, the array of self glycans that shield much of the viral spike, and the immunodominance of the surface-exposed variable regions. Some B cell responses may be downregulated by self-tolerance mechanisms (196) or by other immunosuppressive properties of Env (197). To overcome some of these potential problems, investigators have designed immunogens that lack one or more of the variable regions (181, 183, 198, 199) or that mask immunodominant regions by introducing additional carbohydrate moieties to the protein (200). Unfortunately, these alterations alone have not yet resulted in major improvements in the potency or breadth of the NAbs elicited.

Env immunogens can also be stabilized into a specific known conformation (18, 201). Recall that the HIV-1 Env undergoes a substantial conformational change upon engaging its primary receptor CD4, leading to exposure of the site for coreceptor binding (22, 24). Thermodynamic analysis suggests that the initial contact of gp120 with CD4 results in a conformational alteration that locks Env into a CD4-bound state (49, 202). Thus, although the CD4bs and coreceptor regions of Env are relatively well conserved, they are not fully formed on the native Env trimer. This line of evidence has led to the design of immunogens that mimic the CD4-bound conformation of Env in order to better elicit antibodies to the receptor and coreceptor regions of Env. Starting with a pared down core region of gp120 that lacks the major variable regions, specific disulfide bonds and amino acid substitutions can be introduced that restrict movement of gp120 subdomains, stabilize the CD4 binding surface, and expose the formed coreceptor region (49, 201, 202). Initial studies with stabilized immunogens demonstrate proof of concept that the antibody response can be directed to the coreceptor binding region, but this has not yet translated to a more effective NAb response (189, 201). Current stabilized Env immunogens apparently do not elicit antibodies that can access the CD4bs or coreceptor region on the functional viral spike, but it is hoped that an improved understanding of Env structure and NAb binding will lead to the design of improved immunogens.

Much effort to create improved immunogens now centers on structure-assisted vaccine design (3, 18, 21, 22, 170). Here, a viral neutralization epitope is defined by the binding of one of a handful of specific neutralizing mAbs. The liganded crystal structure can then be solved to determine the atomic-level Env contact surface bound by the neutralizing mAb. As an example, the recent crystal structure of the neutralizing mAb b12 bound to the CD4bs region of gp120 provides the potential to mimic the b12 contact region in a vaccine immunogen. The CD4bs of gp120 is composed of regions of the inner and outer domains of gp120, but interestingly the structural data demonstrate that b12 binds mainly to the outer domain (49). Hence, outer domain constructs have recently been designed as potential vaccine immunogens (203) (**Figure 1**). Further iterative structure-based design and immunogenicity studies will be required to determine if such immunogens can begin to elicit NAbs directed to the CD4bs. It is also possible to combine immunogen design approaches. Initial immunization with a limited region or epitope of gp120 can be followed by immunization with the native trimeric immunogen to elicit epitope-specific antibodies that are then focused on binding the native viral spike (18).

The conserved MPER of gp41 is also a target for structure-assisted vaccine design. Crystal structures of mAbs 2F5 and 4E10 with their cognate peptide epitope have been solved; these have provided insights into the contact residues and secondary structure of the binding surface (34, 87). These analyses also suggest that hydrophobic residues within the antibody-combining site may be required for the antibody to access this region of gp41 that lies close to the viral membrane (87, 204). Because immunization with peptide forms of the MPER does not elicit NAbs, structural information will likely be needed to guide improved design of MPER-based immunogens. One recent approach is to transplant the MPER peptide epitope into a protein scaffold that can stabilize the conformation recognized by the neutralizing mAb. Various forms of such protein scaffolds can then be used as immunogens to focus the antibody response on the epitope of interest. These structure-assisted vaccine design efforts are in relatively early stages of testing (18).

WINDOW OF OPPORTUNITY FOR VACCINE-ELICITED NAbs

Primary virus: strains of HIV-1 that are derived directly from primary human tissue and were not cultured or passaged in a continuous cell line

It is uncertain whether a successful HIV-1 vaccine must prevent the acquisition of infection (sterilizing immunity) rather than aim for an adequate level of viremia control that protects against the immunosuppressive sequelae of infection and reduces the probability of subsequent transmission (**Figure 2**). Considerable obstacles exist for both paradigms. Many successful vaccines for other viral pathogens do not prevent infection; rather, initial rounds of replication that occur at or near the portal of entry trigger a rapid escalation of vaccine-elicited immune responses, leading to eradication of the virus at an early stage of dissemination prior to disease onset (205). Unlike HIV-1, eradication of these other viruses is possible because they neither integrate genetically nor establish a latent pool of infected cells that conceal the virus from immune recognition, thus adding to viral persistence. Because of this latent pool, even the most effective antiretroviral therapies are unable to eradicate HIV-1 once infection is firmly established (205). Thus, the biology of a chronically replicating lentivirus such as HIV-1 is particularly problematic for effective vaccination.

Preexisting NAbs are arguably the best hope for preventing the acquisition of HIV-1 infection. To be effective in this capacity, protective levels of the antibodies need to be sustained over many years. Current evidence suggests that this may be a difficult task. Peak NAb responses in human clinical trials of many candidate HIV-1 vaccines have waned rapidly, with an approximate half-life of only eight weeks (133, 134, 136, 141, 153, 154). This short half-life is in stark contrast to the remarkably stable antiviral antibody responses seen with live attenuated vaccines, such as those for smallpox, measles, mumps, rubella, and varicella-zoster, where the serum half-life of the antibodies is 50–200 years (206). The mechanisms for poor antibody maintenance with HIV-1 Env immunogens are not understood (207, 208). Of potential importance, B cell memory for some vaccine-elicited NAbs against HIV-1 appears to be maintained for prolonged periods of time. Individuals primed with a recombinant canarypox vaccine expressing gp120 and boosted with gp120 protein possessed detectable serum titers of NAbs against sensitive viruses five years after final immunization, and these titers increased dramatically within two weeks after an additional boost with gp160 protein (209). Sustained serologic memory in these vaccinated subjects is consistent with the presence of either long-lived plasma cells or memory B cells, with the boosting effect strongly implying a memory B cell component (207, 208). Dramatic increases in NAbs also have been observed within 2–3 weeks of SIV and SHIV challenge in previously immunized rhesus monkeys—a response that was not seen post-challenge in nonimmunized control animals (210–214).

The failure of most current Env immunogens to elicit sustained titers of NAbs even against sensitive tier 1 viruses suggests the same will be true for NAb responses against primary viruses, and this highlights the obstacle of achieving long-lasting protective antibody-based immunity with future immunogens. A greater understanding of B cell biology and the complex signaling pathways that drive long-lived serum antibody responses is needed to facilitate progress in this area. An alternate strategy is to prime for rapid recall NAb responses that impact the virus in its earliest stages of replication and dissemination, preferably in concert with virus-specific $CD8^+$ T cells. By controlling the virus early, it is hoped that initial damage to the immune system will be minimized to the extent that long-term viremia control and prevention of AIDS are possible (**Figure 2**). Moreover, because the risk of transmitting infection is proportional to the viral load of the donor (215), a vaccine that reduces the viral load should also reduce the rate of transmission as an indirect means of achieving sterilizing immunity in a population (216).

Many questions remain about the potential value of a rapid secondary NAb response during acute HIV-1 infection. Interpretations based on vaccine studies in the SIV and SHIV models

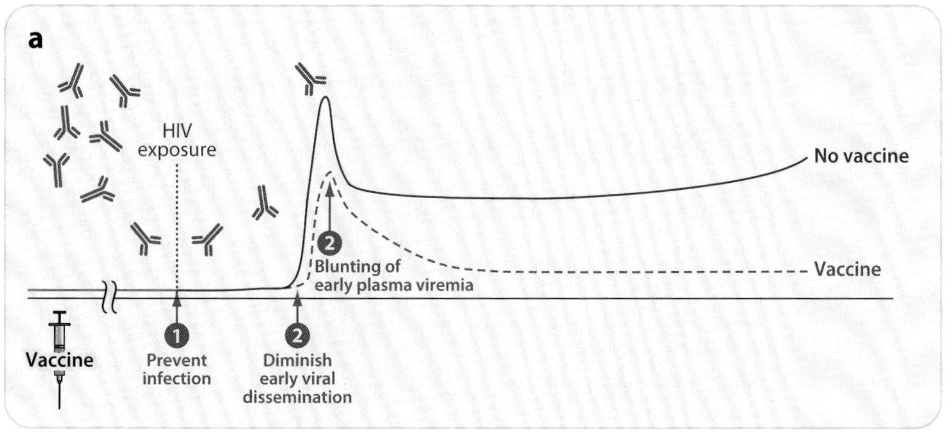

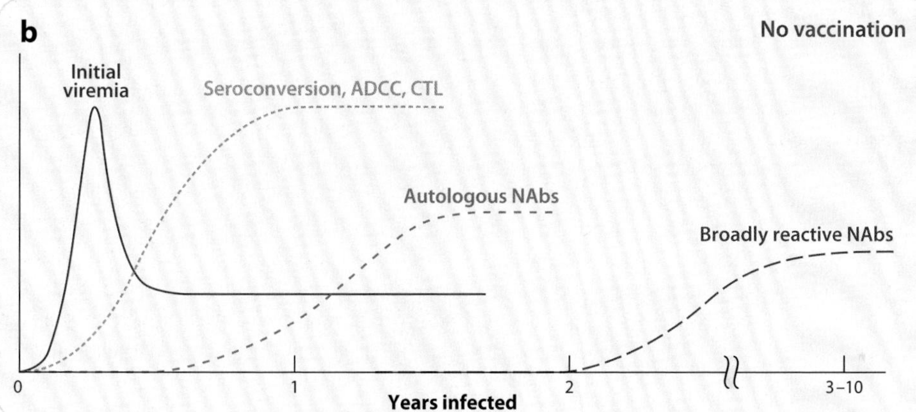

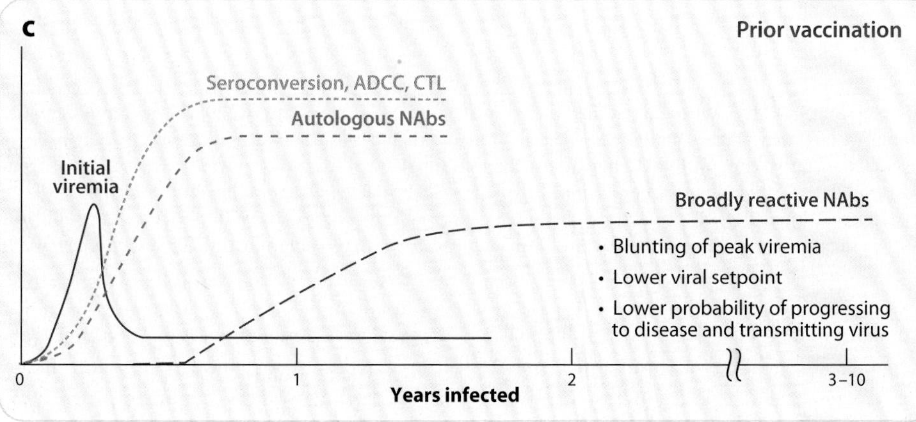

Figure 2

The effect of antibodies on the course of HIV-1 infection. (*a*) Anti-HIV-1 antibodies present prior to viral exposure could prevent the acquisition of infection or could diminish initial viral dissemination and immunologic dysfunction, leading to a blunting of systemic plasma viremia and an augmentation of the adaptive immune response that can control long-term viral replication. (*b* and *c*) The evolution of the anti-Env antibody response after HIV-1 infection. Vaccination prior to viral exposure could lead to a robust secondary antibody response, as shown in (*c*). The more rapid evolution of autologous NAbs and more broadly reactive NAbs could dampen viral replication and work in concert with T cell responses to control long-term viral replication.

are complicated by the coelicitation of virus-specific $CD8^+$ T cells. Additionally, studies of B cell depletion during acute SIV infection in nonhuman primates have yielded conflicting results (217–219). One reported case of a rapid and potent autologous NAb response that coincided with the downregulation and chronic control of rebound viremia after treatment

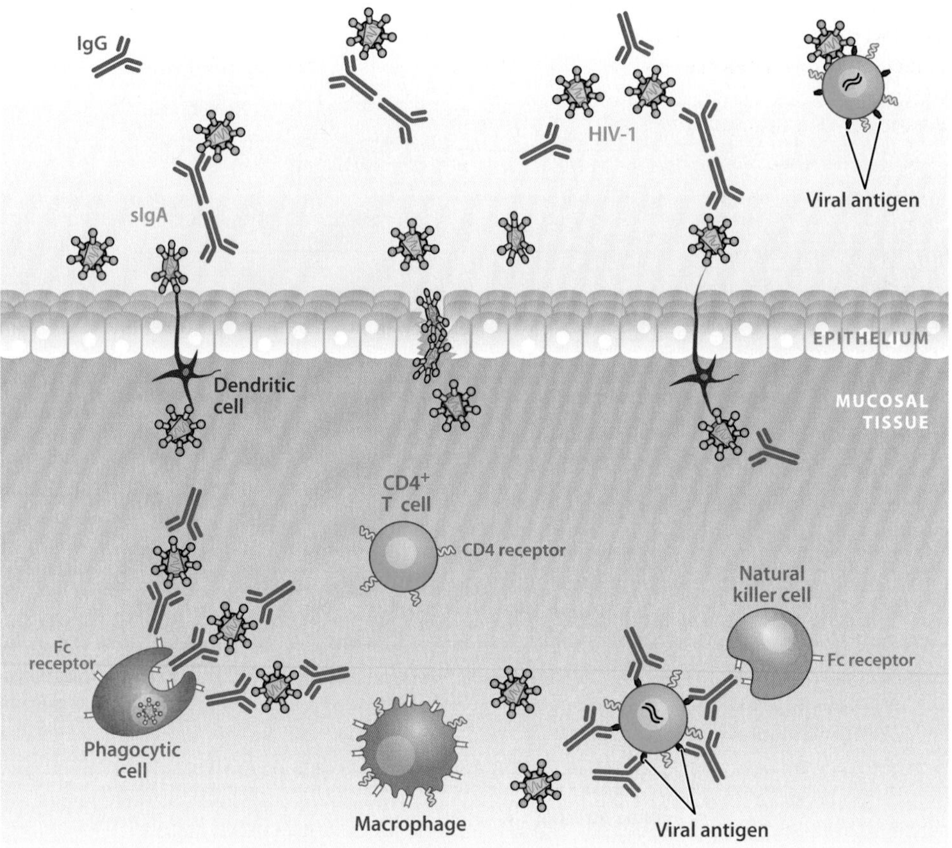

Figure 3

Antibody activities in mucosal tissues. IgG and IgA antibodies at the mucosal surface could bind and inactivate HIV-1, thus potentially preventing initial infection. Dendritic cells may take up unbound virions and transfer them across the mucosal surface, or they may reach the submucosa via a breach in the epithelium. Antibodies may also act within submucosal tissues to neutralize free virus or to bind virus and activate Fc-mediated antibody effector functions. For example, free virus can be coated by antibodies and cleared by phagocytic cells. The initially infected cells (e.g., $CD4^+$ T cells, dendritic cells, macrophages) will express viral antigen and could be eradicated by natural killer cells via the process of antibody-dependent cellular cytotoxicity. Activation of natural killer cells may also lead to the local production of antiviral chemokines and cytokines.

interruption in an HIV-1-infected individual is intriguing (220); however, until other similar cases are identified, general conclusions are not possible. Additional insights into the potential value of a rapid NAb response come from our current understanding of the initial transmission events leading to infection and early viral dissemination (**Figure 3**). Much of this information comes from studies of experimental mucosal SIV transmission in macaques and from studies with human explant tissues (221, 222). Most HIV-1 transmissions occur through exposure of mucosal surfaces to virus-containing secretions, making the mucosa an ideal location for NAbs (either IgG or IgA) to initially intercept the virus. Virus that is not intercepted appears to breach a normal intact mucosal barrier within hours of exposure, infecting intraepithelial and submucosal dendritic cells and CD4+ T lymphocytes. In the female genital tract, HIV-1 must first transverse a thick mucus layer containing several innate antiviral factors, including lysozyme, lactoferrin, secretory leukocyte protease inhibitor, and defensins (223), all of which may account for a relatively low transmission rate during vaginal intercourse. After breaching the mucosa, the virus disseminates locally for several days, infecting CD4+ T cells, dendritic cells, and macrophages, and soon reaches the draining lymph nodes. Systemic dissemination and detection of plasma viremia occur at approximately day 10 (range 7–21 days). Plasma viremia peaks about three weeks after exposure and is soon downregulated to variable lower levels as virus-specific CD8+ T cells are generated. After a considerable delay (3–9 months on average), autologous virus NAbs are detected. Within the first few weeks of infection, massive destruction of CD4+ T cells and loss of germinal centers are seen in the gastrointestinal tract; this coincides with the onset of systemic immune activation (224, 225). Immunologic abnormalities are among the earliest clinical manifestations of overt infection, the degree of which in chronic infection is predictive of progression to disease (226). Early resolution of acute phase immune activation is a feature that distinguishes nonpathogenic SIV infection in natural hosts (227, 228).

It has been argued that a successful HIV-1 vaccine must prevent the establishment of the latent pool of infected cells (205, 221, 229). The exact time when this pool is established is unknown but almost certainly precedes the time when plasma viremia is first detected and perhaps occurs sooner (205, 229). This leaves little time for a secondary NAb response to emerge, especially considering the limited quantity of circulating viral antigen that would be available to drive the response during the initial days of infection. The alternate paradigm of viremia control aims to cope with this latent pool of infected cells by minimizing early damage to the immune system, allowing a healthier immune system to impact viral dissemination during acute HIV-1 infection and gain chronic immune control of the virus (205). This paradigm drives the rationale for T cell–based HIV-1 vaccines (6–8, 230) and may also be relevant for NAbs. HIV-1 has evolved to survive under conditions of long delays in NAb production after primary infection, leaving open the possibility that its survival is sensitive to a more rapid NAb response that is primed by a vaccine.

NON-NEUTRALIZING ANTIVIRAL ANTIBODIES

NAbs that block virus entry (conventional neutralization) are not the only antibodies of interest for HIV-1 vaccines. Some antibodies lack conventional neutralizing activity but nonetheless inhibit cell-free HIV-1 through an Fcγ-receptor (FcγR)-mediated mechanism that most likely involves endocytosis and intracellular degradation (231, 232). In some cases, FcγR might also provide a kinetic advantage for conventional neutralization (233). These mechanisms are relevant for HIV-1-susceptible cells that express FcγR (e.g., monocytes, macrophages, dendritic cells) but would have little value for CD4+ T cells, which rarely express FcγR. In addition to their effects on cell-free virions, certain antibodies appear capable of targeting HIV-1-infected cells for destruction by FcγR-bearing effector cells, such as natural killer cells, monocytes, and macrophages (234, 235). Antibody-mediated activation of these effector cells also leads to the production of antiviral chemokines and cytokines (235). In the mucosal compartment, IgA has potential to block transcytosis of HIV-1 across the epithelial barrier (236, 237) and to mediate intraepithelial neutralization (238). Because conventional entry inhibition is not involved in these effector mechanisms, antiviral antibodies that operate through FcγR or that prevent transcytosis do not necessarily need to bind functional Env spikes. These antibodies might exhibit antiviral effector functions when bound to exposed epitopes on defective Env spikes (239). Antibodies that bind defective Env spikes might be easier to elicit with vaccines; however, the lack of efficacy of high-titer gp120-binding antibodies in certain efficacy trials (e.g., Vax003, Vax004) indicates that they will not always be protective (16). It will be important to determine whether FcR effector functions or mucosal antibodies correlate with the modest efficacy seen in RV144. In an earlier phase 2 trial of this vaccine, ADCC was detected in a majority of vaccinated subjects (240).

CONCLUSIONS

The design of an HIV-1 vaccine that induces broadly cross-reactive NAbs remains a critical goal of HIV-1 researchers. The potent neutralizing activity displayed by some mAbs and sera from HIV-1-infected individuals is evidence that this goal should be obtainable. While results with initial Env immunogens and vaccine concepts have been disappointing, the modest protection seen in a recent efficacy trial in Thailand (RV144) may indicate that weak NAb responses and/or other antiviral antibody effector mechanisms have greater value than previously thought. Although it is not yet known what role antibodies played in this protection, it remains likely that anti-Env antibody responses will be a critical component of an optimally effective HIV-1 vaccine. Thus, additional improvements in immunogen design are needed to achieve a more acceptable level of antibody-mediated protection. Scientists are now challenged to test new ideas as additional insights are gained about vulnerable epitopes on the virus and about the complex innate and adaptive immune pathways that give rise to broadly reactive NAb responses in HIV-1-infected individuals. A better understanding of effective antiviral antibody responses together with iterative immunogenicity studies that provide information to improve immunogen design, is our best hope for overcoming the current impasse in designing a NAb-based HIV-1 vaccine (21, 241).

DISCLOSURE STATEMENT

The authors are not aware of any affiliations, memberships, funding, or financial holdings that might be perceived as affecting the objectivity of this review.

ACKNOWLEDGMENTS

We thank Rich Wyatt, Peter Kwong, Jonathan Stuckey, Leo Kong, and Gary Nabel for contributing figures used in this manuscript, and Brenda Hartman for graphical assistance.

LITERATURE CITED

1. Plotkin SA. 2008. Vaccines: correlates of vaccine-induced immunity. *Clin. Infect. Dis.* 47:401–9
2. Haynes BF, Montefiori DC. 2006. Aiming to induce broadly reactive neutralizing antibody responses with HIV-1 vaccine candidates. *Expert Rev. Vaccines* 5:579–95
3. Burton DR, Desrosiers RC, Doms RW, Koff WC, Kwong PD, et al. 2004. HIV vaccine design and the neutralizing antibody problem. *Nat. Immunol.* 5:233–36
4. Mascola JR. 2003. Defining the protective antibody response for HIV-1. *Curr. Mol. Med.* 3:209–16
5. Montefiori DC, Morris L, Ferrari G, Mascola JR. 2007. Neutralizing and other antiviral antibodies in HIV-1 infection and vaccination. *Curr. Opin. HIV AIDS* 2:169–76
6. McMichael A, Hanke T. 2002. The quest for an AIDS vaccine: is the $CD8^+$ T-cell approach feasible? *Nat. Rev. Immunol.* 2:283–91
7. Pantaleo G, Koup RA. 2004. Correlates of immune protection in HIV-1 infection: what we know, what we don't know, what we should know. *Nat. Med.* 10:806–10
8. Letvin NL. 2006. Progress and obstacles in the development of an AIDS vaccine. *Nat. Rev. Immunol.* 6:930–39

9. McMichael AJ. 2006. HIV vaccines. *Annu. Rev. Immunol.* 24:227–55
10. Wyatt R, Kwong PD, Desjardins E, Sweet RW, Robinson J, et al. 1998. The antigenic structure of the HIV gp120 envelope glycoprotein. *Nature* 393:705–11
11. Montefiori D, Sattentau Q, Flores J, Esparza J, Mascola J. 2007. Antibody-based HIV-1 vaccines: recent developments and future directions. *PLoS Med.* 4:e348
12. Burke B, Barnett SW. 2007. Broadening our view of protective antibody responses against HIV. *Curr. HIV Res.* 5:625–41
13. Mascola JR, Snyder SW, Weislow OS, Belay SM, Belshe RB, et al. 1996. Immunization with envelope subunit vaccine products elicits neutralizing antibodies against laboratory-adapted but not primary isolates of human immunodeficiency virus type 1. The National Institute of Allergy and Infectious Diseases AIDS Vaccine Evaluation Group. *J. Infect. Dis.* 173:340–48
14. Wrin T, Nunberg JH. 1994. HIV-1MN recombinant gp120 vaccine serum, which fails to neutralize primary isolates of HIV-1, does not antagonize neutralization by antibodies from infected individuals. *AIDS* 8:1622–23
15. Flynn NM, Forthal DN, Harro CD, Judson FN, Mayer KH, et al. 2005. Placebo-controlled phase 3 trial of a recombinant glycoprotein 120 vaccine to prevent HIV-1 infection. *J. Infect. Dis.* 191:654–65
16. Gilbert PB, Peterson ML, Follmann D, Hudgens MG, Francis DP, et al. 2005. Correlation between immunologic responses to a recombinant glycoprotein 120 vaccine and incidence of HIV-1 infection in a phase 3 HIV-1 preventive vaccine trial. *J. Infect. Dis.* 191:666–77
17. Graham BS, Mascola JR. 2005. Lessons from failure—preparing for future HIV-1 vaccine efficacy trials. *J. Infect. Dis.* 191:647–49
18. Phogat S, Wyatt R. 2007. Rational modifications of HIV-1 envelope glycoproteins for immunogen design. *Curr. Pharm. Des.* 13:213–27
19. Kwong PD, Wilson IA. 2009. HIV-1 and influenza antibodies: seeing antigens in new ways. *Nat. Immunol.* 10:573–78
20. Dormitzer PR, Ulmer JB, Rappuoli R. 2008. Structure-based antigen design: a strategy for next generation vaccines. *Trends Biotechnol.* 26:659–67
21. Stamatatos L, Morris L, Burton DR, Mascola JR. 2009. Neutralizing antibodies generated during natural HIV-1 infection: good news for an HIV-1 vaccine? *Nat. Med.* 15:866–70
22. Pantophlet R, Burton DR. 2006. GP120: target for neutralizing HIV-1 antibodies. *Annu. Rev. Immunol.* 24:739–69
23. Zolla-Pazner S. 2004. Identifying epitopes of HIV-1 that induce protective antibodies. *Nat. Rev. Immunol.* 4:199–210
24. Wyatt R, Sodroski J. 1998. The HIV-1 envelope glycoproteins: fusogens, antigens, and immunogens. *Science* 280:1884–88
25. Korber B, Gaschen B, Yusim K, Thakallapally R, Kesmir C, et al. 2001. Evolutionary and immunological implications of contemporary HIV-1 variation. *Br. Med. Bull.* 58:19–42
26. Moore JP, Cao Y, Leu J, Qin L, Korber B, et al. 1996. Inter- and intraclade neutralization of human immunodeficiency virus type 1: genetic clades do not correspond to neutralization serotypes but partially correspond to gp120 antigenic serotypes. *J. Virol.* 70:427–44
27. Mascola JR, Louwagie J, McCutchan FE, Fischer CL, Hegerich PA, et al. 1994. Two antigenically distinct subtypes of human immunodeficiency virus type 1: viral genotype predicts neutralization serotype. *J. Infect. Dis.* 169:48–54
28. Binley JM, Wrin T, Korber B, Zwick MB, Wang M, et al. 2004. Comprehensive cross-clade neutralization analysis of a panel of anti-human immunodeficiency virus type 1 monoclonal antibodies. *J. Virol.* 78:13232–52
29. Karlsson Hedestam GB, Fouchier RA, Phogat S, Burton DR, Sodroski J, Wyatt RT. 2008. The challenges of eliciting neutralizing antibodies to HIV-1 and to influenza virus. *Nat. Rev. Microbiol.* 6:143–55
30. McCutchan FE. 2006. Global epidemiology of HIV. *J. Med. Virol.* 78(Suppl. 1):S7–12
31. Burton DR, Stanfield RL, Wilson IA. 2005. Antibody vs. HIV in a clash of evolutionary titans. *Proc. Natl. Acad. Sci. USA* 102:14943–48

32. Scanlan CN, Pantophlet R, Wormald MR, Ollmann Saphire E, Stanfield R, et al. 2002. The broadly neutralizing anti-human immunodeficiency virus type 1 antibody 2G12 recognizes a cluster of α1–>2 mannose residues on the outer face of gp120. *J. Virol.* 76:7306–21
33. Burton DR, Pyati J, Koduri R, Sharp SJ, Thornton GB, et al. 1994. Efficient neutralization of primary isolates of HIV-1 by a recombinant human monoclonal antibody. *Science* 266:1024–27
34. Cardoso RM, Zwick MB, Stanfield RL, Kunert R, Binley JM, et al. 2005. Broadly neutralizing anti-HIV antibody 4E10 recognizes a helical conformation of a highly conserved fusion-associated motif in gp41. *Immunity* 22:163–73
35. Zwick MB, Labrijn AF, Wang M, Spenlehauer C, Saphire EO, et al. 2001. Broadly neutralizing antibodies targeted to the membrane-proximal external region of human immunodeficiency virus type 1 glycoprotein gp41. *J. Virol.* 75:10892–905
36. Muster T, Steindl F, Purtscher M, Trkola A, Klima A, et al. 1993. A conserved neutralizing epitope on gp41 of human immunodeficiency virus type 1. *J. Virol.* 67:6642–47
37. Trkola A, Pomales AB, Yuan H, Korber B, Maddon PJ, et al. 1995. Cross-clade neutralization of primary isolates of human immunodeficiency virus type 1 by human monoclonal antibodies and tetrameric CD4-IgG. *J. Virol.* 69:6609–17
38. Deeks SG, Schweighardt B, Wrin T, Galovich J, Hoh R, et al. 2006. Neutralizing antibody responses against autologous and heterologous viruses in acute versus chronic human immunodeficiency virus (HIV) infection: evidence for a constraint on the ability of HIV to completely evade neutralizing antibody responses. *J. Virol.* 80:6155–64
39. Doria-Rose NA, Klein RM, Manion MM, O'Dell S, Phogat A, et al. 2009. Frequency and phenotype of human immunodeficiency virus envelope-specific B cells from patients with broadly cross-neutralizing antibodies. *J. Virol.* 83:188–99
40. Binley JM, Lybarger EA, Crooks ET, Seaman MS, Gray E, et al. 2008. Profiling the specificity of neutralizing antibodies in a large panel of plasmas from patients chronically infected with human immunodeficiency virus type 1 subtypes B and C. *J. Virol.* 82:11651–68
41. Sather DN, Armann J, Ching LK, Mavrantoni A, Sellhorn G, et al. 2009. Factors associated with the development of cross-reactive neutralizing antibodies during human immunodeficiency virus type 1 infection. *J. Virol.* 83:757–69
42. Dhillon AK, Donners H, Pantophlet R, Johnson WE, Decker JM, et al. 2007. Dissecting the neutralizing antibody specificities of broadly neutralizing sera from human immunodeficiency virus type 1-infected donors. *J. Virol.* 81:6548–62
43. Li Y, Migueles SA, Welcher B, Svehla K, Phogat A, et al. 2007. Broad HIV-1 neutralization mediated by CD4-binding site antibodies. *Nat. Med.* 13:1032–34
44. Li Y, Svehla K, Louder MK, Wycuff D, Phogat S, et al. 2009. Analysis of neutralization specificities in polyclonal sera derived from human immunodeficiency virus type 1-infected individuals. *J. Virol.* 83:1045–59
45. Simek MD, Rida W, Priddy FH, Pung P, Carrow E, et al. 2009. Human immunodeficiency virus type 1 elite neutralizers: individuals with broad and potent neutralizing activity identified by using a high-throughput neutralization assay together with an analytical selection algorithm. *J. Virol.* 83:7337–48
46. Kulkarni SS, Lapedes A, Tang H, Gnanakaran S, Daniels MG, et al. 2009. Highly complex neutralization determinants on a monophyletic lineage of newly transmitted subtype C HIV-1 Env clones from India. *Virology* 385:505–20
47. Wu X, Zhou T, O'Dell S, Wyatt RT, Kwong PD, Mascola JR. 2009. Mechanism of HIV-1 resistance to monoclonal antibody b12 that effectively targets the site of CD4 attachement. *J. Virol.* 83:10892–907
48. Zhang MY, Xiao X, Sidorov IA, Choudhry V, Cham F, et al. 2004. Identification and characterization of a new cross-reactive human immunodeficiency virus type 1-neutralizing human monoclonal antibody. *J. Virol.* 78:9233–42
49. Zhou T, Xu L, Dey B, Hessell AJ, Van Ryk D, et al. 2007. Structural definition of a conserved neutralization epitope on HIV-1 gp120. *Nature* 445:732–37
50. Chen L, Kwon YD, Zhou T, Wu X, O'Dell X, et al. 2009. Structural basis of immune evasion at the site of CD4 attachment on HIV-1 gp120. *Science* 326:1123–27

51. Trkola A, Purtscher M, Muster T, Ballaun C, Buchacher A, et al. 1996. Human monoclonal antibody 2G12 defines a distinctive neutralization epitope on the gp120 glycoprotein of human immunodeficiency virus type 1. *J. Virol.* 70:1100–8
52. Calarese DA, Scanlan N, Zwick MB, Deechongkit S, Mimura Y, et al. 2003. Antibody domain exchange is an immunological solution to carbohydrate cluster recognition. *Science* 300:2065–71
53. Li M, Salazar-Gonzalez JF, Derdeyn CA, Morris L, Williamson C, et al. 2006. Genetic and neutralization properties of subtype C human immunodeficiency virus type 1 molecular env clones from acute and early heterosexually acquired infections in Southern Africa. *J. Virol.* 80:11776–90
54. Thali M, Moore JP, Furman C, Charles M, Ho DD, et al. 1993. Characterization of conserved human immunodeficiency virus type 1 gp120 neutralization epitopes exposed upon gp120-CD4 binding. *J. Virol.* 67:3978–88
55. Xiang SH, Doka N, Choudhary RK, Sodroski J, Robinson JE. 2002. Characterization of CD4-induced epitopes on the HIV type 1 gp120 envelope glycoprotein recognized by neutralizing human monoclonal antibodies. *AIDS Res. Hum. Retrovir.* 18:1207–17
56. Moulard M, Phogat SK, Shu Y, Labrijn AF, Xiao X, et al. 2002. Broadly cross-reactive HIV-1-neutralizing human monoclonal Fab selected for binding to gp120-CD4-CCR5 complexes. *Proc. Natl. Acad. Sci. USA* 99:6913–18
57. Decker JM, Bibollet-Ruche F, Wei X, Wang S, Levy DN, et al. 2005. Antigenic conservation and immunogenicity of the HIV coreceptor binding site. *J. Exp. Med.* 201:1407–19
58. Labrijn AF, Poignard P, Raja A, Zwick MB, Delgado K, et al. 2003. Access of antibody molecules to the conserved coreceptor binding site on glycoprotein gp120 is sterically restricted on primary human immunodeficiency virus type 1. *J. Virol.* 77:10557–65
59. Binley JM, Cayanan CS, Wiley C, Schulke N, Olson WC, et al. 2003. Redox-triggered infection by disulfide-shackled human immunodeficiency virus type 1 pseudovirions. *J. Virol.* 77:5678–84
60. Yuste E, Sanford HB, Carmody J, Bixby J, Little S, et al. 2006. Simian immunodeficiency virus engrafted with human immunodeficiency virus type 1 (HIV-1)-specific epitopes: replication, neutralization, and survey of HIV-1-positive plasma. *J. Virol.* 80:3030–41
61. Gray ES, Taylor N, Wycuff D, Moore PL, Tomaras GD, et al. 2009. Antibody specificities associated with neutralization breadth in plasma from HIV-1 subtype C-infected blood donors. *J. Virol.* 83:8925–37
62. Shen X, Parks RJ, Montefiori DC, Kirchherr JL, Keele BF, et al. 2009. In vivo gp41 antibodies targeting the 2F5 monoclonal antibody epitope mediate human immunodeficiency virus type 1 neutralization breadth. *J. Virol.* 83:3617–25
63. Haynes BF, Fleming J, St Clair EW, Katinger H, Stiegler G, et al. 2005. Cardiolipin polyspecific autoreactivity in two broadly neutralizing HIV-1 antibodies. *Science* 308:1906–8
64. Moore JP, Cao Y, Ho DD, Koup RA. 1994. Development of the anti-gp120 antibody response during seroconversion to human immunodeficiency virus type 1. *J. Virol.* 68:5142–55
65. Tomaras GD, Yates NL, Liu P, Qin L, Fouda GG, et al. 2008. Initial B-cell responses to transmitted human immunodeficiency virus type 1: virion-binding immunoglobulin M (IgM) and IgG antibodies followed by plasma anti-gp41 antibodies with ineffective control of initial viremia. *J. Virol.* 82:12449–63
66. Albert J, Abrahamsson B, Nagy K, Aurelius E, Gaines H, et al. 1990. Rapid development of isolate-specific neutralizing antibodies after primary HIV-1 infection and consequent emergence of virus variants which resist neutralization by autologous sera. *AIDS* 4:107–12
67. Montefiori DC, Zhou IY, Barnes B, Lake D, Hersh EM, et al. 1991. Homotypic antibody responses to fresh clinical isolates of human immunodeficiency virus. *Virology* 182:635–43
68. Tremblay M, Wainberg MA. 1990. Neutralization of multiple HIV-1 isolates from a single subject by autologous sequential sera. *J. Infect. Dis.* 162:735–37
69. Arendrup M, Nielsen C, Hansen JE, Pedersen C, Mathiesen L, et al. 1992. Autologous HIV-1 neutralizing antibodies: emergence of neutralization-resistant escape virus and subsequent development of escape virus neutralizing antibodies. *J. Acquir. Immune Defic. Syndr.* 5:303–7
70. Wrin T, Crawford L, Sawyer L, Weber P, Sheppard HW, et al. 1994. Neutralizing antibody responses to autologous and heterologous isolates of human immunodeficiency virus. *J Acquir. Immune Defic. Syndr.* 7:211–19

71. Bradney AP, Scheer S, Crawford JM, Buchbinder SP, Montefiori DC. 1999. Neutralization escape in human immunodeficiency virus type 1-infected long-term nonprogressors. *J. Infect. Dis.* 179:1264–67
72. Richman DD, Wrin T, Little SJ, Petropoulos CJ. 2003. Rapid evolution of the neutralizing antibody response to HIV type 1 infection. *Proc. Natl. Acad. Sci. USA* 100:4144–49
73. Wei X, Decker JM, Wang S, Hui H, Kappes JC, et al. 2003. Antibody neutralization and escape by HIV-1. *Nature* 422:307–12
74. Gray ES, Moore PL, Choge IA, Decker JM, Bibollet-Ruche F, et al. 2007. Neutralizing antibody responses in acute human immunodeficiency virus type 1 subtype C infection. *J. Virol.* 81:6187–96
75. Mahalanabis M, Jayaraman P, Miura T, Pereyra F, Chester EM, et al. 2009. Continuous viral escape and selection by autologous neutralizing antibodies in drug-naive human immunodeficiency virus controllers. *J. Virol.* 83:662–72
76. Frost SD, Wrin T, Smith DM, Kosakovsky Pond SL, Liu Y, et al. 2005. Neutralizing antibody responses drive the evolution of human immunodeficiency virus type 1 envelope during recent HIV infection. *Proc. Natl. Acad. Sci. USA* 102:18514–19
77. Bunnik EM, Pisas L, van Nuenen AC, Schuitemaker H. 2008. Autologous neutralizing humoral immunity and evolution of the viral envelope in the course of subtype B human immunodeficiency virus type 1 infection. *J. Virol.* 82:7932–41
78. Moore PL, Gray ES, Choge IA, Ranchobe N, Mlisana K, et al. 2008. The c3-v4 region is a major target of autologous neutralizing antibodies in human immunodeficiency virus type 1 subtype C infection. *J. Virol.* 82:1860–69
79. Li B, Decker JM, Johnson RW, Bibollet-Ruche F, Wei X, et al. 2006. Evidence for potent autologous neutralizing antibody titers and compact envelopes in early infection with subtype C human immunodeficiency virus type 1. *J. Virol.* 80:5211–18
80. Davis KL, Gray ES, Moore PL, Decker JM, Salomon A, et al. 2009. High titer HIV-1 V3-specific antibodies with broad reactivity but low neutralizing potency in acute infection and following vaccination. *Virology* 387:414–26
81. Salazar-Gonzalez JF, Salazar MG, Keele BF, Learn GH, Giorgi EE, et al. 2009. Genetic identity, biological phenotype, and evolutionary pathways of transmitted/founder viruses in acute and early HIV-1 infection. *J. Exp. Med.* 206:1273–89
82. Rong R, Bibollet-Ruche F, Mulenga J, Allen S, Blackwell JL, et al. 2007. Role of V1V2 and other human immunodeficiency virus type 1 envelope domains in resistance to autologous neutralization during clade C infection. *J. Virol.* 81:1350–59
83. Rong R, Gnanakaran S, Decker JM, Bibollet-Ruche F, Taylor J, et al. 2007. Unique mutational patterns in the envelope α2 amphipathic helix and acquisition of length in gp120 hypervariable domains are associated with resistance to autologous neutralization of subtype C human immunodeficiency virus type 1. *J. Virol.* 81:5658–68
84. Moore PL, Ranchobe N, Lambson BE, Gray ES, Cave E, et al. 2009. Limited neutralizing antibody specificities drive neutralization escape in early HIV-1 subtype C infection. *PLoS Pathog.* 5:e1000598
85. Rong R, Li B, Lynch RM, Haaland RE, Murphy MK, et al. 2009. Escape from autologous neutralizing antibodies in acute/early subtype C HIV-1 infection requires multiple pathways. *PLoS Pathog.* 5:e1000594
86. Gorny MK, Stamatatos L, Volsky B, Revesz K, Williams C, et al. 2005. Identification of a new quaternary neutralizing epitope on human immunodeficiency virus type 1 virus particles. *J. Virol.* 79:5232–37
87. Ofek G, Tang M, Sambor A, Katinger H, Mascola JR, et al. 2004. Structure and mechanistic analysis of the anti-human immunodeficiency virus type 1 antibody 2F5 in complex with its gp41 epitope. *J. Virol.* 78:10724–37
88. Stanfield RL, Gorny MK, Williams C, Zolla-Pazner S, Wilson IA. 2004. Structural rationale for the broad neutralization of HIV-1 by human monoclonal antibody 447–52D. *Structure* 12:193–204
89. Saphire EO, Parren PW, Pantophlet R, Zwick MB, Morris GM, et al. 2001. Crystal structure of a neutralizing human IgG against HIV-1: a template for vaccine design. *Science* 293:1155–59
90. Scheid JF, Mouquet H, Feldhahn N, Walker BD, Pereyra F, et al. 2009. A method for identification of HIV gp140 binding memory B cells in human blood. *J. Immunol. Methods* 343:65–67
91. Scheid JF, Mouquet H, Feldhahn N, Seaman MS, Velinzon K, et al. 2009. Broad diversity of neutralizing antibodies isolated from memory B cells in HIV-infected individuals. *Nature* 458:636–40

92. Traggiai E, Becker S, Subbarao K, Kolesnikova L, Uematsu Y, et al. 2004. An efficient method to make human monoclonal antibodies from memory B cells: potent neutralization of SARS coronavirus. *Nat. Med.* 10:871–75
93. Kwong PD, Mascola JR, Nabel GJ. 2009. Mining the B cell repertoire for broadly neutralizing monoclonal antibodies to HIV-1. *Cell Host Microbe* 6:292–94
94. Walker LM, Phogat SK, Chan-Hui PY, Wagner D, Phung P, et al. 2009. Broad and potent neutralizing antibodies from an African donor reveal a new HIV-1 vaccine target. *Science* 326:285–89
95. Scarlatti G, Albert J, Rossi P, Hodara V, Biraghi P, et al. 1993. Mother-to-child transmission of human immunodeficiency virus type 1: correlation with neutralizing antibodies against primary isolates. *J. Infect. Dis.* 168:207–10
96. Lathey JL, Tsou J, Brinker K, Hsia K, Meyer WA 3rd, et al. 1999. Lack of autologous neutralizing antibody to human immunodeficiency virus type 1 (HIV-1) and macrophage tropism are associated with mother-to-infant transmission. *J. Infect. Dis.* 180:344–50
97. Calarota SA, Libonatti OV. 2000. Maternal antibodies to HIV-1 envelope domains: No correlation with HIV-1 vertical transmission in patients from Argentina. *Scand. J. Immunol.* 52:292–97
98. Bongertz V, Costa CI, Veloso VG, Grinsztejn B, João Filho EC, et al. 2001. Vertical HIV-1 transmission: importance of neutralizing antibody titer and specificity. *Scand J. Immunol.* 53:302–9
99. Dickover R, Garratty E, Yusim K, Miller C, Korber B, et al. 2006. Role of maternal autologous neutralizing antibody in selective perinatal transmission of human immunodeficiency virus type 1 escape variants. *J. Virol.* 80:6525–33
100. Wu X, Parast AB, Richardson BA, Nduati R, John-Stewart G, et al. 2006. Neutralization escape variants of human immunodeficiency virus type 1 are transmitted from mother to infant. *J. Virol.* 80:835–44
101. Barin F, Jourdain G, Brunet S, Ngo-Giang-Huong N, Weerawatgoompa S, et al. 2006. Revisiting the role of neutralizing antibodies in mother-to-child transmission of HIV-1. *J. Infect. Dis.* 193:1504–11
102. Smith DM, Strain MC, Frost SD, Pillai SK, Wong JK, et al. 2006. Lack of neutralizing antibody response to HIV-1 predisposes to superinfection. *Virology* 355:1–5
103. Reimann KA, Li JT, Voss G, Lekutis C, Tenner-Racz K, et al. 1996. An env gene derived from a primary human immunodeficiency virus type 1 isolate confers high in vivo replicative capacity to a chimeric simian/human immunodeficiency virus in rhesus monkeys. *J. Virol.* 70:3198–206
104. Shibata R, Maldarelli F, Siemon C, Matano T, Parta M, et al. 1997. Infection and pathogenicity of chimeric simian-human immunodeficiency viruses in macaques: determinants of high virus loads and CD4 cell killing. *J. Infect. Dis.* 176:362–73
105. Shibata R, Igarashi T, Haigwood N, Buckler-White A, Ogert R, et al. 1999. Neutralizing antibody directed against the HIV-1 envelope glycoprotein can completely block HIV-1/SIV chimeric virus infections of macaque monkeys. *Nat. Med.* 5:204–10
106. Foresman L, Jia F, Li Z, Wang C, Stephens EB, et al. 1998. Neutralizing antibodies administered before, but not after, virulent SHIV prevent infection in macaques. *AIDS Res. Hum. Retrovir.* 14:1035–43
107. Mascola JR, Lewis MG, Stiegler G, Harris D, VanCott TC, et al. 1999. Protection of Macaques against pathogenic simian/human immunodeficiency virus 89.6PD by passive transfer of neutralizing antibodies. *J. Virol.* 73:4009–18
108. Mascola JR, Stiegler G, VanCott TC, Katinger H, Carpenter CB, et al. 2000. Protection of macaques against vaginal transmission of a pathogenic HIV- 1/SIV chimeric virus by passive infusion of neutralizing antibodies. *Nat. Med.* 6:207–10
109. Baba TW, Liska V, Hofmann-Lehmann R, Vlasak J, Xu W, et al. 2000. Human neutralizing monoclonal antibodies of the IgG1 subtype protect against mucosal simian-human immunodeficiency virus infection. *Nat. Med.* 6:200–6
110. Hofmann-Lehmann R, Vlasak J, Rasmussen RA, Smith BA, Baba TW, et al. 2001. Postnatal passive immunization of neonatal macaques with a triple combination of human monoclonal antibodies against oral simian-human immunodeficiency virus challenge. *J. Virol.* 75:7470–80
111. Parren PW, Marx PA, Hessell AJ, Luckay A, Harouse J, et al. 2001. Antibody protects macaques against vaginal challenge with a pathogenic R5 simian/human immunodeficiency virus at serum levels giving complete neutralization in vitro. *J. Virol.* 75:8340–47

112. Nishimura Y, Igarashi T, Haigwood N, Sadjadpour R, Plishka RJ, et al. 2002. Determination of a statistically valid neutralization titer in plasma that confers protection against simian-human immunodeficiency virus challenge following passive transfer of high-titered neutralizing antibodies. *J. Virol.* 76:2123–30
113. Mascola JR, Lewis MG, VanCott TC, Stiegler G, Katinger H, et al. 2003. Cellular immunity elicited by human immunodeficiency virus type 1/simian immunodeficiency virus DNA vaccination does not augment the sterile protection afforded by passive infusion of neutralizing antibodies. *J. Virol.* 77:10348–56
114. Hessell AJ, Rakasz EG, Poignard P, Hangartner L, Landucci G, et al. 2009. Broadly neutralizing human anti-HIV antibody 2G12 is effective in protection against mucosal SHIV challenge even at low serum neutralizing titers. *PLoS Pathog* 5:e1000433
115. Hessell AJ, Poignard P, Hunter M, Hangartner L, Tehrani DM, et al. 2009. Effective, low-titer antibody protection against low-dose repeated mucosal SHIV challenge in macaques. *Nat. Med.* 15:951–54
116. Hessell AJ, Hangartner L, Hunter M, Havenith CE, Beurskens FJ, et al. 2007. Fc receptor but not complement binding is important in antibody protection against HIV. *Nature* 449:101–4
117. Whitney JB, Ruprecht RM. 2004. Live attenuated HIV vaccines: pitfalls and prospects. *Curr. Opin. Infect. Dis.* 17:17–26
118. Stott EJ. 1994. Towards a vaccine against AIDS: lessons from simian immunodeficiency virus vaccines. *Curr. Top. Microbiol. Immunol.* 188:221–37
119. Belshe RB, Graham BS, Keefer MC, Gorse GJ, Wright P, et al. 1994. Neutralizing antibodies to HIV-1 in seronegative volunteers immunized with recombinant gp120 from the MN strain of HIV-1. NIAID AIDS Vaccine Clinical Trials Network. *JAMA* 272:475–80
120. Gorse GJ, McElrath MJ, Matthews TJ, Hsieh RH, Belshe RB, et al. 1998. Modulation of immunologic responses to HIV-1MN recombinant gp160 vaccine by dose and schedule of administration. National Institute of Allergy and Infectious Diseases AIDS Vaccine Evaluation Group. *Vaccine* 16:493–506
121. Gorse GJ, Corey L, Patel GB, Mandava M, Hsieh RH, et al. 1999. HIV-1MN recombinant glycoprotein 160 vaccine-induced cellular and humoral immunity boosted by HIV-1MN recombinant glycoprotein 120 vaccine. National Institute of Allergy and Infectious Diseases AIDS Vaccine Evaluation Group. *AIDS Res. Hum. Retrovir.* 15:115–32
122. Dolin R, Graham BS, Greenberg SB, Tacket CO, Belshe RB, et al. 1991. The safety and immunogenicity of a human immunodeficiency virus type 1 (HIV-1) recombinant gp160 candidate vaccine in humans. NIAID AIDS Vaccine Clinical Trials Network. *Ann. Intern. Med.* 114:119–27
123. Kovacs JA, Vasudevachari MB, Easter M, Davey RT, Falloon J, et al. 1993. Induction of humoral and cell-mediated anti-human immunodeficiency virus (HIV) responses in HIV sero-negative volunteers by immunization with recombinant gp160. *J. Clin. Invest.* 92:919–28
124. Schwartz DH, Gorse G, Clements ML, Belshe R, Izu A, et al. 1993. Induction of HIV-1-neutralising and syncytium-inhibiting antibodies in uninfected recipients of HIV-1IIIB rgp120 subunit vaccine. *Lancet* 342:69–73
125. Keefer MC, Graham BS, Belshe RB, Schwartz D, Corey L, et al. 1994. Studies of high doses of a human immunodeficiency virus type 1 recombinant glycoprotein 160 candidate vaccine in HIV type 1-seronegative humans. The AIDS Vaccine Clinical Trials Network. *AIDS Res. Hum. Retrovir.* 10:1713–23
126. Bures R, Gaitan A, Zhu T, Graziosi C, McGrath KM, et al. 2000. Immunization with recombinant canarypox vectors expressing membrane-anchored glycoprotein 120 followed by glycoprotein 160 boosting fails to generate antibodies that neutralize R5 primary isolates of human immunodeficiency virus type 1. *AIDS Res. Hum. Retrovir.* 16:2019–35
127. Pitisuttithum P, Gilbert P, Gurwith M, Heyward W, Martin M, et al. 2006. Randomized, double-blind, placebo-controlled efficacy trial of a bivalent recombinant glycoprotein 120 HIV-1 vaccine among injection drug users in Bangkok, Thailand. *J. Infect. Dis.* 194:1661–71
128. Huang Y, Gilbert PB, Montefiori D, Self SG. 2009. Simultaneous evaluation of the magnitude and breadth of a left and right censored multivariate response, with application to HIV vaccine development. *Stat. Biopharm. Res.* 1:81–91
129. Mascola JR, D'Souza P, Gilbert P, Hahn BH, Haigwood NL, et al. 2005. Recommendations for the design and use of standard virus panels to assess neutralizing antibody responses elicited by candidate human immunodeficiency virus type 1 vaccines. *J. Virol.* 79:10103–7

130. Kwong PD, Doyle ML, Casper DJ, Cicala C, Leavitt SA, et al. 2002. HIV-1 evades antibody-mediated neutralization through conformational masking of receptor-binding sites. *Nature* 420:678–82
131. Li M, Gao F, Mascola JR, Stamatatos L, Polonis VR, et al. 2005. Human immunodeficiency virus Type 1 env clones from acute and early subtype B infections for standardized assessments of vaccine-elicited neutralizing antibodies. *J. Virol.* 79:10108–25
132. Seaman MS, Janes H, Hawkins N, Grandpre LE, Devoy C, et al. 2010. Tiered categorization of a diverse panel of human immunodeficiency virus type 1 Env pseudoviruses for neutralizing antibody assessment. *J. Virol.* 84:1439–52
133. Russell ND, Graham BS, Keefer MC, McElrath MJ, Self SG, et al. 2007. Phase 2 study of an HIV-1 canarypox vaccine (vCP1452) alone and in combination with rgp120: negative results fail to trigger a phase 3 correlates trial. *J. Acquir. Immune Defic. Syndr.* 44:203–12
134. Goepfert PA, Tomaras GD, Horton H, Montefiori D, Ferrari G, et al. 2007. Durable HIV-1 antibody and T-cell responses elicited by an adjuvanted multi-protein recombinant vaccine in uninfected human volunteers. *Vaccine* 25:510–18
135. Wang S, Kennedy JS, West K, Montefiori DC, Coley S, et al. 2008. Cross-subtype antibody and cellular immune responses induced by a polyvalent DNA prime-protein boost HIV-1 vaccine in healthy human volunteers. *Vaccine* 26:3947–57
136. Cleghorn F, Pape JW, Schechter M, Bartholomew C, Sanchez J, et al. 2007. Lessons from a multi-site international trial in the Caribbean and South America of an HIV-1 Canarypox vaccine (ALVAC-HIV vCP1452) with or without boosting with MN rgp120. *J. Acquir. Immune Defic. Syndr.* 46:222–30
137. Nitayaphan S, Khamboonruang C, Sirisophana N, Morgan P, Chiu J, et al. 2000. A phase I/II trial of HIV SF2 gp120/MF59 vaccine in seronegative Thais. *Vaccine* 18:1448–55
138. Pitisuttithum P, Nitayaphan S, Thongcharoen P, Khamboonruang C, Kim J, et al. 2003. Safety and immunogenicity of combinations of recombinant subtype E and B human immunodeficiency virus type 1 envelope glycoprotein 120 vaccines in healthy Thai adults. *J. Infect. Dis.* 188:219–27
139. Nitayaphan S, Pitisuttithum P, Karnasuta C, Eamsila C, de Souza M, et al. 2004. Safety and immunogenicity of an HIV subtype B and E prime-boost vaccine combination in HIV-negative Thai adults. *J. Infect. Dis.* 190:702–6
140. Evans TG, McElrath MJ, Matthews T, Montefiori D, Weinhold K, et al. 2001. QS-21 promotes an adjuvant effect allowing for reduced antigen dose during HIV-1 envelope subunit immmunization in humans. *Vaccine* 19:2080–91
141. McElrath MJ, Corey L, Montefiori D, Wolff M, Schwartz D, et al. 2000. A phase II study of two HIV type 1 envelope vaccines, comparing their immunogenicity in populations at risk for acquiring HIV type 1 infection. AIDS Vaccine Evaluation Group. *AIDS Res. Hum. Retrovir.* 16:907–19
142. Montefiori DC, Metch B, McElrath MJ, Self S, Weinhold KJ, et al. 2004. Demographic factors that influence the neutralizing antibody response in recipients of recombinant HIV-1 gp120 vaccines. *J. Infect. Dis.* 190:1962–69
143. Mulligan MJ, Russell ND, Celum C, Kahn J, Noonan E, et al. 2006. Excellent safety and tolerability of the human immunodeficiency virus type 1 pGA2/JS2 plasmid DNA priming vector vaccine in HIV type 1 uninfected adults. *AIDS Res. Hum. Retrovir.* 22:678–83
144. Graham BS, Koup RA, Roederer M, Bailer RT, Enama ME, et al. 2006. Phase 1 safety and immunogenicity evaluation of a multiclade HIV-1 DNA candidate vaccine. *J. Infect. Dis.* 194:1650–60
145. Catanzaro AT, Roederer M, Koup RA, Bailer RT, Enama ME, et al. 2007. Phase I clinical evaluation of a six-plasmid multiclade HIV-1 DNA candidate vaccine. *Vaccine* 25:4085–92
146. Cooney EL, Collier AC, Greenberg PD, Coombs RW, Zarling J, et al. 1991. Safety of and immunological response to a recombinant vaccinia virus vaccine expressing HIV envelope glycoprotein. *Lancet* 337:567–72
147. Cooney EL, McElrath MJ, Corey L, Hu SL, Collier AC, et al. 1993. Enhanced immunity to human immunodeficiency virus (HIV) envelope elicited by a combined vaccine regimen consisting of priming with a vaccinia recombinant expressing HIV envelope and boosting with gp160 protein. *Proc. Natl. Acad. Sci. USA* 90:1882–86

148. Montefiori DC, Graham BS, Kliks S, Wright PF. 1992. Serum antibodies to HIV-1 in recombinant vaccinia virus recipients boosted with purified recombinant gp160. NIAID AIDS Vaccine Clinical Trials Network. *J. Clin. Immunol.* 12:429–39
149. Graham BS, Belshe RB, Clements ML, Dolin R, Corey L, et al. 1992. Vaccination of vaccinia-naive adults with human immunodeficiency virus type 1 gp160 recombinant vaccinia virus in a blinded, controlled, randomized clinical trial. The AIDS Vaccine Clinical Trials Network. *J. Infect. Dis.* 166:244–52
150. Harari A, Bart PA, Stohr W, Tapia G, Garcia M, et al. 2008. An HIV-1 clade C DNA prime, NYVAC boost vaccine regimen induces reliable, polyfunctional, and long-lasting T cell responses. *J. Exp. Med.* 205:63–77
151. Goepfert PA, Horton H, McElrath MJ, Gurunathan S, Ferrari G, et al. 2005. High-dose recombinant canarypox vaccine expressing HIV-1 protein, in seronegative human subjects. *J. Infect. Dis.* 192:1249–59
152. Evans TG, Keefer MC, Weinhold KJ, Wolff M, Montefiori D, et al. 1999. A canarypox vaccine expressing multiple human immunodeficiency virus type 1 genes given alone or with rgp120 elicits broad and durable $CD8^+$ cytotoxic T lymphocyte responses in seronegative volunteers. *J. Infect. Dis.* 180:290–98
153. Clements-Mann ML, Weinhold K, Matthews TJ, Graham BS, Gorse GJ, et al. 1998. Immune responses to human immunodeficiency virus (HIV) type 1 induced by canarypox expressing HIV-1MN gp120, HIV-1SF2 recombinant gp120, or both vaccines in seronegative adults. NIAID AIDS Vaccine Evaluation Group. *J. Infect. Dis.* 177:1230–46
154. AIDS Vaccine Evaluation Group 022 Protocol Team. 2001. Cellular and humoral immune responses to a canarypox vaccine containing human immunodeficiency virus type 1 Env, Gag, and Pro in combination with rgp120. *J. Infect. Dis.* 183:563–70
155. Gupta K, Hudgens M, Corey L, McElrath MJ, Weinhold K, et al. 2002. Safety and immunogenicity of a high-titered canarypox vaccine in combination with rgp120 in a diverse population of HIV-1-uninfected adults: AIDS Vaccine Evaluation Group Protocol 022A. *J. Acquir. Immune Defic. Syndr.* 29:254–61
156. Belshe RB, Stevens C, Gorse GJ, Buchbinder S, Weinhold K, et al. 2001. Safety and immunogenicity of a canarypox-vectored human immunodeficiency virus Type 1 vaccine with or without gp120: a phase 2 study in higher- and lower-risk volunteers. *J. Infect. Dis.* 183:1343–52
157. Pialoux G, Excler JL, Riviere Y, Gonzalez-Canali G, Feuillie V, et al. 1995. A prime-boost approach to HIV preventive vaccine using a recombinant canarypox virus expressing glycoprotein 160 (MN) followed by a recombinant glycoprotein 160 (MN/LAI). The AGIS Group, and l'Agence Nationale de Recherche sur le SIDA. *AIDS Res. Hum. Retrovir.* 11:373–81
158. Catanzaro AT, Koup RA, Roederer M, Bailer RT, Enama ME, et al. 2006. Phase 1 safety and immunogenicity evaluation of a multiclade HIV-1 candidate vaccine delivered by a replication-defective recombinant adenovirus vector. *J. Infect. Dis.* 194:1638–49
159. Robinson HL, Weinhold KJ. 2006. Phase 1 clinical trials of the National Institutes of Health Vaccine Research Center HIV/AIDS candidate vaccines. *J. Infect. Dis.* 194:1625–27
160. Robinson HL. 2007. HIV/AIDS vaccines: 2007. *Clin. Pharmacol. Ther.* 82:686–93
161. Belshe RB, Gorse GJ, Mulligan MJ, Evans TG, Keefer MC, et al. 1998. Induction of immune responses to HIV-1 by canarypox virus (ALVAC) HIV-1 and gp120 SF-2 recombinant vaccines in uninfected volunteers. NIAID AIDS Vaccine Evaluation Group. *AIDS* 12:2407–15
162. Graham BS, Matthews TJ, Belshe RB, Clements ML, Dolin R, et al. 1993. Augmentation of human immunodeficiency virus type 1 neutralizing antibody by priming with gp160 recombinant vaccinia and boosting with rgp160 in vaccinia-naive adults. The NIAID AIDS Vaccine Clinical Trials Network. *J. Infect. Dis.* 167:533–37
163. Mascola JR, Sambor A, Beaudry K, Santra S, Welcher B, et al. 2005. Neutralizing antibodies elicited by immunization of monkeys with DNA plasmids and recombinant adenoviral vectors expressing human immunodeficiency virus type 1 proteins. *J. Virol.* 79:771–79
164. Graham BS, Gorse GJ, Schwartz DH, Keefer MC, McElrath MJ, et al. 1994. Determinants of antibody response after recombinant gp160 boosting in vaccinia-naive volunteers primed with gp160-recombinant vaccinia virus. The National Institute of Allergy and Infectious Diseases AIDS Vaccine Clinical Trials Network. *J. Infect. Dis.* 170:782–86
165. Rerks-Ngarm S, Pitisuttithum P, Nitayaphan S, Kaewkungwal J, Chiu J, et al. 2009. Vaccination with ALVAC and AIDSVAX to prevent HIV-1 infection in Thailand. *N. Engl. J. Med.* 361:2209–20

166. Dolin R. 2009. HIV vaccine trial results—an opening for further research. *N. Engl. J. Med.* 361:2279–80
167. Broder CC, Earl PL, Long D, Abedon ST, Moss B, et al. 1994. Antigenic implications of human immunodeficiency virus type 1 envelope quaternary structure: oligomer-specific and -sensitive monoclonal antibodies. *Proc. Natl. Acad. Sci. USA* 91:11699–703
168. Fouts TR, Binley JM, Trkola A, Robinson JE, Moore JP. 1997. Neutralization of the human immunodeficiency virus type 1 primary isolate JR-FL by human monoclonal antibodies correlates with antibody binding to the oligomeric form of the envelope glycoprotein complex. *J. Virol.* 71:2779–85
169. Pancera M, Wyatt R. 2005. Selective recognition of oligomeric HIV-1 primary isolate envelope glycoproteins by potently neutralizing ligands requires efficient precursor cleavage. *Virology* 332:145–56
170. Lin G, Nara PL. 2007. Designing immunogens to elicit broadly neutralizing antibodies to the HIV-1 envelope glycoprotein. *Curr. HIV Res.* 5:514–41
171. Li Y, Svehla K, Mathy NL, Voss G, Mascola JR, et al. 2006. Characterization of antibody responses elicited by human immunodeficiency virus type 1 primary isolate trimeric and monomeric envelope glycoproteins in selected adjuvants. *J. Virol.* 80:1414–26
172. Ching LK, Vlachogiannis G, Bosch KA, Stamatatos L. 2008. The first hypervariable region of the gp120 Env glycoprotein defines the neutralizing susceptibility of heterologous human immunodeficiency virus type 1 isolates to neutralizing antibodies elicited by the SF162gp140 immunogen. *J. Virol.* 82:949–56
173. Wu L, Yang ZY, Xu L, Welcher B, Winfrey S, et al. 2006. Cross-clade recognition and neutralization by the V3 region from clade C human immunodeficiency virus-1 envelope. *Vaccine* 24:4995–5002
174. Hu SL, Stamatatos L. 2007. Prospects of HIV Env modification as an approach to HIV vaccine design. *Curr. HIV Res.* 5:507–13
175. Rossio JL, Esser MT, Suryanarayana K, Schneider DK, Bess JW Jr, et al. 1998. Inactivation of human immunodeficiency virus type 1 infectivity with preservation of conformational and functional integrity of virion surface proteins. *J. Virol.* 72:7992–8001
176. Poon B, Safrit JT, McClure H, Kitchen C, Hsu JF, et al. 2005. Induction of humoral immune responses following vaccination with envelope-containing, formaldehyde-treated, thermally inactivated human immunodeficiency virus type 1. *J. Virol.* 79:4927–35
177. Wang BZ, Liu W, Kang SM, Alam M, Huang C, et al. 2007. Incorporation of high levels of chimeric human immunodeficiency virus envelope glycoproteins into virus-like particles. *J. Virol.* 81:10869–78
178. Yang X, Wyatt R, Sodroski J. 2001. Improved elicitation of neutralizing antibodies against primary human immunodeficiency viruses by soluble stabilized envelope glycoprotein trimers. *J. Virol.* 75:1165–71
179. Pancera M, Lebowitz J, Schon A, Zhu P, Freire E, et al. 2005. Soluble mimetics of human immunodeficiency virus type 1 viral spikes produced by replacement of the native trimerization domain with a heterologous trimerization motif: characterization and ligand binding analysis. *J. Virol.* 79:9954–69
180. Earl PL, Sugiura W, Montefiori DC, Broder CC, Lee SA, et al. 2001. Immunogenicity and protective efficacy of oligomeric human immunodeficiency virus type 1 gp140. *J. Virol.* 75:645–53
181. Xu R, Srivastava IK, Kuller L, Zarkikh I, Kraft Z, et al. 2006. Immunization with HIV-1 SF162-derived Envelope gp140 proteins does not protect macaques from heterologous simian-human immunodeficiency virus SHIV89.6P infection. *Virology* 349:276–89
182. Kraft Z, Strouss K, Sutton WF, Cleveland B, Tso FY, et al. 2008. Characterization of neutralizing antibody responses elicited by clade A envelope immunogens derived from early transmitted viruses. *J. Virol.* 82:5912–21
183. Srivastava IK, Stamatatos L, Kan E, Vajdy M, Lian Y, et al. 2003. Purification, characterization, and immunogenicity of a soluble trimeric envelope protein containing a partial deletion of the V2 loop derived from SF162, an R5-tropic human immunodeficiency virus type 1 isolate. *J. Virol.* 77:11244–59
184. Grundner C, Li Y, Louder M, Mascola J, Yang X, et al. 2005. Analysis of the neutralizing antibody response elicited in rabbits by repeated inoculation with trimeric HIV-1 envelope glycoproteins. *Virology* 331:33–46
185. Grundner C, Mirzabekov T, Sodroski J, Wyatt R. 2002. Solid-phase proteoliposomes containing human immunodeficiency virus envelope glycoproteins. *J. Virol.* 76:3511–21
186. Binley JM, Sanders RW, Clas B, Schuelke N, Master A, et al. 2000. A recombinant human immunodeficiency virus type 1 envelope glycoprotein complex stabilized by an intermolecular disulfide bond

between the gp120 and gp41 subunits is an antigenic mimic of the trimeric virion-associated structure. *J. Virol.* 74:627–43

187. Beddows S, Schulke N, Kirschner M, Barnes K, Franti M, et al. 2005. Evaluating the immunogenicity of a disulfide-stabilized, cleaved, trimeric form of the envelope glycoprotein complex of human immunodeficiency virus type 1. *J. Virol.* 79:8812–27
188. Beddows S, Franti M, Dey AK, Kirschner M, Iyer SP, et al. 2007. A comparative immunogenicity study in rabbits of disulfide-stabilized, proteolytically cleaved, soluble trimeric human immunodeficiency virus type 1 gp140, trimeric cleavage-defective gp140 and monomeric gp120. *Virology* 360:329–40
189. Morner A, Douagi I, Forsell MN, Sundling C, Dosenovic P, et al. 2009. Human immunodeficiency virus type 1 env trimer immunization of macaques and impact of priming with viral vector or stabilized core protein. *J. Virol.* 83:540–51
190. Srivastava IK, VanDorsten K, Vojtech L, Barnett SW, Stamatatos L. 2003. Changes in the immunogenic properties of soluble gp140 human immunodeficiency virus envelope constructs upon partial deletion of the second hypervariable region. *J. Virol.* 77:2310–20
191. Vaine M, Wang S, Crooks ET, Jiang P, Montefiori DC, et al. 2008. Improved induction of antibodies against key neutralizing epitopes by human immunodeficiency virus type 1 gp120 DNA prime-protein boost vaccination compared to gp120 protein-only vaccination. *J. Virol.* 82:7369–78
192. Wang S, Pal R, Mascola JR, Chou TH, Mboudjeka I, et al. 2006. Polyvalent HIV-1 Env vaccine formulations delivered by the DNA priming plus protein boosting approach are effective in generating neutralizing antibodies against primary human immunodeficiency virus type 1 isolates from subtypes A, B, C, D and E. *Virology* 350:34–47
193. Liao HX, Sutherland LL, Xia SM, Brock ME, Scearce RM, et al. 2006. A group M consensus envelope glycoprotein induces antibodies that neutralize subsets of subtype B and C HIV-1 primary viruses. *Virology* 353:268–82
194. Korber B, Gnanakaran S. 2009. The implications of patterns in HIV diversity for neutralizing antibody induction and susceptibility. *Curr. Opin. HIV AIDS* 4:408–17
195. Stamatos NM, Mascola JR, Kalyanaraman VS, Louder MK, Frampton LM, et al. 1998. Neutralizing antibodies from the sera of human immunodeficiency virus type 1-infected individuals bind to monomeric gp120 and oligomeric gp140. *J. Virol.* 72:9656–67
196. Haynes BF, Moody MA, Verkoczy L, Kelsoe G, Alam SM. 2005. Antibody polyspecificity and neutralization of HIV-1: a hypothesis. *Hum. Antibodies* 14:59–67
197. Shan M, Klasse PJ, Banerjee K, Dey AK, Iyer SP, et al. 2007. HIV-1 gp120 mannoses induce immunosuppressive responses from dendritic cells. *PLoS Pathog.* 3:e169
198. Barnett SW, Lu S, Srivastava I, Cherpelis S, Gettie A, et al. 2001. The ability of an oligomeric human immunodeficiency virus type 1 (HIV-1) envelope antigen to elicit neutralizing antibodies against primary HIV-1 isolates is improved following partial deletion of the second hypervariable region. *J. Virol.* 75:5526–40
199. Lin G, Bertolotti-Ciarlet A, Haggarty B, Romano J, Nolan KM, et al. 2007. Replication-competent variants of human immunodeficiency virus type 2 lacking the V3 loop exhibit resistance to chemokine receptor antagonists. *J. Virol.* 81:9956–66
200. Pantophlet R, Wilson IA, Burton DR. 2003. Hyperglycosylated mutants of human immunodeficiency virus (HIV) type 1 monomeric gp120 as novel antigens for HIV vaccine design. *J. Virol.* 77:5889–901
201. Dey B, Svehla K, Xu L, Wycuff D, Zhou T, et al. 2009. Structure-based stabilization of HIV-1 gp120 enhances humoral immune responses to the induced co-receptor binding site. *PLoS Pathog.* 5:e1000445
202. Dey B, Pancera M, Svehla K, Shu Y, Xiang SH, et al. 2007. Characterization of human immunodeficiency virus type 1 monomeric and trimeric gp120 glycoproteins stabilized in the CD4-bound state: antigenicity, biophysics, and immunogenicity. *J. Virol.* 81:5579–93
203. Wu L, Zhou T, Yang ZY, Svehla K, O'Dell S, et al. 2009. Enhanced exposure of the CD4-binding site to neutralizing antibodies by structural design of a membrane-anchored human immunodeficiency virus type 1 gp120 domain. *J. Virol.* 83:5077–86
204. Alam SM, Scearce RM, Parks RJ, Plonk K, Plonk SG, et al. 2008. Human immunodeficiency virus type 1 gp41 antibodies that mask membrane proximal region epitopes: antibody binding kinetics, induction, and potential for regulation in acute infection. *J. Virol.* 82:115–25

205. Johnston MI, Fauci AS. 2007. An HIV vaccine–evolving concepts. *N. Engl. J. Med.* 356:2073–81
206. Amanna IJ, Carlson NE, Slifka MK. 2007. Duration of humoral immunity to common viral and vaccine antigens. *N. Engl. J. Med.* 357:1903–15
207. Dorner T, Radbruch A. 2007. Antibodies and B cell memory in viral immunity. *Immunity* 27:384–92
208. Radbruch A, Muehlinghaus G, Luger EO, Inamine A, Smith KG, et al. 2006. Competence and competition: the challenge of becoming a long-lived plasma cell. *Nat. Rev. Immunol.* 6:741–50
209. Evans TG, Frey S, Israel H, Chiu J, El-Habib R, et al. 2004. Long-term memory B-cell responses in recipients of candidate human immunodeficiency virus type 1 vaccines. *Vaccine* 22:2626–30
210. Ourmanov I, Bilska M, Hirsch VM, Montefiori DC. 2000. Recombinant modified vaccinia virus ankara expressing the surface gp120 of simian immunodeficiency virus (SIV) primes for a rapid neutralizing antibody response to SIV infection in macaques. *J. Virol.* 74:2960–65
211. Buckner C, Gines LG, Saunders CJ, Vojtech L, Srivastava I, et al. 2004. Priming B cell-mediated anti-HIV envelope responses by vaccination allows for the long-term control of infection in macaques exposed to a R5-tropic SHIV. *Virology* 320:167–80
212. Rose NF, Marx PA, Luckay A, Nixon DF, Moretto WJ, et al. 2001. An effective AIDS vaccine based on live attenuated vesicular stomatitis virus recombinants. *Cell* 106:539–49
213. Amara RR, Villinger F, Altman JD, Lydy SL, O'Neil SP, et al. 2001. Control of a mucosal challenge and prevention of AIDS by a multiprotein DNA/MVA vaccine. *Science* 292:69–74
214. Barouch DH, Santra S, Kuroda MJ, Schmitz JE, Plishka R, et al. 2001. Reduction of simian-human immunodeficiency virus 89.6P viremia in rhesus monkeys by recombinant modified vaccinia virus Ankara vaccination. *J. Virol.* 75:5151–58
215. Pilcher CD, Tien HC, Eron JJ Jr, Vernazza PL, Leu SY, et al. 2004. Brief but efficient: acute HIV infection and the sexual transmission of HIV. *J. Infect. Dis.* 189:1785–92
216. Wilson DP, Law MG, Grulich AE, Cooper DA, Kaldor JM. 2008. Relation between HIV viral load and infectiousness: a model-based analysis. *Lancet* 372:314–20
217. Schmitz JE, Kuroda MJ, Santra S, Simon MA, Lifton MA, et al. 2003. Effect of humoral immune responses on controlling viremia during primary infection of rhesus monkeys with simian immunodeficiency virus. *J. Virol.* 77:2165–73
218. Miller CJ, Genesca M, Abel K, Montefiori D, Forthal D, et al. 2007. Antiviral antibodies are necessary for control of simian immunodeficiency virus replication. *J. Virol.* 81:5024–35
219. Gaufin T, Gautam R, Kasheta M, Ribeiro R, Ribka E, et al. 2009. Limited ability of humoral immune responses in control of viremia during infection with SIVsmmD215 strain. *Blood* 113:4250–61
220. Montefiori DC, Altfeld M, Lee PK, Bilska M, Zhou J, et al. 2003. Viremia control despite escape from a rapid and potent autologous neutralizing antibody response after therapy cessation in an HIV-1-infected individual. *J. Immunol.* 170:3906–14
221. Pope M, Haase AT. 2003. Transmission, acute HIV-1 infection and the quest for strategies to prevent infection. *Nat. Med.* 9:847–52
222. Broliden K, Haase AT, Ahuja SK, Shearer GM, Andersson J. 2009. Introduction: Back to basics: mucosal immunity and novel HIV vaccine concepts. *J. Intern. Med.* 265:5–17
223. Cole AM, Cole AL. 2008. Antimicrobial polypeptides are key anti-HIV-1 effector molecules of cervicovaginal host defense. *Am. J. Reprod. Immunol.* 59:27–34
224. Brenchley JM, Price DA, Douek DC. 2006. HIV disease: fallout from a mucosal catastrophe? *Nat. Immunol.* 7:235–39
225. Levesque MC, Moody MA, Hwang KK, Marshall DJ, Whitesides JF, et al. 2009. Polyclonal B cell differentiation and loss of gastrointestinal tract germinal centers in the earliest stages of HIV-1 infection. *PLoS Med.* 6:e1000107
226. Giorgi JV, Hultin LE, McKeating JA, Johnson TD, Owens B, et al. 1999. Shorter survival in advanced human immunodeficiency virus type 1 infection is more closely associated with T lymphocyte activation than with plasma virus burden or virus chemokine coreceptor usage. *J. Infect. Dis.* 179:859–70
227. Silvestri G, Sodora DL, Koup RA, Paiardini M, O'Neil SP, et al. 2003. Nonpathogenic SIV infection of sooty mangabeys is characterized by limited bystander immunopathology despite chronic high-level viremia. *Immunity* 18:441–52

228. Kaur A, Di Mascio M, Barabasz A, Rosenzweig M, McClure HM, et al. 2008. Dynamics of T- and B-lymphocyte turnover in a natural host of simian immunodeficiency virus. *J. Virol.* 82:1084–93
229. Haynes BF, Shattock RJ. 2008. Critical issues in mucosal immunity for HIV-1 vaccine development. *J. Allergy Clin. Immunol.* 122:3–9; quiz 10–1
230. Lifson JD, Rossio JL, Piatak M Jr, Parks T, Li L, et al. 2001. Role of $CD8^+$ lymphocytes in control of simian immunodeficiency virus infection and resistance to rechallenge after transient early antiretroviral treatment. *J. Virol.* 75:10187–99
231. Holl V, Peressin M, Decoville T, Schmidt S, Zolla-Pazner S, et al. 2006. Nonneutralizing antibodies are able to inhibit human immunodeficiency virus type 1 replication in macrophages and immature dendritic cells. *J. Virol.* 80:6177–81
232. Holl V, Peressin M, Schmidt S, Decoville T, Zolla-Pazner S, et al. 2006. Efficient inhibition of HIV-1 replication in human immature monocyte-derived dendritic cells by purified anti-HIV-1 IgG without induction of maturation. *Blood* 107:4466–74
233. Perez LG, Costa MR, Todd CA, Haynes BF, Montefiori DC. 2009. Utilization of immunoglobulin G Fc receptors by human immunodeficiency virus type 1: a specific role for antibodies against the membrane-proximal external region of gp41. *J. Virol.* 83:7397–410
234. Koup RA, Sullivan JL, Levine PH, Brewster F, Mahr A, et al. 1989. Antigenic specificity of antibody-dependent cell-mediated cytotoxicity directed against human immunodeficiency virus in antibody-positive sera. *J. Virol.* 63:584–90
235. Forthal DN, Landucci G, Daar ES. 2001. Antibody from patients with acute human immunodeficiency virus (HIV) infection inhibits primary strains of HIV type 1 in the presence of natural-killer effector cells. *J. Virol.* 75:6953–61
236. Bomsel M, Heyman M, Hocini H, Lagaye S, Belec L, et al. 1998. Intracellular neutralization of HIV transcytosis across tight epithelial barriers by anti-HIV envelope protein dIgA or IgM. *Immunity* 9:277–87
237. Alfsen A, Iniguez P, Bouguyon E, Bomsel M. 2001. Secretory IgA specific for a conserved epitope on gp41 envelope glycoprotein inhibits epithelial transcytosis of HIV-1. *J. Immunol.* 166:6257–65
238. Huang YT, Wright A, Gao X, Kulick L, Yan H, et al. 2005. Intraepithelial cell neutralization of HIV-1 replication by IgA. *J. Immunol.* 174:4828–35
239. Moore PL, Crooks ET, Porter L, Zhu P, Cayanan CS, et al. 2006. Nature of nonfunctional envelope proteins on the surface of human immunodeficiency virus type 1. *J. Virol.* 80:2515–28
240. Karnasuta C, Paris RM, Cox JH, Nitayaphan S, Pitisuttithum P, et al. 2005. Antibody-dependent cell-mediated cytotoxic responses in participants enrolled in a phase I/II ALVAC-HIV/AIDSVAX® B/E prime-boost HIV-1 vaccine trial in Thailand. *Vaccine* 23:2522–29
241. Montefiori D, Mascola JR. 2009. Neutralizing antibodies against HIV-1: can we elicit them with vaccines and how much do we need? *Curr. Opin. HIV AIDS* 4:347–51

Differentiation of Effector CD4 T Cell Populations*

Jinfang Zhu, Hidehiro Yamane, and William E. Paul

Laboratory of Immunology, National Institute of Allergy and Infectious Diseases, National Institutes of Health, Bethesda, Maryland 20892-1892; email: jfzhu@niaid.nih.gov, hyamane@niaid.nih.gov, wpaul@niaid.nih.gov

Annu. Rev. Immunol. 2010. 28:445–89

First published online as a Review in Advance on January 4, 2010

The *Annual Review of Immunology* is online at immunol.annualreviews.org

This article's doi:
10.1146/annurev-immunol-030409-101212

0732-0582/10/0423-0445$20.00

Key Words

CD4 effector T cells, regulatory T cells, T cell differentiation, cytokines, transcription factors, human diseases

Abstract

CD4 T cells play critical roles in mediating adaptive immunity to a variety of pathogens. They are also involved in autoimmunity, asthma, and allergic responses as well as in tumor immunity. During TCR activation in a particular cytokine milieu, naive CD4 T cells may differentiate into one of several lineages of T helper (Th) cells, including Th1, Th2, Th17, and iTreg, as defined by their pattern of cytokine production and function. In this review, we summarize the discovery, functions, and relationships among Th cells; the cytokine and signaling requirements for their development; the networks of transcription factors involved in their differentiation; the epigenetic regulation of their key cytokines and transcription factors; and human diseases involving defective CD4 T cell differentiation.

INTRODUCTION

CD4 T cells play central roles in the function of the immune system: They help B cells make antibody, enhance and maintain responses of CD8 T cells, regulate macrophage function, orchestrate immune responses against a wide variety of pathogenic microorganisms, and regulate/suppress immune responses both to control autoimmunity and to adjust the magnitude and persistence of responses. CD4 T cells are important mediators of immunologic memory, and when their numbers are diminished or their functions are lost, the individual becomes susceptible to a wide range of infectious disorders. Indeed, in HIV infection, it is when CD4 T cell numbers in blood fall below 200/mm^3 that opportunistic infections are most likely to occur.

The Th1/Th2 Paradigm

These various functions are achieved through the differentiation of naive CD4 T cells as they are stimulated by their cognate antigen presented by competent antigen-presenting cells to become effector and/or memory cells of specialized phenotypes. The initial understanding of the existence of distinctive populations of differentiated CD4 T cells came from the analysis of mouse CD4 T cell clones that were shown by Mosmann & Coffman (1) and slightly later by Bottomly and her colleagues (2) to be divisible into two major groups, designated Th1 and Th2 cells by Mosmann & Coffman. Th1 and Th2 clones could be distinguished mainly by the cytokines produced by the cells, but also through the expression of different patterns of cell surface molecules. With regard to cytokine expression, Th1 cells make IFN-γ as their signature cytokine and also uniquely produce lymphotoxin. Th1 cells tend to be good IL-2 producers, and many make TNF-α as well. By contrast, Th2 cells fail to produce IFN-γ or lymphotoxin. Their signature cytokines are IL-4, IL-5, and IL-13. They also make TNF-α, and some produce IL-9. Although initially thought to be unable to make IL-2, later results indicated that Th2 cells could often produce relatively modest amounts of IL-2.

For some time, investigative concern focused on whether the Th1/Th2 dichotomy was principally applicable in mice but not in humans and on whether it was mainly a property of in vitro–differentiated cells. Indeed, although the study of clones had clearly shown a dichotomy between the two cell types, one could often observe cells obtained directly from mice or humans that produced both IL-4 and IFN-γ. Nonetheless, with growing experience, it has become clear that specialization in patterns of cytokine production and other phenotypic characterstics do occur in vivo in mice and in humans. Still important is to compare, in detail, IFN-γ-producing and IL-4-producing CD4 T cells (i.e., Th1 and Th2 cells) generated in vitro and those that appear in vivo in mice and humans to determine the degree to which in vitro–generated cells truly reflect the biology of responses generated under physiologic conditions.

Within a few years of the description of distinct populations existing among CD4 T cell clones, methods were developed to differentiate naive CD4 T cells into IL-4-producing (Th2) cells in vitro (3–6). Such Th2 differentiation required the activation of naive cells, initially with polyclonal stimuli such as anti-CD3 and anti-CD28, and later with cognate antigen, in the presence of a particular set of cytokines. To obtain Th2 cells, the presence of both IL-2 and IL-4 during the differentiation process was essential. The particularly provocative aspect here was that a major product of the Th2 cell, IL-4, was also a critical inducer. The significance of this finding is now clear in vitro and is discussed in detail below.

It was subsequently shown that Th1 cells could be differentiated in vitro from naive CD4 T cells if IL-4 was neutralized and IL-12 was added to the culture (7). Experiments in which single naive CD4 T cells were primed in vitro indicate that individual CD4 T cells can be made to differentiate into Th1 or Th2 cells (8–10). There was considerable controversy as to whether the inducing cytokines led individual

CD4 T cells to adopt a Th1 or Th2 phenotype or whether such adoption was a stochastic event and the added cytokines functioned by selectively promoting the outgrowth of differentiated cells. Several lines of evidence strongly support the notion that the cytokines play a major role in inducing the transcription factors that determine differentiation (11, 12), although there may be elements of selective outgrowth (12, 13).

Th17 Cells and iTregs

That two major cell types differentiate from naive CD4 T cells dominated the field for more than a decade and a half. Other types of CD4 T cells were recognized, such as NKT cells and natural regulatory T cells (nTregs), but these cells were not derived in the periphery from the naive cells that could also give rise to Th1 and Th2 cells. Rather, they were members of lineages that developed in the thymus and that were distinct from the cells undergoing parallel thymic differentiation to become the naive "conventional" CD4 T cells that were progenitors of Th1 and Th2 cells (14, 15).

In 2003, a third major effector population of CD4 T cell that could be derived from naive CD4 T cells was shown to exist (16–18). These cells, designated Th17 cells (19–21), were characterized by the production of IL-17A, IL-17F, and IL-22 as signature cytokines, molecules not produced by Th1 or Th2 cells. Th17 cells also were good producers of IL-21 (22–24), although IL-21 can be made by several Th cell types.

At the same time, it was shown that cells with the characteristics of regulatory T cells could be induced to differentiate in vitro from naive CD4 T cells (25–28). These cells were designated induced Tregs (iTregs) to distinguish them from nTregs. In mice, iTregs show in vitro and in vivo functions similar to those of nTregs (29), but iTregs in humans have thus far failed to demonstrate activity in an in vitro Treg functional assay (30).

Thus, four major T cell populations clearly emerge from naive CD4 T cells. It is virtually certain that the same precursor can be caused to differentiate either into a Th1 or a Th2 cell. Although not yet definitively shown for Th17 cells or iTregs, it is most likely the case for those cells as well.

Are Tfh Cells a Fifth Lineage?

The activation of CD4 T cells in vivo in response to appropriate stimulation results in the generation of effector populations that have the capacity to enter the tissues and to mediate their immune functions at the site of pathogen invasion. In parallel, a population develops of central memory cells that reside principally in the lymph nodes and spleen and, presumably, are available to reconstitute effector cells upon subsequent antigenic challenge. Both central memory and effector (sometimes effector/memory) cells appear to be distinctive states of each of the Th1, Th2, and Th17 populations and possibly also of Tregs.

A major function of CD4 T cells is to help B cells produce antibody in response to T-dependent antigens. CD4 T cells are also important in the induction and control of immunoglobulin class switching and somatic hypermutation. These events occur mainly within germinal centers, and the CD4 T cells that enter the germinal center to mediate their helper function for antibody production are often designated T follicular helper (Tfh) cells (31).

Whether Tfh cells are an independent lineage (essentially parallel to Th1, Th2, and Th17 cells) or a phenotypic state of each of the three effector lineages remains uncertain. Recently, several studies have appeared in which Tfh cells were analyzed in germinal centers of mice infected with different parasites that induce responses typically associated with Th2 cell development and with immunoglobulin class switching to IgE, an Ig isotype for which IL-4 is essential (32–34). In each instance, cells with the Tfh phenotype produced IL-4, and these cells could be shown to reside within germinal centers and to form contacts with responding B cells (32). This finding implies that individual Tfh cells mediate both help and class switching. In other experiments, individual Tfh cells directly interacting with B cells in the germinal center produced either IL-4 or IFN-γ, depending upon how they had been primed (31). This implies that the issue of Tfh lineage is not limited to the IL-4 pathway but is general.

The demonstration that Tfh cells produce IL-4 or IFN-γ, depending on how they are primed, does not distinguish the possibility that a cell of the Tfh lineage subsequently acquires the capacity to produce IL-4 or IFN-γ from the possibility that Th2 or Th1 cells acquire the capacity to act as Tfh cells. Pearce and colleagues (33) harvested antigen-responsive non-Tfh cells that were competent to produce IL-4 but that were not actually producing the cytokine from lymph nodes of mice infected with *Schistosoma mansoni*. When these cells were transferred into mice also infected with *S. mansoni*, some of the transferred cells acquired the Tfh phenotype, consistent with the concept that Th2 cells can become Tfh cells. However, one cannot rule out the possibility that among the cells harvested from the lymph nodes, there were subpopulations already determined to become conventional Th2 CD4 T cells and others committed to become Tfh cells. It has recently been reported that the bulk of memory cells that participate in affinity maturation reside within the bone marrow, raising the possibility that such T cells are specialized as Tfh memory cells (35).

It is not yet clear whether Tfh cells are a distinct lineage. Further studies are awaited to clarify this interesting and important question. Detailed analysis of the pattern of gene expression or of genome-wide chromatin accessibility might well allow one to determine whether IL-4- and IFN-γ-producing Tfh cells are more closely related to one another than are IL-4-producing Th2 and Tfh cells or vice versa. Such data would provide a reasonable basis upon which to reach a conclusion as to whether Tfh cells are an independent lineage.

More on Lineage Relationships

The discussion as to whether Tfhs should be regarded as a distinctive differentiated state of the major effector lineages (i.e., Th1, Th2, or Th17 cells that acquire Tfh character) or an independent lineage of cells, parallel to Th1, Th2, and Th17, that can subsequently acquire the capacity to produce the distinct regulatory cytokines that control switching to different immunoglobulin isotypes raises the possibility that other lineage relationships may be more complex than previously thought. Principal among these are Tregs, where recent work suggests that different Treg populations may be specialized to control mainly the function of particular subsets of CD4 T cells.

Campbell and colleagues (36) have reported that in response to IFN-γ, Foxp3$^+$ Tregs upregulated T-bet and that T-bet-expressing Tregs accumulated at sites of Th1 cell–mediated inflammation. Furthermore, T-bet$^-$ Tregs proliferated less well than T-bet$^+$ Tregs, and when T-bet was lacking from Tregs, they were relatively ineffective in controlling the expansion of T-bet$^+$ conventional CD4 T cells, whereas they seemed as effective as conventional Tregs in controlling Th2 and Th17 cells.

Rudensky and colleagues (37) reported that conditionally deleting *Irf4* in Tregs selectively allowed the uncontrolled expansion of Th2 cells, suggesting that IFN regulatory factor 4 (IRF4) expression, important in Th2 differentiation, also played a role in differentiation of those Tregs that could control Th2 cells. Similarly, STAT3 expression in Tregs seems to be essential for the ability of Tregs to suppress immune pathology mediated by Th17 cells, whose differentiation requires STAT3 (38). Thus, iTregs should not necessarily be considered as one of a set of distinct fates of CD4 T cells, equivalent to Th1, Th2, and Th17 cells, but possibly as a lineage parallel to the effector CD4 T cells (Th1, Th2, and Th17) as a whole and capable of differentiating into specialized cells that show distinctiveness in their regulatory targets. The finding that transcription factors associated with a particular Th fate differentiation are also important in the specialization of Tregs suggests that the priming conditions that lead conventional cells to adopt one of their possible fates may be the same conditions that call forth Tregs specialized to control these very Th cells.

THE CYTOKINE ENVIRONMENT PLAYS A CENTRAL ROLE IN FATE DETERMINATION AND EFFECTOR FUNCTION

The distinctive differentiated states of the various CD4 effector/regulatory subpopulations are determined largely by the set of transcription factors they express and the genes they transcribe. The induction of the distinctive patterns of gene expression may be achievable in several ways, but in vitro the major determinants of the differentiated state of the cell are the set of cytokines present during the T cell receptor (TCR)-mediated activation process. Our understanding of this process has evolved over an extended period and is described in detail below.

As discussed above, it was first demonstrated that naive CD4 T cells could differentiate into IL-4-producing CD4 T cells if the cytokines IL-4 and IL-2 were present at the time of stimulation by cognate antigen (3–6). That one of the key inducing cytokines is also a major product was a striking finding; this has proven not to be unique for Th2 differentiation. For Th1 differentiation, it was first shown that IL-12 (7) played a central role and only somewhat later was it appreciated that IFN-γ also played an important role in the induction of Th1 cells (39), of which IFN-γ is a signature cytokine. Indeed, in vitro neutralization of IFN-γ will often markedly diminish Th1 development.

Understanding of Th17 differentiation went through a complex evolution, beginning with the recognition of the existence of an IL-12 congener (IL-23) that shared one chain with IL-12 (p40) but expressed a unique chain (p19), distinct from IL-12 p35 (40). This led to the recognition that, in much research that had relied on deleting p40 to block Th1 differentiation, the development/maintenance of both Th1 and Th17 cells were blocked and that IL-23 played an important role in the development and/or maintenance of Th17 cells. However, it was soon appreciated that IL-23 did not act on naive CD4 T cells, but rather was more important later in the Th17 priming process or in the maintenance of the Th17 phenotype.

Further analysis revealed that in vitro Th17 differentiation was most efficient when TGF-β and IL-6 were available (21, 41, 42) but that IL-21 could mediate many of the functions of IL-6 (22–24). IL-6, IL-21, and IL-23 can be regarded, at least at one level, as congeners since each mediates its function through the activation of STAT3. The relative efficacy of the three cytokines may be determined, at least in part, by the number of specific receptors that exist at any one time. For example, IL-23 receptors appear not to be expressed until after the naive cell has partially completed its differentiation to becoming a Th17 cell, and consequently IL-23 plays little part in the initial determination of Th17 differentiation (21, 41, 43). In accord with the importance of products of the differentiated cells playing a role in differentiation, Th17 cells produce IL-21, and IL-21 can certainly propagate the Th17 differentiation process, even if it is less effective than IL-6 in initiating differentiation.

The induction of iTregs from naive CD4 T cells relies on T cell activation in the presence of TGF-β and IL-2. Since Tregs are good TGF-β producers, the principle that a major product of the differentiated cell plays a major role in induction is also applicable to iTregs.

Reliable means of developing Tfh cells in vitro are still being uncovered. It has been proposed that the inclusion of IL-6 or IL-21 together with a TCR-mediated stimulation will induce these cells (44, 45), but this idea is still controversial. Some of these difficulties may

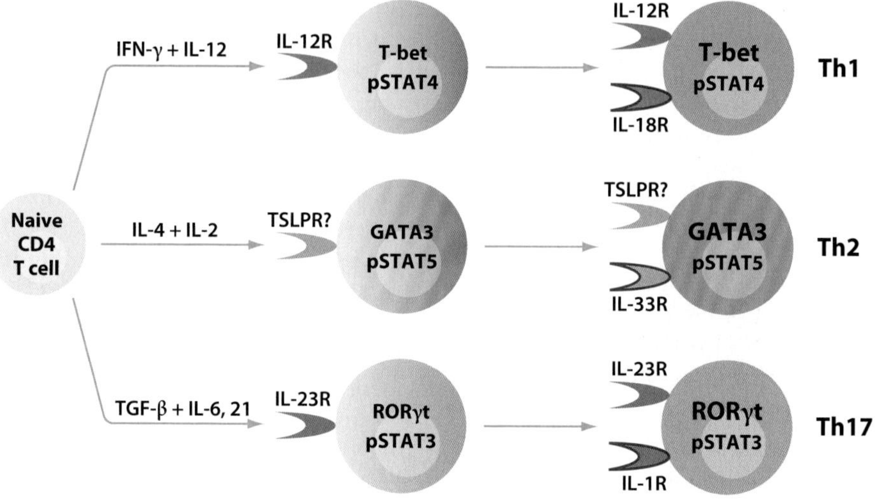

Figure 1

Cytokines play critical roles in differentiation and effector functions of Th1, Th2, and Th17 cells. Upon TCR activation triggered by antigen-presenting cells, naive CD4 T cells differentiate into distinct Th lineages in the context of combinations of cytokines. The differentiation processes involve upregulation of master transcriptional regulators and activation of STAT proteins (185). Each lineage expresses unique cytokine receptors, which can respond to cytokines produced by accessory cells. At later stages of Th cell differentiation, different Th cells preferentially express an IL-1 family receptor. Together with a STAT activator, an IL-1 family cytokine is capable of inducing effector cytokine production from Th cells in a TCR-independent manner (46–49).

stem from an uncertainty as to the proper starting cells for such differentiation—be they naive CD4 T cells or already differentiated Th cells—and the possibility that environmental factors from the germinal center or provided by B cells may play an important role in such differentiation (33, 34).

Cytokines may also play a role in effector cytokine production by differentiated Th1, Th2, and Th17 cells (**Figure 1**). At later stages of Th cell differentiation, a distinct member of the family of IL-1 receptors is selectively upregulated in each lineage. Together with a STAT5 inducer including IL-2, IL-7, or TSLP (thymic stromal lymphopoietin), the IL-1 analog IL-33 causes TCR-independent IL-13 production in a cyclosporine A–independent manner in Th2 cells (46), suggesting an innate-like effector function of Th cells. TCR-independent cytokine production can also be induced in Th1 and Th17 cells by IL-12/IL-18 and IL-23/IL-1, respectively (46–49).

TRANSCRIPTION FACTORS FOR T HELPER CELL FATE DETERMINATION

The master transcription factors and the signaling transducer and activator of transcription (STAT) proteins are indispensable for Th cell fate determination and cytokine production. The activities of the master transcription factors are mainly determined by their expression levels, whereas those of the STATs are regulated by cytokine-mediated posttranslational modification, including tyrosine and/or serine/threonine phosphorylation. Not only do the activated STAT proteins, in collaboration with master transcription factors, regulate the production of the key cytokines by Th cells, they also play important roles in the induction of the master transcription factors. Other transcription factors, either constitutively expressed or induced by TCR and/or cytokine-mediated signaling, are also involved in executing or

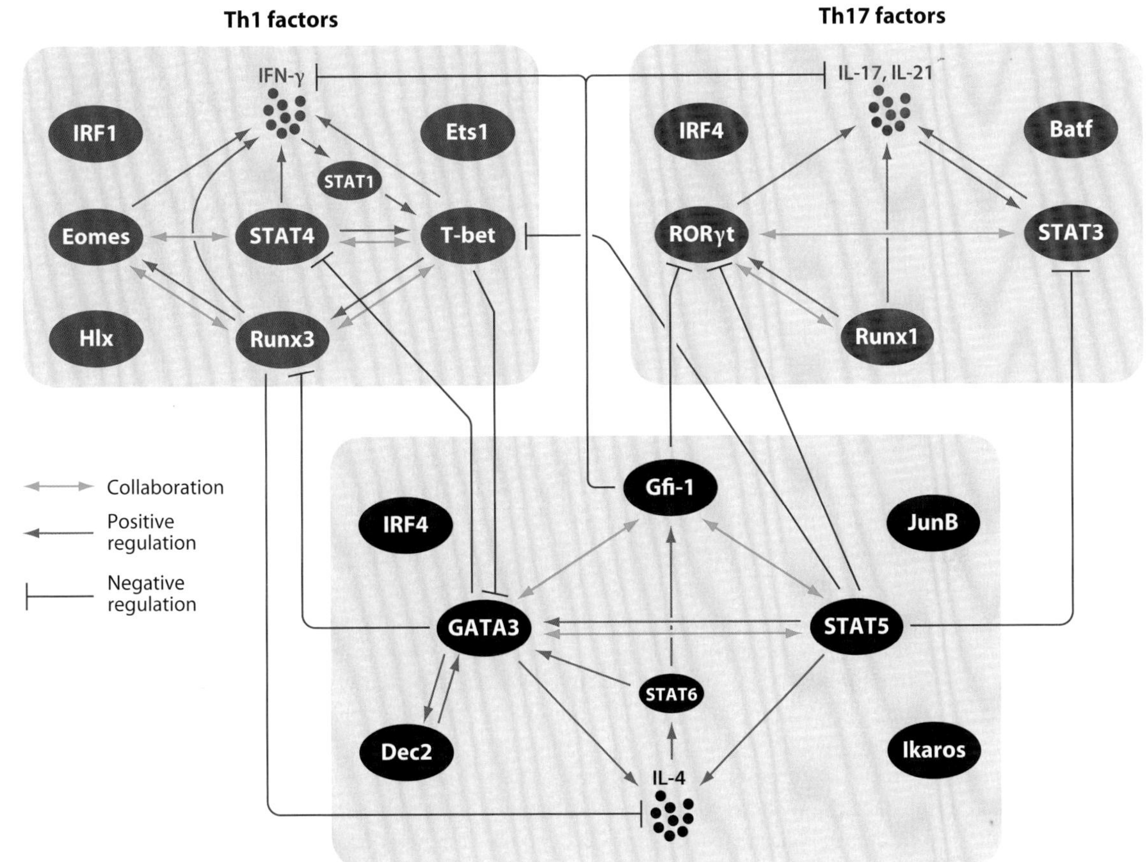

Figure 2

Networks of transcription factors for Th cell differentiation. Critical transcription factors involved in Th1, Th2, and Th17 differentiation and the relationships among these factors are shown. The cell fate of each Th lineage is determined by many transcription factors, including master regulators and STAT family proteins. There are collaborations and positive regulations among the transcription factors during Th cell differentiation and lineage-specific cytokine production. Some factors negatively regulate expression or function of transcription factors of other Th lineages.

fine-tuning Th cell functions. These molecules form a sophisticated transcription factor network (**Figure 2**), which is critical for Th cell fate determination, expansion, and function.

Master Transcription Factors for Each Lineage

GATA3. GATA3, the Th2 master regulator, was the first master regulator to be identified (50, 51). GATA3 is also critical for the development of CD4 T cells, and naive CD4 T cells express it at detectable levels (52). GATA3 expression is upregulated or downregulated during Th2 or Th1 differentiation, respectively (51, 53, 54). Expression of retrovirally encoded GATA3 in Th1 cells makes these cells competent to produce IL-4 and induces endogenous GATA3 production (53, 55). Introducing a dominant-negative (DN) form of GATA3 in T cells reduces Th2 cytokine expression and, in vivo, blocks induction of airway hypersensitivity (56). Th2 differentiation is totally abolished in vitro and in vivo in the absence of GATA3, as shown by the failure of such differentiation in mice in which *Gata3* is deleted in peripheral CD4 T cells (57, 58). Deleting *Gata3* from fully differentiated Th2 cells by the introduction of retrovirally encoded Cre has only a modest effect on IL-4 production but completely blocks the production of IL-5 and IL-13 (57), consistent with direct GATA3 binding to the IL-5 (59) and IL-13 (60, 61) promoters, but only to IL-4 enhancers (62).

GATA3 promotes Th2 differentiation through instructing Th2 commitment, selectively stimulating the growth of Th2 cells, and suppressing Th1 differentiation (63). GATA3 is also expressed at intermediate levels in NKT cells (64) and Treg cells (J. Zhu and W.E. Paul, unpublished observations). NKT cell development and survival is defective in *Gata3* conditional knockout mice (64), but the function of GATA3 in Tregs is not clear.

T-bet/Eomes. T-bet is a major factor for inducing IFN-γ production and Th1 cell differentiation (65). Overexpression of T-bet either during Th2 differentiation or in fully differentiated Th2 cells causes such cells to acquire competence to produce IFN-γ while, at the same time, suppressing their capacity to produce IL-4. T-bet induces IFN-γ partly through remodeling the *Ifng* gene and by upregulating IL-12Rβ2 expression, thus promoting both IFN-γ expression and selective Th1 cell expansion in response to IL-12 (12, 66). *Tbx21*$^{-/-}$ (T-bet knockout) cells have severe defects in Th1 cell differentiation both in vitro and in vivo (67). IFN-γ responses to *Leishmania major* are significantly diminished, although not abolished, in *Tbx21*$^{-/-}$ mice; these mice show increased IL-4 and IL-5 production (67) in response to *L. major* infection. Notably, *Tbx21*$^{+/-}$ cells display a partial phenotype.

T-bet-expressing CD4 T cells are dramatically reduced in human asthmatic airways, and *Tbx21*$^{-/-}$ mice spontaneously develop airway hypersensitivity (68). Despite the very important role of T-bet in Th1 differentiation and in the acquisition of competence to produce IFN-γ, it has been reported that *Tbx21*$^{-/-}$ cells can produce normal amounts of IFN-γ in vitro when naive cells are differentiated under Th1 conditions (i.e., when IL-4 was neutralized), suggesting that a main function of T-bet is to inhibit GATA3 expression and that IFN-γ may be redundantly controlled (54). However, others have reported that, although capable of inducing IL-12Rβ2 expression, T-bet fails to suppress GATA3 and Th2 cytokine production (69). The controversy among these studies regarding T-bet function has not been resolved. Possibly, differences in the timing and/or culture conditions of the experiments account for the different observations. T-bet deficiency also causes defective IFN-γ production by NK cells. However, IFN-γ production by CD8 T cells from *Tbx21*$^{-/-}$ mice is relatively normal (67), although it has been reported recently that T-bet contributes to optimal IFN-γ production at early stages of the CD8 response (70).

The differential requirement for T-bet for IFN-γ production by CD4 and CD8 T cells may be explained by the heightened expression of another T-box family member, Eomesodermin (Eomes), in CD8 T cells (71). Indeed, it has recently been reported that CD8 T cells from T-bet/Eomes double knockouts but not single knockouts produce very little IFN-γ and fail to control lymphocytic choriomeningitis virus (LCMV) infection. Rather, such CD8 T cells aberrantly produce IL-17, which results in a wasting disease after LCMV infection (72). IL-21 inhibition of Th1 cell IFN-γ production may be mediated by suppression of Eomes, not T-bet (73), suggesting that Eomes is also upregulated during Th1 differentiation and involved in optimal IFN-γ production by CD4 T cells. Indeed, CD4 T cells from T-bet/Eomes double knockout mice infected with LCMV fail to produce any IFN-γ in response to challenge with the GP61–81 LCMV envelope peptide (72).

T-bet and Eomes are also involved in regulating IL-2Rβ, whose expression is critical for IL-15-mediated CD8 T cell memory (74). Furthermore, T-bet suppresses IL-7Rα expression and thus affects the generation of central memory CD8 T cells (75, 76). A subset of Treg cells also express T-bet, and these Tregs are important for controlling Th1 responses (36). T-bet is also important for the development and/or function of other immune cells, including B cells, NK cells, NKT cells, and dendritic cells (DCs) (77). Therefore, one should consider the multiple functions of T-bet in the immune system while interpreting results obtained from the analysis of T-bet germline knockout mice; conditional deletion of *Tbx21* may help in dissecting the functions of T-bet in different cell types.

Foxp3. Scurfy mice and patients with IPEX (immunodeficiency, polyendocrinopathy, and enteropathy, X-linked syndrome) lack detectable nTregs. Both the mutant mice and the patients have mutations in *Foxp3* (78–80), which is reported to be the master transcriptional regulator for nTregs (81, 82). Continuous expression of Foxp3 in Tregs is required to maintain the suppressive activity of such cells (83). In addition, conventional T cells transduced with retroviral Foxp3 acquired a Treg phenotype, including the inability to produce cytokines (anergy) and suppressive activity (81). By contrast, limiting Foxp3 expression appears to divert cells that would have differentiated into Tregs to develop into Th2-like cells, implying a close relationship of the Th2 and Treg lineages (84).

Culturing Foxp3$^-$ naive CD4 T cells with a TCR stimulus and TGF-β converts these cells into Foxp3$^+$ CD4 T cells, which have been designated iTregs (25). TGF-β is also critical for the development, homeostasis, and function of nTregs (85–88). Smad3 and NFAT, activated by TGF-β and TCR-mediated signaling, respectively, cooperate in *Foxp3* gene remodeling and expression (89).

RORγt/RORα. Th17 cells do not express GATA3 or T-bet (19, 20); instead, they express high levels of RORγt (90). RORγt is induced in naive CD4 T cells within 8 h of TCR stimulation in association with TGF-β and IL-6. RORγt is the master regulator of Th17 cells; ~50% of activated cells overexpressing RORγt produce IL-17, and RORγt-deficient cells produce very little IL-17. Furthermore, RORγt-deficient mice are partially resistant to experimental autoimmune encephalomyelitis. The residual IL-17 production in RORγt-deficient cells appears to be dependent on the activity of a related nuclear receptor, RORα, which is also upregulated in Th17 cells (91). Although deleting RORα resulted in minimal reduction of IL-17 expression, deficiency of both RORγt and RORα completely abolished IL-17 production. RORγt is also expressed in double-positive (DP) thymocytes (92) and other cell types including lymphoid tissue inducer (LTi) cells, where IL-17 is also produced (93).

Bcl-6. Bcl-6 is a transcriptional repressor. Bcl-6 germline knockout mice develop Th2 diseases even in the absence of STAT6 (94, 95), possibly due to the derepression of GATA3 in the absence of Bcl-6 (96). Bcl-6 is frequently translocated and hypermutated in diffuse large B cell lymphoma and is critical for germinal center B cell differentiation and thus germinal center formation (94). In addition, Bcl-6 expression is greater in CD25$^+$ germinal center B cells than in CD25$^-$ B cells in the germinal center (97). Unlike plasma cells, the CD25$^+$ B cells, representing memory B cells, express lower levels of Blimp-1. STAT5 activation, critical for the self-renewal of these cells, directly induces Bcl-6 expression. Bcl-6 is also expressed in Tfh cells (98) as is CXCR5, a critical chemokine receptor that allows cells to home to B cell follicles (99). Indeed, three recent reports showed that Bcl-6 is critical for Tfh cell differentiation (100–102). Bcl-6 is necessary and sufficient to induce Tfh-related molecules, including CXCR5, PD-1, IL-6R, and IL-21R, but has no effect on IL-21 production. Bcl-6 also suppresses the expression of Th1, Th2, and Th17 cytokines. In addition, enforced Bcl-6 expression induces endogenous Bcl-6 transcription (100), and Blimp-1 represses Bcl-6 (101).

Signaling Transducer and Activator of Transcription (STAT) Proteins

As mentioned above, the cytokine milieu present during TCR-mediated activation of naive CD4 T cells is the most important determinant of CD4 T cell fate. The major signaling pathway triggered by cytokines is the activation of the STAT family of proteins. STATs play critical roles in the differentiation and expansion of Th cells. They are important both for the induction of the master regulators and for cytokine production in collaboration with master regulators.

STAT1. Activation of STAT1 by IFN-γ is important for the induction of T-bet during in vitro Th1 differentiation (39, 69). IFN-γ, through STAT1 activation, also induces T-bet expression in monocytes, macrophages, DCs, and B cells. The existence of a positive feedback loop in which IFN-γ, acting through T-bet, induces more IFN-γ indicates that STAT1 serves as a critical mediator for the amplification of in vitro Th1 responses. However, in the acute phase of *Toxoplasma gondii* infection in mice, the appearance of CD4 T cells capable of producing IFN-γ does not require STAT1 (103). Serum IFN-γ levels in *Stat1*$^{-/-}$ mice 7 days after *T. gondii* infection are comparable to those in wild-type mice. Furthermore, *Stat1*$^{-/-}$ CD4 T cells from *T. gondii*–infected mice produce amounts of IFN-γ in response to soluble *T. gondii* antigen comparable to cells from similarly infected wild-type mice, although these knockout CD4 T cells expressed lower levels of T-bet than did wild-type CD4 T cells. *Stat1*$^{-/-}$ mice have an increased parasite burden and died 7–12 days after infection, most likely owing to the failure of macrophage activation. Thus, to determine whether the IFN-γ/STAT1 autocrine pathway plays an important role in in vivo CD4 T cell differentiation will require a T cell–specific conditional *Stat1* knockout mouse. The need for STAT1 in order for CD4 T cells from *T. gondii*–infected mice to obtain optimal expression of T-bet suggests that the IFN-γ/STAT1 pathway has a role during in vivo Th1 responses and may be particularly important for IFN-γ production in responses that are less robust than those elicited by *T. gondii*.

STAT2. STAT2 forms a heterodimer with STAT1 in response to type I IFNs. *Stat2*-deficient mice have increased susceptibility to viral infection owing to defective type I interferon responses (104). Although type I IFNs have been reported to influence CD4 T cell differentiation, such function is largely attributed to the activation of a STAT1 homodimer, and possibly also of STAT4, by type I IFNs.

STAT3. STAT3 is activated by IL-6, IL-21, and IL-23, cytokines that are involved in Th17 cell differentiation, amplification, and maintenance (21–24, 41, 42). Deletion of *Stat3* in mice and DN STAT3 mutations in humans result in the loss of IL-17-producing CD4 T cells (22, 23, 105–109). STAT3 binds to *Il17* (110) and *Il21* (111) and is responsible for the induction of RORγt and the IL-23R (22, 23, 108). In parallel, STAT3 activation by IL-6 is responsible for Foxp3 downregulation in both differentiating and differentiated Tregs (24, 108, 112, 113), accounting for the critical role of IL-6 in determining the balance between Th17 and iTreg induction. In the absence of STAT3, Foxp3 is upregulated when cells are cultured under Th17 conditions (108). Curiously, IL-10 and IL-27, which are negatively involved in Th17 differentiation, also activate STAT3. IL-6, -21, or -23, through the activation of STAT3, together with IL-1, an NF-κB activator, induce TCR-independent, cyclosporine A–independent IL-17A production (46).

STAT4. STAT4, activated mainly by IL-12, is important for Th1 responses in vitro (114, 115) and in vivo in response to *T. gondii* infection (116). STAT4 expression is higher in Th1 than in Th2 cells (117). STAT4 expression is likely to be regulated positively by IFN-γ (118) and negatively by IL-4 and GATA3 (117, 118). Activated STAT4 can directly induce IFN-γ production and expression of IL-12Rβ2 and T-bet during Th1 differentiation (54, 117). IL-12, by activating STAT4, together with IL-18, an NF-κB activator, induces TCR-independent IFN-γ production (48, 49). STAT4 also plays an important role in IL-12-mediated activation of NK cells (114, 115).

STAT5. STAT5a and STAT5b, the two isoforms of STAT5, are critical for the signaling of many cytokines that utilize the common γ chain as a subunit of their receptors (119). Deletion of both STAT5a and STAT5b affects many aspects of cellular responses, including cell proliferation (120). Low levels of STAT5 activation are sufficient for cell proliferation and survival; however, strong STAT5 signaling is required for Th2 differentiation (121, 122). Thus, even in the presence of STAT5b activation, STAT5a single knockout cells displayed profound defects in Th2 cell differentiation both in vitro and in vivo (121–124). STAT5 directly binds to the DNase I hypersensitive sites (HS) II and HSIII in the second intron of the *Il4* locus in Th2 but not in Th1 cells (122). Such binding may be critical for IL-2-mediated induction and maintenance of accessibility at the HSII site of the *Il4* locus. In addition, STAT5a-deficient cells are hyperresponsive to IL-12, which leads to better Th1 differentiation (125).

STAT5 activation by IL-2 is also critical for Treg development (126–128). STAT5 may contribute to Foxp3 induction by binding to its promoter (127, 129). STAT5 activation also regulates the activity of the *Bcl6* promoter in B cells (97); in view of the expression of Bcl-6 in Tfh cells, this regulation raises the possibility that such an effect may be important in Tfh cell differentiation. On the other hand, STAT5 suppresses Th17 cell differentiation (107) but is required for the expansion of differentiated Th17 cells (130). It has been reported recently that STAT5 serves as a pioneer factor in regulating the accessibility of the *Ifng* locus and thus is also involved in Th1 differentiation (131). Therefore, a low level of STAT5 activation is required for cell proliferation and survival, possibly also for Th1 differentiation and Th17 cell expansion. However, enhanced STAT5 activation suppresses Th1 and Th17 differentiation while Th2 and Treg differentiation is promoted, which correlates with higher expression levels of CD25 in Th2 and Treg cells. The quantitative regulation of STAT5 signaling that results in qualitative differences in Th cell differentiation may be explained by the differential affinity of STAT5 binding to the different gene targets in distinct cell types.

STAT6. STAT6 is the major signal transducer in IL-4-mediated Th2 differentiation and expansion (132–134). In vitro, STAT6 activation is necessary and sufficient for inducing high expression levels of the Th2 master regulator gene, GATA3 (135, 136). STAT6 does not regulate IL-4 transcription directly, but it may regulate the activity of the *Il4/Il13* locus control region (137). Although STAT6 appears indispensable for Th2 differentiation in vitro, one can induce STAT6-independent Th2 cell differentiation in vivo. Despite their STAT6 independence, these responses are still GATA3-dependent (138–142). However, some in vivo Th2 responses such as those elicited by *Trichuris muris* (143), as well as the accumulation of Th2 cells in lung tissue in response to *Nippostrongylus brasiliensis* infection, depend on the IL-4/STAT6 pathway (141). STAT6 may also be important for the amplification of Th2 responses at later stages and/or for the generation of Th2 memory cells in vivo (139).

Other Factors Involved in Fine-Tuning Th Differentiation

Runx family members. Runx3, a transcriptional repressor important for silencing CD4 during CD8 T cell development, is highly expressed in both CD8 and Th1 CD4 T cells (144, 145). In CD8 T cells, Runx3 appears to be responsible for the induction of Eomes, granzyme B, and perforin and for optimal expression of IFN-γ at later stages of responses (70), although such Runx3 functions need to be further verified in *Runx3* conditional knockout mice, given that *Runx3* germline knockout mice show aberrant CD8 development. Our unpublished data also indicate that enforced expression of Runx3 in Th2 cells induces the capacity to produce IFN-γ independent of T-bet and that such IFN-γ induction is partly due to upregulation of Eomes.

Runx3-deficient cells produce less IFN-γ than wild-type Th1 cells (70, 145). Runx3 also represses IL-4 transcription through its binding to the DNase I HSIV region of the *Il4* gene (144).

The Runx family includes Runx1, Runx2, and Runx3; only Runx1 and Runx3 are expressed in T cells. Runx1 is required for CD4 T cell development (146) and may be responsible for IL-2 production by naive CD4 T cells (147). In Tregs, Runx1 interacts with Foxp3, an interaction that is required for the function of Tregs (147) and through which Foxp3 suppresses IL-2 production. Recently, Runx1 has been shown to be critical for maintaining Foxp3 expression and suppressive function of Tregs (148, 149). Naive CD4 T cells from mice conditionally lacking CBFβ, the cofactor for Runx protein, express reduced Foxp3 when stimulated by TGF-β, possibly because the induction of Foxp3 expression requires Runx binding to the *Foxp3* promoter (150, 151). Runx1 also interacts with RORγt and induces optimal RORγt expression and IL-17 production in Th17 cells (152).

Since Runx1 can interact with Foxp3 and RORγt and Runx3 can interact with T-bet and GATA3 (J. Zhu, R. Yagi, W.E. Paul, unpublished data), Runx family members should be considered as important fine-tuners of the master regulator genes. That Runx3 negatively regulates Runx1 expression adds complexity to this transcriptional regulatory network (70).

IFN regulatory factor family members. IRF4 expression is important for Th2 cell differentiation (153, 154). IRF4-deficient Th2 cells produce diminished amounts of IL-4, but this defect can be rescued by overexpression of GATA3, suggesting that IRF4 is involved in upregulating GATA3 (153). In addition, IRF4 may be important in regulating IL-4 expression by collaborating with NFATc2 and c-Maf (154). IRF4 is also indispensable for Th17 differentiation (155). *Irf4*$^{-/-}$ T cells fail to produce IL-17, and *Irf4*$^{-/-}$ mice are resistant to experimental autoimmune encephalomyelitis induction. IRF4 appears to play a role in regulating RORγt expression but not Foxp3 expression. Mice with a conditional *Irf4* deletion in Tregs may develop Th2-like diseases, although the number of Foxp3^{+} cells in these mice appears to be normal (37). IRF4 seems to play an important role in regulating some Foxp3 functions through protein-protein interactions, but the detailed mechanisms for such regulation have not been determined.

IRF1 is an IFN-γ-inducible transcription factor. It was recently reported to regulate IL-12Rα expression in Th1 and Th17 cells. Deletion of *Irf1* resulted in decreased levels of IL-12Rα expression, leading to loss of the responsiveness of such cells to IL-12 (156). Although IL-12Rα is also a component of the receptor complex for IL-23, such decreased IL-12Rα expression did not affect the cells' responsiveness to IL-23. Thus, fine-tuning of IL-12Rα expression by IRF1 may regulate Th1 and Th17 differentiation and expansion in response to IL-12 and IL-23, respectively.

Gfi-1. Growth factor independent 1 (Gfi-1) is a transcriptional repressor. Its locus is the most frequent insertion site in Moloney murine leukemia virus (MoMLV)-induced lymphomas (157). Gfi-1 is involved in many aspects of immune cell functions, including homeostasis of hematopoietic stem cells and development of neutrophils, T cells, and mature DCs, as revealed by the phenotypes of *Gfi1* germline knockout mice (158). Loss of Gfi-1 also results in myeloid leukemias. TCR activation transiently induces Gfi-1, and IL-4 prolongs its expression (13). Gfi-1 selects GATA3^{hi} cells for growth by modulating both upstream and downstream IL-2 signaling events, suggesting that it mediates a selective function during Th2 cell differentiation (13, 159).

Gfi-1 also suppresses non-Th2 lineages. IFN-γ and IL-17 production are increased in *Gfi1* conditional knockout T cells (159, 160). In addition, loss of Gfi-1 results in increased numbers of CD103^{+} Tregs (160). Overexpression of Gfi-1 suppresses TGF-β-mediated functions, and TGF-β downregulates Gfi-1 expression, suggesting a reciprocal regulation between TGF-β signaling and Gfi-1 expression.

Ikaros family members. Ikaros is critical for the development of T and B lymphocytes and NK cells (161). The Ikaros family consists of five members, Ikaros, Helios, Aiolos, Eos, and Pegasus. Their functions require the formation of homo- or heterodimers. Recently, Ikaros was reported to be important for Th2 cell differentiation (162). In the absence of Ikaros, IFN-γ and T-bet are dramatically upregulated even under Th2 polarizing conditions, suggesting that Ikaros plays an important role in suppressing Th1 differentiation. Eos has been reported to play an important role in regulating the repressive activity of Foxp3 in Tregs through interacting with Foxp3 (163). Another family member, Helios, is among the very few genes that are highly expressed in nTregs but not in iTregs, but its function in nTregs is unknown (164).

c-Maf. c-Maf, selectively upregulated in Th2 cells, enhances production of IL-4 but not of other Th2 cytokines (165). c-Maf was also reported to induce CD25 (IL-2Rα) expression (166). Recently, c-Maf has been found to be highly expressed in Tfh cells that are capable of producing IL-17, and IL-17-producing Tfh cells are less frequent in *Maf* knockout mice (167). However, the function of c-Maf in Tfh cells in general has not been established.

Other transcription factors. Many other transcription factors are involved in the differentiation of at least one Th lineage. Selected examples follow: Hlx, a transcription factor induced by T-bet, enhances T-bet-mediated IFN-γ production (66). Ets-1, a cofactor for T-bet for Th1 differentiation, plays a negative role in Th17 cell differentiation (168, 169). JunB, whose expression is selectively upregulated in Th2 cells, collaborates with c-Maf in inducing IL-4 production through binding to the *Il4* promoter (170). Expression of Blimp-1, an important transcription factor for long-lived plasma cells, is induced in Th2 cells where it suppresses IFN-γ and IL-2 production (171–173). Blimp-1 has recently been reported to oppose the expression of Bcl-6 and thus to inhibit Tfh differentiation (101). TIEG1, a TGF-β inducible transcription factor, together with Itch, an E3 ubiquitin ligase, play important roles in Foxp3 induction (174). The aryl hydrocarbon receptor (AhR), induced in Th17 cells independent of RORγt, plays a critical role in the production of Th17 cytokines, particularly IL-22 (175). Cell culture medium IMDM (Iscove's Modified Dulbecco's Medium), which contains higher levels of AhR ligands than RPMI medium 1640, supports better Th17 differentiation (176). BATF (basic leucine zipper transcription factor, ATF-like), an AP-1 family transcription factor, plays a critical role in Th17 but not in Th1 and Th2 cell differentiation (177). BATF is required for RORγt induction, but overexpression of RORγt in *Batf*$^{-/-}$ T cells fails to completely restore IL-17 production. Indeed, BATF binds to the *Il17* gene directly. Dec2 is able to induce GATA3 expression, and Dec2 deficiency leads to impaired Th2 responses both in vitro and in vivo (178). GATA3 also regulates Dec2 expression, suggesting that Dec2 and GATA3 form a positive regulatory feedback loop during Th2 differentiation. In addition, Dec2 upregulates IL-2Rα expression, which may be partially responsible for Dec2-mediated enhancement of Th2 responses (179).

COLLABORATION BETWEEN TRANSCRIPTION FACTORS

GATA3 and STAT5

Both IL-4 and IL-2 are required for Th2 differentiation in vitro (3, 121). IL-4 can be either provided exogenously or produced by the cultured T cells. In either case, IL-4-mediated STAT6 activation enhances GATA3 expression (135, 136). GATA3 binds to regions of the *Il4/Il13* locus, including DNase I HSV_A (62), whereas STAT5 binds to HSII of the *Il4* gene (121, 122). Our unpublished data show that GATA3 also binds to HSII. However, GATA3 alone is not sufficient to induce IL-4 production in the absence of STAT5 activation (121), and a constitutively active form of STAT5a loses its ability to induce IL-4 when basal GATA3 expression is eliminated by gene deletion (57). Thus, both GATA3 and STAT5 are required for IL-4 production, and a higher degree of STAT5 activation can lower the GATA3 level required to induce IL-4.

In differentiated Th2 cells, STAT5 activation is critical to maintain the expression of GATA3 (46). We also found that in Th2 cells GATA3 binds to the *Cd25* locus and maintains CD25 expression (J. Zhu and W.E. Paul, unpublished observation). In addition, a recent report showed that STAT5 regulates IL-4Rα expression, especially during the initiation of Th2 differentiation (180). These data indicate a positive crosstalk between the IL-2/STAT5 and the IL-4/STAT6/GATA3 pathways. Thus, the collaboration of STAT5 and GATA3 at different regulatory levels accounts for full Th2 differentiation.

Besides the collaborative effect between GATA3 and STAT5, other factors, including NFAT, c-Maf, IRF4, and JunB, are also involved in IL-4 production through formation of a transcriptional complex in the promoter region of *Il4* gene, as mentioned above.

T-bet and STAT4

Similar to the collaborative effects between GATA3 and STAT5, T-bet and STAT4 also synergize in the induction of many Th1-specific genes, including IFN-γ, IL-18R1, IL-12Rβ2, and Hlx, although the expression of some Th1 molecules, like CXCR3, is T-bet-dependent but STAT4-independent (181). T-bet expression is partially reduced in *Stat4*$^{-/-}$ Th1 cells, which cannot be rescued by the addition of exogenous IFN-γ. However, enforced expression of T-bet in *Tbx21/Stat4* double knockout failed to restore the defects in the induction of Th1 genes. Both STAT4 and T-bet bind to the IFN-γ promoter; optimal binding of one factor requires the presence of the other. Consistent with this observation, both STAT4 and T-bet are required for the chromatin remodeling at the IFN-γ locus. As mentioned above, Runx3, Hlx, and Ets-1 are also cofactors of T-bet for IFN-γ induction.

RORγt and STAT3

Both RORγt and STAT3 are critical for Th17 cell differentiation (22, 90). Both directly bind to the *Il17a/Il17f* locus (91, 110, 152). The collaborative effect of these two molecules is indicated by the findings that deletion of either results in almost complete loss of IL-17 production and that enforced expression of RORγt and STAT3C, an active form of STAT3, synergistically induces IL-17 production. STAT3 activation or TGF-β signaling alone induces RORγt expression; however, induction is further enhanced when both are present (22). Even in the absence of TGF-β signaling, STAT3 activation fully induces the expression of two Th17-related molecules, IL-21 and IL-23R (22, 23). IL-21 expression induced by the STAT3 pathway is independent of RORγt, but optimal IL-23R expression requires RORγt. Although induction of RORγt in response to STAT3 activation alone is much lower in the absence than in the presence of TGF-β signaling (22), it is sufficient for IL-23R expression. Importantly, TGF-β-mediated induction of Foxp3, a negative regulator of RORγt function, is suppressed by the IL-6/STAT3 pathway (24, 182), providing another mechanism for the collaboration between STAT3 and RORγt.

CROSS-REGULATION AMONG TRANSCRIPTION FACTORS DURING Th DIFFERENTIATION

Transcriptional Repression of Transcription Factors and Cytokines

During Th cell differentiation toward one lineage, the other lineage fates are usually suppressed. There are several mechanisms for such inhibition. An important cross-regulation during Th differentiation is through repression of transcription factors that are important for lineage determination. For example, GATA3 downregulates expression of STAT4, which is the important factor for mediating IL-12 signaling and Th1 differentiation (117). A constitutively active form of STAT5 inhibits T-bet expression while it also promotes Th2 differentiation (122). On the other hand, GATA3 expression is suppressed by T-bet during Th1 differentiation (54).

The transcription factors expressed in one lineage also suppress the production of cytokines of other lineages. In Tregs, Foxp3 inhibits IL-2 production, possibly by binding NFAT (183) and Runx1 (147). In Th1 cells, Runx3 inhibits IL-4 production through binding the *Il4* locus at the HSIV region (144). Gfi-1, which is a regulator for Th2 cell growth, suppresses both IFN-γ (58) and IL-17 production (160). A Th17-specific factor(s) that suppresses Th1 or Th2 cytokines has not been identified.

Cross-Regulation between Transcription Factors through Protein-Protein Interaction

Another interesting mechanism of cross-regulation is suppressive protein-protein interaction between master regulators. Itk-mediated phosphorylation of T-bet at position Y525 induces its interaction with GATA3 and the repression of GATA3 function (184). The Y525F T-bet mutant fails to suppress GATA3-mediated IL-4, IL-5, and IL-13 production while maintaining its ability to suppress IL-2 and to induce IFN-γ. GATA3 may also suppress T-bet function through such interaction.

Our unpublished data indicate that Runx3 induces IFN-γ in the absence of T-bet by upregulating Eomes expression. GATA3 blocks this Runx3-Eomes-IFN-γ pathway presumably through interaction with Runx3. Therefore, when *Gata3* is deleted from Th2 cells, the Runx3-Eomes pathway becomes active and IFN-γ is produced even when IL-12 and IFN-γ are neutralized.

TGF-β is required to differentiate both Th17 and Treg cells. At an intermediate stage of Th17 or Treg differentiation, both RORγt and Foxp3 are induced. Foxp3 interacts with RORγt and, by blocking its function, inhibits IL-17 production (182). A low concentration of TGF-β in combination with a STAT3 activator (IL-6, IL-21, or IL-23) is sufficient to induce RORγt expression; however, Foxp3 induction requires high concentrations of TGF-β. Thus, the relative expression of RORγt and Foxp3, controlled by the amount of TGF-β and of the STAT3-activating proinflammatory cytokines, determines whether the Th17 or Treg fate is adopted.

The mutual exclusivity among master transcription factors, at the transcriptional level, appears to be the major mechanism for cross-regulation during Th cell differentiation. However, suppressive protein-protein interactions play an important role in background "cleanup" during the polarization process by neutralizing the function of any aberrantly expressed transcription factors, most of whose expression may be driven to some extent by TCR activation. Such protein-protein interactions may also be important in maintaining the flexibility of the cells when a final fate decision has not yet been made, such as at early stages of Th differentiation.

TRANSCRIPTION FACTORS EXPRESSED AT LOW LEVELS CAN BE FUNCTIONALLY IMPORTANT

High levels of master regulator gene expression are usually correlated with the phenotype of the appropriate Th lineage. However, some effector functions may not require these factors to be highly expressed. Indeed, the functionality of the factor may depend on the cell context or, more precisely, on the relative amounts of other critical transcription factors. Forced expression of GATA3 in Th2 cells does not generally further enhance Th2 cytokine production; it appears that the endogenous level of GATA3 is already capable of inducing a maximum response. On the other hand, a small amount of GATA3, equivalent to or lower than that expressed in Th1 cells, can be sufficient for inducing IL-4 production given strong STAT5 activation (57). Similarly, although T-bet expression is lower in *Stat1*$^{-/-}$ CD4 T cells than that in wild-type CD4 T cells in response to *T. gondii* infection, such cells produced normal levels of IFN-γ (103). Furthermore, low expression of T-bet in a subset of Tregs is sufficient to induce these cells to produce CXCR3 but not IFN-γ (36). RORγt is modestly induced by IL-6 or IL-21 in the absence of TGF-β signaling, but this level of RORγt expression, although not sufficient to induce IL-17 production, can induce IL-23R expression (22). Therefore, despite the absolute requirement for master regulators, their expression level may not be correlated with the degree of a response. Caution is needed when interpreting data obtained from knockout cells, especially when a factor is already expressed at measurable levels before its upregulation occurs. Loss of function proves the importance of a regulator but does not necessarily establish the importance of the induction. Under such circumstances, a knockdown experiment may be more appropriate.

Taking this argument further, some in vivo–generated Th2 cells express lower levels of GATA3 than do in vitro–differentiated Th2 cells (J. Zhu and W.E. Paul, unpublished data), although GATA3 is absolutely required for in vivo Th2 cell differentiation (57). In addition, IL-4 strongly induces GATA3 in vitro and is needed for in vitro Th2 responses but is not required for in vivo Th2 cell differentiation under several conditions. Although it is possible that IL-4-independent upregulation of GATA3 expression is important in inducing in vivo Th2 differentiation, it is equally possible that another pathway such as STAT5 activation, but not the upregulation of GATA3, is the main driving force in inducing Th2 cell differentiation in some in vivo models. That is, the level of GATA3 found in any activated CD4 T cells may be sufficient for Th2 differentiation provided that high levels of STAT5 activation can be achieved and thus no preferential induction of GATA3 is required.

POSITIVE FEEDBACK DURING Th CELL DIFFERENTIATION

Each Th lineage can produce a cytokine with the potential to play a positive feedback role in promoting differentiation, i.e., IFN-γ for Th1, IL-4 for Th2, IL-21 for Th17, and TGF-β for Tregs (185). Furthermore, the master regulators and STAT proteins not only directly regulate lineage-specific cytokine production and induce important positive feedback at differentiation levels (**Figure 3**), but also regulate genes that are associated either with selective growth of this lineage or with repression of alternative lineage fates. In Th1 cells, T-bet and STAT4 are involved in IFN-γ production (positive feedback), IL-12Rβ2 upregulation (selective growth), and GATA3 downregulation (alternative fate repression). In Th2 cells, GATA3 and STAT5 induce IL-4 production (positive feedback) and CD25 (IL-2Rα) upregulation (both positive feedback and selective growth), and suppress IFN-γ and IL-17 expression (alternative fate repression). Transcription factors that are highly expressed in Th2 cells, including c-Maf and Gfi-1, are also involved in modulating IL-2/STAT5 signaling, which is critical for Th2 cell expansion. In Th17 cells, STAT3 is responsible for the upregulation of IL-21 and IL-23R, so that IL-21 and IL-23 can promote the expansion and terminal differentiation of Th17 cells at later stages (positive feedback and selective growth). Therefore, fully polarized Th cells are generated through lineage commitment, selective growth of committed cells, and active suppression of alternative lineage fates.

The negative feedback of Th cell differentiation is less well studied. Each lineage can produce IL-10 under certain circumstances, which may serve as an example of negative feedback (186).

SIGNALING PATHWAYS CONTROL THE REGULATION OF TRANSCRIPTION FACTORS AND CYTOKINES

As indicated above, naive CD4 T cells stimulated by their cognate antigen can, when

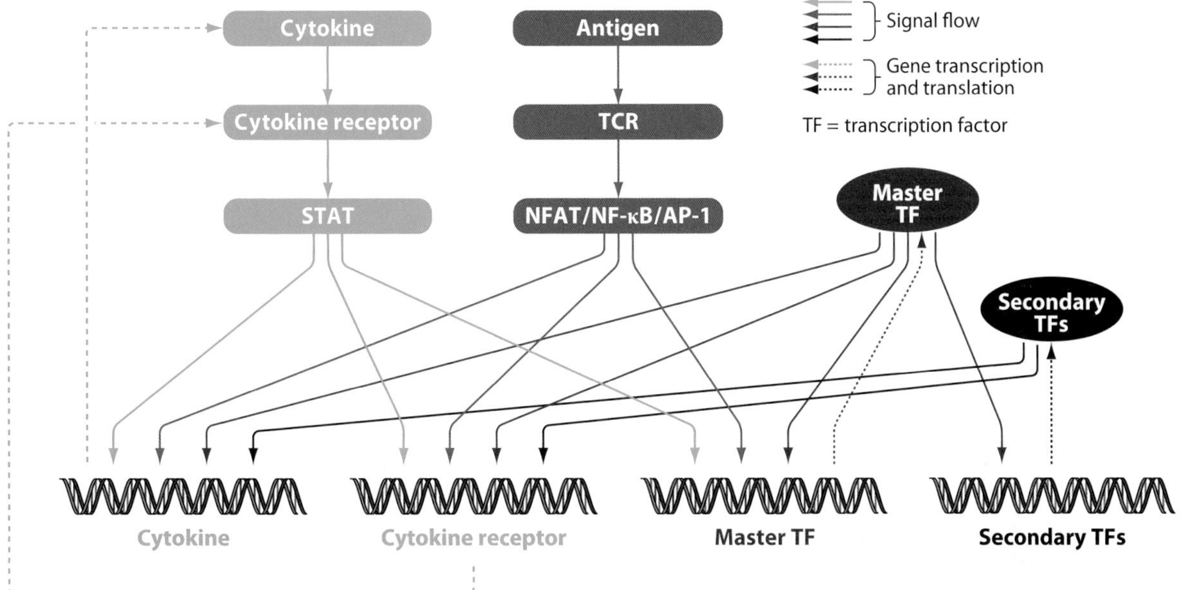

Figure 3

Positive regulatory circuits for Th cell differentiation. Both TCR- and cytokine-mediated signaling, through activation of NFAT/NFκB/AP-1 and STAT proteins, respectively, are critical for early cytokine production and upregulation of a master transcription factor. The master transcription factor induces secondary transcription factors, which collaborate with the master transcription factor to enhance the expression of cytokine and cytokine receptors. In some cases, the master transcription factor also promotes its own expression. Elevated cytokine production and cytokine receptor expression provide powerful positive feedback loops for promoting Th cell fate determination as well as for selective expansion of committed Th cells.

conditions are correct, rapidly express master transcriptional regulators and cytokines important for the differentiation of particular Th phenotypes. This process has been studied intensively for Th2 cells, but the paradigm applies to all three of the effector Th lineages and probably for iTregs and even for Tfh cells.

For Th2 cells, TCR engagement, under the appropriate conditions (discussed in the next section), results in GATA3 expression and IL-2 production/STAT5 activation. Jointly, these result in early IL-4 production, which is IL-4-independent but TCR dependent. This early IL-4 (produced in the induction phase of Th2 polarization) then acts through the IL-4 receptor and STAT6 to further enhance GATA3 expression and, together with continued STAT5 phosphorylation in response to endogenous IL-2 or possibly other STAT5 activators such as IL-7 or TSLP, leads to marked enhancement of IL-4 production and completion of the Th2 polarization process. This latter phase can be thought of as the polarization phase.

Analysis of how various signaling pathways impinge on Th differentiation is best understood in the context of this two-phase process and in terms of the need for early induction of a master transcription factor and early activation of a critical STAT. As noted above, the pairs are as follows: Th2, GATA3/STAT5; Th1, T-bet/STAT4; Th17, RORγt/STAT3; iTregs, Foxp3/STAT5. Recent studies suggest that Tfh cells may also fit the paradigm, with the factors being Bcl6/STAT3. In many instances, the STAT involved also plays a role in the induction of the master transcriptional regulator.

Pathways Downstream of TCR Signaling

The strength of TCR signaling during in vitro differentiation regulates Th1/Th2 polarization. In general, weak signaling favors Th2 differentiation and stronger signaling leads to Th1 differentiation (187). Priming of TCR-transgenic T cells, specific for moth cytochrome *c* (MCC), with an altered peptide ligand (K99R), preferentially induces Th2 differentiation (188). Jorritsma et al. (189) showed that K99R stimulates weak and transient activation of extracellular signal-regulated kinase (ERK), compared with the "cognate" MCC peptide. The reduced ERK activation by K99R is associated with early IL-4 production by naive CD4 T cells and with a distinct pattern of DNA-binding activity of AP-1 to the *Il4* promoter, dominated by a JunB homodimer (189). This finding is consistent with a previous report showing that JunB, when directly bound to the *Il4* promoter, synergizes with c-Maf to activate an *Il4* luciferase reporter gene (170).

When naive TCR-transgenic CD4 T cells are stimulated with low concentrations of cognate peptide, ERK activation is weak and transient (190). The "low concentration–stimulated" T cells rapidly produce GATA3 and activate STAT5 in response to endogenously produced IL-2. GATA3 and STAT5 synergize to result in TCR-dependent, IL-4-independent early IL-4 transcription (induction). These T cells go on to complete their differentiation into Th2 cells by responding to the endogenously produced IL-4 and continued STAT5 activation (polarization) (190). By contrast, stimulating TCR-transgenic naive CD4 T cells with high concentrations of cognate peptide results in failure of Th2 differentiation. TCR-dependent IL-4-independent early GATA3 expression is suppressed and IL-2R-mediated STAT5 activation is transiently blocked, resulting in failure of early IL-4 production. Under these stimulation conditions, strong and prolonged ERK activation is observed. Blockade of the ERK pathway with an inhibitor of MAPK/ERK kinase (MEK) allows T cells stimulated with high peptide concentrations to express early GATA3 and to respond to endogenously produced IL-2, leading to the restoration of early IL-4 production, completion of the induction phase, and subsequent completion of the Th2 polarization process. These results imply that strong ERK activation prevents early GATA3 production and "desensitizes" the IL-2 receptor, thus blocking the Th2 induction phase.

However, cells expressing a DN Lck transgene or a DN H-Ras transgene under the control of the *Lck*-proximal promoter show diminished in vitro Th2 differentiation. This result has been interpreted by the authors to indicate that TCR-mediated Ras/ERK activation is required for Th2 differentiation, possibly by enhancing tyrosine phosphorylation of STAT6 in response to IL-4 (191) and/or preventing ubiquitin/proteasome-mediated degradation of GATA3 in developing Th2 cells by inhibiting the activity of Mdm2, an E3 ubiquitin ligase for GATA3 (192).

The difference in these views of the role of ERK function in Th2 differentiation needs to be considered in terms of the two-phase model of T cell polarization. Indeed, naive CD4 T cells from the mice expressing DN Lck actually produce significantly more IL-4 than do those from the littermate control mice during the early induction phase (193), implying that the Lck/Ras/ERK cascade inhibits early IL-4 production and the Th2 induction phase. However, IL-2 production by naive CD4 T cells from mice expressing DN Lck is significantly decreased compared with that by control cells (193). Diminished IL-2 production could account for diminished Th2 differentiation since STAT5 activation is essential for both the induction and polarization phase of Th2 differentiation, and the degree of activation may have fallen below the threshold level during the polarization phase. Indeed, this suggestion is consistent with our data showing that blockade of the ERK pathway leads to a substantial diminution in IL-2 production by CD4 T cells stimulated with low peptide concentrations (190) and that, in the presence of a MEK inhibitor, low-peptide-concentration Th2 differentiation requires exogenous IL-2.

TCR-Proximal Src Family Tyrosine Kinases: Lck and Fyn

Lck and Fyn belong to the Src family of tyrosine kinases and are involved in optimal T cell activation. *Lck*$^{-/-}$ mice exhibit a prominent but incomplete developmental arrest at the transition from the DN to the DP stage during thymocyte development. The few peripheral T cells that do develop have markedly impaired responses to TCR stimulation (194). By contrast, *Fyn*$^{-/-}$ mice show virtually no abnormality in thymocyte development and in the compartment of peripheral T cells (195, 196). Naive CD4 T cells from *Fyn*$^{-/-}$ mice on a C57BL/6 background display enhanced Th2 polarization upon TCR/CD28 stimulation under neutral conditions (197). Similarly, *Fyn*$^{-/-}$ DO11.10 TCR-transgenic CD4 T cells, on a BALB/c background, are more ready to differentiate into IL-4-producing cells than are wild-type DO11.10 TCR-transgenic cells when activated by cognate peptide in vitro (198). Our unpublished data suggest that activated *Fyn*$^{-/-}$ CD4 T cells have increased STAT6 phosphorylation in response to limited amounts of IL-4, implying that Fyn negatively regulates Th2 differentiation by attenuating IL-4R signaling and thus diminishes the polarization phase of Th2 differentiation. The effects of Fyn on IL-4-mediated STAT6 phosphorylation may be explained by a functional association between Fyn and PTP1B phosphatase (199, 200), which could result in desensitization of activated CD4 T cells to IL-4 (201).

Tec Family Kinases: Itk and Rlk

T cells express three different Tec family kinases, Itk, Rlk (also known as Txk), and Tec. The role of Itk during T cell activation and Th1/Th2 differentiation is well established. Following TCR ligation, Itk is recruited to LAT/SLP-76/PLC-γ1 complex and activates PLC-γ1, which induces hydrolysis of PIP_3 to IP_3 and DAG, resulting in Ca^{2+} release from the endoplasmic reticulum and PKC activation, respectively (202). *Itk*$^{-/-}$ mice exhibit diminished in vivo Th2 responses to *Leishmania major*, and CD4 T cells from these mice show impaired Th2 differentiation in vitro due to a deficit in the Ca^{2+}/NFATc1 pathway (203), which presumably results in a decrease in early IL-2 and/or IL-4 production. Berg and colleagues (204) reported that naive *Itk*$^{-/-}$ TCR-transgenic CD4 T cells have aberrant expression of T-bet and polarize toward the Th1 phenotype in response to a weak TCR signal that would normally have induced Th2 differentiation. Recently, Schwartzberg and colleagues (205) found that a defect in the Ca^{2+}/NFAT pathway in *Itk*$^{-/-}$ CD4 T cells results in diminished IL-17A but not IL-17F production when naive *Itk*$^{-/-}$ CD4 T cells are stimulated under Th17-polarizing conditions. Rlk has been reported to be involved in Th1 responses (206–208).

Itk$^{-/-}$*Rlk*$^{-/-}$ mice show enhanced Th2 responses to *Schistosoma mansoni* eggs in vivo, although *Itk*$^{-/-}$ mice have a defect in Th2 responses to the same organism, and *Rlk*$^{-/-}$ mice behave just as wild-type mice do (209). Consistent with these data, our unpublished data indicate that naive CD4 T cells from *Itk*$^{-/-}$*Rlk*$^{-/-}$ TCR transgenic mice undergo Th2 differentiation in response to high concentrations of cognate peptide that would have caused Th1 polarization in wild-type cells. The *Itk*$^{-/-}$*Rlk*$^{-/-}$ cells show a marked diminution in ERK activation at high peptide concentration, presumably allowing them to express early GATA3 and to respond to endogenously produced IL-2, implying the involvement of Itk and Rlk in TCR-mediated signal strength and thus in inhibition of the induction phase of Th2 differentiation in response to high peptide concentrations.

NF-κB Pathway

Nfkb1$^{-/-}$ CD4 T cells have been reported to undergo diminished Th2 differentiation in vitro and in vivo due to impaired GATA3 expression in the nucleus (210). Because NF-κB1 has no transactivation domain, it must form a complex with other protein(s) to activate NF-κB1-dependent gene expression. Boothby and colleagues (211) identified Bcl-3, which belongs to the IκB family and possesses a transactivation domain, as the partner of NF-κB1 for binding to the κB-like consensus sequence located at 310 to 301 bp upstream of the *Gata3* transcriptional initiation site, implying the potential importance of NF-κB1 and Bcl-3 in regulating TCR-driven GATA3 expression (212). However, because the NF-κB pathway also plays a critical role in the expression of IL-2 and CD25 (213), entities essential for Th2 differentiation, a careful study is needed to determine the relative importance of NF-κB-mediated GATA3 upregulation versus enhanced STAT5 phosphorylation during Th2 cell differentiation induced by this pathway.

Ca^{2+}/NFAT Pathway

The NFAT family consists of five members, of which four, NFAT1 (also known as NFATp, NFATc2), NFAT2 (NFATc, NFATc1), NFAT3 (NFATc4), and NFAT4 (NFATx, NFATc3), are regulated by calcium and the fifth member, NFAT5/TonEBP (tonicity-responsive enhancer-binding protein), by osmotic shock (214). T cells express NFAT1, NFAT2, and NFAT4. TCR ligation increases intracellular Ca^{2+} concentration. Ca^{2+} binds to calmodulin, which in turn triggers the activation of calcineurin. Activated calcineurin dephosphorylates NFAT proteins, which results in the translocation of NFAT to the nucleus and the subsequent induction of NFAT-dependent gene transcription (214).

NFAT proteins are indispensable for effector cytokine production upon TCR activation in already differentiated Th cells and also play important roles in regulating Th differentiation. Here, we focus on the functions of NFAT1, NFAT2, and NFAT4 during the differentiation of Th1/Th2 cells.

The role of NFAT1 in regulating Th1/Th2 differentiation has been the subject of controversy. Naive CD4 T cells from *Nfat1*$^{-/-}$ mice are biased toward Th2 differentiation owing to an increased production of IL-4 in response to anti-CD3 stimulation (215). They exhibit diminished IFN-γ production and subsequent Th1 differentiation through mechanisms independent of IL-4, GATA3, and c-Maf (216). However, NFAT1 binds to the *Il4* promoter in cooperation with IRF4 and c-Maf and enhances *Il4* transcription (154). NFAT1 also binds to the 3′ enhancer of the *Il4* gene (HSV_A), whose activity is Ca^{2+}-dependent (62). In agreement with these reports, the enhancement of Th2 differentiation by IL-6 is mediated through induction of NFAT1 and preferential accumulation of NFAT1 in the nucleus (217).

Nfat4$^{-/-}$ mice have impaired development of CD4 and CD8 SP thymocytes due to diminished Bcl-2 expression, which leads to increased apoptosis (218). Peripheral T cells from these mice exhibit an increased frequency of CD4 T cells of an activated/memory phenotype and become hyperactive in response to anti-CD3 stimulation, although skewing toward either Th1 or Th2 lineage is not observed (218). A combined deficiency in NFAT1 and NFAT4 results in greater Th2 responses with increased expression of Th2 cytokines and increased serum IgG1 and IgE levels (219, 220).

T cells from mice lacking NFAT2 in the lymphoid system generated by blastocyst complementation show impaired Th2 cytokine production, and the sera from these mice display reduced IgG1 and IgE levels (221, 222), implying that NFAT2 is required for Th2 differentiation. Consistent with these results, Th2 differentiation of naive MCC-specific TCR-transgenic CD4 T cells induced by K99R is accompanied by greater expression of nuclear NFAT2 than that of NFAT1 (223). Moreover, the inducible costimulator (ICOS) molecule substantially upregulates *Nfat2* gene transcription, leading to enhanced TCR/CD28-driven early IL-4 production and IL-4-dependent c-Maf expression (224).

Notch Signaling

The Notch pathway plays a crucial role in the development of the central nervous system and vascular system, among others. The mammalian Notch family has four members, Notch1, 2, 3, and 4. They are expressed on the cell surface following various posttranslational modifications, such as fucosylation by Pofut, glucosylation by Fringe, and S1 cleavage by a Furin-like protease. In mammals, there are five Notch ligands: Jagged (Jag) 1 and 2 and Delta-like (Dll) 1, 3, and 4. When a Notch interacts with a Notch ligand, the γ-secretase complex proteolytically releases the Notch intracellular domain (NICD). NICD translocates into the nucleus, where it displaces a corepressor complex from CBF1/Su(H)/Lag-1 (CSL, also known as RBP-J) and recruits a coactivator complex, leading to Notch-dependent gene transcription (225).

In the immune system, Notch is important in thymic T cell differentiation and in the development of marginal zone B cells (226). Notch also plays a role in regulating differentiation of naive CD4 T cells into distinct Th lineages. It was first reported that the Notch3-Dll1 interaction results in Th1 differentiation (227). Skokos & Nussenzweig (228) found that LPS induces MyD88-dependent Dll4 expression on $CD8\alpha^-$ DCs and that these DCs then direct Th1 differentiation in an IL-12-independent, Notch-dependent manner. Enforced expression of Dll1 and Dll4 on IL-12 $p40^{-/-}$ bone marrow–derived DCs has been reported to promote Th1 differentiation in a T-bet-dependent manner and to suppress Th2 development (229). Osborne and colleagues (230, 231) found that Notch1 ICD (N1ICD) can form a complex with NF-κB1 and c-Rel, allowing these NF-κB isoforms to be retained in the nucleus and, with the binding of the N1ICD/NF-κB complex to the IFN-γ promoter, to activate IFN-γ expression. Also reported is that the N1ICD/CSL complex binds to the T-bet promoter and that T-bet gene expression is directly regulated by the Notch1 pathway (232).

Notch has also been reported to be important in directing Th2 lineage commitment. CD4 T cells from mice with a conditional deletion of *Rbpj* (which specifies CSL) by CD4-Cre fail to undergo Th2 differentiation under nonpolarizing conditions (233, 234). Amsen et al. (233) reported that Jag1/Notch interaction directs Th2 differentiation, whereas Dll1/Notch interaction leads to Th1 polarization. They identified a CSL-binding site in the HSV site of the *Il4* gene and found that the binding of the N1ICD/CSL complex to this site upregulates IL-4 gene expression. The N1ICD/CSL complex is also reported to directly regulate *Gata3* gene transcription in a STAT6-independent manner through its binding to an alternative *Gata3* promoter located ~10 kb upstream of the conventional *Gata3* promoter (235). Mice that overexpress a DN form of Mastermind-like 1, one of the coactivator components required for Notch-dependent gene expression, also have a defect in Th2 responses (236, 237).

The Notch pathway also regulates naive CD4 T cell differentiation into iTreg and Th17 cells. Pretreatment of CD4 T cells with a γ-secretase inhibitor diminishes the frequency of $Foxp3^+$ cells induced by TGF-β1 and reduces the binding of the N1ICD/CSL complex to the *Foxp3* promoter (238). γ-secretase inhibitor treatment also blocks the recruitment of Smad proteins to the Foxp3 promoter (238), consistent with a previous finding that N1ICD associates with Smad3 to integrate Notch and TGF-β signals in myogenic cells (239). The interaction of Notch with Dll4 has recently been reported to cause a substantial increase in expression of Th17-related genes in CD4 T cells stimulated under Th17-polarizing conditions (240). Binding of CSL to the RORγt and IL-17A promoter regions is greatly enhanced by Notch ligation by Dll4 but abrogated by treatment with a γ-secretase inhibitor.

Collectively, the Notch pathway appears to govern differentiation of naive CD4 T cells into each of the Th lineages by directly controlling expression of lineage-specific transcription factors and cytokines. However, given the common machinery to activate the Notch pathway upon interaction with any Notch ligand, it is difficult to provide a reasonable explanation for how different Notch ligands instruct naive CD4 T cells to undergo such a diverse set of Th differentiation outcomes.

An alternative view is that the Notch pathway does not instruct Th1/Th2 fate determination but rather regulates the cellular expansion and cytokine production of differentiated cells (241). It was recently reported that neither Dll1- nor Jag1-expressing artificial antigen-presenting cells instruct naive DO11.10 CD4 T cells to differentiate into Th1 or Th2 cells under nonpolarizing conditions (241). Rather, conditional deletion of *Rbpj* or of presenilin, one component of the γ-secretase complex, in mature CD4 T cells does not affect T-bet or GATA3 expression at day 6 of priming under Th1- and Th2-polarizing conditions, respectively. However, loss of RBP-J or presenilin reduces the capacity of differentiated cells to secrete effector cytokines upon challenge, which is associated with decreased T cell proliferation during the priming period. These results are consistent with those in earlier reports suggesting that Notch signaling controls T cell activation. Osborne and colleagues (231) showed that inhibition of Notch activation dramatically decreases the division of both CD4 and CD8 T cells in response to TCR stimulation. γ-secretase inhibition causes a decrease in IL-2 production and CD25 expression, resulting in diminished proliferation of activated CD4 T cells (242). These data suggest an important costimulatory role of Notch signaling in controlling optimal T cell activation.

Our unpublished results indicate that Notch is required for Th2 differentiation induced by weak TCR signaling under nonpolarizing conditions. An analysis of the kinetics of early expression of genes essential for Th2 commitment reveals that IL-4-independent early induction of GATA3 and IL-4 by a weak TCR signal is intact in CD4 T cells deprived of Notch signal, but that IL-2 gene expression is greatly reduced. Consistent with our previous reports demonstrating the central role of IL-2 in Th2 differentiation (121, 190), Notch signal–deprived CD4 T cells fail to complete the polarization phase of Th2 differentiation because of diminished IL-4-dependent late *Gata3* and *Il4* gene expression resulting from limited STAT5 signaling. Exogenous IL-2 corrects the defect in late expression of Gata3 and *Il4* and thus fully restores Th2 differentiation in Notch signal–deprived CD4 T cells. These results imply that during Th2 differentiation, *Gata3* and *Il4* expression do not require direct binding of Notch to their genes, but rather that, in the absence of Notch signaling, it is the failure to produce sufficient amounts of IL-2 needed to sustain IL-4 production that is responsible for defective Th2 differentiation.

TRANSCRIPTION FACTOR–MEDIATED EPIGENETIC MODIFICATIONS

Th cell differentiation involves epigenetic modification and chromatin remodeling at specific loci (243–245). Epigenetic regulation includes modification of both DNA and histones, including DNA CpG methylation, histone methylation and acetylation, as well as DNase I HS induction. Epigenetic modification and chromatin remodeling play critical roles in determining specific gene expression induced by common transcription factors such as NFAT. Indeed, NFAT binding to the *Il4* promoter increases, whereas its binding to the *Ifng* promoter decreases during Th2 differentiation, possibly owing to opposite epigenetic modifications at these two loci during Th2 differentiation (246).

Rao and colleagues (247) identified Th cell lineage–specific HSs in the *Il4* and *Ifng* loci. A series of specific HSs in different Th cells identified at these loci have proven to be critical regulatory elements. Most of these HSs, located in the promoter and enhancer regions, exert positive function in cytokine production, but some, such as HSIV within the *Il4* gene, serve as silencers. Deletion of HSIV results in IL-4 production from Th1 cells both in vitro and in vivo (246). The appearance of the lineage-specific HSs may depend on the induction of master regulator genes. Indeed, many studies show that GATA3 and T-bet are directly responsible for chromatin remodeling at cytokine loci (12, 55, 248, 249). DNA CpG methylation plays an important role in gene silencing. Binding of a DNA methyltransferase, Dnmt-1, to the *Il4* locus is dramatically reduced during Th2 differentiation, and Dnmt-1 deficiency results in abnormal IL-4 expression in CD8 T cells without GATA3 upregulation (250). Deficiency in a methyl CpG-binding domain protein-2 (MBD2) also results in heritable, aberrant IL-4 production in Th1 cells without induction of GATA3 expression (251). GATA3 can block the binding of MBD2 to methyl CpG, suggesting an interesting mechanism through which GATA3 induces IL-4 production.

Recently, genome-wide histone modification patterns have been profiled in human and mouse T cells using next-generation high-throughput DNA sequencing (164, 252, 253). High-throughput DNA sequencing has also been used in genome-wide mapping of DNase I HS sites in Th cells (254).

There are at least 20 different histone modifications involving multiple positions in individual histones. Among these, histone H3 trimethylation at lysine position 4 (H3K4me3) is strongly associated with active chromatin, whereas H3K27me3 is associated with repressed chromatin. Genome-wide profiling of these two histone modifications in different Th lineages, including nTregs, iTregs, Th1, Th2, and Th17 cells, confirms the specificity of epigenetic modification at cytokine loci. For example, the *Il4/Il13* locus displays H3K4me3 in Th2 cells but H3K27me3 in Th1 cells (164). The molecule responsible for H3K4 methylation at the *Il4/Il13* locus during Th2 differentiation does not appear to be the histone H3K4 methyltransferase MLL, which is required for maintaining H3K4 modification at the *Gata3* and *Il4/Il13* loci in memory Th2 cells (255). EZH2, a H3K27 methyltransferase, binds to the *Il4/Il13* locus and may be responsible for suppressive H3K27me3 *Il4/Il13* modification in Th1 cells (256). The genome-wide profiling of H3K4 and H3K27 modifications also revealed the flexibility of master regulator expression in different lineages, as indicated by bivalent H3K4me3 and H3K27me3 modifications, particularly for the *Tbx21* locus (164). Indeed, T-bet can be induced in differentiated Th17 cells and even in nTregs. Strikingly, T-bet associates with RbBp5, a core component of H3K4 methyltransferase complexes, and JMJD3, a H3K27 demethylase (257). These data suggest that the flexibility of T-bet expression underlies the plasticity of Th cells to produce IFN-γ, possibly by reversing the repressive epigenetic modifications at the *Ifng* locus. Differential epigenetic modification at the *Foxp3* locus between nTregs and iTregs has been observed (164, 258).

Through transcription factor binding and epigenetic modification studies, many critical regulatory elements have been identified at each signature cytokine gene locus (**Figure 4**).

IFN-γ. Using a combination of computational analysis, epigenetic profiling of histone H3 modification, DNA CpG methylation and DNase I HS and functional assays, Wilson and colleagues (259) identified several important conserved noncoding sequence (CNS) sites within 100 kb of the *Ifng* gene, representing enhancers and insulators. IfngCNS–6, located 6 kb upstream of the *Ifng* transcription start site, has enhancer activity consistent with an earlier report (260). However, this site was not shown to be hypersensitive to DNase I in primary Th1 cells in this study (259). IfngCNS+29, located 29 kb downstream of the transcription start site, is also an enhancer; it displays DNase I hypersensitivity in Th1 but not in Th2 cells. IfngCNS–22 and IfngCNS–34 contain T-bet responsive elements. These two CNS sites show strong H3K4 methylation and CpG DNA demethylation in Th2 cells, both usually associated with active chromatin, which suggests that they may be the silencers of IFN-γ in Th2 cells or that they are critical elements in maintaining plasticity. However, deletion of CNS–22 from a BAC transgene reduces expression of the IFN-γ reporter in T cells and in NK cells (261). Finally, IfngCNS–54 and IfngCNS+46, serving as insulators, may be the boundaries of the IFN-γ transcription unit (259).

IL-4/IL-13. The *Il4/Il13* Th2 cytokine locus is the most extensively studied among those of

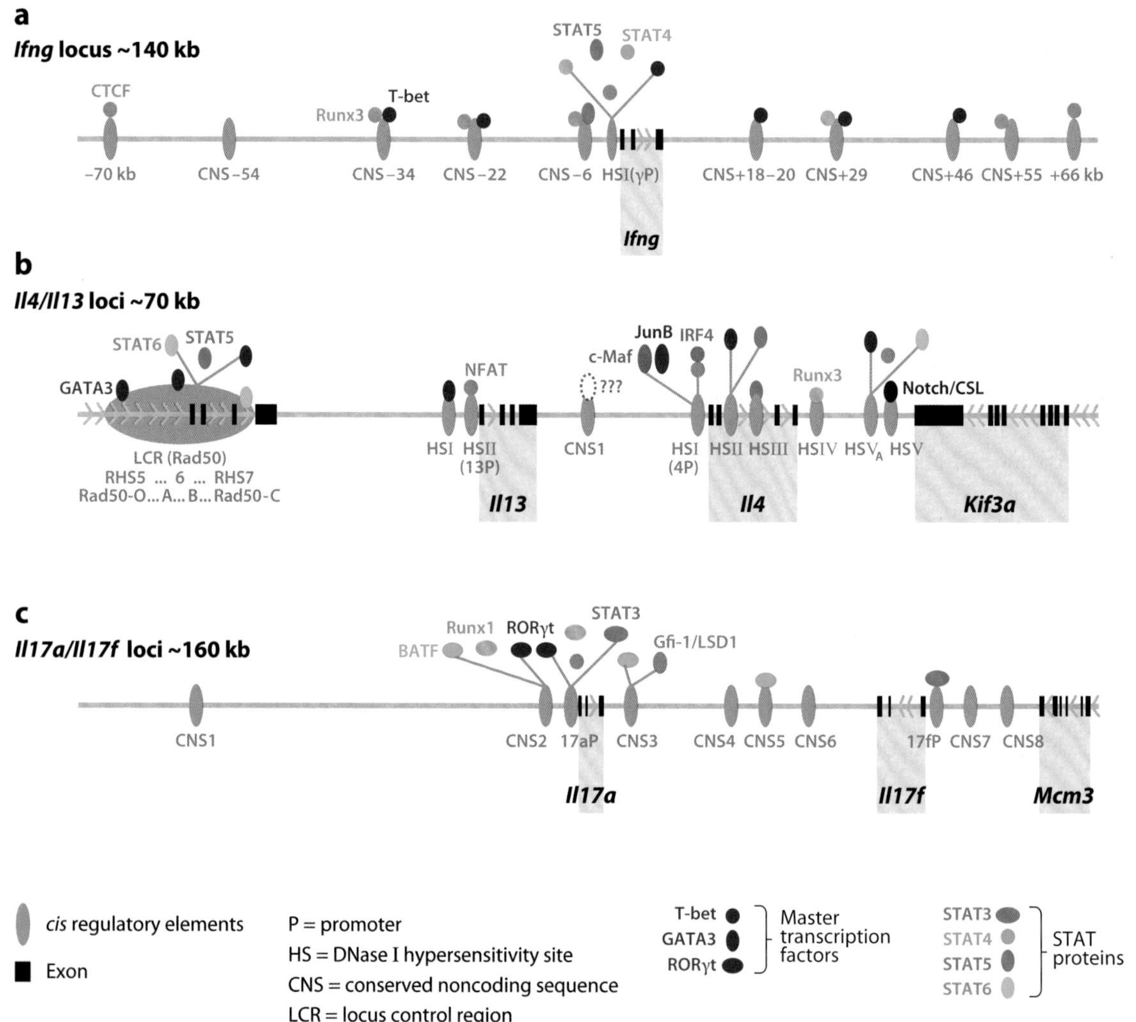

Figure 4

Important *cis*-regulatory elements at the *Ifng*, *Il4/Il13*, and *Il17a/Il17f* loci and binding of transcription factors to these sites. (*a*) Within ~140 kb flanking the *Ifng* gene, many conserved noncoding sequences and their epigenetic modifications have been studied (259). CNS–22 has been shown to be critical for IFN-γ production (261). Many transcription factors, including T-bet, STAT4, Runx3, STAT5, and CTCF, bind to different regions of the *Ifng* gene (65, 131, 144, 181, 243, 261, 262). Our unpublished data suggest that Runx3 also binds to other regulatory elements in addition to the *Ifng* promoter. (*b*) Within ~70 kb flanking the *Il4/Il13* genes, several important regulatory elements, including the locus control region (LCR), CNS1, *Il4* HSII, *Il4* HSIV, and *Il4* HSV_A/V, have been identified (62, 246, 263–267). Many transcription factors, including GATA3, c-Maf, STAT5, STAT6, Runx3, NFAT, and Notch/CSL, directly bind to different regions of the *Il4/Il13* locus (61, 62, 122, 137, 144, 165, 233). Our unpublished data obtained from anti-GATA3 ChIPseq showed six GATA3-binding sites across this ~70-kb region in Th2 cells, with three located in LCR at RHS4, 5, and 6 and the other three at ~1.6 kb upstream of *Il13*, *Il4* HSII, and *Il4* HSV_A. (*c*) Epigenetic modifications of the CNSs across ~160 kb of *Il17a/Il17f* have been reported (268). Some transcription factors critical for regulation of IL-17 expression, including RORγt, STAT3, BATF, Runx1, NFAT, and Gfi-1/LSD1, directly bind to the CNS or promoter regions of *Il17a/Il17f* (90, 110, 152, 160, 177, 205).

the Th "signature" cytokines. GATA3 has been reported to bind to the *Il13* but not to the *Il4* promoter. In addition to the promoters, there are several important regulatory elements within the locus including CNS1 (263), HSVa (264), HSII (265), the locus control region (LCR) (266, 267), and HSIV (246). All these elements except HSII have been shown by genetic deletion studies to be important in regulating IL-4 or IL-13 expression.

IL-17A/IL-17F. The *Il17a/Il17f* locus is less well studied, partly because of the relatively short time since Th17 cells were recognized. Nevertheless, STAT3-binding sites have been identified in the *Il17a* and *Il17f* promoters (110). Chen and colleagues (268) studied chromatin remodeling of *Il17a/Il17f* in Th17 cells and found eight CNS sites, all associated with histone 3 acetylation. These modifications are specific for Th17 cells at all but the CNS5 site, which is located in the intergenic region between *Il17a* and *Il17f*. In addition, functional ROR response elements have been identified within the CNS2 region (also called CNS-5), located ~5 kb upstream of *Il17a* and within 2 kb of the *Il17a* promoter region (91, 152). Both RORγt and Runx1 bind to these two regions and play important roles in regulating IL-17 production (152). We have recently identified a Gfi-1/LSD1 complex binding element located ~10 kb downstream of the *Il17a* transcription start site (CNS3), which may negatively regulate IL-17 production (160). BATF, an AP-1 factor critical for IL-17 production, also strongly binds to this region (177), suggesting that CNS3 contains both positive and negative regulatory elements for IL-17 transcription.

microRNA AND T CELL DIFFERENTIATION

By targeting the 3′ UTR of a transcript, miRNAs can repress translation and/or reduce mRNA stability. Approximately 400 miRNAs have been identified in humans, and more than half of mammalian transcripts are predicted to be targets of miRNAs. Not surprisingly, many reports indicate that miRNAs play important roles in regulating virtually all biological processes including hematopoiesis and the functions of immune cells, including T cells (269).

Dicer and Drosha are the RNase III enzymes critical for generating mature miRNA (270). Deletion of Dicer at an early stage of T cell development by Lck-cre greatly reduces the cellularity of the thymi owing to the increased death of CD4/CD8 DP cells (271). When Dicer is deleted at DP stages, by CD4-cre, the total number of thymocytes is normal (272), but the frequency of CD8 T cells is dramatically reduced, especially in the periphery. CD4 T cell proliferation in response to TCR stimulation is also impaired, correlated with poor IL-2 production by these cells. In addition, Dicer-deficient Th2 cells produce a substantial amount of IFN-γ, suggesting that miRNAs play a negative role in Th1 differentiation and/or IFN-γ production (272). The specific miRNA(s) responsible for these defects remains to be identified. miRNAs are also involved in the generation and expansion of Tregs. Dicer deletion by CD4-cre results in reduced numbers of Tregs and affects the induction of $Foxp3^+$ cells from $CD4^+CD25^-$ T cells by TGF-β (273).

miRNA-155-deficient mice have reduced numbers of Tregs. miRNA-155, whose expression is regulated by Foxp3, directly suppresses SOCS-1 translation and promotes sensitivity of Tregs to IL-2, thereby enhancing Treg proliferation (274). However, the expression of miRNA-155 is not restricted to Tregs. T cell activation by anti-CD3/anti-CD28 dramatically induces miRNA-155 expression within 5 h (275), suggesting that miRNA-155 also plays an important role in conventional T cells. Indeed, miRNA-155-deficient T cells show a Th2 differentiation bias with increased IL-4 and decreased IFN-γ production possibly due to the increased expression of c-Maf, which is a direct target of miRNA-155 (276, 277).

Given the critical importance of both the master transcription factors and miRNAs, study of the regulation of miRNA expression by master transcription factors and of the involvement of miRNAs in modulating master transcription factors promises to be of great importance in understanding Th cell differentiation.

HETEROGENEITY OF THE Th CELLS

Th cells are very diverse owing to the existence of different lineages and heterogeneity within each lineage. As discussed above, Th cells can be classified in at least four lineages, Th1, Th2, Th17, and Treg cells. Some labs have also described TGF-β-producing Th3 cells (278), IL-10-producing TR1 (279) cells, IL-9-producing Th9 cells (280, 281), and T follicular helper Tfh cells (31, 44, 45) as separate lineages. However, Tregs also produce TGF-β, and all Th cells are capable of producing IL-10 under certain circumstances, whereas IL-9 was originally described as a Th2 cytokine and Th9 cells are developmentally related to Th2 cells. Therefore, the Th3, TR1, and Th9 cells may not be members of lineages that are distinct from Th1, Th2, Th17, and Treg cells but that rather represent diversity within Th lineages. Tfh cells may be members of a separate lineage, although this is still a matter of debate. As discussed above, Tfh cells generated in vivo in the course of Th1, Th2, or Th17 responses may express Th1, Th2, or Th17 signature cytokines in addition to IL-21 and CXCR5 (32–34, 167). Are these further differentiated Tfh cells or do each of the effector lineages have the potential to express the molecules that allow them to mediate Tfh function? In the gut, Tfh cells appear to originate mainly from Tregs (282). A possible relationship among conventional Th2, IL-4-producing Tfh, and Th9 cells is illustrated in **Figure 5**.

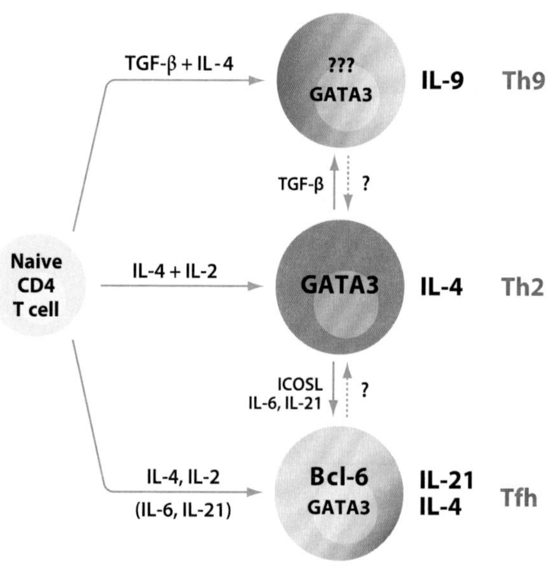

Figure 5

Possible relationships among classic Th2, IL-4-producing Tfh, and Th9 cells. Depending on the cytokine milieu, naive CD4 T cells may differentiate directly into Th2, Tfh, and Th9 cells once they are activated (33, 121, 280, 281). Classic Th2 cells may become IL-4-producing Tfh cells upon receiving IL-6/IL-21 and ICOSL stimulation or IL-9-producing cells upon receiving TGF-β signaling. Whether Th9 cells or IL-4-producing Tfh cells can become classic Th2 cells is not known. The transcription factor directly responsible for IL-9 production has not been identified.

Heterogeneity exists within each cell lineage. Some of the heterogeneity results from the pattern of cytokine production. Each lineage is able to express a set of cytokines. For example, Th2 cells express IL-4, IL-5, IL-10, and IL-13. But some cells produce more of one cytokine than of the others, although there are many double or triple expressors. Even for a given cytokine, the probability of expression from the two alleles may differ, which is largely determined by different epigenetic modifications at each allele (283, 284). Heterogeneity of cytokine production is also true for Th1 and Th17 cells. For example, the IFN-γ^+TNF-α^+IL-2^+ multifunctional Th1 cells, but not the single cytokine producers, are likely to be the long-lasting memory cells (285). In addition to differential epigenetic modification and stochastic events during T cell signaling, variable expression of some transcription factors may also be responsible for heterogeneity in cytokine secretory capacity. For example, PU.1 is selectively expressed in IL-4-nonproducing Th2 cells; such cells are capable of producing more CCL22 (286). Within Th17 cells, differential expression of IL-17 and IL-22 may be due to the induction and activation of the aryl

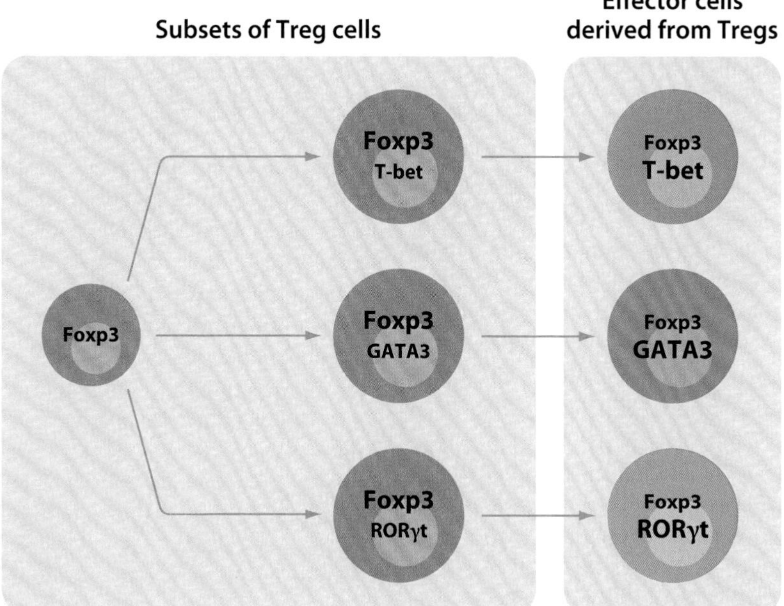

Figure 6

Complexity of Tregs. Foxp3 is the master regulator for Tregs. Recent reports and our unpublished data show that the transcription factors for Th1, Th2, and Th17 cells, T-bet, GATA3, and RORγt, respectively, can also be coexpressed in some Tregs (36, 113, 182). A relatively high expression ratio of Foxp3 over another master transcription factor prevents the induction of effector cytokines. Different combinations of transcription factors subdivide the Tregs with possible distinct regulatory functions. In some cases, the level of Foxp3 expression may fall, leading to expression of effector cytokines controlled by the other master regulator expressed by the cell. Effector cells derived from Tregs, because of their unique antigen specificity, may participate in normal immune responses to infections or contribute to autoimmune diseases (287).

hydrocarbon receptor (AhR) (175). Although both RORγt and AhR have been shown to be highly expressed in Th17 cells, whether they are coexpressed in all Th17 cells or the AhR is preferentially expressed in IL-22-producing Th17 cells has not been determined.

Recent reports suggest that the Tregs are more complex than originally thought. Cells coexpressing RORγt and Foxp3 exist in vivo. Although such cells were thought to represent an intermediate stage in the process of Th17 or iTreg differentiation (182), it has now been shown that treatment of differentiated nTregs with IL-6 will induce them to express RORγt and IL-17 (112, 113). Furthermore, T-bet-expressing Tregs exist in normal mice, and loss of T-bet from Tregs diminishes both the capacity of these Th1-like Tregs to proliferate and their capacity to suppress Th1-related autoimmune diseases (36). Our unpublished data indicate that GATA3 is expressed in some Tregs and may contribute to certain Treg functions. Indeed, Tregs may consist of Th1-, Th2-, and Th17-like populations in which differentiation is accompanied by the upregulation of Th1, Th2, and Th17 master regulators; under certain circumstances, these Tregs may become effector cells (287) (**Figure 6**).

PLASTICITY OF T HELPER CELLS

A multipotential precursor cell can differentiate into distinct lineages, a process that was generally thought to move toward a fixed fate. However, an increasing number of studies have shown that the differentiated cells retain the flexibility to dedifferentiate or redifferentiate. Even terminally differentiated fibroblasts can be reprogrammed to become inducible pluripotent stem cells by the transduction of the transcription factors Oct4/Klf4/Sox2/Myc (288, 289). Likewise, *Pax5* deletion in B cells causes them to lose B cell identity and to gain the potential to develop into T cells (290). Deleting *Gata3* from Th2 cells allows the production of IFN-γ (57); reduction of Foxp3 in Tregs renders them able to gain a Th2 phenotype (84); *Gfi1* deletion from Th2 cells results in active epigenetic modifications at Th17- and iTreg-related gene loci, including *Rorc*, *Il23r*, and *Cd103* (160).

Not only can artificial genetic modification cause the reversal of differentiation, so too can physiologic stimuli. For example, Th2 cells can be induced by IL-12 to produce IFN-γ; Th17 cells isolated using an IL-17F-Thy1.1 reporter, upon transfer, lose IL-17-producing capacity while gaining competence to produce IFN-γ, where IFN-γ production is dependent on STAT4 and T-bet (291). Tregs cultured under Th1 conditions gain the capacity to produce IFN-γ (164). These examples imply that although IFN-γ is the Th1 signature cytokine, each of the other lineages retains the capacity to produce it. Such flexibility may be determined by the bivalent H3K4 and H3K27 modification of the *Tbx21* gene as well as by the accessibility of IfngCNS-22 in non-Th1 cells (164, 259). Interestingly, by using mice with indicators for Foxp3 and IL-17F (Foxp3-GFP/IL-17F-RFP mice), Dong and colleagues (113) reported the existence of GFP$^+$RFP$^+$ cells and showed that Tregs can produce IL-17 when they are treated with IL-6. Acquisition of IL-6-producing capacity correlated with upregulation of RORγt. Strober's group had earlier reported a similar observation (112). Thus, differentiated Th cells are somewhat plastic and can be reprogrammed into other lineages given appropriate stimulation. Understanding the detailed mechanisms through which switching of one Th cell type to the other is achieved has important implications for immune intervention.

IN VITRO/IN VIVO

Another important point is to draw a comparison between effector/regulatory CD4 T cell populations differentiated in vitro and those that occur in vivo in response to infectious agents or other naturally occurring stimulants. Substantial evidence suggests that the in vivo cells may have undergone pathways of differentiation that differ from those established in vitro, and hence the cell types could be quite different from one another. In turn, this finding could imply that the highly polarized cells seen in vitro may either represent more extreme cases than those that occur in vivo or only occur under unusual circumstances. Indeed, partial states of differentiation, in which components of individual phenotypes are coexpressed, may dominate physiologic effector/memory CD4 cell populations. Analysis and comparison of the in vitro and in vivo populations would now seem essential. A particularly cogent example of this potential difference is exemplified in the Th2 lineage. In vitro, IL-4, acting through the IL-4 receptor/STAT6/GATA3 pathway, is virtually essential for Th2 differentiation. In vivo, however, although GATA3 remains critical (57), differentiation can often be obtained in mice that lack the IL-4 receptor and/or STAT6 (142).

MONOGENIC HUMAN DISEASES EFFECTING Th CELL DIFFERENTIATION OR FUNCTION

One of the most convincing lines of evidence establishing the importance of a given differentiation process for human physiology is the existence of monogenic abnormalities in particular differentiation processes or effector functions resulting in disease. A growing set of human disorders in the Th differentiation/function pathways has been identified, with a concomitant proliferation of data establishing the importance of these differentiation processes in humans.

Abnormalities in Th1 Differentiation or Function

To our knowledge, there are no defects that uniquely block the Th1 differentiation of CD4 T cells. However, there is a set of monogenic disorders each with a relatively similar phenotype consistent with the absence of Th1 function. These disorders include deficiencies in *IFNGR1*, *IFNGR2*, *STAT1*, *IL12RB1*, *IL12B*, and *nuclear factor-kappaB-essential modulator* (*NEMO*) (292). In each case, the dominant phenotype is susceptibility to infection with mycobacterial species, including poorly infectious agents such as BCG and atypical mycobacteria, as well as to infection with *Mycobacterium tuberculosis*. In general, other infectious agents are not a problem for these patients, with the exception of *Salmonella*.

Of the mutations described, three block the IFN-γ-signaling pathway and two inhibit the IL-12/23 pathway. IFN-γ is not uniquely produced by Th1 cells; in particular, NK cells are an excellent source of IFN-γ. Defects in IL-12RB1 and IL-12B should block or diminish both Th1 and Th17 differentiation, because these receptor and cytokine chains are important in assembling both the IL-12 and IL-23 receptors and the IL-12 and IL-23 proteins (40, 293). Mutations in IL-12RB1 and IL-12B do indeed impair the capacity of patients' CD4 T cells to develop into Th17 cells (294). However, patients with a defect in Th17 development do not show susceptibility to mycobacterial infection. Taken together, these observations strongly suggest a critical role of human Th1 cells in resistance to infection with various mycobacteria. In mice, although *M. tuberculosis* infection induces both a Th1 and Th17 response (295), the protective response is dependent mainly upon Th1 cells. Human Th1 cells play a dominant role in protection against mycobacterial infection and surprisingly few other intracellular infectious agents.

Abnormalities in Th2 Function

GATA3 mutations have been detected in human populations, and in the heterozygous form they account for the hypoparathyroidism, deafness, and renal dysplasia (HDR) syndrome (296). Although haploinsufficiency of GATA3 also causes reduced Th2 differentiation (297), it does not result in any major immunologic abnormalities. By contrast, there is a human disorder resulting from mutations that cause diminished TCR repertoire complexity. As noted above, low peptide concentration and low affinity of the TCR for the peptide/MHC complex are associated with an increased likelihood of Th2 differentiation in experimental systems. Similarly, mutations in key elements of TCR signaling are also associated with Th2 differentiation and often with elevated IgE. Does the same hold for human conditions?

Omenn syndrome, an autosomal recessive disease of neonates characterized by erythroderma, chronic diarrhea, hepatosplenogaly, and lymphadenopathy (298), is fatal unless treated with bone marrow transplantation. Patients display elevated numbers of Th2 cells and overproduction of IL-4 and IL-5 as well as eosinophilia and elevated serum IgE. The disease results from mutations that significantly impair T cell development in the thymus. Most cases are associated with hypomorphic mutations in RAG1 or RAG2, leading to the development of relatively limited numbers of T cells and B cells (298). As a result, the cells that reach the periphery have a very limited repertoire, although they expand greatly in number in the periphery. Thus, while large numbers of CD4 T cells exist in patients, they represent expansions from relatively small numbers of thymic emigrants, and the individuals have a very limited peripheral CD4 T cell repertoire. In one report, a patient with what appears to be a major but not complete absence of ZAP70 presented with eczematous skin lesions simulating atopic dermatitis and with eosinophilia and elevated IgE, suggesting that a thymic signaling defect may result in a limited TCR repertoire (299). Alternatively, this patient's abnormalities may have resulted from signaling defects among the peripheral CD4 T cells.

Why a limited repertoire should lead to a Th2-mediated disease is not entirely clear.

However, we have argued that low repertoire complexity may favor Th2 differentiation because the likelihood of a newly introduced antigen binding T cells that recognize it with high affinity is small, and thus low-affinity responses will predominate, which should favor Th2 differentiation (300). Mouse models of Omenn syndrome with mutations in RAG genes have a phenotype similar to that of the human Omenn syndrome (301, 302), and, as already noted, intentionally providing mice with a limited T cell repertoire by transferring a small number of CD4 T cells to *Rag2*$^{-/-}$ recipients results in a fulminant, although delayed, Th2 inflammatory disease (300).

Abnormalities in Th17 Differentiation

As noted above, humans with a mutation in IL-12B and IL-12RB1 may display some defects in IL-17 differentiation, but their principal abnormalities are more likely explained by deficiencies in Th1 induction. A very striking example exists of a human deficiency in the development of Th17 cells in patients with mutations in STAT3 that account for Job syndrome, also known as hyper-IgE syndrome (303). The mutations in Job syndrome, which occur mainly in the SH2 domain or the DNA-binding domain of STAT3 (304, 305), have been shown to act as dominant negatives, consistent with the autosomal dominant pattern of inheritance of the syndrome. The striking abnormalities of affected individuals are heightened susceptibility to infection with *Staphylococcus aureus* and *Streptococcus pneumoniae* as well as to *Candida albicans* and other fungi. Blood of such patients lacks CD4 T cells capable of producing IL-17, and their purified naive CD4 T cells fail to differentiate into Th17 cells under conditions in which MHC-matched normal cells differentiate quite efficiently (109).

With the growing body of data indicating an important role for IL-1β in Th17 differentiation or stabilization (47, 306), there will be an interest in mutations affecting IL-1β production, such as those in the inflammasome pathway or in caspsase 1. Thus far, activating mutations have been described that result in several autoinflammatory disorders (307).

Abnormalities in Treg Differentiation

Immunodeficiency, polyendocrinopathy, enteropathy, X-linked syndrome (IPEX) results from mutations in *FOXP3* (80, 308). Because *FOXP3* is on the X chromosome, the affected population is mainly boys. The syndrome often includes insulin-dependent diabetes and elevated serum IgE with aspects of both eczema and psoriasis. Other autoimmune symptoms include hypothyroidism, anemia, thrombocytopenia, and neutropenia. Patients often show an excess production of Th2 cytokines. IPEX-like syndromes have been reported in patients with *IL2RA* mutations (309).

Significance of Evidence for Differentiation

There is no doubt that the effector cytokines of various Th cell types have a critical role in humans. For both Th17 cells and Tregs, mutations of key molecules in the differentiation pathway lead both to the failure of the cells of that type to appear and to severe abnormalities, very much as expected from the mouse studies. For Th1 and Th2 cells, the human results as to the critical role of the differentiation process are less certain as mutations in the key factors associated with differentiation have not been observed. For Th1 cells, the importance of the differentiated cells is inferred either from the similarity of the phenotype in individuals with mutations that block a key Th1 product or from mutations that block Th1 differentiation but also control another lineage. For Th2 cells, the support from human disease lies in the consequence of overactivity of the cell population, particularly where the TCR repertoire is limited.

Although space does not permit an extended discussion of the role of various genes that regulate either signature cytokines or transcription factors in susceptibility to complex human disorders, there is a very large body of data on this point. Genome-wide association studies have implicated many genes known to play a role in Th differentiation as being associated with specific disorders.

SUMMARY POINTS

1. There are at least four types of Th cells, Th1, Th2, Th17, and iTregs. Th1, Th2, and Th17 cells are important for eradicating intracellular pathogens, helminth, and extracellular bacteria/fungi, respectively. Th1 and Th17 cells are also involved in many types of autoimmune diseases, whereas Th2 cells contribute to allergic responses (185). iTreg as well as nTreg cells are critical in maintaining self-tolerance and in modulating immune responses to infections (310).
2. Cytokines play critical roles in determining Th cell differentiation. A combination of cytokines is required for the differentiation of each lineage: IL-12 and IFN-γ for Th1, IL-4 and IL-2/IL-7/TSLP for Th2, TGF-β and IL-6/IL-21/IL-23 for Th17, and TGF-β and IL-2 for iTreg. One of the effector cytokines produced by Th cells further promotes the differentiation process, providing a powerful positive amplification loop. IL-1 family cytokines may also participate in inducing TCR-independent effector cytokine production by Th cells: IL-18 for Th1, IL-33 for Th2, and IL-1 for Th17.
3. Transcription factors involved in Th cell differentiation form a sophisticated network involving collaboration and positive and negative regulation. The master regulators and STAT family members collaborate in T cell differentiation and expansion: T-bet and STAT4 for Th1, GATA3 and STAT5 for Th2, RORγt and STAT3 for Th17, Foxp3 and STAT5 for iTreg. Other transcription factors are either secondary to master regulators and STAT proteins or responsible for the induction of master regulators. Mutual repression between transcription factors of different lineages also exists. Therefore, Th cell differentiation involves lineage commitment, selective growth of committed cells, and active suppression of alternative lineage fates.
4. Most transcription factors involved in Th cell differentiation have been shown to directly bind to the effector cytokine genes (*Ifng*, *Il4/Il13*, and *Il17a/Il17f*) at promoters, enhancers, insulators, and locus control regions (LCR). These genetic elements are generally found at conserved noncoding sequence (CNS) and DNase I hypersensitivity (HS) regions. The binding of transcription factors to the different sites induces gene activation or repression as well as epigenetic modification.
5. Our knowledge of the Th cells has expanded greatly owing to massive Th cell heterogeneity and their plasticity. T cell heterogeneity and plasticity open new opportunities for targeting or redirecting specific subsets in autoimmune and allergic diseases. These targets may become clinically feasible when we fully understand the regulation of Th cell subsets and their relationships.
6. Many signaling molecules and transcription factors shown to be critical in Th cell differentiation in a mouse model are also defective in some human diseases related to abnormal Th cell differentiation. Linking animal models with clinical studies should provide greater insight into the details of Th cell differentiation.

FUTURE ISSUES

1. Identification of Th cell subsets in vivo and comparison of in vitro and in vivo differentiated Th cells remain important issues for future research.
2. We need to understand the cellular and molecular mechanisms underlying in vivo Th differentiation decisions.
3. Specific signaling pathways for regulating master transcription factors of each Th cell lineage have yet to be identified.
4. The component of transcription factor complexes mediating gene activation and repression is also an area requiring further research.
5. Genome-wide profiling of transcription factor binding and epigenetic modifications in each Th lineage are needed.
6. Involvement of specific miRNAs in each Th lineage must be elucidated.
7. Researchers must discover the relationships between classic Th1/Th2 and newly defined Th17/iTreg/Tfh/Th9 cells and between effector cells and regulatory T cells.

DISCLOSURE STATEMENT

The authors are not aware of any affiliations, memberships, funding, or financial holdings that might be perceived as affecting the objectivity of this review.

ACKNOWLEDGMENTS

This work was supported by the Division of Intramural Research, National Institute of Allergy and Infectious Diseases, National Institutes of Health.

LITERATURE CITED

1. Mosmann TR, Cherwinski H, Bond MW, Giedlin MA, Coffman RL. 1986. Two types of murine helper T cell clone. I. Definition according to profiles of lymphokine activities and secreted proteins. *J. Immunol.* 136:2348–57
2. Killar L, MacDonald G, West J, Woods A, Bottomly K. 1987. Cloned, Ia-restricted T cells that do not produce interleukin 4(IL 4)/B cell stimulatory factor 1(BSF-1) fail to help antigen-specific B cells. *J. Immunol.* 138:1674–79
3. Le Gros G, Ben-Sasson SZ, Seder R, Finkelman FD, Paul WE. 1990. Generation of interleukin 4 (IL-4)-producing cells in vivo and in vitro: IL-2 and IL-4 are required for in vitro generation of IL-4-producing cells. *J. Exp. Med.* 172:921–29
4. Swain SL, Weinberg AD, English M, Huston G. 1990. IL-4 directs the development of Th2-like helper effectors. *J. Immunol.* 145:3796–806
5. Seder RA, Paul WE, Davis MM, Fazekas de St Groth B. 1992. The presence of interleukin 4 during in vitro priming determines the lymphokine-producing potential of $CD4^+$ T cells from T cell receptor transgenic mice. *J. Exp. Med.* 176:1091–98
6. Hsieh CS, Heimberger AB, Gold JS, O'Garra A, Murphy KM. 1992. Differential regulation of T helper phenotype development by interleukins 4 and 10 in an $\alpha\beta$ T-cell-receptor transgenic system. *Proc. Natl. Acad. Sci. USA* 89:6065–69
7. Hsieh CS, Macatonia SE, Tripp CS, Wolf SF, O'Garra A, Murphy KM. 1993. Development of TH1 $CD4^+$ T cells through IL-12 produced by *Listeria*-induced macrophages. *Science* 260:547–49

8. Rocken M, Saurat JH, Hauser C. 1992. A common precursor for $CD4^+$ T cells producing IL-2 or IL-4. *J. Immunol.* 148:1031–36
9. Sad S, Mosmann TR. 1994. Single IL-2-secreting precursor CD4 T cell can develop into either Th1 or Th2 cytokine secretion phenotype. *J. Immunol.* 153:3514–22
10. Noben-Trauth N, Hu-Li J, Paul WE. 2002. IL-4 secreted from individual naive $CD4^+$ T cells acts in an autocrine manner to induce Th2 differentiation. *Eur. J. Immunol.* 32:1428–33
11. Grogan JL, Mohrs M, Harmon B, Lacy DA, Sedat JW, Locksley RM. 2001. Early transcription and silencing of cytokine genes underlie polarization of T helper cell subsets. *Immunity* 14:205–15
12. Mullen AC, High FA, Hutchins AS, Lee HW, Villarino AV, et al. 2001. Role of T-bet in commitment of TH1 cells before IL-12-dependent selection. *Science* 292:1907–10
13. Zhu J, Guo L, Min B, Watson CJ, Hu-Li J, et al. 2002. Growth factor independent-1 induced by IL-4 regulates Th2 cell proliferation. *Immunity* 16:733–44
14. Bendelac A, Killeen N, Littman DR, Schwartz RH. 1994. A subset of $CD4^+$ thymocytes selected by MHC class I molecules. *Science* 263:1774–78
15. Sakaguchi S, Sakaguchi N, Asano M, Itoh M, Toda M. 1995. Immunologic self-tolerance maintained by activated T cells expressing IL-2 receptor α-chains (CD25). Breakdown of a single mechanism of self-tolerance causes various autoimmune diseases. *J. Immunol.* 155:1151–64
16. Murphy CA, Langrish CL, Chen Y, Blumenschein W, McClanahan T, et al. 2003. Divergent pro- and antiinflammatory roles for IL-23 and IL-12 in joint autoimmune inflammation. *J. Exp. Med.* 198:1951–57
17. Aggarwal S, Ghilardi N, Xie MH, de Sauvage FJ, Gurney AL. 2003. Interleukin-23 promotes a distinct CD4 T cell activation state characterized by the production of interleukin-17. *J. Biol. Chem.* 278:1910–14
18. Cua DJ, Sherlock J, Chen Y, Murphy CA, Joyce B, et al. 2003. Interleukin-23 rather than interleukin-12 is the critical cytokine for autoimmune inflammation of the brain. *Nature* 421:744–48
19. Park H, Li Z, Yang XO, Chang SH, Nurieva R, et al. 2005. A distinct lineage of CD4 T cells regulates tissue inflammation by producing interleukin 17. *Nat. Immunol.* 6:1133–41
20. Harrington LE, Hatton RD, Mangan PR, Turner H, Murphy TL, et al. 2005. Interleukin 17-producing $CD4^+$ effector T cells develop via a lineage distinct from the T helper type 1 and 2 lineages. *Nat. Immunol.* 6:1123–32
21. Veldhoen M, Hocking RJ, Atkins CJ, Locksley RM, Stockinger B. 2006. TGFβ in the context of an inflammatory cytokine milieu supports de novo differentiation of IL-17-producing T cells. *Immunity* 24:179–89
22. Zhou L, Ivanov II, Spolski R, Min R, Shenderov K, et al. 2007. IL-6 programs T_H -17 cell differentiation by promoting sequential engagement of the IL-21 and IL-23 pathways. *Nat. Immunol.* 8:967–74
23. Nurieva R, Yang XO, Martinez G, Zhang Y, Panopoulos AD, et al. 2007. Essential autocrine regulation by IL-21 in the generation of inflammatory T cells. *Nature* 448:480–83
24. Korn T, Bettelli E, Gao W, Awasthi A, Jager A, et al. 2007. IL-21 initiates an alternative pathway to induce proinflammatory T_H 17 cells. *Nature* 448:484–87
25. Chen W, Jin W, Hardegen N, Lei KJ, Li L, et al. 2003. Conversion of peripheral $CD4^+CD25^-$ naive T cells to $CD4^+CD25^+$ regulatory T cells by TGF-β induction of transcription factor Foxp3. *J. Exp. Med.* 198:1875–86
26. Fu S, Zhang N, Yopp AC, Chen D, Mao M, et al. 2004. TGF-β induces $Foxp3^+$ T-regulatory cells from $CD4^+$ CD25–precursors. *Am. J. Transplant.* 4:1614–27
27. Fantini MC, Becker C, Monteleone G, Pallone F, Galle PR, Neurath MF. 2004. Cutting edge: TGF-β induces a regulatory phenotype in $CD4^+CD25^-$ T cells through Foxp3 induction and down-regulation of Smad7. *J. Immunol.* 172:5149–53
28. Zheng SG, Wang JH, Gray JD, Soucier H, Horwitz DA. 2004. Natural and induced $CD4^+CD25^+$ cells educate $CD4^+CD25^-$ cells to develop suppressive activity: the role of IL-2, TGF-β, and IL-10. *J. Immunol.* 172:5213–21
29. DiPaolo RJ, Brinster C, Davidson TS, Andersson J, Glass D, Shevach EM. 2007. Autoantigen-specific TGFβ-induced $Foxp3^+$ regulatory T cells prevent autoimmunity by inhibiting dendritic cells from activating autoreactive T cells. *J. Immunol.* 179:4685–93

30. Tran DQ, Ramsey H, Shevach EM. 2007. Induction of FOXP3 expression in naive human $CD4^+FOXP3$ T cells by T-cell receptor stimulation is transforming growth factor-β dependent but does not confer a regulatory phenotype. *Blood* 110:2983–90
31. King C, Tangye SG, Mackay CR. 2008. T follicular helper (TFH) cells in normal and dysregulated immune responses. *Annu. Rev. Immunol.* 26:741–66
32. Reinhardt RL, Liang HE, Locksley RM. 2009. Cytokine-secreting follicular T cells shape the antibody repertoire. *Nat. Immunol.* 10:385–93
33. Zaretsky AG, Taylor JJ, King IL, Marshall FA, Mohrs M, Pearce EJ. 2009. T follicular helper cells differentiate from Th2 cells in response to helminth antigens. *J. Exp. Med.* 206:991–99
34. King IL, Mohrs M. 2009. IL-4-producing $CD4^+$ T cells in reactive lymph nodes during helminth infection are T follicular helper cells. *J. Exp. Med.* 206:1001–7
35. Tokoyoda K, Zehentmeier S, Hegazy AN, Albrecht I, Grun JR, et al. 2009. Professional memory $CD4^+$ T lymphocytes preferentially reside and rest in the bone marrow. *Immunity* 30:721–30
36. Koch MA, Tucker-Heard G, Perdue NR, Killebrew JR, Urdahl KB, Campbell DJ. 2009. The transcription factor T-bet controls regulatory T cell homeostasis and function during type 1 inflammation. *Nat. Immunol.* 10:595–602
37. Zheng Y, Chaudhry A, Kas A, deRoos P, Kim JM, et al. 2009. Regulatory T-cell suppressor program co-opts transcription factor IRF4 to control T_H2 responses. *Nature* 458:351–56
38. Chaudhry A, Rudra D, Treuting P, Samstein RM, Liang Y, et al. 2009. $CD4^+$ regulatory T cells control TH17 responses in a Stat3-dependent manner. *Science* 326:986–91
39. Lighvani AA, Frucht DM, Jankovic D, Yamane H, Aliberti J, et al. 2001. T-bet is rapidly induced by interferon-γ in lymphoid and myeloid cells. *Proc. Natl. Acad. Sci. USA* 98:15137–42
40. Oppmann B, Lesley R, Blom B, Timans JC, Xu Y, et al. 2000. Novel p19 protein engages IL-12p40 to form a cytokine, IL-23, with biological activities similar as well as distinct from IL-12. *Immunity* 13:715–25
41. Bettelli E, Carrier Y, Gao W, Korn T, Strom TB, et al. 2006. Reciprocal developmental pathways for the generation of pathogenic effector TH17 and regulatory T cells. *Nature* 441:235–38
42. Mangan PR, Harrington LE, O'Quinn DB, Helms WS, Bullard DC, et al. 2006. Transforming growth factor-β induces development of the T_H17 lineage. *Nature* 441:231–34
43. Korn T, Bettelli E, Oukka M, Kuchroo VK. 2009. IL-17 and Th17 cells. *Annu. Rev. Immunol.* 27:485–517
44. Nurieva RI, Chung Y, Hwang D, Yang XO, Kang HS, et al. 2008. Generation of T follicular helper cells is mediated by interleukin-21 but independent of T helper 1, 2, or 17 cell lineages. *Immunity* 29:138–49
45. Vogelzang A, McGuire HM, Yu D, Sprent J, Mackay CR, King C. 2008. A fundamental role for interleukin-21 in the generation of T follicular helper cells. *Immunity* 29:127–37
46. Guo L, Wei G, Zhu J, Liao W, Leonard WJ, et al. 2009. IL-1 family members and STAT activators induce cytokine production by Th2, Th17, and Th1 cells. *Proc. Natl. Acad. Sci. USA* 106:13463–68
47. Chung Y, Chang SH, Martinez GJ, Yang XO, Nurieva R, et al. 2009. Critical regulation of early Th17 cell differentiation by interleukin-1 signaling. *Immunity* 30:576–87
48. Yang J, Zhu H, Murphy TL, Ouyang W, Murphy KM. 2001. IL-18-stimulated GADD45 beta required in cytokine-induced, but not TCR-induced, IFN-γ production. *Nat. Immunol.* 2:157–64
49. Robinson D, Shibuya K, Mui A, Zonin F, Murphy E, et al. 1997. IGIF does not drive Th1 development but synergizes with IL-12 for interferon-γ production and activates IRAK and NFκB. *Immunity* 7:571–81
50. Zheng W, Flavell RA. 1997. The transcription factor GATA-3 is necessary and sufficient for Th2 cytokine gene expression in CD4 T cells. *Cell* 89:587–96
51. Zhang DH, Cohn L, Ray P, Bottomly K, Ray A. 1997. Transcription factor GATA-3 is differentially expressed in murine Th1 and Th2 cells and controls Th2-specific expression of the interleukin-5 gene. *J. Biol. Chem.* 272:21597–603
52. Ho IC, Tai TS, Pai SY. 2009. GATA3 and the T-cell lineage: essential functions before and after T-helper-2-cell differentiation. *Nat. Rev. Immunol.* 9:125–35
53. Ouyang W, Ranganath SH, Weindel K, Bhattacharya D, Murphy TL, et al. 1998. Inhibition of Th1 development mediated by GATA-3 through an IL-4-independent mechanism. *Immunity* 9:745–55

54. Usui T, Preiss JC, Kanno Y, Yao ZJ, Bream JH, et al. 2006. T-bet regulates Th1 responses through essential effects on GATA-3 function rather than on *IFNG* gene acetylation and transcription. *J. Exp. Med.* 203:755–66
55. Ouyang W, Lohning M, Gao Z, Assenmacher M, Ranganath S, et al. 2000. Stat6-independent GATA-3 autoactivation directs IL-4-independent Th2 development and commitment. *Immunity* 12:27–37
56. Zhang DH, Yang L, Cohn L, Parkyn L, Homer R, et al. 1999. Inhibition of allergic inflammation in a murine model of asthma by expression of a dominant-negative mutant of GATA-3. *Immunity* 11:473–82
57. Zhu J, Min B, Hu-Li J, Watson CJ, Grinberg A, et al. 2004. Conditional deletion of Gata3 shows its essential function in T_H1-T_H2 responses. *Nat. Immunol.* 5:1157–65
58. Pai SY, Truitt ML, Ho IC. 2004. GATA-3 deficiency abrogates the development and maintenance of T helper type 2 cells. *Proc. Natl. Acad. Sci. USA* 101:1993–98
59. Siegel MD, Zhang DH, Ray P, Ray A. 1995. Activation of the interleukin-5 promoter by cAMP in murine EL-4 cells requires the GATA-3 and CLE0 elements. *J. Biol. Chem.* 270:24548–55
60. Kishikawa H, Sun J, Choi A, Miaw SC, Ho IC. 2001. The cell type-specific expression of the murine *IL-13* gene is regulated by GATA-3. *J. Immunol.* 167:4414–20
61. Yamashita M, Ukai-Tadenuma M, Kimura M, Omori M, Inami M, et al. 2002. Identification of a conserved GATA3 response element upstream proximal from the interleukin-13 gene locus. *J. Biol. Chem.* 277:42399–408
62. Agarwal S, Avni O, Rao A. 2000. Cell-type-restricted binding of the transcription factor NFAT to a distal IL-4 enhancer in vivo. *Immunity* 12:643–52
63. Zhu J, Yamane H, Cote-Sierra J, Guo L, Paul WE. 2006. GATA-3 promotes Th2 responses through three different mechanisms: induction of Th2 cytokine production, selective growth of Th2 cells and inhibition of Th1 cell-specific factors. *Cell Res.* 16:3–10
64. Kim PJ, Pai SY, Brigl M, Besra GS, Gumperz J, Ho IC. 2006. GATA-3 regulates the development and function of invariant NKT cells. *J. Immunol.* 177:6650–59
65. Szabo SJ, Kim ST, Costa GL, Zhang X, Fathman CG, Glimcher LH. 2000. A novel transcription factor, T-bet, directs Th1 lineage commitment. *Cell* 100:655–69
66. Mullen AC, Hutchins AS, High FA, Lee HW, Sykes KJ, et al. 2002. Hlx is induced by and genetically interacts with T-bet to promote heritable T_H 1 gene induction. *Nat. Immunol.* 3:652–58
67. Szabo SJ, Sullivan BM, Stemmann C, Satoskar AR, Sleckman BP, Glimcher LH. 2002. Distinct effects of T-bet in TH1 lineage commitment and IFN-γ production in CD4 and CD8 T cells. *Science* 295:338–42
68. Finotto S, Neurath MF, Glickman JN, Qin S, Lehr HA, et al. 2002. Development of spontaneous airway changes consistent with human asthma in mice lacking T-bet. *Science* 295:336–38
69. Afkarian M, Sedy JR, Yang J, Jacobson NG, Cereb N, et al. 2002. T-bet is a STAT1-induced regulator of IL-12R expression in naive $CD4^+$ T cells. *Nat. Immunol.* 3:549–57
70. Cruz-Guilloty F, Pipkin ME, Djuretic IM, Levanon D, Lotem J, et al. 2009. Runx3 and T-box proteins cooperate to establish the transcriptional program of effector CTLs. *J. Exp. Med.* 206:51–59
71. Pearce EL, Mullen AC, Martins GA, Krawczyk CM, Hutchins AS, et al. 2003. Control of effector $CD8^+$ T cell function by the transcription factor *Eomesodermin*. *Science* 302:1041–43
72. Intlekofer AM, Banerjee A, Takemoto N, Gordon SM, Dejong CS, et al. 2008. Anomalous type 17 response to viral infection by $CD8^+$ T cells lacking T-bet and *Eomesodermin*. *Science* 321:408–11
73. Suto A, Wurster AL, Reiner SL, Grusby MJ. 2006. IL-21 inhibits IFN-γ production in developing Th1 cells through the repression of *Eomesodermin* expression. *J. Immunol.* 177:3721–27
74. Intlekofer AM, Takemoto N, Wherry EJ, Longworth SA, Northrup JT, et al. 2005. Effector and memory $CD8^+$ T cell fate coupled by T-bet and eomesodermin. *Nat. Immunol.* 6:1236–44
75. Joshi NS, Cui W, Chandele A, Lee HK, Urso DR, et al. 2007. Inflammation directs memory precursor and short-lived effector $CD8^+$ T cell fates via the graded expression of T-bet transcription factor. *Immunity* 27:281–95
76. Intlekofer AM, Takemoto N, Kao C, Banerjee A, Schambach F, et al. 2007. Requirement for T-bet in the aberrant differentiation of unhelped memory $CD8^+$ T cells. *J. Exp. Med.* 204:2015–21
77. Glimcher LH. 2007. Trawling for treasure: tales of T-bet. *Nat. Immunol.* 8:448–50

78. Brunkow ME, Jeffery EW, Hjerrild KA, Paeper B, Clark LB, et al. 2001. Disruption of a new forkhead/winged-helix protein, scurfin, results in the fatal lymphoproliferative disorder of the scurfy mouse. *Nat. Genet.* 27:68–73
79. Patel DD. 2001. Escape from tolerance in the human X-linked autoimmunity-allergic disregulation syndrome and the Scurfy mouse. *J. Clin. Investig.* 107:155–57
80. Wildin RS, Ramsdell F, Peake J, Faravelli F, Casanova JL, et al. 2001. X-linked neonatal diabetes mellitus, enteropathy and endocrinopathy syndrome is the human equivalent of mouse Scurfy. *Nat. Genet.* 27:18–20
81. Fontenot JD, Gavin MA, Rudensky AY. 2003. Foxp3 programs the development and function of $CD4^+CD25^+$ regulatory T cells. *Nat. Immunol.* 4:330–36
82. Hori S, Nomura T, Sakaguchi S. 2003. Control of regulatory T cell development by the transcription factor Foxp3. *Science* 299:1057–61
83. Williams LM, Rudensky AY. 2007. Maintenance of the Foxp3-dependent developmental program in mature regulatory T cells requires continued expression of Foxp3. *Nat. Immunol.* 8:277–84
84. Wan YY, Flavell RA. 2007. Regulatory T-cell functions are subverted and converted owing to attenuated Foxp3 expression. *Nature* 445:766–70
85. Li MO, Wan YY, Flavell RA. 2007. T cell-produced transforming growth factor-β1 controls T cell tolerance and regulates Th1- and Th17-cell differentiation. *Immunity* 26:579–91
86. Li MO, Sanjabi S, Flavell RA. 2006. Transforming growth factor-β controls development, homeostasis, and tolerance of T cells by regulatory T cell-dependent and -independent mechanisms. *Immunity* 25:455–71
87. Marie JC, Liggitt D, Rudensky AY. 2006. Cellular mechanisms of fatal early-onset autoimmunity in mice with the T cell-specific targeting of transforming growth factor-β receptor. *Immunity* 25:441–54
88. Liu Y, Zhang P, Li J, Kulkarni AB, Perruche S, Chen W. 2008. A critical function for TGF-β signaling in the development of natural $CD4^+CD25^+Foxp3^+$ regulatory T cells. *Nat. Immunol.* 9:632–40
89. Tone Y, Furuuchi K, Kojima Y, Tykocinski ML, Greene MI, Tone M. 2008. Smad3 and NFAT cooperate to induce Foxp3 expression through its enhancer. *Nat. Immunol.* 9:194–202
90. Ivanov II, McKenzie BS, Zhou L, Tadokoro CE, Lepelley A, et al. 2006. The orphan nuclear receptor RORγt directs the differentiation program of proinflammatory $IL\text{-}17^+$ T helper cells. *Cell* 126:1121–33
91. Yang XO, Pappu BP, Nurieva R, Akimzhanov A, Kang HS, et al. 2008. T helper 17 lineage differentiation is programmed by orphan nuclear receptors ROR α and ROR γ. *Immunity* 28:29–39
92. Sun Z, Unutmaz D, Zou YR, Sunshine MJ, Pierani A, et al. 2000. Requirement for RORγ in thymocyte survival and lymphoid organ development. *Science* 288:2369–73
93. Takatori H, Kanno Y, Watford WT, Tato CM, Weiss G, et al. 2009. Lymphoid tissue inducer-like cells are an innate source of IL-17 and IL-22. *J. Exp. Med.* 206:35–41
94. Dent AL, Shaffer AL, Yu X, Allman D, Staudt LM. 1997. Control of inflammation, cytokine expression, and germinal center formation by BCL-6. *Science* 276:589–92
95. Dent AL, Doherty TM, Paul WE, Sher A, Staudt LM. 1999. BCL-6-deficient mice reveal an IL-4-independent, STAT6-dependent pathway that controls susceptibility to infection by *Leishmania major*. *J. Immunol.* 163:2098–103
96. Kusam S, Toney LM, Sato H, Dent AL. 2003. Inhibition of Th2 differentiation and GATA-3 expression by BCL-6. *J. Immunol.* 170:2435–41
97. Scheeren FA, Naspetti M, Diehl S, Schotte R, Nagasawa M, et al. 2005. STAT5 regulates the self-renewal capacity and differentiation of human memory B cells and controls Bcl-6 expression. *Nat. Immunol.* 6:303–13
98. Chtanova T, Tangye SG, Newton R, Frank N, Hodge MR, et al. 2004. T follicular helper cells express a distinctive transcriptional profile, reflecting their role as non-Th1/Th2 effector cells that provide help for B cells. *J. Immunol.* 173:68–78
99. Breitfeld D, Ohl L, Kremmer E, Ellwart J, Sallusto F, et al. 2000. Follicular B helper T cells express CXC chemokine receptor 5, localize to B cell follicles, and support immunoglobulin production. *J. Exp. Med.* 192:1545–52
100. Nurieva RI, Chung Y, Martinez GJ, Yang XO, Tanaka S, et al. 2009. Bcl6 mediates the development of T follicular helper cells. *Science* 325:1001–5

101. Johnston RJ, Poholek AC, DiToro D, Yusuf I, Eto D, et al. 2009. Bcl6 and Blimp-1 are reciprocal and antagonistic regulators of T follicular helper cell differentiation. *Science* 325:1006–10
102. Yu D, Rao S, Tsai LM, Lee SK, He Y, et al. 2009. The transcriptional repressor Bcl-6 directs T follicular helper cell lineage commitment. *Immunity* 31:457–68
103. Lieberman LA, Banica M, Reiner SL, Hunter CA. 2004. STAT1 plays a critical role in the regulation of antimicrobial effector mechanisms, but not in the development of Th1-type responses during toxoplasmosis. *J. Immunol.* 172:457–63
104. Park C, Li S, Cha E, Schindler C. 2000. Immune response in Stat2 knockout mice. *Immunity* 13:795–804
105. Harris TJ, Grosso JF, Yen HR, Xin H, Kortylewski M, et al. 2007. Cutting edge: An in vivo requirement for STAT3 signaling in TH17 development and TH17-dependent autoimmunity. *J. Immunol.* 179:4313–17
106. Mathur AN, Chang HC, Zisoulis DG, Stritesky GL, Yu Q, et al. 2007. Stat3 and Stat4 direct development of IL-17-secreting Th cells. *J. Immunol.* 178:4901–7
107. Laurence A, Tato CM, Davidson TS, Kanno Y, Chen Z, et al. 2007. Interleukin-2 signaling via STAT5 constrains T helper 17 cell generation. *Immunity* 26:371–81
108. Yang XO, Panopoulos AD, Nurieva R, Chang SH, Wang D, et al. 2007. STAT3 regulates cytokine-mediated generation of inflammatory helper T cells. *J. Biol. Chem.* 282:9358–63
109. Milner JD, Brenchley JM, Laurence A, Freeman AF, Hill BJ, et al. 2008. Impaired T_H17 cell differentiation in subjects with autosomal dominant hyper-IgE syndrome. *Nature* 452:773–76
110. Chen Z, Laurence A, Kanno Y, Pacher-Zavisin M, Zhu BM, et al. 2006. Selective regulatory function of Socs3 in the formation of IL-17-secreting T cells. *Proc. Natl. Acad. Sci. USA* 103:8137–42
111. Wei L, Laurence A, Elias KM, O'Shea JJ. 2007. IL-21 is produced by Th17 cells and drives IL-17 production in a STAT3-dependent manner. *J. Biol. Chem.* 282:34605–10
112. Xu L, Kitani A, Fuss I, Strober W. 2007. Cutting edge: Regulatory T cells induce $CD4^+CD25^-Foxp3^-$ T cells or are self-induced to become Th17 cells in the absence of exogenous TGF-β. *J. Immunol.* 178:6725–29
113. Yang XO, Nurieva R, Martinez GJ, Kang HS, Chung Y, et al. 2008. Molecular antagonism and plasticity of regulatory and inflammatory T cell programs. *Immunity* 29:44–56
114. Kaplan MH, Sun YL, Hoey T, Grusby MJ. 1996. Impaired IL-12 responses and enhanced development of Th2 cells in Stat4-deficient mice. *Nature* 382:174–77
115. Thierfelder WE, van Deursen JM, Yamamoto K, Tripp RA, Sarawar SR, et al. 1996. Requirement for Stat4 in interleukin-12-mediated responses of natural killer and T cells. *Nature* 382:171–74
116. Cai G, Radzanowski T, Villegas EN, Kastelein R, Hunter CA. 2000. Identification of STAT4-dependent and independent mechanisms of resistance to *Toxoplasma gondii*. *J. Immunol.* 165:2619–27
117. Usui T, Nishikomori R, Kitani A, Strober W. 2003. GATA-3 suppresses Th1 development by down-regulation of Stat4 and not through effects on IL-12Rβ2 chain or T-bet. *Immunity* 18:415–28
118. Frucht DM, Aringer M, Galon J, Danning C, Brown M, et al. 2000. Stat4 is expressed in activated peripheral blood monocytes, dendritic cells, and macrophages at sites of Th1-mediated inflammation. *J. Immunol.* 164:4659–64
119. Lin JX, Leonard WJ. 2000. The role of Stat5a and Stat5b in signaling by IL-2 family cytokines. *Oncogene* 19:2566–76
120. Moriggl R, Topham DJ, Teglund S, Sexl V, McKay C, et al. 1999. Stat5 is required for IL-2-induced cell cycle progression of peripheral T cells. *Immunity* 10:249–59
121. Cote-Sierra J, Foucras G, Guo L, Chiodetti L, Young HA, et al. 2004. Interleukin 2 plays a central role in Th2 differentiation. *Proc. Natl. Acad. Sci. USA* 101:3880–85
122. Zhu J, Cote-Sierra J, Guo L, Paul WE. 2003. Stat5 activation plays a critical role in Th2 differentiation. *Immunity* 19:739–48
123. Kagami S, Nakajima H, Suto A, Hirose K, Suzuki K, et al. 2001. Stat5a regulates T helper cell differentiation by several distinct mechanisms. *Blood* 97:2358–65
124. Kagami S, Nakajima H, Kumano K, Suzuki K, Suto A, et al. 2000. Both stat5a and stat5b are required for antigen-induced eosinophil and T-cell recruitment into the tissue. *Blood* 95:1370–77

125. Takatori H, Nakajima H, Kagami S, Hirose K, Suto A, et al. 2005. Stat5a inhibits IL-12-induced Th1 cell differentiation through the induction of suppressor of cytokine signaling 3 expression. *J. Immunol.* 174:4105–12
126. Davidson TS, DiPaolo RJ, Andersson J, Shevach EM. 2007. Cutting Edge: IL-2 is essential for TGF-β-mediated induction of Foxp3^{+} T regulatory cells. *J. Immunol.* 178:4022–26
127. Burchill MA, Yang J, Vogtenhuber C, Blazar BR, Farrar MA. 2007. IL-2 receptor beta-dependent STAT5 activation is required for the development of Foxp3^{+} regulatory T cells. *J. Immunol.* 178:280–90
128. Burchill MA, Yang J, Vang KB, Moon JJ, Chu HH, et al. 2008. Linked T cell receptor and cytokine signaling govern the development of the regulatory T cell repertoire. *Immunity* 28:112–21
129. Yao Z, Kanno Y, Kerenyi M, Stephens G, Durant L, et al. 2007. Nonredundant roles for Stat5a/b in directly regulating Foxp3. *Blood* 109:4368–75
130. Amadi-Obi A, Yu CR, Liu X, Mahdi RM, Clarke GL, et al. 2007. TH17 cells contribute to uveitis and scleritis and are expanded by IL-2 and inhibited by IL-27/STAT1. *Nat. Med.* 13:711–18
131. Shi M, Lin TH, Appell KC, Berg LJ. 2008. Janus-kinase-3-dependent signals induce chromatin remodeling at the *Ifng* locus during T helper 1 cell differentiation. *Immunity* 28:763–73
132. Kaplan MH, Schindler U, Smiley ST, Grusby MJ. 1996. Stat6 is required for mediating responses to IL-4 and for development of Th2 cells. *Immunity* 4:313–19
133. Shimoda K, van Deursen J, Sangster MY, Sarawar SR, Carson RT, et al. 1996. Lack of IL-4-induced Th2 response and IgE class switching in mice with disrupted *Stat6* gene. *Nature* 380:630–33
134. Takeda K, Tanaka T, Shi W, Matsumoto M, Minami M, et al. 1996. Essential role of Stat6 in IL-4 signaling. *Nature* 380:627–30
135. Kurata H, Lee HJ, O'Garra A, Arai N. 1999. Ectopic expression of activated Stat6 induces the expression of Th2-specific cytokines and transcription factors in developing Th1 cells. *Immunity* 11:677–88
136. Zhu J, Guo L, Watson CJ, Hu-Li J, Paul WE. 2001. Stat6 is necessary and sufficient for IL-4's role in Th2 differentiation and cell expansion. *J. Immunol.* 166:7276–81
137. Lee DU, Rao A. 2004. Molecular analysis of a locus control region in the T helper 2 cytokine gene cluster: a target for STAT6 but not GATA3. *Proc. Natl. Acad. Sci. USA* 101:16010–15
138. Jankovic D, Kullberg MC, Noben-Trauth N, Caspar P, Paul WE, Sher A. 2000. Single cell analysis reveals that IL-4 receptor/Stat6 signaling is not required for the in vivo or in vitro development of CD4^{+} lymphocytes with a Th2 cytokine profile. *J. Immunol.* 164:3047–55
139. Finkelman FD, Morris SC, Orekhova T, Mori M, Donaldson D, et al. 2000. Stat6 regulation of in vivo IL-4 responses. *J. Immunol.* 164:2303–10
140. Min B, Prout M, Hu-Li J, Zhu J, Jankovic D, et al. 2004. Basophils produce IL-4 and accumulate in tissues after infection with a Th2-inducing parasite. *J. Exp. Med.* 200:507–17
141. Voehringer D, Shinkai K, Locksley RM. 2004. Type 2 immunity reflects orchestrated recruitment of cells committed to IL-4 production. *Immunity* 20:267–77
142. van Panhuys N, Tang SC, Prout M, Camberis M, Scarlett D, et al. 2008. In vivo studies fail to reveal a role for IL-4 or STAT6 signaling in Th2 lymphocyte differentiation. *Proc. Natl. Acad. Sci. USA* 105:12423–28
143. Else KJ, Finkelman FD, Maliszewski CR, Grencis RK. 1994. Cytokine-mediated regulation of chronic intestinal helminth infection. *J. Exp. Med.* 179:347–51
144. Djuretic IM, Levanon D, Negreanu V, Groner Y, Rao A, Ansel KM. 2007. Transcription factors T-bet and Runx3 cooperate to activate *Ifng* and silence *Il4* in T helper type 1 cells. *Nat. Immunol.* 8:145–53
145. Naoe Y, Setoguchi R, Akiyama K, Muroi S, Kuroda M, et al. 2007. Repression of interleukin-4 in T helper type 1 cells by Runx/Cbfβ binding to the *Il4* silencer. *J. Exp. Med.* 204:1749–55
146. Egawa T, Tillman RE, Naoe Y, Taniuchi I, Littman DR. 2007. The role of the Runx transcription factors in thymocyte differentiation and in homeostasis of naive T cells. *J. Exp. Med.* 204:1945–57
147. Ono M, Yaguchi H, Ohkura N, Kitabayashi I, Nagamura Y, et al. 2007. Foxp3 controls regulatory T-cell function by interacting with AML1/Runx1. *Nature* 446:685–89
148. Kitoh A, Ono M, Naoe Y, Ohkura N, Yamaguchi T, et al. 2009. Indispensable role of the Runx1-Cbfβ transcription complex for in vivo-suppressive function of FoxP3^{+} regulatory T cells. *Immunity* 31:609–20
149. Rudra D, Egawa T, Chong MM, Treuting P, Littman DR, Rudensky AY. 2009. Runx-CBFβ complexes control expression of the transcription factor Foxp3 in regulatory T cells. *Nat. Immunol.* 10:1170–77

150. Bruno L, Mazzarella L, Hoogenkamp M, Hertweck A, Cobb BS, et al. 2009. Runx proteins regulate Foxp3 expression. *J. Exp. Med.* 206:2329–37
151. Klunker S, Chong MM, Mantel PY, Palomares O, Bassin C, et al. 2009. Transcription factors RUNX1 and RUNX3 in the induction and suppressive function of Foxp3$^+$ inducible regulatory T cells. *J. Exp. Med.* 206:2701–15
152. Zhang F, Meng G, Strober W. 2008. Interactions among the transcription factors Runx1, RORγt and Foxp3 regulate the differentiation of interleukin 17-producing T cells. *Nat. Immunol.* 9:1297–306
153. Lohoff M, Mittrucker HW, Prechtl S, Bischof S, Sommer F, et al. 2002. Dysregulated T helper cell differentiation in the absence of interferon regulatory factor 4. *Proc. Natl. Acad. Sci. USA* 99:11808–12
154. Rengarajan J, Mowen KA, McBride KD, Smith ED, Singh H, Glimcher LH. 2002. Interferon regulatory factor 4 (IRF4) interacts with NFATc2 to modulate interleukin 4 gene expression. *J. Exp. Med.* 195:1003–12
155. Brustle A, Heink S, Huber M, Rosenplanter C, Stadelmann C, et al. 2007. The development of inflammatory T_H-17 cells requires interferon-regulatory factor 4. *Nat. Immunol.* 8:958–66
156. Kano S, Sato K, Morishita Y, Vollstedt S, Kim S, et al. 2008. The contribution of transcription factor IRF1 to the interferon-γ-interleukin 12 signaling axis and T_H1 versus T_H-17 differentiation of CD4$^+$ T cells. *Nat. Immunol.* 9:34–41
157. Gilks CB, Bear SE, Grimes HL, Tsichlis PN. 1993. Progression of interleukin-2 (IL-2)-dependent rat T cell lymphoma lines to IL-2-independent growth following activation of a gene (Gfi-1) encoding a novel zinc finger protein. *Mol. Cell. Biol.* 13:1759–68
158. Duan Z, Horwitz M. 2005. Gfi-1 takes center stage in hematopoietic stem cells. *Trends Mol. Med.* 11:49–52
159. Zhu J, Jankovic D, Grinberg A, Guo L, Paul WE. 2006. Gfi-1 plays an important role in IL-2-mediated Th2 cell expansion. *Proc. Natl. Acad. Sci. USA* 103:18214–19
160. Zhu J, Davidson TS, Wei G, Jankovic D, Cui K, et al. 2009. Down-regulation of Gfi-1 expression by TGF-β is important for differentiation of Th17 and CD103$^+$ inducible regulatory T cells. *J. Exp. Med.* 206:329–41
161. Georgopoulos K, Winandy S, Avitahl N. 1997. The role of the Ikaros gene in lymphocyte development and homeostasis. *Annu. Rev. Immunol.* 15:155–76
162. Quirion MR, Gregory GD, Umetsu SE, Winandy S, Brown MA. 2009. Cutting edge: Ikaros is a regulator of Th2 cell differentiation. *J. Immunol.* 182:741–45
163. Pan F, Yu H, Dang EV, Barbi J, Pan X, et al. 2009. Eos mediates Foxp3-dependent gene silencing in CD4$^+$ regulatory T cells. *Science* 325:1142–46
164. Wei G, Wei L, Zhu J, Zang C, Hu-Li J, et al. 2009. Global mapping of H3K4me3 and H3K27me3 reveals specificity and plasticity in lineage fate determination of differentiating CD4$^+$ T cells. *Immunity* 30:155–67
165. Kim JI, Ho IC, Grusby MJ, Glimcher LH. 1999. The transcription factor c-Maf controls the production of interleukin-4 but not other Th2 cytokines. *Immunity* 10:745–51
166. Hwang ES, White IA, Ho IC. 2002. An IL-4-independent and CD25-mediated function of c-maf in promoting the production of Th2 cytokines. *Proc. Natl. Acad. Sci. USA* 99:13026–30
167. Bauquet AT, Jin H, Paterson AM, Mitsdoerffer M, Ho IC, et al. 2009. The costimulatory molecule ICOS regulates the expression of c-Maf and IL-21 in the development of follicular T helper cells and TH-17 cells. *Nat. Immunol.* 10:167–75
168. Grenningloh R, Kang BY, Ho IC. 2005. Ets-1, a functional cofactor of T-bet, is essential for Th1 inflammatory responses. *J. Exp. Med.* 201:615–26
169. Moisan J, Grenningloh R, Bettelli E, Oukka M, Ho IC. 2007. Ets-1 is a negative regulator of Th17 differentiation. *J. Exp. Med.* 204:2825–35
170. Li B, Tournier C, Davis RJ, Flavell RA. 1999. Regulation of IL-4 expression by the transcription factor JunB during T helper cell differentiation. *EMBO J.* 18:420–32
171. Cimmino L, Martins GA, Liao J, Magnusdottir E, Grunig G, et al. 2008. Blimp-1 attenuates Th1 differentiation by repression of *ifng*, *tbx21*, and *bcl6* gene expression. *J. Immunol.* 181:2338–47
172. Martins G, Calame K. 2008. Regulation and functions of Blimp-1 in T and B lymphocytes. *Annu. Rev. Immunol.* 26:133–69

173. Wang L, van Panhuys N, Hu-Li J, Kim S, Le Gros G, Min B. 2008. Blimp-1 induced by IL-4 plays a critical role in suppressing IL-2 production in activated CD4 T cells. *J. Immunol.* 181:5249–56
174. Venuprasad K, Huang H, Harada Y, Elly C, Subramaniam M, et al. 2008. The E3 ubiquitin ligase Itch regulates expression of transcription factor Foxp3 and airway inflammation by enhancing the function of transcription factor TIEG1. *Nat. Immunol.* 9:245–53
175. Veldhoen M, Hirota K, Westendorf AM, Buer J, Dumoutier L, et al. 2008. The aryl hydrocarbon receptor links TH17-cell-mediated autoimmunity to environmental toxins. *Nature* 453:106–9
176. Veldhoen M, Hirota K, Christensen J, O'Garra A, Stockinger B. 2009. Natural agonists for aryl hydrocarbon receptor in culture medium are essential for optimal differentiation of Th17 T cells. *J. Exp. Med.* 206:43–49
177. Schraml BU, Hildner K, Ise W, Lee WL, Smith WA, et al. 2009. The AP-1 transcription factor Batf controls T_H17 differentiation. *Nature* 460:405–9
178. Yang XO, Angkasekwinai P, Zhu J, Peng J, Liu Z, et al. 2009. Requirement for the basic helix-loop-helix transcription factor Dec2 in initial TH2 lineage commitment. *Nat. Immunol.* 10:1260–66
179. Liu Z, Li Z, Mao K, Zou J, Wang Y, et al. 2009. Dec2 promotes Th2 cell differentiation by enhancing IL-2R signaling. *J. Immunol.* 183:6320–29
180. Liao W, Schones DE, Oh J, Cui Y, Cui K, et al. 2008. Priming for T helper type 2 differentiation by interleukin 2-mediated induction of interleukin 4 receptor α-chain expression. *Nat. Immunol.* 9:1288–96
181. Thieu VT, Yu Q, Chang HC, Yeh N, Nguyen ET, et al. 2008. Signal transducer and activator of transcription 4 is required for the transcription factor T-bet to promote T helper 1 cell-fate determination. *Immunity* 29:679–90
182. Zhou L, Lopes JE, Chong MM, Ivanov II, Min R, et al. 2008. TGF-β-induced Foxp3 inhibits T_H17 cell differentiation by antagonizing RORγt function. *Nature* 453:236–40
183. Wu Y, Borde M, Heissmeyer V, Feuerer M, Lapan AD, et al. 2006. FOXP3 controls regulatory T cell function through cooperation with NFAT. *Cell* 126:375–87
184. Hwang ES, Szabo SJ, Schwartzberg PL, Glimcher LH. 2005. T helper cell fate specified by kinase-mediated interaction of T-bet with GATA-3. *Science* 307:430–33
185. Zhu J, Paul WE. 2008. CD4 T cells: fates, functions, and faults. *Blood* 112:1557–69
186. O'Garra A, Vieira P. 2007. T_H1 cells control themselves by producing interleukin-10. *Nat. Rev. Immunol.* 7:425–28
187. Constant SL, Bottomly K. 1997. Induction of Th1 and Th2 $CD4^+$ T cell responses: the alternative approaches. *Annu. Rev. Immunol.* 15:297–322
188. Tao X, Grant C, Constant S, Bottomly K. 1997. Induction of IL-4-producing $CD4^+$ T cells by antigenic peptides altered for TCR binding. *J. Immunol.* 158:4237–44
189. Jorritsma PJ, Brogdon JL, Bottomly K. 2003. Role of TCR-induced extracellular signal-regulated kinase activation in the regulation of early IL-4 expression in naive $CD4^+$ T cells. *J. Immunol.* 170:2427–34
190. Yamane H, Zhu J, Paul WE. 2005. Independent roles for IL-2 and GATA-3 in stimulating naive $CD4^+$ T cells to generate a Th2-inducing cytokine environment. *J. Exp. Med.* 202:793–804
191. Yamashita M, Kimura M, Kubo M, Shimizu C, Tada T, et al. 1999. T cell antigen receptor-mediated activation of the Ras/mitogen-activated protein kinase pathway controls interleukin 4 receptor function and type-2 helper T cell differentiation. *Proc. Natl. Acad. Sci. USA* 96:1024–29
192. Yamashita M, Shinnakasu R, Asou H, Kimura M, Hasegawa A, et al. 2005. Ras-ERK MAPK cascade regulates GATA3 stability and Th2 differentiation through ubiquitin-proteasome pathway. *J. Biol. Chem.* 280:29409–19
193. Yamashita M, Hashimoto K, Kimura M, Kubo M, Tada T, Nakayama T. 1998. Requirement for $p56^{lck}$ tyrosine kinase activation in Th subset differentiation. *Int. Immunol.* 10:577–91
194. Molina TJ, Kishihara K, Siderovski DP, van Ewijk W, Narendran A, et al. 1992. Profound block in thymocyte development in mice lacking $p56^{lck}$. *Nature* 357:161–64
195. Stein PL, Lee HM, Rich S, Soriano P. 1992. $pp59^{fyn}$ mutant mice display differential signaling in thymocytes and peripheral T cells. *Cell* 70:741–50
196. Appleby MW, Gross JA, Cooke MP, Levin SD, Qian X, Perlmutter RM. 1992. Defective T cell receptor signaling in mice lacking the thymic isoform of $p59^{fyn}$. *Cell* 70:751–63

197. Tamura T, Igarashi O, Hino A, Yamane H, Aizawa S, et al. 2001. Impairment in the expression and activity of Fyn during differentiation of naive CD4$^+$ T cells into the Th2 subset. *J. Immunol.* 167:1962–69
198. Mamchak AA, Sullivan BM, Hou B, Lee LM, Gilden JK, et al. 2008. Normal development and activation but altered cytokine production of Fyn-deficient CD4$^+$ T cells. *J. Immunol.* 181:5374–85
199. Sharma P, Chakraborty R, Wang L, Min B, Tremblay ML, et al. 2008. Redox regulation of interleukin-4 signaling. *Immunity* 29:551–64
200. Lu X, Malumbres R, Shields B, Jiang X, Sarosiek KA, et al. 2008. PTP1B is a negative regulator of interleukin 4-induced STAT6 signaling. *Blood* 112:4098–108
201. Zhu J, Huang H, Guo L, Stonehouse T, Watson CJ, et al. 2000. Transient inhibition of interleukin 4 signaling by T cell receptor ligation. *J. Exp. Med.* 192:1125–34
202. Schwartzberg PL, Finkelstein LD, Readinger JA. 2005. TEC-family kinases: regulators of T-helper-cell differentiation. *Nat. Rev. Immunol.* 5:284–95
203. Fowell DJ, Shinkai K, Liao XC, Beebe AM, Coffman RL, et al. 1999. Impaired NFATc translocation and failure of Th2 development in Itk-deficient CD4$^+$ T cells. *Immunity* 11:399–409
204. Miller AT, Wilcox HM, Lai Z, Berg LJ. 2004. Signaling through Itk promotes T helper 2 differentiation via negative regulation of T-bet. *Immunity* 21:67–80
205. Gomez-Rodriguez J, Sahu N, Handon R, Davidson TS, Anderson SM, et al. 2009. Differential expression of IL-17A and IL-17F is coupled to TCR signaling via Itk-mediated regulation of NFATc1. *Immunity* 31:587–97
206. Kashiwakura J, Suzuki N, Nagafuchi H, Takeno M, Takeba Y, et al. 1999. Txk, a nonreceptor tyrosine kinase of the Tec family, is expressed in T helper type 1 cells and regulates interferon γ production in human T lymphocytes. *J. Exp. Med.* 190:1147–54
207. Takeba Y, Nagafuchi H, Takeno M, Kashiwakura J, Suzuki N. 2002. Txk, a member of nonreceptor tyrosine kinase of Tec family, acts as a Th1 cell-specific transcription factor and regulates IFN-γ gene transcription. *J. Immunol.* 168:2365–70
208. Sahu N, Venegas AM, Jankovic D, Mitzner W, Gomez-Rodriguez J, et al. 2008. Selective expression rather than specific function of Txk and Itk regulate Th1 and Th2 responses. *J. Immunol.* 181:6125–31
209. Schaeffer EM, Yap GS, Lewis CM, Czar MJ, McVicar DW, et al. 2001. Mutation of Tec family kinases alters T helper cell differentiation. *Nat. Immunol.* 2:1183–88
210. Das J, Chen CH, Yang L, Cohn L, Ray P, Ray A. 2001. A critical role for NF-κB in GATA3 expression and TH2 differentiation in allergic airway inflammation. *Nat. Immunol.* 2:45–50
211. Nolan GP, Fujita T, Bhatia K, Huppi C, Liou HC, et al. 1993. The bcl-3 proto-oncogene encodes a nuclear IκB-like molecule that preferentially interacts with NF-κB p50 and p52 in a phosphorylation-dependent manner. *Mol. Cell. Biol.* 13:3557–66
212. Corn RA, Hunter C, Liou HC, Siebenlist U, Boothby MR. 2005. Opposing roles for RelB and Bcl-3 in regulation of T-box expressed in T cells, GATA-3, and Th effector differentiation. *J. Immunol.* 175:2102–10
213. Ghosh S, May MJ, Kopp EB. 1998. NF-κB and Rel proteins: evolutionarily conserved mediators of immune responses. *Annu. Rev. Immunol.* 16:225–60
214. Macian F. 2005. NFAT proteins: key regulators of T-cell development and function. *Nat. Rev. Immunol.* 5:472–84
215. Kiani A, Viola JP, Lichtman AH, Rao A. 1997. Down-regulation of IL-4 gene transcription and control of Th2 cell differentiation by a mechanism involving NFAT1. *Immunity* 7:849–60
216. Kiani A, Garcia-Cozar FJ, Habermann I, Laforsch S, Aebischer T, et al. 2001. Regulation of interferon-γ gene expression by nuclear factor of activated T cells. *Blood* 98:1480–88
217. Diehl S, Chow CW, Weiss L, Palmetshofer A, Twardzik T, et al. 2002. Induction of NFATc2 expression by interleukin 6 promotes T helper type 2 differentiation. *J. Exp. Med.* 196:39–49
218. Oukka M, Ho IC, de la Brousse FC, Hoey T, Grusby MJ, Glimcher LH. 1998. The transcription factor NFAT4 is involved in the generation and survival of T cells. *Immunity* 9:295–304
219. Ranger AM, Oukka M, Rengarajan J, Glimcher LH. 1998. Inhibitory function of two NFAT family members in lymphoid homeostasis and Th2 development. *Immunity* 9:627–35
220. Rengarajan J, Tang B, Glimcher LH. 2002. NFATc2 and NFATc3 regulate T_H2 differentiation and modulate TCR-responsiveness of naive T_H cells. *Nat. Immunol.* 3:48–54

221. Yoshida H, Nishina H, Takimoto H, Marengere LE, Wakeham AC, et al. 1998. The transcription factor NF-ATc1 regulates lymphocyte proliferation and Th2 cytokine production. *Immunity* 8:115–24
222. Ranger AM, Hodge MR, Gravallese EM, Oukka M, Davidson L, et al. 1998. Delayed lymphoid repopulation with defects in IL-4-driven responses produced by inactivation of NF-ATc. *Immunity* 8:125–34
223. Brogdon JL, Leitenberg D, Bottomly K. 2002. The potency of TCR signaling differentially regulates NFATc/p activity and early IL-4 transcription in naive CD4$^+$ T cells. *J. Immunol.* 168:3825–32
224. Nurieva RI, Duong J, Kishikawa H, Dianzani U, Rojo JM, et al. 2003. Transcriptional regulation of Th2 differentiation by inducible costimulator. *Immunity* 18:801–11
225. Kopan R, Ilagan MX. 2009. The canonical Notch signaling pathway: unfolding the activation mechanism. *Cell* 137:216–33
226. Stanley P, Guidos CJ. 2009. Regulation of Notch signaling during T- and B-cell development by O-fucose glycans. *Immunol. Rev.* 230:201–15
227. Maekawa Y, Tsukumo S, Chiba S, Hirai H, Hayashi Y, et al. 2003. Delta1-Notch3 interactions bias the functional differentiation of activated CD4$^+$ T cells. *Immunity* 19:549–59
228. Skokos D, Nussenzweig MC. 2007. CD8- DCs induce IL-12-independent Th1 differentiation through Delta 4 Notch-like ligand in response to bacterial LPS. *J. Exp. Med.* 204:1525–31
229. Sun J, Krawczyk CJ, Pearce EJ. 2008. Suppression of Th2 cell development by Notch ligands Delta1 and Delta4. *J. Immunol.* 180:1655–61
230. Shin HM, Minter LM, Cho OH, Gottipati S, Fauq AH, et al. 2006. Notch1 augments NF-κB activity by facilitating its nuclear retention. *EMBO J.* 25:129–38
231. Palaga T, Miele L, Golde TE, Osborne BA. 2003. TCR-mediated Notch signaling regulates proliferation and IFN-γ production in peripheral T cells. *J. Immunol.* 171:3019–24
232. Minter LM, Turley DM, Das P, Shin HM, Joshi I, et al. 2005. Inhibitors of γ-secretase block in vivo and in vitro T helper type 1 polarization by preventing Notch upregulation of Tbx21. *Nat. Immunol.* 6:680–88
233. Amsen D, Blander JM, Lee GR, Tanigaki K, Honjo T, Flavell RA. 2004. Instruction of distinct CD4 T helper cell fates by different Notch ligands on antigen-presenting cells. *Cell* 117:515–26
234. Tanigaki K, Tsuji M, Yamamoto N, Han H, Tsukada J, et al. 2004. Regulation of αβ/γδ T cell lineage commitment and peripheral T cell responses by Notch/RBP-J signaling. *Immunity* 20:611–22
235. Amsen D, Antov A, Jankovic D, Sher A, Radtke F, et al. 2007. Direct regulation of Gata3 expression determines the T helper differentiation potential of Notch. *Immunity* 27:89–99
236. Tu L, Fang TC, Artis D, Shestova O, Pross SE, et al. 2005. Notch signaling is an important regulator of type 2 immunity. *J. Exp. Med.* 202:1037–42
237. Fang TC, Yashiro-Ohtani Y, Del Bianco C, Knoblock DM, Blacklow SC, Pear WS. 2007. Notch directly regulates Gata3 expression during T helper 2 cell differentiation. *Immunity* 27:100–10
238. Samon JB, Champhekar A, Minter LM, Telfer JC, Miele L, et al. 2008. Notch1 and TGFβ1 cooperatively regulate Foxp3 expression and the maintenance of peripheral regulatory T cells. *Blood* 112:1813–21
239. Blokzijl A, Dahlqvist C, Reissmann E, Falk A, Moliner A, et al. 2003. Cross-talk between the Notch and TGF-β signaling pathways mediated by interaction of the Notch intracellular domain with Smad3. *J. Cell Biol.* 163:723–28
240. Mukherjee S, Schaller MA, Neupane R, Kunkel SL, Lukacs NW. 2009. Regulation of T cell activation by Notch ligand, DLL4, promotes IL-17 production and Rorc activation. *J. Immunol.* 182:7381–88
241. Ong CT, Sedy JR, Murphy KM, Kopan R. 2008. Notch and presenilin regulate cellular expansion and cytokine secretion but cannot instruct Th1/Th2 fate acquisition. *PLoS One* 3:e2823
242. Adler SH, Chiffoleau E, Xu L, Dalton NM, Burg JM, et al. 2003. Notch signaling augments T cell responsiveness by enhancing CD25 expression. *J. Immunol.* 171:2896–903
243. Wilson CB, Rowell E, Sekimata M. 2009. Epigenetic control of T-helper-cell differentiation. *Nat. Rev. Immunol.* 9:91–105
244. Lee GR, Kim ST, Spilianakis CG, Fields PE, Flavell RA. 2006. T helper cell differentiation: regulation by cis elements and epigenetics. *Immunity* 24:369–79
245. Ansel KM, Djuretic I, Tanasa B, Rao A. 2006. Regulation of Th2 differentiation and *Il4* locus accessibility. *Annu. Rev. Immunol.* 24:607–56

246. Ansel KM, Greenwald RJ, Agarwal S, Bassing CH, Monticelli S, et al. 2004. Deletion of a conserved *Il4* silencer impairs T helper type 1-mediated immunity. *Nat. Immunol.* 5:1251–59
247. Agarwal S, Rao A. 1998. Modulation of chromatin structure regulates cytokine gene expression during T cell differentiation. *Immunity* 9:765–75
248. Seki N, Miyazaki M, Suzuki W, Hayashi K, Arima K, et al. 2004. IL-4-induced GATA-3 expression is a time-restricted instruction switch for Th2 cell differentiation. *J. Immunol.* 172:6158–66
249. Lee HJ, Takemoto N, Kurata H, Kamogawa Y, Miyatake S, et al. 2000. GATA-3 induces T helper cell type 2 (Th2) cytokine expression and chromatin remodeling in committed Th1 cells. *J. Exp. Med.* 192:105–15
250. Makar KW, Perez-Melgosa M, Shnyreva M, Weaver WM, Fitzpatrick DR, Wilson CB. 2003. Active recruitment of DNA methyltransferases regulates interleukin 4 in thymocytes and T cells. *Nat. Immunol.* 4:1183–90
251. Hutchins AS, Mullen AC, Lee HW, Sykes KJ, High FA, et al. 2002. Gene silencing quantitatively controls the function of a developmental trans-activator. *Mol. Cell* 10:81–91
252. Barski A, Cuddapah S, Cui K, Roh TY, Schones DE, et al. 2007. High-resolution profiling of histone methylations in the human genome. *Cell* 129:823–37
253. Schones DE, Cui K, Cuddapah S, Roh TY, Barski A, et al. 2008. Dynamic regulation of nucleosome positioning in the human genome. *Cell* 132:887–98
254. Boyle AP, Davis S, Shulha HP, Meltzer P, Margulies EH, et al. 2008. High-resolution mapping and characterization of open chromatin across the genome. *Cell* 132:311–22
255. Yamashita M, Hirahara K, Shinnakasu R, Hosokawa H, Norikane S, et al. 2006. Crucial role of MLL for the maintenance of memory T helper type 2 cell responses. *Immunity* 24:611–22
256. Koyanagi M, Baguet A, Martens J, Margueron R, Jenuwein T, Bix M. 2005. EZH2 and histone 3 trimethyl lysine 27 associated with *Il4* and *Il13* gene silencing in Th1 cells. *J. Biol. Chem.* 280:31470–77
257. Miller SA, Huang AC, Miazgowicz MM, Brassil MM, Weinmann AS. 2008. Coordinated but physically separable interaction with H3K27-demethylase and H3K4-methyltransferase activities are required for T-box protein-mediated activation of developmental gene expression. *Genes Dev.* 22:2980–93
258. Floess S, Freyer J, Siewert C, Baron U, Olek S, et al. 2007. Epigenetic control of the *foxp3* locus in regulatory T cells. *PLoS Biol.* 5:e38
259. Schoenborn JR, Dorschner MO, Sekimata M, Santer DM, Shnyreva M, et al. 2007. Comprehensive epigenetic profiling identifies multiple distal regulatory elements directing transcription of the gene encoding interferon-γ. *Nat. Immunol.* 8:732–42
260. Lee DU, Avni O, Chen L, Rao A. 2004. A distal enhancer in the interferon-γ (IFN-γ) locus revealed by genome sequence comparison. *J. Biol. Chem.* 279:4802–10
261. Hatton RD, Harrington LE, Luther RJ, Wakefield T, Janowski KM, et al. 2006. A distal conserved sequence element controls *Ifng* gene expression by T cells and NK cells. *Immunity* 25:717–29
262. Sekimata M, Perez-Melgosa M, Miller SA, Weinmann AS, Sabo PJ, et al. 2009. CCCTC-binding factor and the transcription factor T-bet orchestrate T helper 1 cell-specific structure and function at the interferon-γ locus. *Immunity* 31:551–64
263. Mohrs M, Blankespoor CM, Wang ZE, Loots GG, Afzal V, et al. 2001. Deletion of a coordinate regulator of type 2 cytokine expression in mice. *Nat. Immunol.* 2:842–47
264. Solymar DC, Agarwal S, Bassing CH, Alt FW, Rao A. 2002. A 3′ enhancer in the IL-4 gene regulates cytokine production by Th2 cells and mast cells. *Immunity* 17:41–50
265. Hural JA, Kwan M, Henkel G, Hock MB, Brown MA. 2000. An intron transcriptional enhancer element regulates IL-4 gene locus accessibility in mast cells. *J. Immunol.* 165:3239–49
266. Lee GR, Fields PE, Griffin TJ, Flavell RA. 2003. Regulation of the Th2 cytokine locus by a locus control region. *Immunity* 19:145–53
267. Lee GR, Spilianakis CG, Flavell RA. 2005. Hypersensitive site 7 of the TH2 locus control region is essential for expressing TH2 cytokine genes and for long-range intrachromosomal interactions. *Nat. Immunol.* 6:42–48
268. Akimzhanov AM, Yang XO, Dong C. 2007. Chromatin remodeling of interleukin-17 (IL-17)-IL-17F cytokine gene locus during inflammatory helper T cell differentiation. *J. Biol. Chem.* 282:5969–72

269. Baltimore D, Boldin MP, O'Connell RM, Rao DS, Taganov KD. 2008. MicroRNAs: new regulators of immune cell development and function. *Nat. Immunol.* 9:839–45
270. Carmell MA, Hannon GJ. 2004. RNase III enzymes and the initiation of gene silencing. *Nat. Struct. Mol. Biol.* 11:214–18
271. Cobb BS, Nesterova TB, Thompson E, Hertweck A, O'Connor E, et al. 2005. T cell lineage choice and differentiation in the absence of the RNase III enzyme Dicer. *J. Exp. Med.* 201:1367–73
272. Muljo SA, Ansel KM, Kanellopoulou C, Livingston DM, Rao A, Rajewsky K. 2005. Aberrant T cell differentiation in the absence of Dicer. *J. Exp. Med.* 202:261–69
273. Cobb BS, Hertweck A, Smith J, O'Connor E, Graf D, et al. 2006. A role for Dicer in immune regulation. *J. Exp. Med.* 203:2519–27
274. Lu LF, Thai TH, Calado DP, Chaudhry A, Kubo M, et al. 2009. Foxp3-dependent microRNA155 confers competitive fitness to regulatory T cells by targeting SOCS1 protein. *Immunity* 30:80–91
275. Haasch D, Chen YW, Reilly RM, Chiou XG, Koterski S, et al. 2002. T cell activation induces a noncoding RNA transcript sensitive to inhibition by immunosuppressant drugs and encoded by the proto-oncogene, BIC. *Cell. Immunol.* 217:78–86
276. Thai TH, Calado DP, Casola S, Ansel KM, Xiao C, et al. 2007. Regulation of the germinal center response by microRNA-155. *Science* 316:604–8
277. Rodriguez A, Vigorito E, Clare S, Warren MV, Couttet P, et al. 2007. Requirement of bic/microRNA-155 for normal immune function. *Science* 316:608–11
278. Chen Y, Kuchroo VK, Inobe J, Hafler DA, Weiner HL. 1994. Regulatory T cell clones induced by oral tolerance: suppression of autoimmune encephalomyelitis. *Science* 265:1237–40
279. Groux H, O'Garra A, Bigler M, Rouleau M, Antonenko S, et al. 1997. A $CD4^+$ T-cell subset inhibits antigen-specific T-cell responses and prevents colitis. *Nature* 389:737–42
280. Veldhoen M, Uyttenhove C, van Snick J, Helmby H, Westendorf A, et al. 2008. Transforming growth factor-β 'reprograms' the differentiation of T helper 2 cells and promotes an interleukin 9-producing subset. *Nat. Immunol.* 9:1341–46
281. Dardalhon V, Awasthi A, Kwon H, Galileos G, Gao W, et al. 2008. IL-4 inhibits TGF-β-induced $Foxp3^+$ T cells and, together with TGF-β, generates $IL\text{-}9^+IL\text{-}10^+$ $Foxp3^-$ effector T cells. *Nat. Immunol.* 9:1347–55
282. Tsuji M, Komatsu N, Kawamoto S, Suzuki K, Kanagawa O, et al. 2009. Preferential generation of follicular B helper T cells from $Foxp3^+$ T cells in gut Peyer's patches. *Science* 323:1488–92
283. Guo L, Hu-Li J, Zhu J, Watson CJ, Difilippantonio MJ, et al. 2002. In TH2 cells the *Il4* gene has a series of accessibility states associated with distinctive probabilities of IL-4 production. *Proc. Natl. Acad. Sci. USA* 99:10623–28
284. Guo L, Hu-Li J, Paul WE. 2005. Probabilistic regulation in TH2 cells accounts for monoallelic expression of IL-4 and IL-13. *Immunity* 23:89–99
285. Darrah PA, Patel DT, De Luca PM, Lindsay RW, Davey DF, et al. 2007. Multifunctional TH1 cells define a correlate of vaccine-mediated protection against *Leishmania major*. *Nat. Med.* 13:843–50
286. Chang HC, Zhang S, Thieu VT, Slee RB, Bruns HA, et al. 2005. PU.1 expression delineates heterogeneity in primary Th2 cells. *Immunity* 22:693–703
287. Zhou X, Bailey-Bucktrout SL, Jeker LT, Penaranda C, Martinez-Llordella M, et al. 2009. Instability of the transcription factor Foxp3 leads to the generation of pathogenic memory T cells in vivo. *Nat. Immunol.* 10:1000–7
288. Woltjen K, Michael IP, Mohseni P, Desai R, Mileikovsky M, et al. 2009. piggyBac transposition reprograms fibroblasts to induced pluripotent stem cells. *Nature* 458:766–70
289. Takahashi K, Yamanaka S. 2006. Induction of pluripotent stem cells from mouse embryonic and adult fibroblast cultures by defined factors. *Cell* 126:663–76
290. Cobaleda C, Jochum W, Busslinger M. 2007. Conversion of mature B cells into T cells by dedifferentiation to uncommitted progenitors. *Nature* 449:473–77
291. Lee YK, Turner H, Maynard CL, Oliver JR, Chen D, et al. 2009. Late developmental plasticity in the T helper 17 lineage. *Immunity* 30:92–107

292. Filipe-Santos O, Bustamante J, Chapgier A, Vogt G, de Beaucoudrey L, et al. 2006. Inborn errors of IL-12/23- and IFN-γ-mediated immunity: molecular, cellular, and clinical features. *Semin. Immunol.* 18:347–61
293. Trinchieri G, Pflanz S, Kastelein RA. 2003. The IL-12 family of heterodimeric cytokines: new players in the regulation of T cell responses. *Immunity* 19:641–44
294. de Beaucoudrey L, Puel A, Filipe-Santos O, Cobat A, Ghandil P, et al. 2008. Mutations in STAT3 and IL12RB1 impair the development of human IL-17-producing T cells. *J. Exp. Med.* 205:1543–50
295. Khader SA, Cooper AM. 2008. IL-23 and IL-17 in tuberculosis. *Cytokine* 41:79–83
296. Van Esch H, Groenen P, Nesbit MA, Schuffenhauer S, Lichtner P, et al. 2000. GATA3 haplo-insufficiency causes human HDR syndrome. *Nature* 406:419–22
297. Skapenko A, Leipe J, Niesner U, Devriendt K, Beetz R, et al. 2004. GATA-3 in human T cell helper type 2 development. *J. Exp. Med.* 199:423–28
298. Marrella V, Poliani PL, Sobacchi C, Grassi F, Villa A. 2008. Of Omenn and mice. *Trends Immunol.* 29:133–40
299. Turul T, Tezcan I, Artac H, de Bruin-Versteeg S, Barendregt BH, et al. 2009. Clinical heterogeneity can hamper the diagnosis of patients with ZAP70 deficiency. *Eur. J. Pediatr.* 168:87–93
300. Milner JD, Ward JM, Keane-Myers A, Paul WE. 2007. Lymphopenic mice reconstituted with limited repertoire T cells develop severe, multiorgan, Th2-associated inflammatory disease. *Proc. Natl. Acad. Sci. USA* 104:576–81
301. Khiong K, Murakami M, Kitabayashi C, Ueda N, Sawa S, et al. 2007. Homeostatically proliferating CD4 T cells are involved in the pathogenesis of an Omenn syndrome murine model. *J. Clin. Investig.* 117:1270–81
302. Marrella V, Poliani PL, Casati A, Rucci F, Frascoli L, et al. 2007. A hypomorphic R229Q Rag2 mouse mutant recapitulates human Omenn syndrome. *J. Clin. Investig.* 117:1260–69
303. Buckley RH. 2001. The hyper-IgE syndrome. *Clin. Rev. Allergy Immunol.* 20:139–54
304. Minegishi Y, Saito M, Tsuchiya S, Tsuge I, Takada H, et al. 2007. Dominant-negative mutations in the DNA-binding domain of STAT3 cause hyper-IgE syndrome. *Nature* 448:1058–62
305. Holland SM, DeLeo FR, Elloumi HZ, Hsu AP, Uzel G, et al. 2007. STAT3 mutations in the hyper-IgE syndrome. *N. Engl. J. Med.* 357:1608–19
306. Ben-Sasson SZ, Hu-Li J, Quiel J, Cauchetaux S, Ratner M, et al. 2009. IL-1 acts directly on CD4 T cells to enhance their antigen-driven expansion and differentiation. *Proc. Natl. Acad. Sci. USA* 106:7119–24
307. Masters SL, Simon A, Aksentijevich I, Kastner DL. 2009. *Horror autoinflammaticus*: the molecular pathophysiology of autoinflammatory disease. *Annu. Rev. Immunol.* 27:621–68
308. Bennett CL, Christie J, Ramsdell F, Brunkow ME, Ferguson PJ, et al. 2001. The immune dysregulation, polyendocrinopathy, enteropathy, X-linked syndrome (IPEX) is caused by mutations of FOXP3. *Nat. Genet.* 27:20–21
309. Caudy AA, Reddy ST, Chatila T, Atkinson JP, Verbsky JW. 2007. CD25 deficiency causes an immune dysregulation, polyendocrinopathy, enteropathy, X-linked-like syndrome, and defective IL-10 expression from CD4 lymphocytes. *J. Allergy Clin. Immunol.* 119:482–87
310. Belkaid Y, Tarbell K. 2009. Regulatory T cells in the control of host-microorganism interactions. *Annu. Rev. Immunol.* 27:551–89

Molecular Basis of Calcium Signaling in Lymphocytes: STIM and ORAI

Patrick G. Hogan,[1] Richard S. Lewis,[2] and Anjana Rao[1,*]

[1]Department of Pathology, Harvard Medical School, Immune Disease Institute and Program in Cellular and Molecular Medicine, Children's Hospital Boston, Boston, Massachusetts 02115; email: hogan@idi.harvard.edu, arao@idi.harvard.edu

[2]Department of Molecular and Cellular Physiology, Stanford University School of Medicine, Stanford, California 94305; email: rslewis@stanford.edu

Annu. Rev. Immunol. 2010. 28:491–533

The *Annual Review of Immunology* is online at immunol.annualreviews.org

This article's doi:
10.1146/annurev.immunol.021908.132550

0732-0582/10/0423-0491$20.00

*Authors are listed in alphabetical order.

Key Words

CRAC channels, store-operated calcium entry, T cell activation, primary immunodeficiencies

Abstract

Ca^{2+} entry into cells of the peripheral immune system occurs through highly Ca^{2+}-selective channels known as CRAC (calcium release-activated calcium) channels. CRAC channels are a very well-characterized example of store-operated Ca^{2+} channels, so designated because they open when the endoplasmic reticulum (ER) Ca^{2+} store becomes depleted. Physiologically, Ca^{2+} is released from the ER lumen into the cytoplasm when activated receptors couple to phospholipase C and trigger production of the second messenger inositol 1,4,5-trisphosphate (IP_3). IP_3 binds to IP_3 receptors in the ER membrane and activates Ca^{2+} release. The proteins STIM and ORAI were discovered through limited and genome-wide RNAi screens, respectively, performed in *Drosophila* cells and focused on identifying modulators of store-operated Ca^{2+} entry. STIM1 and STIM2 sense the depletion of ER Ca^{2+} stores, whereas ORAI1 is a pore subunit of the CRAC channel. In this review, we discuss selected aspects of Ca^{2+} signaling in cells of the immune system, focusing on the roles of STIM and ORAI proteins in store-operated Ca^{2+} entry.

Nuclear factor of activated T cells (NFAT): a family of four Ca^{2+}-regulated transcription factors whose translocation from the cytoplasm of resting cells to the nucleus of activated cells requires dephosphorylation of a regulatory domain by the Ca^{2+}-dependent serine/threonine phosphatase calcineurin

OVERVIEW

Ca^{2+} signaling is essential for diverse biological processes (reviewed in 1–4). Ca^{2+} ions are especially suited as intracellular second messengers because of the strong homeostatic mechanisms that maintain intracellular free Ca^{2+} concentrations ($[Ca^{2+}]_i$) in resting cells at 100 nM or less, in the face of extracellular Ca^{2+} concentrations ($[Ca^{2+}]_o$) that are four orders of magnitude higher (1–2 mM). Cytoplasmic Ca^{2+} concentrations are maintained at low levels primarily through the action of plasma membrane Ca^{2+}-ATPases (PMCAs) that pump Ca^{2+} out of the cell across the plasma membrane, and the sarco-endoplasmic reticulum Ca^{2+}-ATPases (SERCAs) that pump Ca^{2+} into the lumen of the endoplasmic reticulum (ER) (**Figure 1**). Secondary regulators of $[Ca^{2+}]_i$ include the mitochondrial Ca^{2+} uniporter (MCU) that transports Ca^{2+} across the inner mitochondrial membrane and the electrogenic Na^+-Ca^{2+} exchanger (NCX), which uses the entry of Na^+ to power the extrusion of Ca^{2+} across the plasma membrane.

The molecular mechanisms and consequences of Ca^{2+} signaling are especially well characterized in cells of the immune system, the focus of this review. In the short term (minutes), Ca^{2+} entry is required for mast cell degranulation and for lysis of infected or cancerous target cells by cytolytic T cells (reviewed in 5, 6). In the longer term (hours), sustained Ca^{2+} entry is critical for essentially all responses initiated through T cell, B cell, and Fc receptors, including proliferation and cytokine production by T cells, cytokine production by mast cells and natural killer (NK) cells, differentiation of B cells into plasma cells, and the differentiation of naive T cells into Th1, Th2, and Th17 effector subtypes. Many of these longer-term processes are regulated by the transcription factor NFAT (nuclear factor of activated T cells), which is present in a heavily phosphorylated state in the cytoplasm of resting cells, but which becomes dephosphorylated and translocates into the nucleus when $[Ca^{2+}]_i$ elevation activates the calmodulin (CaM)-dependent phosphatase calcineurin (reviewed in 7, 8) (**Figure 1**).

The primary mechanism of Ca^{2+} influx into cells of the peripheral immune system is a process known as store-operated Ca^{2+} entry (reviewed in 9–13). The "store" is the ER, from which Ca^{2+} is released when the antigen

Figure 1

Schematic diagram of the signaling pathway that connects store-operated Ca^{2+} entry with NFAT-dependent gene transcription in T cells. (*a*) Resting T cells have a membrane potential (maintained primarily by Kv1.3 K^+ channels) of approximately −50 mV and intracellular free Ca^{2+} concentrations ($[Ca^{2+}]_i$) of 50–100 nM that are maintained by the plasma membrane Ca^{2+} ATPase (PMCA), the sarco-endoplasmic reticulum Ca^{2+}-ATPase (SERCA) that pumps Ca^{2+} into the lumen of the endoplasmic reticulum (ER), and electrogenic Na^+-Ca^{2+} exchangers (NCX, not shown). Immunoreceptors include antigen receptors on T and B cells (TCR, BCR), Fcε receptors on mast cells, or Fcγ receptors on NK cells. The concentration of free Ca^{2+} in the ER ($[Ca^{2+}]_{ER}$) is several hundred μM; hence the EF-hand of STIM1 is saturated with Ca^{2+}, and STIM1 does not form higher-order oligomers (dimers are depicted, but the oligomerization state of STIM1 in resting cells is not fully defined). The transcription factor NFAT is heavily phosphorylated and localized to the cytoplasm. (*b*) Activated T cells. T cell receptors assemble into signaling complexes that contain scaffold proteins such as LAT and SLP-76, tyrosine kinases such as Lck, ZAP70, and Itk, and phospholipase C (PLC)γ (not all of which are shown). Inositol 1,4,5-trisphosphate (IP_3) produced by PLCγ binds to IP_3 receptors in the ER membrane, causing the release of Ca^{2+} from the ER. As a result of the depletion of ER Ca^{2+} stores, Ca^{2+} dissociates from EF-hand 1 of STIM1 and causes a conformational change (unfolding of the EF-SAM domain in the ER lumen) that leads to oligomerization (tetramers are depicted, but the oligomerization state of STIM1 in activated cells is not fully defined). The STIM oligomers move to sites of ER–plasma membrane apposition, recruit ORAI proteins to these sites, and cause CRAC channels to open. The resulting increase in $[Ca^{2+}]_i$ causes the universal and abundant cytoplasmic Ca^{2+} sensor calmodulin (CaM) to bind to many channels and enzymes and modulate their activity. Among the targets of CaM are the phosphatase calcineurin, which dephosphorylates NFAT and causes its nuclear translocation, thus activating NFAT-dependent transcription; the PMCA pump whose activity is increased by CaM binding; and the KCa3.1 K^+ channel that maintains membrane potential and the driving force for Ca^{2+} entry. Activated cells also show relocalization of mitochondria toward the plasma membrane, a process expected to maintain CRAC channel activity by diminishing Ca^{2+}-dependent inactivation. MCU: mitochondrial Ca^{2+} uniporter. CK1, GSK3, DYRK: NFAT kinases.

Resting T cells

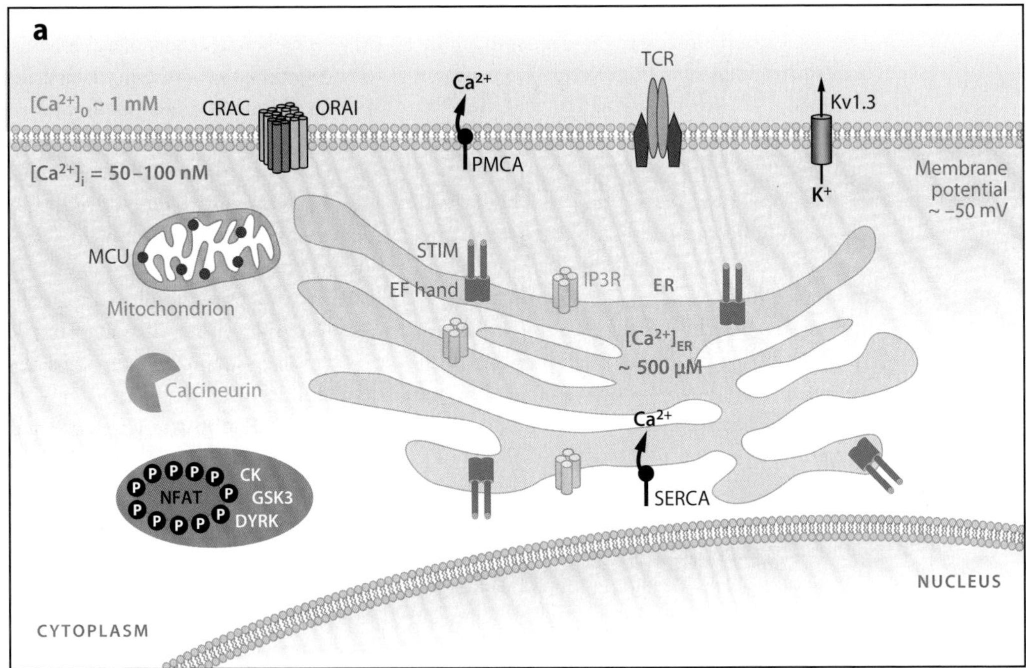

Activated T cells

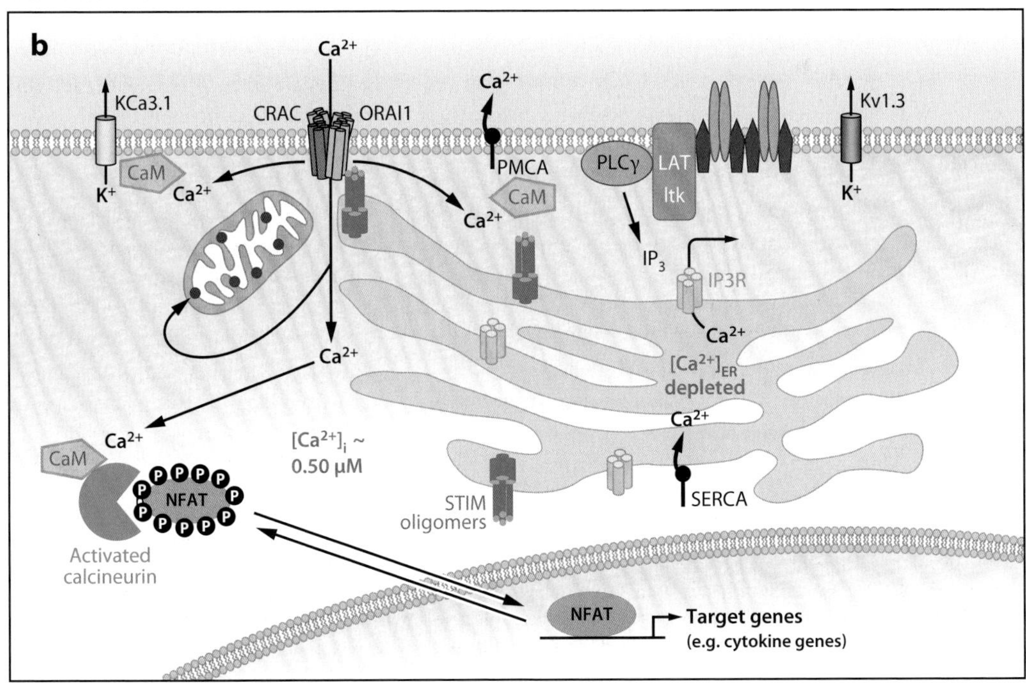

CRAC channel: a store-operated Ca^{2+} channel composed of ORAI proteins and gated by STIM proteins

receptors of T and B cells and the Fc receptors of mast cells and NK cells bind their appropriate ligands. Ligand binding to these receptors initiates a cascade of signaling events, among them activation of Src, Syk/ZAP70, and Tec/Btk family tyrosine kinases; kinase activation culminates in phosphorylation and activation of phospholipase C, an enzyme that hydrolyzes phosphatidylinositol 4,5-bisphosphate (PIP_2) in the plasma membrane to produce the second messengers inositol 1,4,5-trisphosphate (IP_3) and diacylglycerol. When IP_3 binds to IP_3 receptors (IP_3R) in the ER membrane, it effects the release of ER Ca^{2+} stores, causing the free Ca^{2+} concentration in the ER to drop below its resting value of ~400–600 μM (9, 11, 13, 14) (**Figure 1**). However, store release by itself does not elevate $[Ca^{2+}]_i$ sufficiently to promote long-term immune responses: Cytokine production, for instance, requires sustained calcineurin activation to support the prolonged nuclear residence of NFAT necessary for effective transcriptional activity (7, 15).

In 1986, Putney suggested that depletion of ER Ca^{2+} stores could evoke sustained Ca^{2+} influx across the plasma membrane of nonexcitable cells independently of receptor engagement, generation of second messengers, or the brief elevation of $[Ca^{2+}]_i$ that results from ER Ca^{2+} release (16) (**Figure 1**). Parallel biophysical (patch-clamp) experiments established that lymphocytes and mast cells indeed express store-operated Ca^{2+} channels that can be opened in response to store depletion by various agents (reviewed in 9–12). These channels—termed CRAC (calcium release–activated calcium) channels—were eventually well characterized electrophysiologically (reviewed in 9, 10, 17), but their molecular identities, and the nature of their coupling to store depletion, remained unknown for almost 20 years.

It is now known that CRAC channels contain as their pore subunits a class of four-pass transmembrane proteins termed ORAI, gated by ER-resident single-pass transmembrane proteins known as STIM. In a notable illustration of the fact that new technologies are powerful drivers of scientific advances, STIM was discovered only after RNA interference (RNAi) had come into general use as a method for protein depletion in cultured cells (18, 19) and ORAI just as whole-genome RNAi screens were beginning to realize their potential (20–22). As described in detail in a subsequent section, we now know that ORAI1 is the pore subunit of the CRAC channel (23–25); that STIM proteins are ER Ca^{2+} sensors that sense ER Ca^{2+} concentration through an N-terminal Ca^{2+}-binding EF-hand located in the ER lumen (13, 19, 26–28, 31); and that upon store depletion, STIM forms multimers in the ER membrane, then moves to sites of ER–plasma membrane apposition (19, 26, 29–31), where a portion of its C-terminal region gates ORAI channels directly (32–36) (**Figure 1**).

Here we review selected aspects of Ca^{2+} signaling in cells of the immune system, focusing on recent work on the molecules and mechanisms involved in Ca^{2+} entry through CRAC channels. Predictably, there has been an explosion of papers in the field since *Drosophila Stim* and mammalian STIM1 and STIM2 were identified in 2005 (18, 19) and *Drosophila Orai* and mammalian ORAI1, ORAI2, and ORAI3 were identified in 2006 (20–22). Several excellent reviews—indeed, volumes of reviews—summarizing each advance have been published (11–13, 17, 37–41), and the reader is referred to these for details that cannot be covered here because of space limitations. We have attempted to synthesize a large body of information for readers with an interest in immunology, and we apologize to those whose primary work has not been cited here for lack of space.

CELLULAR PATHWAYS OF CALCIUM SIGNALING IN LYMPHOCYTES

Engagement of receptors at the surface of immune cells generates intracellular messengers that create Ca^{2+} signals from two sources: intracellular organelles and the extracellular space. These sources are discussed below as they apply to all cells and specifically to lymphocytes.

Calcium Release from Intracellular Stores

Ca^{2+} signaling in response to stimulation of antigen and Fc receptors is initiated by the release of Ca^{2+} from intracellular stores, and several intracellular messengers have been implicated in this process. IP_3 is the most extensively studied of these, dating back to 1985 when Imboden & Stobo (42) showed that anti-CD3 stimulation of Jurkat T lymphoma cells increased IP_3 levels, released Ca^{2+} from stores, and promoted sustained Ca^{2+} influx. Three isoforms of the IP_3R are expressed in lymphocytes, each with a characteristic sensitivity to activation by IP_3 and to allosteric regulation by Ca^{2+} (reviewed in 43). The particular combination of isoforms and heteromultimers that are expressed can influence the dynamic patterns of Ca^{2+} release that occur upon antigen receptor engagement (44). Elimination of all three IP_3R isoforms by homologous recombination in chicken DT40 pre-B cells completely prevents Ca^{2+} release in response to B cell receptor (BCR) cross-linking (45). Similarly, treatment of Jurkat T cells with IP_3R1 antisense oligonucleotides or IP_3R antagonists diminishes the release from Ca^{2+} stores in response to T cell receptor (TCR) cross-linking (46, 47), again establishing the requirement for IP_3Rs in antigen receptor responses.

CRAC channels can be activated for long periods by sustained TCR engagement even though IP_3 levels decline to near resting levels within 10 min (48), raising questions about whether additional second messengers may be involved in prolonging receptor-regulated Ca^{2+} release from the ER. One possible explanation, as yet untested, is that local IP_3 generation not detectable globally may suffice to deplete Ca^{2+} locally in ER subregions physically involved in STIM-ORAI interaction and CRAC channel activation. On the other hand, substantial evidence suggests that cyclic ADP-ribose (cADPR) may act as a Ca^{2+}-releasing messenger in T cells. cADPR levels rise for more than 60 min after anti-CD3 stimulation in Jurkat T cells through activation of an ADP-ribosyl cyclase; injection of cADPR releases Ca^{2+} from stores through type 3 ryanodine receptors, and a membrane-permeant cADPR antagonist increases the latency and decreases the duration of Ca^{2+} release triggered through the TCR (49). Interestingly, IP_3 and cADPR appear to interact functionally: Even though they bind to distinct receptors, inhibition of IP_3R signaling by IP_3R antagonists also prevents Ca^{2+} signaling by cADPR (47). It is possible that Ca^{2+} released from the ER through the IP_3R acts as a coactivating cofactor for the ryanodine receptor.

Nicotinic acid adenine dinucleotide phosphate (NAADP) is the most recent addition to the arsenal of Ca^{2+} mobilizing messengers in T cells. NAADP is the most potent Ca^{2+}-releasing agent known, roughly 1000 times more effective than IP_3. Following TCR stimulation, NAADP is produced in a biphasic fashion, reaching a transient peak approximately eightfold above baseline within 30 s, followed by a decline to baseline and a secondary smaller rise lasting more than 20 min (50). This time course is consistent with a role for NAADP in both the initiation of Ca^{2+} signals and their maintenance over much longer periods. Recent evidence indicates that in some cells NAADP releases Ca^{2+} from acidic stores such as lysosomes, endosomes, or melanosomes through twin-pore channels (TPCs) (51, 52). However, in T cells the action of NAADP is not inhibited by bafilomycin (which neutralizes acidic compartments) but is blocked by the SERCA pump inhibitor thapsigargin (which depletes ER Ca^{2+} stores) and is sensitive to ryanodine receptor antagonists, suggesting that NAADP instead releases Ca^{2+} through ryanodine receptors in the ER (53, 54).

Further work is needed to understand how the Ca^{2+} mobilizing actions of IP_3, cADPR, and NAADP may be integrated in lymphocytes and under what conditions they are recruited. Importantly, although these messenger systems may contribute to transient release of Ca^{2+} under conditions of mild stimulation in vivo, activation of transcriptional pathways, most notably NFAT, requires sustained entry over tens

Thapsigargin: a highly selective and irreversible inhibitor of SERCA Ca^{2+} ATPases, which pump Ca^{2+} from the cytoplasm back into the ER. Treatment with thapsigargin reduces the free Ca^{2+} concentration in the ER lumen ($[Ca^{2+}]_{ER}$) because the Ca^{2+} that leaves the ER through unspecified leak pathways is not effectively restored

FINGERPRINTING THE CRAC CHANNEL

Patch-clamp recording techniques have been used to characterize the CRAC channel in T cells and mast cells. For whole-cell recording, a glass recording micropipette (tip diameter ~1 μm) is sealed to the cell membrane, and suction is used to break the membrane patch beneath the pipette lumen, thereby establishing electrical and physical continuity between the pipette lumen and the cytoplasm. The patch-clamp circuitry is then used to control the membrane potential and measure the total ionic current flowing through CRAC (and other) channels in the plasma membrane. During whole-cell recording, the cytoplasm of the cell slowly exchanges with the larger volume of the pipette contents. The perforated-patch technique is a less invasive mode in which the cell membrane is not broken, but a pore-forming antibiotic such as amphotericin is included in the pipette solution and inserts into the membrane under the pipette, thus providing the electrical connection to the cytoplasm that is necessary for the voltage clamp, without allowing diffusion of compounds into or out of the cell.

To measure CRAC currents specifically, K^+ currents are most commonly suppressed by replacing K^+ in the pipette with the impermeant cation Cs^+, and TRPM7 channels are inhibited by including Mg^{2+} in the pipette. To make the inward Ca^{2+} current as large as possible, the external solution typically contains high Ca^{2+} (10–20 mM) and the cells are subjected to a voltage step or ramp that clamps the membrane potential to very negative values, both of which increase the driving force for Ca^{2+} entry.

A cluster of biophysical characteristics constitutes a unique fingerprint that distinguishes the CRAC channel from other channels. Among the most useful for discrimination are pore properties such as ion selectivity and conductance. The CRAC channel is among the most Ca^{2+}-selective ion channels known, selecting for Ca^{2+} over monovalent cations such as Na^+ and K^+ by more than 1000:1. The Ca^{2+} conductance of a single CRAC channel (the unitary conductance) is estimated to be ~30 femtosiemens, which corresponds to ~10^4 Ca^{2+} ions flowing through the channel per second at a membrane potential of –100 mV. Notably, the CRAC channel resembles L-type Ca_V channels in its Ca^{2+} selectivity, but its conductance is about 100 times smaller than that of Ca_V, suggesting major differences in pore structure. Other distinguishing features of CRAC channels include distinct fast and slow inactivation processes driven by the elevation of intracellular Ca^{2+}. STIM1 and CaM bind to Orai1 to favor fast inactivation, but the mechanism of slow inactivation is less well understood.

of minutes to several hours. Because the content of the ER is finite, and recovery of released Ca^{2+} into the ER by SERCA pumps is incomplete owing to extrusion of a fraction of Ca^{2+} across the plasma membrane, Ca^{2+} entry from the extracellular space must occur to replenish the ER stores. The next section discusses Ca^{2+} channels in the plasma membrane that fulfill this sustained signaling function.

Calcium Entry Across the Plasma Membrane: The History of CRAC Channels

Since the early 1970s, from studies using $^{45}Ca^{2+}$ to monitor Ca^{2+} handling it was known that mitogens like phytohemagglutinin (PHA) stimulate sustained Ca^{2+} uptake by human T cells and that this is essential for the stimulation of T cell proliferation (55, 56). By the 1980s, the development of vital Ca^{2+} indicator dyes by Tsien and colleagues (57) and patch-clamp recording by Neher, Sakmann and coworkers (58) provided the essential tools needed to begin examining this process mechanistically. Although it became known that TCR cross-linking generated IP_3, which in turn released Ca^{2+} from the ER pool, the role of IP_3 in driving Ca^{2+} entry was initially unclear. Early efforts to identify the entry pathway using patch-clamp recording (see sidebar, Fingerprinting the CRAC Channel) suggested a role for IP_3-gated channels in the plasma membrane (59, 60). However, despite later biochemical evidence in support of plasma membrane IP_3Rs (61, 62), other labs were not able to confirm the presence of IP_3-gated currents in T cells or relate them directly to changes in $[Ca^{2+}]_i$, and their existence was questioned.

Meanwhile, by combining single-cell Ca^{2+} imaging with whole-cell recording from Jurkat cells, Lewis & Cahalan (63) identified a miniscule Ca^{2+} current that activated spontaneously during whole-cell recordings and was temporally correlated with a large increase in $[Ca^{2+}]_i$. The spontaneous activation was absent in perforated-patch recordings, which prevents dialysis of the cytoplasm by the pipette contents, but under these less invasive conditions the current could be activated in an oscillatory manner by PHA, a T cell mitogen. Several critical characteristics of the mitogen-regulated Ca^{2+} channel were established, including insensitivity to membrane potential, extremely high Ca^{2+} selectivity, and a very low Ca^{2+} conductance (as indicated by the nearly complete lack of current noise); however, its mode of activation, and in particular the role of IP_3, was unclear.

During the same period, evidence was accumulating for the existence of a Ca^{2+} entry pathway activated by depletion of Ca^{2+} from the ER. In 1986, Putney formalized the concept as capacitative calcium entry, later renamed store-operated Ca^{2+} entry (16). Shortly thereafter, thapsigargin was introduced as a highly selective and effectively irreversible inhibitor of SERCA pumps that could deplete Ca^{2+} stores and activate store-operated Ca^{2+} entry while bypassing receptor activation and the production of IP_3 (64). Thapsigargin was an extremely useful tool for demonstrating that store-operated channels exist in many if not all nonexcitable cells, including mast cells, thymocytes, and T cells (65), and in a growing number of excitable cells as well. Several other strategies were developed to reduce the free Ca^{2+} concentration ($[Ca^{2+}]_{ER}$) in the ER lumen, including exposure to the reversible SERCA inhibitor cyclopiazonic acid; the membrane-permeant Ca^{2+} buffer TPEN, which crosses the ER membrane and reduces $[Ca^{2+}]_{ER}$ to low levels; and the Ca^{2+} ionophore ionomycin, which accumulates in ER membranes and ferries ER Ca^{2+} into the cytosol.

Building on these advances, Hoth & Penner (66) identified a store-operated Ca^{2+} current in whole-cell recordings from mast cells that was activated by intracellular Ca^{2+} buffers [consistent with the spontaneous activation seen earlier in Jurkat cells (63)], by ionomycin, or by IP_3 in the recording pipette. They called this current the Ca^{2+} release-activated Ca^{2+}, or CRAC, current. Zweifach & Lewis (67) used a different approach—thapsigargin treatment during perforated-patch recording—to identify a similar store-operated current in Jurkat T cells. Importantly, they related the properties of the CRAC current activated by thapsigargin to those of the PHA-activated current described earlier: Both had similar selectivity among Ca^{2+}, Ba^{2+}, and Sr^{2+}, an extremely small apparent unitary conductance of 10–30 fS (femtosiemens), and sensitivity to inhibition by Ni^{2+} (67). Together, these and subsequent studies (68, 69) established the existence of store-operated Ca^{2+} channels in T cells and mast cells and showed that they were activated in T cells by TCR engagement and in mast cells by FcR cross-linking (70), consistent with the idea that IP_3, rather than gating the channels directly, controlled them through depletion of Ca^{2+} from the ER.

TRP channels: transient receptor potential channels

Considerable effort was spent over the ensuing ten years to characterize the biophysical and pharmacological characteristics of the CRAC channel, thereby generating a biophysical fingerprint (see sidebar on Fingerprinting). The fingerprint, summarized in detail elsewhere (71, 72), encompasses such features as store dependency, ion selectivity, pore diameter, unitary conductance, Ca^{2+}-dependent inactivation and potentiation, and pharmacological profile. This unique collection of properties, and in particular the extremely high Ca^{2+} selectivity and small unitary conductance, created a stringent benchmark for judging potential molecular candidates for the CRAC channel. For example, members of the transient receptor potential (TRP) protein family were often proposed as store-operated or CRAC channel candidates (reviewed in 73). For many of these, particularly members of the TRPC subfamily of TRP channels, their unitary conductance was much too large, and their Ca^{2+} selectivity far too low, to be compatible with the CRAC fingerprint. For others, such as TRPV6, many properties initially appeared to be consistent (74), and a dominant-negative TRPV6 mutant was in fact able to suppress CRAC current in Jurkat cells (75). However, subsequent studies showed discrepancies with CRAC channel pore properties (76), and the TRPV6 unitary conductance of ~40 pS for monovalent cations, initially thought to be compatible with the CRAC channel, was later found to be much too large because the CRAC channel conductance had previously been overestimated (77).

While the similar fingerprints of channels activated by thapsigargin and PHA suggested that the CRAC channel is the primary route for Ca^{2+} entry evoked by the TCR, subsequent genetic studies provided more definitive evidence for this conclusion. In mutant Jurkat T cells selected for a lack of store-operated Ca^{2+} entry, CRAC current was lost, and TCR stimulation with anti-CD3 failed to activate Ca^{2+} entry (78). Several human patients with hereditary severe immunodeficiency syndromes lacked thapsigargin-activated CRAC channel activity, and TCR stimulation of their T cells failed to evoke significant Ca^{2+} entry or Ca^{2+} currents detectable by electrophysiology (79–82). In one study, transfection with TRPC3 increased TCR-mediated Ca^{2+} influx in Jurkat mutant cells with partial defects in CRAC current (83); however, analysis of T cells from two related immunodeficient patients showed that despite normal expression of other candidate Ca^{2+} entry channels (TRPC1, TRPC3, TRPC4, TRPC5, TRPC7, TRPV5, and TRPV6), TCR stimulation failed to evoke Ca^{2+} entry (79). Although loss-of-function mutations in these potential Ca^{2+} entry channels were not ruled out, the Ca^{2+} signaling defect in these patients' T cells was ultimately traced to a loss-of-function mutation in ORAI1, and transduction with wild-type ORAI1 was sufficient to restore normal levels of store-operated Ca^{2+} entry and CRAC current (20) (see following section).

RNAi SCREENS IN *DROSOPHILA* CELLS

The discovery of ORAI proteins awaited the emergence of a platform for genome-wide RNAi screens in *Drosophila* cells (85), which preceded genome-wide screens in mammalian cells by several years (85, 86). *Drosophila* cells have several advantages for RNAi screens (85, 87). They readily take up long double-stranded RNAs and process them into multiple overlapping 21- to 22-nucleotide small interfering RNAs that, by providing extensive coverage of the cDNA, evoke efficient knockdown of the target proteins; they lack an interferon response, and hence their use avoids the complications introduced by interferon-induced phenotypic changes in cells; the redundancy of the *Drosophila* genome is much lower than that of the mammalian genome, increasing the chances of observing strong loss-of-function phenotypes; and finally, off-target effects in *Drosophila* cells can actually be an advantage because the overlapping 21- to 22-nucleotide small interfering RNAs produced by Dicer from long double-stranded RNAs often also target mRNAs encoding several related members of a protein family.

MOLECULAR ASPECTS OF CALCIUM SIGNALING IN LYMPHOCYTES

The Discovery of STIM and ORAI

STIM and ORAI were discovered as RNAi began to be widely used as a method for the unbiased discovery of proteins in biological pathways. Meyer and colleagues (19) performed a limited RNAi screen in HeLa cells that identified human STIM1 and STIM2 as proteins whose depletion downregulated store-operated Ca^{2+} entry. At essentially the same time, Roos and colleagues (18) performed a limited RNAi screen in *Drosophila* cells, based on the demonstration by Cahalan and coworkers that *Drosophila* S2 cells had Ca^{2+}-selective channels with most of the electrophysiological characteristics of mammalian CRAC channels (84). This screen identified *Drosophila* Stim and human STIM1 as playing key roles in store-operated Ca^{2+} entry. STIM was placed on the candidate list because it contained a Ca^{2+}-binding EF-hand and a protein-protein interaction domain (a SAM domain) that led to its annotation as a signaling protein.

Drosophila Orai was discovered in the course of RNAi screens performed nearly concurrently by three separate groups (20–22) in *Drosophila* cells, which have several advantages for RNAi screens (85–87) (see sidebar). The Kinet and Cahalan groups used $[Ca^{2+}]_i$ increases, imaged in a high-throughput format, as a direct readout: Cells were treated with thapsigargin in the absence of Ca^{2+} to evoke store depletion, and the medium was then reconstituted with Ca^{2+} to allow Ca^{2+} influx (21, 22). In both cases, knockdown of *Drosophila* Stim served as a positive control. Rao and colleagues (20) used an indirect screen that monitored nuclear translocation of an NFAT-GFP fusion protein ectopically expressed in *Drosophila* S2R+ cells. Even though Ca^{2+}-regulated NFAT transcription factors are not represented in *Drosophila* (their first emergence is in vertebrates), the NFAT-GFP fusion protein translocated correctly to the nucleus of *Drosophila* cells in a manner that was Ca^{2+}- and calcineurin-dependent and blocked by the calcineurin inhibitor cyclosporin A. This likely reflects the evolutionary conservation of calcineurin and NFAT kinases (CK1, DYRK, and GSK3) between *Drosophila* and vertebrates (88).

All three screens yielded *Drosophila* Orai as a robust hit. In the Ca^{2+} screens, which monitored $[Ca^{2+}]_i$ for 5–10 min, depletion of hundreds or thousands of candidate proteins altered the rate or magnitude of thapsigargin-evoked calcium increase, a result that is not surprising given the tight regulation of Ca^{2+} homeostasis in cells (1–4). In contrast, in the NFAT translocation screen, which integrated the effect of increased $[Ca^{2+}]_i$ over 60 min, Stim and Orai were 2 of only 16 hits that included calcineurin components and nuclear transport proteins, as expected (89).

The physiological validation of Stim and Orai as players in the store-operated Ca^{2+} entry pathway used several approaches. The first was genetic: A familial severe immunodeficiency syndrome in two human patients was traced to a point mutation in ORAI1. The patients had presented with a rare immunodeficiency characterized by an inability to produce NFAT-dependent cytokines, whose molecular basis had progressively been traced backwards to an inability to dephosphorylate NFAT and translocate it to the nucleus and, later, to a complete absence of store-operated Ca^{2+} entry and CRAC current in the patients' T cells (79, 80, 90). Notably, the patients' parents and other heterozygous carriers of the mutant allele (who exhibited no clinical symptoms whatsoever) could be distinguished from normal individuals because their T cells showed a decrease in store-operated Ca^{2+} entry when $[Ca^{2+}]_o$ was dropped to below physiological levels (0.2–0.5 mM, compared with normal $[Ca^{2+}]_o$ levels of ~1.25 mM) (20). This permitted the unambiguous identification, through a genome-wide SNP (single nucleotide polymorphism) screen, of a 9.8 MB genomic region linked with high confidence to the mutant allele. The gene encoding ORAI1, one of the three human homologs of *Drosophila* Orai, fell within this interval, and it quickly became apparent that a C-to-T transition, resulting in an arginine-to-tryptophan substitution at position 91 of ORAI1, was the mutation underlying the immunodeficiency syndrome (20). More recently, investigators have shown that a nonsense mutation in STIM1 is the basis for a second hereditary immunodeficiency (91, 92), and two additional families with mutations in ORAI1 have been identified (81, 82, 93). These immunodeficiency syndromes, and mouse models of Stim and Orai deficiency, are discussed in more detail below.

A second mode of validation was reconstitution of store-operated Ca^{2+} entry and CRAC current in the patients' cells by expression of wild-type ORAI1 (20); a third involved electrophysiological (whole-cell patch-clamp) studies of cells coexpressing STIM and ORAI. Soon after the first discovery of ORAI proteins, several groups reported that coexpression of *Drosophila* Stim and Orai in *Drosophila* S2 cells (22) or of human STIM1 and ORAI1 in various mammalian cell types led to a large increase in a Ca^{2+}-selective current with the biophysical characteristics of CRAC current (94–96). The ease of studying these "monster" CRAC currents quickly led to extensive mutational, functional, and comparative analyses of the two mammalian STIM proteins, STIM1 and STIM2, and the three mammalian ORAI proteins, ORAI1, ORAI2, and ORAI3 (reviewed below). More recently, several groups have also demonstrated that the STIM1 C terminus and various fragments derived from it are capable of

Punctum (*pl.* puncta): bright spots observed by fluorescence microscopy where fluorescently labeled STIM proteins accumulate after depletion of ER Ca^{2+} stores

decorating the plasma membrane and activating constitutive CRAC currents when introduced into ORAI-expressing cells (32–36). A wealth of information has been accumulated that will inform future analyses of the structural basis for STIM-ORAI interaction. These biochemical and cell-biological studies are described in the following sections.

STIM1

STIM1 was originally assumed to be a secreted or plasma membrane protein of bone marrow stromal cells, hence the original name stromal interaction molecule (97), and it was experimentally identified as a plasma membrane protein of the chronic myeloid leukemia cell line K562 (98). In fact, STIM1 is predominantly localized in the ER (19, 29–31), and it is believed that ER-resident STIM1, not plasma membrane STIM1, controls CRAC channel opening (19, 29, 96, 99, 100). STIM1 has an ER-luminal portion of ~22 kDa after cleavage of its signal sequence, a single transmembrane segment, and a cytoplasmic portion of ~51 kDa (**Figures 2, 3**). ER-resident STIM1 carries out two basic functions in the CRAC channel pathway: sensing ER Ca^{2+} store depletion and repletion and communicating the level of Ca^{2+} stores to Ca^{2+} channels in the plasma membrane.

Sensing ER Ca^{2+} concentration. The sensing of ER Ca^{2+} levels is the most thoroughly understood step in the STIM-ORAI pathway at the molecular level: Dissociation of Ca^{2+} from a binding site in the luminal portion of STIM1 triggers a structural change in STIM1 (27, 101). The cellular correlate of Ca^{2+} sensing is a relocalization of STIM1, conveniently visualized by light microscopy with GFP-fusion proteins. STIM1 is distributed throughout the ER prior to Ca^{2+} store depletion and collects at numerous individual spots, or puncta, upon depletion of ER Ca^{2+} stores (19, 29, 31, 96, 99).

The ER-luminal domain of STIM1 is responsible for Ca^{2+} sensing. An NMR structure of a recombinant fragment [human STIM1(58–201)] encompassing most of the STIM1 luminal domain shows a classical paired arrangement of two EF-hands followed by a sterile α motif (SAM) domain (27). Only the first EF-hand binds Ca^{2+}, and the EF-SAM protein fragment with bound Ca^{2+} is monomeric (27, 101). The EF-hand pair engages an α-helix of the SAM domain in much the same way that a corresponding EF-hand pair in Ca^{2+}-CaM engages its target peptides (13, 27) (**Figure 2*c***). The structure of the recombinant STIM1 luminal domain in the absence of Ca^{2+} has not yet been determined, but biophysical measurements indicate that dissociation of Ca^{2+} is accompanied by substantial protein unfolding and by a

Figure 2

Structure and properties of STIM1. (*a*) Domain structure of human STIM1 (adapted with permission from Reference 27). Shown are the signal peptide (S), the canonical EF-hand 1 (cEF1), the noncanonical EF-hand 2 (ncEF2), the SAM (sterile α-motif) domain, the transmembrane domain (TM), three predicted coiled-coil regions (cc1, cc2, and cc3), the proline- and serine-rich region, and the lysine-rich (polybasic) region at the C terminus. The EF-SAM fragment whose structure was determined by NMR spectroscopy is indicated. The region to the left of the TM is located in the ER lumen, whereas the region to the right is located in the cytoplasm. Residue numbers at the approximate boundaries of the domains are indicated above the diagram. Coiled-coils cc1 and cc2 have long been recognized in STIM proteins (97, 98, 105) and are assigned high probability in STIM1 by COILS; the predicted coiled-coil cc3 is assigned a low probability by COILS in STIM1, but a relatively high probability in *Aedes aegypti* Stim and *Anopheles gambiae* Stim, and in STIM2 when core hydrophobic positions are weighted. The existence and precise boundaries of cc3 require experimental confirmation. (*b*) Sequence conservation in the STIM C-terminal region. Each horizontal black bar represents the human STIM1 sequence, with gaps introduced as necessary to maintain alignment with human STIM2, fish STIM1 orthologs, or insect Stim proteins, as indicated. Vertical green lines indicate identity of the human STIM1 residue with the residue at the corresponding position of human STIM2; vertical magenta lines indicate identity of the human STIM1 residue with residues at the corresponding position in at least four of five fish orthologs; vertical blue lines indicate identity with residues in at least two of three insect Stim proteins. Adapted from Reference 36. (*c*) Structure of the EF-SAM fragment deduced by NMR spectroscopy (adapted with permission from Reference 27). Alpha-helices are depicted as cylinders. (The canonical EF-hand 1 is *magenta*, the noncanonical EF-hand 2 is *beige*, and the SAM domain is *green*; the Ca^{2+} ion bound to EF-hand 1 is a *yellow sphere*.) Two views related by a 90° rotation are shown.

transition from monomers to a mixture of dimers and larger aggregates (27, 101).

Given that the typical concentration of Ca^{2+} in the ER lumen is hundreds of micromolar, STIM1 must have a relatively low affinity for Ca^{2+} to function as a sensor. The measured K_d for Ca^{2+} binding to recombinant STIM1 luminal domain is ~500–600 μM at 20°C (101), and the K_d for isolated STIM1 EF-hand 1 grafted into a loop of rat CD2 domain 1 is ~500 μM at 25°C (102). Although the conditions of these in vitro determinations were not identical to conditions in cells, the values are in reasonable agreement with the sensitivity of STIM1 redistribution in cells to ER Ca^{2+} concentration (14, 26).

Store depletion leads to oligomerization of STIM1. Direct evidence that STIM1 in cells dimerizes or oligomerizes during Ca^{2+} sensing is the increased FRET between CFP-STIM1 donor and YFP-STIM1 acceptor upon store depletion (103, 104). This step precedes the appearance of STIM1 puncta subjacent to the

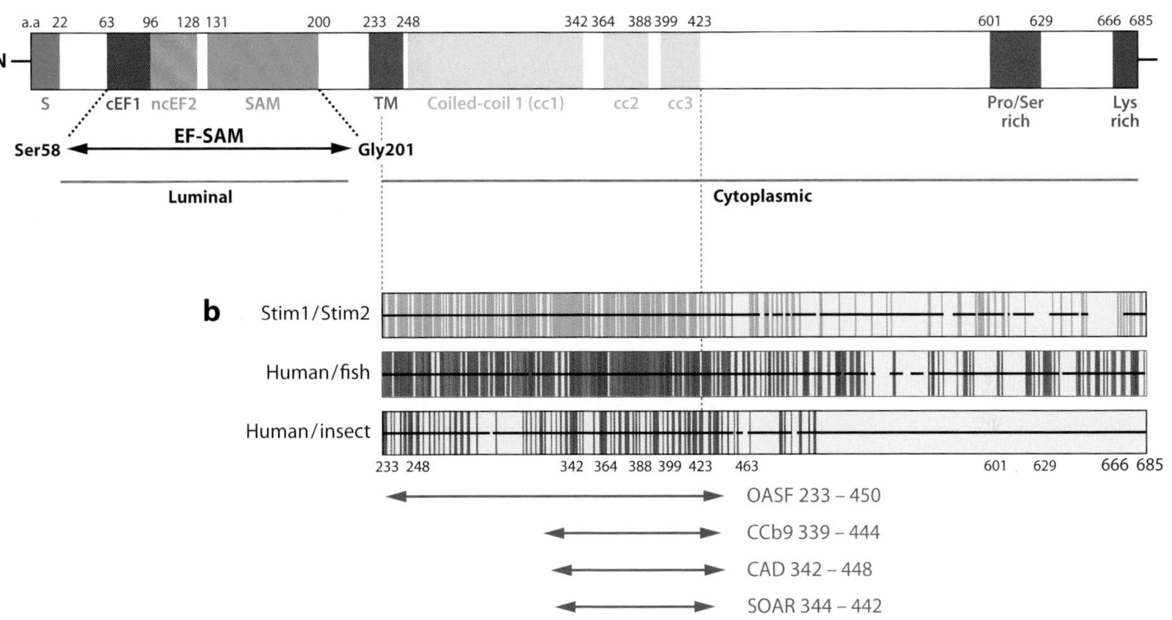

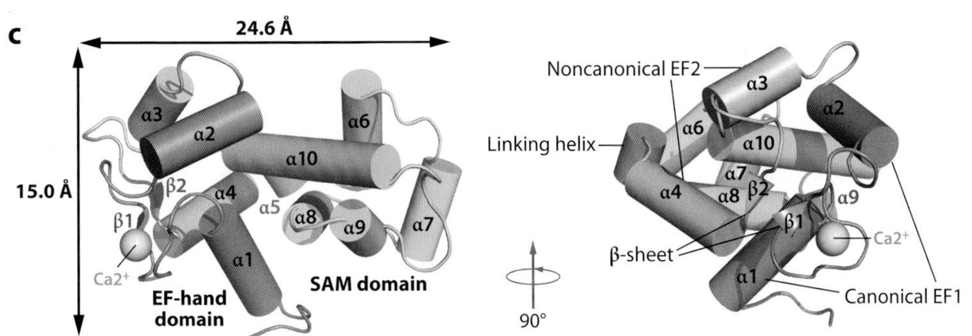

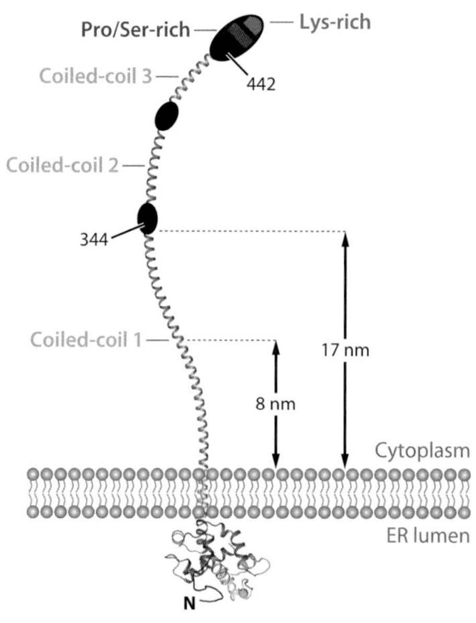

Figure 3

Schematic representation of full-length STIM1. The cytoplasmic region contains three predicted coiled-coil regions (*cyan*), a serine- and proline-rich region (*red*), and a polybasic tail (*blue*). The coiled coils can span the distance, estimated to be 8 nm (109) or ~17 nm (29), that separates the ER and the plasma membrane at the junctions where STIM and ORAI accumulate upon ER Ca^{2+} store depletion. For an explanation of the three coiled-coil regions, see the caption to **Figure 2*a***.

plasma membrane (103) and thus is the earliest indicator of Ca^{2+} sensing by STIM1 in cells (**Figure 4**).

Ca^{2+} dissociation from STIM1 leads to unfolding and oligomerization of the STIM1 luminal domain. EF-hand 1 of STIM1 was recognized from its amino acid sequence (105), and disabling Ca^{2+} binding by point mutations in EF-hand 1 leads to constitutive localization of STIM1 in puncta (19, 31). Moreover, the same substitutions lead to constitutive activation of store-operated Ca^{2+} entry and CRAC current (19, 31, 106), demonstrating that disruption of Ca^{2+} binding to EF-hand 1 is functionally equivalent to dissociation of Ca^{2+} upon store depletion. Targeted, structure-based substitutions in the second EF-hand and in the SAM domain surface, intended to destabilize the close interaction between the paired EF-hands and the SAM domain, caused unfolding of the STIM1 luminal domain as predicted and also caused constitutive formation of STIM1 puncta and constitutively elevated Ca^{2+} entry (27).

The authors of the structural study (27) have carefully left open the question of whether the large aggregates observed with STIM1 luminal domain in solution represent the state of STIM1 luminal domain in Ca^{2+}-depleted ER. SAM domains are in fact protein interaction domains that can assemble into large oligomeric structures (107), and one possible scenario is that the EF-hands release the SAM domain, after which the SAM domains oligomerize. However, STIM1 aggregation deviates from assembly of other characterized SAM domain multimers in two respects (27): STIM1 luminal domain in the absence of Ca^{2+} is seen as amorphous aggregates by electron microscopy, not in ordered polymers as with other SAM domains; and mutations in STIM1 residues that correspond to protein-protein contact sites of other SAM domains fail to impede aggregation of the STIM1 domain. In cells, oligomerization may be constrained by the tethering of STIM1 monomers to the ER membrane, by interaction with chaperones in the ER lumen, or by the protein-protein interactions of the STIM1 cytoplasmic region. Thus, it remains an open question whether the STIM1 luminal domain in cells forms large aggregates, as in vitro, or smaller ordered oligomers.

Redistribution of STIM1. The STIM1 puncta visible by light microscopy are localized at sites of close apposition between the ER and the plasma membrane, as observed by electron microscopy (29) (**Figure 4**). The time course of STIM1 redistribution to these sites has been followed by TIRF microscopy using fluorescently labeled STIM1 proteins. The redistribution is completed over tens of seconds (19, 29, 103), and the reverse movement of STIM1 from puncta to ER upon repletion of ER stores is comparably rapid (19, 108). The accumulation of STIM1 near the

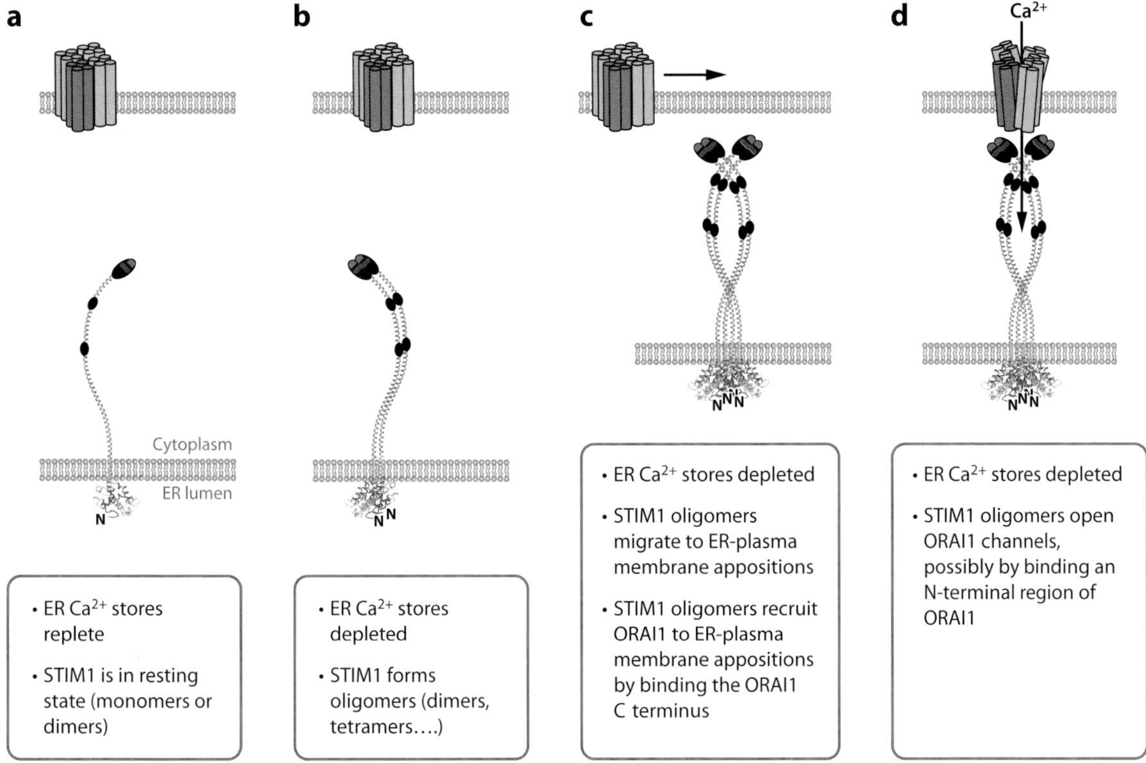

a
b
c
d
Ca2+
Cytoplasm
ER lumen
N
N N
NNN
• ER Ca2+ stores replete
• STIM1 is in resting state (monomers or dimers)
• ER Ca2+ stores depleted
• STIM1 forms oligomers (dimers, tetramers....)
• ER Ca2+ stores depleted
• STIM1 oligomers migrate to ER-plasma membrane appositions
• STIM1 oligomers recruit ORAI1 to ER-plasma membrane appositions by binding the ORAI1 C terminus
• ER Ca2+ stores depleted
• STIM1 oligomers open ORAI1 channels, possibly by binding an N-terminal region of ORAI1

Figure 4

Sequence of steps in store-operated Ca^{2+} entry. (*a*) Schematic diagrams of STIM1 and ORAI1 in the resting state, when ER Ca^{2+} stores are replete. ORAI is depicted as a tetramer for reasons discussed in the text. STIM1 is depicted as a monomer for convenience, but its oligomerization state in resting cells is not yet fully defined. (*b*) STIM1 oligomerization. STIM1 forms oligomers when ER stores are depleted. Oligomers are depicted here as dimers for convenience, but their stoichiometry in activated cells is unknown. (*c*) STIM1 redistribution. Oligomerization of STIM1 in the ER membrane is followed by migration of STIM1 to ER–plasma membrane appositions. This redistribution involves binding of the STIM1 polybasic regions to PIP_2 and PIP_3 in the plasma membrane. STIM1 oligomers then recruit ORAI1 to ER–plasma membrane junctions by binding a C-terminal region of ORAI1. (*d*) STIM1-ORAI1 gating. STIM1 oligomers open ORAI channels, possibly by binding to an N-terminal region of ORAI1.

plasma membrane is further accentuated by a modest increase in the ER–plasma membrane junctional area upon store depletion in Jurkat cells (29) and by a larger increase in HeLa cells (109).

Movement of STIM1 into puncta is believed to involve local diffusion within the ER membrane, with STIM1 collecting at ER–plasma membrane contacts owing to interactions with specific proteins or lipids (103). Consistent with a diffusive mechanism, local depletion of ER stores, which may be the rule in the case of physiological stimulation, is effective in activating the CRAC current (110), and movement of STIM1 is estimated to be over a short distance, averaging approximately 2 μm, even when stores are globally depleted (103).

The interactions that retain STIM1 at ER–plasma membrane contacts are not fully defined. One key interaction maps to the short polybasic segment at the STIM1 C terminus (33, 103, 111) (see **Figure 2**). Involvement of the polybasic segment has led to the hypothesis that STIM is recruited by negatively charged phospholipids such as PIP_2 and PIP_3 (103), an established mechanism for targeting cytoplasmic and cytoskeletal proteins to the plasma membrane.

Depleting PIP_2 from the plasma membrane of COS-7 cells did not prevent formation of STIM1 puncta but did lead to a modest reduction in preformed puncta (112, 113). Experience with other proteins indicates that it may be necessary to deplete both PIP_2 and PIP_3 to alter localization (114). Prior depletion either of PIP_2 by recruitment of phosphatase to the plasma membrane or of PIP_3 and PIP by inhibition of PI3K and PI4K decreased the initial migration of STIM1-EYFP to puncta in HeLa cells (115). Prior depletion of both polyphosphoinositides nearly abolished STIM1 migration to puncta (115), although a similar treatment did not dissociate preformed YFP-STIM1 puncta in COS-7 cells (113), leaving open the possibility that puncta once formed are stabilized by other interactions. Complementary in vitro data show binding of the STIM1 C terminus to liposomes containing either PIP_2 or PIP_3 (116). Because PIP_3 is absent from the plasma membrane of naive T cells, it will be of interest to investigate whether STIM-ORAI signaling in T cells is influenced by costimulatory signals that trigger production of PIP_3. Whether the net effect of costimulation would be increased CRAC channel activity is unclear, given that STIM-polyphosphoinositide interactions may have negative effects on STIM-ORAI signaling downstream of STIM1 redistribution (115).

A second factor that may contribute to STIM targeting, at least when ORAI is overexpressed, is interaction with the ORAI channel complex itself (33, 115). Neither PIP_2 nor ORAI1 is preferentially localized to ER–plasma membrane contacts in resting cells, although their interaction with STIM1 is necessarily limited to these sites. Proteins known to be preferentially localized to ER–plasma membrane contacts, such as junctophilin (117, 118), have thus far not been shown to interact directly with STIM, although such interactions have not been ruled out.

A critical upstream signaling mechanism for formation of puncta is oligomerization of the STIM1 luminal domain. This has been clearly shown by introducing artificial oligomerization domains, an FRB domain and tandem FKBP12 domains, in place of the luminal domain of STIM1, and expressing the engineered proteins in cells (14). A cell-permeant ligand, rapalog, capable of bridging the inserted domains and causing assembly of multimers, triggered puncta formation and activated CRAC current in the absence of ER Ca^{2+} store depletion.

Why oligomerization occurring in the ER lumen would cause STIM1 to collect at ER–plasma membrane contacts is not immediately obvious. Redistribution is not directed purely by protein-protein associations within the ER lumen because removing the ~14-residue polybasic tail at the STIM1 C terminus prevents redistribution (33, 103, 116) unless the deletion is compensated by overexpression of ORAI (33). Likewise, the inhibitory effect of depleting PIP_2 and PIP_3 from the plasma membrane can be compensated by overexpression of ORAI (115). Evidently, the changes in the luminal domain are conveyed in some manner to the cytoplasmic domain of STIM1. Two nonexclusive possibilities have been proposed (14, 103): (*a*) that oligomerization increases the avidity of STIM for plasma membrane sites in the same way that IgG or IgM avidity exceeds that of a single combining site, and (*b*) that oligomerization induces a conformational change in the C-terminal cytoplasmic domain of STIM1 and exposes a previously buried polybasic C-terminal segment or other sites that interact at ER–plasma membrane contacts.

STIM1 redistribution in cells shows marked cooperativity with respect to ER-luminal Ca^{2+} concentration (14, 26). Because each STIM1 monomer has a single Ca^{2+}-binding site, the cooperativity indicates that oligomeric STIM1 is involved in at least one step of redistribution. The data on concentration dependence do not discriminate between whether the oligomer makes a transitory appearance or is stable. It is tempting to view the increased FRET between CFP-STIM1 and YFP-STIM1, maintained throughout redistribution to ER–plasma membrane contacts (103, 104), as evidence that a single oligomeric state is maintained. However, the solidity of this argument depends on the extent to which FRET distinguishes among dimers, small oligomers, and larger oligomers, which has not been investigated experimentally.

Importantly, physiological stimuli can elicit significant Ca^{2+} entry without generating large puncta. For example, puncta are not prominent in mast cells stimulated by cross-linking surface IgE with antigen (119), and STIM redistribution detected by TIRF microscopy is absent or modest in HEK293 cells stimulated with a low concentration of muscarinic agonist (120), even though these conditions elicit robust STIM-ORAI-dependent Ca^{2+} elevation or Ca^{2+} oscillations (119–121). In these examples, partial refilling of the Ca^{2+} stores during stimulation may limit the size of STIM-ORAI coclusters. In contrast, T cells stimulated through the TCR by treatment with superantigens or anti-CD3 antibodies exhibit clear puncta and larger clusters of STIM1 (29, 122, 123), which may reflect strong signaling and a greater degree of local store depletion, although this remains to be tested.

Additional protein-protein interactions. A portion of ER-resident GFP-STIM1 colocalizes in cells with microtubules (96, 100, 124). The prominence of the association with microtubules is variable, and it may be accentuated by GFP-STIM1 overexpression. Association with microtubules is mediated by STIM1 binding to the microtubule plus end tracking protein EB1 through a TxIP motif in STIM1 (125, 126). EB1 recruits STIM1 to sites of physical contact between growing microtubule tips and ER. Time-lapse images initially gave the impression that a fraction of cellular STIM1 is traveling along microtubules at any given moment (100). However, a later study established that individual STIM1 molecules do not move with the microtubule tip, but rather are recruited transiently from nearby in the ER and then disperse as the tip grows onward and recruits new STIM1 molecules (125).

It is not clear whether STIM1 association with extending microtubule tips has a physiological role in Ca^{2+} signaling. Microtubules are not required for initial CRAC channel gating in T cells and mast cells (127, 128), although microtubules contribute to the sustained Ca^{2+} plateau through a Ca^{2+}-dependent movement of mitochondria toward the plasma membrane that limits slow Ca^{2+}-dependent inactivation of the CRAC channel (128). Likewise, in HeLa cells where the STIM-microtubule interaction has been extensively studied, EB1 knockdown or treatment with taxol to suppress microtubule growth and shortening eliminated STIM-microtubule colocalization, but did not affect store-operated Ca^{2+} entry (125). Thus, current evidence indicates that any effect of STIM-microtubule interaction on the CRAC current is indirect, through remodeling of ER or ER–plasma membrane contacts or through regulating the availability of STIM1.

STIM1 interacts directly with TRPC proteins in biochemical and functional assays (108, 129, 130), leading to the proposal of a specific mechanism by which STIM1 gates TRPC channels (130). The relevance of this interaction to cellular Ca^{2+} signaling is controversial (131). Nevertheless, activation of TRPC channels offers a possible explanation for Ca^{2+} influx not accounted for by ORAI channels.

STIM1 is also required for activation of the ARC (arachidonate-regulated Ca^{2+}-selective) channel, which, as indicated by the acronym, is a Ca^{2+} channel activated by arachidonic acid (132). The function of the ARC channel in immune cells has not been investigated, but in other cell types it does not appear to be activated by store depletion, nor is depletion required for its activation by arachidonic acid.

Lastly, activated STIM1 controls an adenylate cyclase (133). Stringent controls appear to eliminate the possibility that activation of the cyclase is through a local STIM1-dependent Ca^{2+} signal. The finding is very important as a first example of STIM1 integrating intracellular Ca^{2+} signaling with signaling in other intracellular pathways. Its biological ramifications have not been fully explored.

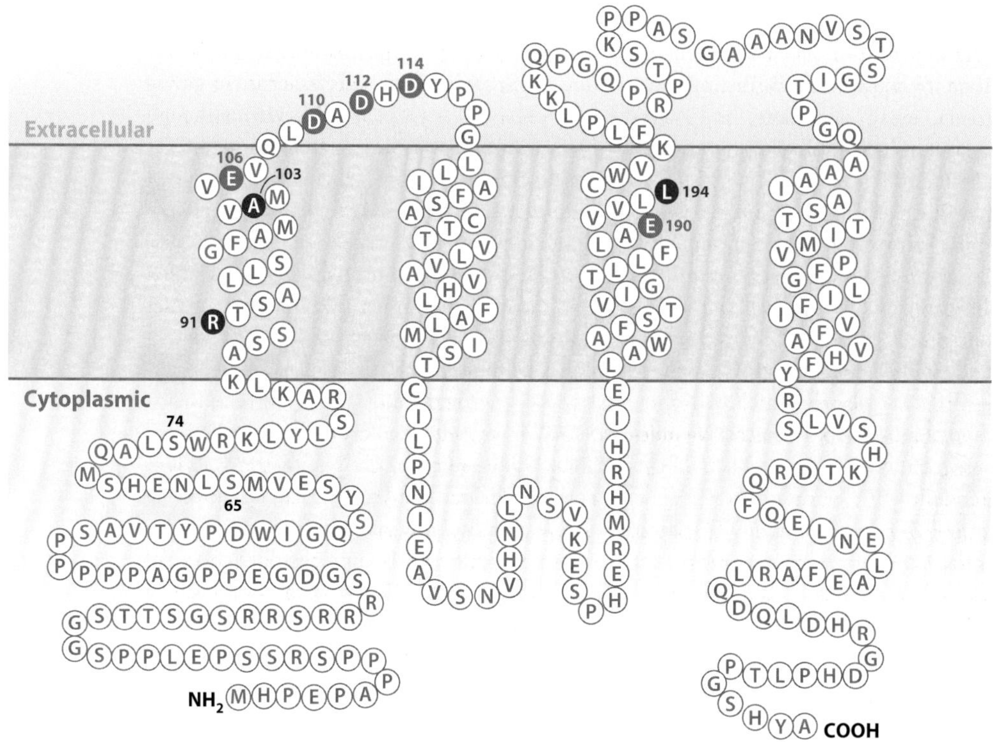

Figure 5

Amino acid sequence of human ORAI1. Residues E106, D110, D112, D114, and E190, that when mutated affect channel properties, are shown in blue. Residues R91, A103, and L194, that when mutated to W, E, and P, respectively, are associated with human immunodeficiency, are shown in red (20, 93). Residues 65 and 74 are indicated; truncated ORAI1 proteins that begin at either residue are able to assemble and function as CRAC channels (33, 36, 150).

ORAI1

The ORAI1 monomer is a ~33-kDa plasma membrane protein with four transmembrane helices (**Figure 5**); glycosylation increases its apparent molecular weight on SDS gels (24, 89). There is persuasive evidence that ORAI1 assembles as a tetrameric CRAC channel (134–136). The channel opens in response to the signal conveyed by STIM1, conducts Ca^{2+} selectively, and, in certain cases, directs the intracellular Ca^{2+} signal to privileged effectors.

The ORAI1 channel. The transmembrane topology of the ORAI monomer (**Figure 5**) was established by (*a*) the intracellular location of N-terminal and C-terminal epitope tags and the extracellular location of an epitope tag introduced into the TM3-TM4 loop (24), (*b*) verification that an N-glycosylation site in the TM3-TM4 loop is glycosylated and therefore extracellular (24, 89), and (*c*) evidence that substitutions in the TM1-TM2 loop alter channel block by extracellular lanthanide ions (23).

The best evidence that the assembled channel is a tetramer comes from electrophysiological studies of channels made from concatenated ORAI1 monomers. CRAC currents in cells expressing a tandem tetramer of ORAI1 (unlike CRAC currents in cells expressing the monomer, tandem dimer, or tandem trimer) are insensitive to coexpression of the dominant negative E106Q monomer (134). Given that even a single E106Q substitution within the tandem tetramer compromises channel function, these results are most readily explained if the tandem tetramer forms a closed unit unable to incorporate a further monomer (134). The inability of a tandem tetramer to incorporate an ORAI monomer has been confirmed by FRET (135). Physical evidence also suggests that the channel is a tetramer because four individual bleaching steps are often resolved in single-molecule photobleaching of ORAI-GFP channels sparsely expressed in the plasma membrane (135, 136). These are technically difficult experiments in which the number of steps cannot be scored reliably for most channels (135), but two laboratories have independently concluded that open CRAC channels are tetramers (135, 136). However, one of the laboratories reports only two bleaching steps for closed *Drosophila* Orai channels (136). Finally, size-exclusion chromatography of purified detergent-solubilized ORAI1 complexes has supported the conclusion that the channel is a multimer (33, 137) but has not provided an accurate assessment of the number of subunits.

Redistribution of ORAI1. An outline has emerged of how the depleted-stores signal is relayed to ORAI1 channels. ORAI1 is recruited to ER–plasma membrane contacts through engagement of a C-terminal cytoplasmic segment of ORAI1 by STIM1, and a further STIM1-ORAI1 interaction gates the channel (**Figure 4**). The direct interactions of STIM1 with ORAI1, and their involvement in gating, are discussed below in the section on STIM-ORAI signaling.

Selectively conducting Ca^{2+}. The biological role of the CRAC channel is to provide a permeation pathway for Ca^{2+} influx that effectively excludes the more abundant Na^+ of physiological solutions. The negatively charged side chains of ORAI1 residues E106 in TM1 and E190 in TM3 help to create this permeation pathway, as evidenced by the markedly reduced selectivity for Ca^{2+} in channels with the specific replacements E106D or E190Q (23–25). More subtle changes observed on replacement of acidic residues in the TM1-TM2 loop indicate that residues immediately external to E106 also influence ion permeation (23, 25). Wild-type ORAI channels do not conduct monovalent ions in physiological solutions containing Mg^{2+} or Ca^{2+}. However, in the absence of divalent ions, the currents carried by monovalent ions are sensitive probes of pore configuration. Additional experiments examining the ability of mutated channels to discriminate between Na^+ and Cs^+ further support the notion that residues E106 and E190 are close to the ion permeation pathway (23–25).

In an ORAI1 tetramer, four E106 side chains likely coordinate Ca^{2+} directly within the pore. The strict requirement for negative charges at this position in the channel is supported by the findings that ORAI1(E106A) and *Drosophila* Orai with the corresponding substitution fail to conduct Ca^{2+} (23, 24) and that a single E106Q replacement prevents Ca^{2+} flux when incorporated into a tandem tetramer with wild-type ORAI1 monomers (134). In contrast, the proposal that the negative charges of E190 side chains or the external acidic residues form essential Ca^{2+} coordination sites in the pore (25) is inconsistent with the evidence that ORAI1(E190A) and ORAI1(D110A/D112A) channels conduct Ca^{2+} perfectly well (24, 25). The distinctive structural contribution of these other acidic residues remains to be determined.

Other key properties that the ORAI1 channel has in common with the native CRAC channel are its very small single-channel current (138), which will contribute to tightly graded control of local and global Ca^{2+} concentrations, and its regulation by feedback mechanisms that will limit Ca^{2+} entry when local or global Ca^{2+} concentration is elevated (138–143) (see the sidebar above, Fingerprinting the CRAC Channel).

Communicating to effectors. The calcineurin-NFAT pathway in T cells is thought to respond primarily to global cytoplasmic Ca^{2+} transients. However, other effector pathways downstream of CRAC currents respond to local Ca^{2+} signals in microdomains near the sites of Ca^{2+} influx. Following the precedent of voltage-dependent Ca^{2+} channels and neuronal synaptic channels that conduct Ca^{2+}, Ca^{2+}-activated effector proteins could be localized in ORAI channel complexes or at adjacent sites within ER–plasma membrane appositions.

CRAC channel signaling is clearly restricted to microdomains in RBL (rat basophilic leukemia)-1 mast cells because loading cells with the fast Ca^{2+} chelator BAPTA [bis(2-aminophenoxy)ethane-*N*,*N*,*N*′,*N*′-tetra-acetate] diminishes Ca^{2+}-dependent induction of the *c-fos* gene in these cells, whereas loading them with the slow Ca^{2+} chelator EGTA [ethyleneglycol-bis(beta-aminoethyl ether)-*N*,*N*′-tetra-acetic acid] has no effect (144, 145). The membrane-proximal effector appears to be the Syk kinase, which couples through intermediate steps to STAT5 signaling in the cell nucleus and to phospholipase A_2 and 5-lipoxygenase to elicit leukotriene production in the cytoplasm (144–147). Endothelial nitric oxide synthase (148) and Ca^{2+}-sensitive adenylate cyclases (149) are also activated selectively by a local increase in subplasmalemmal Ca^{2+} occurring after store depletion, although these older studies did not show that ORAI channels, rather than TRPC or other channels, are the local source of Ca^{2+}. The molecular tools are now available to investigate which enzymes and signaling proteins are activated in microdomains near ORAI channels in cells of the immune system.

ORAI1 is excluded from artificially close ER–plasma membrane contacts made by engineering inducible cross-links between the two membranes (112). This result suggests that the ORAI channel complex protrudes more than ~9 nm into the cytoplasm, a result that was first interpreted as indicating the presence of associated proteins. A model of the channel reconstructed from electron microscopic images of purified ORAI1 has raised the possibility that ORAI itself extends ~10 nm into the cytoplasm (137). If this conclusion is correct, the bulk of the protruding region of ORAI1 would necessarily be composed of the N-terminal section of ORAI that is dispensable for channel function. The extended surface could contribute additional interactions with STIM proteins or other regulatory proteins or serve as a scaffold for effector proteins.

STIM1-ORAI1 Signaling

Prior to store depletion, ORAI1 is distributed throughout the plasma membrane. The sequential steps in the activation of CRAC channels are that STIM1 moves to puncta, STIM1 recruits ORAI1 to puncta, and ORAI1 channels open (**Figure 4**). The latter two steps, which are described next, depend on direct physical interactions between STIM1 and ORAI1.

ORAI1 recruitment to puncta. Ca^{2+} entry through CRAC channels occurs at STIM1 puncta (30). ORAI1 colocalizes with STIM1 at puncta (30, 99, 150), and FRET between labeled STIM and labeled ORAI indicates that the proteins are closely juxtaposed (104, 119, 123, 151). STIM1 redistributes to puncta in the absence of overexpressed ORAI (19, 29, 31, 33, 99), but overexpressed ORAI does not relocalize appreciably to puncta unless it is coexpressed with STIM (33, 99), indicating that STIM is necessary to recruit ORAI to puncta.

Recruitment of ORAI1 depends on its C-terminal cytoplasmic tail, as is evident from the failure of ORAI1 lacking its C-terminal tail to colocalize with STIM1 and support CRAC current upon store depletion (104, 150). Electrophysiological recording of CRAC currents indicates that the relevant segment ends before residue 283 (141). The conclusion based on C-terminal deletion is strongly supported by studies of ORAI1 channels with the individual replacements L273S or L276D, which fail to interact with STIM1 upon store depletion (104, 151). The basis for recruitment is most likely a direct protein-protein interaction of the ORAI1 C terminus with STIM1 (33, 36, 104), with the corollary that STIM1 spans the ER–plasma membrane distance, because the short C-terminal tail of ORAI1 cannot project so far (**Figures 3**, **4**).

ORAI1 channel gating. Studies with fully recombinant proteins expressed in bacteria or insect cells show that the STIM1 cytoplasmic region and the minimal CAD (CRAC activation domain) fragment bind directly to the C-terminal region of ORAI1 in vitro (33, 36). Circumstantial evidence suggests that this interaction is not by itself sufficient for gating. The ORAI1 ΔN truncation, missing all of the N-terminal cytoplasmic region, is expressed in the plasma membrane and accumulates at STIM1 puncta following store depletion, but it does not support the CRAC current (104, 150). In contrast, truncated ORAI1 proteins that include a short segment just N-terminal to ORAI TM1 can assemble and function as Ca^{2+} channels (33, 36, 150), focusing attention on the segment ORAI1(65–91).

ORAI1(R91W), the variant identified in two human patients with a hereditary immunodeficiency, interacts with STIM1 and is recruited to puncta upon store depletion (104, 151), yet it fails to conduct CRAC current (20, 79, 104, 142). The defect is intrinsic to ORAI, as shown by the fact that the corresponding R66W mutant of ORAI3 is activated neither by store depletion via STIM1 nor by 2-aminoethoxydiphenyl borate (2-APB), a compound that directly activates wild-type ORAI3 channels (152). There is no specific requirement for arginine at position 91 because ORAI1 proteins with nonconservative R91G and R91E replacements are fully functional, but replacement of R91 by residues with bulky nonpolar side chains interferes with channel function (153). These results could be explained if channel gating requires movement of this N-terminal segment of ORAI1, and substitution of bulky nonpolar residues at position 91 impairs the gating movement, but a more general effect of the N-terminal truncations or substitutions on channel structure has not been excluded (151–154).

Intriguingly, assays in vitro have detected a weak interaction of STIM1 with ORAI1 peptides corresponding to the segment ORAI1(65–91) (33, 36). Direct tests of whether this second identified STIM-ORAI interaction occurs with full-length ORAI, and whether it participates in gating, are warranted. Movement of STIM1 and ORAI1 to puncta is not obligatory for channel gating. Expression of the STIM1 cytoplasmic region alone, divorced from the luminal domain and the transmembrane tether, activates endogenous CRAC channels in *Stim1*$^{-/-}$ T cells, Jurkat T cells, and RBL cells (34, 36, 111, 140). Expression of the fragment together with ORAI1 can result in large constitutive CRAC currents in HEK293 cells (34, 104, 135, 140), without formation of visible STIM1 puncta and without visible relocalization of ORAI1 (104, 136). This finding rules out obligatory participation of specialized proteins or a distinctive lipid environment at the ER–plasma membrane contacts in channel gating. Conveniently, the finding has also provided tools to approach several questions that were not amenable to study at puncta.

The ability of the STIM1 cytoplasmic domain to activate ORAI1 channels directly has been tested in experiments with human ORAI1 channels expressed in the yeast *Saccharomyces cerevisiae*, which does not possess a STIM-ORAI pathway. The recombinant STIM1 C terminus elicited Ca^{2+} efflux from membrane vesicles isolated from yeast expressing ORAI1, but not from control vesicles containing no ORAI1 (36). As in mammalian cells, the SCID mutant ORAI1(R91W) and the pore mutant ORAI1(E106Q) did not support Ca^{2+} flux. The results imply that STIM1 and ORAI1 communicate directly at ER–plasma membrane contacts in mammalian cells, but they do not exclude the possibility that additional proteins in mammalian cells further modulate the efficiency of STIM-ORAI coupling.

N-terminal and C-terminal truncations of the soluble STIM1 cytoplasmic region have pinpointed a minimal fragment of STIM1 that can activate overexpressed ORAI1 and, in T cells and mast cells, native ORAI1 (32–35). The minimal region, termed SOAR (STIM-ORAI activating region), CAD, or CCb9, encompasses roughly residues 344–442 (32, 33, 35) and is contained within the functionally similar fragment termed OASF (ORAI1 activating STIM1 small C-terminal fragment) (34) (**Figure 2**). Notably, this region is positioned approximately 110 residues past the single transmembrane segment that tethers STIM1 to the ER. This accords with the geometry of ER–plasma membrane contacts (29, 109) and allows the part of STIM that interacts physically with ORAI proteins to be positioned near the plasma membrane by the lengthy STIM1 coiled-coil regions (**Figures 3**, **4**).

STIM1-ORAI1 stoichiometry. Use of the STIM1 C-terminal fragment has permitted a direct approach to the stoichiometry of STIM-ORAI interaction (135). Labeled STIM C terminus and labeled ORAI, when coexpressed, do not coalesce into puncta visible by fluorescence microscopy (104, 136). Visualization of single ORAI channels by TIRF microscopy further indicates that they do not form submicroscopic aggregates, even though ORAI channels are open (135). These observations led to an experimental design in which labeled STIM1 was expressed at low levels in order to resolve its interactions with endogenous channels. Under these conditions, photobleaching of STIM1 C-terminal-EGFP bound to or near the plasma membrane proceeded in one or two steps (135). Two-step bleaching was assigned to a STIM-ORAI complex because cells expressing modestly higher levels of STIM showed increased one-step bleaching, whereas, in contrast, cells expressing exogenous ORAI1 in addition to STIM1 showed increased two-step bleaching. The interpretation that two STIM1 C-terminal domain molecules interact with ORAI in cells is in line with the finding that the recombinant C-terminal region of STIM1 exists as a dimer in vitro (32, 36), but the photobleaching result was taken to support the stronger conclusion that two STIM1 molecules activate an ORAI channel. Weaknesses in the argument are (*a*) the rather indirect evidence that the population with two bleaching steps corresponds to STIM-ORAI complexes, and (*b*) the lack of measurements to confirm that the STIM C terminus expressed at these low levels activated endogenous ORAI channels.

The picture of a STIM1 dimer, or two independent STIM1 molecules, gating an ORAI1 tetramer channel is seemingly in tension with another view: that multimer formation is necessary for CRAC current activation. The presence of a specific multimerization domain in STIM1 cytoplasmic fragments may correlate with their ability to activate the CRAC channel (34). Experimentally, the activating CAD fragment of STIM1 forms tetramers in solution, and complexes of CAD fragment and ORAI1 that have been coexpressed in insect cells, solubilized, and purified are visible as large aggregates by electron microscopy (33). However, it has not been shown that the truncated STIM1 fragment oligomerizes in the same way as the full-length protein or that the solubilized and purified ORAI channels are in an active conformation. The finding that coexpression of CAD lowers the effective diffusion coefficient of ORAI in the plasma membrane, as determined by FRAP (33), furnishes some support for ORAI1 oligomerization in cells, but it could be explained, for example, by transitory interactions of CAD with immobile cellular proteins that lower the effective concentration of freely diffusing ORAI1.

It thus remains an open question whether ORAI1 activated in situ by the STIM1 C terminus and ORAI1 activated after recruitment to puncta by full-length STIM1 are in identical complexes. The estimated average density of channels at puncta in HEK293 cells overexpressing recombinant STIM and ORAI is ~1,000 per μm^2 (135), compared with a density greater than 10,000 per μm^2 for the slightly larger nicotinic acetylcholine receptor in postsynaptic membranes (155). This estimate does not require that the channels be tightly packed, even in cells overexpressing ORAI and producing large currents; however, it does not rule out the ordered assembly of closely packed ORAI channels into patches with dimensions below the resolution of conventional light microscopy. The question of STIM1-ORAI1 stoichiometry will be resolved only through structural determination of the conformations and oligomerization states of full-length STIM1 and ORAI1, as well as investigations of the actual organization of STIM and ORAI at puncta in T cells and mast cells.

Additional gating mechanisms. There are continuing reports that CRAC channels can be activated by an unidentified calcium influx factor (CIF) extracted and partially purified from ER Ca^{2+}-depleted human platelets, Jurkat T cells, and other sources (156, 157). RNAi experiments have placed CIF downstream of STIM1 and upstream of the membrane-associated phospholipase iPLA$_2\beta$ and ORAI1 (158). The model proposed is that CIF releases iPLA$_2\beta$ from inhibition by CaM, and iPLA$_2\beta$ in turn generates products that activate CRAC channels (159) and, in some cells, less selective Ca^{2+}-permeable channels (160). The effectiveness of the STIM1 C terminus in activating ORAI1 channels in vitro argues strongly that CIF is not required for STIM1 to communicate with ORAI1. However, it remains possible that CIF provides a parallel pathway for ORAI activation or modulation; purification and identification of the active component of CIF will be needed to test this hypothesis.

STIM2, ORAI2, ORAI3

STIM2. STIM2 bears a marked resemblance to STIM1 in its overall structure (105). Its ER-luminal domain has paired canonical and noncanonical EF-hands and a SAM domain, and its cytoplasmic domain displays sequence similarity to STIM1 extending through a long predicted coiled-coil and beyond the C-terminal boundary of the minimal activating fragment of STIM1, as well as a polybasic C-terminal tail. The protein sequences diverge in a short segment at the N terminus and a longer segment near the C terminus. STIM2 in cells is reportedly localized exclusively in the ER (161).

STIM2 also recapitulates the basic functional properties of STIM1. Recombinant STIM2 luminal domain binds Ca^{2+} in vitro with an affinity suitable for sensing ER Ca^{2+} levels (162). Its monomeric luminal domain is somewhat more stable in the absence of Ca^{2+} than is the STIM1 domain, but nonetheless on loss of Ca^{2+} the STIM2 EF-SAM fragment undergoes a conformational change and oligomerizes (28, 162). In cells, upon depletion of Ca^{2+} stores, STIM2 redistributes to puncta at ER–plasma membrane contacts (26). In fact, STIM2 redistributes to puncta at higher ER Ca^{2+} concentrations—that is, with a smaller reduction in Ca^{2+} stores—than STIM1, and a fraction of STIM2 is already activated in cells with replete Ca^{2+} stores (26). STIM2 may also have a distinctive propensity to interact with plasma membrane lipids. In vitro data indicate that the cytoplasmic domain and the isolated polybasic tail of STIM2 bind more avidly to PIP_2/PIP_3 than do the corresponding fragments of STIM1 (116). Tending to counteract the partial activation in cells with replete stores and the more avid targeting to ER–plasma membrane contacts, a STIM2 EF-hand mutant that is constitutively localized at ER–plasma membrane junctions couples less effectively to ORAI1 than does the corresponding EF-hand mutant of STIM1 (120).

There has been considerable debate over the role of STIM2 in Ca^{2+} signaling. Overexpression of STIM2 has produced variable results, ranging from an inhibition of store-operated Ca^{2+} entry when STIM2 is expressed alone (161) to increases in constitutive or store-operated Ca^{2+} influx when STIM2 is coexpressed with ORAI1 (26, 95, 163). Overexpression of STIM2 alone partially rescues store-operated Ca^{2+} entry in STIM1$^{-/-}$ T cells (15). Collectively, these data indicate that STIM2 can engage in the same signaling pathway as STIM1, and that overexpression is not a sufficiently precise tool to tease out its biological role.

Currently, the only established role for STIM2 is a contribution to maintaining basal cytoplasmic Ca^{2+} levels (26), and in many cells STIM2 may have no acute signaling role. Thus, STIM1, not STIM2, is essential for agonist-driven Ca^{2+} oscillations in HEK293 cells (120). This does not minimize the physiological importance of STIM2. The absence of STIM2 in

STIM2$^{-/-}$ T cells causes at most minor impairment in a short-term Ca^{2+} influx assay in stimulated cells, but it results in severe deficits in the sustained nuclear localization of the transcription factor NFAT and in cytokine production (15).

ORAI2 and ORAI3. ORAI2 and ORAI3 exhibit strong sequence similarity to ORAI1 in the transmembrane segments TM1–TM4. Glutamate residues corresponding to E106 and E190, which contribute to the selective Ca^{2+} permeability of ORAI1, are present. Overexpression of ORAI2 or ORAI3 together with STIM1 yields large Ca^{2+}-selective currents in some expression systems (96, 139, 141, 152, 164), and the substitutions E81D and E165Q in ORAI3 have the same deleterious effect on Ca^{2+} selectivity as the corresponding replacements, E106D and E190Q, in ORAI1 (152). The N-terminal and C-terminal intracellular segments implicated in STIM1-ORAI1 interaction are also conserved, as is the intracellular region between TM2 and TM3 to which no function has yet been assigned. Experiments probing the interaction of STIM1 with chimeric ORAI proteins further strengthen the argument that the ORAI C terminus is essential in recruiting ORAI channels to puncta (165). On the basis of the latter work, Romanin and colleagues (165) have suggested a direct interaction between the second predicted coiled-coil of STIM1 and a predicted coiled-coil of ORAI1, although the authors note that neither a coiled-coil structure nor a direct interaction between these regions has been documented.

ORAI2 mRNA is present at high levels in murine T cells, and ORAI2 may support store-operated Ca^{2+} entry in ORAI1$^{-/-}$ T cells (166). This ORAI1-independent Ca^{2+} influx is especially apparent in naive T cells, but a residual store-operated Ca^{2+} entry and a CRAC-like current are also present in differentiated ORAI1$^{-/-}$ T cells (167). However, the failure of recombinant ORAI2 to reconstitute store-operated Ca^{2+} entry in ORAI1$^{-/-}$ T cells (167), despite strong recombinant protein expression at the cell surface, leaves the contribution of ORAI2 in doubt.

Several lines of evidence converge on the conclusion that ORAI3 is a subunit of the ARC channel, another highly selective Ca^{2+} channel that responds to arachidonic acid rather than to store depletion (168, 169). As mentioned previously, the role of the ARC channel in immune responses remains to be delineated. Another report raises the alternative possibility that ORAI1-ORAI3 hetero-multimeric channels could account for store-operated currents that are less Ca^{2+}-selective than CRAC currents (170).

MOVEMENTS OF STIM1 AND ORAI1 IN ANTIGEN-STIMULATED T CELLS

Two groups have examined the redistribution of STIM1 and ORAI1 in stimulated T cells (122, 123). Cahalan and colleagues (122) used Jurkat cells and primary human T cells transfected with GFP-ORAI1 and untagged or YFP-tagged STIM1, and stimulated them with dendritic cells (DCs) pulsed with the superantigen SEB (staphylococcal enterotoxin B). The tagged and endogenous proteins moved rapidly (within 5–10 min) to the vicinity of the T cell–DC interface [a region termed the immunological synapse, where T cell and costimulatory receptors cluster with signaling proteins (171)], and remained colocalized there for at least 30 min. A pore mutant of ORAI1 (E106A) was also able to redistribute to the T cell–DC interface, even though its expression interfered dominantly with the function of the endogenous ORAI channel and abolished Ca^{2+} entry through endogenous CRAC channels. These authors also showed that TCR stimulation resulted in upregulation of *STIM1*, *ORAI1*, *ORAI2*, and *ORAI3* mRNA in activated T cells and in a corresponding increase in both thapsigargin-stimulated and TCR-stimulated Ca^{2+} influx.

Samelson and colleagues (123) used a different system in which Jurkat cells coexpressing ORAI1-CFP and STIM1-YFP were plated onto coverslips coated with stimulatory anti-CD3 antibodies. Under these conditions STIM1 and ORAI1 colocalized at puncta near the stimulatory surface, and at least some STIM1 and ORAI1 molecules were close enough for FRET between them to be observed. However the regions of STIM1-ORAI1 colocalization were distinct from the signaling microclusters containing TCRs and marked by phosphotyrosine, suggesting that sites of tyrosine kinase activation in the contact interface do not necessarily overlap with sites of Ca^{2+} influx.

Surprisingly, a large fraction of endogenous as well as fluorescently tagged STIM1 and ORAI1 proteins moved away from the stimulatory surface, eventually colocalizing in stable cap structures at the opposite pole of the cell (123). The average FRET efficiency between ORAI1-CFP and STIM1-YFP was consistently higher in the caps than in the puncta, and photobleaching experiments showed that both proteins were notably less mobile in the caps than when diffusely distributed in the ER and plasma membrane, respectively, of unstimulated cells. Formation of the caps required TCR stimulation, the activation of tyrosine kinases, and an intact cytoskeleton, but it was not dependent on Ca^{2+} influx. Based on their observation that the caps appeared more dynamic when Jurkat T cells were stimulated with B cells pulsed with the superantigen SEE (staphylococcal enterotoxin E) and were sometimes seen to donate STIM1 and ORAI1 to a second contact interface formed by the T cell with a newly arriving superantigen-pulsed B cell, the authors speculated that the cap may serve as a repository of STIM and ORAI proteins that could be rapidly mobilized.

OTHER PATHWAYS FOR Ca^{2+} ENTRY IN LYMPHOCYTES

As discussed above, the bulk of the available evidence suggests that CRAC channels form the primary route for Ca^{2+} entry in T cells and mast cells. Nevertheless, several studies have proposed that additional Ca^{2+} entry pathways contribute to Ca^{2+} signaling in lymphocytes. The regulation and activity of these alternative pathways are not as well understood as those of the CRAC channel. In the following sections, we discuss the current evidence for these pathways and suggest experiments that may provide more definitive tests for their roles in lymphocyte Ca^{2+} signaling.

Ca^{2+} Entry in B Cells: IP_3 Receptors in the Plasma Membrane or B-SOC?

The high sensitivity of CRAC channels to inhibition by trivalent cations has been exploited to reveal other routes of Ca^{2+} entry into lymphocytes. In two studies, treatment of chicken DT40 pre-B cells with 300 nM Gd^{3+} or La^{3+} (sufficient to fully block CRAC current) failed to fully suppress BCR-triggered Ca^{2+} entry (172, 173). What is the source of this residual BCR-dependent Ca^{2+} entry? Taylor and colleagues (173) propose that it occurs through plasma membrane IP_3Rs, based on recordings of single-channel currents in whole-cell recordings from DT40 and mouse B cells. Several lines of evidence support the argument that the currents reflect IP_3Rs in the plasma membrane: Channel activity was absent in IP_3R–knockout DT40 cells, the single-channel conductance varied with expression of known IP_3R pore mutants, and the currents could be blocked by extracellular bungarotoxin when IP_3Rs with bungarotoxin-binding sites were expressed. Surprisingly, however, regardless of the amount of IP_3R cDNA used to transfect, only two to three IP_3-gated channels were detected in the plasma membrane. This constancy of expression is apparently not regulated by feedback from channel activity or Ca^{2+} entry, as it also applies to mutant IP_3Rs with reduced IP_3 binding or low conductance (174). Together, the findings of Taylor and colleagues (173, 174) suggest that just two to three high-conductance IP_3Rs account for about half of the Ca^{2+} entry triggered by BCR stimulation, whereas the remainder is conducted by thousands of low-conductance CRAC channels. If true, this could exert a powerful influence on the specificity of Ca^{2+} signaling, particularly if specific effector proteins are localized within

Ca^{2+} microdomain: a local region near Ca^{2+} channels where free Ca^{2+} concentration is elevated. Microdomains are often too small to be visualized by Ca^{2+} imaging but their presence can be inferred by showing that a fast Ca^{2+} chelator (BAPTA) blocks a downstream effect, whereas a slow Ca^{2+} chelator (EGTA) does not

Ca_V channels: voltage-gated Ca^{2+} channels that open when the membrane potential becomes depolarized

the Ca^{2+} microdomains of the IP_3R. One essential test of these results would be to identify the individual sites of influx through the IP_3Rs using Ca^{2+} imaging techniques; knowing the location of these Ca^{2+} hotspots not only would confirm the electrophysiological results, but also would likely offer helpful clues regarding downstream pathways or mechanisms of channel regulation.

A second group recently confirmed that BCR stimulation evoked trivalent-insensitive, non-CRAC-mediated Ca^{2+} entry into DT40 cells but concluded that it was not conducted through IP_3Rs (175). Morita and colleagues (175) observed that BCR stimulation could elicit La^{3+}-insensitive Ca^{2+} entry into IP_3R–deficient DT40 cells, but only if stores had first been fully depleted with thapsigargin. The response in DT40 cells required STIM1 expression but was not affected by knocking down Orai1 or Orai2. These and other findings suggest a pathway, referred to as B-SOC, that is STIM1-dependent and regulated by the combination of store depletion and a signal from the BCR. The channel underlying this process has not been identified. To validate this B-SOC pathway, it will be necessary to distinguish it from the CRAC channel by characterizing its biophysical and pharmacological properties using patch-clamp techniques; because biochemical factors and membrane potential can also influence Ca^{2+} signals, Ca^{2+} imaging experiments alone cannot describe the underlying pathway directly or in enough detail to allow a meaningful comparison. Further work will be needed to clarify the relation between B-SOC and the IP_3Rs described by Taylor et al.

Ca_V Channels in T Cells

Voltage-gated Ca^{2+} (Ca_V) channels execute diverse roles in electrically excitable cells: Ca_V channels open upon membrane depolarization, and the resulting Ca^{2+} entry initiates muscle contraction and vesicle exocytosis and shapes electrical activity, to name but a few functions. The roles of Ca_V channels in electrically inexcitable cells such as lymphocytes have been more controversial. The inhibitory effects of L-type Ca_V antagonists (nifedipine, diltiazem, and verapamil, among others) on TCR-mediated Ca^{2+} responses originally prompted the notion that human T cells express functional Ca_V channels (176, 177). However, the lack of specificity of these drugs for Ca_V channels creates complications: At the high doses that were used they also block K^+ channels, which can indirectly inhibit Ca^{2+} signaling via CRAC channels by depolarizing the membrane and diminishing the driving force for Ca^{2+} entry (178–180). Moreover, one Ca_V antagonist, nifedipine, may affect the store-operated Ca^{2+} entry process itself (181). Finally, depolarization of T cells fails to elicit a $[Ca^{2+}]_i$ rise or to evoke inward Ca^{2+} currents (122, 182, 183). Thus, if a Ca_V channel were to conduct Ca^{2+} in T cells, it would have to be activated through a novel biochemical pathway rather than through membrane depolarization.

Molecular studies have provided additional evidence for Ca_V channel expression in T cells. Cav1.1, 1.2, and 1.4 transcripts and proteins as well as auxiliary β subunits have been detected in murine T cells, and their levels of expression increased after stimulation with anti-CD3 and anti-CD28 in vitro (183). Alternatively spliced transcripts of Cav1.4 channels have been detected in human T, B, and Jurkat cells; these splicing events are predicted to create deletions that might account for the observed lack of voltage-dependent gating (182, 184). $[Ca^{2+}]_i$ elevations evoked by anti-CD3 were partially suppressed in $CD4^+$ T cells from mice lacking either β3 or β4 subunits (183), possibly explaining the cytokine secretion defects in these mice. Similarly, TCR-mediated Ca^{2+} signaling was partially inhibited in $CD4^+$ T cells from mice genetically disrupted for expression of the scaffold protein AHNAK1 (185). AHNAK1 is a very large scaffold protein (~700 kDa) that binds several proteins, including PLCγ, S100b, the annexin 2 complex, and the Ca_V β2 subunit (185). Cav1.1 and Cav1.2 protein levels were diminished in $AHNAK1^{-/-}$ cells, and Cav1.1 in the membrane fraction was reduced, correlating with the smaller Ca^{2+} responses

(185). Interestingly, AHNAK1 is expressed in $CD8^+$ T cells only after they differentiate to CTLs, and expression of Cav1.1 is upregulated in parallel. Like AHNAK1$^{-/-}$ $CD4^+$ T cells, CTLs from AHNAK1$^{-/-}$ mice show reduced Ca^{2+} elevation in response to TCR stimulation, as well as reduced granzyme B production and cytolytic activity (186).

Can these studies be reconciled with the evidence that Orai Ca^{2+} channels are responsible for Ca^{2+} influx in peripheral mouse and human T cells? In humans, loss of expression or function of ORAI1 results in a complete lack of TCR-mediated Ca^{2+} influx as well as in profound immunodeficiency (79–82, 93). Murine T cells deficient in β4, β3, or AHNAK1 fail to exhibit substantial Ca^{2+} entry following TCR stimulation, but are not impaired for Ca^{2+} entry evoked by store depletion with thapsigargin, implying that CRAC channel activation by full store depletion is intact. One possibility is that Ca_V β subunits and the AHNAK1 scaffold influence Ca^{2+} influx and T cell effector functions indirectly, perhaps by influencing the local generation of IP_3 [bulk IP_3 generation was unaffected in AHNAK1$^{-/-}$ T cells (185)], or some additional mechanism that does not directly involve Ca^{2+} permeation through Ca_V channels.

An essential step in validating Ca_V channels as a Ca^{2+} permeation pathway in peripheral T cells is to demonstrate that they conduct a measurable Ca^{2+} current after activation by the TCR. The most straightforward way to do this is to confirm that mutations of the critical ion selectivity–producing glutamate residues in the Ca_V pore alter the ion selectivity of the TCR-induced current. This type of experiment was done originally with Cav1 channels (187), and an analogous mutagenesis of the Orai1 subunit of the CRAC channel supplied the definitive proof that Orai1 forms the pore of the CRAC channel (23–25). A direct demonstration of currents carried by Ca_V channels in T cells will help settle the debate regarding their role as a parallel pathway for TCR-triggered Ca^{2+} influx.

In conclusion, further studies will be needed to determine the contributions of Ca_V channels, IP_3Rs, or other modes of non-store-operated Ca^{2+} entry to Ca^{2+} influx in lymphocytes, particularly in defined subsets of immune cells and under a range of stimulation conditions. Notably, murine thymocytes that completely lack store-operated Ca^{2+} entry as a result of targeted disruption of the *Stim1* and *Stim2* genes show no developmental impairment (discussed below), suggesting that STIM-independent modes of Ca^{2+} entry may operate during T cell development. These possibilities deserve further investigation.

Kv channel: voltage-gated K^+ channel that maintains the negative membrane potential that drives Ca^{2+} influx

Modulation of Calcium Signals

The rate at which Ca^{2+} enters the cell through open CRAC channels is determined by the Ca^{2+} concentration gradient and the voltage difference across the plasma membrane (membrane potential). Thus, even though they do not conduct Ca^{2+} directly, various channels can modulate calcium signals in T cells through their ability to alter the T cell membrane potential (normally ~−50 mV, with the cell interior at negative potential relative to the outside) (188). The most thoroughly understood are the K^+-selective channels. These have been extensively reviewed elsewhere (41, 180); here, we give a brief overview of their functions.

K^+ channels. Kv1.3 is expressed in human and mouse T cells. It is a voltage-gated channel (hence Kv channel), which opens upon depolarization beyond ~−50 mV (i.e., when the difference in potential between the inside and outside of the cell is reduced, as would occur upon opening of nonselective cation channels or Ca^{2+}-selective CRAC channels). By allowing K^+ to leave the cells, opening of the Kv1.3 channel sets the resting membrane potential of the T cell near this value (i.e., ~−50 mV), thus resisting the depolarizing influence of Ca^{2+} influx through CRAC channels. Blockade of Kv1.3 with highly specific blockers inhibits T cell activation in vitro in a dose-dependent manner, which has been linked mechanistically to depolarization and reduced Ca^{2+} entry (41, 189).

KCa channel: K^+ channel that is activated by increased intracellular Ca^{2+}

In addition, human T and B cells also express KCa3.1, a class of intermediate-conductance K^+ channels. This channel is voltage-independent but is activated by Ca^{2+} (hence KCa channel). The KCa3.1 channel opens when Ca^{2+} binds to CaM bound to the channel C terminus (half-maximal activation by ~0.5 μM Ca^{2+}) and hyperpolarizes the cell, thus increasing the driving force for Ca^{2+} influx and causing a greater overall increase of $[Ca^{2+}]_i$. Interestingly, KCa3.1 is negatively regulated by the histidine phosphatase PHPT-1, and knockdown of PHPT-1 has been associated with increased Ca^{2+} signals and proliferation (190).

Recent studies have revealed important changes in Kv1.3 and KCa3.1 expression during T cell activation and differentiation in vivo. Kv1.3 is more abundant than KCa3.1 in naive resting T cells and central and effector memory T cells, enabling this K^+ channel to play the dominant role in maintaining membrane potential and Ca^{2+} influx. However, upon activation, central memory cells upregulate KCa3.1, whereas effector memory cells upregulate Kv1.3 (180). This creates a difference in their dependency on K^+ channel subtypes that may be exploited for therapeutic purposes. Kv1.3 levels are high in T cells from human patients with a variety of autoimmune diseases (191), and clofazimine, a Kv1.3 channel inhibitor, has been used successfully in treatment of lupus, psoriasis, and chronic graft-versus-host disease in human patients (192), while other selective Kv1.3 inhibitors have been effective in treating diverse autoimmune disease models in animals (191, 193).

Recently, members of the twin-pore class of K^+ channels (K_{2P}) have been reported in T cells. In one study, a voltage-independent K^+ current developed during whole-cell recording from Jurkat cells and resembled in some ways TRESK, a K_{2P} family member that contributes to the resting potential in diverse cells (194). In human T cells, there is immunological evidence for the acid-sensitive TWIK-related channels TASK1 and TASK3, and an anandamide-sensitive current in these cells has been attributed to TASK channels (195). Anandamide suppressed experimental allergic encephalomyelitis in rats, raising the possibility that these channels could provide an additional therapeutic target in T cells (195), but the general lack of specificity of anandamide and other TASK inhibitors complicates efforts to assess TASK channel functions in vivo. Given reports that K^+ currents in human and rat T cells are completely inhibited after treatment with highly specific blockers of Kv1.3 and KCa3.1 (ShK-Dap[22] and TRAM-34, respectively) (41, 196), further work will be needed to establish roles for the K_{2P} family of K^+ channels in lymphocytes.

TRPM4. The nonselective cation channel TRPM4 (197) may also play an important role in regulating membrane potential and Ca^{2+} signaling in T cells. TRPM4 is activated by Ca^{2+}, and once open it would be expected to drive the lymphocyte membrane potential toward 0 mV, just the opposite of the KCa channel. Launay et al. (198) show evidence that TRPM4 protein is present in thymocytes, the D10 T cell line (Th2), and Jurkat T cells and that increased $[Ca^{2+}]_i$ activated a nonselective current in Jurkat that was inhibited by transfection with a dominant-negative TRPM4 mutant. The same inhibitory mutant suppressed PHA-induced $[Ca^{2+}]_i$ oscillations and IL-2 production, leading to the suggestion that TRPM4 causes periodic depolarization that provides negative feedback to help terminate each oscillation and prevent $[Ca^{2+}]_i$ from climbing to a high plateau. These results differ from earlier studies on Jurkat T cells in several respects. First, Launay et al. did not observe the prominent KCa current that was activated by μM $Ca^{2+}{}_i$ in prior studies (199). Also, PHA had been shown previously to evoke oscillations of CRAC current in Jurkat cells without any apparent nonselective current (63). The reasons for these discrepancies are not clear but could reflect clonal variation in Jurkat cell lines. However, previous studies of primary human T cells also failed to reveal a Ca^{2+}-activated nonselective cation channel like TRPM4, and intracellular dialysis of resting or activated human

T cells with up to 10 μM $Ca^{2+}{}_i$ evoked large KCa currents without any detectable nonselective current (200). Characterization of TRPM4 currents in normal human T cells will be an important step toward establishing their functional roles.

Mitochondria. The activity of CRAC channels can be modulated by mitochondria, and recent studies suggest that this may serve to sustain the activity of CRAC channels during interactions of T cells with antigen-presenting cells (APCs). Shortly after Ca^{2+} enters the cell through CRAC channels, energized mitochondria take up a portion of it through the MCU, accumulate it, and release it back into the cytosol through a Na^+-Ca^{2+} exchange mechanism (201). In human T cells and Jurkat cells, sustained elevation of $[Ca^{2+}]_i$ in response to store depletion requires uptake and release of Ca^{2+} by the mitochondria (201). One mechanism by which energized mitochondria may sustain CRAC channel activity is by preventing slow Ca^{2+}-dependent inactivation of CRAC channels (202). Mitochondria are thought to inhibit inactivation by taking up Ca^{2+} and thereby reducing the free Ca^{2+} near the inactivation site or by locally generating ATP, a Ca^{2+} buffer (203–205). Interestingly, in Jurkat T cells Ca^{2+} influx through CRAC channels causes mitochondria to move toward the plasma membrane through a microtubule- and kinesin-dependent process, and sustained $[Ca^{2+}]_i$ elevation is reduced when translocation is prevented, e.g., by treatment with nocodazole or by loading with antikinesin mAb (206). The accumulation of mitochondria near sources of Ca^{2+} has also been observed in other cells and occurs by a mechanism in which local $[Ca^{2+}]_i$ elevation uncouples mitochondria from kinesin-driven movement along microtubules (207, 208).

Directed mitochondrial movement also results from polarized signaling through the TCR. Mitochondria accumulate at contacts between T cells and anti-CD3 beads, and this is dependent on Ca^{2+} entry through CRAC channels (209). The movement in this case is not nocodazole-sensitive, however; instead, it is inhibited by actin filament depolymerization with latrunculin B. Preventing the movement with latrunculin B did reduce the sustained component of Ca^{2+} signaling, but the actin dependency of immune synapse formation and strength of TCR signaling makes it difficult to draw a firm conclusion about the specific role of mitochondrial movement in this case. However, it is intriguing that CRAC channels also localize to the synapse (122, 123), raising the possibility that mitochondria function as part of a self-regulating signaling complex that promotes sustained Ca^{2+} entry at the synapse.

The dynamics of Ca^{2+} signaling in T cells are also modulated by time-dependent changes in Ca^{2+} pumping across the plasma membrane (210). In Jurkat T cells, Ca^{2+} extrusion occurs via PMCA4b. At resting $[Ca^{2+}]_i$, the PMCA is autoinhibited through an interaction between its C terminus and a region near the Ca^{2+} transport site (211). After $[Ca^{2+}]_i$ rises, pump activity is initially low, but over tens of seconds Ca^{2+}-CaM binds to the C terminus, displacing the inhibitory domain and allowing pump activity to increase. The effect of this PMCA modulation is to act as a high-pass filter, allowing transients to pass relatively unimpeded but effectively reducing sustained signals. This behavior contributes to the generation of biphasic spike and plateau responses commonly seen with strong TCR stimulation (210).

Mechanisms and Functions of Complex Calcium Signaling Patterns

The diversity of mechanisms that create and modulate Ca^{2+} signals in lymphocytes creates the potential for complex signaling dynamics, which is likely to have important consequences for the strength and specificity of signaling through downstream pathways. At high levels of stimulation using strong antigens, anti-TCR cross-linking, or artificial store depletion, a biphasic response is typical. This consists of an early rise to a peak, followed by a gradual decline over tens of seconds to an elevated plateau. Under these strong stimulation conditions, one would expect Ca^{2+} store depletion to remain relatively constant. Quantitative modeling has shown how this dynamic signature can arise from PMCA modulation (210).

At lower levels of stimulation, either with antigen or anti-TCR cross-linking or partial depletion of stores, $[Ca^{2+}]_i$ oscillations are the more common response. A particularly dramatic example is seen with human T cells stimulated with a variety of agents (SERCA inhibitors, ionomycin, or anti-CD3) that only partially deplete the intracellular stores (212). Under these conditions, $[Ca^{2+}]_i$ oscillates with a regular period of 100–200 s. The complete mechanism of this response is not known; however, evidence suggests that the oscillations are derived from the repetitive and coordinated opening and closing of CRAC channels, rather than from repetitive Ca^{2+} release from the ER. In support of this idea, PHA-evoked $[Ca^{2+}]_i$ oscillations are terminated immediately by block of CRAC Ca^{2+} fluxes, and, in perforated-patch recordings from Jurkat cells, PHA evokes oscillations of CRAC current even under voltage-clamp conditions (63). Single-cell measurements from human T cells show that store content and the Ca^{2+} influx rate oscillate out of phase with each other (212). One model proposed to explain this oscillatory behavior is that intrinsic delays in the feedback between changes in store content and CRAC channel activity cause each to overshoot and undershoot its equilibrium value. Given our current understanding of the mechanism for CRAC channel activation, these delays may arise from the time it takes STIM1 to accumulate at ER–plasma membrane junctions following store depletion and to dissipate after stores refill. Other processes may also contribute to the oscillations, such as activation of Ca^{2+}-activated K^+ channels and TRPM4 channels, which could provide positive or negative feedback, respectively, during the rise and fall of each oscillation through their influence on membrane potential (198). However, the ability of CRAC current to oscillate at a constant membrane potential (63) shows that the basic oscillatory machinery does not require these other channels. A fuller understanding of the oscillation mechanism will entail quantitative modeling that incorporates an accurate characterization of each conductance and their interactions through changes in membrane potential and $[Ca^{2+}]_i$. Given the current pace of progress in understanding the CRAC channel, this may soon become possible.

$[Ca^{2+}]_i$ oscillations may serve important functions in lymphocytes by enhancing the efficiency and the specificity of Ca^{2+} signaling to the nucleus. In Jurkat cells and RBL cells, artificially generated oscillations enhance the efficiency of signaling through NFAT by a limited amount of Ca^{2+} or IP_3 (213–215). In addition, the activation of different transcriptional pathways shows a distinct dependency on oscillation frequency that enhances the specificity with which pathways are recruited; NFAT requires frequent spikes (period <200 s) for significant activity, whereas NF-κB is activated by spike periods as long as 30 min (213). The mechanism underlying these differences is likely to derive from the kinetics of transcription factor activation and deactivation. For example, NFAT translocation to the nucleus is regulated by a relatively rapid dephosphorylation/phosphorylation cycle; in this case, oscillations enhance the nuclear accumulation of NFAT provided that their period is shorter than the lifetime of the dephosphorylated state, so that each pulse of Ca^{2+} causes an incremental increase in nuclear NFAT (215). In contrast, NF-κB is activated through the proteolysis of the inhibitory IκB subunit; because resynthesis of IκB is a slow process, deactivation is also slow, and even infrequent oscillations are able to drive NF-κB accumulation in the nucleus (216).

These studies highlight the possibility that lymphocytes may receive specific information encoded in the amplitude and pattern of Ca^{2+} signals. To assess whether such a decoding system operates in vivo, naturally occurring Ca^{2+} signals must be characterized in cells exposed to the physiological stimuli that control their behavior and developmental fate. Several recent studies have used two-photon microscopy to measure $[Ca^{2+}]_i$ signals as T cells navigate within three-dimensional immune tissues. In thymic slices, thymocytes undergoing positive selection display irregular oscillations that are associated strongly with immotility, and increased $[Ca^{2+}]_i$ appears to be necessary and sufficient to stop cell migration (217). Thus, during development Ca^{2+} signals act in a positive feedback loop that stops the cells from migrating once they encounter and recognize an antigen-MHC complex; this "stop signal" then may help prolong the signaling that drives transcriptional programs leading to positive selection. Mature T cells in lymph node explants also display $[Ca^{2+}]_i$ fluctuations that increase in frequency and amplitude on contact with antigen-primed DCs (218). As in the thymus, Ca^{2+} spikes in naive lymph node T cells were associated with decreased velocity, consistent with the ability of Ca^{2+} to slow T cell motility. $[Ca^{2+}]_i$ elevation and oscillations have also been seen in B cells contacting antigen-bearing DCs in the lymph node (219). A third study showed that only high-potency peptides can cause a $[Ca^{2+}]_i$ rise in lymph node T cells in vivo, and again, the Ca^{2+} signal was necessary for motility arrest (220). It remains to be seen whether Ca^{2+} is a universal motility stop signal in the immune system, what other signals participate in immobilizing cells at sites of productive contacts with APCs, and how the balance between these influences may change during development.

BIOLOGICAL CONSEQUENCES OF STIM AND ORAI DEFICIENCIES

Hereditary Immunodeficiencies in Humans Resulting from Mutations in STIM1 and ORAI1

In human patients, defects in CRAC channel function lead primarily to severe immunodeficiency. A handful of patients with rare hereditary immunodeficiencies have been identified who display a concomitant loss of T cell cytokine expression, store-operated Ca^{2+} entry, and CRAC current (20, 79–82, 90–93). Three sets of siblings from three families have mutations in ORAI1, and three others from a single family have mutations in STIM1 (**Figure 6**). The mutations are recessive because the heterozygous relatives are not immunodeficient. Because other family members (STIM2, ORAI2, ORAI3) do not compensate for mutations in STIM1 and ORAI1, the data suggest strongly that ORAI1 and STIM1 are the predominant family members responsible for store-operated Ca^{2+} entry in human T cells. Patients with mutations in STIM2, ORAI2, or ORAI3 have not yet been identified.

R91W, a loss-of-function mutation in ORAI1. T cells from the two patients who have been most completely characterized were unable to produce some NFAT-dependent cytokines or to show changes in the expression of diverse Ca^{2+}-regulated genes, upon stimulation (80, 90). This was traced to an almost complete loss of store-operated Ca^{2+} entry and CRAC channel current, resulting in very minor, transient dephosphorylation and nuclear translocation of NFAT in stimulated T cells (79, 80, 90). Relatives who were heterozygous carriers of the mutant allele were identified by the fact that they showed decreased store-operated Ca^{2+} entry, but only at subphysiological $[Ca^{2+}]_o$ (20). Genome-wide SNP analyses, together with the *Drosophila* RNAi screen, established the genetic basis for the immunodeficiency as an R91W mutation in ORAI1, near the beginning of the first transmembrane domain (20) (**Figure 6**). Why this mutation is nonfunctional is not yet understood at a biochemical level (see previous section).

The defect in store-operated Ca^{2+} entry in the T cells and fibroblasts of these patients could be rescued by expression of wild-type ORAI1, but not by overexpression of ORAI2 above its endogenous levels in cells. There was a minor degree of rescue by overexpressed ORAI3. The biophysical differences in the channel formed by ORAI1, ORAI2, and ORAI3 were discussed above; in particular, channels formed by ORAI2 may not be gated by store depletion in a physiological context, although

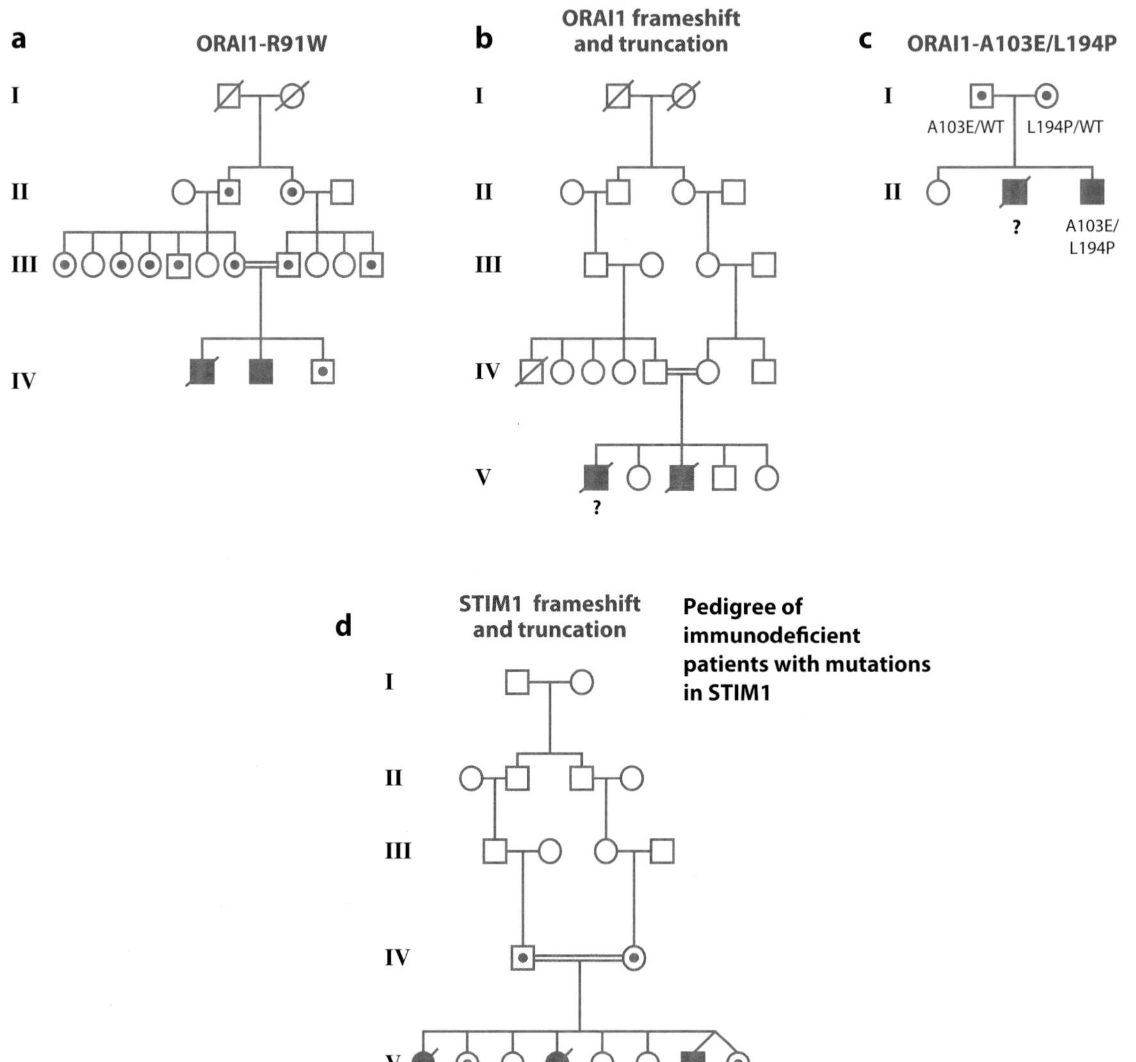

Figure 6

Pedigrees of immunodeficient patients with mutations in (*a–c*) ORAI1 and (*d*) STIM1. (*Filled symbols*, patients; *strike-through*, deceased; ?, DNA unavailable for sequencing; dot within symbol, individual is heterozygous for the mutant allele.) Adapted with permission from References 91, 93.

overexpression of ORAI2 and STIM1 does result in increased Ca^{2+} entry evoked by store depletion.

ORAI1 mutations leading to loss of ORAI1 protein expression. ORAI1 mutations are also responsible for two other familial severe immunodeficiency syndromes, originally described in the mid-1990s (81, 82). In each case, the underlying mutations result in an essentially null phenotype for ORAI1 (93) (**Figure 6**). In one of the families, where the parents were second cousins and their two affected children were homozygous for the mutant allele, insertion of an adenine in exon 1 of *ORAI1* gave rise to a frameshift mutation that altered the sequence of the first transmembrane domain and introduced a stop codon that terminated the protein at residue 112 (81, 93). There was no detectable expression of the mutant protein (or mRNA, possibly due to nonsense-mediated decay) and no detectable Ca^{2+} entry into the patient's fibroblasts upon store depletion with thapsigargin. Store-operated Ca^{2+} entry was restored upon reconstitution of the mutant fibroblasts with wild-type ORAI1, but not with STIM1.

In the second family, where the parents were unrelated, the affected patient appears to have inherited a different mutant *ORAI1* allele from each of his heterozygous (and clinically normal) parents (82, 93) (**Figure 6**). This patient's two independent missense mutations, A103E and L194P, are located in the first and third transmembrane regions of ORAI1, respectively, in relative proximity to two essential glutamate residues, E106 and E190, in the Ca^{2+}-conducting pore. Nevertheless, both mutations result in loss of protein expression rather than in loss of function with unimpaired expression. Endogenous ORAI1 protein levels appeared to be diminished in the patient's fibroblasts, and ORAI1 cDNAs bearing the individual mutations were not expressed at detectable levels even in HEK293 cells. As with T cells and fibroblasts bearing the R91W mutant in ORAI1 discussed above, the defect in store-operated Ca^{2+} entry in this patient's fibroblasts was rescued by expression of wild-type ORAI1 and to some degree by overexpression of ORAI3 above its endogenous levels in these cells. Again, as with the R91W mutant T cells and fibroblasts, there was no rescue upon overexpression of ORAI2.

A STIM1 mutation leading to loss of STIM1 protein expression. A fourth hereditary immunodeficiency was traced to a nonsense mutation in STIM1 (91) (**Figure 6**). In two patients from this family, insertion of an adenine in the third exon of STIM1 resulted in a frameshift that introduced a stop codon shortly thereafter, at residue 136. The predicted short N-terminal fragment of STIM1 was not detected in the patient's fibroblasts. Store-operated Ca^{2+} entry was almost undetectable but could be restored by reintroduction of wild-type STIM1. There was also considerable rescue by overexpressed STIM2, indicating that both STIM1 and STIM2 can couple to ORAI1 and suggesting that endogenous STIM2 is not expressed at high enough levels to contribute to CRAC channel function or does not couple as effectively as STIM1 to ORAI1 in fibroblasts. These possibilities may be distinguished by measuring the relative levels of endogenous and ectopically expressed STIM1 and STIM2 and by measuring the ability of purified recombinant STIM1 and STIM2 to open the ORAI1 channel in cell-free systems.

Clinical manifestations. The clinical manifestations of patients with homozygous STIM1 and ORAI1 mutations have been described in detail (90–93) and are summarized very briefly here. The predominant clinical phenotype is a severe T cell immunodeficiency, marked in the affected infants by recurrent viral, fungal, and bacterial infections. Lymphocyte development is unaffected, with total lymphocyte counts, numbers of T, B, and NK cells, and serum immunoglobulin levels generally falling in the normal range, but T cell activation and proliferation are strongly impaired. Another consistent symptom is a congenital, nonprogressive myopathy that manifests in infants as muscular hypotonia and persists in surviving patients whose immune deficiency has been rescued by transfer of hematopoietic precursor cells. Histological examination of one of the patients showed atrophy of type II muscle fibers (93). Clinically, the myopathy eventually results in severe chronic pulmonary disease with increased mucus retention in the airways. The myopathy is consistent with the well-established requirement for ORAI1 and STIM1 in store-operated Ca^{2+} entry in skeletal muscle and for STIM1 in myoblast differentiation (reviewed in 92, 221, 222). A less consistent manifestation, observed in some but not all surviving patients, is ectodermal dysplasia, a syndrome that encompasses defects in formation of dental enamel as well as anhydrosis with impaired sweat production and consequent heat intolerance (90–93).

These data suggest that the major clinical consequences of loss-of-function mutations in ORAI1 and STIM1 are limited to the immune system, skeletal muscle, and certain ectodermally derived tissues. Such selective impairment is surprising given that ORAI1 and STIM1 are both widely expressed and that store-operated Ca^{2+} channels with the characteristics of CRAC channels have been described in diverse nonimmune cell types (reviewed in 92). The most likely explanation is that in most nonimmune cell types deficiencies in ORAI1 and STIM1 are compensated for by expression of other STIM and ORAI family members. The therapeutic implications are obvious—compounds that selectively inhibit the channel function of ORAI1 or coupling between ORAI1 and STIM1 have the potential to suppress immune function selectively, without having deleterious effects on other organ systems. As such they might lack the toxicity of current immunosuppressive agents, such as cyclosporin A and FK506.

Patients with STIM1 mutations also showed evidence of lymphoproliferation and autoimmune disease, presenting with thrombocytopenia and (in some cases) autoimmune hemolytic anemia (91, 92). In the one patient in whom this determination could be made, the autoimmunity correlated with decreased numbers of regulatory T cells (Tregs) (91). This phenotype is reminiscent of that observed in mice lacking Stim1 and Stim2 selectively in T cells (15), as discussed below.

Functional Consequences of Stim1, Stim2, and Orai1 Mutations in Mice

The immunological and extraimmunological phenotypes of mice with targeted disruptions of the *Stim1*, *Stim2*, and *Orai1* genes are only briefly described here, given that they have been exhaustively covered in several recent reviews (39, 92, 221–225). All three genes are required for survival: On the C57BL/6 background, mice with a targeted global deletion of *Orai1* or *Stim1* (or an R93W knock-in mutation introduced into the *Orai1* gene) die at late embryonic ages in utero or perinatally within a day of birth, and *Stim2*-deficient mice survive for only ~5 weeks (15, 166, 167, 226–228). Crossing to outbred mouse strains prolongs the survival of some *Stim1*-deficient mice to approximately 7 days and rescues the neonatal lethality of a fraction of *Orai1*-deficient mice (15, 166, 167). Surviving *Orai1*-deficient mice show a strong phenotype of thin skin, sporadic hair loss, and cyclical alopecia (167), resembling that described in mice with a keratinocyte-specific deletion of the *Cnb1* gene (which encodes a regulatory subunit of calcineurin) (229).

Here, we focus on T cells and mast cells, the cells of the immune system whose phenotypes have been best characterized in these mice. Briefly, the effect of Orai1 and Stim1 deficiency varies depending on cell type. To illustrate, mast cell degranulation and leukotriene production are almost completely abolished with individual deletions of either *Stim1* or *Orai1* (166, 227); the function of Tregs is more resistant because they are present and functional in the absence of *Stim1* but are severely compromised in numbers and suppressive function upon deletion of both *Stim1* and *Stim2* (15); and, finally, thymocyte development is surprisingly unaffected even when all Stim function is lost, as in fetal liver chimeras generated with precursors doubly deficient in *Stim1* and *Stim2* (M. Oh-hora, personal communication). A possible scenario is that Ca^{2+} influx in developing thymocytes occurs through a STIM-independent, non-store-operated pathway, for instance one of those discussed in the context of peripheral T cells in the previous section.

Orai1 deficiency. Mice with a gene-trap mutation in the *Orai1* gene were used to investigate the role of Orai1 in mast cell and T cell function (166). Mast cells developed normally in the absence of Orai1 but showed essentially no degranulation or synthesis of leukotriene C4 in response to stimulation with antigen IgE, even though store-operated Ca^{2+} entry was not completely abolished. Thymic T cell development was unaffected in these mice, as in mice with a targeted deletion of the *Orai1* gene (167). In both strains of mice, store-operated Ca^{2+} entry and cytokine production were moderately impaired in naive *Orai1*-deficient T cells compared with wild-type T cells, possibly because of compensation by other Orai family members (166, 167) (discussed above). However, previously activated or differentiated T cells showed considerable downregulation of *Orai2* and *Orai3* mRNA and displayed a much more striking decrease in cytokine production (167). Store-operated Ca^{2+} entry in response to anti-IgM stimulation was also diminished, albeit not completely lost, in *Orai1*-deficient B cells relative to wild-type B cells (167). It remains to be tested whether the T and B cell impairments translate into immune deficiency in vivo.

Stim1 and Stim2 deficiencies. As observed for mast cells from mice with a gene trap mutation in *Orai1* (166), mast cells from mice with a targeted disruption of the *Stim1* gene were poorly functional in vitro and in vivo (227). In T cells, Stim1 deficiency resulted in a profound loss of store-operated Ca^{2+} entry, whereas the lack of Stim2 had only a minor effect in these short-term (10–60 min) assays, possibly because Stim2 constitutes less than 5% of total Stim protein in T cells (15). However, T cells lacking Stim2 were unable to sustain NFAT nuclear translocation and showed a disproportionate decrease in cytokine production (15), consistent with the hypothesis that, as ER stores refill, STIM1 is more rapidly inactivated, whereas STIM2 may remain active and continue to gate ORAI channels for a prolonged time (26).

Perhaps the most unexpected immune phenotypes were observed when both the *Stim1* and *Stim2* genes were conditionally and selectively deleted in T cells using *CD4Cre*. Over the course of approximately four months, these doubly deficient mice developed a notable lymphoproliferative phenotype characterized by splenomegaly, lymphadenopathy, infiltration of leukocytes into many organs, and signs of autoimmunity in the form of blepharitis and dermatitis (15). The lymphoproliferative phenotype was associated with a striking decrease in the number and function of Tregs. The Treg loss of function was at least partly cell intrinsic because mixed bone marrow chimera experiments showed that the Treg developmental and functional defects persisted even in the presence of circulating wild-type T cells in the recipient chimeric mice. However, the development of splenomegaly and lymphadenopathy was mostly prevented in the chimeras, as well as in *Stim1*$^{fl/fl}$, *Stim2*$^{fl/fl}$, *CD4Cre* mice that received wild-type $CD4^+$ $CD25^+$ Tregs at a young age. Together, these findings suggest that store-operated Ca^{2+} entry through the STIM-Orai1 pathway is essential for Treg development and function (15), a finding confirmed in *Stim1*-null bone marrow chimeras generated independently by another group (228).

CONCLUSIONS AND PERSPECTIVES

To summarize, our view of Ca^{2+} signaling in immune cells, and of the field of store-operated Ca^{2+} entry more generally, was revolutionized 3–4 years ago with the discovery of STIM and ORAI. These discoveries were followed quickly by a dramatic increase in our understanding of how these proteins work together in lymphocytes and other nonexcitable cells to effect store-operated Ca^{2+} entry. Many challenges remain. From a structural and biophysical point of view, we are far from a precise understanding of how ORAI channels are gated by STIM1. From a signaling and cell biological point of view, we have almost no information on the many factors that are likely to modulate STIM-ORAI coupling in cells. Much remains to be learned about how STIM-ORAI signaling contributes to the development and function of different subsets of immune cells; the possible contributions of other channels to processes such as thymocyte development need to be explored; and the physiological functions of ORAI2 and

ORAI3 remain to be elucidated. We encourage the community to participate in these efforts and hope that the coming years bring many important advances.

DISCLOSURE STATEMENT

P.H. and A.R. are founders and scientific advisors to Calcimedica, Inc. The authors are not aware of any affiliations, memberships, funding, or financial holdings that might be perceived as affecting the objectivity of this review.

ACKNOWLEDGMENTS

We thank Dr. Yubin Zhou for help with the illustrations, Jake Banfield-Weir for administrative and secretarial assistance, and the National Institutes of Health for support.

LITERATURE CITED

1. Berridge MJ, Lipp P, Bootman MD. 2000. The versatility and universality of calcium signaling. *Nat. Rev. Mol. Cell Biol.* 1:11–21
2. Berridge MJ, Bootman MD, Roderick HL. 2003. Calcium signaling: dynamics, homeostasis and remodelling. *Nat. Rev. Mol. Cell Biol.* 4:517–29
3. Carafoli E. 2002. Calcium signaling: a tale for all seasons. *Proc. Natl. Acad. Sci. USA* 99:1115–22
4. Clapham DE. 2007. Calcium signaling. *Cell* 131:1047–58
5. Di Capite J, Parekh AB. 2009. CRAC channels and Ca^{2+} signaling in mast cells. *Immunol. Rev.* 231:45–58
6. Pores-Fernando AT, Zweifach A. 2009. Calcium influx and signaling in cytotoxic T-lymphocyte lytic granule exocytosis. *Immunol. Rev.* 231:160–73
7. Hogan PG, Chen L, Nardone J, Rao A. 2003. Transcriptional regulation by calcium, calcineurin, and NFAT. *Genes Dev.* 17:2205–32
8. Macian F. 2005. NFAT proteins: key regulators of T-cell development and function. *Nat. Rev. Immunol.* 5:472–84
9. Lewis RS. 2001. Calcium signaling mechanisms in T lymphocytes. *Annu. Rev. Immunol.* 19:497–521
10. Parekh AB, Putney JW Jr. 2005. Store-operated calcium channels. *Physiol. Rev.* 85:757–810
11. Hogan PG, Rao A. 2007. Dissecting I_{CRAC}, a store-operated calcium current. *Trends Biochem. Sci.* 32:235–45
12. Feske S. 2007. Calcium signaling in lymphocyte activation and disease. *Nat. Rev. Immunol.* 7:690–702
13. Stathopulos PB, Ikura M. 2009. Structurally delineating stromal interaction molecules as the endoplasmic reticulum calcium sensors and regulators of calcium release-activated calcium entry. *Immunol. Rev.* 231:113–31
14. Luik RM, Wang B, Prakriya M, Wu MM, Lewis RS. 2008. Oligomerization of STIM1 couples ER calcium depletion to CRAC channel activation. *Nature* 454:538–42
15. Oh-Hora M, Yamashita M, Hogan PG, Sharma S, Lamperti E, et al. 2008. Dual functions for the endoplasmic reticulum calcium sensors STIM1 and STIM2 in T cell activation and tolerance. *Nat. Immunol.* 9:432–43
16. Putney JW. 1986. A model for receptor-regulated calcium entry. *Cell Calcium* 7:1–12
17. Prakriya M. 2009. The molecular physiology of CRAC channels. *Immunol. Rev.* 231:88–98
18. Roos J, DiGregorio PJ, Yeromin AV, Ohlsen K, Lioudyno M, et al. 2005. STIM1, an essential and conserved component of store-operated Ca^{2+} channel function. *J. Cell Biol.* 169:435–45
19. Liou J, Kim ML, Heo WD, Jones JT, Myers JW, et al. 2005. STIM is a Ca^{2+} sensor essential for Ca^{2+}-store-depletion-triggered Ca^{2+} influx. *Curr. Biol.* 15:1235–41
20. Feske S, Gwack Y, Prakriya M, Srikanth S, Puppel S, et al. 2006. A mutation in Orai1 causes immune deficiency by abrogating CRAC channel function. *Nature* 441:179–85

21. Vig M, Peinelt C, Beck A, Koomoa DL, Rabah D, et al. 2006. CRACM1 is a plasma membrane protein essential for store-operated Ca^{2+} entry. *Science* 312:1220–23
22. Zhang SL, Yeromin AV, Zhang XH, Yu Y, Safrina O, et al. 2006. Genome-wide RNAi screen of Ca^{2+} influx identifies genes that regulate Ca^{2+} release-activated Ca^{2+} channel activity. *Proc. Natl. Acad. Sci. USA* 103:9357–62
23. Yeromin AV, Zhang SL, Jiang W, Yu Y, Safrina O, Cahalan MD. 2006. Molecular identification of the CRAC channel by altered ion selectivity in a mutant of Orai. *Nature* 443:226–29
24. Prakriya M, Feske S, Gwack Y, Srikanth S, Rao A, Hogan PG. 2006. Orai1 is an essential pore subunit of the CRAC channel. *Nature* 443:230–33
25. Vig M, Beck A, Billingsley JM, Lis A, Parvez S, et al. 2006. CRACM1 multimers form the ion-selective pore of the CRAC channel. *Curr. Biol.* 16:2073–79
26. Brandman O, Liou J, Park WS, Meyer T. 2007. STIM2 is a feedback regulator that stabilizes basal cytosolic and endoplasmic reticulum Ca^{2+} levels. *Cell.* 131:1327–39
27. Stathopulos PB, Zheng L, Li GY, Plevin MJ, Ikura M. 2008. Structural and mechanistic insights into STIM1-mediated initiation of store-operated calcium entry. *Cell* 135:110–22
28. Stathopulos PB, Zheng L, Ikura M. 2009. Stromal interaction molecule (STIM) 1 and STIM2 calcium sensing regions exhibit distinct unfolding and oligomerization kinetics. *J. Biol. Chem.* 284:728–32
29. Wu MM, Buchanan J, Luik RM, Lewis RS. 2006. Ca^{2+} store depletion causes STIM1 to accumulate in ER regions closely associated with the plasma membrane. *J. Cell Biol.* 174:803–13
30. Luik RM, Wu MM, Buchanan J, Lewis RS. 2006. The elementary unit of store-operated Ca^{2+} entry: local activation of CRAC channels by STIM1 at ER-plasma membrane junctions. *J. Cell Biol.* 174:815–25
31. Zhang SL, Yu Y, Roos J, Kozak JA, Deerinck TJ, et al. 2005. STIM1 is a Ca^{2+} sensor that activates CRAC channels and migrates from the Ca^{2+} store to the plasma membrane. *Nature* 437:902–5
32. Yuan JP, Zeng W, Dorwart MR, Choi YJ, Worley PF, Muallem S. 2009. SOAR and the polybasic STIM1 domains gate and regulate Orai channels. *Nat. Cell Biol.* 11:337–43
33. Park CY, Hoover PJ, Mullins FM, Bachhawat P, Covington ED, et al. 2009. STIM1 clusters and activates CRAC channels via direct binding of a cytosolic domain to Orai1. *Cell* 136:876–90
34. Muik M, Fahrner M, Derler I, Schindl R, Bergsmann J, et al. 2009. A cytosolic homomerization and a modulatory domain within STIM1 C terminus determine coupling to ORAI1 channels. *J. Biol. Chem.* 284:8421–26
35. Kawasaki T, Lange I, Feske S. 2009. A minimal regulatory domain in the C terminus of STIM1 binds to and activates ORAI1 CRAC channels. *Biochem. Biophys. Res. Commun.* 385:49–54
36. Zhou Y, Meraner P, Kwon HT, Machnes D, Oh-hora M, et al. 2010. Minimal requirement for store-operated calcium entry: STIM1 gates ORAI1 channels in vitro. *Nat. Struct. Mol. Biol.* 17:112–16
37. Lewis RS. 2007. The molecular choreography of a store-operated calcium channel. *Nature* 446:284–87
38. Cahalan MD. 2009. STIMulating store-operated Ca^{2+} entry. *Nat. Cell Biol.* 11:669–77
39. Vig M, Kinet JP. 2009. Calcium signaling in immune cells. *Nat. Immunol.* 10:21–27
40. Rao A, Hogan PG. 2009. Calcium signaling in cells of the immune and hematopoietic systems. *Immunol. Rev.* 231:5–9
41. Cahalan MD, Chandy KG. 2009. The functional network of ion channels in T lymphocytes. *Immunol. Rev.* 231:59–87
42. Imboden JB, Stobo JD. 1985. Transmembrane signaling by the T cell antigen receptor. Perturbation of the T3-antigen receptor complex generates inositol phosphates and releases calcium ions from intracellular stores. *J. Exp. Med.* 161:446–56
43. Taylor CW, Rahman T, Tovey SC, Dedos SG, Taylor EJ, Velamakanni S. 2009. IP_3 receptors: some lessons from DT40 cells. *Immunol. Rev.* 231:23–44
44. Miyakawa T, Maeda A, Yamazawa T, Hirose K, Kurosaki T, Iino M. 1999. Encoding of Ca^{2+} signals by differential expression of IP_3 receptor subtypes. *EMBO J.* 18:1303–8
45. Sugawara H, Kurosaki M, Takata M, Kurosaki T. 1997. Genetic evidence for involvement of type 1, type 2 and type 3 inositol 1,4,5-trisphosphate receptors in signal transduction through the B-cell antigen receptor. *EMBO J.* 16:3078–88
46. Jayaraman T, Ondriasová E, Ondrias K, Harnick DJ, Marks AR. 1995. The inositol 1,4,5-trisphosphate receptor is essential for T-cell receptor signaling. *Proc. Natl. Acad. Sci. USA* 92:6007–11

47. Guse AH, da Silva CP, Berg I, Skapenko AL, Weber K, et al. 1999. Regulation of calcium signaling in T lymphocytes by the second messenger cyclic ADP-ribose. *Nature* 398:70–73
48. Guse AH, Roth E, Emmrich F. 1993. Intracellular Ca^{2+} pools in Jurkat T-lymphocytes. *Biochem. J.* 291:447–51
49. Kunerth S, Langhorst MF, Schwarzmann N, Gu X, Huang L, et al. 2004. Amplification and propagation of pacemaker Ca^{2+} signals by cyclic ADP-ribose and the type 3 ryanodine receptor in T cells. *J. Cell Sci.* 117:2141–49
50. Gasser A, Bruhn S, Guse AH. 2006. Second messenger function of nicotinic acid adenine dinucleotide phosphate revealed by an improved enzymatic cycling assay. *J. Biol. Chem.* 281:16906–13
51. Brailoiu E, Churamani D, Cai X, Schrlau MG, Brailoiu GC, et al. 2009. Essential requirement for two-pore channel 1 in NAADP-mediated calcium signaling. *J. Cell Biol.* 186:201–9
52. Calcraft PJ, Ruas M, Pan Z, Cheng X, Arredouani A, et al. 2009. NAADP mobilizes calcium from acidic organelles through two-pore channels. *Nature* 459:596–600
53. Steen M, Kirchberger T, Guse AH. 2007. NAADP mobilizes calcium from the endoplasmic reticular Ca^{2+} store in T-lymphocytes. *J. Biol. Chem.* 282:18864–71
54. Dammermann W, Guse AH. 2005. Functional ryanodine receptor expression is required for NAADP-mediated local Ca^{2+} signaling in T-lymphocytes. *J. Biol. Chem.* 280:21394–99
55. Whitney RB, Sutherland RM. 1973. Characteristics of calcium accumulation by lymphocytes and alterations in the process induced by phytohemagglutinin. *J. Cell. Physiol.* 82:9–20
56. Whitney RB, Sutherland RM. 1972. Requirement for calcium ions in lymphocyte transformation stimulated by phytohemagglutinin. *J. Cell. Physiol.* 80:329–37
57. Grynkiewicz G, Poenie M, Tsien RY. 1985. A new generation of Ca^{2+} indicators with greatly improved fluorescence properties. *J. Biol. Chem.* 260:3440–50
58. Hamill OP, Marty A, Neher E, Sakmann B, Sigworth FJ. 1981. Improved patch-clamp techniques for high-resolution current recording from cells and cell-free membrane patches. *Pflugers Arch.* 391:85–100
59. Kuno M, Gardner P. 1987. Ion channels activated by inositol 1,4,5-trisphosphate in plasma membrane of human T-lymphocytes. *Nature* 326:301–4
60. Kuno M, Goronzy J, Weyand CM, Gardner P. 1986. Single-channel and whole-cell recordings of mitogen-regulated inward currents in human cloned helper T lymphocytes. *Nature* 323:269–73
61. Khan AA, Steiner JP, Klein MG, Schneider MF, Snyder SH. 1992. IP3 receptor: localization to plasma membrane of T cells and cocapping with the T cell receptor. *Science* 257:815–18
62. Khan AA, Steiner JP, Snyder SH. 1992. Plasma membrane inositol 1,4,5-trisphosphate receptor of lymphocytes: selective enrichment in sialic acid and unique binding specificity. *Proc. Natl. Acad. Sci. USA* 89:2849–53
63. Lewis RS, Cahalan MD. 1989. Mitogen-induced oscillations of cytosolic Ca^{2+} and transmembrane Ca^{2+} current in human leukemic T cells. *Cell Regul.* 1:99–112
64. Thastrup O, Dawson AP, Scharff O, Foder B, Cullen PJ, et al. 1989. Thapsigargin, a novel molecular probe for studying intracellular calcium release and storage. *Agents Actions* 27:17–23
65. Putney JW, Bird GS. 1993. The inositol phosphate-calcium signaling system in nonexcitable cells. *Endocr. Rev.* 14:610–31
66. Hoth M, Penner R. 1992. Depletion of intracellular calcium stores activates a calcium current in mast cells. *Nature* 355:353–56
67. Zweifach A, Lewis RS. 1993. Mitogen-regulated Ca^{2+} current of T lymphocytes is activated by depletion of intracellular Ca^{2+} stores. *Proc. Natl. Acad. Sci. USA* 90:6295–99
68. Premack BA, McDonald TV, Gardner P. 1994. Activation of Ca^{2+} current in Jurkat T cells following the depletion of Ca^{2+} stores by microsomal Ca^{2+}-ATPase inhibitors. *J. Immunol.* 152:5226–40
69. Hoth M, Penner R. 1993. Calcium release-activated calcium current in rat mast cells. *J. Physiol.* 465:359–86
70. Zhang L, McCloskey MA. 1995. Immunoglobulin E receptor-activated calcium conductance in rat mast cells. *J. Physiol.* 483:59–66
71. Prakriya M, Lewis RS. 2003. CRAC channels: activation, permeation, and the search for a molecular identity. *Cell Calcium* 33:311–21

72. Cahalan M, Zhang S, Yeromin A, Ohlsen K, Roos J, Stauderman K. 2007. Molecular basis of the CRAC channel. *Cell Calcium* 42:133–44
73. Ramsey IS, Delling M, Clapham DE. 2006. An introduction to TRP channels. *Annu. Rev. Physiol.* 68:619–47
74. Yue L, Peng JB, Hediger MA, Clapham DE. 2001. CaT1 manifests the pore properties of the calcium-release-activated calcium channel. *Nature* 410:705–9
75. Cui J, Bian J-S, Kagan A, McDonald TV. 2002. CaT1 contributes to the stores-operated calcium current in Jurkat T-lymphocytes. *J. Biol. Chem.* 277:47175–83
76. Voets T, Prenen J, Fleig A, Vennekens R, Watanabe H, et al. 2001. CaT1 and the calcium release-activated calcium channel manifest distinct pore properties. *J. Biol. Chem.* 276:47767–70
77. Clapham DE. 2002. Sorting out MIC, TRP, and CRAC ion channels. *J. Gen. Physiol.* 120:217–20
78. Fanger CM, Hoth M, Crabtree GR, Lewis RS. 1995. Characterization of T cell mutants with defects in capacitative calcium entry: genetic evidence for the physiological roles of CRAC channels. *J. Cell Biol.* 131:655–67
79. Feske S, Prakriya M, Rao A, Lewis R. 2005. A severe defect in CRAC Ca^{2+} channel activation and altered K^+ channel gating in T cells from immunodeficient patients. *J. Exp. Med.* 202:651–62
80. Feske S, Giltnane J, Dolmetsch R, Staudt LM, Rao A. 2001. Gene regulation mediated by calcium signals in T lymphocytes. *Nat. Immunol.* 2:316–24
81. Partiseti M, Le Deist F, Hivroz C, Fischer A, Korn H, Choquet D. 1994. The calcium current activated by T cell receptor and store depletion in human lymphocytes is absent in a primary immunodeficiency. *J. Biol. Chem.* 269:32327–35
82. Le Deist F, Hivroz C, Partiseti M, Thomas C, Buc HA, et al. 1995. A primary T-cell immunodeficiency associated with defective transmembrane calcium influx. *Blood.* 85:1053–62
83. Philipp S, Strauss B, Hirnet D, Wissenbach U, Mery L, et al. 2003. TRPC3 mediates T-cell receptor-dependent calcium entry in human T-lymphocytes. *J. Biol. Chem.* 278:26629–38
84. Yeromin AV, Roos J, Stauderman KA, Cahalan MD. 2004. A store-operated calcium channel in *Drosophila* S2 cells. *J. Gen. Physiol.* 123:167–82
85. Echeverri CJ, Perrimon N. 2006. High-throughput RNAi screening in cultured cells: a user's guide. *Nat. Rev. Genet.* 7:373–84
86. Moffat J, Sabatini DM. 2006. Building mammalian signaling pathways with RNAi screens. *Nat. Rev. Mol. Cell Biol.* 7:177–87
87. Sharma S, Rao A. 2009. RNAi screening: tips and techniques. *Nat. Immunol.* 10:799–804
88. Gwack Y, Sharma S, Nardone J, Tanasa B, Iuga A, et al. 2006. A genome-wide *Drosophila* RNAi screen identifies DYRK-family kinases as regulators of NFAT. *Nature* 441:646–50
89. Gwack Y, Srikanth S, Feske S, Cruz-Guilloty F, Oh-hora M, et al. 2007. Biochemical and functional characterization of Orai proteins. *J. Biol. Chem.* 282:16232–43
90. Feske S, Dräger R, Peter HH, Eichmann K, Rao A. 2000. The duration of nuclear residence of NFAT determines the pattern of cytokine expression in human SCID T cells. *J. Immunol.* 165:297–305
91. Picard C, McCarl CA, Papolos A, Khalil S, Lüthy K, et al. 2009. STIM1 mutation associated with a syndrome of immunodeficiency and autoimmunity. *N. Engl. J. Med.* 360:1971–80
92. Feske S. 2009. ORAI1 and STIM1 deficiency in human and mice: roles of store-operated Ca^{2+} entry in the immune system and beyond. *Immunol. Rev.* 231:189–209
93. McCarl C, Picard C, Khalil S, Kawasaki T, Rother J, et al. 2009. ORAI1 deficiency and lack of store-operated Ca^{2+} entry cause immunodeficiency, myopathy, and ectodermal dysplasia. *J. Allergy Clin. Immunol.* 124:1311–18
94. Peinelt C, Vig M, Koomoa DL, Beck A, Nadler MJS, et al. 2006. Amplification of CRAC current by STIM1 and CRACM1 (Orai1). *Nat. Cell Biol.* 8:771–73
95. Soboloff J, Spassova MA, Tang XD, Hewavitharana T, Xu W, Gill DL. 2006. Orai1 and STIM reconstitute store-operated calcium channel function. *J. Biol. Chem.* 281:20661–65
96. Mercer JC, Dehaven WI, Smyth JT, Wedel B, Boyles RR, et al. 2006. Large store-operated calcium selective currents due to coexpression of Orai1 or Orai2 with the intracellular calcium sensor, Stim1. *J. Biol. Chem.* 281:24979–90

97. Oritani K, Kincade PW. 1996. Identification of stromal cell products that interact with pre-B cells. *J. Cell Biol.* 134:771–82
98. Manji SS, Parker NJ, Williams RT, van Stekelenburg L, Pearson RB, et al. 2000. STIM1: a novel phosphoprotein located at the cell surface. *Biochim. Biophys. Acta* 1481:147–55
99. Xu P, Lu J, Li Z, Yu X, Chen L, Xu T. 2006. Aggregation of STIM1 underneath the plasma membrane induces clustering of Orai1. *Biochem. Biophys. Res. Commun.* 350:969–76
100. Baba Y, Hayashi K, Fujii Y, Mizushima A, Watarai H, et al. 2006. Coupling of STIM1 to store-operated Ca^{2+} entry through its constitutive and inducible movement in the endoplasmic reticulum. *Proc. Natl. Acad. Sci. USA* 103:16704–9
101. Stathopulos PB, Li GY, Plevin MJ, Ames JB, Ikura M. 2006. Stored Ca^{2+} depletion-induced oligomerization of stromal interaction molecule 1 (STIM1) via the EF-SAM region: an initiation mechanism for capacitive Ca^{2+} entry. *J. Biol. Chem.* 281:35855–62
102. Huang Y, Zhou Y, Wong HC, Chen Y, Chen Y, et al. 2009. A single EF-hand isolated from STIM1 forms dimer in the absence and presence of Ca^{2+}. *FEBS Lett.* 276:5589–97
103. Liou J, Fivaz M, Inoue T, Meyer T. 2007. Live-cell imaging reveals sequential oligomerization and local plasma membrane targeting of stromal interaction molecule 1 after Ca^{2+} store depletion. *Proc. Natl. Acad. Sci. USA* 104:9301–6
104. Muik M, Frischauf I, Derler I, Fahrner M, Bergsmann J, et al. 2008. Dynamic coupling of the putative coiled-coil domain of ORAI1 with STIM1 mediates ORAI1 channel activation. *J. Biol. Chem.* 283:8014–22
105. Williams RT, Manji SS, Parker NJ, Hancock MS, Van Stekelenburg L, et al. 2001. Identification and characterization of the STIM (stromal interaction molecule) gene family: coding for a novel class of transmembrane proteins. *Biochem. J.* 357:673–85
106. Spassova MA, Soboloff J, He LP, Xu W, Dziadek MA, Gill DL. 2006. STIM1 has a plasma membrane role in the activation of store-operated Ca^{2+} channels. *Proc. Natl. Acad. Sci. USA* 103:4040–45
107. Qiao F, Bowie JU. 2005. The many faces of SAM. *Sci. STKE* 2005:re7
108. Smyth JT, Dehaven WI, Bird GS, Putney JW Jr. 2008. Ca^{2+}-store-dependent and -independent reversal of Stim1 localization and function. *J. Cell Sci.* 121:762–72
109. Orci L, Ravazzola M, Le Coadic M, Shen WW, Demaurex N, Cosson P. 2009. STIM1-induced precortical and cortical subdomains of the endoplasmic reticulum. *Proc. Natl. Acad. Sci. USA* 106:19358–62
110. Ong HL, Liu X, Tsaneva-Atanasova K, Singh BB, Bandyopadhyay BC, et al. 2007. Relocalization of STIM1 for activation of store-operated Ca^{2+} entry is determined by the depletion of subplasma membrane endoplasmic reticulum Ca^{2+} store. *J. Biol. Chem.* 282:12176–85
111. Huang GN, Zeng W, Kim JY, Yuan JP, Han L, et al. 2006. STIM1 carboxyl-terminus activates native SOC, I_{crac} and TRPC1 channels. *Nat. Cell Biol.* 8:1003–10
112. Várnai P, Tóth B, Tóth DJ, Hunyady L, Balla T. 2007. Visualization and manipulation of plasma membrane-endoplasmic reticulum contact sites indicates the presence of additional molecular components within the STIM1-Orai1 complex. *J. Biol. Chem.* 282:29678–90
113. Korzeniowski MK, Popovic MA, Szentpetery Z, Varnai P, Stojilkovic SS, Balla T. 2009. Dependence of STIM1/Orai1-mediated calcium entry on plasma membrane phosphoinositides. *J. Biol. Chem.* 284:21027–35
114. Heo WD, Inoue T, Park WS, Kim ML, Park BO, et al. 2006. PI(3,4,5)P3 and PI(4,5)P2 lipids target proteins with polybasic clusters to the plasma membrane. *Science* 314:1458–61
115. Walsh CM, Chvanov M, Haynes LP, Petersen OH, Tepikin AV, Burgoyne RD. 2009. Role of phosphoinositides in STIM1 dynamics and store-operated calcium entry. *Biochem. J.* 425:159–68
116. Ercan E, Momburg F, Engel U, Temmerman K, Nickel W, Seedorf M. 2009. A conserved, lipid-mediated sorting mechanism of yeast Ist2 and mammalian STIM proteins to the peripheral ER. *Traffic* 10:1802–18
117. Takeshima H, Komazaki S, Nishi M, Iino M, Kangawa K. 2000. Junctophilins: a novel family of junctional membrane complex proteins. *Mol. Cell* 6:11–22
118. Cuttell L, Vaughan A, Silva E, Escaron CJ, Lavine M, et al. 2008. Undertaker, a *Drosophila* Junctophilin, links Draper-mediated phagocytosis and calcium homeostasis. *Cell* 135:524–34

119. Calloway N, Vig M, Kinet JP, Holowka D, Baird B. 2009. Molecular clustering of STIM1 with Orai1/CRACM1 at the plasma membrane depends dynamically on depletion of Ca^{2+} stores and on electrostatic interactions. *Mol. Biol. Cell* 20:389–99
120. Bird GS, Hwang SY, Smyth JT, Fukushima M, Boyles RR, Putney JW Jr. 2009. STIM1 is a calcium sensor specialized for digital signaling. *Curr. Biol.* 19:1724–29
121. Wedel B, Boyles RR, Putney JW Jr, Bird GS. 2007. Role of the store-operated calcium entry proteins Stim1 and Orai1 in muscarinic cholinergic receptor-stimulated calcium oscillations in human embryonic kidney cells. *J. Physiol.* 579:679–89
122. Lioudyno MI, Kozak JA, Penna A, Safrina O, Zhang SL, et al. 2008. Orai1 and STIM1 move to the immunological synapse and are up-regulated during T cell activation. *Proc. Natl. Acad. Sci. USA* 105:2011–16
123. Barr VA, Bernot KM, Srikanth S, Gwack Y, Balagopalan L, et al. 2008. Dynamic movement of the calcium sensor STIM1 and the calcium channel Orai1 in activated T-cells: puncta and distal caps. *Mol. Biol. Cell* 19:2802–17
124. Smyth JT, DeHaven WI, Bird GS, Putney JW Jr. 2007. Role of the microtubule cytoskeleton in the function of the store-operated Ca^{2+} channel activator STIM1. *J. Cell Sci.* 120:3762–71
125. Grigoriev I, Gouveia SM, Van Der Vaart B, Demmers J, Smyth JT, et al. 2008. STIM1 is a MT-plus-end-tracking protein involved in remodeling of the ER. *Curr. Biol.* 18:177–82
126. Honnappa S, Gouveia SM, Weisbrich A, Damberger FF, Bhavesh NS, et al. 2009. An EB1-binding motif acts as a microtubule tip localization signal. *Cell* 138:366–76
127. Bakowski D, Glitsch MD, Parekh AB. 2001. An examination of the secretion-like coupling model for the activation of the Ca^{2+} release-activated Ca^{2+} current I_{CRAC} in RBL-1 cells. *J. Physiol.* 532:55–71
128. Quintana A, Schwarz EC, Schwindling C, Lipp P, Kaestner L, Hoth M. 2006. Sustained activity of calcium release-activated calcium channels requires translocation of mitochondria to the plasma membrane. *J. Biol. Chem.* 281:40302–9
129. Yuan JP, Zeng W, Huang GN, Worley PF, Muallem S. 2007. STIM1 heteromultimerizes TRPC channels to determine their function as store-operated channels. *Nat. Cell Biol.* 9:636–45
130. Zeng W, Yuan JP, Kim MS, Choi YJ, Huang GN, et al. 2008. STIM1 gates TRPC channels, but not Orai1, by electrostatic interaction. *Mol. Cell* 32:439–48
131. DeHaven WI, Jones BF, Petranka JG, Smyth JT, Tomita T, et al. 2009. TRPC channels function independently of STIM1 and Orai1. *J. Physiol.* 587:2275–98
132. Mignen O, Thompson JL, Shuttleworth TJ. 2007. STIM1 regulates Ca^{2+} entry via arachidonate-regulated Ca^{2+}-selective (ARC) channels without store depletion or translocation to the plasma membrane. *J. Physiol.* 579:703–15
133. Lefkimmiatis K, Srikanthan M, Maiellaro I, Moyer MP, Curci S, Hofer AM. 2009. Store-operated cyclic AMP signaling mediated by STIM1. *Nat. Cell Biol.* 11:433–42
134. Mignen O, Thompson JL, Shuttleworth TJ. 2008. Orai1 subunit stoichiometry of the mammalian CRAC channel pore. *J. Physiol.* 586:419–25
135. Ji W, Xu P, Li Z, Lu J, Liu L, et al. 2008. Functional stoichiometry of the unitary calcium-release-activated calcium channel. *Proc. Natl. Acad. Sci. USA* 105:13668–73
136. Penna A, Demuro A, Yeromin AV, Zhang SL, Safrina O, et al. 2008. The CRAC channel consists of a tetramer formed by Stim-induced dimerization of Orai dimers. *Nature* 456:116–20
137. Maruyama Y, Ogura T, Mio K, Kato K, Kaneko T, et al. 2009. Tetrameric Orai1 is a teardrop-shaped molecule with a long, tapered cytoplasmic domain. *J. Biol. Chem.* 284:13676–85
138. Yamashita M, Navarro-Borelly L, McNally BA, Prakriya M. 2007. Orai1 mutations alter ion permeation and Ca^{2+}-dependent fast inactivation of CRAC channels: evidence for coupling of permeation and gating. *J. Gen. Physiol.* 130:525–40
139. Lis A, Peinelt C, Beck A, Parvez S, Monteilh-Zoller M, et al. 2007. CRACM1, CRACM2, and CRACM3 are store-operated Ca^{2+} channels with distinct functional properties. *Curr. Biol.* 17:794–800
140. Zhang SL, Kozak JA, Jiang W, Yeromin AV, Chen J, et al. 2008. Store-dependent and -independent modes regulating Ca^{2+} release-activated Ca^{2+} channel activity of human Orai1 and Orai3. *J. Biol. Chem.* 283:17662–71

141. Lee KP, Yuan JP, Zeng W, So I, Worley PF, Muallem S. 2009. Molecular determinants of fast Ca^{2+}-dependent inactivation and gating of the Orai channels. *Proc. Natl. Acad. Sci. USA* 106:14687–92
142. Derler I, Fahrner M, Muik M, Lackner B, Schindl R, et al. 2009. A Ca^{2+} release-activated Ca^{2+} (CRAC) modulatory domain (CMD) within STIM1 mediates fast Ca^{2+}-dependent inactivation of ORAI1 channels. *J. Biol. Chem.* 284:24933–38
143. Mullins FM, Park CY, Dolmetsch RE, Lewis RS. 2009. STIM1 and calmodulin interact with Orai1 to induce Ca^{2+}-dependent inactivation of CRAC channels. *Proc. Natl. Acad. Sci. USA* 106:15495–500
144. Ng SW, Nelson C, Parekh AB. 2009. Coupling of Ca^{2+} microdomains to spatially and temporally distinct cellular responses by the tyrosine kinase Syk. *J. Biol. Chem.* 284:24767–72
145. Parekh AB. 2009. Local Ca^{2+} influx through CRAC channels activates temporally and spatially distinct cellular responses. *Acta Physiol. (Oxf)*. 195:29–35
146. Chang WC, Di Capite J, Singaravelu K, Nelson C, Halse V, Parekh AB. 2008. Local Ca^{2+} influx through Ca^{2+} release-activated Ca^{2+} (CRAC) channels stimulates production of an intracellular messenger and an intercellular proinflammatory signal. *J. Biol. Chem.* 283:4622–31
147. Ng SW, di Capite J, Singaravelu K, Parekh AB. 2008. Sustained activation of the tyrosine kinase Syk by antigen in mast cells requires local Ca^{2+} influx through Ca^{2+} release-activated Ca^{2+} channels. *J. Biol. Chem.* 283:31348–55
148. Lin S, Fagan KA, Li KX, Shaul PW, Cooper DM, Rodman DM. 2000. Sustained endothelial nitric-oxide synthase activation requires capacitative Ca^{2+} entry. *J. Biol. Chem.* 275:17979–85
149. Cooper DM. 2003. Regulation and organization of adenylyl cyclases and cAMP. *Biochem. J.* 375:517–29
150. Li Z, Lu J, Xu P, Xie X, Chen L, Xu T. 2007. Mapping the interacting domains of STIM1 and Orai1 in Ca^{2+} release-activated Ca^{2+} channel activation. *J. Biol. Chem.* 282:29448–56
151. Navarro-Borelly L, Somasundaram A, Yamashita M, Ren D, Miller RJ, Prakriya M. 2008. STIM1-Orai1 interactions and Orai1 conformational changes revealed by live-cell FRET microscopy. *J. Physiol.* 586:5383–401
152. Schindl R, Bergsmann J, Frischauf I, Derler I, Fahrner M, et al. 2008. 2-aminoethoxydiphenyl borate alters selectivity of Orai3 channels by increasing their pore size. *J. Biol. Chem.* 283:20261–67
153. Derler I, Fahrner M, Carugo O, Muik M, Bergsmann J, et al. 2009. Increased hydrophobicity at the N terminus/membrane interface impairs gating of the severe combined immunodeficiency-related ORAI1 mutant. *J. Biol. Chem.* 284:15903–15
154. Thompson JL, Mignen O, Shuttleworth TJ. 2009. The Orai1 severe combined immune deficiency mutation and calcium release-activated Ca^{2+} channel function in the heterozygous condition. *J. Biol. Chem.* 284:6620–26
155. Heuser JE, Salpeter SR. 1979. Organization of acetylcholine receptors in quick-frozen, deep-etched, and rotary-replicated Torpedo postsynaptic membrane. *J. Cell Biol.* 82:150–73
156. Bolotina VM, Csutora P. 2005. CIF and other mysteries of the store-operated Ca^{2+}-entry pathway. *Trends Biochem. Sci.* 30:378–87
157. Bolotina VM. 2008. Orai, STIM1 and iPLA$_2\beta$: a view from a different perspective. *J. Physiol.* 586:3035–42
158. Csutora P, Peter K, Kilic H, Park KM, Zarayskiy V, et al. 2008. Novel role for STIM1 as a trigger for calcium influx factor production. *J. Biol. Chem.* 283:14524–31
159. Csutora P, Zarayskiy V, Peter K, Monje F, Smani T, et al. 2006. Activation mechanism for CRAC current and store-operated Ca^{2+} entry: calcium influx factor and Ca^{2+}-independent phospholipase A$_2\beta$-mediated pathway. *J. Biol. Chem.* 281:34926–35
160. Trepakova ES, Csutora P, Hunton DL, Marchase RB, Cohen RA, Bolotina VM. 2000. Calcium influx factor directly activates store-operated cation channels in vascular smooth muscle cells. *J. Biol. Chem.* 275:26158–63
161. Soboloff J, Spassova MA, Hewavitharana T, He LP, Xu W, et al. 2006. STIM2 is an inhibitor of STIM1-mediated store-operated Ca^{2+} entry. *Curr. Biol.* 16:1465–70
162. Zheng L, Stathopulos PB, Li GY, Ikura M. 2008. Biophysical characterization of the EF-hand and SAM domain containing Ca^{2+} region of STIM1 and STIM2. *Biochem. Biophys. Res. Commun.* 369:240–46
163. Parvez S, Beck A, Peinelt C, Soboloff J, Lis A, et al. 2008. STIM2 protein mediates distinct store-dependent and store-independent modes of CRAC channel activation. *FASEB J.* 22:752–61

164. DeHaven WI, Smyth JT, Boyles RR, Putney JW Jr. 2007. Calcium inhibition and calcium potentiation of Orai1, Orai2, and Orai3 calcium release-activated calcium channels. *J. Biol. Chem.* 282:17548–56
165. Frischauf I, Muik M, Derler I, Bergsmann J, Fahrner M, et al. 2009. Molecular determinants of the coupling between STIM1 and Orai channels: differential activation of Orai1–3 channels by a STIM1 coiled-coil mutant. *J. Biol. Chem.* 284:21696–706
166. Vig M, DeHaven WI, Bird GS, Billingsley JM, Wang H, et al. 2008. Defective mast cell effector functions in mice lacking the CRACM1 pore subunit of store-operated calcium release-activated calcium channels. *Nat. Immunol.* 9:89–96
167. Gwack Y, Srikanth S, Oh-hora M, Hogan PG, Lamperti ED, et al. 2008. Hair loss and defective T- and B-cell function in mice lacking ORAI1. *Mol. Cell. Biol.* 28:5209–22
168. Mignen O, Thompson JL, Shuttleworth TJ. 2008. Both Orai1 and Orai3 are essential components of the arachidonate-regulated Ca^{2+}-selective (ARC) channels. *J. Physiol.* 586:185–95
169. Mignen O, Thompson JL, Shuttleworth TJ. 2009. The molecular architecture of the arachidonate-regulated Ca^{2+}-selective ARC channel is a pentameric assembly of Orai1 and Orai3 subunits. *J. Physiol.* 587:4181–97
170. Schindl R, Frischauf I, Bergsmann J, Muik M, Derler I, et al. 2009. Plasticity in Ca^{2+} selectivity of Orai1/Orai3 heteromeric channel. *Proc. Natl. Acad. Sci. USA* 106:19623–28
171. Dustin ML. 2009. The cellular context of T cell signaling. *Immunity* 30:482–92
172. Morita T, Tanimura A, Nezu A, Kurosaki T, Tojyo Y. 2004. Functional analysis of the green fluorescent protein-tagged inositol 1,4,5-trisphosphate receptor type 3 in Ca^{2+} release and entry in DT40 B lymphocytes. *Biochem. J.* 382:793–801
173. Dellis O, Dedos SG, Tovey SC, Taufiq-Ur-Rahman, Dubel SJ, Taylor CW. 2006. Ca^{2+} entry through plasma membrane IP3 receptors. *Science* 313:229–33
174. Dellis O, Rossi AM, Dedos SG, Taylor CW. 2008. Counting functional inositol 1,4,5-trisphosphate receptors into the plasma membrane. *J. Biol. Chem.* 283:751–55
175. Morita T, Tanimura A, Baba Y, Kurosaki T, Tojyo Y. 2009. A Stim1-dependent, noncapacitative Ca^{2+}-entry pathway is activated by B-cell-receptor stimulation and depletion of Ca^{2+}. *J. Cell Sci.* 122:1220–28
176. Stokes L, Gordon J, Grafton G. 2004. Non-voltage-gated L-type Ca^{2+} channels in human T cells: pharmacology and molecular characterization of the major alpha pore-forming and auxiliary beta-subunits. *J. Biol. Chem.* 279:19566–73
177. Kotturi MF, Hunt SV, Jefferies WA. 2006. Roles of CRAC and Cav-like channels in T cells: more than one gatekeeper? *Trends Pharmacol. Sci.* 27:360–67
178. Randriamampita C, Bismuth G, Debré P, Trautmann A. 1991. Nitrendipine-induced inhibition of calcium influx in a human T-cell clone: role of cell depolarization. *Cell Calcium* 12:313–23
179. DeCoursey TE, Chandy KG, Gupta S, Cahalan MD. 1985. Voltage-dependent ion channels in T-lymphocytes. *J. Neuroimmunol.* 10:71–95
180. Chandy KG, Wulff H, Beeton C, Pennington M, Gutman GA, Cahalan MD. 2004. K^+ channels as targets for specific immunomodulation. *Trends Pharmacol. Sci.* 25:280–89
181. Colucci A, Giunti R, Senesi S, Bygrave FL, Benedetti A, Gamberucci A. 2009. Effect of nifedipine on capacitive calcium entry in Jurkat T lymphocytes. *Arch. Biochem. Biophys.* 481:80–85
182. Stokes L, Gordon J, Grafton G. 2004. Non-voltage-gated L-type Ca^{2+} channels in human T cells: pharmacology and molecular characterization of the major alpha pore-forming and auxiliary beta-subunits. *J. Biol. Chem.* 279:19566–73
183. Badou A, Jha MK, Matza D, Mehal WZ, Freichel M, et al. 2006. Critical role for the beta regulatory subunits of Cav channels in T lymphocyte function. *Proc. Natl. Acad. Sci. USA* 103:15529–34
184. Kotturi MF, Jefferies WA. 2005. Molecular characterization of L-type calcium channel splice variants expressed in human T lymphocytes. *Mol. Immunol.* 42:1461–74
185. Matza D, Badou A, Kobayashi KS, Goldsmith-Pestana K, Masuda Y, et al. 2008. A scaffold protein, AHNAK1, is required for calcium signaling during T cell activation. *Immunity* 28:64–74
186. Matza D, Badou A, Jha MK, Willinger T, Antov A, et al. 2009. Requirement for AHNAK1-mediated calcium signaling during T lymphocyte cytolysis. *Proc. Natl. Acad. Sci. USA* 106:9785–90
187. Sather WA, McCleskey EW. 2003. Permeation and selectivity in calcium channels. *Annu. Rev. Physiol.* 65:133–59

188. Lewis RS, Cahalan MD. 1995. Potassium and calcium channels in lymphocytes. *Annu. Rev. Immunol.* 13:623–53

189. Wulff H, Beeton C, Chandy KG. 2003. Potassium channels as therapeutic targets for autoimmune disorders. *Curr. Opin. Drug Discov. Dev.* 6:640–47

190. Srivastava S, Zhdanova O, Di L, Li Z, Albaqumi M, et al. 2008. Protein histidine phosphatase 1 negatively regulates CD4 T cells by inhibiting the K^+ channel KCa3.1. *Proc. Natl. Acad. Sci. USA* 105:14442–46

191. Beeton C, Wulff H, Standifer NE, Azam P, Mullen KM, et al. 2006. Kv1.3 channels are a therapeutic target for T cell-mediated autoimmune diseases. *Proc. Natl. Acad. Sci. USA* 103:17414–19

192. Ren YR, Pan F, Parvez S, Fleig A, Chong CR, et al. 2008. Clofazimine inhibits human Kv1.3 potassium channel by perturbing calcium oscillation in T lymphocytes. *PLoS One* 3:e4009

193. Beeton C, Pennington MW, Wulff H, Singh S, Nugent D, et al. 2005. Targeting effector memory T cells with a selective peptide inhibitor of Kv1.3 channels for therapy of autoimmune diseases. *Mol. Pharmacol.* 67:1369–81

194. Pottosin II, Bonales-Alatorre E, Valencia-Cruz G, Mendoza-Magaña ML, Dobrovinskaya OR. 2008. TRESK-like potassium channels in leukemic T cells. *Pflugers Arch.* 456:1037–48

195. Meuth SG, Bittner S, Meuth P, Simon OJ, Budde T, Wiendl H. 2008. TWIK-related acid-sensitive K^+ channel 1 (TASK1) and TASK3 critically influence T lymphocyte effector functions. *J. Biol. Chem.* 283:14559–70

196. Beeton C, Wulff H, Barbaria J, Clot-Faybesse O, Pennington M, et al. 2001. Selective blockade of T lymphocyte K^+ channels ameliorates experimental autoimmune encephalomyelitis, a model for multiple sclerosis. *Proc. Natl. Acad. Sci. USA* 98:13942–47

197. Launay P, Fleig A, Perraud AL, Scharenberg AM, Penner R, Kinet JP. 2002. TRPM4 is a Ca^{2+}-activated nonselective cation channel mediating cell membrane depolarization. *Cell* 109:397–407

198. Launay P, Cheng H, Srivatsan S, Penner R, Fleig A, Kinet JP. 2004. TRPM4 regulates calcium oscillations after T cell activation. *Science* 306:1374–77

199. Grissmer S, Lewis RS, Cahalan MD. 1992. Ca^{2+}-activated K^+ channels in human leukemic T cells. *J. Gen. Physiol.* 99:63–84

200. Grissmer S, Nguyen AN, Cahalan MD. 1993. Calcium-activated potassium channels in resting and activated human T lymphocytes. Expression levels, calcium dependence, ion selectivity, and pharmacology. *J. Gen. Physiol.* 102:601–30

201. Hoth M, Fanger CM, Lewis RS. 1997. Mitochondrial regulation of store-operated calcium signaling in T lymphocytes. *J. Cell Biol.* 137:633–48

202. Zweifach A, Lewis RS. 1995. Slow calcium-dependent inactivation of depletion-activated calcium current. Store-dependent and -independent mechanisms. *J. Biol. Chem.* 270:14445–51

203. Hoth M, Button DC, Lewis RS. 2000. Mitochondrial control of calcium-channel gating: a mechanism for sustained signaling and transcriptional activation in T lymphocytes. *Proc. Natl. Acad. Sci. USA* 97:10607–12

204. Gilabert JA, Parekh AB. 2000. Respiring mitochondria determine the pattern of activation and inactivation of the store-operated Ca^{2+} current I_{CRAC}. *EMBO J.* 19:6401–7

205. Parekh AB. 2008. Mitochondrial regulation of store-operated CRAC channels. *Cell Calcium* 44:61–63

206. Quintana A, Schwarz EC, Schwindling C, Lipp P, Kaestner L, Hoth M. 2006. Sustained activity of calcium release-activated calcium channels requires translocation of mitochondria to the plasma membrane. *J. Biol. Chem.* 281:40302–9

207. Yi M, Weaver D, Hajnóczky G. 2004. Control of mitochondrial motility and distribution by the calcium signal: a homeostatic circuit. *J. Cell Biol.* 167:661–72

208. Wang X, Schwarz TL. 2009. The mechanism of Ca^{2+}-dependent regulation of kinesin-mediated mitochondrial motility. *Cell* 136:163–74

209. Quintana A, Schwindling C, Wenning AS, Becherer U, Rettig J, et al. 2007. T cell activation requires mitochondrial translocation to the immunological synapse. *Proc. Natl. Acad. Sci. USA* 104:14418–23

210. Bautista DM, Hoth M, Lewis RS. 2002. Enhancement of calcium signaling dynamics and stability by delayed modulation of the plasma-membrane calcium-ATPase in human T cells. *J. Gen. Physiol.* 541:877–94

211. Caride AJ, Elwess NL, Verma AK, Filoteo AG, Enyedi A, et al. 1999. The rate of activation by calmodulin of isoform 4 of the plasma membrane Ca^{2+} pump is slow and is changed by alternative splicing. *J. Biol. Chem.* 274:35227–32
212. Dolmetsch RE, Lewis RS. 1994. Signaling between intracellular Ca^{2+} stores and depletion-activated Ca^{2+} channels generates $[Ca^{2+}]_i$ oscillations in T lymphocytes. *J. Gen. Physiol.* 103:365–88
213. Dolmetsch RE, Xu K, Lewis RS. 1998. Calcium oscillations increase the efficiency and specificity of gene expression. *Nature* 392:933–36
214. Li W, Llopis J, Whitney M, Zlokarnik G, Tsien RY. 1998. Cell-permeant caged InsP3 ester shows that Ca^{2+} spike frequency can optimize gene expression. *Nature* 392:936–41
215. Tomida T, Hirose K, Takizawa A, Shibasaki F, Iino M. 2003. NFAT functions as a working memory of Ca^{2+} signals in decoding Ca^{2+} oscillation. *EMBO J.* 22:3825–32
216. Lewis RS. 2003. Calcium oscillations in T-cells: mechanisms and consequences for gene expression. *Biochem. Soc. Trans.* 31:925–29
217. Bhakta NR, Oh DY, Lewis RS. 2005. Calcium oscillations regulate thymocyte motility during positive selection in the three-dimensional thymic environment. *Nat. Immunol.* 6:143–51
218. Wei SH, Safrina O, Yu Y, Garrod KR, Cahalan MD, Parker I. 2007. Ca^{2+} signals in $CD4^+$ T cells during early contacts with antigen-bearing dendritic cells in lymph node. *J. Immunol.* 179:1586–94
219. Qi H, Egen JG, Huang AYC, Germain RN. 2006. Extrafollicular activation of lymph node B cells by antigen-bearing dendritic cells. *Science* 312:1672–76
220. Skokos D, Shakhar G, Varma R, Waite JC, Cameron TO, et al. 2007. Peptide-MHC potency governs dynamic interactions between T cells and dendritic cells in lymph nodes. *Nat. Immunol.* 8:835–44
221. Rosenberg PB. 2009. Calcium entry in skeletal muscle. *J. Physiol.* 13:3149–51
222. Dirksen RT. 2009. Checking your SOCCs and feet: the molecular mechanisms of Ca^{2+} entry in skeletal muscle. *J. Physiol.* 13:3139–47
223. Varga-Szabo D, Braun A, Nieswandt B. 2009. Calcium signaling in platelets. *J. Thromb. Haemost.* 7:1057–66
224. Baba Y, Kurosaki T. 2009. Physiological function and molecular basis of STIM1-mediated calcium entry in immune cells. *Immunol. Rev.* 231:174–88
225. Oh-hora M. 2009. Calcium signaling in the development and function of T-lineage cells. *Immunol. Rev.* 231:210–24
226. Bergmeier W, Oh-Hora M, McCarl CA, Roden RC, Bray PF, Feske S. 2009. R93W mutation in Orai1 causes impaired calcium influx in platelets. *Blood* 113:675–78
227. Baba Y, Nishida K, Fujii Y, Hirano T, Hikida M, Kurosaki T. 2008. Essential function for the calcium sensor STIM1 in mast cell activation and anaphylactic responses. *Nat. Immunol.* 9:81–88
228. Beyersdorf N, Braun A, Vögtle T, Varga-Szabo D, Galdos RR, et al. 2009. STIM1-independent T cell development and effector function in vivo. *J. Immunol.* 182:3390–97
229. Mammucari C, di Vignano AT, Sharov AA, Neilson J, Havdra MC, et al. 2006. Integration of Notch1 and calcineurin/NFAT signaling pathways in keratinocyte growth and differentiation control. *Dev. Cell* 8:666–76

A Genomic Approach to Human Autoimmune Diseases

Virginia Pascual,[1] Damien Chaussabel,[1] and Jacques Banchereau[1,2]

[1]Baylor Institute for Immunology Research, INSERM U-899, Dallas, Texas 75204; email: Virginip@baylorhealth.edu, Damienc@baylorhealth.edu, Jacquesb@baylorhealth.edu

[2]Department of Gene and Cell Medicine, Department of Medicine, Immunology Institute, Mount Sinai School of Medicine, New York, New York 10029

Annu. Rev. Immunol. 2010. 28:535–71

First published online as a Review in Advance on January 4, 2010

The *Annual Review of Immunology* is online at immunol.annualreviews.org

This article's doi:
10.1146/annurev-immunol-030409-101221

0732-0582/10/0423-0535$20.00

Key Words

microarray, blood, biomarkers, lupus, juvenile arthritis

Abstract

The past decade has seen an explosion in the use of DNA-based microarrays. These techniques permit assessment of RNA abundance on a genome-wide scale. Medical applications emerged in the field of cancer, with studies of both solid tumors and hematological malignancies leading to the development of tests that are now used to personalize therapeutic options. Microarrays have also been used to analyze the blood transcriptome in a wide range of diseases. In human autoimmune diseases, these studies are showing potential for identifying therapeutic targets as well as biomarkers for diagnosis, assessment of disease activity, and response to treatment. More quantitative and sensitive high-throughput RNA profiling methods are starting to be available and will be necessary for transcriptome analyses to become routine tests in the clinical setting. We expect this to crystallize within the coming decade, as these methods become part of the personalized medicine armamentarium.

INTRODUCTION

The immune system is a powerful defense operation. Protective immunity results from the interplay between two cardinal systems: nonspecific innate immunity and antigen-specific adaptive immunity. Dysfunctions of the immune system lie at the center of a wide variety of diseases, including autoimmunity, allergy, infections, cancer, and even some cardiovascular diseases.

Like most diseases of the immune system, autoimmune diseases arise from interactions between environmental, epigenetic, and genetic factors that result in downstream perturbations of complex and interactive biological networks. Attempts to identify single causative factors (i.e., genes or cytokines) with the use of classic genetic approaches or in vitro studies focusing on a limited number of genes and/or cell types have, for the most part, not succeeded. Furthermore, in vivo studies using animal models of human immune-mediated diseases have been of limited value in the identification of relevant therapeutic targets (1). For example, the many existing murine lupus models have not yet led to the development of specific treatments for human lupus (2). Likewise, animal models of rheumatoid arthritis (RA) predicted IL-1β to be an appropriate target in human RA (3). Blocking IL-1 was indeed effective only in a minor fraction of patients (4), and that fraction unfortunately cannot be identified using currently available disease markers. The successful blockade of TNF-α in RA patients represents considerable progress (5), but many autoimmune diseases continue to be treated with nonspecific medications such as corticosteroids and chemotherapeutic drugs. The use of these later medications is unfortunately associated with considerable adverse events. Additional challenges in the field of autoimmunity include the lack of specific biomarkers that can be used for diagnosis, assessment of disease activity, and prediction of flares. These problems are especially significant as these diseases are lifelong with a relapsing and remitting course.

An integrative evaluation of the complex network of alterations underlying the pathogenesis of autoimmune diseases was until recently difficult to conceive. Technological advances in the past 10 years, however, now permit us to analyze DNA, RNA, or protein in patient samples on a genome-wide scale. These techniques, combined with bioinformatics, are changing the face of clinical research and opening the path for novel approaches to patient care. DNA microarrays can assess in a single sample the activity of the entire transcriptome (6, 7). Current techniques detect mRNA species from known genes as immunofluorescent labeled cRNA hybridized to arrays of either cDNA or oligonucleotide fragments, but novel approaches are rapidly emerging (8). Tissue samples, blood, purified cells, and even saliva can be tested in these assays.

The first hint that genomic studies could have clinical applications came in 1999, when microarray-based transcriptional profiling was proposed for the differential diagnosis of acute myeloid and lymphocytic leukemias (9). These studies have since resulted in the identification of gene expression signatures correlating with clinical outcomes both in hematological and solid tumors (10, 11). In breast cancer, for example, microarray studies have helped identify subgroups of patients that may benefit from adjuvant therapy (12). When applied to diseases of the immune system in humans, restricted access to sampling relevant tissue(s), such as the brain in multiple sclerosis (MS) or the joints in RA, becomes a major limitation. Cells of the immune system, however, get educated and implement their functions by recirculating between central and peripheral lymphoid organs as well as by migrating to and from sites of injury via the blood. The blood therefore represents the pipeline of the immune system. Indeed, it is the preferred route for immune cells to reach the lymph nodes. After exiting through outgoing lymphatic vessels, these cells again reach the bloodstream to be transported to tissues throughout the body. Upon patrolling these tissues, they gradually drift back into the lymphatic system to begin the cycle all over again. The complex patterns of recirculation depend on the state of cell activation, the adhesion molecules expressed by immune and endothelial cells, and the presence of chemotactic molecules that selectively attract particular populations of blood cells. Sampling the blood therefore provides a "snap shot" of the complex immune networks that operate throughout the entire body. Indeed, profiling blood sample RNA from patients with both systemic as well as organ-specific autoimmune diseases has proved to be a valid approach to find clues about pathogenesis as well as to identify potential biomarkers **(Figure 1)** (13, 14).

Furthermore, in addition to providing a static view of the transcriptional activity of blood cells in the steady state, the transcriptome of whole blood, peripheral blood mononuclear cells (PBMCs), or purified blood cell populations can be assessed with DNA microarray technology after exposure in vivo (15, 16) or in vitro (17) to a variety of immune stimuli. This approach, also known as "exercising the genome" (18), has the potential to reveal alterations in gene pathways that are only visible after specific types of activation. The transcriptional effects of patient serum factors on healthy blood cells can also be studied using this approach. Indeed, we and others have successfully applied this "reverse proteomics" or reporter

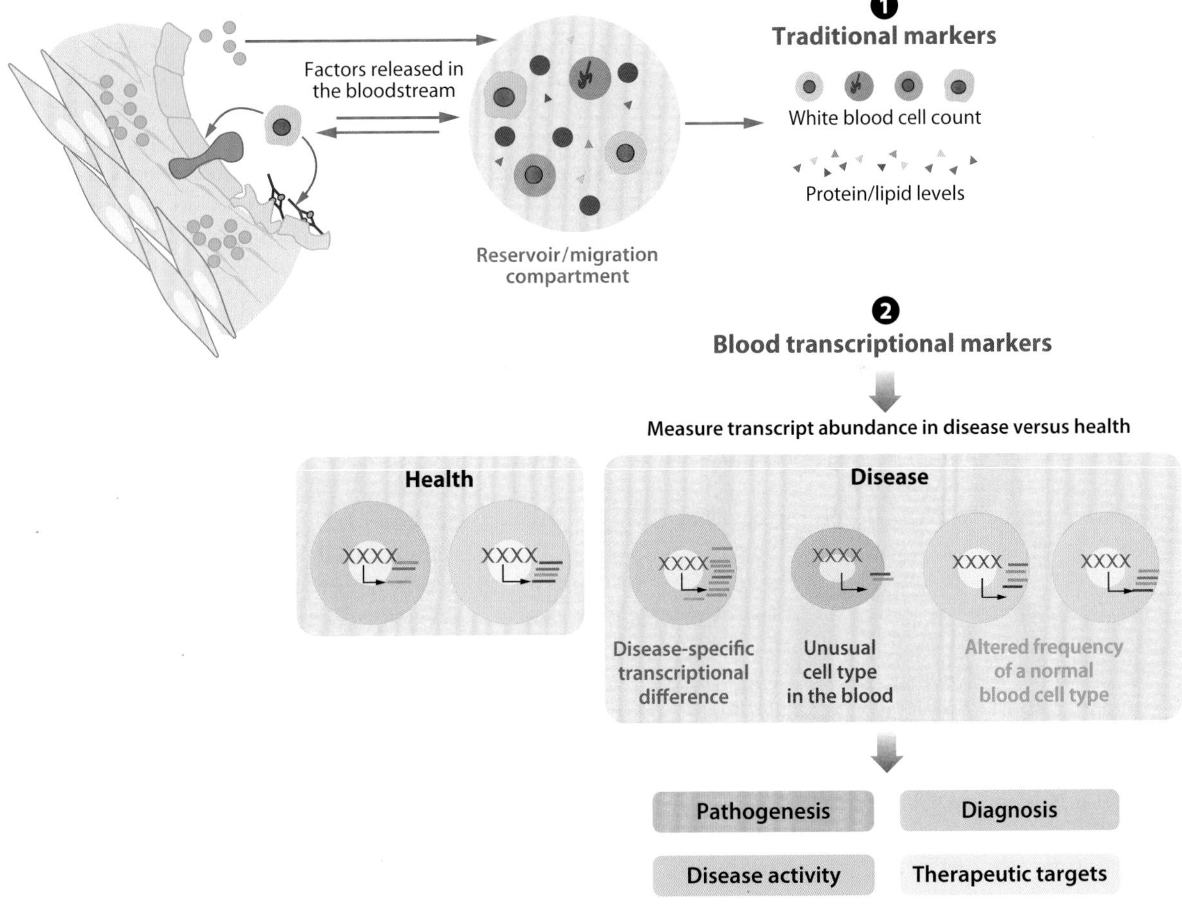

Figure 1

The blood can be used as a source of transcriptional biomarkers to understand the pathogenesis, diagnose, assess severity, and find therapeutic targets for human autoimmune diseases.

assay approach to understand autoimmune disease pathogenesis (19, 20).

About 10 years ago, we surmised that analyzing the blood transcriptome of patients with autoimmune diseases would help us understand their pathogenesis and ultimately provide better care to these patients. Here we describe our experience and that of others using this powerful yet challenging approach. We especially focus on systemic lupus erythematosus (SLE) and systemic-onset juvenile idiopathic arthritis (SoJIA), two diseases in which microarray technology has led to the identification of pathogenic pathways, therapeutic targets, as well as potential biomarkers to diagnose and follow patient disease activity and response to therapy.

HUMAN SYSTEMIC LUPUS ERYTHEMATOSUS

SLE occurs in 17–48/100,000 people. There is a spectrum of human lupus ranging from solely skin involvement to systemic disease, which is characterized by a relapsing and remitting course with flares of high morbidity. SLE patients are predominantly women who present with chronic nonspecific symptoms such as fever, weight loss, and fatigue that is often associated with lymphadenopathy and especially lymphopenia. Some patients may present with severe acute illness characterized by seizures, psychosis, renal failure, profound anemia, pulmonary hemorrhage, or sepsis. Confirming the diagnosis of SLE requires the fulfillment of 4 out of 11 criteria, one of those being the presence of antinuclear antibodies (ANA), which are detected in more than 95% of patients. Loss of tolerance to nuclear antigens focuses on chromatin components (such as dsDNA, histones, and nucleosomes) and U-rich ribonucleoproteins [such as RNP and Sm, which are Toll-like receptor 9 (TLR9) and TLR7 ligands, respectively] (195). Antibodies against phospholipids (complexed to β2-glycoprotein) exposed on the surface of dying cells are also frequently detected in SLE patients and correlate with the development of thromboembolic complications. Autoantibodies directed to cell surface molecules, especially those expressed on cells of hematopoietic origin, cause hemolytic anemia, neutropenia, and thrombocytopenia. Antibodies against antigens expressed in target organs like the kidney (glomerular extracts) are also found in patients with severe kidney disease. In addition to the direct damage caused by cellular and/or tissue antigen-antibody interactions, many lupus symptoms result from indirect damage through the deposition of immune complexes on tissues (i.e., nephritis, arthritis, and vasculitis).

BLOOD DNA MICROARRAYS TO UNDERSTAND AUTOIMMUNE DISEASE PATHOGENESIS

The first reports on blood gene expression profiling in autoimmune/inflammatory diseases date back to 2002–2003. SLE (21–24), juvenile idiopathic arthritis (19, 25–28), MS (29, 30), RA (31–34), Sjögren's syndrome (35), diabetes (36, 37), inflammatory bowel disease (38), psoriasis and psoriatic arthritis (PsA) (39, 40), inflammatory myopathies (41, 42), scleroderma (43, 44), vasculitis (45), and antiphospholipid syndrome (46) have been studied using this approach. Overall, these studies have shown that diseases with diverse pathogenesis and clinical manifestations may share common mediators, which represent therapeutic targets for intervention. Blood RNA profiling has also rapidly extended to other diseases involving the immune system, especially infections caused by viruses such as HIV (47), adenovirus (48, 49), influenza (50), or dengue (51); bacteria such as *Staphylococcus aureus*, *Streptococcus pneumoniae*, or *Escherichia coli* (52); *Mycobacterium tuberculosis* (53); and parasites *(Plasmodium)* (54); as well as sepsis (55). The blood of transplant recipients has also been profiled in kidney (56), liver (57), heart (58), and hematopoietic cell transplant recipients (59). Furthermore, disease signatures have been detected in the blood cells of patients with cardiovascular diseases (60) and nonhematological malignancies (61, 62).

Systemic Lupus Erythematosus

SLE and type I IFN. Multiple cell types and soluble mediators, including IL-10 (63, 64) and IFN-γ (65–67), but not type I IFN, have been proposed to be at the center of lupus pathogenesis (see sidebar, Human Systemic Lupus Erythematosus). Yet, in the late 1960s, polyI:C, a known inducer of type I IFN, was reported to accelerate disease in young NZB × NZW

(F1) female mice (68). Then, 10 years later, increased IFN levels were detected in the sera of patients with SLE (69). Intriguingly, treatment with recombinant IFN-α resulted in autoantibody formation in up to 20% of patients and in the appearance of SLE-specific symptoms in a fraction of them (reviewed in 70). In the late 1990s, the number of natural IFN-producing cells, later identified as plasmacytoid dendritic cells (pDCs), were reported to be decreased in lupus blood (71) but increased at sites of injury (i.e., the skin) (72, 73). Furthermore, DNA and/or nucleic acid–containing immune complexes could induce these cells to secrete type I IFN (74, 75). At this time, we described how monocytes from some children with SLE displayed dendritic cell (DC) function and that the serum of these patients was able to induce the differentiation of healthy monocytes into mature DCs in an IFN-α-dependent manner (76). These studies, together with those describing the numerous effects of type I IFN on adaptive immunity (77–80), now converged to place this family of cytokines at the center of lupus pathogenesis (see sidebar, The Central Role of Type I IFN in SLE Pathogenesis). Yet several observations did not support the hypothesis: First, not every SLE patient has detectable serum type I IFN levels (81); second, dysregulation of type I IFN production is not obvious in most murine SLE models (2); and third, genetic linkage and association studies had not identified candidate lupus susceptibility genes within the IFN pathway (82). Gene expression profiling helped address some of these questions.

THE CENTRAL ROLE OF TYPE I IFN IN SLE PATHOGENESIS

Different genetic alterations may lead to type I IFN overproduction in human systemic lupus erythematosus (SLE). The increased bioavailability of type I IFN contributes to peripheral tolerance breakdown through the activation of immature myeloid dendritic cells (mDCs). These cells, together with plasmacytoid DCs (pDCs), help expand autoreactive B cells. IFN-matured DCs also activate cytotoxic CD8^{+} T cells, possibly increasing the apoptotic cell load. The capture of apoptotic cells by mDCs and of nucleic acid–containing immune complexes by pDCs and B cells amplifies the autoimmune reaction by increasing the antigenic load, type I IFN production, and B cell activation, respectively. Endogenous proteins such as HMGB1 (196) and LL37 (197, 198) have been recently shown to alter the conformation and/or trafficking and subsequently increase the interferogenic capacity of immune complex–bound endogenous DNA and RNA.

Because serum levels of type I IFN family members are difficult to measure, we explored whether leukocyte gene expression profiling might help us assess the prevalence of lupus patients' exposure to these cytokines. Thirty children with SLE (representing four ethnicities, 60% female), 9 healthy children, and a group of 12 patients with juvenile chronic arthritis were recruited. PBMCs from the pediatric SLE patients displayed striking transcriptional differences compared to healthy controls (375 transcripts) (**Figure 2**). After correction for multiple testing-related errors, the very conservative Bonferroni correction (see the section below, Data Analysis Primer) selected 15 genes, 14 of which were IFN inducible. A less conservative correction (Benjamini and Hochberg) selected 33 genes, 26 of which were IFN regulated (21).

All but one of the pediatric patients in our study exhibited upregulation of IFN-inducible genes, and the only patient lacking this signature had been in remission for over two years (21). Similar studies performed with adult SLE PBMCs showed an IFN signature in approximately 50% of patients (22–24). The higher prevalence of the signature in children might have been due to sample selection, as more patients with newly diagnosed, untreated disease were included in the pediatric study. It might also reflect a higher degree of disease severity and/or a unique genetic background responsible for the earlier appearance of disease manifestations in the pediatric cohort. Larger population studies are required to resolve the source of this difference.

All nucleated cells express the type I IFN receptor (IFNAR) and respond to type I IFN with phosphorylation of STAT1 and STAT2, which ultimately leads to the transcription of

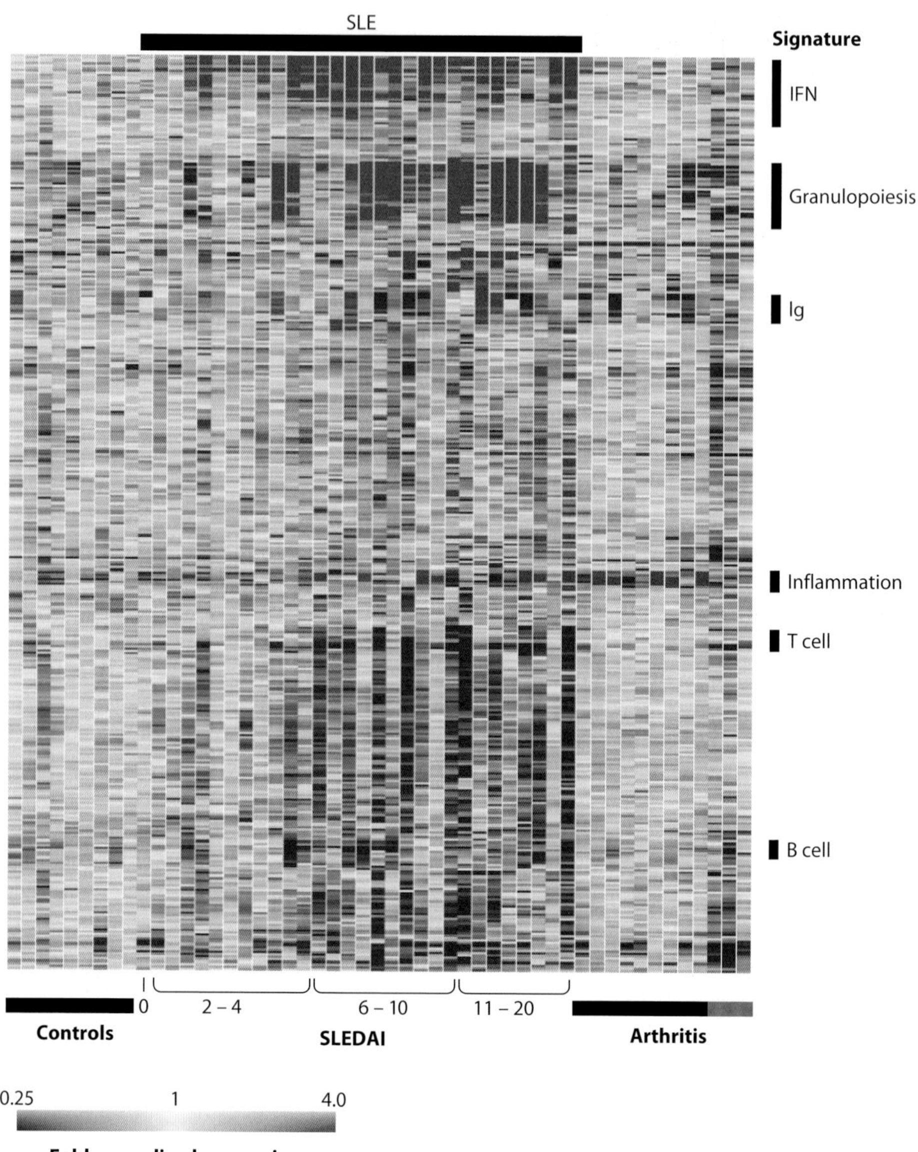

Figure 2

SLE signature. Hierarchical clustering of gene expression from blood leukocytes of 9 healthy children, 30 children with SLE, and 12 patients with juvenile chronic arthritis. SLE patients were ranked according to their SLE disease activity index (SLEDAI) at the time of blood draw. Each row represents a separate gene and each column a separate patient. 374 transcript sequences were selected as being differentially expressed in SLE compared to healthy patients. The normalized expression index for each transcript sequence (*rows*) in each sample (*columns*) is indicated by a color code. Red, yellow, and blue squares indicate that expression of the gene is greater than, equal to, or less than the mean level of expression across 9 healthy controls, respectively. The scale extends from fluorescence ratios of 0.25 to 4.0. Original figure published in *J. Exp. Med.* 2003. 197:711–23.

IFN-responsive genes (83). A notable exception is represented by immature neutrophils, which do not phosphorylate STAT1 in response to receptor ligation (84). All type I IFNs signal through this receptor and give rise to similar signaling and transcriptional cascades. Sequence differences between type I IFNs result, however, in different binding affinities with each IFNAR chain and consequent biological activities (85). Hundreds of genes are induced or repressed (86), including among others classical antiviral/proliferative transcripts (i.e., OAS, MX1, etc.), IFN regulatory factors (IRF5 and IRF7), proapoptotic molecules (i.e., FAS and TRAIL), B cell differentiation factors (i.e., BLyS/BAFF), chemokines and chemokine receptors (CCL2 and CXCL10) and, interestingly, even lupus autoantigens such as Ro/SSA (21). Many IFN-inducible proteins might indeed play a significant role in disease pathogenesis. Fas and TRAIL can, for example, contribute to nucleosome overload and therefore to increased nuclear antigen presentation. BLyS/BAFF induces the proliferation and differentiation of mature B cells into antibody-secreting cells. Indeed, a neutralizing anti-BAFF/BLyS antibody being tested in clinical trials appears to reduce SLE disease activity and prevent flares (87).

Treating SLE patients with high-dose intravenous steroids, which are used to control disease flares, results in the silencing of the IFN signature (21) (**Figure 3**). This is associated with pDC depletion (88), although both the blood pDCs and the IFN signature return in less than one week after intravenous steroid administration (V. Pascual, D. Chaussabel, and J. Banchereau, unpublished data). Altogether, these observations support the central role of pDCs as producers of type I IFN in lupus pathogenesis.

A surprise from these initial studies was the absence of type I IFN gene transcripts in the face of an abundance of IFN-inducible gene transcripts in SLE PBMCs. A likely explanation is that the cells producing type I IFN, and therefore transcribing these genes, migrate to sites of injury. Indeed, IFN-inducible genes and/or

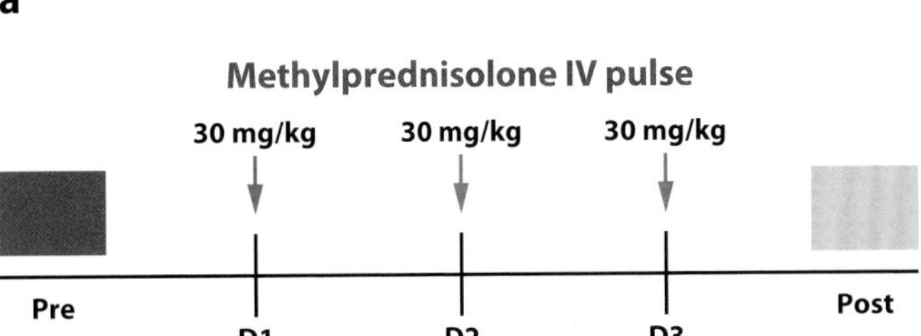

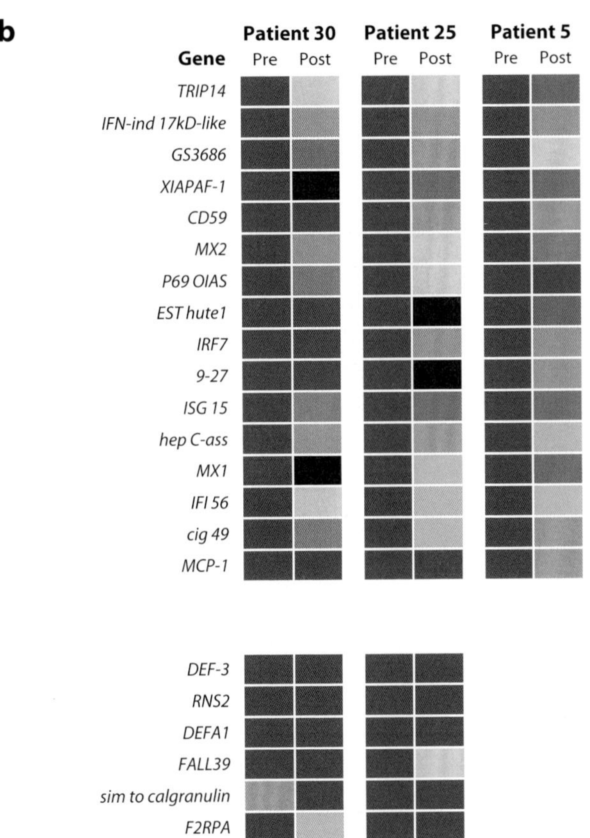

Figure 3

High-dose steroid intravenous pulse extinguishes the type I IFN signature in systemic lupus erythematosus (SLE) blood. Peripheral blood mononuclear cells were analyzed from three pediatric SLE patients before and after treatment with high-dose intravenous methylprednisolone (1 g day^{-1} for three days). All patients showed downregulation of IFN-regulated transcripts (*a*), whereas expression of non–type I IFN–inducible transcripts (i.e., granulopoiesis, *b*) does not change significantly. Patient #5 did not display granulopoiesis signature before high-dose glucocorticoid therapy. Original figure published in *J. Exp. Med.* 2003. 197:711–23.

proteins can be detected in lupus kidney (89), skin (73), and synovial biopsies from SLE patients (90). These tissues are all infiltrated with pDCs (72, 91), further supporting the theory that they are the source of type I IFN in SLE. Increased levels of Flt3L, a pDC growth factor, in SLE serum (92) suggest that this cytokine might contribute to the increased numbers of these cells at the sites of inflammation.

Type I IFN and murine lupus. A number of murine lupus models have been available for decades (2), yet they did not predict that type I IFN might be an important mediator of human SLE. However, in line with the human studies, two independent groups showed that the crossing of NZB and B6 *lpr/lpr* mice, respectively, with a type I IFN receptor knockout strain significantly decreased morbidity and prolonged the survival of these animals (93, 94). Additionally, delivering type I IFN to young (6–8 weeks old) preautoimmune NZB/W F(1) mice resulted in the rapid development of severe SLE, possibly explaining the deleterious effect of poly I:C reported decades ago (95). Conversely, administration of a type I IFN immunogen that induced transient specific neutralizing antibodies delayed/prevented lupus manifestations, including proteinuria, histological renal lesions, and death in these mice (96).

Introduction of the Yaa locus into lupus-prone mice accelerates the development of autoimmune manifestations (97). The Yaa phenotype results from a duplication of the TLR7 gene (98, 99). Engagement of TLR7, which can be triggered by viruses or immune complexes containing RNA and by RNA-associated autoantigens, induces pDCs to secrete type I IFN (100–102). B cells, which also express this receptor, respond to the same triggers with activation and proinflammatory cytokine production (103). A role for TLR7 in the induction of autoimmunity is further demonstrated in transgenic mice, which spontaneously develop autoimmunity. Whereas a modest increase in TLR7 gene dosage promotes autoreactive lymphocytes with RNA specificities and myeloid cell proliferation, a substantial increase in TLR7 expression causes fatal acute inflammatory pathology and profound DC dysregulation (104). Using the Unc93b1 3d mutation that selectively abolishes nucleic acid–binding TLR3, 7, and 9 signaling, endosomal TLR signaling has been shown to be required for optimal production of IgG autoantibodies, IgM rheumatoid factor, and other clinical parameters of disease in lupus-prone mice as well (105). Although there is currently no evidence that TLR7 mutations contribute to human SLE, polymorphisms in TLR8 have been recently reported to be associated with SLE in pediatric and adult populations (106).

Genome in the Footsteps of Transcriptome Analyses

Traditional genetic approaches had not pointed to type I IFN as a contributor to lupus pathogenesis. Instead, the HLA locus, Fcγ receptors, complement components, etc., were among the candidates to explain disease susceptibility (82). Nevertheless, the evidence accumulated through some of the studies described above led some geneticists to perform a "genome-focused" search for polymorphisms in 13 type I IFN–related genes (107). This study revealed a strong association between SLE and certain variants of the IFN regulatory factor 5 (IRF5), which has since been confirmed in several genome-wide association (GWA) studies (108, 109). Indeed, the IRF5 SLE risk haplotype is associated with higher serum type I IFN activity in patients (110). A correlation between serum IFN-α activity in patients and their first-degree healthy relatives has also been described (111). In addition to IRF5, polymorphisms in other genes connected with the IFN signaling pathway, such as *STAT4* and *IRAK1*, have emerged as conferring susceptibility to SLE (112–114). More recently, mutations in the human *TREX1* gene, which cause Aicardi-Goutieres syndrome and chilblain lupus (115), have also been linked to SLE (116). TREX1 is a negative regulator of the IFN stimulatory DNA response, and single-stranded DNA derived from endogenous retroelements accumulates in

Trex1-deficient cells (117). The persistent presence of dsDNA from dying cells could also lead to an aberrant immune response in patients carrying Trex1 mutations (118). Finally, polymorphisms in the autophagy-related gene *ATG5* have been described in SLE (109). ATG-deficient pDCs seem to be less able to produce type I IFN in response to certain viruses (119). The specific mechanisms through which these lupus-related polymorphisms affect IFN production in response to environmental and/or endogenous triggers remain for the most part to be elucidated.

The IFN pathway is not the only genetic pathway predisposing to SLE. Genes within the HLA locus, TLR signaling, B cell– and myeloid lineage–specific, FcRs, etc., have been confirmed to be associated with disease. Altogether, however, IFN-related genetic alterations rank among the highest, closely behind the HLA locus, in the lupus susceptibility scale (120) (**Figure 4**).

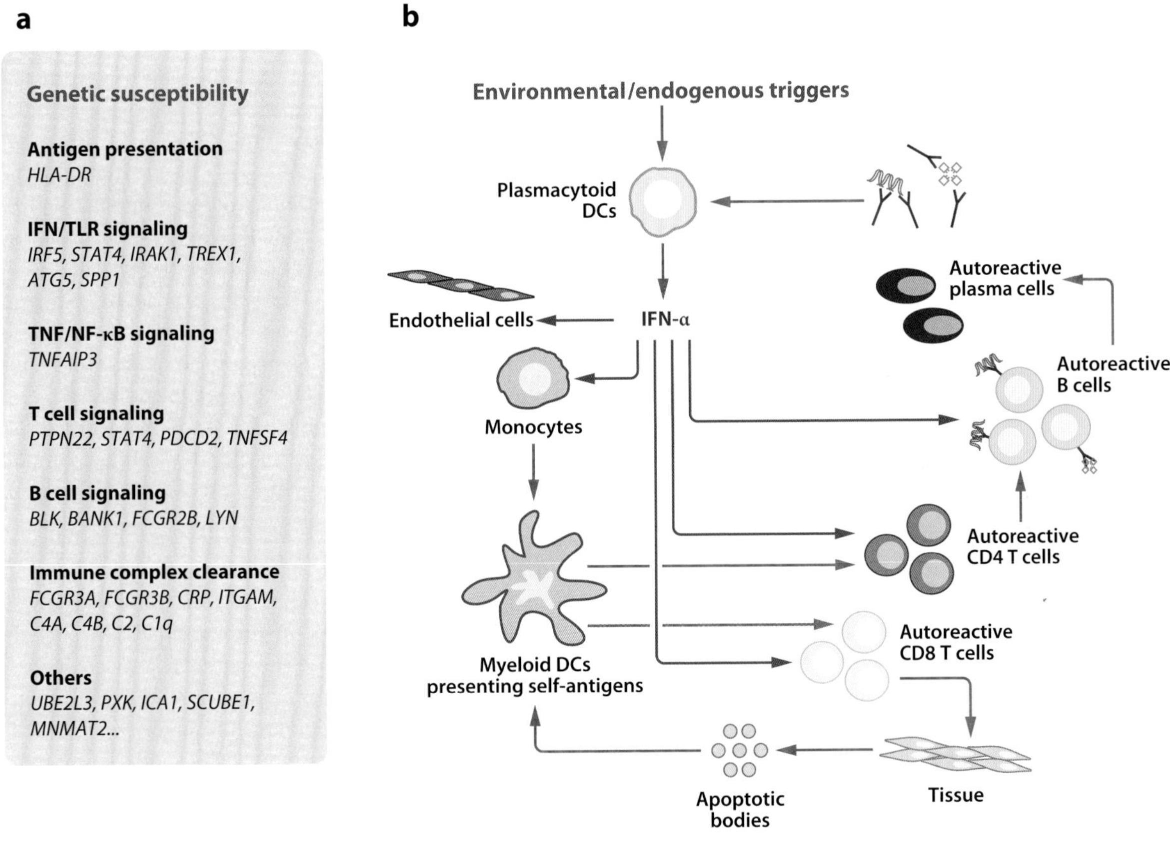

Figure 4

A unified view of systemic lupus erythematosus pathogenesis. (*a*) HLA and non-HLA gene polymorphisms contribute to SLE susceptibility. Among them, TLR/IFN signaling pathway–related genes have recently been described. (*b*) Both environmental triggers (i.e., viral infections) and chromatin-containing immune complexes might contribute to the unabated production of type I IFN by plasmacytoid dendritic cells (pDCs) in SLE patients. Increased bioavailability of type I IFN induces and maintains the generation of mature DCs, tilting the fate of autoreactive T lymphocytes that have escaped central tolerance from deletion to activation. These mature DCs activate cytotoxic CD8^{+} T cells to generate nucleosomes that can be captured and presented by IFN-DCs. Together with IL-6, type I IFN promotes the differentiation of mature B cells into plasma cells, which secrete autoantibodies. A direct effect of IFN-α on endothelial cells could also contribute to premature atherosclerosis in SLE patients.

Drug-Induced Lupus and Type I IFN

Microarray analyses of PBMCs have also shed some light on the pathogenesis of drug-induced lupus. Upon treatment with TNF antagonists, up to 20% of patients with RA and Crohn's disease develop anti-dsDNA antibodies, and a fraction of them even progress to reversible SLE (70). In line with those clinical observations, the PBMCs of juvenile arthritis patients treated with anti-TNF antibodies display an overt IFN signature. In vitro studies revealed that addition of TNF antagonists induced pDCs exposed to viruses to secrete higher levels of type I IFN (121). This is best explained by the inhibition of TNF-dependent pDC maturation, which normally shuts down type I IFN secretion. Further studies are necessary to understand if this mechanism extends to other drugs, such as hydralazine, antiepileptic medications, etc., that can induce lupus-like syndromes.

Non-IFN-related signatures in SLE blood. Type I IFN–inducible transcripts represent only a fraction of the transcriptional alterations observed in SLE patient PBMCs (21, 22). A different set of signatures reflects changes in blood cell composition. Thus, the second most prevalent signature in our study (21) consisted of genes expressed by granulocytes at varying stages of development (e.g., elastase, myeloperoxidase, and bactericidal proteins such as defensins). This finding was surprising, as Ficoll-purified PBMCs, which are normally freed from neutrophils, were the source of RNA for these arrays. However, phenotypic examination of the isolated PBMCs revealed a large population of low-density neutrophils in the mononuclear cell fraction from patients but not from controls. The expression of neutrophil-specific transcripts (e.g., the defensin *DEF3*) correlated with the frequency of low-density neutrophils in the patients' samples (**Figure 5**). Next, and as expected, the well-known lupus-associated lymphopenia resulted in a relative decrease in B cell–, T cell–, and NK cell–specific transcripts (e.g., TCRα/β, Lck, and CD3γ). Transcripts encoding variable and constant regions of immunoglobulins (Igs) together with plasma cell–lineage markers were increased in several patients, a finding correlating with the expansion of CD19^{low} CD20^{-} CD38^{high} CD27^{high} plasma cell precursors (PCPs) (21). These cells, which are oligoclonal and highly proliferative, are not specific to SLE but can be detected in situations where there is immune activation, i.e., vaccinations, infections, and other autoimmune diseases (122–124). Although type I IFN induces in vitro the differentiation of memory B cells into PCPs very similar to those found in SLE patients (77), the IFN and PCP signatures do not always correlate in individual patients. This discordance might be explained by the fact that some of the medications used to treat SLE, such as mycophenolate mofetil, target proliferative cells and suppress the PCP signature, while having few effects on the overall IFN signature (Z. Xu, L. Bennett, J. Banchereau, and V. Pascual, unpublished data).

Proof of concept: clinical trials with IFN-α antagonists in human SLE. A phase Ia trial to evaluate the safety, pharmacokinetics, and immunogenicity of an anti-IFN-α monoclonal antibody (mAb) therapy in adult SLE patients was recently conducted (125). The antibody elicited a specific and dose-dependent inhibition of expression of type I IFN–inducible

Figure 5

A non–type I IFN–induced signature in SLE peripheral blood mononuclear cells (granulopoiesis signature). (*a*) Genes are divided into three categories: enzymes and their inhibitors, bactericidal proteins, and others. Median expression and the number of patients who display more than twofold increase (*red*) in gene expression. (*b*) Presence of granular cells in leukocytes that display granulopoiesis-related RNA. Flow cytometry analysis (forward scatter versus side scatter) of Ficoll-separated mononuclear cells. The gated cells are immature neutrophils. (*c*) Correlation between the defensin alpha (DEF3) levels and the numbers of cells gated as shown in *b*. Abbreviations: FSC, forward scatter; SLE, systemic lupus erythematosus; SLEDAI, SLE disease activity index; SSC, side scatter.

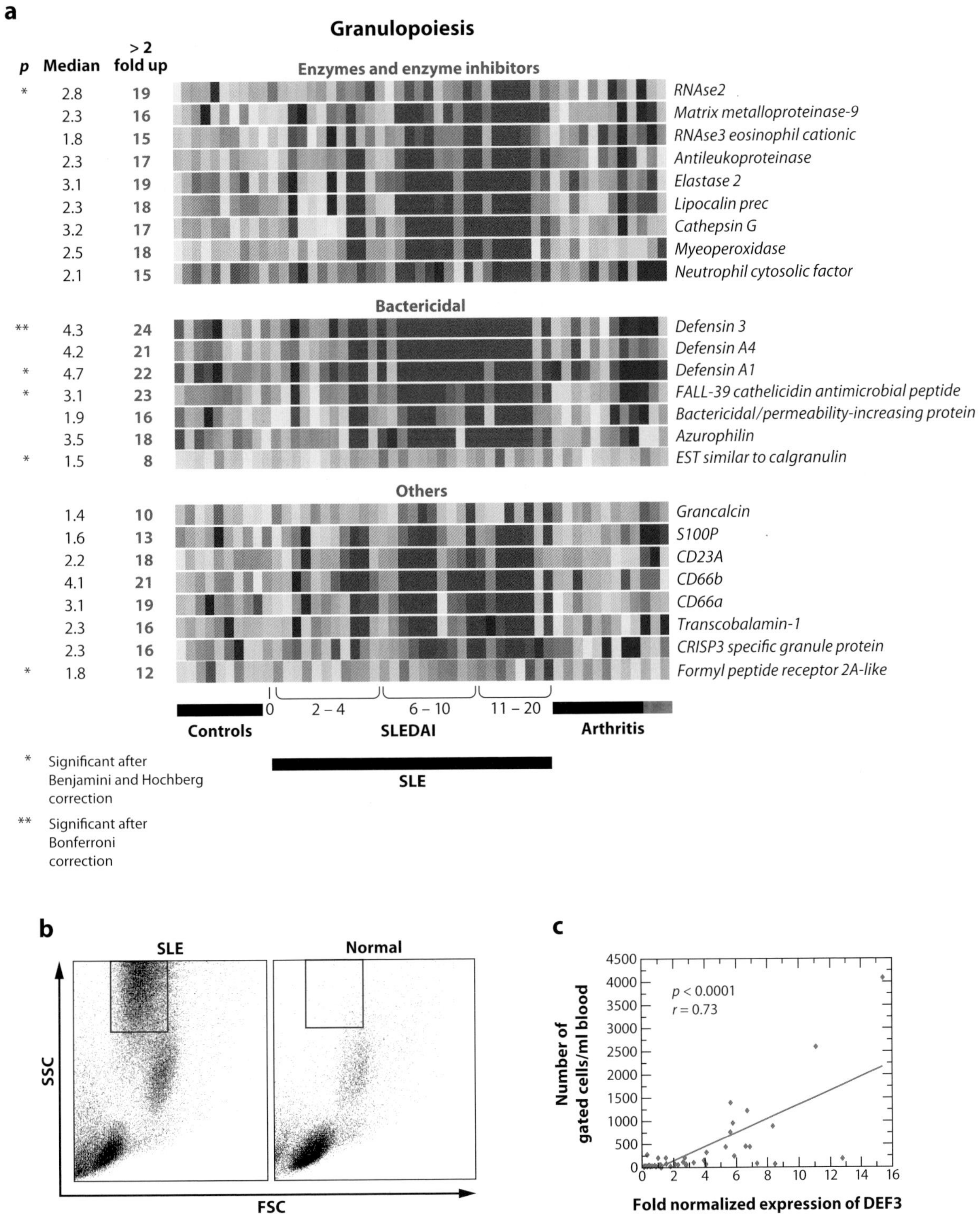

a

Granulopoiesis

p	Median	> 2 fold up	Gene
			Enzymes and enzyme inhibitors
*	2.8	19	*RNAse2*
	2.3	16	*Matrix metalloproteinase-9*
	1.8	15	*RNAse3 eosinophil cationic*
	2.3	17	*Antileukoproteinase*
	3.1	19	*Elastase 2*
	2.3	18	*Lipocalin prec*
	3.2	17	*Cathepsin G*
	2.5	18	*Myeoperoxidase*
	2.1	15	*Neutrophil cytosolic factor*
			Bactericidal
**	4.3	24	*Defensin 3*
	4.2	21	*Defensin A4*
*	4.7	22	*Defensin A1*
*	3.1	23	*FALL-39 cathelicidin antimicrobial peptide*
	1.9	16	*Bactericidal/permeability-increasing protein*
	3.5	18	*Azurophilin*
*	1.5	8	*EST similar to calgranulin*
			Others
	1.4	10	*Grancalcin*
	1.6	13	*S100P*
	2.2	18	*CD23A*
	4.1	21	*CD66b*
	3.1	19	*CD66a*
	2.3	16	*Transcobalamin-1*
	2.3	16	*CRISP3 specific granule protein*
*	1.8	12	*Formyl peptide receptor 2A-like*

* Significant after Benjamini and Hochberg correction

** Significant after Bonferroni correction

b

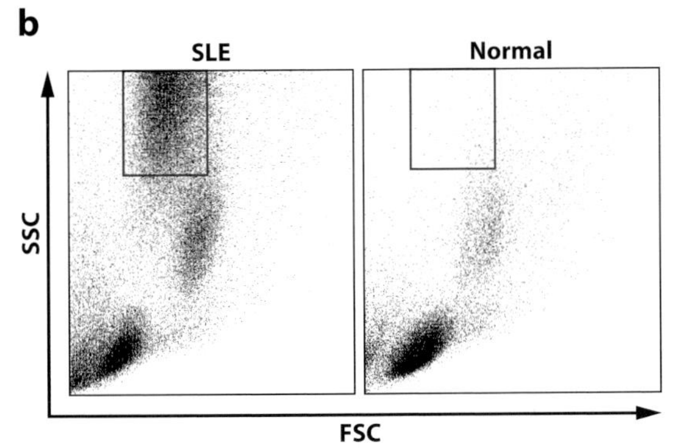

c

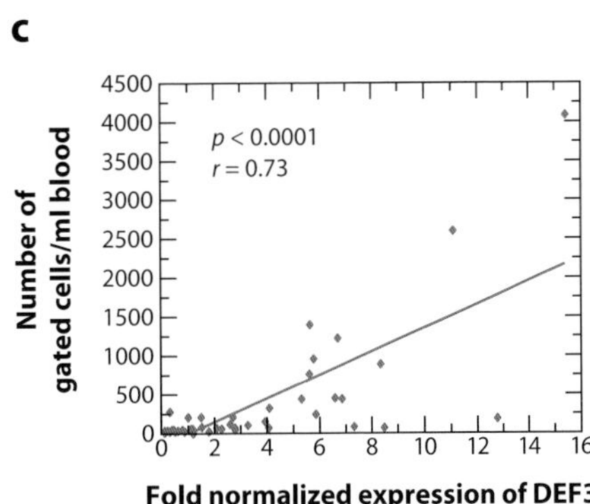

genes in both whole blood and skin lesions from SLE patients, at both the transcript and the protein levels. As expected, overexpression of BLyS/BAFF, a type I IFN–inducible gene, decreased as well with treatment. Interestingly, however, TNF-α, IL-10, IL-1β, GM-CSF, and their respective downstream signatures were also suppressed upon treatment with anti-IFN-α mAb (125). These data suggest that, beyond the IFN signature, many of the transcriptional alterations detected in SLE might be connected to the type I IFN pathway. Thus, this first trial supports the proposed central role of type I IFN in human SLE.

JUVENILE IDIOPATHIC ARTHRITIS

JIA is the most common rheumatic disease in childhood and an important cause of short- and long-term disability. The term JIA includes a heterogeneous group of diseases characterized by the development of chronic peripheral arthritis starting in the first 16 years of life. JIA is classified according to three major types of disease presentation: oligoarthritis, polyarthritis, and systemic onset (SoJIA). Each of these groups is defined by a constellation of clinical signs and symptoms during the first six months of illness. SoJIA represents up to 20% of all the cases of JIA. This disease is unique in terms of clinical manifestations, prognosis, and lack of response to conventional therapies. High spiking fever, a salmon-color rash that follows the fever spikes, anemia, leukocytosis, and elevated erythrocyte sedimentation rate are the main initial features of the disease, sometimes lasting several months before the diagnosis can be established at the time arthritis appears. Most SoJIA patients lack classical autoantibodies. As the symptoms are nonspecific and found in other diseases such as infections and malignancies, patients undergo a series of very costly diagnostic tests and prolonged hospitalizations. The systemic manifestations may last from weeks to months and eventually subside, to be followed by chronic arthritis. About 50% of patients will present oligoarticular involvement and will recover. The other half will evolve into a polyarticular pattern. Almost half of children with SoJIA will have active arthritis 10 years after diagnosis is made. These patients display an increased risk of developing hemophagocytic syndrome, also known as macrophage activation syndrome, a disorder associated with serious morbidity and/or death.

Juvenile Idiopathic Arthritis (JIA)

SoJIA is one of the most challenging pediatric rheumatic diseases (see sidebar, Juvenile Idiopathic Arthritis). Its pathogenesis had been for years linked to proinflammatory cytokines, as elevated serum levels of IL-6 and TNF had been found in active patients (126, 127). IL-6 antagonists are not yet available in the United States, however, and TNF antagonists did not prove to be efficacious in treating these patients. To try to understand SoJIA pathogenesis, we developed two complementary approaches based on microarray technology: (*a*) analysis of transcriptional patterns in active patient PBMCs (25), and (*b*) analysis of the transcriptional changes induced by serum from active patients in healthy PBMCs (19). The development of biomarkers for disease diagnosis and patient follow-up is described in a later section of this review.

Transcriptional analysis of SoJIA PBMCs revealed alterations in the expression of >800 transcripts. Most of these changes, however, were also found in patients suffering from systemic inflammation caused by bacterial and viral infections and did not point toward any specific molecular pathway (25). The clue came from in vitro experiments designed to test the effect of active patient sera on the transcriptional profile of healthy PBMCs. These "reverse proteomics" experiments revealed that SoJIA serum upregulates the transcription and secretion of IL-1β in healthy leukocytes (**Figure 6**). SoJIA serum also upregulates the expression of genes known to be induced by IL-1β and/or involved in innate immunity pathways (19).

This unexpected finding led us to consider the role of IL-1β in disease pathogenesis. An IL-1 receptor antagonist (anakinra) had been developed to treat patients with RA but had shown limited clinical efficacy (4). We thus treated two SoJIA patients who were refractory to all conventional therapies and observed remarkable clinical and hematological responses. Fever and rash disappeared within 48 h. Laboratory parameters of inflammation soon

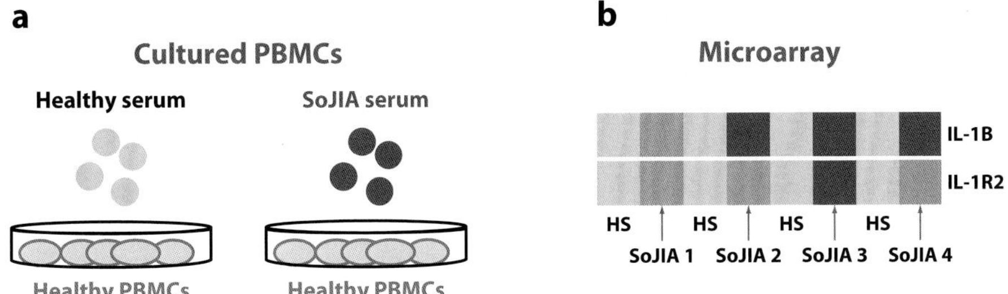

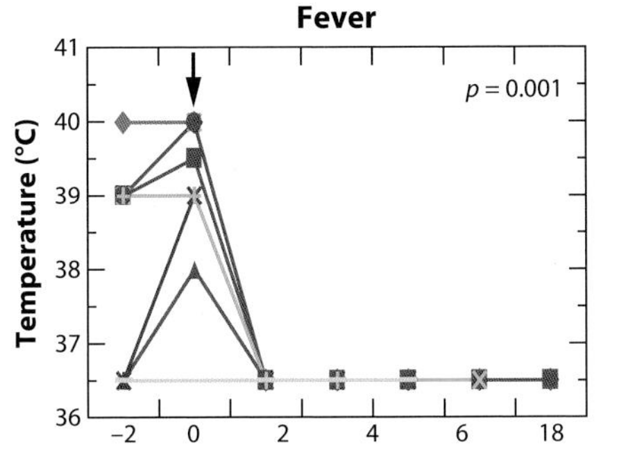

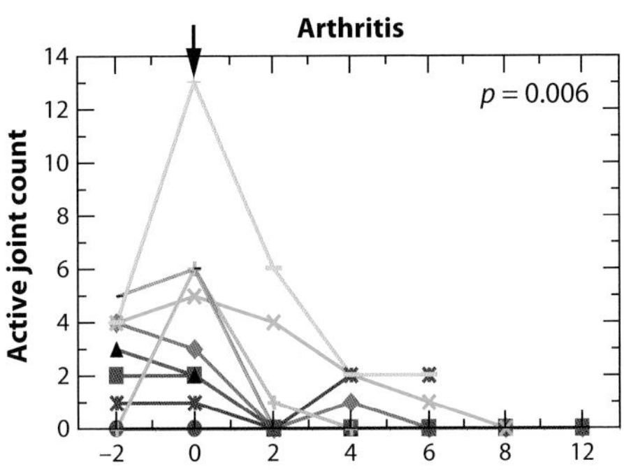

Figure 6

Gene expression profiling led to the identification of IL-1β in the pathogenesis of SoJIA. (*a*) Incubation of healthy PBMCs with autologous sera (AS) or sera from four patients with active SoJIA. (*b*) Transcriptional changes induced by SoJIA sera included the upregulation of IL-1β and its receptors. (*c*) Treatment with daily injections of anakinra induced the resolution of systemic symptoms (fever) and arthritis in 9 out of 9 and 7 out of 9 patients, respectively. Adapted from *Curr. Opin. Immunol.* 2007. 19:623–32.

followed, and, most importantly, refractory arthritis responded within a few weeks to anakinra treatment. Seven additional patients were similarly treated, and 5 out of 7 quickly went into complete remission (19) (**Figure 6**). Since then, 30 patients have been treated in our clinic, and 72% of them have attained full and long-lasting remission (V. Pascual, M. Punaro, D. Chaussabel, and J. Banchereau, unpublished data). The efficacy of anakinra to treat SoJIA patients has been recently confirmed in a randomized clinical trial (P. Quartier, F. Allantaz, R. Cimaz, P. Pillet, C. Messiaen C, et al., manuscript submitted). Rapid and sustained responses to IL-1β blockade have also been described in patients with refractory adult-onset Still's disease (128), which is the adult equivalent of SoJIA. These patients display a blood microarray signature almost identical to that of SoJIA patients (V. Pascual, J. Cush, F. Allantaz, D. Chaussabel, and J. Banchereau, unpublished data).

The origin of dysregulated IL-1β production in SoJIA remains unknown. A common infectious or inflammatory trigger could lead to an excessive production of IL-1 in patients with underlying mutations in genes controlling the regulation of this cytokine. In favor of this hypothesis, nonspecific activation of PBMCs from a group of SoJIA patients in vitro results in excessive IL-1β secretion (19). Because IL-1β can upregulate its own transcription, IL-1β itself could also be responsible for the serum effects described above. This cytokine is difficult to detect in the serum, however, because it binds to large proteins such as β2-macroglobulin, complement, and the soluble type II IL-1 receptor (129). Alternatively, some members of the S100A family (S100A8 and S100A9) have been described as being elevated in SoJIA serum and postulated to induce IL-1β secretion (130, 131).

Thus, simple experiments performed with active patient sera helped focus our attention on the IL-1 pathway. This pathway had been obscured by the many transcriptional alterations found in the blood of patients.

Other Rheumatic Diseases

Sjögren's syndrome (SS). SS is an autoimmune disease characterized by lymphocytic infiltration and progressive functional disruption of lacrimal and salivary glands. Extraglandular manifestations, however, are also common. The production of autoantibodies is a prominent feature, as antinuclear antibodies are found in about 80% of patients, and anti-SSA/Ro and anti-SSB/La autoantibodies in 65% and 40%, respectively. Although the etiology of SS is unknown, a genetic predisposition has long been recognized. Indeed, the major polymorphisms in type I IFN–related genes (*IRF5* and *STAT4*) found associated with SLE are also associated with primary SS patients (132, 133). Transcriptome analyses performed on blood (35), salivary gland tissue (134), and even saliva (135) of patients have also revealed an upregulation of IFN-inducible genes remarkably similar to those described in SLE.

Inflammatory myopathies. Gene expression profiling of muscle and skin from patients with inflammatory myopathies has revealed unexpected signatures and led to the identification of previously unrecognized cell types and signaling pathways in involved tissues (see sidebar, Inflammatory Myopathies). The vast majority of upregulated transcripts in samples from dermatomyositis (DM) and polymyositis (PM) patients are type I IFN inducible (136). Indeed, pDCs account for most of the CD4^{+} T cells present in DM muscle (41). These cells, which had been previously interpreted as T-helper cells (137), are also present in DM skin (138). Juvenile DM (JDM), the most common pediatric inflammatory myopathy, is strongly associated with HLA class II region genes (139). A type I IFN signature is also found in JDM muscle biopsies (140). Microarray analyses of PM and inclusion body myositis (IBM) muscle revealed an overexpression of Ig gene transcripts. Consequently, abundant CD20^{-} CD138^{+} plasma cells were identified by immunohistochemistry as the source of this signature (41).

Blood samples from JDM, DM, and PM patients reflect the main signatures found in muscle with a distinct overexpression of type I IFN–inducible genes. Accordingly, clinical improvement during immunosuppressive treatment is generally associated with the disappearance of this signature (42, 141). Thus, microarray analyses have revealed new molecular and cellular alterations in inflammatory myopathies. These might enable the identification of novel therapeutic targets and open the door for biomarker development in these diseases. The prominent IFN signature in DM and PM patients advocates for the conduction of clinical trials with type I IFN antagonists.

Psoriasis and psoriatic arthritis (PsA). Psoriasis vulgaris is a chronic inflammatory

INFLAMMATORY MYOPATHIES

The inflammatory myopathies include dermatomyositis (DM), polymyositis (PM), and inclusion body myositis (IBM). DM muscle pathology is quite distinct, with perivascular inflammatory cells and abnormal capillaries and perimysial perifascicular myofibers. Both PM and IBM have larger infiltrates of inflammatory cells into muscle that surround, displace, and even invade the myofibers. DM and PM are treated with corticosteroids and nonspecific immunosuppressive drugs. IBM is refractory to these therapies. A challenge common to these diseases is the lack of simple and specific tests, other than muscle biopsy and magnetic resonance imaging, for the diagnosis and disease activity assessment of patients.

condition characterized by hyperproliferation of keratinocytes, dermal infiltration of activated $CD4^+$ T cells, and lesional production of proinflammatory cytokines (142). The disease has a strong genetic component, and inflammatory arthritis develops in as many as 30% of patients. Microarray studies revealed signatures corresponding to cytokines and chemokines within involved skin and markers of DC activation in uninvolved skin. Several members of the IL-1 cytokine family as well as IFN-inducible genes are upregulated in psoriatic lesions of patients (143–146).

PBMC gene expression profiling of PsA patients identified a signature that differentiated these patients from healthy individuals and RA patients. Downregulated transcripts clustered to certain chromosomal regions, including those containing the psoriasis susceptibility loci PSORS1 and PSORS2. Genes involved in downregulation or suppression of innate and acquired immune responses were most downregulated, possibly explaining the proinflammatory responses associated with this disease. One gene, nucleoporin 62 kDa, could correctly classify all controls and 94.7% of the PsA patients. The combination of two genes, *MAP3K3* and *CACNA1S*, correctly classified all RA and PsA patients (40). Larger studies are necessary to confirm these tantalizing data. This is particularly relevant regarding PsA, as diagnosing early and/or predicting who will develop this complication might lead to early therapeutic interventions, thus preventing the development of erosive arthritis.

Rheumatoid arthritis. RA is a systemic autoimmune disorder characterized by chronic inflammation and destruction of bone and cartilage in diarthrodial joints. There is clearly a need for improved clinical laboratory evaluation and classification of patients with RA, as diagnosis is based on clinical observations and a combination of serological markers (i.e., rheumatoid factor and anticyclic citrullinated peptide antibodies) that are not present in every patient (147). Furthermore, although effective treatments are now available, their efficacy is not universal. Indeed, more than one-third of RA patients do not respond to current biological agents, including TNF antagonists, and there are no available biomarkers to predict response to therapy.

Gene expression profiling has been used to study both synovial tissues of affected joints and peripheral blood. Initial studies comparing RA synovial tissue to osteoarthritis revealed upregulation in RA of transcripts specific to antigen-presenting cells, T cells, and B cells (148). STAT1-inducible genes were found to be upregulated in another study (149), suggesting the involvement of the IFN pathway in the disease process of at least a subgroup of patients. Synovial tissue microarrays have also been used to predict responsiveness to anti-TNF therapy in a limited number of patients (150). Overall, patients with high levels of tissue inflammation were more likely to benefit from anti-TNF treatment.

The transcriptome analysis of RA PBMCs revealed a signature significantly correlated with the percentage of circulating monocytes, in line with the known monocytosis and monocyte activation often seen in RA patients (34). Other studies support the results described in synovial tissue and reveal the presence of a type I IFN signature in a subgroup of patients (32). More studies are necessary to determine whether this information might help researchers understand the heterogeneity of this disease and better classify and/or predict treatment success in subsets of RA patients.

Systemic sclerosis (SSc). SSc is a clinically heterogeneous disease characterized by vascular dysfunction, tissue fibrosis, and internal organ damage. Initial symptoms are difficult to recognize, and patients are often diagnosed late in the disease process, when irreversible damage has already occurred. Antinuclear antibodies are present in most patients. In a significant number of them, however, these antibodies do not display specificities that help with the diagnosis. There are no effective therapies for this disease (151).

Skin biopsies from patients with early diffuse SSc show nearly identical patterns of gene expression at clinically affected and unaffected sites. Upregulation of genes from endothelial cells, B lymphocytes, fibroblasts, cytotoxic T cells, macrophages, and DCs have been described. Identified gene pathways include those of TGF-β, as well as a "cell proliferation signature" (152). Patient PBMCs showed increased expression of a cluster of IFN-regulated genes (43, 153), including Siglec-1 (CD169, sialoadhesin), which was confirmed by finding increased Siglec-1 surface expression on $CD14^+$ monocytes (44). Risk alleles in the *IRF5* and *STAT4* genes have been reported in SSc patients (154). These observations indicate a potential role for type I IFN and call for testing IFN antagonists in this disease.

Other Autoimmune Diseases

Multiple sclerosis. MS is a chronic autoimmune disease characterized by demyelination of the central nervous system (CNS) white matter (155). Microarray studies in MS have focused on identifying gene expression differences in CNS lesions of patients to assess pathogenesis, and in blood to assess response to treatment. Differentially expressed genes in MS lesions belong to immunological and inflammatory pathways, stress-response, and antioxidant processes, as well as metabolic and CNS markers (156, 157). Of particular interest are a number of genes localized to susceptible loci previously linked with MS (158). Transcriptome analyses of purified blood T cells from MS patients showed altered expression of genes involved in apoptosis (159). Overall, due to the heterogeneity of the samples and the small scale of these expression studies, it is still difficult to define which of the identified gene pathways are directly associated to the pathogenesis of this disease.

As IFN-β represents an effective therapy in MS, attempts have been made to identify predictors of response to therapy using blood transcriptome analyses. As expected, IFN-regulated transcripts could be identified in treated patients (160–162). Larger studies are necessary to establish definitive gene expression profiles predicting disease onset, flare, or response to therapy.

Diabetes. Following the identification of a major signature in SLE, we wondered whether an organ-specific autoimmune disease such as diabetes would be associated with alterations in the blood transcriptome. We even hypothesized that these patients might display a type I IFN signature because of previous reports of elevated IFN-α in pancreatic tissue from patients (163). Thus, expression profiles of PBMCs from children with newly diagnosed Type 1 diabetes (T1D) were compared to those from healthy controls, and one- and four-month follow-up samples were obtained from a subgroup of patients. PBMCs from children with new-onset Type 2 diabetes (T2D) were also analyzed (36). These studies identified changes in expression of IL-1β, early growth response gene 3, and prostaglandin-endoperoxide synthase 2, which resolved within four months of insulin therapy in both T1D and T2D. IL-1β was highly overexpressed in both diseases, suggesting that they likely share a final common pathway for β-cell dysfunction that includes secretion of IL-1β, which exacerbates existing β-cell dysfunction and causes further hyperglycemia.

The presence of proinflammatory factors in serum of T1D patients has also been investigated using the genomic strategy of "reverse proteomics" described above for SoJIA patients (20). Thus, sera from recent-onset diabetes patients, long-standing diabetes patients, at-risk siblings of diabetes patients, and healthy controls were tested for the induction of gene expression patterns in unrelated, healthy PBMCs (20). All recent-onset sera induced an expression signature that included IL-1 cytokine family members and chemokines involved in monocyte/macrophage and neutrophil chemotaxis. This molecular signature was not induced with the sera of healthy controls or long-standing diabetes patients. Furthermore, longitudinal analyses of at-risk siblings before and after onset support the hypothesis that the signature emerges years before onset.

Overall, these results identify IL-1β as a target of disease-modifying therapy for diabetes. Indeed, clinical trials using IL-1 antagonists have already proven some efficacy in adults with T2D (164, 165) and are under way for patients with T1D. Additionally, these studies support the theory that proinflammatory serum markers may be used as inclusion criteria or endpoint measures in clinical trials aimed at preventing T1D.

BLOOD MICROARRAYS AND BIOMARKER DISCOVERY

In addition to the identification of disease signatures that may yield critical insight regarding underlying immune dysfunctions and identify potential therapeutic targets in autoimmune diseases, blood transcriptional studies have been used to identify biomarkers for diagnosis, monitoring of disease activity, and prediction of clinical outcomes. We have applied this approach to SoJIA and SLE because there are no available diagnostic tests or disease activity measures (SoJIA) or because current measures are too burdensome to apply in the clinical setting (SLE). In order to select specific biomarkers, we had to devise in both cases novel genomic analysis strategies.

Analysis of Significance Patterns

The diagnosis of SoJIA takes weeks to months, as it is based on clinical criteria that lack specificity (166). Indeed, initial symptoms mimic infections or malignancies, and it is only when arthritis appears that the disease can be recognized. We surmised that the blood transcriptome of SoJIA-afflicted children could be a source of diagnostic biomarkers. The profiles that differentiate SoJIA patients from healthy controls, however, were highly similar to those of children with febrile infectious diseases of both bacterial and viral origin (25). Because SoJIA can present at any age during childhood, matching the control groups for this disease and for infections that predominate at earlier or later times during childhood was a challenge, however. Thus, we devised a custom meta-analysis strategy for biomarker selection relying on the analysis of patterns of significance (see sidebar, Analysis of Significance Patterns) (167). This approach can be used to compare diseases across multiple data sets, each being analyzed in relation to its own set of healthy controls. First, statistical comparisons were performed between each group of patients (SoJIA, *S. aureus*, *S. pneumoniae*, *E. coli*, influenza A, and SLE) and their respective control groups composed of age- and gender-matched healthy donors. The *P* values obtained from each comparison were then subjected to selection criteria. This permitted us to identify genes significantly changed in SoJIA patients versus their control group, and not in any of the other diseases versus their own control groups. The SoJIA-specific signature that we obtained using this algorithm was composed of 88 transcripts (**Figure 7**). Treatment with IL-1 antagonists was able to extinguish this signature in the majority of patients. Using a more stringent analysis, 12 out of 88 transcripts seemed to be enough to correctly classify an independent

ANALYSIS OF SIGNIFICANCE PATTERNS

The strategy is based on the comparison of *P* values obtained by generating gene expression data from well-defined groups of patients and their corresponding healthy controls, which are well matched for age, sex, ethnicity, etc. Genes significantly changed ($P < 0.01$) in the study group are divided into two sets: overexpressed versus control and underexpressed versus control. *P* values of the genes forming the overexpressed set are obtained for the reference groups. *P* values of the reference groups are set to 1 when genes are underexpressed. The same procedure is used in the set of genes that are underexpressed in the study group, only this time *P* values of the reference group are set to 1 when genes are overexpressed. *P* value data are then processed to perform hierarchical clustering, and groups of genes are based on significance patterns (25, 167).

group of patients during the systemic phase of the disease against healthy and febrile disease controls. However, these 12 genes were not dysregulated in SoJIA patients who had resolved the systemic phase and were left with chronic arthritis, suggesting that they are specifically dysregulated in the initial phase of the disease, probably the time of greatest sensitivity to IL-1

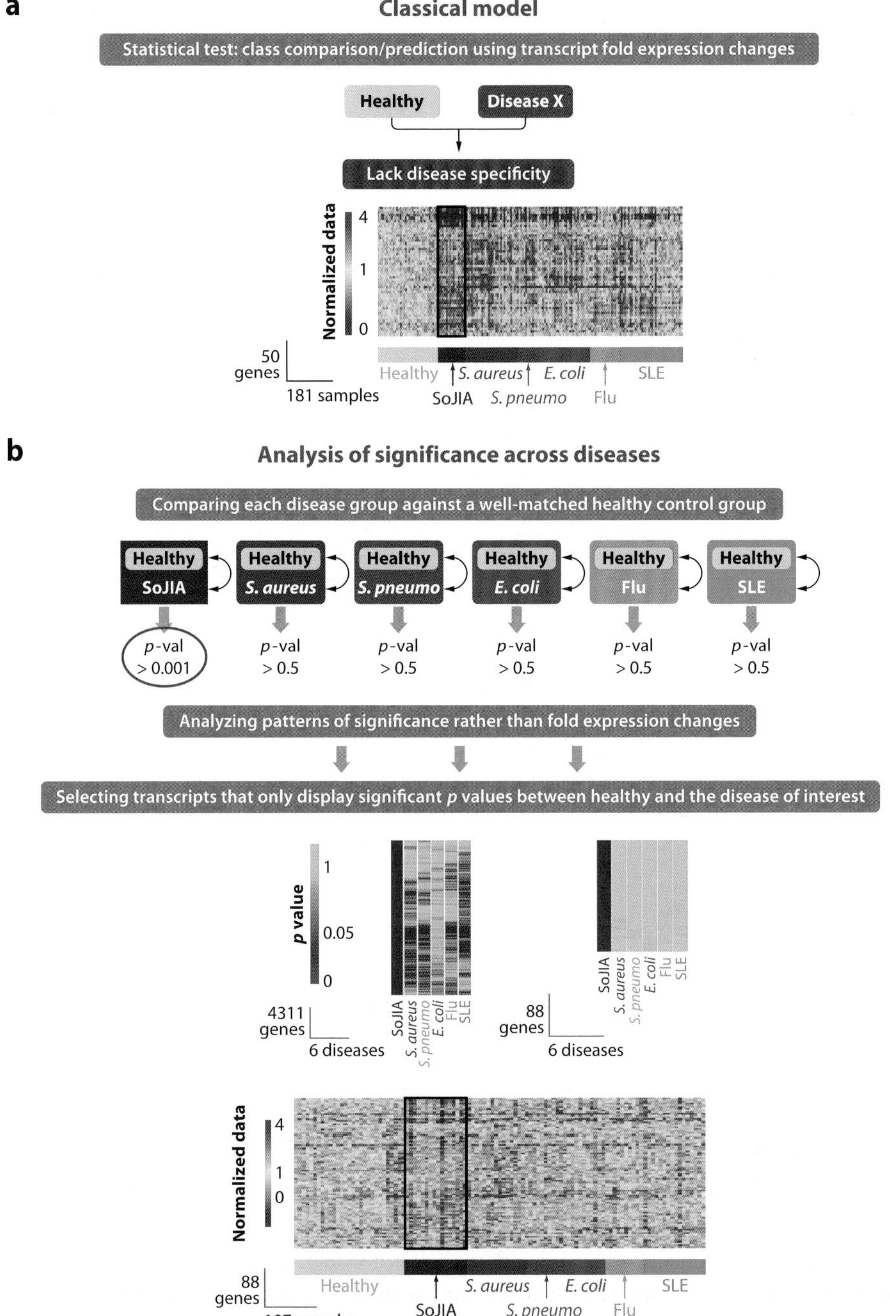

blockade. The specificity of 7 out of 12 genes has been recently validated in an independent study of PBMC transcriptional profiles, including different types of JIA patients (28). The same type of analysis has allowed the identification of blood disease–specific transcriptional markers differentiating SLE patients from patients with diseases that also display a type I IFN signature such as influenza infection (167).

Modular Analysis Framework for Blood Genomic Studies

The exploitation of large-scale data can be hindered by our limited ability to separate signal from noise and to grasp the overall biological significance of the results. Numerous approaches have been developed (168–171), including our modular analysis framework (172) that reduces the dimension of blood transcriptional data in order (*a*) to facilitate functional interpretation, (*b*) to enable comparative analyses across multiple data sets and diseases, (*c*) to minimize noise and improve robustness of biomarker signatures, and (*d*) to derive multivariate metrics that can be used at the bedside. The steps involved in the development of this framework are depicted in the sidebar, Module-Based Analysis of Gene Expression.

Once the framework has been established, transcriptional changes can then be mapped for individual diseases on a modular basis (**Figure 8**). Briefly, differences in expression levels between study groups are displayed on a grid. Each position on the grid is assigned to a given module; a red spot indicates an increase, whereas a blue spot indicates a decrease, in transcript abundance. The spot intensity is determined by the proportion of transcripts reaching significance for a given module. A posteriori, biological interpretation has linked several modules to immune cells or pathways as indicated by a color code on the figure legend (**Figure 8**).

We have explored the use of transcriptional modules as a basis for biomarker discovery in

MODULE-BASED ANALYSIS OF GENE EXPRESSION

Transcriptionally coregulated transcripts emerging from the blood profiles of patients with eight different diseases were identified using a clustering algorithm. Once patterns were identified for each disease, the cluster membership of individual transcripts was compared across all other diseases. A module is formed of transcripts found always to belong to the same clusters across all diseases (eight out of eight in our example). The stringency of this requirement was progressively relaxed during the subsequent rounds of selection so that modules are formed when transcripts fall in the same clusters in any combination of seven (round 2) or six (round 3) diseases. This stepwise reduction of the stringency of filtering criteria accounts for the fact that transcripts may not be "turned on" in all diseases. Indeed, modules linked to IFN or inflammation (M3.1 and M3.2) were, for instance, not formed until round 3 of selection. As should be expected of transcriptional modules, literature profiling of genes forming each module revealed significant functional convergence, with half of the modules associated with clearly identifiable functional themes (**Figure 8**). By including profiles from a wide range of diseases, we identified a "universal" set of modules that could be used as a stable framework for subsequent analysis of any PBMC data set (172).

Figure 7

Analysis of significance across diseases identifies 88 systemic-onset juvenile idiopathic arthritis (SoJIA)-specific transcripts. (*a*) Eight healthy and eight SoJIA samples were used as a training set to generate a list of 50 classifier genes displaying the best ability to discriminate SoJIA patients from healthy controls. Those classifier genes were hierarchically clustered in a test set composed of 35 healthy controls, 16 SoJIA, 31 *Staphylococcus aureus*, 12 *Streptococcus pneumoniae*, 31 *Escherichia coli*, 18 influenza A, and 38 SLE patients. (*b*) Genes expressed at statistically different levels in SoJIA patients compared to healthy volunteers ($P < 0.01$, Wilcoxon-Mann-Whitney test) were selected (4311 probe sets). Out of those, 88 were expressed at statistically different levels in SoJIA patients compared to healthy volunteers ($P < 0.01$, Wilcoxon-Mann-Whitney test) but not in all the other groups ($P > 0.5$, Wilcoxon-Mann-Whitney test). The 88 genes are hierarchically clustered in the 107 samples from different disease groups used in (*a*). Expression values of the genes are normalized per gene to the healthy group. Adapted from *Curr. Opin. Immunol.* 2007. 19:623–32.

SLE (172), a disease that presents with a wide range of clinical and laboratory abnormalities (see sidebar, above, Human Systemic Lupus Erythematosus). Objectively assessing disease activity across patients or longitudinally in individual patients can therefore be challenging. At least six composite measures of SLE global disease activity have been developed and used to assess disease progression during clinical trials (173). These measures, however, rely on many clinical and laboratory findings and are cumbersome to obtain. Additionally,

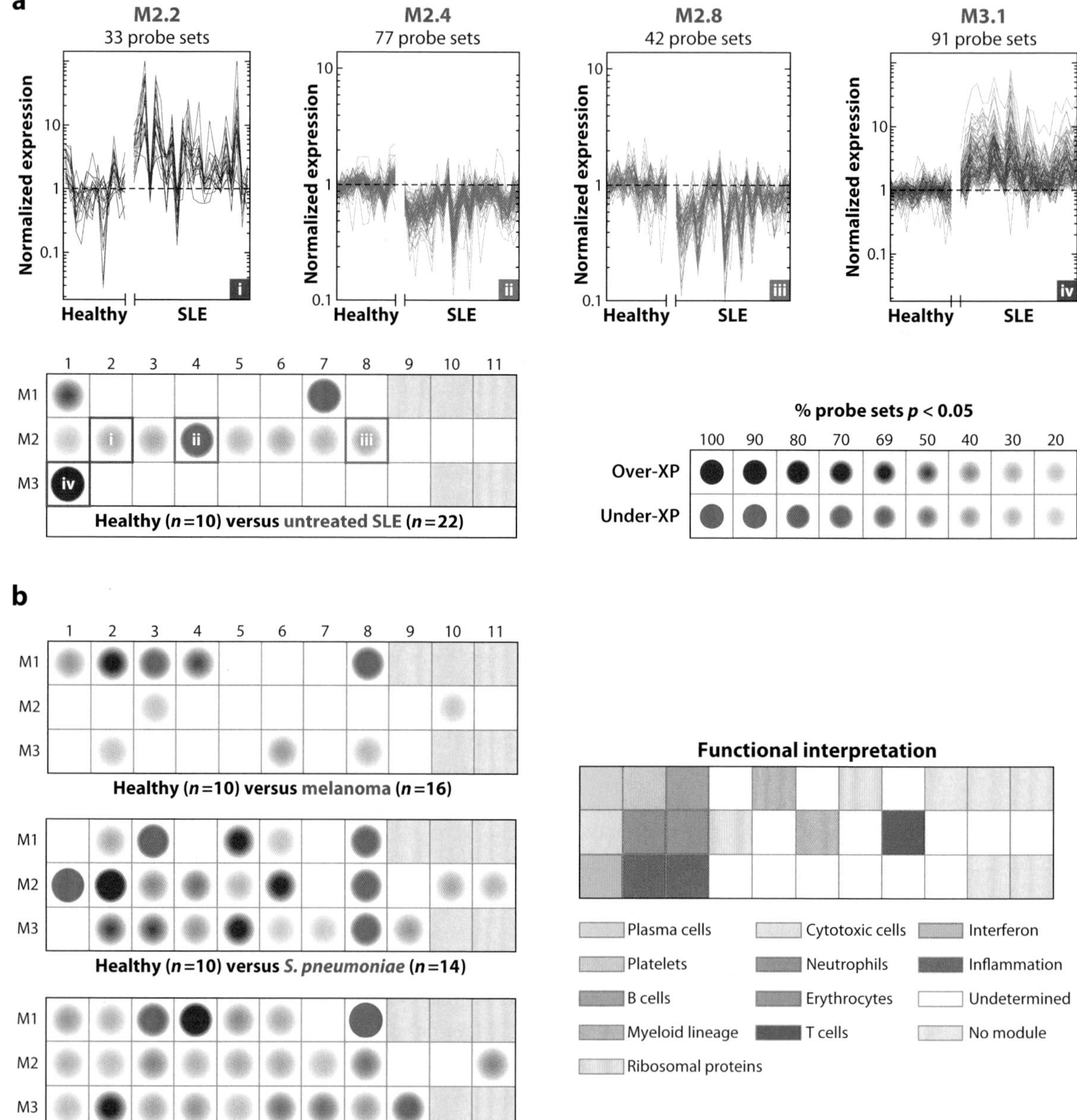

given the heterogeneous nature of the clinical disease, not all SLE manifestations are computed within these measures, making the overall assessment of the patient sometimes difficult. The SLEDAI (174), one of the simplest measures, considers 24 different attributes that need to be obtained at every clinic visit. Thus, establishment of a simple and objective disease activity index would be beneficial.

We attempted to assess whether such an activity index could be generated from blood leukocyte microarray transcriptional data applying the modular interpretation described above. The idea was that this approach would permit us to focus on biologically relevant transcripts, while reducing the dimension of microarray data from over 44,000 variables to about 5,000 distributed in 28 modules. Comparisons carried out on a module-by-module basis identified 11 submodules with a minimum of 15% of transcripts over- or underexpressed compared to healthy children. We next transformed the expression values of the transcripts within these modules into 11 composite values (or expression vectors) and summarized the results as one single multivariate score. These multivariate transcriptional scores were correlated to clinical disease activity indices in both cross-sectional and longitudinal sets of samples. Indeed, upon longitudinal follow-up of patients, severity of disease was in some cases more accurately assessed, and even predicted, by the transcriptional score than by the SLEDAI. A striking example is represented in **Figure 9**, which displays the discordance between a very low SLEDAI, suggestive of low disease activity, and a high transcriptional score in a seven-year-old patient with SLE (SLE 78). This patient was subsequently diagnosed with severe pulmonary hypertension, an uncommon but serious complication of SLE that is not recorded within the classic SLEDAI. Although this approach needs to be validated in large multicentric studies, it might prove useful for the discovery of diagnostic/prognostic markers and the monitoring of disease progression and response to treatment in other diseases.

CHALLENGES IN TRANSCRIPTOME-BASED BIOMARKER DISCOVERY

To date, few diseases besides cancer have received the level of attention required to provide robust assays that could be used in clinical practice. Most published data on autoimmune diseases, including our own data, result from proof-of-principle studies that need to be validated. Interindividual variability, whether driven by genetic or environmental factors, and inherent disease heterogeneity require these studies to be performed on large data sets and in multiple centers. Indeed, progress in this complex field is more likely to be achieved through concerted, focused consortium-type efforts.

Disease heterogeneity is an important initial limiting step in autoimmune disease biomarker discovery. Thus, patient clinical characteristics and disease stages should be taken into account and carefully recorded at the time of sample selection for the study. The importance of implementation of common methods and standards

Figure 8

Modular fingerprints of human immune-mediated diseases. (*a*) Expression levels of four groups of transcriptionally coregulated genes in peripheral blood mononuclear cells (PBMCs) of healthy children and children with systemic lupus erythematosus (SLE) are shown. Transcripts within modules 2.2 (neutrophil-related transcripts) and 3.1 (type I IFN–inducible transcripts) are upregulated, whereas 2.4 (ribosomal protein-encoding transcripts) and 2.8 (T cell–related transcripts) are downregulated in the majority of SLE patients. These differentially expressed modules and seven additional ones are represented on a grid as red (overexpressed) or blue (underexpressed) circles. The intensity of the color reflects the percentage of transcripts within each module that are significantly differentially expressed. Statistical comparisons between patient and healthy control groups were performed independently on a module-by-module basis (Mann-Whitney rank test, $P < 0.05$). (*b*) Modular analysis of PBMC differential gene expression in patients with melanoma, liver transplant under immunosuppression, and *S. pneumoniae* infection. The color code of modules containing transcripts with annotated function is depicted in the lower-right quadrant. Adapted from *Immunity*. 2008. 29:150–64.

for the collection of this type of information, samples, and measurements cannot be stressed enough (175, 176).

Drug treatments and comorbidities may impact blood transcriptional signatures, and those variables cannot always be isolated, as patients cannot be taken off treatments. These factors also pose significant challenges in terms of study design and downstream data analysis. We have found that including samples from recently diagnosed and untreated patients is useful when selecting biomarkers related to disease pathogenesis. Selective inclusion criteria can be subsequently relaxed to broaden the scope and potential clinical impact of a study. Working with pediatric populations is attractive because it is easier to accrue patients in the initial phases of disease and because significantly fewer comorbidities and modalities of treatments are encountered.

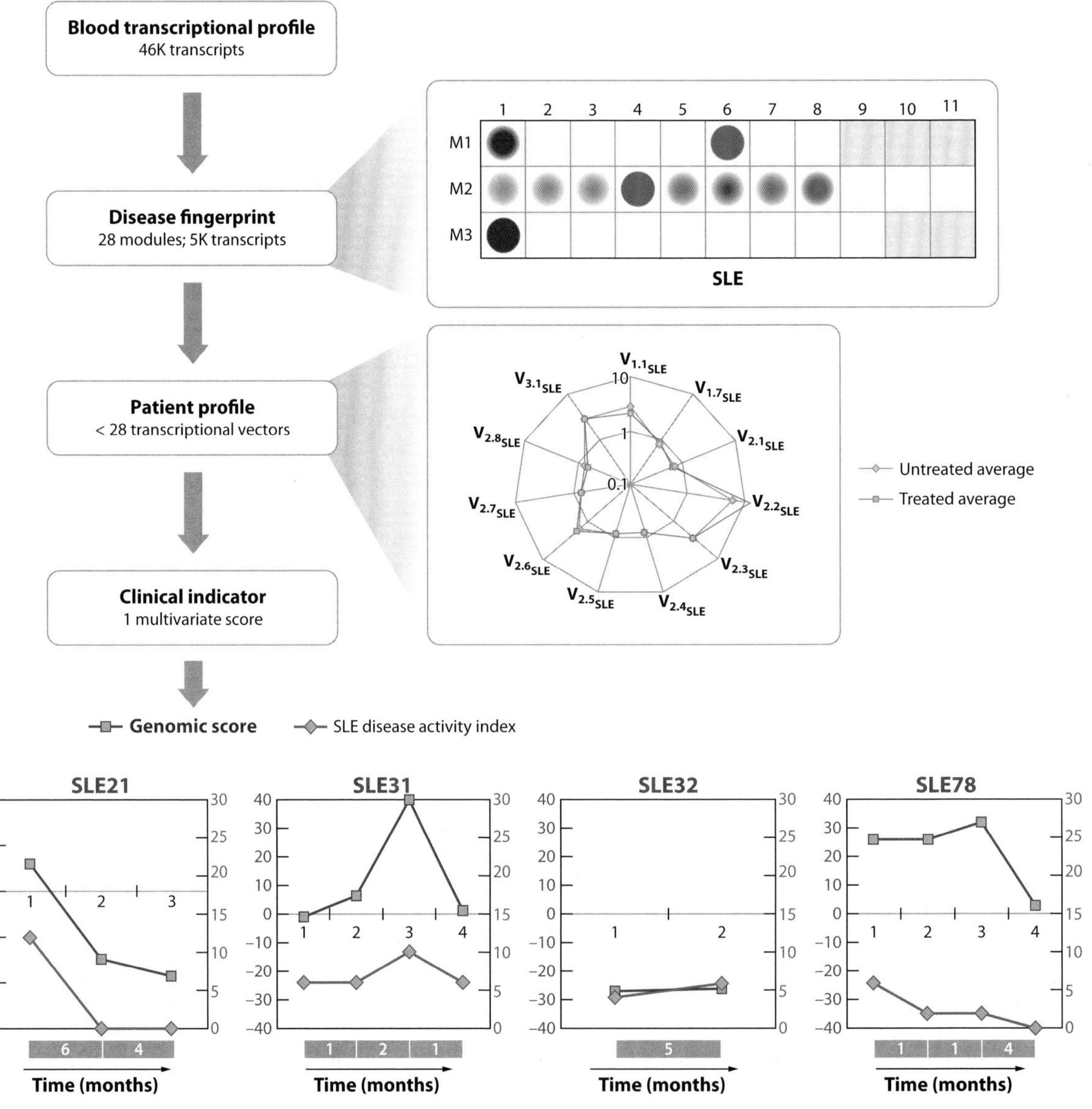

Sample Collection and Logistics

High-quality RNA can be easily isolated from PBMCs. However, cell isolation procedures represent a well-documented source of variability (176, 177). As a result, most transcriptional studies are now carried out using whole blood. Indeed, it has become possible to preserve intact RNA from small volumes of blood collected in tubes under vacuum that can be stored frozen for extended periods without the need for further processing (178, 179). A drawback of using whole blood as a source of RNA is its high content in globin transcripts. Although globin reduction techniques increase sensitivity and data reproducibility (178–180), there is some controversy regarding whether globin removal may interfere with biomarker discovery (179, 181).

Sensitivity

The sensitivity of microarray-based technologies is relatively low when compared to real-time PCR (polymerase chain reaction). Furthermore, the measurement of transcript abundance using microarrays is relative rather than absolute. As a result, data may not be directly compared due to systematic variations introduced, for instance, between manufacturing, sample, or array processing batches. This fact has implications for data reproducibility as well.

Reproducibility

Standardization efforts improve comparability, but the reproducibility of microarray data remains a legitimate concern (182–184). Indeed, no standards have been adopted by the community, and, given the need to keep up with the rapid technology developments that characterize this field, they would be difficult to implement. It is likely, for instance, that microarray technologies will be superseded in the near future by more robust digital expression technologies (discussed below), therefore obviating efforts to standardize microarray-based transcriptome analyses.

Interpretation

The factors affecting data reproducibility across microarray platforms and laboratories can also impact the quality or interpretability of a data set. It is important to avoid confounding the analysis with technical variables. For example, reuse of preexisting data for direct group comparison should be avoided. Samples should be run if possible in one single batch. If this is not possible, case and control samples should be randomized across the different runs. Overall, the availability of cost-effective commercial platforms has reduced the number of formats used for analysis and enhances data quality and

Figure 9

Development of transcriptome-based systemic lupus erythematosus (SLE) disease activity biomarkers. Starting from a full set of 28 modules, 11 modules are selected, for which a minimum proportion of transcripts (>15%) are significantly changed ($P < 0.05$) between the study groups (SLE and healthy). Next, composite values for each sample are generated by calculating the arithmetic average of normalized expression values across significantly overexpressed or underexpressed genes selected from each module. Each resulting "transcriptional vector" recapitulates the expression of a given module (or select set of genes within a module) in a given patient. A spider graph connecting all the vector values in untreated (average in *orange*) and treated (average in *green*) patients is shown. The values are normalized per gene using the median expression value of healthy and are represented on a logarithmic scale. A nonparametric method for analyzing multivariate ordinal data was then used to score the patients based on 5 out of 11 vectors that best correlated individually with SLE disease activity according to the SLE disease activity index (SLEDAI). The correlation achieved by this score was superior to that of its individual components. Upon longitudinal follow-up of patients, parallel trends were observed between transcriptional scores and SLEDAI longitudinal measures in a majority of patients. Disease flaring and subsequent recovery were detected in one patient (SLE31) upon longitudinal follow-up using both SLEDAI and transcriptional score. Interestingly, however, the amplitude of change observed in the case of the transcriptional U-score appears not only to be much greater (0 to 40 versus 6 to 10 for SLEDAI), but an increase could already be detected at the second time point, two months before the worsening of the clinical condition of this patient was detected by SLEDAI. One of the patients (SLE78) showing discrepancy between the SLEDAI (low) and transcriptional score (high) was diagnosed during the follow-up period with a life-threatening complication (pulmonary hypertension) that is not computed within the SLEDAI. Thus, severity of disease was more accurately assessed by the transcriptional score.

reproducibility when compared to early cDNA arrays. Meta-analysis of data obtained using different platforms and from different laboratories is possible, but one must proceed with caution. A common strategy is the use of a control group that is common to all data sets under study (e.g., nonstimulated or healthy controls) (167, 185, 186).

Finally, when interpreting results from blood transcriptome analyses, it is important to consider that changes in transcript abundance might reflect two phenomena: (*a*) transcriptional regulation and (*b*) relative changes in cell composition (**Figure 1**). The latter can also provide reliable and valid clinical correlate/biomarker signatures, as shown in patients with SLE who display PCP and/or immature neutrophil signatures (21). The analysis of purified cell subpopulations might represent a useful way to identify low-frequency biomarkers. Subpopulation frequencies (i.e., shifts in naive, memory, and/or effector populations of T and/or B cells) may still be responsible, however, for transcriptional differences between patients and controls. Cell purification techniques might also be a source of biased results. Positive selection might, for example, alter the steady state transcriptome by delivering signals through surface receptors, whereas enrichment purification methods are more prone to contamination with other cell types.

Data Analysis Primer

Although data acquisition brings its own set of challenges, data analysis might represent the main bottleneck for blood transcriptional studies. It is beyond the scope of this review to examine in detail microarray data analysis methods, but generalizations are provided here for the main analysis steps.

Per-chip normalization. This step allows control of array-wide variations in intensity across multiple samples that form a given data set. After background subtraction, a normalization algorithm is used to rescale the difference in overall intensity to a fixed intensity level for all samples across multiple arrays.

Data filtering. Typically more than half of the probes present on a microarray do not detect a signal for any of the samples in a given analysis. Thus, a detection filter is applied to remove such probes. This step avoids the introduction of unnecessary noise in downstream analyses.

Unsupervised analysis. The aim of this step is to group samples on the basis of their molecular profiles without a priori knowledge of their phenotypic classification. The first step consists of selecting transcripts that are expressed in the data set (detection filter) and that display some degree of variability (which facilitates sample clustering). For instance, this filter could select transcripts with expression levels that deviate by at least twofold from the median intensity calculated across all samples. It is important, though, to apply this filter independently of any knowledge of sample grouping or phenotype (which makes this type of analysis "unsupervised"). Next, a pattern discovery algorithm is applied to identify molecular phenotypes or trends in the data.

Clustering. Clustering is commonly used for the discovery of expression patterns in large data sets. Hierarchical clustering is an iterative agglomerative clustering method that can be used to produce gene trees and condition trees. Condition tree clustering groups samples on the basis of the similarity of their expression profiles across a specified gene list. Other commonly employed clustering algorithms include k-means clustering and self-organizing maps.

Class comparison. Class comparison analyses identify genes differentially expressed among groups and/or time points. The methods for analysis are chosen based on the study design. For studies with independent observations and two or more groups, t-tests, ANOVA, Mann-Whitney U tests, or Kruskal-Wallis tests are used. For more complex studies (e.g., longitudinal), appropriate linear mixed model analyses are chosen.

Multiple testing correction (MTC). MTC methods provide a means to mitigate the level of noise in sets of transcripts identified by class comparison (in order to lower permissiveness to false positives). Although it reduces noise, MTC promotes a higher false negative rate as a result of dampening the signal. The methods available are characterized by varying degrees of stringency, and therefore they produce gene lists with different levels of robustness.

Benjamini and Hochberg false discovery rate. This is the least stringent MTC applied and provides a good balance between discovery of statistically significant genes while limiting false positives. By using this procedure with an alpha of 0.01, 1% of the statistically significant transcripts might be identified as significant by chance alone (false positives).

Bonferroni correction. This is the most stringent method used and can drastically reduce false positive rates. Conversely, it increases the probability of having false negatives.

Class prediction. Class prediction analyses assess the classification capability of gene expression data for a study subject or sample. K-nearest neighbors is a commonly used technique for this task. Using Euclidian distance, this method identifies the user defined "K" number of closest observations for an unclassified sample. Class prediction is then determined by the lowest *P* value, which is calculated for each group. The *P* values are based on the likelihood of obtaining the observed number of neighbors for a specific class given the overall class proportion in the data set. Other available class prediction procedures include, but are not limited to, Discriminant Analysis, General Linear Model Selection, Logistic Regression, Distance Scoring, Partial Least Squares, Partition Trees, and Radial Basis Machine (187, 188).

Sample size. The number of samples necessary for the identification of a robust signature is variable. Indeed, sample size requirements depend on the amplitude of the difference between and the variability within study groups.

Several approaches have been devised for the calculation of sample size for microarray experiments, but to date little consensus exists. Hence, best practices in the field consist of using independent sets of samples to validate candidate signatures. Thus, the robustness of the signature identified relies on a statistically significant association between the predicted and true phenotypic class in the first and the second test sets.

New analytical techniques, including network and global analytical tools, are being devised to facilitate the interpretation of genomics data in the real context of interactive networks where all molecular players influence each other (189). Many computational tools are also being created to help interpret this type of complex data (190). A detailed account of this topic is beyond the scope of this review.

THE FUTURE OF BLOOD GENOMICS

Microarray technologies are limited by several factors, such as hybridization noise (background signal, nonspecific binding) and lack of sensitivity for transcripts expressed at very low or very high levels (dynamic range). Additional limitations derive from the fact that they rely on existing sequence knowledge based on the human genome and lack the capacity to quantify alternative messages, such as splice variants of a given gene. When considering human studies with potential clinical applications, perhaps the main limitation, however, is that direct comparability of data across batches and platforms is sometimes impossible.

Real-time PCR technology is currently considered the gold standard for measurement of gene expression in clinical settings. However, it can be used to measure transcript abundance for only a small number of genes. Thus, there is the interest in other technologies such as the one developed by Nanostring, which detects transcript abundance for up to 500 transcripts with high sensitivity (191). The approach is digital because it counts individual RNA molecules, and therefore there is no need for normalization to a healthy control population. But a distinct advantage of this technology, which like microarrays is hybridization-based, is that sample preparation needs are reduced to a minimum—for instance none of the steps involve enzymatic reactions. Also, given its high sensitivity, fast turnaround time, sample throughput, and intermediate multiplexing ability, this approach seems particularly promising for bedside applications.

The important limitations of current microarray-based technologies might also be lifted by methods relying on high-throughput sequencing for genome-wide measurement of RNA abundance (192). RNA-Seq (RNA sequencing) (193) starts with a population of RNA [total or fractionated, such as poly(A)+] that is converted to a library of cDNA fragments with adaptors attached to one or both ends. Each molecule, with or without amplification, is then sequenced in a high-throughput manner to obtain short sequences from one end (single-end sequencing) or both ends (pair-end sequencing). The reads are typically 30–400 bp, depending on the DNA-sequencing technology used. Thus, this approach does not rely on probe design and instead uses tag-based sequencing. The obtained sequences are then uniquely mapped against a reference genome, which basically eliminates background signals. A detailed genome-wide transcription map for a given sample can thus be obtained by sequencing several tens of millions of tags. From this map it is possible to obtain several types of information, including not only transcript abundance but also transcriptome structure (splice variants), noncoding RNA species such as miRNA, and genetic polymorphisms. Because it uses a high-throughput sequencer, RNA-Seq is also cost effective and is expected to supersede microarray technologies. Another advantage of RNA-Seq compared to DNA microarrays is that RNA-Seq does not have an upper limit for quantification, and therefore it can measure a large dynamic range of expression levels. The data generated should also be reproducible across different platforms. The use of RNA-Seq has not reached the mainstream, with most publications in the field reporting results for a small number of samples that are limited, for the most part, to model organisms. Indeed, challenges ahead are multiple, including sample preparation (laborious, and potentially a source of bias), storage of massive amounts of data, and sequence alignment. The powerful advantage of measuring transcriptome dynamics across different tissues or conditions without sophisticated normalization of data sets confers

Table 1 Characteristics of different methods available for gene expression analysis

	Microarrays	RNA-Seq	PCR	Nanostring
Principle	Hybridization	Sequencing	Hybridization	Hybridization
Necessitates probe design	Yes	No	Yes	Yes
Sensitivity	Low	High	High	High
Amplification	Yes	Yes	Yes	No
Scale	Genome-wide	Genome-wide	Low	Genome-wide
Detects genetic polymorphisms	No	Yes	No	No
Output	Spot intensity	Sequence tag counts	Cycles of amplification	Molecule counts

this technology with a tremendous advantage for understanding transcriptomic dynamics in health and disease (8) (**Table 1**).

Transcriptome analyses have recently been combined with GWA studies to identify networks of genes involved in disease pathogenesis. The abundance of a gene transcript can in fact be directly modified by polymorphisms in regulatory elements. Consequently, expression levels of most genes have statistically significant heritability, and transcript abundance might therefore be considered a quantitative trait. These have been named expression QTLs (eQTLs) (18). By combining genome-wide assays of gene expression and genetic variation, the genetic factors responsible for individual differences in quantitative levels of expression can be mapped. This information could provide significant insight into the biological basis for disease associations identified through GWA studies.

In addition to DNA sequence variants, gene transcription is also modulated by epigenetic modifications (194). Post-translational modifications of histones, for example, modulate DNA accessibility and chromatin stability to provide an enormous variety of alternative interaction surfaces for *trans*-acting factors (18). Epigenetic studies will undoubtedly complement transcriptome studies by providing additional clues to understand gene expression alterations in disease.

We therefore expect that rapid technology developments currently occurring in the genomic field, including genetic, epigenetic, and proteomic studies, will directly impact transcriptome research. Keeping up with these advances will be a challenge for the teams currently engaged in this line of work. In particular, it increases the demands on already strained bioinformatics resources. At the same time, these recent developments hold tremendous promise for understanding and better treating autoimmunity and beyond.

CONCLUSION

Basic immunologists have made great progress in the past 80 years in understanding the cellular and molecular components of the immune system. During the past decade, we have started to see translation of this knowledge to humans, but, as Mark Davis has written, "You can go to the most prestigious medical center in the world and ask, 'How is my immune system?' and, after a short period of eye rolling and looks of amused incomprehension, you might, if they don't throw you out, be offered a white blood cell count" (1). We contend that the quantitative analysis of the blood transcriptome, together with other approaches such as polychromatic flow cytometry and advanced proteomics, will provide physicians with a comprehensive picture of their patient's immune system. The successful identification of pathogenic pathways and therapeutic targets in some human autoimmune diseases through the use of this technology supports that it could be applied to other types of diseases. Furthermore, blood transcriptome studies will facilitate the development of diagnostic biomarkers and personalized treatment options, thus leading to more efficient and cost effective therapies. Eventually, this added knowledge will transform the practice of Medicine into a true Health Care System focusing on monitoring health and preventing disease, rather than the "Sick Care System" that we have today.

SUMMARY POINTS

1. Analysis of the blood transcriptome can be performed using cost effective, commercially available DNA microarrays.
2. Blood transcriptome analyses in autoimmune diseases reveal
   - signatures reflecting activation of molecular pathways that can be targeted in patients;

- signatures that can help genetic studies pinpoint autoimmune disease–specific susceptibility loci;
- signatures shared among different autoimmune diseases;
- disease-specific signatures that might be used to develop diagnostic biomarkers; and
- signatures to assess disease activity and treatment efficacy.

FUTURE ISSUES

1. Novel bioinformatics tools and data analyses remain limiting steps.
2. DNA microarrays allow a genome-wide assessment of gene expression, but they have limited sensitivity, are relatively slow, and are not fully quantitative.
3. Improved data mining tools and expanded data sets will facilitate the identification of both novel therapeutic targets and predictors of autoimmune diseases outcomes.
4. Biomarkers identified through blood transcriptome studies need to be fully validated in large multicentric trials.
5. The mechanisms leading to the expression of disease-specific genomic signatures need to be understood. Information generated through transcriptome analyses must be integrated with genome-wide genetic association and epigenetic studies. Such assimilation will allow the determination of whether or not variation in gene expression underlies susceptibility to complex autoimmune diseases.
6. Autoimmune disease–specific signatures will be used as diagnostic tests using rapid and quantitative methods such as real-time PCR or Nanostring.
7. Blood genomic analyses will become routine assays to assess health status and, as such, represent an essential component of personalized medicine.

DISCLOSURE STATEMENT

J.B. is the coinventor of several patent applications in the field of autoimmunity and owns stock in Illumina. The authors are not aware of any affiliations, memberships, funding, or financial holdings that might be perceived as affecting the objectivity of this review.

ACKNOWLEDGMENTS

This study was partially supported by U19-A1057234, RO1-CA078846, AR054083-01, (J.B.) and Baylor Health Care Foundation (J.B). J.B. holds the W.W. Caruth, Jr. Chair for Transplantation Immunology Research. This study was also supported by R01 AR050770-01, ARO54083-01CORT, NIH ARO55503-01CORT, U19-AI082715-01, Alliance for Lupus Research, and the Mary Kirkland Foundation to V.P.; and U01AI082110 and the DANA Foundation to D.C.

The authors want to thank Florence Allantaz, Lynda Bennett, Quynh-Ahn Nguyen, Charlie Quinn, Pinakeen Patel, and Dorothee Stichweh for their contributions through the past 10 years to autoimmune disease microarray studies; Jeanine Baisch, Romain Banchereau, Patrice Mannoni, Karolina Palucka, and Octavio Ramilo for critical reading of the manuscript; and Barbara and Jerry Nepom for their insightful comments.

LITERATURE CITED

1. Davis MM. 2008. A prescription for human immunology. *Immunity* 29:835–38
2. Liu K, Mohan C. 2006. What do mouse models teach us about human SLE? *Clin. Immunol.* 119:123–30
3. Horai R, Saijo S, Tanioka H, Nakae S, Sudo K, et al. 2000. Development of chronic inflammatory arthropathy resembling rheumatoid arthritis in interleukin 1 receptor antagonist-deficient mice. *J. Exp. Med.* 191:313–20
4. Mertens M, Singh JA. 2009. Anakinra for rheumatoid arthritis: a systematic review. *J. Rheumatol.* 36:1118–25
5. Feldmann M, Maini RN. 2001. Anti-TNFα therapy of rheumatoid arthritis: What have we learned? *Annu. Rev. Immunol.* 19:163–96
6. Schena M, Shalon D, Davis RW, Brown PO. 1995. Quantitative monitoring of gene expression patterns with a complementary DNA microarray. *Science* 270:467–70
7. Shalon D, Smith SJ, Brown PO. 1996. A DNA microarray system for analyzing complex DNA samples using two-color fluorescent probe hybridization. *Genome Res.* 6:639–45
8. Wang Z, Gerstein M, Snyder M. 2009. RNA-Seq: a revolutionary tool for transcriptomics. *Nat. Rev. Genet.* 10:57–63
9. Golub TR, Slonim DK, Tamayo P, Huard C, Gaasenbeek M, et al. 1999. Molecular classification of cancer: class discovery and class prediction by gene expression monitoring. *Science* 286:531–37
10. Alizadeh AA, Eisen MB, Davis RE, Ma C, Lossos IS, et al. 2000. Distinct types of diffuse large B-cell lymphoma identified by gene expression profiling. *Nature* 403:503–11
11. Winnepenninckx V, Lazar V, Michiels S, Dessen P, Stas M, et al. 2006. Gene expression profiling of primary cutaneous melanoma and clinical outcome. *J. Natl. Cancer Inst.* 98:472–82
12. Sotiriou C, Pusztai L. 2009. Gene-expression signatures in breast cancer. *N. Engl. J. Med.* 360:790–800
13. Pascual V, Allantaz F, Patel P, Palucka AK, Chaussabel D, Banchereau J. 2008. How the study of children with rheumatic diseases identified interferon-α and interleukin-1 as novel therapeutic targets. *Immunol. Rev.* 223:39–59
14. Bauer JW, Bilgic H, Baechler EC. 2009. Gene-expression profiling in rheumatic disease: tools and therapeutic potential. *Nat. Rev. Rheumatol.* 5:257–65
15. Calvano SE, Xiao W, Richards DR, Felciano RM, Baker HV, et al. 2005. A network-based analysis of systemic inflammation in humans. *Nature* 437:1032–37
16. Zaas AK, Chen M, Varkey J, Veldman T, Hero AO, et al. 2009. Gene expression signatures diagnose influenza and other symptomatic respiratory viral infections in humans. *Cell Host Microbe* 6:207–17
17. Boldrick JC, Alizadeh AA, Diehn M, Dudoit S, Liu CL, et al. 2002. Stereotyped and specific gene expression programs in human innate immune responses to bacteria. *Proc. Natl. Acad. Sci. USA* 99:972–77
18. Cookson W, Liang L, Abecasis G, Moffatt M, Lathrop M. 2009. Mapping complex disease traits with global gene expression. *Nat. Rev. Genet.* 10:184–94
19. Pascual V, Allantaz F, Arce E, Punaro M, Banchereau J. 2005. Role of interleukin-1 (IL-1) in the pathogenesis of systemic onset juvenile idiopathic arthritis and clinical response to IL-1 blockade. *J. Exp. Med.* 201:1479–86
20. Wang X, Jia S, Geoffrey R, Alemzadeh R, Ghosh S, Hessner MJ. 2008. Identification of a molecular signature in human type 1 diabetes mellitus using serum and functional genomics. *J. Immunol.* 180:1929–37
21. Bennett L, Palucka AK, Arce E, Cantrell V, Borvak J, et al. 2003. Interferon and granulopoiesis signatures in systemic lupus erythematosus blood. *J. Exp. Med.* 197:711–23
22. Baechler EC, Batliwalla FM, Karypis G, Gaffney PM, Ortmann WA, et al. 2003. Interferon-inducible gene expression signature in peripheral blood cells of patients with severe lupus. *Proc. Natl. Acad. Sci. USA* 100:2610–15
23. Crow MK, Wohlgemuth J. 2003. Microarray analysis of gene expression in lupus. *Arthritis Res. Ther.* 5:279–87
24. Han GM, Chen SL, Shen N, Ye S, Bao CD, Gu YY. 2003. Analysis of gene expression profiles in human systemic lupus erythematosus using oligonucleotide microarray. *Genes Immun.* 4:177–86

25. Allantaz F, Chaussabel D, Stichweh D, Bennett L, Allman W, et al. 2007. Blood leukocyte microarrays to diagnose systemic onset juvenile idiopathic arthritis and follow the response to IL-1 blockade. *J. Exp. Med.* 204:2131–44
26. Ogilvie EM, Khan A, Hubank M, Kellam P, Woo P. 2007. Specific gene expression profiles in systemic juvenile idiopathic arthritis. *Arthritis Rheum.* 56:1954–65
27. Fall N, Barnes M, Thornton S, Luyrink L, Olson J, et al. 2007. Gene expression profiling of peripheral blood from patients with untreated new-onset systemic juvenile idiopathic arthritis reveals molecular heterogeneity that may predict macrophage activation syndrome. *Arthritis Rheum.* 56:3793–804
28. Barnes MG, Grom AA, Thompson SD, Griffin TA, Pavlidis P, et al. 2009. Subtype-specific peripheral blood gene expression profiles in recent-onset juvenile idiopathic arthritis. *Arthritis Rheum.* 60:2102–12
29. Achiron A, Feldman A, Mandel M, Gurevich M. 2007. Impaired expression of peripheral blood apoptotic-related gene transcripts in acute multiple sclerosis relapse. *Ann. N. Y. Acad. Sci.* 1107:155–67
30. Singh MK, Scott TF, LaFramboise WA, Hu FZ, Post JC, Ehrlich GD. 2007. Gene expression changes in peripheral blood mononuclear cells from multiple sclerosis patients undergoing beta-interferon therapy. *J. Neurol. Sci.* 258:52–59
31. Edwards CJ, Feldman JL, Beech J, Shields KM, Stover JA, et al. 2007. Molecular profile of peripheral blood mononuclear cells from patients with rheumatoid arthritis. *Mol. Med.* 13:40–58
32. Van Der Pouw Kraan TC, Wijbrandts CA, van Baarsen LG, Voskuyl AE, Rustenburg F, et al. 2007. Rheumatoid arthritis subtypes identified by genomic profiling of peripheral blood cells: assignment of a type I interferon signature in a subpopulation of patients. *Ann. Rheum. Dis.* 66:1008–14
33. Lequerre T, Gauthier-Jauneau AC, Bansard C, Derambure C, Hiron M, et al. 2006. Gene profiling in white blood cells predicts infliximab responsiveness in rheumatoid arthritis. *Arthritis Res. Ther.* 8:R105
34. Batliwalla FM, Baechler EC, Xiao X, Li W, Balasubramanian S, et al. 2005. Peripheral blood gene expression profiling in rheumatoid arthritis. *Genes Immun.* 6:388–97
35. Emamian ES, Leon JM, Lessard CJ, Grandits M, Baechler EC, et al. 2009. Peripheral blood gene expression profiling in Sjogren's syndrome. *Genes Immun.* 10:285–96
36. Kaizer EC, Glaser CL, Chaussabel D, Banchereau J, Pascual V, White PC. 2007. Gene expression in peripheral blood mononuclear cells from children with diabetes. *J. Clin. Endocrinol. Metab.* 92:3705–11
37. Takamura T, Honda M, Sakai Y, Ando H, Shimizu A, et al. 2007. Gene expression profiles in peripheral blood mononuclear cells reflect the pathophysiology of type 2 diabetes. *Biochem. Biophys. Res. Commun.* 361:379–84
38. Burczynski ME, Peterson RL, Twine NC, Zuberek KA, Brodeur BJ, et al. 2006. Molecular classification of Crohn's disease and ulcerative colitis patients using transcriptional profiles in peripheral blood mononuclear cells. *J. Mol. Diagn.* 8:51–61
39. Stoeckman AK, Baechler EC, Ortmann WA, Behrens TW, Michet CJ, Peterson EJ. 2006. A distinct inflammatory gene expression profile in patients with psoriatic arthritis. *Genes Immun.* 7:583–91
40. Batliwalla FM, Li W, Ritchlin CT, Xiao X, Brenner M, et al. 2005. Microarray analyses of peripheral blood cells identifies unique gene expression signature in psoriatic arthritis. *Mol. Med.* 11:21–29
41. Greenberg SA, Pinkus JL, Pinkus GS, Burleson T, Sanoudou D, et al. 2005. Interferon-alpha/beta-mediated innate immune mechanisms in dermatomyositis. *Ann. Neurol.* 57:664–78
42. Baechler EC, Bauer JW, Slattery CA, Ortmann WA, Espe KJ, et al. 2007. An interferon signature in the peripheral blood of dermatomyositis patients is associated with disease activity. *Mol. Med.* 13:59–68
43. Tan FK, Zhou X, Mayes MD, Gourh P, Guo X, et al. 2006. Signatures of differentially regulated interferon gene expression and vasculotrophism in the peripheral blood cells of systemic sclerosis patients. *Rheumatology (Oxford)* 45:694–702
44. York MR, Nagai T, Mangini AJ, Lemaire R, van Seventer JM, Lafyatis R. 2007. A macrophage marker, Siglec-1, is increased on circulating monocytes in patients with systemic sclerosis and induced by type I interferons and Toll-like receptor agonists. *Arthritis Rheum.* 56:1010–20
45. Alcorta DA, Barnes DA, Dooley MA, Sullivan P, Jonas B, et al. 2007. Leukocyte gene expression signatures in antineutrophil cytoplasmic autoantibody and lupus glomerulonephritis. *Kidney Int.* 72:853–64
46. Potti A, Bild A, Dressman HK, Lewis DA, Nevins JR, Ortel TL. 2006. Gene-expression patterns predict phenotypes of immune-mediated thrombosis. *Blood* 107:1391–96

47. Lempicki RA, Polis MA, Yang J, McLaughlin M, Koratich C, et al. 2006. Gene expression profiles in hepatitis C virus (HCV) and HIV coinfection: class prediction analyses before treatment predict the outcome of anti-HCV therapy among HIV-coinfected persons. *J. Infect. Dis.* 193:1172–77
48. Thach DC, Agan BK, Olsen C, Diao J, Lin B, et al. 2005. Surveillance of transcriptomes in basic military trainees with normal, febrile respiratory illness, and convalescent phenotypes. *Genes Immun.* 6:588–95
49. Popper SJ, Watson VE, Shimizu C, Kanegaye JT, Burns JC, Relman DA. 2009. Gene transcript abundance profiles distinguish Kawasaki disease from adenovirus infection. *J. Infect. Dis.* 200:657–66
50. Ramilo O, Allman W, Chung W, Mejias A, Ardura M, et al. 2007. Gene expression patterns in blood leukocytes discriminate patients with acute infections. *Blood* 109:2066–77
51. Simmons CP, Popper S, Dolocek C, Chau TN, Griffiths M, et al. 2007. Patterns of host genome-wide gene transcript abundance in the peripheral blood of patients with acute dengue hemorrhagic fever. *J. Infect. Dis.* 195:1097–107
52. Ardura MI, Banchereau R, Mejias A, Di Pucchio T, Glaser C, et al. 2009. Enhanced monocyte response and decreased central memory T cells in children with invasive *Staphylococcus aureus* infections. *PLoS One* 4:e5446
53. Jacobsen M, Repsilber D, Gutschmidt A, Neher A, Feldmann K, et al. 2007. Candidate biomarkers for discrimination between infection and disease caused by *Mycobacterium tuberculosis*. *J. Mol. Med.* 85:613–21
54. Ockenhouse CF, Hu WC, Kester KE, Cummings JF, Stewart A, et al. 2006. Common and divergent immune response signaling pathways discovered in peripheral blood mononuclear cell gene expression patterns in presymptomatic and clinically apparent malaria. *Infect. Immun.* 74:5561–73
55. Tang BM, McLean AS, Dawes IW, Huang SJ, Lin RC. 2007. The use of gene-expression profiling to identify candidate genes in human sepsis. *Am. J. Respir. Crit. Care Med.* 176:676–84
56. Zhang HQ, Lu H, Enosawa S, Takahara S, Sakamoto S, Suzuki S. 2002. Identification of novel genes associated with immunosuppression in renal transplant patients. *Transplant. Proc.* 34:2733–35
57. Martinez-Llordella M, Puig-Pey I, Orlando G, Ramoni M, Tisone G, et al. 2007. Multiparameter immune profiling of operational tolerance in liver transplantation. *Am. J. Transplant.* 7:309–19
58. Deng MC, Eisen HJ, Mehra MR, Billingham M, Marboe CC, et al. 2006. Noninvasive discrimination of rejection in cardiac allograft recipients using gene expression profiling. *Am. J. Transplant.* 6:150–60
59. Baron C, Somogyi R, Greller LD, Rineau V, Wilkinson P, et al. 2007. Prediction of graft-versus-host disease in humans by donor gene-expression profiling. *PLoS Med.* 4:e23
60. Tang Y, Xu H, Du X, Lit L, Walker W, et al. 2006. Gene expression in blood changes rapidly in neutrophils and monocytes after ischemic stroke in humans: a microarray study. *J. Cereb. Blood Flow Metab.* 26:1089–102
61. Solmi R, Ugolini G, Rosati G, Zanotti S, Lauriola M, et al. 2006. Microarray-based identification and RT-PCR test screening for epithelial-specific mRNAs in peripheral blood of patients with colon cancer. *BMC Cancer* 6:250
62. Osman I, Bajorin DF, Sun TT, Zhong H, Douglas D, et al. 2006. Novel blood biomarkers of human urinary bladder cancer. *Clin. Cancer Res.* 12:3374–80
63. Llorente L, Zou W, Levy Y, Richaud-Patin Y, Wijdenes J, et al. 1995. Role of interleukin 10 in the B lymphocyte hyperactivity and autoantibody production of human systemic lupus erythematosus. *J. Exp. Med.* 181:839–44
64. Llorente L, Richaud-Patin Y, Garcia-Padilla C, Claret E, Jakez-Ocampo J, et al. 2000. Clinical and biologic effects of anti-interleukin-10 monoclonal antibody administration in systemic lupus erythematosus. *Arthritis Rheum.* 43:1790–800
65. Yokoyama H, Takabatake T, Takaeda M, Wada T, Naito T, et al. 1992. Up-regulated MHC-class II expression and γ-IFN and soluble IL-2R in lupus nephritis. *Kidney Int.* 42:755–63
66. Haas C, Ryffel B, Le Hir M. 1997. IFN-γ is essential for the development of autoimmune glomerulonephritis in MRL/Ipr mice. *J. Immunol.* 158:5484–91
67. Horwitz DA, Gray JD, Behrendsen SC, Kubin M, Rengaraju M, et al. 1998. Decreased production of interleukin-12 and other Th1-type cytokines in patients with recent-onset systemic lupus erythematosus. *Arthritis Rheum.* 41:838–44

68. Steinberg AD, Baron S, Talal N. 1969. The pathogenesis of autoimmunity in New Zealand mice, I. Induction of antinucleic acid antibodies by polyinosinic-polycytidylic acid. *Proc. Natl. Acad. Sci. USA* 63:1102–7
69. Hooks JJ, Moutsopoulos HM, Geis SA, Stahl NI, Decker JL, Notkins AL. 1979. Immune interferon in the circulation of patients with autoimmune disease. *N. Engl. J. Med.* 301:5–8
70. Stewart TA. 2003. Neutralizing interferon alpha as a therapeutic approach to autoimmune diseases. *Cytokine Growth Factor Rev.* 14:139–54
71. Cederblad B, Blomberg S, Vallin H, Perers A, Alm GV, Ronnblom L. 1998. Patients with systemic lupus erythematosus have reduced numbers of circulating natural interferon-α-producing cells. *J. Autoimmun.* 11:465–70
72. Blomberg S, Eloranta ML, Cederblad B, Nordlin K, Alm GV, Ronnblom L. 2001. Presence of cutaneous interferon-a producing cells in patients with systemic lupus erythematosus. *Lupus* 10:484–90
73. Farkas L, Beiske K, Lund-Johansen F, Brandtzaeg P, Jahnsen FL. 2001. Plasmacytoid dendritic cells (natural interferon-α/β-producing cells) accumulate in cutaneous lupus erythematosus lesions. *Am. J. Pathol.* 159:237–43
74. Vallin H, Blomberg S, Alm GV, Cederblad B, Ronnblom L. 1999. Patients with systemic lupus erythematosus (SLE) have a circulating inducer of interferon-alpha (IFN-α) production acting on leucocytes resembling immature dendritic cells. *Clin. Exp. Immunol.* 115:196–202
75. Bave U, Vallin H, Alm GV, Ronnblom L. 2001. Activation of natural interferon-α producing cells by apoptotic U937 cells combined with lupus IgG and its regulation by cytokines. *J. Autoimmun.* 17:71–80
76. Blanco P, Palucka AK, Gill M, Pascual V, Banchereau J. 2001. Induction of dendritic cell differentiation by IFN-α in systemic lupus erythematosus. *Science* 294:1540–43
77. Jego G, Palucka AK, Blanck JP, Chalouni C, Pascual V, Banchereau J. 2003. Plasmacytoid dendritic cells induce plasma cell differentiation through type I interferon and interleukin 6. *Immunity* 19:225–34
78. Marrack P, Kappler J, Mitchell T. 1999. Type I interferons keep activated T cells alive. *J. Exp. Med.* 189:521–30
79. Kolumam GA, Thomas S, Thompson LJ, Sprent J, Murali-Krishna K. 2005. Type I interferons act directly on CD8 T cells to allow clonal expansion and memory formation in response to viral infection. *J. Exp. Med.* 202:637–50
80. Le Bon A, Schiavoni G, D'Agostino G, Gresser I, Belardelli F, Tough DF. 2001. Type I interferons potently enhance humoral immunity and can promote isotype switching by stimulating dendritic cells in vivo. *Immunity* 14:461–70
81. Preble OT, Black RJ, Friedman RM, Klippel JH, Vilcek J. 1982. Systemic lupus erythematosus: presence in human serum of an unusual acid-labile leukocyte interferon. *Science* 216:429–31
82. Tsao BP. 2004. Update on human systemic lupus erythematosus genetics. *Curr. Opin. Rheumatol.* 16:513–21
83. Darnell JE Jr, Kerr IM, Stark GR. 1994. Jak-STAT pathways and transcriptional activation in response to IFNs and other extracellular signaling proteins. *Science* 264:1415–21
84. Martinelli S, Urosevic M, Daryadel A, Oberholzer PA, Baumann C, et al. 2004. Induction of genes mediating interferon-dependent extracellular trap formation during neutrophil differentiation. *J. Biol. Chem.* 279:44123–32
85. de Weerd NA, Samarajiwa SA, Hertzog PJ. 2007. Type I interferon receptors: biochemistry and biological functions. *J. Biol. Chem.* 282:20053–57
86. de Veer MJ, Holko M, Frevel M, Walker E, Der S, et al. 2001. Functional classification of interferon-stimulated genes identified using microarrays. *J. Leukoc. Biol.* 69:912–20
87. Ding C. 2008. Belimumab, an anti-BLyS human monoclonal antibody for potential treatment of inflammatory autoimmune diseases. *Expert Opin. Biol. Ther.* 8:1805–14
88. Shodell M, Shah K, Siegal FP. 2003. Circulating human plasmacytoid dendritic cells are highly sensitive to corticosteroid administration. *Lupus* 12:222–30
89. Peterson KS, Huang JF, Zhu J, D'Agati V, Liu X, et al. 2004. Characterization of heterogeneity in the molecular pathogenesis of lupus nephritis from transcriptional profiles of laser-captured glomeruli. *J. Clin. Invest.* 113:1722–33

90. Nzeusseu Toukap A, Galant C, Theate I, Maudoux AL, Lories RJ, et al. 2007. Identification of distinct gene expression profiles in the synovium of patients with systemic lupus erythematosus. *Arthritis Rheum.* 56:1579–88
91. Tucci M, Quatraro C, Lombardi L, Pellegrino C, Dammacco F, Silvestris F. 2008. Glomerular accumulation of plasmacytoid dendritic cells in active lupus nephritis: role of interleukin-18. *Arthritis Rheum.* 58:251–62
92. Gill MA, Blanco P, Arce E, Pascual V, Banchereau J, Palucka AK. 2002. Blood dendritic cells and DC-poietins in systemic lupus erythematosus. *Hum. Immunol.* 63:1172–80
93. Santiago-Raber ML, Baccala R, Haraldsson KM, Choubey D, Stewart TA, et al. 2003. Type-I interferon receptor deficiency reduces lupus-like disease in NZB mice. *J. Exp. Med.* 197:777–88
94. Braun D, Geraldes P, Demengeot J. 2003. Type I interferon controls the onset and severity of autoimmune manifestations in lpr mice. *J. Autoimmun.* 20:15–25
95. Mathian A, Weinberg A, Gallegos M, Banchereau J, Koutouzov S. 2005. IFN-α induces early lethal lupus in preautoimmune (New Zealand black × New Zealand white)F_1 but not in BALB/c Mice. *J. Immunol.* 174:2499–506
96. Zagury D, Le Buanec H, Mathian A, Larcier P, Burnett R, et al. 2009. IFNα kinoid vaccine-induced neutralizing antibodies prevent clinical manifestations in a lupus flare murine model. *Proc. Natl. Acad. Sci. USA* 106:5294–99
97. Izui S, Ibnou-Zekri N, Fossati-Jimack L, Iwamoto M. 2000. Lessons from BXSB and related mouse models. *Int. Rev. Immunol.* 19:447–72
98. Pisitkun P, Deane JA, Difilippantonio MJ, Tarasenko T, Satterthwaite AB, Bolland S. 2006. Autoreactive B cell responses to RNA-related antigens due to TLR7 gene duplication. *Science* 312:1669–72
99. Subramanian S, Tus K, Li QZ, Wang A, Tian XH, et al. 2006. A Tlr7 translocation accelerates systemic autoimmunity in murine lupus. *Proc. Natl. Acad. Sci. USA* 103:9970–75
100. Bave U, Alm GV, Ronnblom L. 2000. The combination of apoptotic U937 cells and lupus IgG is a potent IFN-α inducer. *J. Immunol.* 165:3519–26
101. Vollmer J, Tluk S, Schmitz C, Hamm S, Jurk M, et al. 2005. Immune stimulation mediated by autoantigen binding sites within small nuclear RNAs involves Toll-like receptors 7 and 8. *J. Exp. Med.* 202:1575–85
102. Barrat FJ, Meeker T, Gregorio J, Chan JH, Uematsu S, et al. 2005. Nucleic acids of mammalian origin can act as endogenous ligands for Toll-like receptors and may promote systemic lupus erythematosus. *J. Exp. Med.* 202:1131–39
103. Lau CM, Broughton C, Tabor AS, Akira S, Flavell RA, et al. 2005. RNA-associated autoantigens activate B cells by combined B cell antigen receptor/Toll-like receptor 7 engagement. *J. Exp. Med.* 202:1171–77
104. Deane JA, Pisitkun P, Barrett RS, Feigenbaum L, Town T, et al. 2007. Control of Toll-like receptor 7 expression is essential to restrict autoimmunity and dendritic cell proliferation. *Immunity* 27:801–10
105. Kono DH, Haraldsson MK, Lawson BR, Pollard KM, Koh YT, et al. 2009. Endosomal TLR signaling is required for antinucleic acid and rheumatoid factor autoantibodies in lupus. *Proc. Natl. Acad. Sci. USA* 106:12061–66
106. Armstrong DL, Reiff A, Myones BL, Quismorio FP Jr, Klein-Gitelman M, et al. 2009. Identification of new SLE-associated genes with a two-step Bayesian study design. *Genes Immun.* 10:446–56
107. Sigurdsson S, Nordmark G, Goring HH, Lindroos K, Wiman AC, et al. 2005. Polymorphisms in the tyrosine kinase 2 and interferon regulatory factor 5 genes are associated with systemic lupus erythematosus. *Am. J. Hum. Genet.* 76:528–37
108. Graham RR, Kozyrev SV, Baechler EC, Reddy MV, Plenge RM, et al. 2006. A common haplotype of interferon regulatory factor 5 (IRF5) regulates splicing and expression and is associated with increased risk of systemic lupus erythematosus. *Nat. Genet.* 38:550–55
109. Harley JB, Alarcon-Riquelme ME, Criswell LA, Jacob CO, Kimberly RP, et al. 2008. Genome-wide association scan in women with systemic lupus erythematosus identifies susceptibility variants in ITGAM, PXK, KIAA1542 and other loci. *Nat. Genet.* 40:204–10
110. Niewold TB, Kelly JA, Flesch MH, Espinoza LR, Harley JB, Crow MK. 2008. Association of the IRF5 risk haplotype with high serum interferon-α activity in systemic lupus erythematosus patients. *Arthritis Rheum.* 58:2481–87

111. Niewold TB, Hua J, Lehman TJ, Harley JB, Crow MK. 2007. High serum IFN-α activity is a heritable risk factor for systemic lupus erythematosus. *Genes Immun.* 8:492–502
112. Remmers EF, Plenge RM, Lee AT, Graham RR, Hom G, et al. 2007. STAT4 and the risk of rheumatoid arthritis and systemic lupus erythematosus. *N. Engl. J. Med.* 357:977–86
113. Jacob CO, Reiff A, Armstrong DL, Myones BL, Silverman E, et al. 2007. Identification of novel susceptibility genes in childhood-onset systemic lupus erythematosus using a uniquely designed candidate gene pathway platform. *Arthritis Rheum.* 56:4164–73
114. Jacob CO, Zhu J, Armstrong DL, Yan M, Han J, et al. 2009. Identification of IRAK1 as a risk gene with critical role in the pathogenesis of systemic lupus erythematosus. *Proc. Natl. Acad. Sci. USA* 106:6256–61
115. Rice G, Newman WG, Dean J, Patrick T, Parmar R, et al. 2007. Heterozygous mutations in TREX1 cause familial chilblain lupus and dominant Aicardi-Goutieres syndrome. *Am. J. Hum. Genet.* 80:811–15
116. Lee-Kirsch MA, Gong M, Chowdhury D, Senenko L, Engel K, et al. 2007. Mutations in the gene encoding the 3′–5′ DNA exonuclease TREX1 are associated with systemic lupus erythematosus. *Nat. Genet.* 39:1065–67
117. Stetson DB, Ko JS, Heidmann T, Medzhitov R. 2008. Trex1 prevents cell-intrinsic initiation of autoimmunity. *Cell* 134:587–98
118. Lehtinen DA, Harvey S, Mulcahy MJ, Hollis T, Perrino FW. 2008. The TREX1 double-stranded DNA degradation activity is defective in dominant mutations associated with autoimmune disease. *J. Biol. Chem.* 283:31649–56
119. Tal MC, Sasai M, Lee HK, Yordy B, Shadel GS, Iwasaki A. 2009. Absence of autophagy results in reactive oxygen species-dependent amplification of RLR signaling. *Proc. Natl. Acad. Sci. USA* 106:2770–75
120. Moser KL, Kelly JA, Lessard CJ, Harley JB. 2009. Recent insights into the genetic basis of systemic lupus erythematosus. *Genes. Immun.* 10:373–79
121. Palucka AK, Blanck JP, Bennett L, Pascual V, Banchereau J. 2005. Cross-regulation of TNF and IFN-α in autoimmune diseases. *Proc. Natl. Acad. Sci. USA* 102:3372–77
122. Arce E, Jackson DG, Gill MA, Bennett LB, Banchereau J, Pascual V. 2001. Increased frequency of pregerminal center B cells and plasma cell precursors in the blood of children with systemic lupus erythematosus. *J. Immunol.* 167:2361–69
123. Odendahl M, Jacobi A, Hansen A, Feist E, Hiepe F, et al. 2000. Disturbed peripheral B lymphocyte homeostasis in systemic lupus erythematosus. *J. Immunol.* 165:5970–79
124. Wrammert J, Smith K, Miller J, Langley WA, Kokko K, et al. 2008. Rapid cloning of high-affinity human monoclonal antibodies against influenza virus. *Nature* 453:667–71
125. Yao Y, Richman L, Higgs BW, Morehouse CA, de los Reyes M, et al. 2009. Neutralization of interferon-α/β-inducible genes and downstream effect in a phase I trial of an anti-interferon-α monoclonal antibody in systemic lupus erythematosus. *Arthritis Rheum.* 60:1785–96
126. Prieur AM, Roux-Lombard P, Dayer JM. 1996. Dynamics of fever and the cytokine network in systemic juvenile arthritis. *Rev. Rhum.* (Engl. Ed.) 63:163–70
127. Muller K, Herner EB, Stagg A, Bendtzen K, Woo P. 1998. Inflammatory cytokines and cytokine antagonists in whole blood cultures of patients with systemic juvenile chronic arthritis. *Br. J. Rheumatol.* 37:562–69
128. Fitzgerald AA, Leclercq SA, Yan A, Homik JE, Dinarello CA. 2005. Rapid responses to anakinra in patients with refractory adult-onset Still's disease. *Arthritis Rheum.* 52:1794–803
129. Dinarello CA. 1996. Biologic basis for interleukin-1 in disease. *Blood* 87:2095–147
130. Wittkowski H, Frosch M, Wulffraat N, Goldbach-Mansky R, Kallinich T, et al. 2008. S100A12 is a novel molecular marker differentiating systemic-onset juvenile idiopathic arthritis from other causes of fever of unknown origin. *Arthritis Rheum.* 58:3924–31
131. Frosch M, Ahlmann M, Vogl T, Wittkowski H, Wulffraat N, et al. 2009. The myeloid-related proteins 8 and 14 complex, a novel ligand of Toll-like receptor 4, and interleukin-1β form a positive feedback mechanism in systemic-onset juvenile idiopathic arthritis. *Arthritis Rheum.* 60:883–91
132. Korman BD, Alba MI, Le JM, Alevizos I, Smith JA, et al. 2008. Variant form of STAT4 is associated with primary Sjogren's syndrome. *Genes Immun.* 9:267–70
133. Nordmark G, Kristjansdottir G, Theander E, Eriksson P, Brun JG, et al. 2009. Additive effects of the major risk alleles of IRF5 and STAT4 in primary Sjogren's syndrome. *Genes Immun.* 10:68–76

134. Hjelmervik TO, Petersen K, Jonassen I, Jonsson R, Bolstad AI. 2005. Gene expression profiling of minor salivary glands clearly distinguishes primary Sjogren's syndrome patients from healthy control subjects. *Arthritis Rheum.* 52:1534–44
135. Hu S, Wang J, Meijer J, Ieong S, Xie Y, et al. 2007. Salivary proteomic and genomic biomarkers for primary Sjogren's syndrome. *Arthritis Rheum.* 56:3588–600
136. Greenberg SA. 2007. A gene expression approach to study perturbed pathways in myositis. *Curr. Opin. Rheumatol.* 19:536–41
137. Arahata K, Engel AG. 1984. Monoclonal antibody analysis of mononuclear cells in myopathies. I: Quantitation of subsets according to diagnosis and sites of accumulation and demonstration and counts of muscle fibers invaded by T cells. *Ann. Neurol.* 16:193–208
138. Wenzel J, Schmidt R, Proelss J, Zahn S, Bieber T, Tuting T. 2006. Type I interferon-associated skin recruitment of CXCR3+ lymphocytes in dermatomyositis. *Clin. Exp. Dermatol.* 31:576–82
139. Feldman BM, Rider LG, Reed AM, Pachman LM. 2008. Juvenile dermatomyositis and other idiopathic inflammatory myopathies of childhood. *Lancet* 371:2201–12
140. Tezak Z, Hoffman EP, Lutz JL, Fedczyna TO, Stephan D, et al. 2002. Gene expression profiling in DQA1*0501+ children with untreated dermatomyositis: a novel model of pathogenesis. *J. Immunol.* 168:4154–63
141. Walsh RJ, Kong SW, Yao Y, Jallal B, Kiener PA, et al. 2007. Type I interferon-inducible gene expression in blood is present and reflects disease activity in dermatomyositis and polymyositis. *Arthritis Rheum.* 56:3784–92
142. Lowes MA, Bowcock AM, Krueger JG. 2007. Pathogenesis and therapy of psoriasis. *Nature* 445:866–73
143. Oestreicher JL, Walters IB, Kikuchi T, Gilleaudeau P, Surette J, et al. 2001. Molecular classification of psoriasis disease-associated genes through pharmacogenomic expression profiling. *Pharmacogenomics J.* 1:272–87
144. Nomura I, Gao B, Boguniewicz M, Darst MA, Travers JB, Leung DY. 2003. Distinct patterns of gene expression in the skin lesions of atopic dermatitis and psoriasis: a gene microarray analysis. *J. Allergy Clin. Immunol.* 112:1195–202
145. Bowcock AM, Shannon W, Du F, Duncan J, Cao K, et al. 2001. Insights into psoriasis and other inflammatory diseases from large-scale gene expression studies. *Hum. Mol. Genet.* 10:1793–805
146. Zhou X, Krueger JG, Kao MC, Lee E, Du F, et al. 2003. Novel mechanisms of T-cell and dendritic cell activation revealed by profiling of psoriasis on the 63100-element oligonucleotide array. *Physiol. Genomics* 13:69–78
147. Imboden JB. 2009. The immunopathogenesis of rheumatoid arthritis. *Annu. Rev. Pathol.* 4:417–34
148. Devauchelle V, Marion S, Cagnard N, Mistou S, Falgarone G, et al. 2004. DNA microarray allows molecular profiling of rheumatoid arthritis and identification of pathophysiological targets. *Genes Immun.* 5:597–608
149. Van Der Pouw Kraan TC, van Gaalen FA, Kasperkovitz PV, Verbeet NL, Smeets TJ, et al. 2003. Rheumatoid arthritis is a heterogeneous disease: evidence for differences in the activation of the STAT-1 pathway between rheumatoid tissues. *Arthritis Rheum.* 48:2132–45
150. Van Der Pouw Kraan TC, Wijbrandts CA, van Baarsen LG, Rustenburg F, Baggen JM, et al. 2008. Responsiveness to antitumor necrosis factor α therapy is related to pretreatment tissue inflammation levels in rheumatoid arthritis patients. *Ann. Rheum. Dis.* 67:563–66
151. Gabrielli A, Avvedimento EV, Krieg T. 2009. Scleroderma. *N. Engl. J. Med.* 360:1989–2003
152. Milano A, Pendergrass SA, Sargent JL, George LK, McCalmont TH, et al. 2008. Molecular subsets in the gene expression signatures of scleroderma skin. *PLoS One* 3:e2696
153. Bos CL, van Baarsen LG, Timmer TC, Overbeek MJ, Basoski NM, et al. 2009. Molecular subtypes of systemic sclerosis in association with anticentromere antibodies and digital ulcers. *Genes. Immun.* 10:210–18
154. Rueda B, Broen J, Simeon C, Hesselstrand R, Diaz B, et al. 2009. The STAT4 gene influences the genetic predisposition to systemic sclerosis phenotype. *Hum. Mol. Genet.* 18:2071–77
155. Frohman EM, Racke MK, Raine CS. 2006. Multiple sclerosis–the plaque and its pathogenesis. *N. Engl. J. Med.* 354:942–55

156. Mycko MP, Papoian R, Boschert U, Raine CS, Selmaj KW. 2003. cDNA microarray analysis in multiple sclerosis lesions: detection of genes associated with disease activity. *Brain* 126:1048–57
157. Mycko MP, Papoian R, Boschert U, Raine CS, Selmaj KW. 2004. Microarray gene expression profiling of chronic active and inactive lesions in multiple sclerosis. *Clin. Neurol. Neurosurg.* 106:223–29
158. Iglesias AH, Camelo S, Hwang D, Villanueva R, Stephanopoulos G, Dangond F. 2004. Microarray detection of E2F pathway activation and other targets in multiple sclerosis peripheral blood mononuclear cells. *J. Neuroimmunol.* 150:163–77
159. Satoh J, Nakanishi M, Koike F, Miyake S, Yamamoto T, et al. 2005. Microarray analysis identifies an aberrant expression of apoptosis and DNA damage-regulatory genes in multiple sclerosis. *Neurobiol. Dis.* 18:537–50
160. Koike F, Satoh J, Miyake S, Yamamoto T, Kawai M, et al. 2003. Microarray analysis identifies interferon beta-regulated genes in multiple sclerosis. *J. Neuroimmunol.* 139:109–18
161. Sturzebecher S, Wandinger KP, Rosenwald A, Sathyamoorthy M, Tzou A, et al. 2003. Expression profiling identifies responder and nonresponder phenotypes to interferon-beta in multiple sclerosis. *Brain* 126:1419–29
162. Pappas DJ, Coppola G, Gabatto PA, Gao F, Geschwind DH, et al. 2009. Longitudinal system-based analysis of transcriptional responses to type I interferons. *Physiol. Genomics* 38:362–71
163. Huang X, Yuang J, Goddard A, Foulis A, James RF, et al. 1995. Interferon expression in the pancreases of patients with type I diabetes. *Diabetes* 44:658–64
164. Larsen CM, Faulenbach M, Vaag A, Volund A, Ehses JA, et al. 2007. Interleukin-1-receptor antagonist in type 2 diabetes mellitus. *N. Engl. J. Med.* 356:1517–26
165. Larsen CM, Faulenbach M, Vaag A, Ehses JA, Donath MY, Mandrup-Poulsen T. 2009. Sustained effects of interleukin-1-receptor antagonist treatment in type 2 diabetes mellitus. *Diabetes Care* 32:1663–68
166. Cassidy JT, Petty RE. 2001. Juvenile rheumatoid arthritis. In *Textbook of Pediatric Rheumatology*, ed. JT Cassidy, RE Petty, pp. 218–321. Philadelphia: W.B. Saunders. 3rd ed.
167. Chaussabel D, Allman W, Mejias A, Chung W, Bennett L, et al. 2005. Analysis of significance patterns identifies ubiquitous and disease-specific gene-expression signatures in patient peripheral blood leukocytes. *Ann. N. Y. Acad. Sci.* 1062:146–54
168. Mootha VK, Bunkenborg J, Olsen JV, Hjerrild M, Wisniewski JR, et al. 2003. Integrated analysis of protein composition, tissue diversity, and gene regulation in mouse mitochondria. *Cell* 115:629–40
169. Segal E, Yelensky R, Koller D. 2003. Genome-wide discovery of transcriptional modules from DNA sequence and gene expression. *Bioinformatics* 19(Suppl. 1):i273–82
170. Allison DB, Cui X, Page GP, Sabripour M. 2006. Microarray data analysis: from disarray to consolidation and consensus. *Nat. Rev. Genet.* 7:55–65
171. Horvath S, Dong J. 2008. Geometric interpretation of gene coexpression network analysis. *PLoS Comput. Biol.* 4:e1000117
172. Chaussabel D, Quinn C, Shen J, Patel P, Glaser C, et al. 2008. A modular analysis framework for blood genomics studies: application to systemic lupus erythematosus. *Immunity* 29:150–64
173. Liang MH, Socher SA, Larson MG, Schur PH. 1989. Reliability and validity of six systems for the clinical assessment of disease activity in systemic lupus erythematosus. *Arthritis Rheum.* 32:1107–18
174. Gladman DD, Ibanez D, Urowitz MB. 2002. Systemic lupus erythematosus disease activity index 2000. *J. Rheumatol.* 29:288–91
175. Snyder M, Weissman S, Gerstein M. 2009. Personal phenotypes to go with personal genomes. *Mol. Syst. Biol.* 5:273
176. Whitney AR, Diehn M, Popper SJ, Alizadeh AA, Boldrick JC, et al. 2003. Individuality and variation in gene expression patterns in human blood. *Proc. Natl. Acad. Sci. USA* 100:1896–901
177. Debey S, Zander T, Brors B, Popov A, Eils R, Schultze JL. 2006. A highly standardized, robust, and cost-effective method for genome-wide transcriptome analysis of peripheral blood applicable to large-scale clinical trials. *Genomics* 87:653–64
178. Debey-Pascher S, Eggle D, Schultze JL. 2009. RNA stabilization of peripheral blood and profiling by bead chip analysis. *Methods Mol. Biol.* 496:175–210
179. Tian Z, Palmer N, Schmid P, Yao H, Galdzicki M, et al. 2009. A practical platform for blood biomarker study by using global gene expression profiling of peripheral whole blood. *PLoS One* 4:e5157

180. Vartanian K, Slottke R, Johnstone T, Casale A, Planck SR, et al. 2009. Gene expression profiling of whole blood: comparison of target preparation methods for accurate and reproducible microarray analysis. *BMC Genomics* 10:2
181. Li L, Ying L, Naesens M, Xiao W, Sigdel T, et al. 2008. Interference of globin genes with biomarker discovery for allograft rejection in peripheral blood samples. *Physiol. Genomics* 32:190–97
182. Shi L, Reid LH, Jones WD, Shippy R, Warrington JA, et al. 2006. The MicroArray Quality Control (MAQC) project shows inter- and intraplatform reproducibility of gene expression measurements. *Nat. Biotechnol.* 24:1151–61
183. Shi L, Perkins RG, Fang H, Tong W. 2008. Reproducible and reliable microarray results through quality control: good laboratory proficiency and appropriate data analysis practices are essential. *Curr. Opin. Biotechnol.* 19:10–18
184. Tan PK, Downey TJ, Spitznagel EL Jr, Xu P, Fu D, et al. 2003. Evaluation of gene expression measurements from commercial microarray platforms. *Nucleic Acids Res.* 31:5676–84
185. Butte AJ, Kohane IS. 2006. Creation and implications of a phenome-genome network. *Nat. Biotechnol.* 24:55–62
186. Rhodes DR, Yu J, Shanker K, Deshpande N, Varambally R, et al. 2004. Large-scale meta-analysis of cancer microarray data identifies common transcriptional profiles of neoplastic transformation and progression. *Proc. Natl. Acad. Sci. USA* 101:9309–14
187. Boulesteix AL, Strobl C, Augustin T, Daumer M. 2008. Evaluating microarray-based classifiers: an overview. *Cancer Inform.* 6:77–97
188. Ancona N, Maglietta R, Piepoli A, D'Addabbo A, Cotugno R, et al. 2006. On the statistical assessment of classifiers using DNA microarray data. *BMC Bioinform.* 7:387
189. Fraser ID, Germain RN. 2009. Navigating the network: signaling cross-talk in hematopoietic cells. *Nat. Immunol.* 10:327–31
190. Zak DE, Aderem A. 2009. Systems biology of innate immunity. *Immunol. Rev.* 227:264–82
191. Geiss GK, Bumgarner RE, Birditt B, Dahl T, Dowidar N, et al. 2008. Direct multiplexed measurement of gene expression with color-coded probe pairs. *Nat. Biotechnol.* 26:317–25
192. Wold B, Myers RM. 2008. Sequence census methods for functional genomics. *Nat. Methods* 5:19–21
193. Sultan M, Schulz MH, Richard H, Magen A, Klingenhoff A, et al. 2008. A global view of gene activity and alternative splicing by deep sequencing of the human transcriptome. *Science* 321:956–60
194. Shilatifard A. 2006. Chromatin modifications by methylation and ubiquitination: implications in the regulation of gene expression. *Annu. Rev. Biochem.* 75:243–69
195. Martin DA, Elkon KB. 2005. Autoantibodies make a U-turn: the toll hypothesis for autoantibody specificity. *J. Exp. Med.* 202:1465–9
196. Tian J, Avalos AM, Mao SY, Chen B, Senthil K, et al. 2007. Toll-like receptor 9-dependent activation by DNA-containing immune complexes is mediated by HMGB1 and RAGE. *Nat. Immunol.* 8:487–96
197. Lande R, Gregorio J, Facchinetti V, Chatterjee B, Wang YH, et al. 2007. Plasmacytoid dendritic cells sense self-DNA coupled with antimicrobial peptide. *Nature* 449:564–9
198. Ganguly D, Chamilos G, Lande R, Gregorio J, Meller S, et al. 2009. Self-RNA-antimicrobial peptide complexes activate human dendritic cells through TLR7 and TLR8. *J. Exp. Med.* 206:1983–94

Inflammatory Bowel Disease

Arthur Kaser,[1] Sebastian Zeissig,[2] and Richard S. Blumberg[2]

[1]Department of Medicine II, Medical University Innsbruck, 6020 Innsbruck, Austria

[2]Division of Gastroenterology, Hepatology, and Endoscopy, Brigham and Women's Hospital, Harvard Medical School, Boston, Massachusetts 02115; email: rblumberg@partners.org

Annu. Rev. Immunol. 2010. 28:573–621

First published online as a Review in Advance on January 6, 2010

The *Annual Review of Immunology* is online at immunol.annualreviews.org

This article's doi: 10.1146/annurev-immunol-030409-101225

0732-0582/10/0423-0573$20.00

Key Words

Crohn's disease, ulcerative colitis, intestinal inflammation, genetics, microbiota

Abstract

Insights into inflammatory bowel disease (IBD) are advancing rapidly owing to immunologic investigations of a plethora of animal models of intestinal inflammation, ground-breaking advances in the interrogation of diseases that are inherited as complex genetic traits, and the development of culture-independent methods to define the composition of the intestinal microbiota. These advances are bringing a deeper understanding to the genetically determined interplay between the commensal microbiota, intestinal epithelial cells, and the immune system and the manner in which this interplay might be modified by relevant environmental factors in the pathogenesis of IBD. This review examines these interactions and, where possible, potential lessons from IBD-directed, biologic therapies that may allow for elucidation of pathways that are central to disease pathogenesis in humans.

INTRODUCTION

The two major clinically defined forms of inflammatory bowel disease (IBD), Crohn's disease (CD) and ulcerative colitis (UC), are chronic remittent or progressive inflammatory conditions that may affect the entire gastrointestinal tract and the colonic mucosa, respectively, and are associated with an increased risk for colon cancer. IBD has long been appreciated to have a genetic basis and likely involves a response of the immune system to some environmental agent(s). The discordance of IBD among monozygotic twins (1) and the development of IBD in immigrants to high-prevalence countries (2) and in countries undergoing rapid Westernization also highlights the importance of environmental factors in disease pathogenesis (3).

The discovery that interleukin-2 (IL-2), IL-10, or T cell receptor (TCR) (4–6) mutant mice develop IBD-like enterocolitis, and the success of tumor necrosis factor (TNF)-α blockade in treating patients with CD, stimulated a new era of investigation in the early 1990s. Mechanisms deduced from numerous animal models (7) could be tested for relevance in human IBD by target-specific biologics (8). Since the recent dramatic expansion of studies into the genetic basis of complex diseases such as IBD (9), and the possibility to study the intestinal microbiome by sequencing (10), the pace of pathophysiologic discovery has further quickened. Genetically based interactions between the human intestinal microbiome and mucosal immune system and the manner in which environmental factors modify these relationships appear particularly relevant for the development of IBD. Among the insights that have emerged is the central role played by the innate immune system and its relationship to the commensal microbiota and adaptive immune system in the initiation and perpetuation of IBD. This review aims to integrate recent discoveries in the genetics, microbiology, and immunobiology of IBD together with lessons learned from the application of biologic therapies to emphasize the dynamic relationships of each of these components and the importance of considering them in their totality in order to understand the pathogenesis of these disorders.

GENETIC BASIS OF IBD

Both types of IBD occur in genetically susceptible individuals through interplay with poorly understood environmental factors. IBD, considered a polygenic disorder, is familial in 5–10% of individuals and sporadic in the remainder (1). Monozygotic twins exhibit phenotypic concordance in 50–75% of CD patients, and the relative risk of developing CD is 800-fold greater compared to the general population (1). In UC, phenotypic concordance in monozygotic twins is less frequent (10–20%), suggesting that heritability is less important in UC, that the relevant environmental exposure(s) is less common, or that copy number variations and/or epigenetic differences between twin pairs are more frequent, thus limiting the possibility for true concordance (1). Genetic studies, including candidate gene approaches, linkage mapping studies, and in particular genome-wide association studies (GWASs), have significantly advanced our understanding on the importance of genetic susceptibility in IBD (11). The GWASs performed to date together with a meta-analysis of several GWASs involving CD have identified more than 30 risk-conferring loci (see References 9, 11, and 12 for recent reviews of IBD genetics). These studies highlight pathways previously identified through immunologic studies [e.g., IL-23 and T helper (Th) 17 cells (13)], but have also discovered previously unappreciated pathways such as autophagy (14), raising novel hypotheses about disease pathogenesis (summarized in **Figure 1** and in **Supplemental Table 1**; follow the **Supplemental Material link** from the Annual Reviews home page at **http://www.annualreviews.org**).

Interestingly, GWASs have also revealed a substantial overlap in genetic risk factors between CD and UC (15, 16). However, it is possible that these similarities are not shared at the level of structurally or functionally

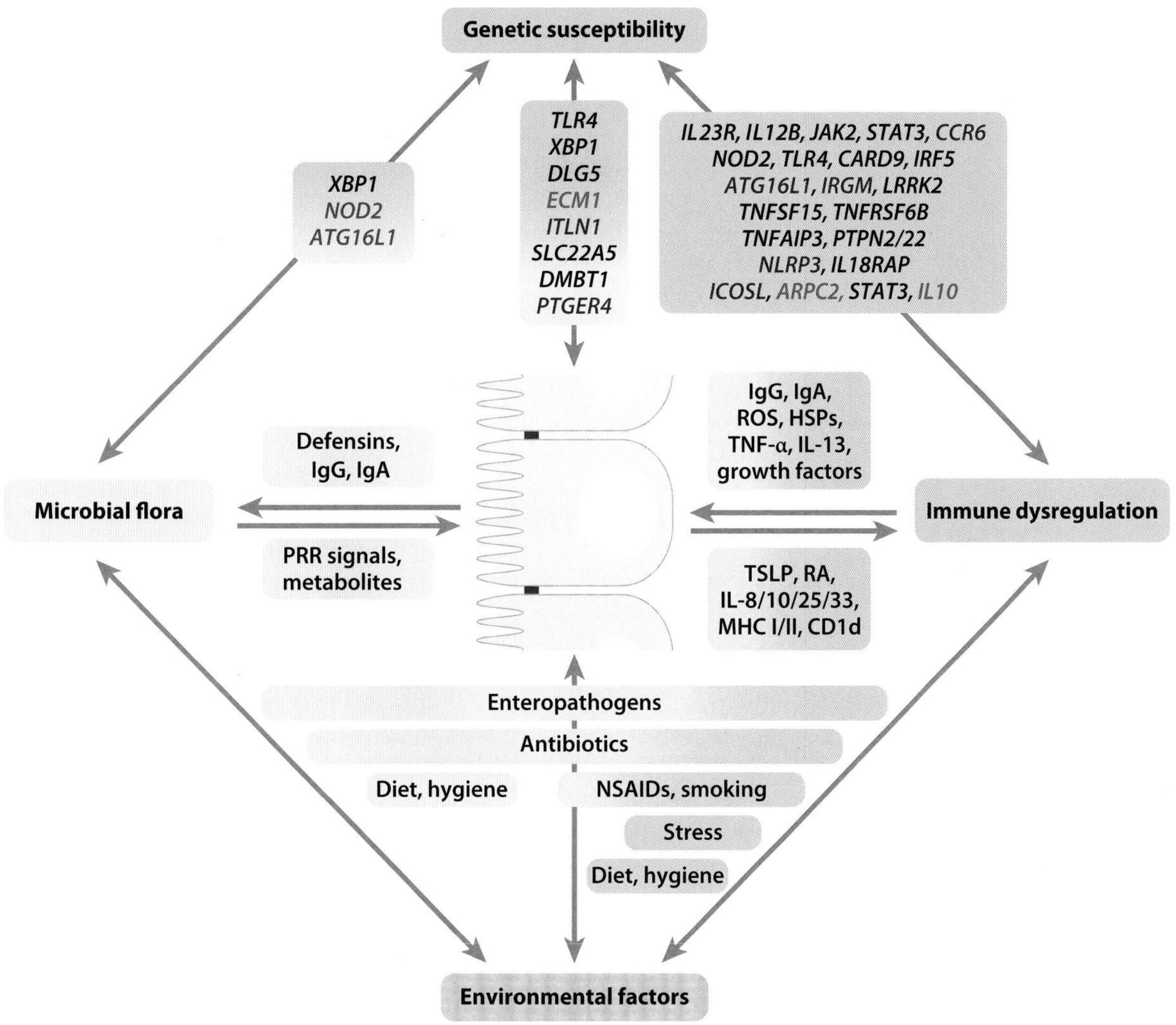

Figure 1

Inflammatory bowel disease (IBD) as a multifactorial disorder. The development and course of IBD are affected by several factors, including genetic susceptibility of the host, the intestinal microbiota, other environmental factors, and the host immune system. In addition, these factors cross-regulate each other in multiple ways, as shown. IBD-associated genes are summarized by molecular pathways with genes belonging to the same pathway arranged next to each other in one line. Polymorphisms in genes specific for Crohn's disease (CD) are shown in magenta text, whereas those specific for ulcerative colitis (UC) are shown in dark blue text. Genetic associations shared between both diseases are shown in black text. Abbreviations: HSPs, heat shock proteins; MHC, major histocompatibility complex; NSAIDs, nonsteroidal anti-inflammatory drugs; PRR, pattern-recognition receptor; RA, retinoic acid; ROS, reactive oxygen species; TSLP, thymic stromal lymphopoietin.

relevant polymorphisms because causal variants are mostly unknown. The wide phenotypic diversity of cystic fibrosis associated with diverse *CFTR* variants might serve as precedent (17). However, some loci are quite unique for CD or UC. For example, autophagy genes (e.g., *ATG16L1*, *IRGM*), NOD-like receptors (e.g., *NOD2*), and intelectins (*ITLN1*) are highly specific for CD, whereas loci related to regulatory pathways (*IL10* and *ARPC2*), intestinal epithelial cell (IEC) function (e.g., *ECM1*), and an E3 ubiquitin ligase (e.g., *HERC2*) appear to be specific for UC (**Supplemental Table 1**). Moreover, associations within the HLA/MHC region are stronger with UC compared to CD, a genetic trait of IBD shared with a number of other autoimmune diseases (9, 15). Although IBD is classified as an immune-mediated disease, there is no evidence to date that autoimmunity plays a direct pathogenic role in either UC or CD despite the existence of detectable autoantibodies that are cross-reactive with bacterial antigens (18). These genetic associations within the HLA/MHC region raise the possibility, however, that autoimmunity may ultimately be defined as another pathogenetic mechanism.

In addition to the HLA/MHC region, a number of other IBD risk loci are also associated with a diverse set of immune-related diseases. These include type 1 diabetes mellitus (e.g., *PTPN2* and *PTPN22*), type 2 diabetes mellitus (e.g., *CDKAL1*), asthma (e.g., *ORMDL3*), psoriasis (e.g., *CDKAL1* and *GCKR*), systemic lupus erythematosus (e.g., *PTPN22*), Graves' disease (e.g., *PTPN22*), and rheumatoid arthritis (e.g., *PTPN22*) (9, 15, 19). The sharing of associations among different diseases implies that a general inherited propensity to develop immune-related diseases may exist and that environmental (or epigenetic) factors may determine not only disease phenotype but also the specific immune-mediated disease that develops. Moreover, IBD risk loci vary remarkably between different populations. For example, *NOD2* and autophagy genes, the major risk loci in the Caucasian population, are not susceptibility factors in the Asian population (3). Hence, despite commonalities in the genetic basis of CD and UC (15), substantial genetic heterogeneity exists within and between populations. However, despite genotypic differences among various populations, the clinicopathologic phenotype is largely similar, as is the overall response to various therapies (3). This might predict that a large variety of genotypes converge on a limited set of phenotypic pathways that are responsible for initiating disease and are amenable to therapeutic manipulation.

A striking but potentially instructive outcome of GWASs is that the vast majority of identified loci individually confer extremely modest risk [odds-ratios (ORs), mostly between 1.11 and 1.29]. Collectively, the loci identified to date represent ≈10–20% of the overall variance of potential disease risk; a dominant contribution is provided by the three common *NOD2* variants (20). Moreover, for most of the confirmed loci the causal gene(s) or variant(s) (ranging from rare to common) is not yet known (9, 11, 12). This "missing heritability" has led to at least two potential interpretations. The genetic basis for common phenotypic traits such as sporadic IBD may be due to the cumulative effect of interactions between an unknown quantity of potentially hundreds or thousands of common single nucleotide polymorphisms (SNPs) of minor individual biologic impact (21) and/or that IBD, especially the familial form, may be due to the effects of rare variants with profound impact that may be modified by more common variants (21, 22). In this latter model, at least a subset of IBD, such as those with a familial pattern of inheritance, may potentially be due to a "more" Mendelian form of heredity, which is supported by several lines of evidence. First, multiple rare primary genetic syndromes with Mendelian inheritance may develop IBD as a part of the syndrome (e.g., Wiskott-Aldrich Syndrome, Hermansky-Pudlak Syndrome, glycogen storage disease type 1b, and immunodeficiency polyendocrinopathy with eczema and X-linked, or IPEX). Second, a familial form of early-onset CD has been recently identified as a monogenic disorder due to homozygous mutations in either *IL10RA* or *IL10RB*, which encode subunits of the IL-10 receptor (23). Moreover, these IL-10R variants appear to functionally map to hematopoietic cells, as cure was observed after allogeneic hematopoietic stem cell transplantation, a modality recognized as of potential utility in a select subset of IBD subjects (24). It is therefore interesting that

Il10$^{-/-}$ (5) and *Il10rb*$^{-/-}$ (25) mice as well as mice with *Stat3* deletion in macrophages (26) all develop spontaneous intestinal inflammation. Although IL-10R1 (encoded by *IL10RA*) is unique to IL-10R, IL-10R2 (encoded by *IL10RB*) is shared with other receptors such as IL-22, which may protect against colitis via goblet cells (27). Thus, rare variants with strong biologic effects and common variants may reside within a functional pathway, as may be the case for IL-10R, IL-10, and STAT3. As spontaneous IBD rarely develops in animal models targeted at IBD susceptibility loci, it may be speculated that those cases that do develop disease in rodents might be monogenically inherited in humans (e.g., IL-10).

ROLE OF THE MICROBIOTA AS A MAJOR ENVIRONMENTAL DRIVER OF IBD

Insight into the genetic basis of IBD has focused attention on the relationships between the immune system and the intestinal microbiota. The intestinal microbiota profoundly affects host immune composition under physiologic conditions and is likely the most important environmental factor in IBD as the target of the inflammatory response (28). This is supported by a wide variety of observations in humans and mouse models, as recently reviewed elsewhere (7, 29). Perhaps most important among these are the observations that numerous genetic mouse models of intestinal inflammation do not develop disease after germ-free rederivation (30), and T cell lines specific for bacterial antigens, but not when nonspecifically activated, can induce intestinal inflammation (31, 32). IBD may represent an inappropriate immune response to the commensal microbiota in a genetically predisposed host. This finding has led to an intense interest in the composition of the intestinal microbiota, its regulation by the host and environmental factors, and the interactions between the microbiota and host.

Regulation of Mucosal Immune Functions by the Commensal Microbiota

Humans (and experimental animals) associate with numerous microorganisms at environmentally exposed surfaces of the body (10). The gastrointestinal tract harbors more than 10^{14} microorganisms of more than 1000 species (33, 34), mostly contained within the colon and not accessible to conventional culture techniques (10). Most (>90%) belong to two different phyla that account for the majority of gram-negative bacteria (Bacteroidetes) and gram-positive bacteria (Firmicutes); the remainder belong to rarer phyla such as Proteobacteria (containing genuses such as *Escherichia* and *Helicobacter*) and Actinobacteria as well as viruses, protists, and fungi (10). Collectively, the microbiota carries out many physiological functions important in mammalian biology (35). In fact, the microbiota is required for the development and differentiation of local and systemic immune and nonimmune components (28). As an example, *Bacteroides thetaiotaomicron* affects innate immune capabilities by regulating antimicrobial peptide (e.g., angiogenin) expression within the intestinal epithelium through direct activation of Toll-like receptors (TLR) on Paneth cells (36). Similarly, adaptive immune functions within the intestines related to TCR$\alpha\beta$ intraepithelial lymphocytes (37), T regulatory cells (Tregs) (38), and Th17 cells (39–41) are determined by specific bacteria, although the mechanisms behind these effects cannot yet be explained by simple rules. Systemic immune responses are also impaired in germ-free mice, including the development of adequate Treg responses leading to increased systemic autoimmunity (38, 42), which may have implications for the development of extraintestinal manifestations in IBD. An example of a microbial mechanism that affects host inflammatory responses and that is also affected by dietary intake, i.e., environmental factors, is that associated with short-chain fatty acids (SCFA). SCFA derive from microbial fermentation of dietary fiber, bind to G protein–coupled receptor 43 (GPR43), and play a profound role in various inflammatory conditions, such as colitis, arthritis, and asthma (43). Consequently, *Gpr43*$^{-/-}$ mice, similar to germ-free mice that lack SCFA, exhibit a profound impairment in the resolution of inflammation (43). Overall, the commensal microbiota has major effects on the composition and function of innate and adaptive immune pathways as they may relate to IBD.

Determinants of Commensal Microbiota Composition: Nature and/or Nurture?

Large throughput and next generation sequencing of variable regions of microbial 16S rRNA have allowed for detailed insights into the composition of the intestinal microbiota and their functional genes (i.e., microbiome) in animal models and humans (10). These studies reveal an astounding degree of complexity as defined by phylotypes, with remarkable interindividual differences observed even in healthy subjects (34) and an important role for environmental as well as genetic factors in determining the microbial niche. Specifically, twin studies revealed only a slightly decreased similarity of community structure in dizygotic compared to monozygotic twins, while exhibiting substantial similarity with their mothers (34). This finding suggests that microbial commensalism is largely "inherited" from the mothers and modified by genetic and other environmental (e.g., dietary) factors. Despite the significant interindividual differences at the phylotype level, there is an apparent effort on the part of the host and microbial communities to achieve the existence of a defined "core microbiome" of predicted metabolic functionality that is shared under disparate genotypes (34). This is perhaps the most important virtue of the microbiota in exerting its influences on homeostasis and/or disease. How this attribute relates to IBD has not yet been studied (10).

Animal studies do support the notion that host factors affect microbial commensalism, however. For example, *Cd1d*$^{-/-}$ mice exhibit an overgrowth of commensal bacteria upon monocolonization from the germ-free state and an alteration of the overall architecture of their microbial communities (44). This effect might be mediated by Paneth cells given their altered morphology and function in *Cd1d*$^{-/-}$ mice. Thus, host innate immune factors that act through Paneth cells (44–47) or other (potentially genetically defined) factors affecting the composition of mucins (48) or microbial adherence to IECs (49) may also be determinants of the microbial niche. One example of altered colonization is the upregulation of carcinoembryonic antigen-related cell adhesion molecule 6 (CEACAM6) on the cell surface of IECs in IBD, which serves as ligand for certain Proteobacteria such as enteroadherent *Escherichia coli* that may bloom in a subset of individuals with intestinal inflammation (50). CEACAM6 on IECs likely accounts for the localization of enteroadherent *E. coli* on inflamed epithelium adjacent to ulcerated areas, implying an important secondary factor in further promoting intestinal inflammation (50). Similarly, adaptive immune factors such as secretory IgA may also affect commensalism, and the commensals in turn drive the generation of secretory IgA (51).

Composition of Commensal Microbiota in Intestinal Inflammation and IBD

Recent studies have sought to determine whether specific alterations can be identified in the intestinal microbiota in IBD. 16S rRNA sequencing revealed a detectable difference between the intestinal microbiota in CD and UC compared to healthy controls (52). This difference in microbial phylotypes largely arises from a distinct subset of CD and UC patients (so-called IBD subset) with the remaining IBD patients being similar to healthy controls, although this awaits further more extensive metagenomic analyses. This IBD subset is characterized by depletion of commensal bacteria with a tenfold lower bacterial load and affects both major classes of commensal phyla, Firmicutes and Bacteroidetes (52). Whether this "dysbiosis" in the IBD subset is associated with particular genotypes (and hence a primary effect antecedent to inflammation) or is a consequence of inflammation per se is unknown (see **Table 1**). Several genetic loci associated with IBD (e.g., *NOD2*, *ATG16L1*, *XBP1*) affect or have been predicted to affect Paneth cells (e.g., *ITLN1* or intelectin 1) (20, 45–47, 53), which secrete abundant quantities of antimicrobial factors. Hence, the function of a number of genes could affect microbial community structure and predispose to inflammation. For example, NOD2 expression is regulated by the microbiota and, in turn, regulates the quantity of bacteria within the intestines, perhaps via Paneth cells (54). However, dysbiosis in the absence of NOD2 appears neither inflammatory in its own right nor secondary to inflammation given the absence of spontaneous inflammation in $Nod2^{-/-}$ mice (47, 55). It is interesting to note that *NOD2* polymorphisms were recently identified as risk factors for *Mycobacterium paratuberculosis* (MAP) infection in cattle (56), which phenocopies IBD of the small intestine (29). However, the major *NOD2* polymorphisms linked to CD are not associated with the presence of MAP in the peripheral blood as detected by PCR (29). Nonetheless, these insights suggest that, in the context of inflammation, an overgrowth of certain organisms (e.g., enteroadherent *E. coli* or MAP) together with altered interactions between these organisms with the host (e.g., increased CEACAM6) may be a relevant secondary factor in driving inflammation in IBD.

A recent study on the transcription factor T-bet (encoded by *Tbx21*) has provided strong support for the possibility that dysbiosis could contribute to intestinal inflammation. Specifically, T-bet deficiency in the innate immune system together with an absence of Tregs led to spontaneous colitis, which was abrogated by antibiotics, supporting a role for the commensal flora (57). Although colonic dendritic cell (DC)-derived TNF was a critical mediator of the induction of colitis and induced IEC apoptosis via TNFR1, colitis was strikingly vertically (mother-pup) and horizontally (adult-adult) transmitted via the intestinal microbiota from $Rag2^{-/-}Tbx21^{-/-}$ mice to T-bet intact immunodeficient and immunocompetent mice (57). Hence, the colonic environment in $Rag2^{-/-}Tbx21^{-/-}$ mice indeed created a milieu that supported the development of a colitogenic microbial community (57). It is therefore intriguing to speculate that TNF could be a decisive factor in regulating microbial community structure including its colitogenic nature, which has important ramifications for both forms of IBD given the responsiveness of both CD and UC to anti-TNF therapies (see below and in **Supplemental Table 2**). Although there is little evidence that human IBD is a transmissible disease, these observations suggest that the host can primarily (perhaps through TNF) or secondarily through inflammatory mediators and their consequences (e.g., altered mucin content or antimicrobial peptides) affect the intestinal microbiota and its relationship with the host in a manner that induces or perpetuates inflammation. Regardless of the mechanism that creates this microbial niche, these studies show that the commensal microbiota can assume an overall structure that is inflammatory.

Host inflammation per se, induced by a pathogen (e.g., the model pathogen *Citrobacter rodentium*), chemically (dextran sodium sulfate, DSS), or genetically through *Il10* deletion, leads to profound alterations of colonic microbial community structure (58) (see **Table 1**). In each of these models, inflammation was associated with a decrease in Bacteroidetes and with maintenance, and thus relative increase, of Proteobacteria, in particular aerobes within Enterobacteriaceae (58). Upon pathogenic invasion, *C. rodentium* filled the void in the microbial niche normally occupied by commensals (58) and appeared to co-opt the inflammatory response to gain a foothold in the intestinal microenvironment. Such a pathogen-induced dysbiosis could be inflammatory in its own right because it would enable the pathogen to maintain its control of the local environment. If dysbiosis includes the overgrowth of other proinflammatory species such as pathogenic *E. coli*, it is possible that inflammation is perpetuated through these other inflammatory allies of the invading pathogen until homeostasis is restored upon removal of the inciting

Table 1 Changes in the microbial flora in selected human diseases and mouse models of disease[a]

		Decreased abundance	Increased abundance	Total bacterial amount	Sample origin
Human	**IBD**	Bacteroidetes including *Bacteroides thetaiotaomicron* (52) Clostridia class of Firmicutes including *Faecalibacterium prausnitzii* (52, 71, 352–354) and butyrate-producing spp. (52) Reduced diversity (353, 355)	Proteobacteria including *Enterobacteriaceae* (relative, not absolute increase) (52, 352, 354, 356) Bacilli class of Firmicutes (52) Increase in mucosal adherent bacteria (particularly in adjacent uninflamed mucosa) (104)	Decreased in recent 16S rRNA studies (52, 352) Increased in DGGE and FISH studies (104, 357)	Intestinal tissue
	Indeterminate colitis	Bacteroidetes (358)	Increase in mucosal adherent bacteria (104, 358)		Intestinal tissue
	Obesity (359)	Bacteroidetes (increase upon calorie restriction)	Firmicutes (decrease upon calorie restriction)		Luminal content
Mouse	**DSS colitis (58)**	Bacteroidetes (twofold)	Firmicutes (twofold; includes *Lachnospiraceae*, *Lactobacillaceae* families)	Reduced (0.7-fold)	Colon tissue and luminal content
	***Il10*$^{-/-}$ (58, 360)**	Bacteroidetes (0.7-fold)	Firmicutes (twofold; includes *Lachnospiraceae* family) *Enterobacteriaceae* (Proteobacteria)	Unchanged	Colon tissue and luminal content
	***Citrobacter rodentium* infection (58)**	Bacteroidetes (threefold)	*Enterobacteriaceae* (Proteobacteria)	Reduced (fourfold)	Colon tissue and luminal content
	ob/ob mice (361, 362)	Bacteroidetes (0.5-fold, division-wide)	Firmicutes (division-wide)		Cecal content
	High fat diet (C57BL/6 versus *Relmb*$^{-/-}$) (363)	Bacteroidetes (diet-induced, independent of obesity)	Firmicutes (Clostridia class) Proteobacteria (Deltaproteobacteria) (both diet-induced, independent of obesity)		Fecal pellets
	***Myd88*$^{-/-}$ on NOD background (42)**	Reduced Firmicutes/ Bacteroidetes ratio	Bacteroidetes (*Rikenellaceae* and *Porphyromonadaceae* families) Firmicutes (*Lactobacillaceae*)		Cecal content

[a]Abbreviations: DGGE, denaturing gradient gel electrophoresis; DSS, dextran sodium sulfate; FISH, fluorescence in situ hybridization.

agent (50). Because chemically or genetically induced inflammation in animal models and human IBD (52) seemingly phenocopies these pathogen-induced changes in the microbiota, inflammation per se may cause dysbiosis with the aforementioned consequences. These studies also support the idea that the genetically susceptible host with IBD responds to the commensal microbiota as if it were a pathogen.

These observations predict that more severe inflammation might be associated with more profound changes in the microbiota, which in turn would increase the quantity of pathogenic bacteria (i.e., commensal microbiota with pathogenic tendencies), thus perpetuating inflammation. It is interesting to speculate whether the IBD subset described by Frank et al. (52) is indeed associated with more severe inflammation together with a more robust host immune response to the commensal microbiota (e.g., robust IgG response to specific microbial antigens including flagellin or outer membrane protein C) (59). Altogether, these observations raise questions concerning the mechanisms whereby inflammation affects microbial composition.

Mechanisms of Host-Commensal Interactions and Their Relationship to Inflammation

The host mechanisms that provide the niche for the gut microbiota and how these change with inflammation are largely unknown. In *Drosophila*, five commensal species dominate the gut microbiota, making *Drosophila* more amenable for study than mice or humans (60). In *Drosophila*, inhibition of the intestinal homeobox gene *Caudal* increases NF-κB-dependent antimicrobial peptide expression, which in turn alters the commensal populations in the intestine (60). The consequential dominance of one particular gut microbe results in gut cell apoptosis and host mortality, whereas reintroduction of the *Caudal* gene restores a healthy microbiota and normal host survival (60). Thus, NF-κB-regulated antimicrobial peptides secreted by IECs including Paneth cells could represent a mechanism whereby specific microorganisms may bloom (34) during inflammation.

The ability of microorganisms to control NF-κB may therefore be critical. Probiotic bacteria, for example, may stabilize IκB or promote peroxisome proliferator-activated receptor γ (PPARγ), which diminishes NF-κB (RelA) retention in the nucleus (61, 62). Another example is NADPH oxidase (or dual oxidase) of *Drosophila* [functionally homologous to *NCF4*, a genetic risk factor for CD (63) that encodes the human neutrophil NADPH oxidase factor 4], which regulates the quantity of bacteria in the gut (64, 65).

Thus, a proper balance of commensal community architecture and antimicrobial activities of the epithelium (including goblet cells, absorptive epithelial cells, and Paneth cells), innate immune cells (e.g., neutrophils, macrophages), and the adaptive immune system (e.g., IgA) are critical in maintaining the proper composition of the "metagenome," the expressed genetic composition of the commensal bacteria and host (33, 34).

The Role of Environmental Factors in Regulating Commensalism and Intestinal Inflammation

These observations on the alterations of microbial composition that are observed in humans with IBD or in experimental model systems may also provide a window into an understanding of the role of certain modifying environmental factors in the pathogenesis of IBD such as diet (66), antibiotics, and most importantly pathogenic infections.

Support for this concept comes from studies with *Helicobacter hepaticus*, a commensal bacterium with pathogenic potential (38, 67). Although colonization of wild-type mice with *H. hepaticus* does not result in inflammation, *H. hepaticus* induces colitis in $Il10^{-/-}$ (68) or *scid*/$Rag2^{-/-}$ hosts that received naive $CD4^{+}CD45RB^{high}$ T cells (67). This colitis is driven by T cells, including those specific for the flagellar hook protein (FlgE) of *H. hepaticus* (69). In both of these cases, *H. hepaticus*–induced colitis requires aggressive T cells in the absence of Tregs, similar to the original observations of Powrie and colleagues (70). Notably, this colitis is prevented by cocolonization with the symbiont *Bacteroides fragilis*, suggesting that, although not specifically shown, this organism may have been depleted by *H. hepaticus* infection (38). Notably, protection by *B. fragilis* is dependent on a single microbial molecule (polysaccharide A, PSA) and involves decreased colonic TNF and increased IL-10 from $CD4^+$ T cells (38). Hence, a symbiotic bacterial molecule might network with the immune system to coordinate anti-inflammatory responses required for homeostasis. Such a symbiont and its protective factor may be lost during infection or in a host genetically susceptible for IBD (38). Along similar lines, decreased *Faecalibacterium prausnitzii*, a major commensal Firmicute, is associated with postoperative recurrence of CD. *F. prausnitzii* exerts anti-inflammatory properties and induces IL-10 in hematopoietic cells (71). In summary, these observations suggest that initiation of chronic intestinal inflammation requires perturbations of both the commensal microbiota and host immune system; in other words, a two-hit hypothesis for the initiation of IBD (72).

Commensal Microbiota, Innate Immunity, and Adaptive Immunity: A Continuum

Although an adaptive immune system is not necessary for development of colitis in *Rag2*$^{-/-}$*Tbx21*$^{-/-}$ mice (57), it is no doubt a critical factor with the involvement of both bacterial antigen–specific T and B cells. Transfer of flagellin-specific $CD4^+$ T cells into immunodeficient *scid* mice can induce colitis (73). Similarly, in human IBD there is a notable serologic switch from a homeostatic IgA-dominant to an IgG-dominant response within the intestines that is largely directed at bacterial antigens (74). This excessive production of IgG in IBD is likely to be inflammatory, as the neonatal Fc receptor (FcRn) within hematopoietic cells promotes intestinal inflammation in response to bacterial flagellins in the presence of anti-flagellin IgG (75). However, mice deficient in innate immune responses (i.e., *Myd88*$^{-/-}$*Trif*$^{-/-}$) do not develop intestinal inflammation despite increased bacterial translocation into the spleen and a dramatic increase in antibacterial IgG responses (76). Hence, though primary alterations in innate immunity may be antecedent to abnormal adaptive immune responses to the commensal microbiota in IBD, they do not necessarily transform into intestinal inflammation.

In this context, one of the most dominant bacterial antigens inducing IgG responses in human CD and mouse models of colitis are flagellins. Although flagellins are expressed by many intestinal commensals, this IgG response is mainly directed at *Clostridia*-related species expressing specific flagellins (CBir1–15) (73). The flagellar antigen recognized by anti-CBir1 is notably present in colitic and noncolitic mouse strains (73), indicating that the presence of the antigen (and the IgG response) itself does not correlate with colitis. Consistent with this, neither *Myd88*$^{-/-}$*Trif*$^{-/-}$ mice (with elevated antibacterial IgG) (76) nor mice transgenic for a TCR specific for a CBir1 flagellin develop intestinal inflammation (77). To the contrary, the flagellin-specific TCR transgene results in enhanced Treg responses that appear to promote IgA production with all of its beneficial consequences (77). Consistent with this, *Tlr5*$^{-/-}$ mice develop spontaneous colitis (78), which suggests that an innate inability to respond to flagellin induces a loss of Treg responses, increased bacterial specific IgG, and bacterial dysbiosis due to a loss of commensal specific IgA; altogether these effects culminate in a loss of tolerance to the microbiota and intestinal inflammation.

Taken together, this suggests that the presence of inflammatory bacterial antigen(s) (e.g., flagellin) within the microbiota is inadequate to induce intestinal inflammation even in the presence of a broad loss of innate immune function, despite an adaptive immune system geared toward inflammation as revealed by the presence of an IgG-dominated B cell response or even an absent adaptive immune response as observed in $Rag2^{-/-}$ mice. Hence, a critical accumulation of irregularities in the intestinal microenvironment is necessary for inflammation to occur; albeit these irregularities may evolve from single critical perturbations, as discussed throughout this review.

THE CENTRAL ROLE OF INNATE IMMUNITY IN IBD AND ITS RELATIONSHIP TO THE COMMENSAL MICROBIOTA

Genetic studies, animal models, and the apparent superior efficacy of biologic agents directed at innate, as opposed to adaptive, immune factors in the treatment of IBD (see **Supplemental Table 2**) suggest abnormal innate immune responses toward the microbiota as a central underlying theme of IBD (**Figure 2**).

NOD2 and Pattern Recognition of the Microbiota

NOD2 polymorphisms were the first firm genetic association between an individual gene and a polygenic disease (79–81). Between 30% and 40% of patients with CD in the Western hemisphere (compared to ≈10% in healthy controls) carry *NOD2* polymorphisms on at least one allele. *NOD2* is not a genetic risk factor for UC, but other *NOD2* polymorphisms have been linked to Blau syndrome (82). NOD2 is structured into two N-terminal caspase-activation and recruitment domains, a central nucleotide-binding and oligomerization domain, and a C-terminal leucine-rich repeat ligand-binding domain (83). Three individually uncommon (minor allele frequency <5%) polymorphisms that affect protein structure, R702W ($NOD2^{C2104T}$, "SNP8"), G908R ($NOD2^{G2722C}$, "SNP12"), and 1007fs ($NOD2^{3020insC}$, "SNP13"), account for 32%, 18%, and 31% of CD-associated variants, respectively, whereas additional rare variants cumulatively account for 19% of the risk associated with *NOD2* (84). Altogether, 93% of the variants are located in the leucine-rich repeat region (84), which is involved in

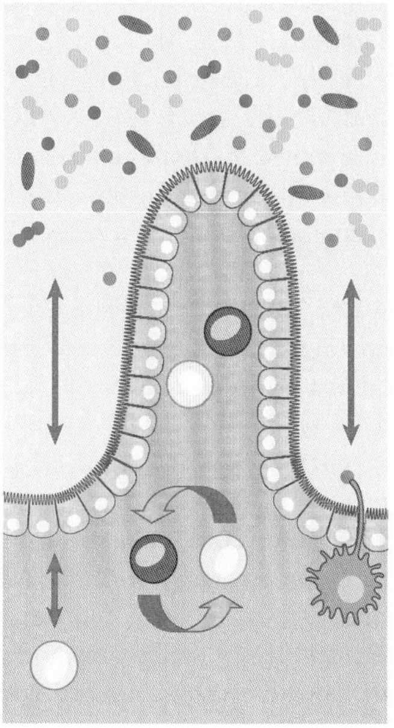

	Target of/altered by	Participant in/ central organizer of
Flora	• Antimicrobial peptides • Host diet • Host genotype • Microbial-microbial interactions	• Lymphatic development via PRRs (NODs, TLRs) • Epithelial homeostasis through PRRs (TLRs, MyD88) • Nutrient digestion and host energy metabolism (butyrate)
IEC	• Proinflammatory cytokines (TNF-α, IFN-γ, IL-13) • PRR signals (TLRs, MyD88) • Cytokines (IL-10, IL-11, IL-22) • Growth factors (EGF, KGF) • Heat-shock proteins	• Cyto-/chemokine production (IL-8, IL-10, TSLP, IL-25, IL-33) • Antimicrobial peptide production • T/B cell priming, homing, cytokine production via retinoic acid • Antigen processing (M cells, FcRn), presentation (MHC I/II, CD1d)
Immune cells	• Epithelial cyto-/chemokines regulating migration (IL-8, CCL2), activation (IL-10, IL-25, IL-33), Ig class switching (TSLP) • Microbial-derived products (PAMPs, butyrate)	• Antigen presentation (DC antigen sampling, MHC I/II, CD1) • Epithelial/microbial homeostasis via cytokines, growth factors, complement, Ig

Figure 2

The microbial flora, intestinal epithelial cells, and lamina propria immune cells as targets, participants, and central organizers in intestinal immune responses. Abbreviations: EGF, epithelial growth factor; KGF, keratinocyte growth factor; PAMPs, pathogen-associated molecular patterns; PRR, pattern-recognition receptor.

binding of *N*-acetyl muramyl dipeptide (MDP) derived from bacterial peptidoglycan (83) and *N*-glycolyl MDP from mycobacteria (85), as well as viral ssRNA (86). The OR for CD for simple *NOD2* heterozygotes is 2.4, and for homozygotes or compound heterozygotes 17.1 in Caucasians (79, 84), rendering *NOD2* as the locus with the strongest effect size among all currently known IBD-associated loci (20).

NOD2 is expressed intracellularly, including in myeloid cells, IECs, Paneth cells (87, 88), and, as recently reported, T cells (89). NOD2 activation by MDP results in binding to receptor-interacting serine-threonine kinase 2 (RIP2; also known as RICK, CARDIAK), which in turn results in NF-κB essential modulator (NEMO; also known as IκB kinase γ) ubiquitination via the E3 ubiquitin ligase TRAF6 (90–92). Ubiquitinated NEMO recruits the TGF-β-activated kinase (TAK1) complex to phosphorylate the IκB kinases (IKK), which promote IκB degradation and consequently release NF-κB into the nucleus to transduce expression of chemokines (e.g., CXCL3/CXCL14 and CCL2) and cytokines (e.g., TNF and IL-6) (92). TLRs signal via a similar pathway with which NOD2 may synergize (92). ssRNA binding to NOD2 results in interaction with mitochondrial antiviral signaling protein, consequent IRF3 activation, and IFN-β production (86). Neither *Nod2*$^{-/-}$ nor *Nod2*^{2939insC} mice (knock-in of human *NOD2*^{3020insC}) develop enteritis or colitis (47, 55), and a comprehensive pathway to disease has not yet been elucidated. In the search for NOD2 functions in CD, several lines of evidence suggest hypomorphic function of the CD-associated variants, which are related to bacterial innate immune recognition, as detailed below.

The three common CD-associated *NOD2* polymorphisms abrogate RIP2 binding and NEMO ubiquitination (90) and result in decreased NF-κB transactivation (93), implying hypomorphic NOD2 function. Consequently, PBMCs from patients homozygous for these variants exhibit decreased inflammatory cytokine secretion upon MDP stimulation or MDP-stimulated TLR ligation (94). Accordingly, macrophages from *Nod2*$^{-/-}$ mice exhibit diminished IκBα phosphorylation upon MDP stimulation and decreased IL-6 and IL-12p40 secretion upon costimulation with TLR ligands (47). However, chronic stimulation of NOD2 via MDP, as predicted to occur in the context of the intestinal microbiota, "tolerizes" against subsequent stimulation through TLRs, which is lost in CD patients homozygous for the *NOD2*^{3020insC} allele (95). Consistent with this, NOD2 signaling may even be inhibitory to TLR2-mediated activation of NF-κB in antigen-presenting cells (APC), which is lost with the murine homolog of the *NOD2*^{3020insC} variant (96). Increased NF-κB activation upon MDP stimulation has also been observed in mice engineered to express the mouse homolog of *NOD2*^{3020insC} (*Nod2*^{2939insC}). These mice were more susceptible to DSS colitis, which could be prevented by recombinant IL-1Ra (55). Along the same lines, *Nod2*$^{-/-}$ APCs induced heightened IFN-γ responses in antigen-specific CD4^{+} T cells, and transfer of OVA-TCR transgenic CD4^{+} T cells into recipient mice and subsequent exposure to OVA expressed by orally administered *E. coli* resulted in more severe colitis compared to *Nod2*$^{+/+}$ recipient mice (97). However, *Nod2*$^{-/-}$ mice also exhibit diminished humoral adaptive immune responses to a model antigen in vivo (47), highlighting the complexity of NOD2 functions.

CD-associated NOD2 variants also exhibit a gain of function through active inhibition of (anti-inflammatory and regulatory) *IL10* transcription via blockade of p38 interactions with nuclear ribonucleoprotein hnRNP-A1 (98), consistent with decreased TLR ligand–induced IL-10 production of monocytes from patients homozygous for *NOD2*^{3020insC} (98, 99). Altogether, these aspects of NOD2 function on NF-κB, TLRs, and IL-10 predict impairment of the normal innate response toward commensal flora required for the maintenance of tolerance.

Nod2$^{-/-}$ mice also exhibit decreased α-defensin expression in Paneth cells and increased systemic translocation of the orally infected model pathogen *Listeria monocytogenes* (47), as well as increased overall bacterial load in the intestinal lumen (54). Similarly, Paneth cells from $NOD2^{3020insC}$ homozygous patients exhibit decreased α-defensin HD4 and HD5 expression (53), though inflammation could also contribute to downregulation (100). Furthermore, IEC-expressed NOD2 may provide protection against intracellular bacteria like *Salmonella typhimurium*, a function lost with the $NOD2^{3020insC}$ variant (88, 101). NOD2 is also involved in the autophagic response to invasive bacteria (see Autophagy and IBD section, below) as it induces the recruitment of the autophagy protein ATG16L1 to the entry site of bacteria at the plasma membrane (102, 103). Notably, the major CD-associated *NOD2* variants fail to induce autophagy via ATG16L1, and consequently autophagic wrapping of invading bacteria is impaired (102, 103). These altered NOD2 functions could contribute to the increased association of intestinal bacteria with the epithelium, which has been observed in IBD (104), as well as lead to an inability to manage pathogens and the commensal flora, setting the stage for an inflammatory environment, as described above (47).

NF-κB and Its Regulation in IBD

As detailed above, there is an intricate relationship between NOD2 and NF-κB, with underlying hypomorphic induction of NF-κB by CD-associated NOD2 variants and its complex outcomes. This relationship draws specific attention to the complex role of the NF-κB pathway (105) in the mucosal immune system with vastly divergent effects in different cellular compartments.

Increased NF-κB activation, associated with increased IL-1β, TNF-α, and IL-6 expression (106), in macrophages and IECs has been reported in CD, UC, nonspecific colitis, and diverticulitis, but not in uninflamed mucosa, and correlates with inflammatory activity (107). NF-κB p65 (RelA) antisense oligonucleotides administered intravenously or rectally ameliorate trinitrobenzene sulfonic acid (TNBS)-induced colitis and colitis in $Il10^{-/-}$ mice (106). Similarly, administration of BMS-345541, a pharmacological inhibitor of IκB destruction, ameliorates DSS colitis (108). Also similarly, deletion of IKKβ (*Ikbkb*) in macrophages and neutrophils improves colitis in $Il10^{-/-}$ mice (109). In contrast, genetic deletion of IKKβ specifically in IECs results in increased severity of DSS colitis (109, 110), which appears secondary to decreased recruitment of inflammatory cells that contribute to production of barrier protective mediators such as IL-11, IL-22, and heat shock protein 70 (109–111). Consistent with this, IEC-specific *Ikbkb* deletion did not affect chronic colitis in $Il10^{-/-}$ mice, in contrast to IKKβ deletion in myeloid cells (109), supporting a protective role for IKKβ in the epithelium in contrast to an inflammatory role in myeloid cells (109). Overall, these divergent outcomes resemble TLR4 signaling in the mucosa (promotion of mucosal healing versus promotion of inflammation) (112, 113).

In addition, IKKβ within IECs can direct adaptive immune functions in the lamina propria via distal effects on DCs (114). Specifically, the intestinal microbiota drives expression of thymic stromal lymphopoietin (TSLP) in IECs via an IKKβ-dependent pathway (115, 116), which renders mucosal DCs noninflammatory, characterized by IL-10 and IL-6, but not IL-12, secretion (117). IEC-specific IKKβ ($Ikbkb^{Villin\text{-}Cre}$) deletion results in decreased TSLP expression in IECs and a consequent inability to eradicate *Trichuris muris* infestation secondary to a failure to develop a protective Th2 response (116, 118). Instead, mucosal DCs in $Ikbkb^{Villin\text{-}Cre}$ or TSLP-receptor (*Crlf2*)-deficient mice exhibit increased IL-12/23p40 and TNF expression and $CD4^+$ T cells deviated to IFN-γ and IL-17 secretion. Consequently, these mice develop severe intestinal inflammation (116). Indeed, neutralization of IL-12/23p40 and IFN-γ in *Trichuris*-infested $Ikbkb^{Villin\text{-}Cre}$ or $Crlf2^{-/-}$ mice results in decreased IFN-γ and IL-17 expression and a concomitant increase in IL-13 expression, restored goblet cell function via increased

RELMβ expression, and worm expulsion (116, 118).

Another important aspect of IECs lies in their roles as physical barrier and source of antimicrobial peptides, both in defense against pathogenic invasions and in the maintenance of bacterial commensalism (36, 44, 76). Deletion of NEMO (*Ikbkg*), or both IKKα (*Ikbka*) and IKKβ, in IECs results in severe spontaneous colitis secondary to apoptosis of colonic IECs (119). This is associated with decreased production of antimicrobial peptides and translocation of bacteria into the mucosa, which triggers a spontaneous MyD88- and TNFR1-dependent chronic inflammatory response in the colon (119).

A20 (*Tnfaip3*) is a potent inhibitor of NF-κB signaling by restricting TNF and TLR signals via ubiquitin editing of RIP (120) and TNF receptor-associated factor 6 (TRAF6) (121), respectively. A20 also restricts MyD88-independent TLR signals by inhibiting Toll/IL-1 receptor domain-containing adaptor inducing IFN-β (TRIF)-dependent NF-κB signals (122) and MDP-induced NOD2 signaling (123). In a direct feed-back loop, A20 is phosphorylated by IKKβ, which increases its ability to inhibit NF-κB activation. Altogether, these properties render A20 a critical negative regulator of microbially derived signals, and *Tnfaip3*$^{-/-}$ mice succumb to severe inflammation in various organs, including the intestine (124). Notably, a polymorphism at *rs7753394*, with the closest gene being *TNFAIP3*, has been associated with CD (and other immune-related diseases) (125), implying a more general role of A20 in disease pathogenesis in addition to its role in restricting NOD2 signals.

METABOLIC ABNORMALITIES AND IMMUNE FUNCTION OF THE INTESTINAL EPITHELIUM IN IBD

The studies on NOD2 and NF-κB summarized above have furthered the interest in the intestinal epithelium in IBD as an immunophysiologic barrier rather than simply as a structural barrier whose "leakiness" might represent the sole factor antecedent to the development of IBD (**Figure 2**).

Endoplasmic Reticulum Stress of the Intestinal Epithelium

The unfolded protein response (UPR) is activated upon accumulation of misfolded proteins, which cause endoplasmic reticulum (ER) stress (126). Among three proximal effector pathways, inositol-requiring enzyme 1 (IRE1)/X-box binding protein 1 (XBP1) is the evolutionarily most conserved (126). UPR molecules are ubiquitously expressed, and the relative contribution of individual pathways in various cell types varies profoundly (126, 127). The intestinal epithelium is unique in that it selectively expresses an additional isoform of IRE1α, IRE1β, predicting critical dependency on an efficient UPR (128). Indeed, *IRE1*β$^{-/-}$ (*Ern2*) mice are more susceptible to DSS colitis in association with increased ER stress (128). IRE1 activates XBP1 via an unconventional splicing mechanism by excising a 26-nucleotide sequence from the unspliced *XBP1* mRNA, resulting in a frameshift and consequent production of an active transcription factor (XBP1s) that contains a DNA transactivating domain at the C terminus (126). *Xbp1* deletion in the intestinal epithelium results in unabated ER stress in the epithelium, spontaneous enteritis in the small intestine, and increased susceptibility to DSS colitis (46). Deletion of only one allele is sufficient to induce profound overactivation of IRE1 and enteritis in approximately one-third of mice (46). XBP1 regulates Paneth cell function, with a consequent defect in handling oral *Listeria monocytogenes* infection (46), similar to *Nod2*$^{-/-}$ mice (47). Deletion of *Xbp1* results in apoptotic depletion of Paneth cells and reduction in goblet cells, whereas IECs exhibit increased inflammatory responsiveness to TLR and cytokine signals (46). A candidate gene study revealed significant associations of the complex *XBP1* locus with both CD and UC (46). Three-fold more rare SNPs in CD and UC compared to healthy controls were found by deep sequencing, and CD-/UC-associated variants exhibit hypomorphic induction of UPR target genes (46).

A forward-genetic approach recently yielded the *Winnie* and *Eeyore* mouse models with spontaneous colitis resembling UC, which mapped to missense mutations in the *Muc2* gene (129). These variants led to aberrant MUC2 oligomerization and induction of ER stress in goblet cells, and goblet cells in UC exhibited a similar phenotype (129). The *woodrat* (*wrt*) forward-genetic model with a missense mutation in the membrane-bound transcription factor peptidase site 1 (S1P)-encoding gene (*Mbtps1*) provides another example of a link between the UPR and intestinal inflammation (130). S1P activates ATF6α, another proximal UPR mediator, upon ER stress (126). *Mbtps1*$^{wrt/wrt}$ mice exhibited increased sensitivity to DSS colitis, with abnormal *Mbtps1* function mapping to nonhematopoietic cells (130). Moreover, administration of the ER stress inducer tunicamycin results in severe colitis in *Mbtps1*$^{wrt/wrt}$ but not in wild-type mice (130).

The HLA-B27 transgenic rat model of spontaneous colitis may serve as a final example of the association between ER stress and intestinal inflammation (30). The human HLA-B27 heavy chain is remarkably unstable, suggesting that its misfolding induces ER stress in certain tissues (e.g., stomach, intestines, joints, liver, skin), which in turn correlates closely with the extent of colitis (131), presumably through mechanisms as described above. This observation could also explain the high prevalence of (asymptomatic) ileitis in patients with HLA-B27-associated spondyloarthropathies.

In summary, a proper ER stress response in the intestinal epithelium appears to be necessary to maintain homeostasis, with the most highly secretory cell types (Paneth and goblet cells) most vulnerable to these effects. XBP1 and ER stress in general may regulate the ability of the intestinal epithelium to both regulate and sense the composition of the luminal microbiota, which sets the inflammatory tone of the IEC. These studies also suggest that alterations in IECs may be a primordial factor in the development of IBD. Environmental and microbial factors can modulate ER stress in beneficial and detrimental ways (72), and increased ER stress may be a common occurrence in human IBD (46, 129, 132). Thus, primary (genetic) or secondary (environmental) pathways (and their interactions) that lead to ER stress within environmentally exposed and highly secretory cells appear to be an important pathway for development of IBD (133).

Autophagy and IBD

Macroautophagy, a fundamental and evolutionary highly conserved response to fasting, is a lysosomal pathway that is involved in the turnover of cellular macromolecules and organelles and plays an important role in a variety of biological processes as diverse as infection, immunity, cancer, and aging (134). Autophagy is activated by a variety of conditions of cellular stress including ER stress (135) and involves formation of double-membraned autophagosomes engulfing cellular contents that later fuse with lysosomes. The connection between ER stress and autophagy involves several levels and likely differs between cell types (135). ER stress may activate autophagy through the ability of IRE1 to associate with TRAF2 and activate JNK or through PERK-mediated inhibition of eIF2α (135).

It is thus interesting that a GWAS discovered *ATG16L1* as a genetic risk factor that is specific for CD, but not for UC (14). Virtually all the risk of this locus was exerted by *rs2241880*, which codes for a T300A substitution (14). *rs2241880* was also one of the main associations reported in another GWAS on CD (63). Together with the identification of polymorphisms close to another gene involved in autophagy, *IRGM* (125), these studies together revealed a previously unanticipated role for autophagy in the pathogenesis of CD.

Insight into the potential mechanism of ATG16L1 in CD stems from studies in *Atg16l1* hypomorphic and deficient mice. ATG16L1 deficiency disrupts the recruitment of the

ATG12-ATG5 conjugate to the isolation membrane, and a consequence is severe impairment in autophagosome formation and degradation of long-lived proteins (136). Stimulation of *Atg16l1*$^{-/-}$ macrophages with LPS resulted in high production of IL-1β and IL-18 via TRIF-dependent activation of caspase-1, showing that ATG16L1 regulates LPS-induced inflammasome activation (136). Deficiency of ATG16L1 in bone marrow resulted in increased susceptibility to DSS colitis, which could be alleviated by IL-1β and IL-18 blockade (136). Hypomorphic ATG16L1 variants and IEC-specific *Atg5* deletion revealed abnormalities in the granule exocytosis pathway of Paneth cells, including disorganized granules and decreased granule numbers (45). Similar alterations were found in CD patients homozygous for the *ATG16L1* risk allele (45). Despite these abnormalities, ATG16L1 hypomorphic mice—in contrast to *Nod2*$^{-/-}$ (47) and *Xbp1*$^{Villin\text{-}Cre}$ (46) mice, which also exhibit Paneth cell defects—exhibited no impairment upon oral *Listeria monocytogenes* infection. Paneth cells in ATG16L1-hypomorphic mice also revealed altered expression of genes involved in PPAR signaling and lipid metabolism together with increased production of the adipocytokines, leptin, and adiponectin (45), implicating them in the regulation of intestinal inflammation. Mice deficient in ATG16L1 in the bone marrow—or ATG16L1 hypomorphic mice—do not, however, develop spontaneous enteritis (45, 136). A knock-down/reconstitution strategy in vitro revealed that the *ATG16L1*^{T300A} variant resembles NOD2 function (88, 101) by exhibiting impaired capture of *Salmonella typhimurium* within autophagosomes with no effect on basal autophagy (137). Consistent with this, the autophagic response can be triggered by NOD1 or NOD2 upon intracellular infection with invasive bacteria, which function in inducing the recruitment of ATG16L1 to the plasma membrane (102, 103). The *ATG16L1*^{T300A} is associated with impaired NOD2-dependent induction of autophagy upon stimulation with MDP (102, 103). Thus, these two genetic risk factors (*NOD2* and *ATG16L1*) function in a common pathway that involves bacterially induced autophagy and the consequent induction of antigen-specific T cells, and this pathway is also impaired in the absence of normal NOD2 function (103).

A 20-kb deletion polymorphism immediately upstream of *IRGM*, resulting in an altered expression pattern (138), was identified as the potential causal variant of the second autophagy gene discovered in association with CD (125, 139). IRGM belongs to the IFN-γ-induced p47 immunity-related GTPase family (140). Its mouse homolog, LRG-47 (encoded by *Irgm1*), controls intracellular pathogens by autophagy (141), and *Irgm1*$^{-/-}$ mice exhibit increased susceptibility to *Toxoplasma gondii*, *Listeria monocytogenes*, and *Mycobacterium tuberculosis* infection (142) due to decreased bacterial killing in *Irgm1*$^{-/-}$ macrophages (142).

These studies reveal a convergence of several genetic risk factors for IBD (*NOD2*, *XBP1*, and *ATG16L1*) on the function of the intestinal epithelium and especially Paneth cells and concurrently on the regulation of inflammatory pathways in both the epithelium and myeloid cells. Hence, these epithelial cell functions, which are likely susceptible to environmental modification, may be important determinants of the propensity to develop IBD. Although Paneth cell dysfunction may lead to dysbiosis or altered adherence of bacteria to the epithelium (36), isolated Paneth cell deletion (143) and inability to activate their antimicrobial function (144) are not associated with spontaneous intestinal inflammation. It might therefore be hypothesized that dysbiosis must be coupled with immune hypersensitivity to the commensal microbiota to develop intestinal inflammation.

Organic Carnitine and Cation Transporters and β-oxidation

The UPR and autophagy pathways regulate important cellular "metabolic" functions associated with diet (145, 146). Given the complex metabolic environment at the host-microbiota interface, and the potential contribution of environmental/nutritional factors to

IBD [e.g., increasing incidence upon "Westernization" (3, 147)], it is notable that another genuine metabolic function, β-oxidation, is implicated in CD pathogenesis. Expression quantitative trait locus (eQTL) analysis suggests that *SLC22A5* (20), encoding OCTN2, is the associated gene at the *IBD5* locus (148). OCTN2 is a Na^+-dependent, high-affinity L-carnitine transporter and a polyspecific Na^+-independent cation transporter (149). Carnitine has an obligatory role for transport of long-chain fatty acids into mitochondria for β-oxidation, which is of particular importance to the energy metabolism of IECs and liver (150). Gastrointestinal carnitine content in *Slc22a5*$^{-/-}$ mice is reduced to 5–10% of normal (151). This is associated with increased IEC apoptosis, abnormal villus structure, and inflammatory infiltration in the mucosa with the spontaneous development of small intestinal perforations and (micro) abscesses (151). Similarly, pharmacological inhibition of gut fatty acid β-oxidation also results in experimental colitis (152). Genetically decreased *SLC22A5* expression in CD (20) may become particularly relevant in metabolically "challenged" IECs owing to alterations in the microbiota or, in the context of inflammation, when energy needs are increased, due to increased catabolism.

Role of CD1d-Restricted Natural Killer T Cells in IBD

In concluding a discussion of metabolic factors and immune function, we briefly consider the biology of natural killer T (NKT) cells in relationship to IBD. NKT cells respond to phospholipids or glycolipids that are presented by CD1d on an APC leading to an "innate-like" rapid response through secretion of abundant numbers of Th1, Th2, and Th17 cytokines that subsequently trigger almost all branches of the innate and adaptive immune systems (153). NKT cells can be activated by various mechanisms, including direct activation by presentation of self- or microbial-derived lipids by the nonclassical MHC class I molecule CD1d and indirect cytokine-mediated activation mainly through IL-12 and IL-18 (153). The inflamed lamina propria of UC but not of CD patients contains increased numbers of T cells expressing the NK marker CD161, which respond to CD1d with increased secretion of IL-13 (154). However, in humans these NKT cells do not react with CD1d tetramers loaded with the invariant (i) NKT cell ligand α-galactosylceramide and therefore must be considered as type II or noninvariant NKT cells (154). Consistent with this, mice deficient in CD1d and NKT cells are resistant to oxazolone colitis, a murine model of ulcerative colitis (155). However, in contrast to human UC, invariant NKT cells were observed to be the main effectors in oxazolone colitis (155).

The mechanism(s) by which CD1d and NKT cells may be involved in UC pathogenesis remains to be established, but several possibilities exist. Many different cell types that are present in the intestines express CD1d, including DCs, macrophages, B cells, and IECs (156). This raises the questions of whether a particular cell type is responsible for NKT cell activation in colitis and whether the various CD1d-expressing cells in the intestines play differential, protective, or pathogenic roles in colitis as previously described for NF-κB (109, 157) and TLR4 (112). Interestingly, IEC-specific deletion of the microsomal triglyceride transfer protein that normally lipidates apolipoprotein-B during absorption of dietary lipids, and that also assists in loading nascent lipid antigens onto CD1d within the ER and is necessary for CD1d-restricted antigen presentation (158), leads to increased mortality upon oxazolone challenge, which can be prevented by systemic antibody-mediated blockade of CD1d (T. Olszack, S. Zeissig, A. Kaser, and R.S. Blumberg, unpublished observations). These findings suggest a protective role of CD1d on IECs in murine oxazolone colitis in contrast to a pathogenic role of CD1d on hematopoietic cells. The importance of these findings is highlighted by the fact that IECs of IBD subjects exhibit decreased CD1d expression (159) while overall CD1d expression in the lamina propria is increased, presumably owing to mononuclear cell infiltration (160). This proinflammatory effect of CD1d on hematopoietic cells may be mediated by IL-23 and the IL-23R, both of which are genetic risk factors for both CD and UC (see below). IL-23R is expressed on NKT cells and regulates IL-17 expression by NKT cells (161). CD1d-restricted NKT cells have also been linked to the pathogenesis of asthma, which, similar to UC, is associated with increased secretion of IL-13 (162).

INNATE IMMUNE CYTOKINE PATHWAYS AND IBD

Abnormalities of innate immune function and their relationship to the commensal microbiota have been identified to be key properties that characterize the immunogenetic profile of human IBD and animal models of intestinal inflammation, as described in detail above. Another line of evidence that supports a central role of innate immune functional abnormalities in IBD pathogenesis is the cytokine environment that is observed, as well as the efficacy of therapies that are directed at the specific cytokines and the cells that are responsible for their production. The experience with biologic therapies in humans with IBD is particularly instructive in furthering our understanding of the immunogenetic pathogenesis of these disorders and in assigning relevance to potential functional pathways (see **Supplemental Table 2**).

TNF and TNF-Related Cytokines (TL1A)

The currently most efficacious treatment for IBD is anti-TNF antibodies (8). Surprisingly, the mechanistic basis of their effectiveness remains enigmatic, as does the specific relationship of TNF to the genetic underpinning of IBD. It is noteworthy that *TNF* is located 1 MB apart from the MHC locus, which has been associated with UC more so than with CD (163). The dramatic efficacy of anti-TNF antibodies predicts it is a major factor on which many pathways associated with IBD converge.

TNF acts as a transmembrane or soluble protein by transducing signals ranging from cellular activation and proliferation to cytotoxicity and apoptosis through two distinct TNF receptors, TNFR1 (p55) and TNFR2 (p75) (164). NF-κB and NF-AT control *Tnf* transcription, and AU-rich elements (ARE) in the 5′ UTR control mRNA destabilization and translational repression (165). $Tnf^{\Delta ARE}$ mice overproduce TNF and develop inflammatory polyarthritis and spondyloarthritis and CD-like deep transmural intestinal inflammation with granulomas primarily in the terminal ileum (165, 166). Intestinal pathology is attenuated in $Tnfr2^{-/-}Tnf^{\Delta ARE}$ double mutants and is absent in $Tnfr1^{-/-}Tnf^{\Delta ARE}$ mice (165). $Rag1^{-/-}Tnf^{\Delta ARE}$ mice exhibit only mild inflammation confined to the intestinal mucosa (165). This suggests that TNF can inflict superficial injury in the absence of mature B and T cells, but such are required for transmural inflammation typical of CD and severe disease observed in $Tnf^{\Delta ARE}$ mice. The superficial inflammation observed in $Rag1^{-/-}Tnf^{\Delta ARE}$ mice is reminiscent of TNFR1-dependent inflammation observed in $Rag2^{-/-}Tbx21^{-/-}$ mice (57). Bone marrow and parenchymal cells are equally responsive to the pathogenic effects of TNF in the development of intestinal inflammation in the $Tnf^{\Delta ARE}$ model (166, 167). Interestingly, TNFR1 on mesenchymal cells adjacent to IECs appears to be particularly important for disease in $Tnf^{\Delta ARE}$ mice, which may regulate the balance of matrix metalloproteinases (MMP) and inhibitor of MMP (TIMP) expression, leading to leukocyte recruitment and tissue destruction (166, 168). Thus, one mechanism of anti-TNF therapies may be through blockade of a superficial pathway of tissue injury that is common to both UC and CD and involves TNF production by parenchymal cells or innate immune cells that act upon TNFR1 within superficial cellular structures of the gut. Consistent with this, human colon IECs express TNF (along with GM-CSF, CXCL8, CCL2, and IL-6) ex vivo upon exposure to inflammatory stimuli or pathogenic bacteria (169). Moreover, IEC apoptosis is increased in CD and reduced upon anti-TNF antibody treatment (170). In a similar manner, blockade of TNF reduces IEC apoptosis in the *Rag2*$^{-/-}$*Tbx21*$^{-/-}$ (57), *Ikbkg*$^{\Delta IEC}$ (119), and SAMP1/YitFc (171) models.

Transmural, CD-like inflammation in *Tnf*$^{\Delta ARE}$ mice requires CD8^{+} T cells, is dependent on IL-12/23p40 and IFN-γ, and is regulated by CD4^{+} T cells (167). IFN-γ-secreting CD8^{+} effector T cells are also involved in a hapten-mediated colitis model (172), suggesting that CD8 effectors are more important in IBD than currently appreciated. Myeloid cells or T (Th1) lymphocytes may be sources of TNF (167). However, numerous other cell types, including Paneth cells and adipocytes, exist that may promote inflammation within their specific intestinal microenvironments (173). TNF also plays an important role in other models of intestinal inflammation, like TNBS-induced models (174), in *Il10*$^{-/-}$ mice (175), and in the spontaneous UC-like disease in the cotton-top tamarin model (176). Notably, nonlymphocyte-derived TNF was sufficient for the development of colitis in the CD45RB^{high} transfer model with TNF found in macrophages (localized close to epithelial erosions) and colonic epithelial cells, especially during early phases of disease (177). In the CD45RB^{high} transfer model of colitis, continuous anti-TNF antibody treatment was required to decrease disease severity (178). Expression of noncleavable membrane-bound TNF in *Rag2*$^{-/-}$*Tnf*$^{-/-}$ recipients that lack soluble TNF is sufficient to cause colitis upon transfer of TNF-deficient CD4^{+}CD45RB^{high} T cells (179). TNF^{+} cells are increased in the lamina propria of both UC and CD, with localization confined to subepithelial macrophages (UC) or evenly distributed throughout the lamina propria (CD) (180). Overall, these studies suggest that in transmural colitis, TNF is likely derived from many different cell types and that pathogenic T cells may create a permissive environment for the inflammatory effects of TNF to occur. Moreover, they highlight the pathologic potential of TNF in both UC and CD and the importance of the membrane-bound TNF in its own right, which is consistent with the role of anti-TNF-induced apoptosis as a therapeutic pathway in CD (181). Specifically, retrograde signaling via transmembrane TNF has been suggested to distinguish effective (anti-TNF) and ineffective (TNFR2-Fc) TNF-targeted therapies in CD (8, 181). However, it should be noted that in oxazolone-induced colitis (155, 182), a TNFR1-IgG$_1$-fusion protein led to more extensive disease (183), which was associated with decreased TGF-β_1. TGF-β_1 usually limits the extent of disease to the distal part of the colon (184). Because TNFR1-Fc (and TNFR2-Fc) may bind both soluble TNF and lymphotoxin-α, this may reflect a role for lymphotoxin-α in regulating TGF-β production and intestinal inflammation.

Polymorphisms in *TNFSF15* (encoding TL1A, TNF ligand–related molecule 1A), another TNF-related family member, confer substantial risk for CD in Japanese and Korean cohorts with ORs of up to 2.40 and 3.49, respectively (185, 186), as compared to the relatively modest OR of 1.22 exhibited in the Caucasian GWAS meta-analysis (20). TL1A is a TNF-like cytokine that is increased in CD and interacts with the death domain receptor (DR3), which signals through NF-κB (187). TL1A is produced by human DCs and monocytes and enhances IFN-γ production by T and NK cells (187). Both DSS-induced colitis and the spontaneous colitis in SAMP1/Yit mice exhibit increased expression of TL1A, DR3, and Th1 and Th17 cytokines, which are decreased together with mucosal inflammation by neutralization of TL1A (188, 189). This highlights TL1A as another example of an innate immune-derived (TNF-related) molecule that drives adaptive immune-mediated, intestinal inflammation, and it is tantalizing to speculate that this might be a particularly interesting therapeutic target in Asians with IBD.

IL-6, gp130, JAK2, and STAT3

IL-6 signals through the IL-6R expressed on the cell surface and through soluble IL-6R (sIL-6R) via binding of the sIL-6R/IL-6 complex to the transmembrane receptor β subunit gp130 (*trans* signaling) (190). Redundancy within the IL-6 family, which comprises IL-6, IL-11, leukemia inhibitory factor, oncostatin M, ciliary neurotrophic factor, and cardiotrophin-1, is attributed to the common use of gp130. gp130 signals via two distinct pathways: The first is Janus kinase (JAK) 1, JAK2, and tyrosine kinase 2 (Tyk2) and consequent signal transducer and activator of transcription 3 (STAT3) activation. The second pathway is through STAT1 leading to activation of NF-κB. The second pathway involves engagement of src-homology tyrosine phosphatase (SHP2) and subsequent activation of the Ras-ERK pathway.

IL-6 and sIL-6 secretion is increased in both CD and UC mucosa and likely derives predominantly from non-T cells (191). Phosphorylated STAT3 expression indicates T cells and macrophages as the major targets of IL-6 signaling (191). IL-6 *trans* signaling is important for the survival of $CD4^+$ T cells, and possibly macrophages, and for their production of inflammatory cytokines such as TNF, IFN-γ, and IL-1β (191, 192). IL-6 plays an important role in immune-deviating T cells from a Treg fate toward an inflammatory (i.e., Th17) phenotype (193–195). Consistent with this, blockade of IL-6 *trans* signaling via a gp130-Fc decoy receptor or complete IL-6R signaling via an anti-IL-6R antibody ameliorates colitis in the $CD45RB^{high}$ transfer model, in the TNBS model, and in *Il10*$^{-/-}$ mice (191, 192). This is associated with increased apoptosis of lamina propria mononuclear cells implying that excess IL-6 secretion by innate immune cells promotes the survival and activity of proinflammatory T cells (and possibly macrophages), which drive inflammation (191, 192).

Accordingly, a placebo-controlled pilot trial reported benefit of an anti-IL-6R in active CD (**Supplemental Table 2**). Polymorphisms close to *STAT3* and within *STAT3* have been associated with CD (20, 125) and UC (196). Moreover, a polymorphism in the *JAK2* promoter region also associates with CD (20) and UC (197), highlighting the importance of IL-6-gp130-JAK2-STAT3 related pathways in both forms of IBD. However, the pleiotropic relationships that JAK2 (e.g., gp130 family members, IFN-γ, IL-12) and STAT3 (e.g., gp130 family members; IL-10; leptin; IL-12; and γ_c family members such as IL-2, IL-7, IL-9, IL-15, and IL-21) have with cytokine signaling pathways are considerable such that it cannot be concluded that the associations identified between *JAK2* and *STAT3* and IBD are definitively related to the biology of IL-6-mediated signaling.

Additional complexity stems from the fact that gp130 signaling involves two cascades with distinct biologic consequences (STAT1/STAT3-NF-κB mediated and SHP2-Ras-ERK mediated) that have unique effects on the intestinal epithelium. Deletion of the STAT binding domain (*gp130*$^{\Delta STAT}$) leads to spontaneous ulcerations of the rectum (198) and augments DSS-induced colitis (199), implying a cytoprotective role for gp130-induced STAT3 (and STAT1) signaling in IECs (200, 201). In line with this, IEC-specific *Stat3* deletion results in augmented DSS-induced epithelial erosions and subsequent mucosal inflammation, whereas STAT3 overactivation confers protection (202). *Gp130*$^{\Delta STAT}$ mice also lack intestinal epithelial trefoil factor (TFF) 3 expression (199), a cytoprotective molecule associated with mucins, and *Tff3*$^{-/-}$ mice consequently phenocopy the sensitivity to DSS administration (203) observed in *gp130*$^{\Delta STAT}$ mice. IECs also express the IL-6R on the basal surface, and its ligation activates NF-κB (200, 201), which, as discussed above, provides important protective signals to the epithelium.

Mice with disabled gp130-related SHP2-Ras-ERK activation, however, do not exhibit spontaneous mucosal ulcerations, are protected from DSS colitis, and exhibit increased levels of TFF3 expression and increased STAT1/STAT3 activation (199). If one takes together (*a*) the genetic studies that find an association of *JAK2* and *STAT3* with IBD, (*b*) the amelioration of colitis in mouse models through blockade of

IL-6 signaling (191, 192), and (*c*) the potential benefit of anti-IL-6R therapy in human CD (**Supplemental Table 2**), then in IBD there may be loss of epithelial cytoprotective function of IL-6. This loss of function is due to disabled STAT1/STAT3-mediated, gp130-associated signaling together with excess promotion of inflammatory pathways by IL-6, derived predominantly from innate immune cells within the lamina propria.

Apart from IECs, STAT3 activation by IL-6, IL-10, and other cytokines (mentioned above) in myeloid cells also has important implications for IBD. Deletion of floxed exon 22 of *Stat3* in macrophages and neutrophils via *LysM-Cre* results in spontaneous transmural enterocolitis with depletion of goblet cells (26), along with augmented LPS-induced expression of inflammatory cytokines (26). A comparable phenotype is observed upon deletion of exons 18–20 of *Stat3* in bone marrow and endothelial cells by *Tie2-Cre* (204), which is associated with the formation of granuloma-like structures and crypt abscesses. Similar to $Stat3^{LysM\text{-}Cre}$, LPS-stimulation of $Stat3^{Tie2\text{-}Cre}$ myeloid cells leads to increased IκBα phosphorylation along with increased NF-κB DNA binding activity (204).

These studies suggest that, in the context of a specific inability of macrophages in the intestines to respond to STAT3-mediated signals as may be delivered by IL-10, augmented responses to microbial signals and consequently intestinal inflammation are observed. Accordingly, enterocolitis is improved in $Tlr4^{-/-}Stat3^{LysM\text{-}Cre}$ mice. Moreover, this macrophage-induced inflammation in the absence of STAT3 requires IL-12p40 and lymphocytes because inflammation is ameliorated in $Il12b\ [p40]^{-/-}Stat3^{LysM\text{-}Cre}$ and $Rag2^{-/-}Stat3^{LysM\text{-}Cre}$ mice, respectively (205). Because inflammation is not ameliorated by loss of STAT1 expression, which is essential for IFN-γ signaling, it might be surmised that the critical cytokine derived from aggressive STAT3-deficient macrophages leading to inflammation is IL-23, although this needs to be directly tested.

NLRP3 and the IL-1 Cytokine Family

Although the prototypical innate proinflammatory mediator IL-1β has been known for decades as an important contributor to mucosal inflammation (206, 207), recent evidence has reinvigorated interest in the relationship of IL-1β to IBD. Specifically, polymorphisms in *NLRP3*, encoding NALP3/cryopyrin, have been associated with CD in a candidate-gene study (208). NALP3 within the inflammasome directs the conversion of procaspase-1 to caspase-1 and generates secretory IL-1β and IL-18 (206, 207). Hypermorphic missense mutations of *NLRP3* and consequently increased IL-1β are linked to rare autoinflammatory disorders (206). Notably, CD-associated *NLRP3* polymorphisms appear to be linked to decreased IL-1β secretion from LPS-stimulated peripheral blood cells (208). A primary relationship between IL-1/IL-18 and IBD is also highlighted by a CD- and UC-associated SNP within the IL-18 receptor accessory protein gene (*IL18RAP*) that identifies a 350-kb haplotype block in strong linkage disequilibrium containing *IL1RL1-IL18R1-IL18RAP-SLC9A4* (209). Decreased IL-1β production upon MDP stimulation has similarly been reported in myeloid cells of patients carrying risk-associated *NOD2* variants (94, 210, 211). These genetic studies suggest that inadequate innate IL-1β (and possibly IL-18) activity could be a risk pathway for CD and UC, perhaps at the level of the epithelial barrier.

However, these considerations contrast with observations in human IBD tissues and in experimental models. IL-1β expression, relative to IL-1 receptor antagonist (IL-1ra), is increased in IBD intestinal tissues (212). Moreover, administration of anti-IL-1β (213) or IL-1ra (214) ameliorates experimental rabbit immune complex colitis, whereas neutralization of IL-1ra increases its severity (215). Similarly, IL-18 expression is increased in IBD, particularly in IECs (216, 217). Neutralization of IL-18 ameliorates DSS colitis, and, of note, increased IL-18 expression in this model localizes to

IECs (218). Administration of the natural IL-18 antagonist, IL-18 binding protein (IL-18BP), also ameliorates DSS colitis (219). A major proinflammatory role of IL-18 in experimental intestinal inflammation was also deduced from experiments in the TNBS (220, 221) and *scid* transfer (222) models of colitis. Genetic deletion of caspase-1, which impairs the downstream function of the NALP3 inflammasome and hence IL-1β and IL-18 processing, similarly ameliorates DSS colitis (223). These studies suggest that excessive IL-1 and IL-18 may promote chronic intestinal inflammation.

To reconcile these data with the genetic studies, it is reasonable to consider the possibility that an inadequate IL-1 (and potentially IL-18) response during innate management of the luminal interface may predispose to IBD through an uncontrolled adaptive immune response. IL-1 and IL-18 are also both important links to balanced expression of Th17 (224–226) and Th1 (206) pathways, respectively. In addition, IL-1 may intersect with other primary (genetically mediated) risk pathways. For example, IL-1β expression is increased in *Atg16l1*$^{-/-}$ myeloid cells (136); IL-1β is an important inducer of IL-6, and, interestingly, several α-defensins, including human α-defensin 5, decrease IL-1β secretion, raising the final possibility that elevated IL-1β may result from Paneth cell dysfunction (227).

ADAPTIVE IMMUNE PATHWAYS AND THEIR RELATIONSHIPS WITH INNATE IMMUNE PATHWAYS

As reviewed above, a model for the pathogenesis of IBD emerges that supports an inappropriate relationship between the commensal microbiota—the IEC barrier—and innate immunity that leads to inappropriate release of cytokines and other mediators that are inflammatory in their own right, abnormalities of the physiologic barrier that exists between the intestinal lumen and lamina propria and its consequences as well as cytokines that promote the inflammatory activity of adaptive immune cells. There are many layers in this model, some of which are outlined above and include both an inappropriate drive to innate immune signaling from an abnormal commensal bacterial architecture and an inadequate degree of innate immune regulation through pathways intrinsic to the pattern-recognition receptor (PRR)-associated pathways themselves. In this section, we review the manner in which innate immune signaling links to the adaptive immune system that leads to the chronic inflammation characteristic of IBD as well as the abnormalities that appear to reside within regulatory pathways that typically provide restraint to both innate and adaptive immune pathways. Because these latter topics have been extensively reviewed recently (228), they are only discussed in an abbreviated manner here.

IL-12 and IL-23

IL-12 and IL-23, secreted by DCs secondary to PRR-derived signals, are highly related heterodimeric cytokines sharing the IL-12p40 subunit (12). IL-12 (p35 and p40 heterodimer) supports Th1, while IL-23 (p19 and p40) supports Th17 pathways (229). IL-12 was originally linked with intestinal inflammation in the TNBS colitis model based upon studies that neutralized the p40 chain (230). Anti-IL-12p40 treatment resulted in decreased IFN-γ production from lamina propria CD4$^+$ T cells (230). Further support for the IL-12/Th1 pathway emerged when abrogation of the Th1 effector cytokine IFN-γ in the CD4$^+$ CD45RB^{high}/*Rag*$^{-/-}$ transfer model potently protected from colitis and when T-bet-deficient CD4$^+$CD45RB^{high} cells were unable to induce colitis in *Rag*$^{-/-}$ recipients (178, 231, 232). Moreover, human lamina propria mononuclear cells exhibit increased IFN-γ secretion in CD in contrast to UC and controls (233). In the context of the epidemiologically detrimental relationship of smoking and CD, it is notable that chronic stimulation of the α_7 nicotinic acetylcholine receptor on T cells leads to Th1 responses (234, 235).

These studies led to the development of anti-IL-12p40 (ABT864 and ustekinumab) and anti-IFN-γ antibodies as potential therapeutics for CD. Treatment with ABT864 increased response rates compared to placebo, although remission rates were not different (**Supplemental Table 2**). Neutralization of IL-12p40 decreased Th1- and Th17-associated cytokines within the intestinal tissues. In contrast, IFN-γ neutralization with fontolizumab was unexpectedly not or only partially effective in CD (**Supplemental Table 2**). Although these studies are consistent with a role for IL-12p40, the effector arm of this pathway in human IBD remains unclear.

The first GWAS in Caucasians detected a strong association of *IL23R* polymorphisms with CD and UC (13). Specifically, an uncommon coding variant (*rs11209026*, $IL23R^{G1142A}$, Arg381Gln) conferred protection from disease, and additional noncoding *IL23R* variants were independently shown to confer risk (13). Because the *IL23R* locus is also associated with psoriasis and ankylosing spondylitis, this pathway may be of general importance for auto-inflammatory diseases (15, 236). Similarly, polymorphisms at *IL12B* (encoding IL-12p40) have been associated with both CD (139) and UC (196, 237).

These observations followed the first report on the then novel cytokine IL-23 in 2000 (238) and the realization that several pathologies, in particular experimental autoimmune encephalitis (EAE) (239) and collagen-induced arthritis (240), that had been ascribed to IL-12 are also linked to IL-23. In EAE and uveitis models, IL-12 and IL-23 are both pathogenic and contribute to distinct patterns of inflammation (241, 242). The relative roles of IL-12 and/or IL-23 have also been reevaluated in experimental colitis. In a model of innate experimental colitis induced in immunodeficient $Rag1^{-/-}$ mice by agonistic anti-CD40 antibodies, IL-23 blockade via anti-IL-23p19 blocked intestinal pathology but did not affect wasting disease or systemic inflammation; in contrast, anti-IL-12p40 blocked all aspects of disease (243). Similar results were obtained in $p19^{-/-}$ and $p40^{-/-}$ mice (243). Notably, in this innate model of colitis lacking T cells (see below), colonic IL-17A mRNA was 65-fold upregulated upon anti-CD40, which was IL-23-dependent (243). A similar role for IL-23 was reported in *Helicobacter hepaticus*–induced typhlocolitis in $Rag2^{-/-}$ mice, which was also associated with upregulation of IL-17 (in granulocytes, monocytes, and $Gr1^{-}CD11b^{-}$ cells) and confined to the colon (244). In a variation of the *H. hepaticus* model in T cell sufficient hosts treated with anti-IL-10R, $p35^{-/-}$ mice developed colitis similar in severity to wild-type mice, but $p40^{-/-}$ mice were protected (245). In the T cell–mediated $CD45RB^{high}$ model, colitis was prevented in $Rag2^{-/-}$ recipients deficient in *p40* or *p19*, but not *p35* (244), again supporting a role for IL-23. The results with $p35^{-/-}$ mice (244) must be interpreted with caution because p35 is also a component of a third IL-12 family member, IL-35 [heterodimer with Epstein Barr virus–induced gene 3 (EBI3)] (246). IL-35 is mainly produced by $FoxP3^{+}$ Tregs and exerts significant regulatory functions (246).

Nonetheless, these studies support a proinflammatory role for IL-23 in intestinal inflammation, and, consistent with this, IL-23 administration accelerates colitis development in $Rag^{-/-}$ mice reconstituted with $CD45RB^{high}$ naive $CD4^{+}$ T cells or with memory $CD4^{+}$ T cells from $Il10^{-/-}$ mice (247). Moreover, blockade of IL-6 and IL-17, but not of either cytokine alone starting prior to reconstitution of $Rag^{-/-}$ mice with $CD45RB^{high}$ T cells (derived from $Il10^{-/-}$ mice), significantly ameliorates colitis (247). IL-17 is thought to exert proinflammatory activities by inducing CXC chemokines and other chemoattractants from endothelial and epithelial cells, which broadly express the IL-17 receptor (248). IL-17 also contributes to an inflammatory response syndrome subsequent to systemic TNF administration; Paneth cells appear to be an important source of IL-17 in this model. Taken together, these studies support an important role for not only IL-12 but also IL-23 derived from innate immune cells as a driver of chronic intestinal inflammation in CD and, potentially, UC and have focused attention on Th17 cells because of the potential role of Th-derived IL-17 in mediating these processes.

Th17 Cells

Th17 cells, characterized by IL-17 (also known as IL-17A), IL-17F, and IL-22 production, constitute a distinct T helper cell lineage that differentiates from naive T helper cells (249, 250). Th17 cells are important in host defense against bacterial and fungal infections, in particular at mucosal surfaces (248). TCR ligation, IL-6, and TGF-β are required for Th17 lineage commitment (193, 224). IL-6 via STAT3 and TGF-β induce transcription of RORγt (251), a member of the retinoic acid–related orphan nuclear hormone receptor family. RORγt directs the differentiation of Th17 cells, and *Rorc*$^{-/-}$ mice lack Th17 cells (251). IL-23R is upregulated on RORγt^{+} Th17 cells by IL-6, and IL-23 expands committed Th17 cells (251). An intriguing feature of IL-23 and Th17 cells is their selective and constitutive presence in the intestinal lamina propria especially within the small intestine, which is dependent on the microbial flora (251, 252). The germ-free state or treatment with broad-spectrum antibiotics decreases lamina propria Th17 cells (39, 251, 253). Specific components drive the expansion of Th17 cells in the intestine, as a single commensal microbe, segmented filamentous bacterium (SFB), which adheres tightly to the surface of IECs in the terminal ileum, induces Th17 cells upon colonization of germ-free mice (40, 41). Adenosine 5′-triphosphate (ATP), which may derive from commensal bacteria, may activate CD70^{high}CD11c^{low} lamina propria cells leading to colonic Th17 differentiation (253). Germ-free mice contain much lower ATP levels in their intestinal lumen compared to specific pathogen–free mice (253) and exhibit a corollary increase in FoxP3^{+} Tregs. Moreover, CD70^{high}CD11c^{low} lamina propria cells express IL-6, IL-23p19, and TGF-β-activating integrin $\alpha_V\beta_8$ after ATP stimulation, which are required for Th17 differentiation and consequently for intestinal inflammation (253, 254). Hence, microbial-derived metabolic factors such as ATP, which act upon purinergic receptors (P2X and P2Y), might be critical factors for Th17 differentiation in the intestine.

A recent study assessed the role of Th17-derived IL-17 in the CD45RB^{high} transfer model (255). Transfer of *Il17a*$^{-/-}$ CD45RB^{high} T cells into *Rag1*$^{-/-}$ hosts unexpectedly increased the severity of colitis compared to wild-type transfer, which was associated with increased IFN-γ in the colon (255). Investigators proposed that IL-17A modulates Th1 polarization, suggesting that excessive IFN-γ is the inflammatory factor in the absence of Th-derived IL-17A. Similarly, transfer of *Il17r*$^{-/-}$ T cells also induced more severe disease compared to wild-type cells, suggesting T cells as both source and target of IL-17 (255). In this context, it is noteworthy that neutralization of IL-17 (256) or genetic deletion of IL-17 (257) is also associated with exacerbation of DSS-induced colitis, while *Il17f*$^{-/-}$ mice were protected from DSS colitis (257). These studies suggest that IL-17A is surprisingly anti-inflammatory through an undefined mechanism. However, to the contrary, in the TNBS colitis model IL-17 is proinflammatory (258). These apparently ambiguous functions of IL-17 as an effector cytokine contrast with the clearly demonstrated proinflammatory role of IFN-γ, at least in the experimental models discussed above (178, 231). Given recent studies showing that reversal of IL-17-mediated inflammation requires neutralization of both IL-17A and IL-17F (259), we may consider that (*a*) IL-17A provides a protective function during mucosal inflammation, perhaps through inhibition of IFN-γ, but that (*b*) unopposed IL-17F may drive intestinal inflammation through a pathway that involves promotion of IFN-γ production. Clearly, the functional relationships between IL-17-related family members and IFN-γ and their relationship with IL-12p40-related cytokines deserves attention in the normal intestine and in IBD.

IL-17 expression, which maps to T lymphocytes and monocytes/macrophages, is increased in both CD and UC (260). In normal human colonic mucosa, IL-17-producing $CD4^+$ T cells are markedly infrequent compared to IFN-γ-producing cells, but their frequency is substantially increased in CD mucosa (261). How this increase in IL-17-producing cells within the lamina propria relates to the presence of SFB and their metabolic factors is unknown, but it appears to be independent of ATP (40). Notably, human Th17 cells in CD mucosa may also express IFN-γ and IL-4, as well as IL-23R and IL-12Rβ2 (Th17/Th1). Furthermore, IL-12 may downregulate RORγt and IL-17 expression while upregulating T-bet (261), consistent with the inhibition of Th17 cells by IFN-γ and IL-4 (262).

Overall, while IL-23-regulated pathways represent an important new concept for understanding the mechanisms of intestinal inflammation, the relative roles of Th17-derived IL-17 (and Th17 cells themselves) and/or non–T cell–derived IL-17 in IBD remain unclear. Similarly, the limited efficacy of IFN-γ blockade in human IBD (**Supplemental Table 2**), in comparison with its clear inflammatory role in experimental colitis, remains a conundrum. A small subset of CD patients exhibit granulomas, the pathologic hallmark of IFN-γ expression, suggesting that this subset might benefit from IFN-γ blockade, which could be tested. The limited efficacy of anti-IFN-γ in humans could also be due to the release of Th17 cells, highlighting the complexity of consequences of pharmacological intervention. What seems clear, however, is the importance of IL-23 in promoting chronic mucosal inflammation in animal models (243–245, 247) and likely human disease (13). This draws attention to the role IL-23 plays in blocking Treg function, suggesting that innate immune cell–derived IL-23 may promote colitis not as much by mediating IL-17 production but by inhibiting $FoxP3^+$ Treg cell function and its consequent regulation of adaptive and innate immune cell–driven inflammation (263, 264).

Th17–T Regulatory Cell Balance in IBD

A fine balance exists between Th17 cells and the $FoxP3^+$ subset of regulatory $CD4^+CD25^+$ T cells that are induced (iTregs) under the control of many of the factors discussed above. The function of natural $FoxP3^+CD4^+CD25^+$ Tregs emanating from the thymus and iTregs has been extensively reviewed in relation to IBD (228). They build upon the now classic studies of Powrie (70, 265) and Sakaguchi (266) showing that transfer of $CD4^+CD45RB^{high}$ or $CD4^+CD25^{-/-}$ T cells into *scid* mice promotes intestinal inflammation or autoimmune gastritis, respectively, with prevention of gastrointestinal inflammation provided by cotransfer of $CD4^+CD25^+$ Tregs. Both Treg and Th17 differentiation requires TGF-β, which induces FoxP3 and RORγ, and their differentiation is reciprocally regulated in a highly dynamic manner depending on further signals (195, 267). Such signals include low concentrations of TGF-β together with IL-6 (193, 224, 268) and IL-21 (269, 270), which induce *Il23r* expression and favor development of Th17 cells, in contrast to high concentrations of TGF-β, which represses *Il23r* expression (267). Similarly, retinoic acid metabolites, provided by IECs and DCs, tip the balance toward Treg differentiation and inhibit Th17 differentiation (271–273). Mechanistically, FoxP3 directly interacts with RORγt to inhibit its function, resulting in decreased *Il17* transcription, while IL-6, IL-21, and IL-23, in turn, decrease the FoxP3-mediated inhibition of RORγt (267). It appears increasingly clear that lineage commitment to either Treg or Th17 is substantially more plastic than previously appreciated and under control of both metabolic and innate factors (195).

Despite the massive evidence in support of a central role for natural $FoxP3^+CD4^+CD25^+$ Tregs and iTregs in experimental intestinal inflammation, mostly obtained through Treg transfer studies into lymphopenic hosts (228), GWASs in CD or UC have not revealed polymorphisms in *FOXP3* or in genes directly related to Treg differentiation

(11, 274). $CD4^+CD25^+FoxP3^+$ Treg numbers are increased in the inflamed lamina propria of patients with CD and UC compared to uninflamed mucosa and healthy controls, whereas their numbers are decreased in peripheral blood (275–277). Moreover, $CD4^+CD25^+$ Tregs from peripheral blood and mesenteric lymph nodes retain their suppressive activity toward the $CD4^+CD25^-$ subset (275, 276). Patients with a rare immunodeficiency due to mutant *FOXP3*, characterized by immune dysregulation, polyendocrinopathy, enteropathy, and inherited as an X-linked monogenic disorder, IPEX, may exhibit profound intestinal inflammation (278), which is in accordance with the *scurfy* mouse model secondary to a *Foxp3* defect (279, 280). Notably, another rare immunodeficiency, Wiskott-Aldrich Syndrome (WAS)—due to genetic defects in the WAS protein—may also develop an UC-like disease along with abnormalities in natural and likely iTregs (281, 282). The WAS protein is functionally linked to specific cytoskeletal elements, making it interesting that genetic polymorphisms in one such protein, encoded by *ARPC2* (Arp2/3), have been specifically linked to UC (283).

There are a number of potential interpretations of these observations. One possibility is that some IBD patients might harbor rare mutations in the genetic programs associated with natural $FoxP3^+CD4^+CD25^+$ Tregs and iTregs, a possibility worth study by novel methodologies in familial and, especially, early-onset IBD. Another possibility is that in sporadic IBD, which is likely to be based upon polygenic inheritance, more subtle abnormalities exist in the pathways that determine the balance between induced Th17-Treg development due to both primary (e.g., *IL23R* polymorphisms) and secondary (e.g., composition of the microbiome) factors. Strategies aimed to increase the relative balance of Tregs to Th17 (and other inflammatory T cells), such as histone-deacetylase inhibitors that ameliorate DSS colitis through expansion of Tregs (284), could thus have therapeutic potential in human IBD. Furthermore, development and suppressive function of Tregs depend on the expression of factors such as the IL-2 receptor α chain (CD25), the glucocorticoid-induced TNFR-related protein (GITR; *TNFRSF18*), and cytotoxic T lymphocyte-associated protein 4 (CTLA-4), predicting that targeting these in the pursuit of limiting inflammatory T cells may unintentionally also target Tregs (**Supplemental Table 2**). Another model that has been promoted by MacDonald and colleagues is that $FoxP3^+$ Tregs are normal in IBD (275–277) but that the effector T cells are resistant to the effects of inhibitory cytokines such as TGF-β in the context of inflammation (285). This is supported by increased phosphorylated SMAD7, an inhibitor of phosphorylated SMAD2/3—which are directly downstream of the TGF-β-receptor—in lamina propria T cells of inflamed intestines (286). Another anti-inflammatory mediator, IL-10, also important in Treg function, is discussed in the next paragraphs.

IL-10 and IL-10 Receptor in IBD

Spontaneous enterocolitis in *Il10*$^{-/-}$ mice represents one of the first models of intestinal inflammation and unequivocally supports the involvement of immune mechanisms in IBD (5). Colitis was attenuated in *Il10*$^{-/-}$ mice held under specific pathogen–free conditions compared to those raised conventionally (5), whereas germ-free *Il10*$^{-/-}$ mice were completely protected (287), highlighting the critical contribution of the microbiota. Moreover, *H. hepaticus* causes severe inflammation in *Il10*$^{-/-}$, but not in wild-type, mice (67), indicating that this bacterium (and potentially others) has pathogenic potential in this context. The importance of IL-10 in preventing intestinal inflammation is further supported by the spontaneous colitis in *Il10rb*$^{-/-}$ mice (25) and *Blimp1*$^{-/-}$ mice, which exhibit a defect in IL-10 production (288).

IL-10 exerts a multitude of anti-inflammatory and immunoregulatory functions and may be produced by a variety of regulatory subsets of T cells, B cells, DCs, parenchymal cells, and IECs (289, 290), making it important to define the sources in intestinal tissues in order to understand the mechanisms of action. In situ hybridization has suggested constitutive expression in human IECs and increased expression in lamina propria mononuclear cells in both CD and UC (290). IL-10 expression in mice (as detected through an IRES GFP knock-in) is low in bone marrow–derived DCs and macrophages but was potently induced in the small intestinal intraepithelial lymphocyte (IEL) and colonic lamina propria lymphocyte compartments upon TCR stimulation, highlighting the intestine as a unique site for induction of IL-10-producing T cells (291). Consistent with this, T cell–specific deletion of floxed *Il10* alleles results in spontaneous colitis under specific pathogen–free conditions (292). Similarly, *Il10* deletion in FoxP3$^+$ Tregs results in spontaneous colitis, but not in systemic autoimmunity (293), which contrasts with the severe autoimmune disease (including enterocolitis) in *FoxP3*$^{-/-}$ mice (294, 295) or in patients with *FOXP3* mutations causing IPEX (280). These studies highlight the unique importance of IL-10 derived primarily from FoxP3$^+$ Tregs, intestinal T cells, and, possibly, IECs in the prevention of inflammation in the intestines. Importantly, whereas most T cell–derived IL-10 in the colon is from natural and induced FoxP3$^+$ Treg, in the small intestine it derives from FoxP3$^-$ T cells, which appear to localize to the epithelium, possibly reflecting other regulatory subsets of T cells such as Tr1 cells (296, 297).

As noted earlier, IL-10 signaling involves STAT3, a genetic risk factor for IBD. IL-10-induced SOCS3 expression is abrogated in *Stat3*-deficient macrophages, leading to unabated IL-12/23p40 expression upon exposure to microbial products like LPS (205). One important pathway maintaining mucosal homeostasis (or tolerance), which is important in IBD, might therefore be mediated by IL-10 derived from FoxP3$^+$ Tregs that act upon IL-10R on mucosal macrophages to stimulate STAT3-induced SOCS3 expression, which quells TLR-mediated secretion of IL-23 and other inflammatory cytokines. Moreover, STAT3 signaling, perhaps via IL-10, further enables FoxP3 in natural Tregs to specifically suppress Th17 cells (298).

Based upon these insights, subcutaneous recombinant IL-10 was examined as a potential therapeutic in CD and UC (**Supplemental Table 2**), but it was not effective. As local delivery could offer advantages, *Lactococcus lactis* engineered to secrete IL-10 ameliorated colitis in the DSS and *Il10*$^{-/-}$ models (299), but efficacy in humans remains to be shown. Nonetheless, it is extremely notable that a recent GWAS discovered polymorphisms in a SNP flanking *IL10* as the most significant association outside the MHC for UC (283). Resequencing of *IL10* revealed numerous rare and private variants; several nsSNPs are predicted to affect binding to the IL-10RA receptor chain (283). The identification of such rare, private variants is notable given the recent identification of a monogenic form of CD associated with mutations in *IL10RA* or *IL10RB*, as discussed earlier (23). In summary, impairment of IL-10-associated regulatory pathways appears to be critical in both forms of IBD as deduced from functional and genetic studies.

LEUKOCYTE HOMING PATHWAYS AS MODIFIERS OF IBD

The ability of the host to regulate the movement of innate (monocytes and DCs) and adaptive (Tregs) regulatory cells relative to inflammatory populations into the intestines via the sequential processes of tethering (e.g., selectins), rolling (e.g., ICAM), adhesion (e.g., integrins), and transmigration (e.g., chemokines) through the endothelium and consequently localization to their specific destinations within the intestinal microenvironment is of increasingly recognized importance in human IBD and has been extensively reviewed (300, 301). Recent studies indicate that environmental and genetic factors might impact these pathways, which are therapeutic targets as well, as detailed below.

Compartmentalization of Leukocyte Homing and the Role of Environmental and Metabolic Factors

Small intestinal homing of T and B cells is imprinted by DCs in Peyer's patches and mesenteric lymph nodes by induction of $\alpha_4\beta_7$ integrin and CCR9 (see below), which interact with mucosal vascular addressin cell adhesion molecule-1 (MAdCAM1) and CCL25, respectively, on the surface of lamina propria postcapillary venules (302, 303). Effector T cell entry into the small IEL compartment involves $\alpha_E\beta_7$ integrin, which interacts with E-cadherin on the basolateral surface of small IECs (301).

The selectins are more broadly expressed, with L-selectin on most leukocytes, P-selectin on inflamed endothelial cells and activated platelets, and E-selectin on inflamed endothelial cells (300). Blockade of the pan-selectin ligand P-selectin glycoprotein ligand-1 (PSGL1) attenuates spontaneous ileitis in SAMP1/YitFc mice (304, 305) and established DSS colitis (306). In contrast, blockade of L-selectin increases severity of TNBS colitis potentially because of effects on neutrophil recruitment (307).

Chemokine receptor signaling is important in homeostasis and inflammation; two pathways, CCL20-CCR6 and CCL25-CCR9, are particularly relevant for IBD in view of genetic insights, the role of environmental factors (e.g., microbiota and metabolic factors), and their therapeutic manipulation. Inflammatory signals, including IL-17, induce CCL20, which exhibits increased expression in the colonic epithelium of IBD (308–310). Th17 cells, in turn, express CCR6 and CCR4 (311, 312). As a result, *Ccr6*$^{-/-}$ Th17 cells exhibit an altered homing pattern and migrate to different compartments of the intestine (312). Adoptive transfer of *Ccr6*$^{-/-}$ Th17 cells into *scid* mice augments intestinal inflammation along with Th1 deviation of intestinal T cells (312), and *Ccr6*$^{-/-}$ mice are more susceptible to TNBS colitis (313), implying a potential regulatory function of Th17 cells as noted above (255). However, CCL20 neutralization ameliorates TNBS colitis (314) and reduces severity in DSS colitis (313). Given the pleiotropic activities of chemokine ligands, it is conceivable that CCL20, although the only CCR6 ligand, may interact with other chemokine receptors. Notably, Tregs also express CCR6, and Th17 cells may express CCL20, which could cross-regulate Treg recruitment as another example of the dynamic tension between these two functional populations (315).

CCR6-CCL20 also affects the development of intestinal lymphoid structures, as *Ccr6* deletion compromises Peyer's patch and isolated lymphoid follicle (ILF) development, and some c-kit$^+$ lymphoid precursors in cryptopatches express CCR6 (316). The generation of ILFs requires signaling from the intestinal microbiota via NOD1 in IECs, resulting in regulation of CCL20/CCR6 signaling and β-defensin 3 production (317). Notably, in the absence of ILFs, the microbial community is profoundly altered in a corollary manner (317). Hence, there might be reciprocal regulation of the bacterial flora and ILFs, which could be relevant for the lymphoid aggregations observed within the colon of IBD.

In contrast to CCL20, CCL25 production is confined to small IECs and tethered to the endothelium, where it recruits T effector populations to the IEL and lamina propria compartments (301). Although microbial factors modify CCL20-CCR6 signaling pathways as discussed above, metabolic factors, specifically retinoic acid metabolites, affect CCL25-CCR9 pathways. Retinoic acids enhance TGF-β-mediated signaling (318), increase FoxP3 expression, and promote expression of $\alpha_4\beta_7$ and CCR9 in gut T cells activated by IECs and DCs from gut-associated lymphoid tissue DCs, but not in other tissues, owing to the restricted presence of the retinoic acid biosynthetic pathway (319). These studies underscore the multidirectional interactions between the (microbial and metabolic) environment, the innate immune system, and the adaptive immune system.

Genetic Factors Controlling Leukocyte Homing in IBD

A meta-analysis of GWAS data identified the *CCR6* locus as associated with CD (20), which might affect lymphocyte homing, but also ILF induction and, hence, host-microbiota homeostasis. Similarly, *NKX2-3*, encoding a homeobox transcription factor involved in the localization of T and B lymphocytes to mesenteric lymph nodes, appears to be a risk factor for UC and CD (139, 196, 237).

Therapeutic Evidence for Leukocyte Homing as a Mediator of Human IBD

Importance of integrin blockade in IBD was originally implied from studies of colitis in the cotton-top tamarin (320). Blockade of specific integrins has been extensively studied in several rodent models of intestinal inflammation. As an illustrative example, $Tnf^{\Delta ARE}\beta_7^{-/-}$ mice are protected from the development of colitis owing to the absence of β_7-integrin- containing ($\alpha_4\beta_7$ and $\alpha_E\beta_7$) heterodimers (321). Consistent with these animal studies, a blocking anti-$\alpha_4\beta_7$ antibody (MLN002) exhibited some evidence of therapeutic efficacy in phase II clinical trials in UC and CD (**Supplemental Table 2**), while an α_4-blocking antibody (Natalizumab) was beneficial in a subpopulation of CD patients (**Supplemental Table 2**). Although no direct comparisons have been performed, the reported remission rates suggest that $\alpha_4\beta_7$-based anti-integrin strategies might be effective in a more confined patient population compared to anti-TNF-based strategies, and this apparently reduced effectiveness could be related to the fact that anti-integrin strategies might affect the homing of effector, but also regulatory populations. Similarly, CCR9 antagonists (Ccx282-B) appear to be efficacious in $Tnf^{\Delta ARE}$-associated enterocolitis (322), albeit mice deficient in either CCL25 or CCR9 were not protected from colitis in the $Tnf^{\Delta ARE}$ model (321). Nonetheless, Ccx282-B exhibits some therapeutic activity in CD in preliminary studies (**Supplemental Table 2**).

LIPID METABOLISM AND ITS ROLE IN THE REGULATION OF INFLAMMATION

Recent evidence from genetic and immunologic studies suggests that metabolism and inflammation are tightly linked processes that cross-regulate each other, with significant implications for IBD (323). Specifically, mammalian and commensal microbial lipids have been demonstrated to play key roles in the regulation of inflammation through their function as (*a*) ligands of lipid-activated nuclear receptors such as PPAR, retinoic acid receptors, and steroid-hormone receptors; (*b*) regulators of gene expression through histone deacetylase inhibition, as demonstrated for SCFA; (*c*) pro- or anti-inflammatory mediators, including those associated with prostaglandins, leukotrienes, lipoxins, resolvins, and protectins; (*d*) intracellular signaling molecules including sphingolipid- and phosphatidylinositol-derived second messengers; and (*e*) antigens in CD1-mediated immune responses as discussed previously in this review. In this final section, we discuss the regulation of intestinal inflammation by arachidonic acid metabolites, PPARs, and polyunsaturated fatty acid (PUFA) derivatives in view of recent available information linking these to the immunogenetic basis of IBD and their special importance as potential environmental modifying agents.

Arachidonic Acid Pathways

The two isoforms of the enzyme cyclooxygenase (COX1 and COX2) catalyze the production of prostanoids from arachidonic acid, including prostaglandin D_2 (PGD_2), PGE_2, $PGF_{2\alpha}$, PGI_2, and thromboxane (TX). These act through their respective receptors, PGD receptor (DP), PGE receptor (EP), PGF receptor (FP), PGI receptor (IP), and TX receptor (TP) (324). Nonsteroidal anti-inflammatory drugs (NSAIDs), which share COX inhibition as a common mechanism, have been associated with the relapse of IBD, hence representing an environmental factor intersecting with the immunogenetic biology of IBD. In line with this is the increased susceptibility of mice deficient in COX1 (*Ptgs1*$^{-/-}$) and COX2 (*Ptgs2*$^{-/-}$) to DSS colitis (325), and pharmacological inhibition of COX1 and COX2 points toward PGE_2 as the protective factor in colitis (326). Indeed, genetic deletion of the aforementioned prostanoid receptors has shown that only mice deficient in EP4 (*Ptger4*$^{-/-}$), the receptor for PGE_2, exhibit increased susceptibility to DSS colitis (326). In human colonic mucosa, EP4 is expressed in the intestinal epithelium and in lamina propria mononuclear cells, including $CD3^+$ and myeloid cells (327, 328). Notably, mucosal barrier function is impaired early after DSS administration upon treatment with an EP4 antagonist (326). It is unclear whether mucosal barrier dysfunction is through a direct effect on IECs or secondary to inflammatory mediators. Consistent with the latter possibility, PGE_2-EP4 signaling has been shown to downregulate lamina propria $CD4^+$ T cell proliferation and IFN-γ production (326), which may directly damage IEC tight junctions (329). PGE_2 may also suppress chemokine secretion from LPS-stimulated macrophages via EP4 (330), stimulate IL-10 production (331), and suppress the degradation of NF-κB1 p105/p50 (331). Thus, PGE_2-EP4 signaling may facilitate mucosal protection through anti-inflammatory IEC, macrophage, and $CD4^+$ T cell function.

However, PGE_2-EP4 and -EP2 signaling was recently shown to facilitate IL-1- and IL-23-mediated Th17 differentiation from naive $CD4^+$ T cells (332, 333). Notably, EP4 antagonist treatment ameliorated EAE and contact hypersensitivity (CHS) (332), suggesting disparate roles of PGE_2-EP4 signaling in experimental colitis compared to EAE and CHS, two models that can be driven by IL-23 and Th17 cells in a specific immunopathologic pathway.

Recently, *PTGER4* has been implicated in the genetic basis of CD (334). Specifically, a GWAS revealed strong evidence for an association of a 250-kb region on chromosome 5p13.1, which is contained within a 1.25 Mb gene desert (334). *PTGER4* is the closest gene, 270 kb proximally from the CD-associated block. Quantitative trait locus analysis revealed that individuals harboring two specific *5p13.1* risk alleles exhibited increased *PTGER4* mRNA expression (possibly through *cis* acting elements), suggesting *PTGER4* as the causal gene (334). However, increased PTGER4 expression associated with CD is at odds with the increased severity of DSS colitis in *Ptger4*$^{-/-}$ mice (326). Further studies are required to reconcile these apparent inconsistencies. Nonetheless, a significant body of epidemiologic, immunologic, and genetic information supports a role for arachidonic acid metabolites in IBD.

PPARγ

PPARs are lipid-activated transcription factors that form obligate heterodimers with the retinoid X receptor (RXR) (323). In the absence of ligands, RXR heterodimers are bound to DNA and repress expression of target genes, whereas ligand binding causes release of corepressors leading to the initiation of gene transcription (323). PPARγ is expressed in liver, adipose tissue, IECs, and hematopoietic cells and plays a key role in the regulation of lipid metabolism, inflammation, and cancer (335). The molecular mechanisms of gene regulation by PPARγ are manifold, including direct peroxisome proliferator response element (PPRE)-driven transcriptional activation and PPRE-independent transrepression through interference with AP1, NF-κB, p38, and transcriptional coactivators and repressors (323).

A variety of naturally occurring ligands have been proposed for PPARγ, including unsaturated fatty acids, eicosanoids (e.g., 15dPGJ2), and lysophosphatidic acid (335). In addition, PPARγ is the target of thiazolidinedione drugs and 5-aminosalicylic acid (5-ASA) (336). PPARγ is highly expressed in the intestinal epithelium, and its expression is dependent on PRR signaling by the intestinal microbiota and direct transcriptional regulation by microbial metabolites such as butyrate (337, 338). Consistent with this, both germ-free and TLR4$^{-/-}$ mice exhibit decreased intestinal epithelial expression of PPARγ (337).

Several lines of evidence suggest involvement of PPARγ in IBD. First, thiazolidinediones were shown to be effective in the treatment of human IBD and various mouse models of intestinal inflammation. Thus, both PPARγ agonists block CXCL8 and CCL2 production through IκBα-dependent inhibition of NF-κB and consequently protect from DSS-induced colitis (339). These findings are confirmed in various other models of colitis induced by chemicals, bacteria, ischemia-reperfusion, T cell transfer into immunocompromised hosts, and spontaneous models of IBD including IL-10-deficient mice and SAMP1/YitFc mice (335). The protective effects of thiazolidinediones in these models seem to be mediated mainly via IECs and not via hematopoietic cells because conditional PPARγ deletion in the intestinal epithelium leads to mild spontaneous colitis, increased susceptibility to DSS colitis, and prevention of the therapeutic effect of some but not all PPARγ agonists (340).

Importantly, these observations extend to human IBD because rosiglitazone was shown to be efficacious in the treatment of mild to moderate UC (341). In addition, the therapeutic efficacy of 5-ASA derivatives seems to be at least partially mediated via PPARγ. Thus, 5-ASA was shown to bind to PPARγ leading to activation of PPRE-driven gene transcription (336). In addition, PPARγ heterozygous mice, which exhibit a 70% decrease in colonic PPARγ levels, exhibit pronounced intestinal inflammation upon TNBS challenge and cannot be protected by 5-ASA (336).

These findings demonstrate a crucial role of PPARγ signaling in the prevention of intestinal inflammation and suggest that agonistic targeting of PPARγ might be an effective treatment for IBD. However, these observations also raise the question of whether impaired PPARγ signaling might be a causal factor in IBD. Support for this idea stems from the notion that patients with UC show decreased expression of PPARγ in IECs but not in hematopoietic cells (337). In addition, resistance to ileitis in Samp1/YitFc mice on the AKR background has been linked to increased PPARγ expression in the intestinal crypt epithelium. The reason for impaired PPARγ expression in UC remains enigmatic. However, given the crucial role of commensal-derived signals in the induction of PPARγ, it is possible that changes in the microbiota or its products contribute to impaired PPARγ expression in UC.

Notably, several genes implicated in IBD pathogenesis are functionally linked to PPARs. Thus, mice hypomorphic for the CD-associated gene *ATG16L1* showed altered Paneth cell morphology and dramatically increased PPAR signaling (45). These findings might explain why CD patients, in contrast to UC patients, show normal PPARγ expression. In addition, recent evidence also suggests cross-regulation of PPAR signaling and ER stress. Specifically, pioglitazone was shown to reduce ER stress leading to pancreatic islet cell protection and prevention of diabetes (342). In addition to being a regulator of the UPR, PPARs also seem to be targets of ER stress, as demonstrated by increased expression of PPARγ but decreased expression of PPARα in response to ER stress (343). These findings demonstrate the existence of a feedback loop between ER stress and PPARγ signaling and suggest that agonistic targeting of PPARγ might exert its beneficial effects at least in part through alleviation of ER stress.

Lipoxins, Resolvins, and Protectins

It is increasingly recognized that resolution of inflammation is not a passive process but is actively regulated not only by cell surface receptors such as CEACAM1 and cytokines (e.g., TGF-β, IL-10, IL-35) but also by several families of lipid-derived signaling molecules, namely lipoxins, resolvins, and protectins (344). Of these, resolvins and protectins are derived from omega-3 PUFAs, whereas lipoxins are derived from arachidonic acid, the same precursors that give rise to proinflammatory leukotrienes and prostaglandins in a process called lipid class switching (345). Thus, after an acute inflammatory phase driven by leukotrienes and prostaglandins, these same mediators, mostly PGE_2 and PGD_2, induce key enzymes involved in the biosynthesis of lipoxins leading to resolution of inflammation (345). Importantly, proresolution pathways driven by lipoxins, resolvins, and protectins are distinct from classical anti-inflammatory pathways in that they are not immunosuppressive but actively accelerate resolution of inflammation by inhibition of neutrophil and eosinophil recruitment and stimulation of macrophage phagocytosis with clearance of microorganisms and apoptotic cells (344). Given that the intestinal mucosa is permanently exposed to microorganisms, it is not surprising that some of these lipid mediators, including lipoxins, are constitutively expressed in the healthy mucosa (346). However, in contrast to healthy controls, patients with UC express significantly lower levels of 15-lipoxygenase-2, a key enzyme involved in lipoxin production, and consequently low levels of lipoxin (346). In addition to the putative role of anti-inflammatory lipid mediators in the pathogenesis of IBD, both resolvins and lipoxins are well characterized for their protective therapeutic role in intestinal inflammation. Thus, resolvin E1 was shown to protect from TNBS colitis through regulation of innate and adaptive immune responses (347), and mice overexpressing n3-PUFA are protected from DSS colitis. In addition, omega-3 PUFA may reduce the rates of relapse in CD (348, 349). Similar observations have been made with lipoxin analogs in that they attenuate TNBS colitis concomitant with decreased expression of proinflammatory cytokines (350). In addition to their anti-inflammatory effects on immune cells, lipoxins regulate immune responses of IECs, given that lipoxin A_4 analogs reduce NF-κB-mediated transcriptional activation, inhibit degradation of IκBα in response to *Salmonella typhimurium* in IECs, and protected from DSS colitis (351). Lipoxins, resolvins, and protectins might therefore be of therapeutic efficacy in the prevention and treatment of intestinal inflammation and await testing in human IBD.

CONCLUDING REMARKS

IBD results from a continuum of complex interactions between a quartet of host-derived and external elements that involve various aspects of the intestinal microbiota, the immune system, the genetic composition of the host, and specific environmental factors. Recent studies into the complexity of these arrangements increasingly support not only the syndromic nature of this disorder, but also the need for systems-based approaches in understanding the biologic pathways involved and the correlation of these arrangements with specific phenotypic outcomes that go beyond the assigned clinical descriptors currently in practice, namely UC and CD. Studies of the microbiota, immune system, and genetics have revealed more similarities than differences between these two extreme phenotypes, suggesting this continuum of interactions is similarly reflected in a continuous lineage of functional pathways and, consequently, phenotypes. Genetic studies, for example, increasingly support the concept of familial and sporadic forms of IBD whose inheritance ranges from monogenic to polygenic and involve a wide range of biologic pathways that affect innate immunity, adaptive immunity, ER stress and autophagy, and metabolic pathways associated with cellular homeostasis and the regulation of inflammation per se. Moreover, these genetic observations, together with immunologic studies, emphasize the particularly important role played by abnormalities of the innate immune functions of hematopoietic and nonhematopoietic cells, especially within the intestinal epithelium and its unique relationship with the commensal microbiota, in influencing and being influenced by the adaptive immune system. Such observations increasingly support a long-held view that the chronic intestinal inflammation associated with IBD may be a secondary consequence of innate immune deficiency (or dysfunction). These immunogenetic observations, together with the "reality-test" provided by biologic therapies in human IBD, also provide a foundation for this model given the evidence to date that supports targets such as TNF, IL-6, and IL-12/23 as important mediators of the major IBD phenotypes. Finally, given these comments, it can be anticipated that environmental factors that modify the risk for development of IBD have the common attribute of affecting the relationship between the commensal microbiota and the immune system in a manner that intersects with the functionally relevant immunogenetic pathway(s) that are uniquely operative within a particular context of IBD.

DISCLOSURE STATEMENT

The authors are not aware of any affiliations, memberships, funding, or financial holdings that might be perceived as affecting the objectivity of this review.

ACKNOWLEDGMENTS

We thank Dr. Stephen B. Hanauer, University of Chicago, and Dr. Andre Franke, Christian-Albrechts University of Kiel, for helpful discussions. The authors acknowledge support by NIH grants DK51362, DK44319, and DK53056, as well as the Harvard Digestive Diseases Center and the Crohn's and Colitis Foundation of America (to R.S.B.); the Deutsche Forschungsgemeinschaft (Ze 814/1-1) and the Crohn's and Colitis Foundation of America (to S.Z.); and grants START-Y446 from the Austrian Ministry of Science, P21530 from the Austrian Science Fund, and MFI 2007-407 from Innsbruck Medical University (to A.K.).

LITERATURE CITED

1. Halme L, Paavola-Sakki P, Turunen U, Lappalainen M, Farkkila M, Kontula K. 2006. Family and twin studies in inflammatory bowel disease. *World J. Gastroenterol.* 12:3668–72
2. Tsironi E, Feakins RM, Probert CS, Rampton DS, Phil D. 2004. Incidence of inflammatory bowel disease is rising and abdominal tuberculosis is falling in Bangladeshis in East London, United Kingdom. *Am. J. Gastroenterol.* 99:1749–55
3. Thia KT, Loftus EV Jr, Sandborn WJ, Yang SK. 2008. An update on the epidemiology of inflammatory bowel disease in Asia. *Am. J. Gastroenterol.* 103:3167–82
4. Sadlack B, Merz H, Schorle H, Schimpl A, Feller AC, Horak I. 1993. Ulcerative colitis-like disease in mice with a disrupted interleukin-2 gene. *Cell* 75:253–61
5. Kühn R, Löhler J, Rennick D, Rajewsky K, Müller W. 1993. Interleukin-10-deficient mice develop chronic enterocolitis. *Cell* 75:263–74
6. Mombaerts P, Mizoguchi E, Grusby MJ, Glimcher LH, Bhan AK, Tonegawa S. 1993. Spontaneous development of inflammatory bowel disease in T cell receptor mutant mice. *Cell* 75:274–82
7. Strober W, Fuss IJ, Blumberg RS. 2002. The immunology of mucosal models of inflammation. *Annu. Rev. Immunol.* 20:495–549
8. Baumgart DC, Sandborn WJ. 2007. Inflammatory bowel disease: clinical aspects and established and evolving therapies. *Lancet* 369:1641–57
9. Gregersen PK, Olsson LM. 2009. Recent advances in the genetics of autoimmune disease. *Annu. Rev. Immunol.* 27:363–91
10. Peterson DA, Frank DN, Pace NR, Gordon JI. 2008. Metagenomic approaches for defining the pathogenesis of inflammatory bowel diseases. *Cell Host Microbe* 3:417–27
11. Van Limbergen J, Wilson DC, Satsangi J. 2009. The genetics of Crohn's disease. *Annu. Rev. Genomics Hum. Genet.* 10:89–116
12. Cho JH. 2008. The genetics and immunopathogenesis of inflammatory bowel disease. *Nat. Rev. Immunol.* 8:458–66

13. Duerr RH, Taylor KD, Brant SR, Rioux JD, Silverberg MS, et al. 2006. A genome-wide association study identifies IL23R as an inflammatory bowel disease gene. *Science* 314:1461–63
14. Hampe J, Franke A, Rosenstiel P, Till A, Teuber M, et al. 2007. A genome-wide association scan of nonsynonymous SNPs identifies a susceptibility variant for Crohn disease in ATG16L1. *Nat. Genet.* 39:207–11
15. Zhernakova A, van Diemen CC, Wijmenga C. 2009. Detecting shared pathogenesis from the shared genetics of immune-related diseases. *Nat. Rev. Genet.* 10:43–55
16. Budarf ML, Labbe C, David G, Rioux JD. 2009. GWA studies: rewriting the story of IBD. *Trends Genet.* 25:137–46
17. Zielenski J. 2000. Genotype and phenotype in cystic fibrosis. *Respiration* 67:117–33
18. Targan SR, Karp LC. 2005. Defects in mucosal immunity leading to ulcerative colitis. *Immunol. Rev.* 206:296–305
19. Hindorff LA, Sethupathy P, Junkins HA, Ramos EM, Mehta JP, et al. 2009. Potential etiologic and functional implications of genome-wide association loci for human diseases and traits. *Proc. Natl. Acad. Sci. USA* 106:9362–67
20. Barrett JC, Hansoul S, Nicolae DL, Cho JH, Duerr RH, et al. 2008. Genome-wide association defines more than 30 distinct susceptibility loci for Crohn's disease. *Nat. Genet.* 40:955–62
21. Goldstein DB. 2009. Common genetic variation and human traits. *N. Engl. J. Med.* 360:1696–98
22. Casanova JL, Abel L. 2009. Revisiting Crohn's disease as a primary immunodeficiency of macrophages. *J. Exp. Med.* 206:1839–43
23. Glocker EO, Kotlarz D, Boztug K, Gertz EM, Schäffer AA, et al. 2009. Inflammatory bowel disease and mutations affecting the interleukin-10 receptor. *N. Engl. J. Med.* 361:2033–45
24. Lopez-Cubero SO, Sullivan KM, McDonald GB. 1998. Course of Crohn's disease after allogeneic marrow transplantation. *Gastroenterology* 114:433–40
25. Spencer SD, Di Marco F, Hooley J, Pitts-Meek S, Bauer M, et al. 1998. The orphan receptor CRF2–4 is an essential subunit of the interleukin 10 receptor. *J. Exp. Med.* 187:571–78
26. Takeda K, Clausen BE, Kaisho T, Tsujimura T, Terada N, et al. 1999. Enhanced Th1 activity and development of chronic enterocolitis in mice devoid of Stat3 in macrophages and neutrophils. *Immunity* 10:39–49
27. Sugimoto K, Ogawa A, Mizoguchi E, Shimomura Y, Andoh A, et al. 2008. IL-22 ameliorates intestinal inflammation in a mouse model of ulcerative colitis. *J. Clin. Invest.* 118:534–44
28. Round JL, Mazmanian SK. 2009. The gut microbiota shapes intestinal immune responses during health and disease. *Nat. Rev. Immunol.* 9:313–23
29. Sartor RB. 2008. Microbial influences in inflammatory bowel diseases. *Gastroenterology* 134:577–94
30. Taurog JD, Richardson JA, Croft JT, Simmons WA, Zhou M, et al. 1994. The germfree state prevents development of gut and joint inflammatory disease in HLA-B27 transgenic rats. *J. Exp. Med.* 180:2359–64
31. Iqbal N, Oliver JR, Wagner FH, Lazenby AS, Elson CO, Weaver CT. 2002. T helper 1 and T helper 2 cells are pathogenic in an antigen-specific model of colitis. *J. Exp. Med.* 195:71–84
32. Cong Y, Brandwein SL, McCabe RP, Lazenby A, Birkenmeier EH, et al. 1998. $CD4^+$ T cells reactive to enteric bacterial antigens in spontaneously colitic C3H/HeJBir mice: increased T helper cell type 1 response and ability to transfer disease. *J. Exp. Med.* 187:855–64
33. Gill SR, Pop M, Deboy RT, Eckburg PB, Turnbaugh PJ, et al. 2006. Metagenomic analysis of the human distal gut microbiome. *Science* 312:1355–59
34. Turnbaugh PJ, Hamady M, Yatsunenko T, Cantarel BL, Duncan A, et al. 2009. A core gut microbiome in obese and lean twins. *Nature* 457:480–84
35. Ley RE, Peterson DA, Gordon JI. 2006. Ecological and evolutionary forces shaping microbial diversity in the human intestine. *Cell* 124:837–48
36. Vaishnava S, Behrendt CL, Ismail AS, Eckmann L, Hooper LV. 2008. Paneth cells directly sense gut commensals and maintain homeostasis at the intestinal host-microbial interface. *Proc. Natl. Acad. Sci. USA* 105:20858–63
37. Umesaki Y, Setoyama H, Matsumoto S, Okada Y. 1993. Expansion of $\alpha\beta$ T-cell receptor-bearing intestinal intraepithelial lymphocytes after microbial colonization in germ-free mice and its independence from thymus. *Immunology* 79:32–37

38. Mazmanian SK, Round JL, Kasper DL. 2008. A microbial symbiosis factor prevents intestinal inflammatory disease. *Nature* 453:620–25
39. Ivanov II, Frutos Rde L, Manel N, Yoshinaga K, Rifkin DB, et al. 2008. Specific microbiota direct the differentiation of IL-17-producing T-helper cells in the mucosa of the small intestine. *Cell Host Microbe* 4:337–49
40. Ivanov II, Atarashi K, Manel N, Brodie EL, Shima T, et al. 2009. Induction of intestinal Th17 cells by segmented filamentous bacteria. *Cell* 139:485–98
41. Gaboriau-Routhiau V, Rakotobe S, Lécuyer E, Mulder I, Lan A, et al. 2009. The key role of segmented filamentous bacteria in the coordinated maturation of gut helper T cell responses. *Immunity* 31:677–89
42. Wen L, Ley RE, Volchkov PY, Stranges PB, Avanesyan L, et al. 2008. Innate immunity and intestinal microbiota in the development of Type 1 diabetes. *Nature* 455:1109–13
43. Maslowski KM, Vieira AT, Ng A, Kranich J, Sierro F, et al. 2009. Regulation of inflammatory responses by gut microbiota and chemoattractant receptor GPR43. *Nature* 461:1282–86
44. Nieuwenhuis EE, Matsumoto T, Lindenbergh D, Willemsen R, Kaser A, et al. 2009. Cd1d-dependent regulation of bacterial colonization in the intestine of mice. *J. Clin. Invest.* 119:1241–50
45. Cadwell K, Liu JY, Brown SL, Miyoshi H, Loh J, et al. 2008. A key role for autophagy and the autophagy gene Atg16l1 in mouse and human intestinal Paneth cells. *Nature* 456:259–63
46. Kaser A, Lee AH, Franke A, Glickman JN, Zeissig S, et al. 2008. XBP1 links ER stress to intestinal inflammation and confers genetic risk for human inflammatory bowel disease. *Cell* 134:743–56
47. Kobayashi KS, Chamaillard M, Ogura Y, Henegariu O, Inohara N, et al. 2005. Nod2-dependent regulation of innate and adaptive immunity in the intestinal tract. *Science* 307:731–34
48. Linden SK, Sutton P, Karlsson NG, Korolik V, McGuckin MA. 2008. Mucins in the mucosal barrier to infection. *Mucosal Immunol.* 1:183–97
49. Sonnenburg JL, Xu J, Leip DD, Chen CH, Westover BP, et al. 2005. Glycan foraging in vivo by an intestine-adapted bacterial symbiont. *Science* 307:1955–59
50. Barnich N, Carvalho FA, Glasser AL, Darcha C, Jantscheff P, et al. 2007. CEACAM6 acts as a receptor for adherent-invasive *E. coli*, supporting ileal mucosa colonization in Crohn disease. *J. Clin. Invest.* 117:1566–74
51. Macpherson AJ, Uhr T. 2004. Induction of protective IgA by intestinal dendritic cells carrying commensal bacteria. *Science* 303:1662–65
52. Frank DN, St Amand AL, Feldman RA, Boedeker EC, Harpaz N, Pace NR. 2007. Molecular-phylogenetic characterization of microbial community imbalances in human inflammatory bowel diseases. *Proc. Natl. Acad. Sci. USA* 104:13780–85
53. Wehkamp J, Salzman NH, Porter E, Nuding S, Weichenthal M, et al. 2005. Reduced Paneth cell alpha-defensins in ileal Crohn's disease. *Proc. Natl. Acad. Sci. USA* 102:18129–34
54. Petnicki-Ocwieja T, Hrncir T, Liu Y-J, Biswas A, Hudcovic T, et al. 2009. Nod2 is required for the regulation of commensal microbiota in the intestine. *Proc. Natl. Acad. Sci. USA* 106:15813–18
55. Maeda S, Hsu LC, Liu H, Bankston LA, Iimura M, et al. 2005. Nod2 mutation in Crohn's disease potentiates NF-κB activity and IL-1β processing. *Science* 307:734–38
56. Pinedo PJ, Buergelt CD, Donovan GA, Melendez P, Morel L, et al. 2009. Association between CARD15/NOD2 gene polymorphisms and paratuberculosis infection in cattle. *Vet. Microbiol.* 134:346–52
57. Garrett WS, Lord GM, Punit S, Lugo-Villarino G, Mazmanian SK, et al. 2007. Communicable ulcerative colitis induced by T-bet deficiency in the innate immune system. *Cell* 131:33–45
58. Lupp C, Robertson ML, Wickham ME, Sekirov I, Champion OL, et al. 2007. Host-mediated inflammation disrupts the intestinal microbiota and promotes the overgrowth of Enterobacteriaceae. *Cell Host Microbe* 2:119–29
59. Targan SR, Landers CJ, Yang H, Lodes MJ, Cong Y, et al. 2005. Antibodies to CBir1 flagellin define a unique response that is associated independently with complicated Crohn's disease. *Gastroenterology* 128:2020–28
60. Ryu JH, Kim SH, Lee HY, Bai JY, Nam YD, et al. 2008. Innate immune homeostasis by the homeobox gene caudal and commensal-gut mutualism in *Drosophila*. *Science* 319:777–82

61. Neish AS, Gewirtz AT, Zeng H, Young AN, Hobert ME, et al. 2000. Prokaryotic regulation of epithelial responses by inhibition of IκB-α ubiquitination. *Science* 289:1560–63
62. Kelly D, Campbell JI, King TP, Grant G, Jansson EA, et al. 2004. Commensal anaerobic gut bacteria attenuate inflammation by regulating nuclear-cytoplasmic shuttling of PPAR-γ and RelA. *Nat. Immunol.* 5:104–12
63. Rioux JD, Xavier RJ, Taylor KD, Silverberg MS, Goyette P, et al. 2007. Genome-wide association study identifies new susceptibility loci for Crohn disease and implicates autophagy in disease pathogenesis. *Nat. Genet.* 39:596–604
64. Ha EM, Oh CT, Bae YS, Lee WJ. 2005. A direct role for dual oxidase in *Drosophila* gut immunity. *Science* 310:847–50
65. Ha EM, Lee KA, Seo YY, Kim SH, Lim JH, et al. 2009. Coordination of multiple dual oxidase-regulatory pathways in responses to commensal and infectious microbes in drosophila gut. *Nat. Immunol.* 10:949–57
66. Bernstein CN, Shanahan F. 2008. Disorders of a modern lifestyle: reconciling the epidemiology of inflammatory bowel diseases. *Gut* 57:1185–91
67. Cahill RJ, Foltz CJ, Fox JG, Dangler CA, Powrie F, Schauer DB. 1997. Inflammatory bowel disease: an immunity-mediated condition triggered by bacterial infection with *Helicobacter hepaticus*. *Infect. Immun.* 65:3126–31
68. Kullberg MC, Ward JM, Gorelick PL, Caspar P, Hieny S, et al. 1998. *Helicobacter hepaticus* triggers colitis in specific-pathogen-free interleukin-10 (IL-10)-deficient mice through an IL-12- and gamma interferon-dependent mechanism. *Infect. Immun.* 66:5157–66
69. Kullberg MC, Andersen JF, Gorelick PL, Caspar P, Suerbaum S, et al. 2003. Induction of colitis by a CD4$^+$ T cell clone specific for a bacterial epitope. *Proc. Natl. Acad. Sci. USA* 100:15830–35
70. Powrie F, Leach MW, Mauze S, Caddle LB, Coffman RL. 1993. Phenotypically distinct subsets of CD4$^+$ T cells induce or protect from chronic intestinal inflammation in C. B-17 scid mice. *Int. Immunol.* 5:1461–71
71. Sokol H, Pigneur B, Watterlot L, Lakhdari O, Bermudez-Humaran LG, et al. 2008. *Faecalibacterium prausnitzii* is an anti-inflammatory commensal bacterium identified by gut microbiota analysis of Crohn disease patients. *Proc. Natl. Acad. Sci. USA* 105:16731–36
72. Kaser A, Blumberg RS. 2009. Endoplasmic reticulum stress in the intestinal epithelium and inflammatory bowel disease. *Semin. Immunol.* 21:156–63
73. Lodes MJ, Cong Y, Elson CO, Mohamath R, Landers CJ, et al. 2004. Bacterial flagellin is a dominant antigen in Crohn disease. *J. Clin. Invest.* 113:1296–306
74. Brandtzaeg P, Carlsen HS, Halstensen TS. 2006. The B-cell system in inflammatory bowel disease. *Adv. Exp. Med. Biol.* 579:149–67
75. Kobayashi K, Qiao SW, Yoshida M, Baker K, Lencer WI, Blumberg RS. 2009. An FcRn-dependent role for anti-flagellin immunoglobulin G in pathogenesis of colitis in mice. *Gastroenterology* 137:1746–56
76. Slack E, Hapfelmeier S, Stecher B, Velykoredko Y, Stoel M, et al. 2009. Innate and adaptive immunity cooperate flexibly to maintain host-microbiota mutualism. *Science* 325:617–20
77. Cong Y, Feng T, Fujihashi K, Schoeb TR, Elson CO. 2009. A dominant, coordinated T regulatory cell-IgA response to the intestinal microbiota. *Proc. Natl. Acad. Sci. USA* 106:19256–61
78. Vijay-Kumar M, Sanders CJ, Taylor RT, Kumar A, Aitken JD, et al. 2007. Deletion of TLR5 results in spontaneous colitis in mice. *J. Clin. Invest.* 117:3909–21
79. Ogura Y, Bonen DK, Inohara N, Nicolae DL, Chen FF, et al. 2001. A frameshift mutation in NOD2 associated with susceptibility to Crohn's disease. *Nature* 411:603–6
80. Hugot JP, Chamaillard M, Zouali H, Lesage S, Cezard JP, et al. 2001. Association of NOD2 leucine-rich repeat variants with susceptibility to Crohn's disease. *Nature* 411:599–603
81. Hampe J, Cuthbert A, Croucher PJ, Mirza MM, Mascheretti S, et al. 2001. Association between insertion mutation in NOD2 gene and Crohn's disease in German and British populations. *Lancet* 357:1925–28
82. Miceli-Richard C, Lesage S, Rybojad M, Prieur AM, Manouvrier-Hanu S, et al. 2001. CARD15 mutations in Blau syndrome. *Nat. Genet.* 29:19–20
83. Meylan E, Tschopp J, Karin M. 2006. Intracellular pattern recognition receptors in the host response. *Nature* 442:39–44

84. Lesage S, Zouali H, Cezard JP, Colombel JF, Belaiche J, et al. 2002. CARD15/NOD2 mutational analysis and genotype-phenotype correlation in 612 patients with inflammatory bowel disease. *Am. J. Hum. Genet.* 70:845–57
85. Coulombe F, Divangahi M, Veyrier F, de Leseleuc L, Gleason JL, et al. 2009. Increased NOD2-mediated recognition of N-glycolyl muramyl dipeptide. *J. Exp. Med.* 206:1709–16
86. Sabbah A, Chang TH, Harnack R, Frohlich V, Tominaga K, et al. 2009. Activation of innate immune antiviral responses by Nod2. *Nat. Immunol.* 10:1073–80
87. Gutierrez O, Pipaon C, Inohara N, Fontalba A, Ogura Y, et al. 2002. Induction of Nod2 in myelomonocytic and intestinal epithelial cells via nuclear factor-κB activation. *J. Biol. Chem.* 277:41701–5
88. Hisamatsu T, Suzuki M, Reinecker HC, Nadeau WJ, McCormick BA, Podolsky DK. 2003. CARD15/NOD2 functions as an antibacterial factor in human intestinal epithelial cells. *Gastroenterology* 124:993–1000
89. Shaw MH, Reimer T, Sánchez-Valdepeñas C, Warner N, Kim YG, et al. 2009. T cell-intrinsic role of Nod2 in promoting type 1 immunity to *Toxoplasma gondii*. *Nat. Immunol.* 10:1267–74
90. Abbott DW, Wilkins A, Asara JM, Cantley LC. 2004. The Crohn's disease protein, NOD2, requires RIP2 in order to induce ubiquitinylation of a novel site on NEMO. *Curr. Biol.* 14:2217–27
91. Ogura Y, Inohara N, Benito A, Chen FF, Yamaoka S, Nunez G. 2001. Nod2, a Nod1/Apaf-1 family member that is restricted to monocytes and activates NF-κB. *J. Biol. Chem.* 276:4812–18
92. Abbott DW, Yang Y, Hutti JE, Madhavarapu S, Kelliher MA, Cantley LC. 2007. Coordinated regulation of Toll-like receptor and NOD2 signaling by K63-linked polyubiquitin chains. *Mol. Cell. Biol.* 27:6012–25
93. Inohara N, Ogura Y, Fontalba A, Gutierrez O, Pons F, et al. 2003. Host recognition of bacterial muramyl dipeptide mediated through NOD2. Implications for Crohn's disease. *J. Biol. Chem.* 278:5509–12
94. van Heel DA, Ghosh S, Butler M, Hunt KA, Lundberg AM, et al. 2005. Muramyl dipeptide and Toll-like receptor sensitivity in NOD2-associated Crohn's disease. *Lancet* 365:1794–96
95. Hedl M, Li J, Cho JH, Abraham C. 2007. Chronic stimulation of Nod2 mediates tolerance to bacterial products. *Proc. Natl. Acad. Sci. USA* 104:19440–45
96. Watanabe T, Kitani A, Murray PJ, Strober W. 2004. NOD2 is a negative regulator of Toll-like receptor 2-mediated T helper type 1 responses. *Nat. Immunol.* 5:800–8
97. Watanabe T, Kitani A, Murray PJ, Wakatsuki Y, Fuss IJ, Strober W. 2006. Nucleotide binding oligomerization domain 2 deficiency leads to dysregulated TLR2 signaling and induction of antigen-specific colitis. *Immunity* 25:473–85
98. Noguchi E, Homma Y, Kang X, Netea MG, Ma X. 2009. A Crohn's disease-associated NOD2 mutation suppresses transcription of human IL10 by inhibiting activity of the nuclear ribonucleoprotein hnRNP-A1. *Nat. Immunol.* 10:471–79
99. Netea MG, Kullberg BJ, de Jong DJ, Franke B, Sprong T, et al. 2004. NOD2 mediates anti-inflammatory signals induced by TLR2 ligands: implications for Crohn's disease. *Eur. J. Immunol.* 34:2052–59
100. Simms LA, Doecke JD, Walsh MD, Huang N, Fowler EV, Radford-Smith GL. 2008. Reduced alpha-defensin expression is associated with inflammation and not NOD2 mutation status in ileal Crohn's disease. *Gut* 57:903–10
101. Barnich N, Aguirre JE, Reinecker HC, Xavier R, Podolsky DK. 2005. Membrane recruitment of NOD2 in intestinal epithelial cells is essential for nuclear factor-κB activation in muramyl dipeptide recognition. *J. Cell Biol.* 170:21–26
102. Travassos LH, Carneiro LA, Ramjeet M, Hussey S, Kim YG, et al. 2009. Nod1 and Nod2 direct autophagy by recruiting ATG16L1 to the plasma membrane at the site of bacterial entry. *Nat. Immunol.* doi:10.1038/ni.1823
103. Cooney R, Baker J, Brain O, Danis B, Pichulik T, et al. 2009. NOD2 stimulation induces autophagy in dendritic cells influencing bacterial handling and antigen presentation. *Nat. Med.* doi:10.1038/nm.2069
104. Swidsinski A, Ladhoff A, Pernthaler A, Swidsinski S, Loening-Baucke V, et al. 2002. Mucosal flora in inflammatory bowel disease. *Gastroenterology* 122:44–54
105. Vallabhapurapu S, Karin M. 2009. Regulation and function of NF-κB transcription factors in the immune system. *Annu. Rev. Immunol.* 27:693–733

106. Neurath MF, Pettersson S, Meyer zum Buschenfelde KH, Strober W. 1996. Local administration of antisense phosphorothioate oligonucleotides to the p65 subunit of NF-κB abrogates established experimental colitis in mice. *Nat. Med.* 2:998–1004

107. Rogler G, Brand K, Vogl D, Page S, Hofmeister R, et al. 1998. Nuclear factor κB is activated in macrophages and epithelial cells of inflamed intestinal mucosa. *Gastroenterology* 115:357–69

108. MacMaster JF, Dambach DM, Lee DB, Berry KK, Qiu Y, et al. 2003. An inhibitor of IκB kinase, BMS-345541, blocks endothelial cell adhesion molecule expression and reduces the severity of dextran sulfate sodium-induced colitis in mice. *Inflamm. Res.* 52:508–11

109. Eckmann L, Nebelsiek T, Fingerle AA, Dann SM, Mages J, et al. 2008. Opposing functions of IKKβ during acute and chronic intestinal inflammation. *Proc. Natl. Acad. Sci. USA* 105:15058–63

110. Greten FR, Eckmann L, Greten TF, Park JM, Li ZW, et al. 2004. IKKβ links inflammation and tumorigenesis in a mouse model of colitis-associated cancer. *Cell* 118:285–96

111. Tanaka K, Namba T, Arai Y, Fujimoto M, Adachi H, et al. 2007. Genetic evidence for a protective role for heat shock factor 1 and heat shock protein 70 against colitis. *J. Biol. Chem.* 282:23240–52

112. Ungaro R, Fukata M, Hsu D, Hernandez Y, Breglio K, et al. 2009. A novel Toll-like receptor 4 antagonist antibody ameliorates inflammation but impairs mucosal healing in murine colitis. *Am. J. Physiol. Gastrointest. Liver Physiol.* 296:G1167–79

113. Rakoff-Nahoum S, Paglino J, Eslami-Varzaneh F, Edberg S, Medzhitov R. 2004. Recognition of commensal microflora by Toll-like receptors is required for intestinal homeostasis. *Cell* 118:229–41

114. Artis D. 2008. Epithelial-cell recognition of commensal bacteria and maintenance of immune homeostasis in the gut. *Nat. Rev. Immunol.* 8:411–20

115. Allakhverdi Z, Comeau MR, Jessup HK, Yoon BR, Brewer A, et al. 2007. Thymic stromal lymphopoietin is released by human epithelial cells in response to microbes, trauma, or inflammation and potently activates mast cells. *J. Exp. Med.* 204:253–58

116. Zaph C, Troy AE, Taylor BC, Berman-Booty LD, Guild KJ, et al. 2007. Epithelial-cell-intrinsic IKK-β expression regulates intestinal immune homeostasis. *Nature* 446:552–56

117. Rimoldi M, Chieppa M, Salucci V, Avogadri F, Sonzogni A, et al. 2005. Intestinal immune homeostasis is regulated by the crosstalk between epithelial cells and dendritic cells. *Nat. Immunol.* 6:507–14

118. Taylor BC, Zaph C, Troy AE, Du Y, Guild KJ, et al. 2009. TSLP regulates intestinal immunity and inflammation in mouse models of helminth infection and colitis. *J. Exp. Med.* 206:655–67

119. Nenci A, Becker C, Wullaert A, Gareus R, van Loo G, et al. 2007. Epithelial NEMO links innate immunity to chronic intestinal inflammation. *Nature* 446:557–61

120. Wertz IE, O'Rourke KM, Zhou H, Eby M, Aravind L, et al. 2004. De-ubiquitination and ubiquitin ligase domains of A20 downregulate NF-κB signaling. *Nature* 430:694–99

121. Boone DL, Turer EE, Lee EG, Ahmad RC, Wheeler MT, et al. 2004. The ubiquitin-modifying enzyme A20 is required for termination of Toll-like receptor responses. *Nat. Immunol.* 5:1052–60

122. Turer EE, Tavares RM, Mortier E, Hitotsumatsu O, Advincula R, et al. 2008. Homeostatic MyD88-dependent signals cause lethal inflammation in the absence of A20. *J. Exp. Med.* 205:451–64

123. Hitotsumatsu O, Ahmad RC, Tavares R, Wang M, Philpott D, et al. 2008. The ubiquitin-editing enzyme A20 restricts nucleotide-binding oligomerization domain containing 2-triggered signals. *Immunity* 28:381–90

124. Lee EG, Boone DL, Chai S, Libby SL, Chien M, et al. 2000. Failure to regulate TNF-induced NF-κB and cell death responses in A20-deficient mice. *Science* 289:2350–54

125. Wellcome Trust Case Control Consort. 2007. Genome-wide association study of 14,000 cases of seven common diseases and 3,000 shared controls. *Nature* 447:661–78

126. Ron D, Walter P. 2007. Signal integration in the endoplasmic reticulum unfolded protein response. *Nat. Rev. Mol. Cell Biol.* 8:519–29

127. Todd DJ, Lee AH, Glimcher LH. 2008. The endoplasmic reticulum stress response in immunity and autoimmunity. *Nat. Rev. Immunol.* 8:663–74

128. Bertolotti A, Wang X, Novoa I, Jungreis R, Schlessinger K, et al. 2001. Increased sensitivity to dextran sodium sulfate colitis in IRE1β-deficient mice. *J. Clin. Invest.* 107:585–93

129. Heazlewood CK, Cook MC, Eri R, Price GR, Tauro SB, et al. 2008. Aberrant mucin assembly in mice causes endoplasmic reticulum stress and spontaneous inflammation resembling ulcerative colitis. *PLoS Med.* 5:e54
130. Brandl K, Rutschmann S, Li X, Du X, Xiao N, et al. 2009. Enhanced sensitivity to DSS colitis caused by a hypomorphic Mbtps1 mutation disrupting the ATF6-driven unfolded protein response. *Proc. Natl. Acad. Sci. USA* 106:3300–5
131. Turner MJ, Sowders DP, DeLay ML, Mohapatra R, Bai S, et al. 2005. HLA-B27 misfolding in transgenic rats is associated with activation of the unfolded protein response. *J. Immunol.* 175:2438–48
132. Shkoda A, Ruiz PA, Daniel H, Kim SC, Rogler G, et al. 2007. Interleukin-10 blocked endoplasmic reticulum stress in intestinal epithelial cells: impact on chronic inflammation. *Gastroenterology* 132:190–207
133. Kaser A, Blumberg RS. 2010. Endoplasmic reticulum stress and intestinal inflammation. *Mucosal Immunol.* 3:11–6
134. Levine B, Kroemer G. 2008. Autophagy in the pathogenesis of disease. *Cell* 132:27–42
135. He C, Klionsky DJ. 2009. Regulation mechanisms and signaling pathways of autophagy. *Annu. Rev. Genet.* 43:67–93
136. Saitoh T, Fujita N, Jang MH, Uematsu S, Yang BG, et al. 2008. Loss of the autophagy protein Atg16L1 enhances endotoxin-induced IL-1β production. *Nature* 456:264–68
137. Kuballa P, Huett A, Rioux JD, Daly MJ, Xavier RJ. 2008. Impaired autophagy of an intracellular pathogen induced by a Crohn's disease associated ATG16L1 variant. *PLoS ONE* 3:e3391
138. McCarroll SA, Huett A, Kuballa P, Chilewski SD, Landry A, et al. 2008. Deletion polymorphism upstream of IRGM associated with altered IRGM expression and Crohn's disease. *Nat. Genet.* 40:1107–12
139. Parkes M, Barrett JC, Prescott NJ, Tremelling M, Anderson CA, et al. 2007. Sequence variants in the autophagy gene IRGM and multiple other replicating loci contribute to Crohn's disease susceptibility. *Nat. Genet.* 39:830–32
140. Taylor GA, Feng CG, Sher A. 2004. p47 GTPases: regulators of immunity to intracellular pathogens. *Nat. Rev. Immunol.* 4:100–9
141. Singh SB, Davis AS, Taylor GA, Deretic V. 2006. Human IRGM induces autophagy to eliminate intracellular mycobacteria. *Science* 313:1438–41
142. MacMicking JD, Taylor GA, McKinney JD. 2003. Immune control of tuberculosis by IFN-γ-inducible LRG-47. *Science* 302:654–59
143. Garabedian EM, Roberts LJ, McNevin MS, Gordon JI. 1997. Examining the role of Paneth cells in the small intestine by lineage ablation in transgenic mice. *J. Biol. Chem.* 272:23729–40
144. Wilson CL, Ouellette AJ, Satchell DP, Ayabe T, Lopez-Boado YS, et al. 1999. Regulation of intestinal alpha-defensin activation by the metalloproteinase matrilysin in innate host defense. *Science* 286:113–17
145. Lee AH, Scapa EF, Cohen DE, Glimcher LH. 2008. Regulation of hepatic lipogenesis by the transcription factor XBP1. *Science* 320:1492–96
146. Singh R, Kaushik S, Wang Y, Xiang Y, Novak I, et al. 2009. Autophagy regulates lipid metabolism. *Nature* 458:1131–35
147. Ouyang Q, Tandon R, Goh KL, Ooi CJ, Ogata H, Fiocchi C. 2005. The emergence of inflammatory bowel disease in the Asian Pacific region. *Curr. Opin. Gastroenterol.* 21:408–13
148. Peltekova VD, Wintle RF, Rubin LA, Amos CI, Huang Q, et al. 2004. Functional variants of OCTN cation transporter genes are associated with Crohn disease. *Nat. Genet.* 36:471–75
149. Koepsell H, Lips K, Volk C. 2007. Polyspecific organic cation transporters: structure, function, physiological roles, and biopharmaceutical implications. *Pharm. Res.* 24:1227–51
150. Rinaldo P, Matern D, Bennett MJ. 2002. Fatty acid oxidation disorders. *Annu. Rev. Physiol.* 64:477–502
151. Shekhawat PS, Srinivas SR, Matern D, Bennett MJ, Boriack R, et al. 2007. Spontaneous development of intestinal and colonic atrophy and inflammation in the carnitine-deficient jvs ($OCTN2^{-/-}$) mice. *Mol. Genet. Metab.* 92:315–24
152. Roediger WE, Nance S. 1986. Metabolic induction of experimental ulcerative colitis by inhibition of fatty acid oxidation. *Br. J. Exp. Pathol.* 67:773–82
153. Tupin E, Kinjo Y, Kronenberg M. 2007. The unique role of natural killer T cells in the response to microorganisms. *Nat. Rev. Microbiol.* 5:405–17

154. Fuss IJ, Heller F, Boirivant M, Leon F, Yoshida M, et al. 2004. Nonclassical CD1d-restricted NK T cells that produce IL-13 characterize an atypical Th2 response in ulcerative colitis. *J. Clin. Invest.* 113:1490–97
155. Heller F, Fuss IJ, Nieuwenhuis EE, Blumberg RS, Strober W. 2002. Oxazolone colitis, a Th2 colitis model resembling ulcerative colitis, is mediated by IL-13-producing NK-T cells. *Immunity* 17:629–38
156. Dougan SK, Kaser A, Blumberg RS. 2007. CD1 expression on antigen-presenting cells. *Curr. Top. Microbiol. Immunol.* 314:113–41
157. Spehlmann ME, Eckmann L. 2009. Nuclear factor-κ B in intestinal protection and destruction. *Curr. Opin. Gastroenterol.* 25:92–99
158. Brozovic S, Nagaishi T, Yoshida M, Betz S, Salas A, et al. 2004. CD1d function is regulated by microsomal triglyceride transfer protein. *Nat. Med.* 10:535–39
159. Perera L, Shao L, Patel A, Evans K, Meresse B, et al. 2007. Expression of nonclassical class I molecules by intestinal epithelial cells. *Inflamm. Bowel Dis.* 13:298–307
160. Page MJ, Poritz LS, Tilberg AF, Zhang WJ, Chorney MJ, Koltun WA. 2000. Cd1d-restricted cellular lysis by peripheral blood lymphocytes: relevance to the inflammatory bowel diseases. *J. Surg. Res.* 92:214–21
161. Rachitskaya AV, Hansen AM, Horai R, Li Z, Villasmil R, et al. 2008. Cutting edge: NKT cells constitutively express IL-23 receptor and RORγt and rapidly produce IL-17 upon receptor ligation in an IL-6-independent fashion. *J. Immunol.* 180:5167–71
162. Akbari O, Stock P, Meyer E, Kronenberg M, Sidobre S, et al. 2003. Essential role of NKT cells producing IL-4 and IL-13 in the development of allergen-induced airway hyperreactivity. *Nat. Med.* 9:582–88
163. Fernando MM, Stevens CR, Walsh EC, De Jager PL, Goyette P, et al. 2008. Defining the role of the MHC in autoimmunity: a review and pooled analysis. *PLoS Genet.* 4:e1000024
164. Ware CF. 2005. Network communications: lymphotoxins, LIGHT, and TNF. *Annu. Rev. Immunol.* 23:787–819
165. Kontoyiannis D, Pasparakis M, Pizarro TT, Cominelli F, Kollias G. 1999. Impaired on/off regulation of TNF biosynthesis in mice lacking TNF AU-rich elements: implications for joint and gut-associated immunopathologies. *Immunity* 10:387–98
166. Armaka M, Apostolaki M, Jacques P, Kontoyiannis DL, Elewaut D, Kollias G. 2008. Mesenchymal cell targeting by TNF as a common pathogenic principle in chronic inflammatory joint and intestinal diseases. *J. Exp. Med.* 205:331–37
167. Kontoyiannis D, Boulougouris G, Manoloukos M, Armaka M, Apostolaki M, et al. 2002. Genetic dissection of the cellular pathways and signaling mechanisms in modeled tumor necrosis factor-induced Crohn's-like inflammatory bowel disease. *J. Exp. Med.* 196:1563–74
168. Pender SL, MacDonald TT. 2004. Matrix metalloproteinases and the gut—new roles for old enzymes. *Curr. Opin. Pharmacol.* 4:546–50
169. Jung HC, Eckmann L, Yang SK, Panja A, Fierer J, et al. 1995. A distinct array of proinflammatory cytokines is expressed in human colon epithelial cells in response to bacterial invasion. *J. Clin. Invest.* 95:55–65
170. Zeissig S, Bojarski C, Buergel N, Mankertz J, Zeitz M, et al. 2004. Downregulation of epithelial apoptosis and barrier repair in active Crohn's disease by tumor necrosis factor α antibody treatment. *Gut* 53:1295–302
171. Marini M, Bamias G, Rivera-Nieves J, Moskaluk CA, Hoang SB, et al. 2003. TNF-α neutralization ameliorates the severity of murine Crohn's-like ileitis by abrogation of intestinal epithelial cell apoptosis. *Proc. Natl. Acad. Sci. USA* 100:8366–71
172. Nancey S, Holvoet S, Graber I, Joubert G, Philippe D, et al. 2006. $CD8^+$ cytotoxic T cells induce relapsing colitis in normal mice. *Gastroenterology* 131:485–96
173. Desreumaux P, Ernst O, Geboes K, Gambiez L, Berrebi D, et al. 1999. Inflammatory alterations in mesenteric adipose tissue in Crohn's disease. *Gastroenterology* 117:73–81
174. Neurath MF, Fuss I, Pasparakis M, Alexopoulou L, Haralambous S, et al. 1997. Predominant pathogenic role of tumor necrosis factor in experimental colitis in mice. *Eur. J. Immunol.* 27:1743–50
175. Gratz R, Becker S, Sokolowski N, Schumann M, Bass D, Malnick SD. 2002. Murine monoclonal anti-TNF antibody administration has a beneficial effect on inflammatory bowel disease that develops in IL-10 knockout mice. *Dig. Dis. Sci.* 47:1723–27

176. Watkins PE, Warren BF, Stephens S, Ward P, Foulkes R. 1997. Treatment of ulcerative colitis in the cottontop tamarin using antibody to tumor necrosis factor α. *Gut* 40:628–33
177. Corazza N, Eichenberger S, Eugster HP, Mueller C. 1999. Nonlymphocyte-derived tumor necrosis factor is required for induction of colitis in recombination activating gene (RAG)$2^{-/-}$ mice upon transfer of $CD4^{+}CD45RB^{hi}$ T cells. *J. Exp. Med.* 190:1479–92
178. Powrie F, Leach MW, Mauze S, Menon S, Caddle LB, Coffman RL. 1994. Inhibition of Th1 responses prevents inflammatory bowel disease in scid mice reconstituted with $CD45RB^{hi}$ $CD4^{+}$ T cells. *Immunity* 1:553–62
179. Corazza N, Brunner T, Buri C, Rihs S, Imboden MA, et al. 2004. Transmembrane tumor necrosis factor is a potent inducer of colitis even in the absence of its secreted form. *Gastroenterology* 127:816–25
180. Murch SH, Braegger CP, Walker-Smith JA, MacDonald TT. 1993. Location of tumor necrosis factor α by immunohistochemistry in chronic inflammatory bowel disease. *Gut* 34:1705–9
181. Lugering A, Lebiedz P, Koch S, Kucharzik T. 2006. Apoptosis as a therapeutic tool in IBD? *Ann. NY Acad. Sci.* 1072:62–77
182. Iijima H, Neurath MF, Nagaishi T, Glickman JN, Nieuwenhuis EE, et al. 2004. Specific regulation of T helper cell 1-mediated murine colitis by CEACAM1. *J. Exp. Med.* 199:471–82
183. Fichtner-Feigl S, Strober W, Kawakami K, Puri RK, Kitani A. 2006. IL-13 signaling through the IL-13α2 receptor is involved in induction of TGF-β1 production and fibrosis. *Nat. Med.* 12:99–106
184. Boirivant M, Fuss IJ, Chu A, Strober W. 1998. Oxazolone colitis: A murine model of T helper cell type 2 colitis treatable with antibodies to interleukin 4. *J. Exp. Med.* 188:1929–39
185. Yamazaki K, McGovern D, Ragoussis J, Paolucci M, Butler H, et al. 2005. Single nucleotide polymorphisms in TNFSF15 confer susceptibility to Crohn's disease. *Hum. Mol. Genet.* 14:3499–506
186. Yang SK, Lim J, Chang HS, Lee I, Li Y, et al. 2008. Association of TNFSF15 with Crohn's disease in Koreans. *Am. J. Gastroenterol.* 103:1437–42
187. Papadakis KA, Prehn JL, Landers C, Han Q, Luo X, et al. 2004. TL1A synergizes with IL-12 and IL-18 to enhance IFN-γ production in human T cells and NK cells. *J. Immunol.* 172:7002–7
188. Bamias G, Mishina M, Nyce M, Ross WG, Kollias G, et al. 2006. Role of TL1A and its receptor DR3 in two models of chronic murine ileitis. *Proc. Natl. Acad. Sci. USA* 103:8441–46
189. Takedatsu H, Michelsen KS, Wei B, Landers CJ, Thomas LS, et al. 2008. TL1A (TNFSF15) regulates the development of chronic colitis by modulating both T-helper 1 and T-helper 17 activation. *Gastroenterology* 135:552–67
190. Kishimoto T. 2005. Interleukin-6: from basic science to medicine—40 years in immunology. *Annu. Rev. Immunol.* 23:1–21
191. Atreya R, Mudter J, Finotto S, Mullberg J, Jostock T, et al. 2000. Blockade of interleukin 6 trans signaling suppresses T-cell resistance against apoptosis in chronic intestinal inflammation: evidence in Crohn disease and experimental colitis in vivo. *Nat. Med.* 6:583–88
192. Yamamoto M, Yoshizaki K, Kishimoto T, Ito H. 2000. IL-6 is required for the development of Th1 cell-mediated murine colitis. *J. Immunol.* 164:4878–82
193. Bettelli E, Carrier Y, Gao W, Korn T, Strom TB, et al. 2006. Reciprocal developmental pathways for the generation of pathogenic effector TH17 and regulatory T cells. *Nature* 441:235–38
194. Lee YK, Turner H, Maynard CL, Oliver JR, Chen D, et al. 2009. Late developmental plasticity in the T helper 17 lineage. *Immunity* 30:92–107
195. Zhou L, Chong MM, Littman DR. 2009. Plasticity of $CD4^{+}$ T cell lineage differentiation. *Immunity* 30:646–55
196. Franke A, Balschun T, Karlsen TH, Hedderich J, May S, et al. 2008. Replication of signals from recent studies of Crohn's disease identifies previously unknown disease loci for ulcerative colitis. *Nat. Genet.* 40:713–15
197. Anderson CA, Massey DC, Barrett JC, Prescott NJ, Tremelling M, et al. 2009. Investigation of Crohn's disease risk loci in ulcerative colitis further defines their molecular relationship. *Gastroenterology* 136:523–29
198. Ernst M, Inglese M, Waring P, Campbell IK, Bao S, et al. 2001. Defective gp130-mediated signal transducer and activator of transcription (STAT) signaling results in degenerative joint disease, gastrointestinal ulceration, and failure of uterine implantation. *J. Exp. Med.* 194:189–203

199. Tebbutt NC, Giraud AS, Inglese M, Jenkins B, Waring P, et al. 2002. Reciprocal regulation of gastrointestinal homeostasis by SHP2 and STAT-mediated trefoil gene activation in gp130 mutant mice. *Nat. Med.* 8:1089–97

200. Wang L, Walia B, Evans J, Gewirtz AT, Merlin D, Sitaraman SV. 2003. IL-6 induces NF-κB activation in the intestinal epithelia. *J. Immunol.* 171:3194–201

201. Becker C, Fantini MC, Schramm C, Lehr HA, Wirtz S, et al. 2004. TGF-β suppresses tumor progression in colon cancer by inhibition of IL-6 trans-signaling. *Immunity* 21:491–501

202. Bollrath J, Phesse TJ, von Burstin VA, Putoczki T, Bennecke M, et al. 2009. gp130-mediated Stat3 activation in enterocytes regulates cell survival and cell-cycle progression during colitis-associated tumorigenesis. *Cancer Cell* 15:91–102

203. Mashimo H, Wu DC, Podolsky DK, Fishman MC. 1996. Impaired defense of intestinal mucosa in mice lacking intestinal trefoil factor. *Science* 274:262–65

204. Welte T, Zhang SS, Wang T, Zhang Z, Hesslein DG, et al. 2003. STAT3 deletion during hematopoiesis causes Crohn's disease-like pathogenesis and lethality: a critical role of STAT3 in innate immunity. *Proc. Natl. Acad. Sci. USA* 100:1879–84

205. Kobayashi M, Kweon MN, Kuwata H, Schreiber RD, Kiyono H, et al. 2003. Toll-like receptor-dependent production of IL-12p40 causes chronic enterocolitis in myeloid cell-specific Stat3-deficient mice. *J. Clin. Invest.* 111:1297–308

206. Dinarello CA. 2009. Immunological and inflammatory functions of the interleukin-1 family. *Annu. Rev. Immunol.* 27:519–50

207. Martinon F, Mayor A, Tschopp J. 2009. The inflammasomes: guardians of the body. *Annu. Rev. Immunol.* 27:229–65

208. Villani AC, Lemire M, Fortin G, Louis E, Silverberg MS, et al. 2009. Common variants in the NLRP3 region contribute to Crohn's disease susceptibility. *Nat. Genet.* 41:71–76

209. Zhernakova A, Festen EM, Franke L, Trynka G, van Diemen CC, et al. 2008. Genetic analysis of innate immunity in Crohn's disease and ulcerative colitis identifies two susceptibility loci harboring CARD9 and IL18RAP. *Am. J. Hum. Genet.* 82:1202–10

210. Li J, Moran T, Swanson E, Julian C, Harris J, et al. 2004. Regulation of IL-8 and IL-1β expression in Crohn's disease associated NOD2/CARD15 mutations. *Hum. Mol. Genet.* 13:1715–25

211. van Beelen AJ, Zelinkova Z, Taanman-Kueter EW, Muller FJ, Hommes DW, et al. 2007. Stimulation of the intracellular bacterial sensor NOD2 programs dendritic cells to promote interleukin-17 production in human memory T cells. *Immunity* 27:660–69

212. Casini-Raggi V, Kam L, Chong YJ, Fiocchi C, Pizarro TT, Cominelli F. 1995. Mucosal imbalance of IL-1 and IL-1 receptor antagonist in inflammatory bowel disease. A novel mechanism of chronic intestinal inflammation. *J. Immunol.* 154:2434–40

213. Cominelli F, Nast CC, Llerena R, Dinarello CA, Zipser RD. 1990. Interleukin 1 suppresses inflammation in rabbit colitis. Mediation by endogenous prostaglandins. *J. Clin. Invest.* 85:582–86

214. Cominelli F, Nast CC, Clark BD, Schindler R, Lierena R, et al. 1990. Interleukin 1 (IL-1) gene expression, synthesis, and effect of specific IL-1 receptor blockade in rabbit immune complex colitis. *J. Clin. Invest.* 86:972–80

215. Ferretti M, Casini-Raggi V, Pizarro TT, Eisenberg SP, Nast CC, Cominelli F. 1994. Neutralization of endogenous IL-1 receptor antagonist exacerbates and prolongs inflammation in rabbit immune colitis. *J. Clin. Invest.* 94:449–53

216. Monteleone G, Trapasso F, Parrello T, Biancone L, Stella A, et al. 1999. Bioactive IL-18 expression is up-regulated in Crohn's disease. *J. Immunol.* 163:143–47

217. Pizarro TT, Michie MH, Bentz M, Woraratanadharm J, Smith MF Jr, et al. 1999. IL-18, a novel immunoregulatory cytokine, is up-regulated in Crohn's disease: expression and localization in intestinal mucosal cells. *J. Immunol.* 162:6829–35

218. Siegmund B, Fantuzzi G, Rieder F, Gamboni-Robertson F, Lehr HA, et al. 2001. Neutralization of interleukin-18 reduces severity in murine colitis and intestinal IFN-γ and TNF-α production. *Am. J. Physiol. Regul. Integr. Comp. Physiol.* 281:R1264–73

219. Sivakumar PV, Westrich GM, Kanaly S, Garka K, Born TL, et al. 2002. Interleukin 18 is a primary mediator of the inflammation associated with dextran sulphate sodium induced colitis: blocking interleukin 18 attenuates intestinal damage. *Gut* 50:812–20
220. Kanai T, Watanabe M, Okazawa A, Sato T, Yamazaki M, et al. 2001. Macrophage-derived IL-18-mediated intestinal inflammation in the murine model of Crohn's disease. *Gastroenterology* 121:875–88
221. Ten Hove T, Corbaz A, Amitai H, Aloni S, Belzer I, et al. 2001. Blockade of endogenous IL-18 ameliorates TNBS-induced colitis by decreasing local TNF-α production in mice. *Gastroenterology* 121:1372–79
222. Wirtz S, Becker C, Blumberg R, Galle PR, Neurath MF. 2002. Treatment of T cell-dependent experimental colitis in SCID mice by local administration of an adenovirus expressing IL-18 antisense mRNA. *J. Immunol.* 168:411–20
223. Siegmund B, Lehr HA, Fantuzzi G, Dinarello CA. 2001. IL-1β-converting enzyme (caspase-1) in intestinal inflammation. *Proc. Natl. Acad. Sci. USA* 98:13249–54
224. Veldhoen M, Hocking RJ, Atkins CJ, Locksley RM, Stockinger B. 2006. TGFβ in the context of an inflammatory cytokine milieu supports de novo differentiation of IL-17-producing T cells. *Immunity* 24:179–89
225. Chung Y, Chang SH, Martinez GJ, Yang XO, Nurieva R, et al. 2009. Critical regulation of early Th17 cell differentiation by interleukin-1 signaling. *Immunity* 30:576–87
226. Wilson NJ, Boniface K, Chan JR, McKenzie BS, Blumenschein WM, et al. 2007. Development, cytokine profile and function of human interleukin 17-producing helper T cells. *Nat. Immunol.* 8:950–57
227. Shi J, Aono S, Lu W, Ouellette AJ, Hu X, et al. 2007. A novel role for defensins in intestinal homeostasis: regulation of IL-1β secretion. *J. Immunol.* 179:1245–53
228. Izcue A, Coombes JL, Powrie F. 2009. Regulatory lymphocytes and intestinal inflammation. *Annu. Rev. Immunol.* 27:313–38
229. Langrish CL, McKenzie BS, Wilson NJ, de Waal Malefyt R, Kastelein RA, Cua DJ. 2004. IL-12 and IL-23: master regulators of innate and adaptive immunity. *Immunol. Rev.* 202:96–105
230. Neurath MF, Fuss I, Kelsall BL, Stuber E, Strober W. 1995. Antibodies to interleukin 12 abrogate established experimental colitis in mice. *J. Exp. Med.* 182:1281–90
231. Ito H, Fathman CG. 1997. CD45RB^{high} CD.4^{+} T cells from IFN-γ knockout mice do not induce wasting disease. *J. Autoimmun.* 10:455–59
232. Neurath MF, Weigmann B, Finotto S, Glickman J, Nieuwenhuis E, et al. 2002. The transcription factor T-bet regulates mucosal T cell activation in experimental colitis and Crohn's disease. *J. Exp. Med.* 195:1129–43
233. Fuss IJ, Neurath M, Boirivant M, Klein JS, de la Motte C, et al. 1996. Disparate CD4^{+} lamina propria (LP) lymphokine secretion profiles in inflammatory bowel disease. Crohn's disease LP cells manifest increased secretion of IFN-γ, whereas ulcerative colitis LP cells manifest increased secretion of IL-5. *J. Immunol.* 157:1261–70
234. Loftus EV Jr. 2004. Clinical epidemiology of inflammatory bowel disease: incidence, prevalence, and environmental influences. *Gastroenterology* 126:1504–17
235. Kikuchi H, Itoh J, Fukuda S. 2008. Chronic nicotine stimulation modulates the immune response of mucosal T cells to Th1-dominant pattern via nAChR by upregulation of Th1-specific transcriptional factor. *Neurosci. Lett.* 432:217–21
236. Xavier RJ, Rioux JD. 2008. Genome-wide association studies: a new window into immune-mediated diseases. *Nat. Rev. Immunol.* 8:631–43
237. Fisher SA, Tremelling M, Anderson CA, Gwilliam R, Bumpstead S, et al. 2008. Genetic determinants of ulcerative colitis include the ECM1 locus and five loci implicated in Crohn's disease. *Nat. Genet.* 40:710–12
238. Oppmann B, Lesley R, Blom B, Timans JC, Xu Y, et al. 2000. Novel p19 protein engages IL-12p40 to form a cytokine, IL-23, with biological activities similar as well as distinct from IL-12. *Immunity* 13:715–25
239. Cua DJ, Sherlock J, Chen Y, Murphy CA, Joyce B, et al. 2003. Interleukin-23 rather than interleukin-12 is the critical cytokine for autoimmune inflammation of the brain. *Nature* 421:744–48
240. Murphy CA, Langrish CL, Chen Y, Blumenschein W, McClanahan T, et al. 2003. Divergent pro- and antiinflammatory roles for IL-23 and IL-12 in joint autoimmune inflammation. *J. Exp. Med.* 198:1951–57

241. Kroenke MA, Carlson TJ, Andjelkovic AV, Segal BM. 2008. IL-12- and IL-23-modulated T cells induce distinct types of EAE based on histology, CNS chemokine profile, and response to cytokine inhibition. *J. Exp. Med.* 205:1535–41
242. Luger D, Silver PB, Tang J, Cua D, Chen Z, et al. 2008. Either a Th17 or a Th1 effector response can drive autoimmunity: conditions of disease induction affect dominant effector category. *J. Exp. Med.* 205:799–810
243. Uhlig HH, McKenzie BS, Hue S, Thompson C, Joyce-Shaikh B, et al. 2006. Differential activity of IL-12 and IL-23 in mucosal and systemic innate immune pathology. *Immunity* 25:309–18
244. Hue S, Ahern P, Buonocore S, Kullberg MC, Cua DJ, et al. 2006. Interleukin-23 drives innate and T cell-mediated intestinal inflammation. *J. Exp. Med.* 203:2473–83
245. Kullberg MC, Jankovic D, Feng CG, Hue S, Gorelick PL, et al. 2006. IL-23 plays a key role in *Helicobacter hepaticus*-induced T cell-dependent colitis. *J. Exp. Med.* 203:2485–94
246. Collison LW, Workman CJ, Kuo TT, Boyd K, Wang Y, et al. 2007. The inhibitory cytokine IL-35 contributes to regulatory T-cell function. *Nature* 450:566–69
247. Yen D, Cheung J, Scheerens H, Poulet F, McClanahan T, et al. 2006. IL-23 is essential for T cell-mediated colitis and promotes inflammation via IL-17 and IL-6. *J. Clin. Invest.* 116:1310–16
248. Ouyang W, Kolls JK, Zheng Y. 2008. The biological functions of T helper 17 cell effector cytokines in inflammation. *Immunity* 28:454–67
249. Harrington LE, Hatton RD, Mangan PR, Turner H, Murphy TL, et al. 2005. Interleukin 17-producing $CD4^+$ effector T cells develop via a lineage distinct from the T helper type 1 and 2 lineages. *Nat. Immunol.* 6:1123–32
250. Park H, Li Z, Yang XO, Chang SH, Nurieva R, et al. 2005. A distinct lineage of CD4 T cells regulates tissue inflammation by producing interleukin 17. *Nat. Immunol.* 6:1133–41
251. Ivanov II, McKenzie BS, Zhou L, Tadokoro CE, Lepelley A, et al. 2006. The orphan nuclear receptor RORγt directs the differentiation program of proinflammatory $IL\text{-}17^+$ T helper cells. *Cell* 126:1121–33
252. Becker C, Wirtz S, Blessing M, Pirhonen J, Strand D, et al. 2003. Constitutive p40 promoter activation and IL-23 production in the terminal ileum mediated by dendritic cells. *J. Clin. Invest.* 112:693–706
253. Atarashi K, Nishimura J, Shima T, Umesaki Y, Yamamoto M, et al. 2008. ATP drives lamina propria T(H)17 cell differentiation. *Nature* 455:808–12
254. Manocha M, Svend R, Laouar A, Liao G, Bhan A, et al. 2009. Blocking CD27-CD70 costimulatory pathway suppresses experimental colitis. *J. Immunol.* 183:270–76
255. O'Connor W Jr, Kamanaka M, Booth CJ, Town T, Nakae S, et al. 2009. A protective function for interleukin 17A in T cell-mediated intestinal inflammation. *Nat. Immunol.* 10:603–9
256. Ogawa A, Andoh A, Araki Y, Bamba T, Fujiyama Y. 2004. Neutralization of interleukin-17 aggravates dextran sulfate sodium-induced colitis in mice. *Clin. Immunol.* 110:55–62
257. Yang XO, Chang SH, Park H, Nurieva R, Shah B, et al. 2008. Regulation of inflammatory responses by IL-17F. *J. Exp. Med.* 205:1063–75
258. Zhang Z, Zheng M, Bindas J, Schwarzenberger P, Kolls JK. 2006. Critical role of IL-17 receptor signaling in acute TNBS-induced colitis. *Inflamm. Bowel Dis.* 12:382–88
259. Leppkes M, Becker C, Ivanov II, Hirth S, Wirtz S, et al. 2009. RORγ-expressing Th17 cells induce murine chronic intestinal inflammation via redundant effects of IL-17A and IL-17F. *Gastroenterology* 136:257–67
260. Fujino S, Andoh A, Bamba S, Ogawa A, Hata K, et al. 2003. Increased expression of interleukin 17 in inflammatory bowel disease. *Gut* 52:65–70
261. Annunziato F, Cosmi L, Santarlasci V, Maggi L, Liotta F, et al. 2007. Phenotypic and functional features of human Th17 cells. *J. Exp. Med.* 204:1849–61
262. Weaver CT, Hatton RD, Mangan PR, Harrington LE. 2007. IL-17 family cytokines and the expanding diversity of effector T cell lineages. *Annu. Rev. Immunol.* 25:821–52
263. Izcue A, Hue S, Buonocore S, Arancibia-Carcamo CV, Ahern PP, et al. 2008. Interleukin-23 restrains regulatory T cell activity to drive T cell-dependent colitis. *Immunity* 28:559–70
264. Maloy KJ, Salaun L, Cahill R, Dougan G, Saunders NJ, Powrie F. 2003. $CD4^+CD25^+$ T(R) cells suppress innate immune pathology through cytokine-dependent mechanisms. *J. Exp. Med.* 197:111–19

265. Powrie F, Mason D. 1990. OX-22high CD4^{+} T cells induce wasting disease with multiple organ pathology: prevention by the OX-22low subset. *J. Exp. Med.* 172:1701–8
266. Sakaguchi S, Sakaguchi N, Asano M, Itoh M, Toda M. 1995. Immunologic self-tolerance maintained by activated T cells expressing IL-2 receptor α-chains (CD25). Breakdown of a single mechanism of self-tolerance causes various autoimmune diseases. *J. Immunol.* 155:1151–64
267. Zhou L, Lopes JE, Chong MM, Ivanov II, Min R, et al. 2008. TGF-β-induced Foxp3 inhibits T(H)17 cell differentiation by antagonizing RORγt function. *Nature* 453:236–40
268. Mangan PR, Harrington LE, O'Quinn DB, Helms WS, Bullard DC, et al. 2006. Transforming growth factor-β induces development of the T(H)17 lineage. *Nature* 441:231–34
269. Nurieva R, Yang XO, Martinez G, Zhang Y, Panopoulos AD, et al. 2007. Essential autocrine regulation by IL-21 in the generation of inflammatory T cells. *Nature* 448:480–83
270. Zhou L, Ivanov II, Spolski R, Min R, Shenderov K, et al. 2007. IL-6 programs T(H)-17 cell differentiation by promoting sequential engagement of the IL-21 and IL-23 pathways. *Nat. Immunol.* 8:967–74
271. Mucida D, Park Y, Kim G, Turovskaya O, Scott I, et al. 2007. Reciprocal TH17 and regulatory T cell differentiation mediated by retinoic acid. *Science* 317:256–60
272. Sun CM, Hall JA, Blank RB, Bouladoux N, Oukka M, et al. 2007. Small intestine lamina propria dendritic cells promote de novo generation of Foxp3 T reg cells via retinoic acid. *J. Exp. Med.* 204:1775–85
273. Denning TL, Wang YC, Patel SR, Williams IR, Pulendran B. 2007. Lamina propria macrophages and dendritic cells differentially induce regulatory and interleukin 17-producing T cell responses. *Nat. Immunol.* 8:1086–94
274. Park O, Grishina I, Leung PS, Gershwin ME, Prindiville T. 2005. Analysis of the Foxp3/scurfin gene in Crohn's disease. *Ann. NY Acad. Sci.* 1051:218–28
275. Maul J, Loddenkemper C, Mundt P, Berg E, Giese T, et al. 2005. Peripheral and intestinal regulatory CD4^{+} CD25^{high} T cells in inflammatory bowel disease. *Gastroenterology* 128:1868–78
276. Saruta M, Yu QT, Fleshner PR, Mantel PY, Schmidt-Weber CB, et al. 2007. Characterization of FOXP3^{+}CD4^{+} regulatory T cells in Crohn's disease. *Clin. Immunol.* 125:281–90
277. Makita S, Kanai T, Oshima S, Uraushihara K, Totsuka T, et al. 2004. CD4^{+}CD25^{bright} T cells in human intestinal lamina propria as regulatory cells. *J. Immunol.* 173:3119–30
278. Bennett CL, Christie J, Ramsdell F, Brunkow ME, Ferguson PJ, et al. 2001. The immune dysregulation, polyendocrinopathy, enteropathy, X-linked syndrome (IPEX) is caused by mutations of FOXP3. *Nat. Genet.* 27:20–21
279. Brunkow ME, Jeffery EW, Hjerrild KA, Paeper B, Clark LB, et al. 2001. Disruption of a new forkhead/winged-helix protein, scurfin, results in the fatal lymphoproliferative disorder of the scurfy mouse. *Nat. Genet.* 27:68–73
280. Wildin RS, Ramsdell F, Peake J, Faravelli F, Casanova JL, et al. 2001. X-linked neonatal diabetes mellitus, enteropathy and endocrinopathy syndrome is the human equivalent of mouse scurfy. *Nat. Genet.* 27:18–20
281. Maillard MH, Cotta-de-Almeida V, Takeshima F, Nguyen DD, Michetti P, et al. 2007. The Wiskott-Aldrich syndrome protein is required for the function of CD4^{+}CD25^{+}Foxp3^{+} regulatory T cells. *J. Exp. Med.* 204:381–91
282. Marangoni F, Trifari S, Scaramuzza S, Panaroni C, Martino S, et al. 2007. WASP regulates suppressor activity of human and murine CD4^{+}CD25^{+}FOXP3^{+} natural regulatory T cells. *J. Exp. Med.* 204:369–80
283. Franke A, Balschun T, Karlsen TH, Sventoraityte J, Nikolaus S, et al. 2008. Sequence variants in IL10, ARPC2 and multiple other loci contribute to ulcerative colitis susceptibility. *Nat. Genet.* 40:1319–23
284. Tao R, de Zoeten EF, Ozkaynak E, Chen C, Wang L, et al. 2007. Deacetylase inhibition promotes the generation and function of regulatory T cells. *Nat. Med.* 13:1299–307
285. Monteleone G, Boirivant M, Pallone F, MacDonald TT. 2008. TGF-β1 and Smad7 in the regulation of IBD. *Mucosal Immunol.* 1(Suppl. 1):S50–53
286. Fantini MC, Rizzo A, Fina D, Caruso R, Sarra M, et al. 2009. Smad7 controls resistance of colitogenic T cells to regulatory T cell-mediated suppression. *Gastroenterology* 136:1308–16
287. Sellon RK, Tonkonogy S, Schultz M, Dieleman LA, Grenther W, et al. 1998. Resident enteric bacteria are necessary for development of spontaneous colitis and immune system activation in interleukin-10-deficient mice. *Infect. Immun.* 66:5224–31

288. Martins GA, Cimmino L, Shapiro-Shelef M, Szabolcs M, Herron A, et al. 2006. Transcriptional repressor Blimp-1 regulates T cell homeostasis and function. *Nat. Immunol.* 7:457–65
289. Maynard CL, Weaver CT. 2008. Diversity in the contribution of interleukin-10 to T-cell-mediated immune regulation. *Immunol. Rev.* 226:219–33
290. Autschbach F, Braunstein J, Helmke B, Zuna I, Schurmann G, et al. 1998. In situ expression of interleukin-10 in noninflamed human gut and in inflammatory bowel disease. *Am. J. Pathol.* 153:121–30
291. Kamanaka M, Kim ST, Wan YY, Sutterwala FS, Lara-Tejero M, et al. 2006. Expression of interleukin-10 in intestinal lymphocytes detected by an interleukin-10 reporter knockin tiger mouse. *Immunity* 25:941–52
292. Roers A, Siewe L, Strittmatter E, Deckert M, Schluter D, et al. 2004. T cell-specific inactivation of the interleukin 10 gene in mice results in enhanced T cell responses but normal innate responses to lipopolysaccharide or skin irritation. *J. Exp. Med.* 200:1289–97
293. Rubtsov YP, Rasmussen JP, Chi EY, Fontenot J, Castelli L, et al. 2008. Regulatory T cell-derived interleukin-10 limits inflammation at environmental interfaces. *Immunity* 28:546–58
294. Fontenot JD, Rudensky AY. 2005. A well adapted regulatory contrivance: regulatory T cell development and the forkhead family transcription factor Foxp3. *Nat. Immunol.* 6:331–37
295. Kim JM, Rasmussen JP, Rudensky AY. 2007. Regulatory T cells prevent catastrophic autoimmunity throughout the lifespan of mice. *Nat. Immunol.* 8:191–97
296. Maynard CL, Harrington LE, Janowski KM, Oliver JR, Zindl CL, et al. 2007. Regulatory T cells expressing interleukin 10 develop from Foxp3$^+$ and Foxp3$^-$ precursor cells in the absence of interleukin 10. *Nat. Immunol.* 8:931–41
297. Groux H, O'Garra A, Bigler M, Rouleau M, Antonenko S, et al. 1997. A CD4$^+$ T-cell subset inhibits antigen-specific T-cell responses and prevents colitis. *Nature* 389:737–42
298. Chaudhry A, Rudra D, Treuting P, Samstein RM, Liang Y, et al. 2009. CD4$^+$ regulatory T cells control Th17 responses in a Stat3-dependent manner. *Science* 326:986–91
299. Steidler L, Hans W, Schotte L, Neirynck S, Obermeier F, et al. 2000. Treatment of murine colitis by *Lactococcus lactis* secreting interleukin-10. *Science* 289:1352–55
300. Luster AD, Alon R, von Andrian UH. 2005. Immune cell migration in inflammation: present and future therapeutic targets. *Nat. Immunol.* 6:1182–90
301. Agace WW. 2008. T-cell recruitment to the intestinal mucosa. *Trends Immunol.* 29:514–22
302. Mora JR, Bono MR, Manjunath N, Weninger W, Cavanagh LL, et al. 2003. Selective imprinting of gut-homing T cells by Peyer's patch dendritic cells. *Nature* 424:88–93
303. Johansson-Lindbom B, Svensson M, Wurbel MA, Malissen B, Marquez G, Agace W. 2003. Selective generation of gut tropic T cells in gut-associated lymphoid tissue (GALT): requirement for GALT dendritic cells and adjuvant. *J. Exp. Med.* 198:963–69
304. Rivera-Nieves J, Burcin TL, Olson TS, Morris MA, McDuffie M, et al. 2006. Critical role of endothelial P-selectin glycoprotein ligand 1 in chronic murine ileitis. *J. Exp. Med.* 203:907–17
305. Kosiewicz MM, Nast CC, Krishnan A, Rivera-Nieves J, Moskaluk CA, et al. 2001. Th1-type responses mediate spontaneous ileitis in a novel murine model of Crohn's disease. *J. Clin. Invest.* 107:695–702
306. Rijcken EM, Laukoetter MG, Anthoni C, Meier S, Mennigen R, et al. 2004. Immunoblockade of PSGL-1 attenuates established experimental murine colitis by reduction of leukocyte rolling. *Am. J. Physiol. Gastrointest. Liver Physiol.* 287:G115–24
307. Kuhl AA, Kakirman H, Janotta M, Dreher S, Cremer P, et al. 2007. Aggravation of different types of experimental colitis by depletion or adhesion blockade of neutrophils. *Gastroenterology* 133:1882–92
308. Kwon JH, Keates S, Bassani L, Mayer LF, Keates AC. 2002. Colonic epithelial cells are a major site of macrophage inflammatory protein 3α (MIP-3α) production in normal colon and inflammatory bowel disease. *Gut* 51:818–26
309. Lee JW, Wang P, Kattah MG, Youssef S, Steinman L, et al. 2008. Differential regulation of chemokines by IL-17 in colonic epithelial cells. *J. Immunol.* 181:6536–45
310. Kaser A, Ludwiczek O, Holzmann S, Moschen AR, Weiss G, et al. 2004. Increased expression of CCL20 in human inflammatory bowel disease. *J. Clin. Immunol.* 24:74–85
311. Acosta-Rodriguez EV, Rivino L, Geginat J, Jarrossay D, Gattorno M, et al. 2007. Surface phenotype and antigenic specificity of human interleukin 17-producing T helper memory cells. *Nat. Immunol.* 8:639–46

312. Wang C, Kang SG, Lee J, Sun Z, Kim CH. 2009. The roles of CCR6 in migration of Th17 cells and regulation of effector T-cell balance in the gut. *Mucosal Immunol.* 2:173–83
313. Varona R, Cadenas V, Flores J, Martinez-A C, Márquez G. 2003. CCR6 has a nonredundant role in the development of inflammatory bowel disease. *Eur. J. Immunol.* 33:2937–46
314. Katchar K, Kelly CP, Keates S, O'Brien MJ, Keates AC. 2007. MIP-3α neutralizing monoclonal antibody protects against TNBS-induced colonic injury and inflammation in mice. *Am. J. Physiol. Gastrointest. Liver Physiol.* 292:G1263–71
315. Yamazaki T, Yang XO, Chung Y, Fukunaga A, Nurieva R, et al. 2008. CCR6 regulates the migration of inflammatory and regulatory T cells. *J. Immunol.* 181:8391–401
316. Williams IR. 2006. CCR6 and CCL20: partners in intestinal immunity and lymphorganogenesis. *Ann. NY Acad. Sci.* 1072:52–61
317. Bouskra D, Brezillon C, Berard M, Werts C, Varona R, et al. 2008. Lymphoid tissue genesis induced by commensals through NOD1 regulates intestinal homeostasis. *Nature* 456:507–10
318. Xiao S, Jin H, Korn T, Liu SM, Oukka M, et al. 2008. Retinoic acid increases Foxp3$^+$ regulatory T cells and inhibits development of Th17 cells by enhancing TGF-β-driven Smad3 signaling and inhibiting IL-6 and IL-23 receptor expression. *J. Immunol.* 181:2277–84
319. Mora JR, Iwata M, von Andrian UH. 2008. Vitamin effects on the immune system: vitamins A and D take center stage. *Nat. Rev. Immunol.* 8:685–98
320. Podolsky DK, Lobb R, King N, Benjamin CD, Pepinsky B, et al. 1993. Attenuation of colitis in the cotton-top tamarin by antialpha 4 integrin monoclonal antibody. *J. Clin. Invest.* 92:372–80
321. Apostolaki M, Manoloukos M, Roulis M, Wurbel MA, Muller W, et al. 2008. Role of β7 integrin and the chemokine/chemokine receptor pair CCL25/CCR9 in modeled TNF-dependent Crohn's disease. *Gastroenterology* 134:2025–35
322. Wei Z, Ertl L, Baumgart T, Rubas W, Hor S-Y, et al. 2005. CC chemokine receptor 9 (CCR9) antagonist ameliorates experimental ileitis and colitis. *Gastroenterology* 128:A204 (Abstr.)
323. Bensinger SJ, Tontonoz P. 2008. Integration of metabolism and inflammation by lipid-activated nuclear receptors. *Nature* 454:470–77
324. Narumiya S, Sugimoto Y, Ushikubi F. 1999. Prostanoid receptors: structures, properties, and functions. *Physiol. Rev.* 79:1193–226
325. Morteau O, Morham SG, Sellon R, Dieleman LA, Langenbach R, et al. 2000. Impaired mucosal defense to acute colonic injury in mice lacking cyclooxygenase-1 or cyclooxygenase-2. *J. Clin. Invest.* 105:469–78
326. Kabashima K, Saji T, Murata T, Nagamachi M, Matsuoka T, et al. 2002. The prostaglandin receptor EP4 suppresses colitis, mucosal damage and CD4 cell activation in the gut. *J. Clin. Invest.* 109:883–93
327. Cosme R, Lublin D, Takafuji V, Lynch K, Roche JK. 2000. Prostanoids in human colonic mucosa: effects of inflammation on PGE(2) receptor expression. *Hum. Immunol.* 61:684–96
328. Takafuji V, Cosme R, Lublin D, Lynch K, Roche JK. 2000. Prostanoid receptors in intestinal epithelium: selective expression, function, and change with inflammation. *Prostaglandins Leukot. Essent. Fatty Acids* 63:223–35
329. Colgan SP, Parkos CA, Delp C, Arnaout MA, Madara JL. 1993. Neutrophil migration across cultured intestinal epithelial monolayers is modulated by epithelial exposure to IFN-γ in a highly polarized fashion. *J. Cell Biol.* 120:785–98
330. Takayama K, Garcia-Cardena G, Sukhova GK, Comander J, Gimbrone MA Jr, Libby P. 2002. Prostaglandin E2 suppresses chemokine production in human macrophages through the EP4 receptor. *J. Biol. Chem.* 277:44147–54
331. Minami M, Shimizu K, Okamoto Y, Folco E, Ilasaca ML, et al. 2008. Prostaglandin E receptor type 4-associated protein interacts directly with NF-κB1 and attenuates macrophage activation. *J. Biol. Chem.* 283:9692–703
332. Yao C, Sakata D, Esaki Y, Li Y, Matsuoka T, et al. 2009. Prostaglandin E2-EP4 signaling promotes immune inflammation through Th1 cell differentiation and Th17 cell expansion. *Nat. Med.* 15:633–40
333. Boniface K, Bak-Jensen KS, Li Y, Blumenschein WM, McGeachy MJ, et al. 2009. Prostaglandin E2 regulates Th17 cell differentiation and function through cyclic AMP and EP2/EP4 receptor signaling. *J. Exp. Med.* 206:535–48

334. Libioulle C, Louis E, Hansoul S, Sandor C, Farnir F, et al. 2007. Novel Crohn disease locus identified by genome-wide association maps to a gene desert on 5p13.1 and modulates expression of PTGER4. *PLoS Genet.* 3:e58
335. Dubuquoy L, Rousseaux C, Thuru X, Peyrin-Biroulet L, Romano O, et al. 2006. PPARγ as a new therapeutic target in inflammatory bowel diseases. *Gut* 55:1341–49
336. Rousseaux C, Lefebvre B, Dubuquoy L, Lefebvre P, Romano O, et al. 2005. Intestinal antiinflammatory effect of 5-aminosalicylic acid is dependent on peroxisome proliferator-activated receptor-γ. *J. Exp. Med.* 201:1205–15
337. Dubuquoy L, Jansson EA, Deeb S, Rakotobe S, Karoui M, et al. 2003. Impaired expression of peroxisome proliferator-activated receptor gamma in ulcerative colitis. *Gastroenterology* 124:1265–76
338. Wachtershauser A, Loitsch SM, Stein J. 2000. PPAR-γ is selectively upregulated in Caco-2 cells by butyrate. *Biochem. Biophys. Res. Commun.* 272:380–85
339. Su CG, Wen X, Bailey ST, Jiang W, Rangwala SM, et al. 1999. A novel therapy for colitis utilizing PPAR-γ ligands to inhibit the epithelial inflammatory response. *J. Clin. Invest.* 104:383–89
340. Bassaganya-Riera J, Reynolds K, Martino-Catt S, Cui Y, Hennighausen L, et al. 2004. Activation of PPAR γ and δ by conjugated linoleic acid mediates protection from experimental inflammatory bowel disease. *Gastroenterology* 127:777–91
341. Lewis JD, Lichtenstein GR, Deren JJ, Sands BE, Hanauer SB, et al. 2008. Rosiglitazone for active ulcerative colitis: a randomized placebo-controlled trial. *Gastroenterology* 134:688–95
342. Evans-Molina C, Robbins RD, Kono T, Tersey SA, Vestermark GL, et al. 2009. Peroxisome proliferator-activated receptor gamma activation restores islet function in diabetic mice through reduction of endoplasmic reticulum stress and maintenance of euchromatin structure. *Mol. Cell. Biol.* 29:2053–67
343. Rutkowski DT, Wu J, Back SH, Callaghan MU, Ferris SP, et al. 2008. UPR pathways combine to prevent hepatic steatosis caused by ER stress-mediated suppression of transcriptional master regulators. *Dev. Cell* 15:829–40
344. Serhan CN, Chiang N, Van Dyke TE. 2008. Resolving inflammation: dual anti-inflammatory and proresolution lipid mediators. *Nat. Rev. Immunol.* 8:349–61
345. Levy BD, Clish CB, Schmidt B, Gronert K, Serhan CN. 2001. Lipid mediator class switching during acute inflammation: signals in resolution. *Nat. Immunol.* 2:612–19
346. Mangino MJ, Brounts L, Harms B, Heise C. 2006. Lipoxin biosynthesis in inflammatory bowel disease. *Prostaglandins Other Lipid Mediat.* 79:84–92
347. Arita M, Yoshida M, Hong S, Tjonahen E, Glickman JN, et al. 2005. Resolvin E1, an endogenous lipid mediator derived from omega-3 eicosapentaenoic acid, protects against 2,4,6-trinitrobenzene sulfonic acid-induced colitis. *Proc. Natl. Acad. Sci. USA* 102:7671–76
348. Hudert CA, Weylandt KH, Lu Y, Wang J, Hong S, et al. 2006. Transgenic mice rich in endogenous omega-3 fatty acids are protected from colitis. *Proc. Natl. Acad. Sci. USA* 103:11276–81
349. Belluzzi A, Brignola C, Campieri M, Pera A, Boschi S, Miglioli M. 1996. Effect of an enteric-coated fish-oil preparation on relapses in Crohn's disease. *N. Engl. J. Med.* 334:1557–60
350. Fiorucci S, Wallace JL, Mencarelli A, Distrutti E, Rizzo G, et al. 2004. A beta-oxidation-resistant lipoxin A4 analog treats hapten-induced colitis by attenuating inflammation and immune dysfunction. *Proc. Natl. Acad. Sci. USA* 101:15736–41
351. Gewirtz AT, Collier-Hyams LS, Young AN, Kucharzik T, Guilford WJ, et al. 2002. Lipoxin a4 analogs attenuate induction of intestinal epithelial proinflammatory gene expression and reduce the severity of dextran sodium sulfate-induced colitis. *J. Immunol.* 168:5260–67
352. Baumgart M, Dogan B, Rishniw M, Weitzman G, Bosworth B, et al. 2007. Culture independent analysis of ileal mucosa reveals a selective increase in invasive *Escherichia coli* of novel phylogeny relative to depletion of Clostridiales in Crohn's disease involving the ileum. *Isme J.* 1:403–18
353. Manichanh C, Rigottier-Gois L, Bonnaud E, Gloux K, Pelletier E, et al. 2006. Reduced diversity of faecal microbiota in Crohn's disease revealed by a metagenomic approach. *Gut* 55:205–11
354. Gophna U, Sommerfeld K, Gophna S, Doolittle WF, Veldhuyzen van Zanten SJ. 2006. Differences between tissue-associated intestinal microfloras of patients with Crohn's disease and ulcerative colitis. *J. Clin. Microbiol.* 44:4136–41

355. Ott SJ, Musfeldt M, Wenderoth DF, Hampe J, Brant O, et al. 2004. Reduction in diversity of the colonic mucosa associated bacterial microflora in patients with active inflammatory bowel disease. *Gut* 53:685–93
356. Martinez-Medina M, Aldeguer X, Gonzalez-Huix F, Acero D, Garcia-Gil LJ. 2006. Abnormal microbiota composition in the ileocolonic mucosa of Crohn's disease patients as revealed by polymerase chain reaction-denaturing gradient gel electrophoresis. *Inflamm. Bowel Dis.* 12:1136–45
357. Bibiloni R, Mangold M, Madsen KL, Fedorak RN, Tannock GW. 2006. The bacteriology of biopsies differs between newly diagnosed, untreated, Crohn's disease and ulcerative colitis patients. *J. Med. Microbiol.* 55:1141–49
358. Conte MP, Schippa S, Zamboni I, Penta M, Chiarini F, et al. 2006. Gut-associated bacterial microbiota in paediatric patients with inflammatory bowel disease. *Gut* 55:1760–67
359. Ley RE, Turnbaugh PJ, Klein S, Gordon JI. 2006. Microbial ecology: human gut microbes associated with obesity. *Nature* 444:1022–23
360. Tsang J, Brown R, Anderson G, Schmidt T, Tannock G, et al. 2004. Selective expansion of colitogenic commensal bacterial species in SPF IL-$10^{-/-}$ mice. *Gastroenterology* 126:A291 (Abstr.)
361. Ley RE, Backhed F, Turnbaugh P, Lozupone CA, Knight RD, Gordon JI. 2005. Obesity alters gut microbial ecology. *Proc. Natl. Acad. Sci. USA* 102:11070–75
362. Turnbaugh PJ, Ley RE, Mahowald MA, Magrini V, Mardis ER, Gordon JI. 2006. An obesity-associated gut microbiome with increased capacity for energy harvest. *Nature* 444:1027–31
363. Hildebrandt MA, Hoffman C, Sherrill-Mix SA, Keilbaugh SA, Hamady M, et al. 2009. High fat diet determines the composition of the murine gut microbiome independently of obesity. *Gastroenterology* 137:1716–24

Intestinal Bacteria and the Regulation of Immune Cell Homeostasis

David A. Hill and David Artis

University of Pennsylvania School of Veterinary Medicine, Department of Pathobiology, Philadelphia, Pennsylvania 19104-4539; email: dartis@vet.upenn.edu

Annu. Rev. Immunol. 2010. 28:623–67

First published online as a Review in Advance on January 5, 2010

The *Annual Review of Immunology* is online at immunol.annualreviews.org

This article's doi:
10.1146/annurev-immunol-030409-101330

0732-0582/10/0423-0623$20.00

Key Words

commensal, bacteria, IBD, allergy, antibiotic, germ-free, microbiota, colitis

Abstract

The human intestine is colonized by an estimated 100 trillion bacteria. Some of these bacteria are essential for normal physiology, whereas others have been implicated in the pathogenesis of multiple inflammatory diseases including IBD and asthma. This review examines the influence of signals from intestinal bacteria on the homeostasis of the mammalian immune system in the context of health and disease. We review the bacterial composition of the mammalian intestine, known bacterial-derived immunoregulatory molecules, and the mammalian innate immune receptors that recognize them. We discuss the influence of bacterial-derived signals on immune cell function and the mechanisms by which these signals modulate the development and progression of inflammatory disease. We conclude with an examination of successes and future challenges in using bacterial communities or their products in the prevention or treatment of human disease.

INTRODUCTION

IBD: inflammatory bowel disease

Microorganisms are the most abundant life form on earth. Although many are free living, some have evolved to participate in close and often long-lasting interactions with multicellular species. Some of these relationships are pathogenic, whereas others are beneficial to the multicellular host. Such beneficial relationships have evolved to represent a conserved feature of multicellular life, important for normal development and physiology in plants (1), insects (2), nematodes (3), fish (4), birds (5), and mammals (6).

After birth, the epithelial surfaces of mammals are colonized with viruses, fungi, bacteria, protozoa, and helminths, creating complex microbial communities in multiple environmental niches. The mammalian intestine is the best studied of these microbial environments. By adulthood, the mammalian intestine is colonized by members of all three domains of life; bacteria are the most abundant, with more than 100 trillion individual organisms (7). Several terms have been used to describe the relationship between microorganisms and multicellular organisms (see sidebar), but for the purposes of this review we use "intestinal bacteria" to refer to all bacteria that inhabit the intestine and the term "beneficial" to specify those that participate in a mutualistic or commensal relationship. In some cases, millennia of evolution have resulted in mutualistic relationships between beneficial bacteria and the multicellular host (8). For example, beneficial bacteria supply essential nutrients, aid in the digestion of otherwise indigestible compounds, promote angiogenesis and enteric nerve function, defend against opportunistic pathogens, and contribute to the development and regulation of the mammalian immune system (9, 10).

Although signals derived from intestinal bacteria are important for normal mammalian development and physiology, alteration of these communities (dysbiosis) in patients or animal models is associated with multiple disease states including inflammatory bowel disease (IBD) (11), obesity (12), cancer (13), diabetes (14), and allergy (15). In many cases, altered immune responses to intestinal bacteria contribute to inflammation (16, 17), implicating dysbiosis as a biomarker and a potential trigger for disease. As such, understanding how signals derived from intestinal bacteria influence the mammalian immune system has important implications for defining the etiology of human inflammatory diseases as well as for the development of preventative or therapeutic intervention strategies.

This review focuses on the influence of intestinal bacteria on the mammalian immune system. We first give an overview of the role of intestinal bacteria in mammalian health and disease. We then review the acquisition and composition of bacterial communities in the mammalian intestine, with particular attention given to genetic and environmental factors that influence bacterial community structure. Next, we discuss immunomodulatory signals derived from intestinal bacteria, the receptors that recognize them, and their influence on innate and adaptive immune cell homeostasis. Finally, we discuss the prospects of exploiting our knowledge of signals from intestinal bacteria to prevent or treat human disease.

COMMON TERMS DESCRIBING INTESTINAL COMMUNITIES

Symbiosis: close and often long-term relationship between different biological species. Symbiotic relationships can be described as

- Mutualistic: both species derive a benefit from the interaction,
- Parasitic: one member benefits and the other is harmed, or
- Commensal: one member benefits and the other is unaffected.

Dysbiosis: the condition of having microbial imbalances on or within the body.

Probiotic: an organism given as a live supplement to confer a biological benefit to the host.

INTESTINAL BACTERIA IN MAMMALIAN HEALTH AND DISEASE

Although beneficial bacteria colonize all mammalian epithelial surfaces, the gastrointestinal tract has the largest bacterial burden, with more than 100 trillion individual organisms at a density of 10^{11} to 10^{14} cells per gram of luminal contents (7, 18). The bacterial communities of the mammalian intestine are also some of the best characterized; studies carried out as early as the 1960s using culture-based and microbiological identification methods began to identify the major bacterial groups present in the mammalian intestine (19). Currently, molecular advances in DNA bar coding and 454 pyrosequencing of 16S ribosomal RNA gene segments are allowing previously unattainable insights into nonculturable bacterial communities (20–23) and are placing species estimates from conservative numbers of 1000–2000 to numbers as high as 15,000–40,000 individual members (24).

Over the past century, studies in animals and humans have identified important roles for bacterial signals in promoting the optimal digestion of food (25), maintaining epithelial homeostasis (26), modulating fat metabolism (27), promoting angiogenesis (28) and enteric nerve function (29), supporting resistance to infection (30), and promoting normal development and regulation of immune cell homeostasis (6) (**Figure 1**). Despite these beneficial sequelae, dysbiosis may be both a biomarker and a potential contributing factor to human inflammatory diseases.

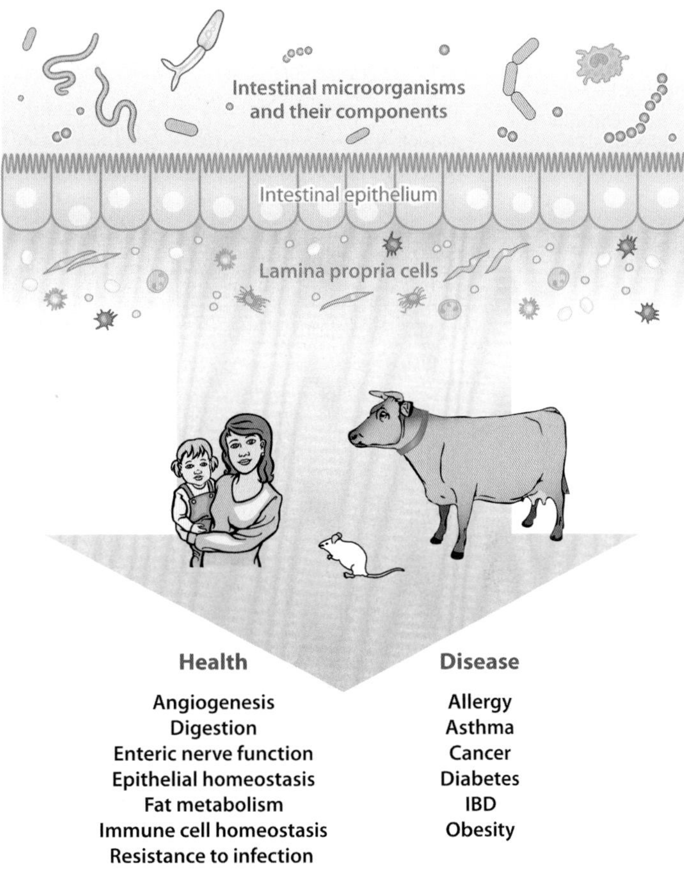

Figure 1

Intestinal bacteria in mammalian health and disease. Schematic of the known influences of intestinal bacteria on normal mammalian physiology and inflammatory disease states.

For example, IBD is thought to result from inappropriate and ongoing mucosal immune responses to normal intestinal bacteria (31). Tolerance to intestinal bacteria is broken in IBD (32), leading to inappropriate local (33) and systemic (34, 35) immune responses to intestinal communities that may contribute to pathogenesis (16). Additionally, bacterial communities from the intestine of IBD patients have a reduced diversity compared with those from healthy individuals (11), and IBD patients display aberrant cytokine production, T cell activation, and IgG antibody responses to intestinal bacteria (32, 33). Genetic susceptibility loci have been identified for the inflammatory bowel diseases Crohn's and ulcerative colitis, including mutations in the pattern-recognition receptor NOD2 (nucleotide-binding oligomerization domain-containing protein 2) (36, 37), a component of the innate immune system that is important for immune recognition and responses to intracellular bacteria (38) (see below). These findings implicate altered immune responses to intestinal bacteria in the pathogenesis of IBD.

LPS: lipopolysaccharide

TLR: Toll-like receptor

Animal models of IBD have provided additional insights into the influence of intestinal bacteria on the pathogenesis of this disease. Reducing microbial stimulation in murine models of IBD, achieved by rearing animals under germ-free conditions, ameliorates intestinal disease. For example, IL-2-deficient mice spontaneously develop intestinal inflammation when raised under conventional conditions but have a delayed and milder disease course when raised under germ-free conditions (39). Similarly, both IL-10-deficient or TCRαβ-deficient mice develop spontaneous colitis associated with inappropriate inflammatory immune cell responses when maintained under conventional conditions but were protected against disease when maintained under germ-free conditions (40, 41). These findings support an essential role for microbial-derived signals in driving pathogenic inflammatory responses in these models.

Antibiotic treatment can also ameliorate disease in murine models of IBD. For example, mice deficient in the multiple drug resistance gene (*mdr1aI*) developed spontaneous colitis when housed under specific pathogen–free conditions but were protected from disease by oral antibiotic treatment (42). In addition, mice deficient in keratin-8, a major intermediate filament protein present in the intestinal epithelia, were protected from spontaneous colitis by oral antibiotic treatment (43), as were IL-10-deficient mice (44, 45). These findings suggest that the role of bacterial-derived signals in disease pathogenesis is not purely developmental; rather, they identify bacterial signals as important in the maintenance of intestinal inflammation.

In addition to contributing to inflammatory states, dysbiosis alone can cause disease in otherwise healthy animals. For example, mice deficient in the inflammatory transcription factor T-bet and the recombinase-activating gene RAG2 (TRUC mice) developed spontaneous colitis that was ameliorated by antibiotic treatment (46). When wild-type mice were cohoused with TRUC mice, they also developed colitis, implicating vertical and horizontal transmission of colitogenic bacterial communities as a cause of disease in immunocompetent animals (46).

Altered signals from intestinal bacteria may also influence risk of developing asthma and other systemic atopic disorders in humans (17). Atopy describes inappropriate, type 2 inflammatory responses to environmental allergens (reviewed in 47), and some patients with atopic diseases have altered intestinal bacterial communities (15). In addition, antibiotic treatment of children increases the risk of developing asthma later in life (48) (presumably as a result of altering intestinal communities), as does early colonization with the intestinal bacterium *Bacteroides fragilis* (49), a bacterial group that increases in frequency upon antibiotic treatment of mice (50). Similarly, colonization with *Bifidobacterium*, *Clostridium difficile*, or *Escherichia coli* is associated with the development of eczema in humans (15, 51, 52), an association that may be related to formula feeding (53), although this hypothesis remains to be tested directly.

Animal models have provided important insights into the influence of intestinal bacteria on systemic immune responses that may contribute to disease states. For example, outgrowths of *Candida albicans* after antibiotic treatment of conventional mice were associated with the development of a $CD4^+$ T cell–mediated allergic airway disease (54). In addition, inflammatory responses following subcutaneous injections of carrageenan, lipopolysaccharide (LPS), TNF-α, IL-1β, or the chemokine CXCL1 were reduced in germ-free mice (55). These immune defects were reversed through conventionalization, or the systemic administration of LPS, implicating bacterial signals in the regulation of systemic inflammatory responses (55). Finally, intestinal bacteria may also influence the development of type 1 diabetes, as nonobese diabetic mice deficient in the Toll-like receptor (TLR) adaptor molecule MyD88 are protected against diabetes development (14). Taken together, these findings implicate signals from intestinal bacteria in the regulation of local and systemic inflammatory responses that contribute to disease pathogenesis.

BACTERIAL COMPOSITION AND COLONIZATION DYNAMICS IN THE MAMMALIAN INTESTINE

Humans and other mammals are born from a sterile environment and subsequently acquire intestinal bacteria during their first months of life (56). Early studies using culture-based and microbiological identification methods identified lactobacilli, anaerobic streptococci, and members of the *Bacteroides* genus as residents of the normal adult human intestine (19). However, a large percentage of intestinal bacteria are anaerobes that lack the enzymes necessary for the detoxification of oxygen. As such, even under ideal conditions, it is estimated that only half of bacteria in stool are culturable (57).

More recently, DNA bar coding and 454 pyrosequencing of 16S ribosomal RNA gene segments have provided more accurate characterization of intestinal communities. These studies have identified the Firmicutes and Bacteroidetes phyla as the major bacterial groups present in the mammalian intestine (20–23) (**Figure 2**). Of the Firmicutes, 95% belong to the Clostridia class, whereas large variations exist in the Bacteroidetes phylotypes among individuals (20–22, 58). Other phyla present in relatively low abundance include the Proteobacteria, Actinobacteria, Fusobacteria, and Verrucomicrobia (20, 21, 23, 58, 59). New sequencing methods also allow for metagenomic analysis of intestinal communities and are providing novel insights into the influence of microbial-derived genes and gene products on normal mammalian physiology (24).

Bacterial communities exhibit differences along the length of the colon and between the luminal and mucosal-associated microenvironments (20, 60, 61), suggesting that defined microbial communities at different anatomical locations may be important for normal

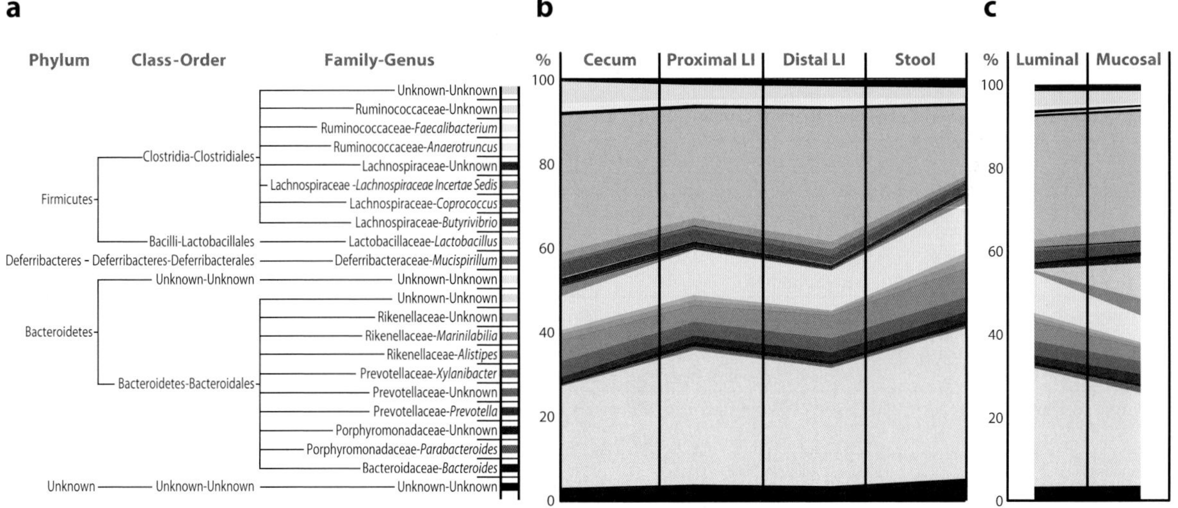

Figure 2

The composition of bacterial communities along the length and between luminal and mucosal compartments of the mammalian intestine. Stool pellet, luminal content, or mucosal-associated communities were sterilely collected. Total sample DNA was extracted and bacterial 16S rRNA gene fragments were PCR amplified with bar code–tagged primers and subjected to pyrosequencing, and taxonomic assignments for each sequence were obtained using RDP Classifier. (*a*) Commonly found bacteria in the murine colon. (*b*) Relative frequencies and distribution of bacteria along the length of the murine colon and in murine stool samples. (*c*) Relative frequencies and distribution of bacteria between luminal and mucosal-associated compartments of the murine colon. Adapted from Reference 50.

mammalian physiology (**Figure 2*b*** and **2*c***). For example, although lactobacilli have been cited for potential probiotic effects (62) and can be isolated from approximately 80% of adults, they represent a relatively low proportion of luminal bacteria (58). However, these potentially beneficial microorganisms represent a much higher proportion of mucosal-associated bacteria (up to 13%) in the mammalian intestine (**Figure 2**) (50).

Although intestinal bacteria are likely to be continuously acquired, mammals undergo two dominant phases of intestinal colonization, the first during breast milk or formula feeding and the second upon weaning to solid foods. Mammalian breast milk is both a continuous source of defined microorganisms and an important source of passive immunity that shapes developing intestinal communities (63). As such, breast-feeding is considered important for the development and maintenance of normal bacterial communities in the intestine (64). The temporal and spatial patterns of intestinal colonization in infants are variable between individuals (65) and depend on multiple factors, including country of birth (66), prematurity (67–69), mode of delivery (67, 70), history of hospitalization (67), antibiotic use (67), feeding practices (53, 56, 67, 71–74), and other factors (**Table 1**). For example, vaginally born and breast-fed infants have a predominance of *Bifidobacteria* in their intestine, with smaller contributions of *E. coli*, *Bacteroides*, and Clostridia species (75). In comparison, infants delivered by Cesarean section have delayed colonization kinetics compared with vaginally born infants, as well as persistent changes to community compositions (70), including lower burdens of *Bifidobacteria* and *Bacteroides* and higher burdens of *C. difficile* (67). Although these individuals likely acquire mature adult bacterial communities upon transition to solid foods, these early alterations may not be benign, given that some associations exist between early alterations to intestinal bacteria and increased risk of atopic disease (76, 77).

The initial immune response to colonization of the mammalian intestine is best described in mice and is characterized by a general inflammatory response that peaks within a week of birth and subsequently stabilizes over the first year of life (78). A hallmark of colonization is the production and secretion

Table 1 Factors influencing the acquisition and/or composition of intestinal bacterial communities

Factor	Reported alteration	References
Birth in North America	Increased *Bacteroides* and *Bifidobacterium* species, decreased *Lactobacillus* and *Eubacterium aerofaciens*	66
Hospitalization/prematurity	Delayed colonization, reduced community diversity, reduced *Bifidobacterium* species, higher *C. difficile*	67–69
Delivery by Cesarean section	Delayed colonization, lower *Bifidobacterium* species and *Bacteroides fragilis*, higher *C. difficile*	67, 70
Antibiotic use	Decreased *Bifidobacterium* and *Bacteroides* species, increased *Campylobacter*	61, 67
Formula feeding	Delayed colonization with *Bifidobacterium* species, more often colonized with staphylococci, *E. coli*, *C. difficile*, *Bacteroides*, and lactobacilli	53, 56, 67, 72, 74
Vegetarian diet	Higher *Clostridium* species	71
Old age	Lower *Clostridium* species, higher *Ruminococcus obeum* and gammaproteobacteria species	377
Older siblings	Higher *Bifidobacterium* species	67
Infectious colitis	Increased *Campylobacter*, decreased *Lactobacillus*	61, 378
Species	Bacterial communities differ between mammalian species	61
Gender	Bacterial communities differ between genders	61
Genetics	Innate immune function regulates intestinal communities in flies	379

of IgA into the intestinal lumen by the host (79) in response to small numbers of intestinal bacteria that penetrate the intestinal epithelium (80, 81). Upon penetration, Peyer's patch dendritic cells (DCs) phagocytose penetrating bacteria and initiate IgA responses through T cell–dependent and –independent mechanisms (82–85). These DCs induce IgA class switching in the mesenteric lymph nodes (mLNs), but not in systemic secondary lymphoid structures (80), indicating that induction of this initial IgA response is compartmentalized to mucosal tissues (86). The resulting secretion of IgA across the intestinal epithelium feeds back in a homeostatic mechanism to reduce epithelial penetration by intestinal bacteria (87).

In addition to IgA responses, the mammalian host mounts an innate immune response upon colonization that contributes to maintenance of the mucosal barrier (reviewed in 88). For example, intestinal Paneth cells directly sense intestinal bacteria through cell-autonomous MyD88 activation, resulting in upregulated expression of the antimicrobial peptide REGIIIγ (89). In addition, intestinal goblet cells upregulate their expression of RELMβ, but not of RELMα or RELMγ, in response to intestinal colonization (90). These early innate responses by intestinal epithelial cells (IECs) have important immunoprotective roles. For example, MyD88-deficient mice fail to upregulate REGIIIγ and are susceptible to *Listeria monocytogenes* infection; reconstitution of MyD88-deficient mice with recombinant REGIIIγ enhances clearance of this pathogen (91).

The systemic response to colonization, and the subsequent development of systemic tolerance, is less well described. Serum antibodies to components of intestinal bacteria are found in humans and other mammals (92), and these antibodies help contain bacteria to the intestine in the absence of innate mechanisms (93, 94). In addition, patients with IBD display systemic immune responses to intestinal bacteria (34, 35), suggesting that tolerance to intestinal bacteria is important for systemic immune cell homeostasis. Although the mechanisms by which the naive host tolerates intestinal bacteria are an ongoing field of study (see below), it will be interesting to examine whether colonization of the intestine with microorganisms early in life influences immunological thresholds from which subsequent proinflammatory or immunoregulatory responses are determined (48, 49).

DC: dendritic cell

IEC: intestinal epithelial cell

NLR: Nod-like receptor

INNATE RECOGNITION OF BACTERIAL-DERIVED SIGNALS IN THE INTESTINE

As discussed above, the colonization of the mammalian intestine results in rapid and dramatic responses by the mucosal immune system that are important for maintaining mucosal homeostasis and protecting against intestinal pathogens. These responses are likely mediated in part through the recognition of bacterial signals (cell wall components, DNA segments, metabolites, etc.) by innate TLRs, NOD-like receptors (NLRs), and G protein–coupled receptors (GPCRs) expressed in hematopoietic and nonhematopoietic cells of the intestine. In this section, we review the signals derived from intestinal bacteria, their innate receptors, and the role that IECs and DCs play in recognizing these signals and modulating subsequent adaptive immune responses (summarized in **Table 2**).

TLR Ligands: Flagellin, Lipopolysaccharide, Polysaccharide A, and CPG Motifs

TLRs are innate pattern-recognition receptors that recognize evolutionarily conserved motifs found in bacteria and other microorganisms (95). TLRs have evolved to recognize multiple microbial-derived products including double-stranded viral RNA (TLR3), gram-negative LPS (TLR4), and gram-negative and gram-positive flagellin (TLR5) (reviewed in 96). Most TLRs are expressed on the surface of cells, with the exception of TLR3, 7, 8, and 9, which are localized to endosomal compartments (97).

Table 2 Bacterial signal receptors, ligands, and immunologic effects

Ligand	Proposed receptor	Immunologic outcome	References
PSA	TLR2	Promotes normal Th1/Th2 balance	110, 113
		Enhances response to abscess-forming bacteria	110, 111
		Suppresses intestinal IL-17 production	112
		Protects against colitis	112
LPS	TLR4	Activates NF-κB	104
		Induces DC migration	105
		Activates systemic DCs	106
		Inhibits mucosal DCs	107
		Protects against colitis	103
Flagellin	TLR5	Positively associated with Crohn's disease	99
		Protects against chemical-, bacterial-, viral-, and radiation-induced mortality	98
CpG	TLR9	Enhances intestinal IFN-γ and IL-17 production	109
		Protects against intestinal parasites	109
		Protects against systemic allergy	108
Muramyl dipeptide	NOD2	Activates NF-κB	114
		Promotes lymphoid tissue development	116
		Regulates intestinal bacterial communities	116
		Promotes antigen-specific immune responses	117
		Protects against colitis	127–129
		Promotes tolerance to bacterial products	130
		Inhibits IL-12p70 production	125
		Protects against IL-12-driven experimental colitis	126, 127
		Protects against Crohn's disease	36, 37
Ado	A2A	Protects against colitis	137
		Drives intestinal Th17 cell differentiation	138
Butyrate	GPR109A	May protect against colon cancer	140–142, 380
		Induces ROS and suppresses NF-κB signaling in IECs	142, 143
		Reduces TNF-α, TNF-β, IL-6, and IL-1β production by LPLs in IBD patients	144, 145, 381
Succinate	GPR91	Acts on intestinal DCs to trigger intracellular calcium release, induce migration, induce proinflammatory cytokine production, and enhance antigen-specific T cell activation	147
SlpA	DC-SIGN	Induces IL-10 and IL-12p70 production by DCs	148

APC: antigen-presenting cell

Several disease models have provided insights into the role of TLR ligands in modulation of the mammalian immune system and indicate both proinflammatory and immunoregulatory functions for TLR signals in various disease settings. As discussed above, nonobese diabetic mice deficient in the TLR signaling molecule MyD88 are protected against the development of type 1 diabetes (14), suggesting that microbial-derived signals are central to disease development in this model. In contrast, treatment with flagellin protects against chemical-, bacterial-, viral-, and radiation-induced mortality in animal models (98), indicating that this molecule has important immunoregulatory roles. In humans, dominant-negative TLR5 polymorphisms reduce adaptive responses to flagellin and are negatively associated with Crohn's disease (99), whereas TLR2 expression is higher in antigen-presenting cells (APCs) from patients with psoriatic arthritis (100). These findings have spurred interest in TLR ligands as therapeutic agents for human disease, and TLR ligands are currently being investigated as treatments for human allergy (101) and as adjuvant therapies for cancer (102).

One mechanism by which TLR ligands may influence disease states is through modulation of mucosal immune cell function. For example, LPS-induced TLR-dependent signaling protects against experimental colitis (103). Cellular studies showed that LPS elicits TLR-dependent NF-κB activation in IECs, providing a possible mechanism by which IECs monitor and initiate immune responses to intestinal bacteria (104). In addition, LPS causes differential DC migration (105) and differential DC activation, depending on anatomical location; TLR4 signaling on DCs promotes antigen-specific $CD4^+$ T cell–mediated pulmonary inflammation (106), whereas intestinal DCs are reported to become hyporesponsive upon TLR4 ligation (107).

Other TLR ligands have proinflammatory and immunoregulatory roles depending on the anatomical location examined. Administration of CpG, a microbial DNA motif that is recognized by TLR9, reduced the susceptibility of TLR4-deficient mice to systemic allergy (108), implicating this molecule in immunoregulatory roles. However, CpG rescued defective IFN-γ and IL-17 production in the intestine of germ-free mice and protected against infection with intestinal parasites (109). In contrast, the *Bacteroides fragilis* cell wall component polysaccharide A (PSA) may have a predominantly immunoregulatory role, given that it promotes normal immune homeostasis (110, 111) and protects against experimental colitis through the suppression of IL-17 production (112, 113).

NLR Ligands: Peptidoglycan

NLRs, such as NOD1 and NOD2, detect intracellular ligands and are recognized as key mediators of proinflammatory and immunoregulatory responses (114). NLRs recognize several bacterial components, including peptidoglycan-containing meso-diaminopimelic acid (NOD1) and muramyl dipeptide (NOD2) (reviewed in 115). In a pathogenic setting, NOD2 ligation initiates NF-κB activation and upregulation of inflammatory cytokines, including IL-12 (114). In addition, recognition of bacterial signals through NLRs is important for the development of intestinal lymphoid tissues (116), the maintenance of normal intestinal bacterial communities (116), and the mounting of antigen-specific immunity (117).

Approximately 15% of patients with Crohn's disease have homozygous or compound heterozygous mutations in the gene that encodes NOD2 (CARD15) (36, 37). Disease-associated alleles were shown to impair NOD2 receptor activity (118), leading to the hypothesis that impaired control of intestinal bacteria was central to disease development (119, 120). However, subsequent studies in NOD2-deficient mice, in particular the seemingly unaltered susceptibility of these mice to some experimental colitis models, suggested a more complex immunomodulatory role for NOD2 signaling (121, 122). Indeed, contrary to the prevailing dogma, it was shown that Crohn's disease–associated NOD2 alleles potentiate rather than attenuate NF-κB signaling (123, 124).

Subsequent studies explored the complex proinflammatory and immunoregulatory roles for NOD2. NOD2 activation was shown to inhibit TLR2-dependent activation of NF-κB, suggesting one possible mechanism by which Crohn's disease–associated NOD2 alleles could result in an inflammatory state (125). Consistent with this, NOD2-deficient mice displayed TLR2-dependent susceptibility to colitis that was characterized by antigen-specific IFN-γ-producing $CD4^+$ T cells (126). Muramyl dipeptide activation of NOD2 also protected mice from experimental colitis (127), and NOD2 transgenic mice exhibited enhanced muramyl dipeptide–mediated resistance to colitis (128). Cellular studies have indicated that administration of muramyl dipeptide decreases the production of IL-12p40, IL-6, and TNF-α by intestinal DCs (127–129). Furthermore,

LPL: lamina propria lymphocyte

APCs from NOD2-deficient mice produced greater IL-12p70 when stimulated with peptidoglycan, whereas addition of muramyl dipeptide to cultures of APCs from NOD2-sufficient mice lead to decreased IL-12p70 responses (125). While these findings suggest that NOD2 plays an important immunoregulatory role in attenuating TLR2-mediated proinflammatory responses to intestinal bacteria (130), other studies have highlighted synergistic inflammatory and immunoregulatory roles for NOD- and TLR-dependent signaling (124, 131, 132).

NOD signaling also modulates production of the immunoregulatory cytokine IL-10. Animal models have shown that TLR2 and NOD2 can act synergistically to induce IL-10 production by macrophages (133), and Crohn's disease–associated NOD2 alleles suppress transcription of human *IL10* by inhibiting the activity of the nuclear ribonucleoprotein hnRNP-A1 (134). As such, both positive and negative interactions between TLRs and NLRs potentially exist to modulate inflammatory and immunoregulatory cytokine responses. While complex, the intricacies of these interactions likely hold important potential for future preventative and therapeutic interventions for IBD and other inflammatory diseases.

G Protein–Coupled and Other Receptors: Adenosine, Short-Chain Fatty Acids, and Surface Layer A Protein

In addition to the TLR and NOD ligands, immunoregulatory GPCR ligands such as the purine adenosine (Ado) are of growing interest in the fields of IBD and other inflammatory disease research (135). Ado may function as an endogenously generated regulator of inflammation, depending on the receptor it binds. For example, an Ado A2A receptor agonist did not alter the course of dextran sodium sulfate (DSS)-induced colitis (136), whereas Ado A2B–deficient mice had increased susceptibility to DSS colitis (137). Additionally, intestinal bacteria can be a source of ATP that can drive Th17 cell differentiation in the lamina propria by inducing IL-6 and IL-23p19 production by a population of CD70^{high} CC11c^{low} cells (138). Consistent with this, germ-free mice exhibited lower concentrations of luminal ATP, as well as fewer numbers of Th17 cells in the lamina propria, a defect that could be reversed through the systemic or rectal administration of ATP.

The normal bacteria of the mammalian intestine also produce significant amounts of butyrate, as well as other short-chain fatty acids (SCFAs) (reviewed in 139). The receptor for butyrate, GPR109A, is expressed on IECs and is downregulated in human colon cancer, in a mouse model of intestinal/colon cancer, and in colon cancer cell lines (140, 141). Consistent with the view that GPR109A is a tumor suppressor, expressing GPR109A in colon cancer cells induces apoptosis in the presence of butyrate (142). Butyrate signals through GPR109A in IECs to suppress NF-κB signaling (142, 143) and reduces production of TNF-α, TNF-β, IL-6, and IL-1β by lamina propria lymphocytes (LPLs) in Crohn's and ulcerative colitis patients (144, 145), implicating this microbial metabolite in the regulation of multiple cell populations. Additionally, the SCFA receptor GPR43 has recently been identified as a key mediator of microbial-derived immunomodulatory signals, as mice deficient in GPR43 show exacerbated or unresolving inflammation in models of colitis, arthritis, and asthma (146).

Succinate, a component of the citric acid cycle, modulates DC function by signaling through the extracellular GPCR GPR91. In one study, succinate signaling triggered intracellular calcium release, induced migratory responses, and acted in synergy with TLR ligands to induce the production of proinflammatory cytokines by DCs (147). In this study, GPR91$^{-/-}$ mice exhibited reduced Langerhans cell migration to draining lymph nodes and succinate enhanced antigen-specific activation of human and mouse CD4^{+} T cells (147). GPR91$^{-/-}$ mice displayed impaired tetanus toxoid–specific recall T cell responses, further implicating GPR91-dependent succinate signaling as a signal of immunologic danger.

Finally, bacterial adhesion via surface proteins can directly modulate immune cell function. For example, *Lactobacillus acidophilus* NCFM attaches to DCs and induces concentration-dependent production of IL-10 and IL-12p70 in a DC-specific, ICAM-3-grabbing nonintegrin (DC-SIGN)-specific manner (148). This immunomodulatory function may depend on the bacterial surface component surface layer protein A (SlpA) because purified SlpA protein binds directly to DC-SIGN, and T cells primed with DCs that are stimulated with *L. acidophilus* NCFM lacking SlpA produce less IL-4 than do those stimulated with wild-type *L. acidophilus* NCFM. In summary, microbial signals can have proinflammatory and immunoregulatory effects on multiple immune cell lineages. The next section examines how recognition of microbial signals by IECs and DCs can result in modulation of both local and systemic immune responses.

RECOGNITION OF INTESTINAL BACTERIA BY EPITHELIAL CELLS

The intestinal epithelium has a diverse set of physiologic functions, including digestion and absorption of nutrients, creating a physical barrier between the external and internal environments, and immunological surveillance of intestinal bacteria and potential pathogens. Epithelial cells are continually replaced from a pool of $Lgr5^+$ multipotent stem cells that reside in crypts of the intestine (149, 150). These epithelial cells provide an effective physical barrier to the outside environment as intercellular tight junctions prevent paracellular traffic and actin-rich microvillar extensions create an apical brush border that impedes microbial attachment and invasion (151). Uptake of macromolecules, particulate antigens, and microorganisms across the intestinal epithelia occurs only by active vesicular transport across epithelial cells, and as such is regulated by multiple mechanisms (reviewed in 152).

In addition to physical adaptations that control transport of solutes across the epithelium, biochemical adaptations have evolved, including production of heavily glycosylated, mucin-rich secretions from goblet cells that create a relatively impermeable, apically adhered glycocalyx (153). The epithelium also produces antimicrobial peptides, including defensins, cathelicidins, and calprotectins that confer broad-spectrum antimicrobial properties through the formation of pores in bacterial cell walls (154). These adaptations are consistent with the view that IECs, in addition to promoting digestion and absorption of nutrients, perform essential barrier functions that obstruct the entry of beneficial and pathogenic bacteria into the underlying lamina propria.

IECs are in continuous contact with beneficial and pathogenic bacteria and, as a result, are ideally located for immunological surveillance of the intestinal lumen. As discussed above, IECs express TLRs (155, 156), NLRs (38), and GPCRs that recognize microbial components and modulate cellular responses (**Figure 3**). IEC expression of innate pattern-recognition receptors is important for mounting immune responses to pathogenic microorganisms (115, 157) by promoting the expression of proinflammatory cytokines (95, 114), chemokines, and antimicrobial peptides (97) as well as the direct induction of IgA class switching by B cells (82, 158, 159). Responses by IECs to intestinal bacteria are not uniform, however: IECs selectively initiate proinflammatory responses to pathogenic bacteria while promoting tolerance to beneficial bacteria (151, 157, 160). One example of this is the gram-negative bacteria *Bacteroides thetaiotaomicron*, which induces IEC expression of the antimicrobial peptide REGIIIγ, whereas the gram-positive *Bifidobacterium longum*, a common component of intestinal communities, does not (161, 162).

Two mechanisms by which IECs may discriminate between beneficial and pathogenic bacteria are (*a*) through subcellular sequestering of pattern-recognition receptors away from luminal signals and (*b*) differential receptor

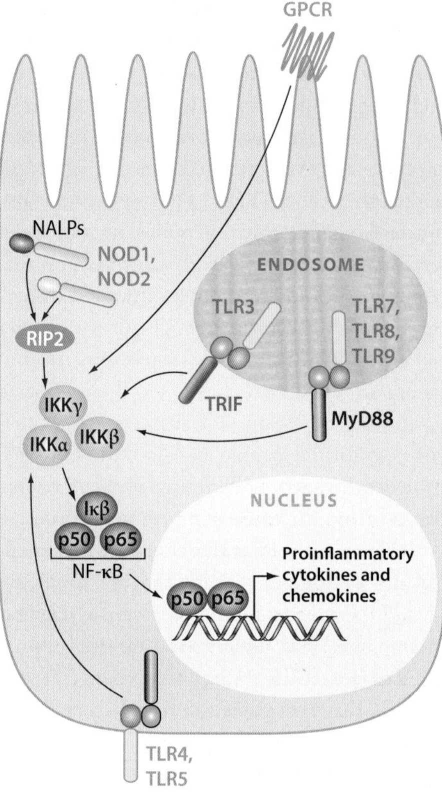

Figure 3

Innate receptors and signaling cascades of mammalian intestinal epithelial cells (IECs). Schematic shows the location of innate pattern-recognition receptors and their signaling cascades in mammalian IEC. Innate pattern-recognition receptors converge on a common NF-κB signaling cascade to regulate transcription of proinflammatory cytokines and chemokines.

expression. For example, TLR5, which recognizes bacterial flagellin, is expressed exclusively on the basolateral surfaces of IECs (reported in Reference 156). Additionally, TLR3, 7, 8, and 9 are reported to be expressed exclusively in intracellular endosomal organelles (97), and NLRs are localized to the cytoplasm, reducing exposure of these receptors to luminal bacteria (163, 164). In addition, under steady-state conditions, IECs express little or no TLR2, TLR4, or CD14, further minimizing stimulation by luminal bacteria (165, 166). However, subcellular localization and differential expression alone cannot account for discrimination between beneficial and pathogenic bacteria, as GPCRs that recognize and initiate responses to bacterial products are continuously expressed on the apical surface of IECs. As such, further investigations are necessary to fully understand how IECs discriminate against beneficial and pathogenic bacteria.

The recognition of bacterial signals by IECs is essential to mucosal homeostasis, implicating IECs as central modulators of inflammatory responses (103, 116, 167). One mechanism by which IECs may regulate mucosal homeostasis is by influencing DCs, macrophages, and lymphocytes through the local expression of immunoregulatory cytokines, including thymic stromal lymphopoietin (TSLP), IL-10, transforming growth factor-β (TGF-β), prostaglandin E2, retinoic acid, and IL-25 (168–174). For example, a population of intestinal DCs induced regulatory T cells (Tregs) that expressed the forkhead box P3 transcription factor ($Foxp3^+$) in a TGF-β- and retinoic acid–dependent manner in vitro, implicating epithelial-derived signals in the conditioning of DCs and subsequent adaptive responses (175, 176). In addition, deletion of NF-κB signaling specifically in IECs resulted in the dysregulated expression of DC-derived proinflammatory cytokines and the development of spontaneous or infection-induced intestinal inflammation (177, 178). These findings provided the first in vivo evidence of a crucial role for IECs in the conditioning of intestinal DC responses. In vitro studies recapitulated the in vivo results as monocyte-derived or circulating DCs conditioned with supernatants from Caco-2 cells or IECs isolated from healthy patients induced $Foxp3^+$ Tregs, whereas IEC supernatants from Crohn's disease patients did not (179). This effect was dependent on the production of TGF-β and retinoic acid by IECs, but not on TSLP production, as DCs deficient in the TSLP receptor ($TSLPR^{-/-}$) and wild-type DCs exhibited a similar capacity to convert naive T cells into Tregs (180).

Epithelial-derived TSLP in particular has important immunomodulatory roles. High levels of *Tslp* mRNA are expressed by epithelial cells at the barrier surfaces of the skin, airways, and intestine, and expression can be upregulated by infection, inflammation, and tissue injury (172, 178, 181–184) in an NF-κB-dependent manner (185). In vitro studies have shown that TSLP-conditioned human DCs can promote Th2 cell responses (172, 186–188) through the inhibition of IL-12 production and the induction of OX40L expression (172, 188). In addition, in vivo studies in the skin and lung (186, 187, 189, 190) have shown that transgenic overexpression of TSLP in cutaneous or pulmonary epithelial cells results in the onset of Th2 cytokine–mediated inflammation resembling atopic dermatitis or asthma, respectively (189, 190). This finding suggests that TSLP is necessary and sufficient for the initiation of Th2 cytokine–driven inflammation (reviewed in 191). Indeed, TLSP expression and TSLP-TSLPR interactions are important for immunity to the intestinal nematode *Trichuris* and for protection against experimental colitis through the in vivo inhibition of IL-12/23p40 production by DCs (173, 178, 192).

Finally, IECs are in direct contact with intraepithelial lymphocytes (IELs) and express all the molecular machinery required for antigen processing and presentation, including proteolytically active cathepsins, the invariant chain, and MHC class II (MHCII) molecules (193). In addition, IECs isolated from patients with IBD were shown to express MHCII molecules and localize exogenous antigens to the late endosome on their basolateral surfaces (194). In vitro studies have shown that rodent IECs, although less potent than professional APCs, could process and present antigen through the MHCII pathway (195). Despite the ability of IECs to process and present antigen, they are reported to lack expression of costimulatory molecules (196), indicating that IECs cannot prime naive T cells and may instead provide tolerogenic signals. However, the intestine contains a large population of memory/activated T cells that exhibit less stringent requirements for costimulation and therefore may be influenced by IEC-intrinsic antigen presentation. Additionally, IECs may deliver inhibitory or tolerogenic signals directly to T cells, consistent with their known role in controlling B cell responses (159). Taken together, these studies highlight that IEC-mediated recognition of intestinal bacteria results in IEC-intrinsic gene expression and the production of immunoregulatory signals that can control innate and adaptive immune cell function.

IEL: intraepithelial lymphocyte

RECOGNITION OF INTESTINAL BACTERIA BY DENDRITIC CELLS

DCs are perhaps the most efficient modulators of adaptive immune responses (reviewed in 197), and they represent an important link between the innate and adaptive immune systems. In the intestine, DCs take on specific phenotypic characteristics and perform distinct functions depending on their anatomical location (198). In the small intestine, DCs reside in the intestinal lamina propria (LP DCs) and in organized lymphoid structures such as Peyer's patches (PP DCs), solitary isolated lymphoid tissue, and mLNs where they function to sample and present luminal and self antigen to T cells (199) (**Figure 4**). PP DCs can be divided into three groups based on chemokine receptor expression, location within the Peyer's patch, and functional characteristics: CX3CR1$^+$ PP DCs are found in close contact with the follicle-associated epithelium, where they participate in a close functional relationship with the epithelial M (microfold) cell (200) to sample luminal antigens in a pattern-recognition receptor–dependent manner (201); CCR6$^+$ PP DCs are found in the subepithelial dome but can quickly migrate to the follicle-associated epithelium in response to microbial stimulation (202); and CCR7$^+$ PP DCs are found in T cell areas (203), where they orchestrate helper T cell responses (204), T cell migration (205, 206), and IgA production (207, 208) in response to microbial signals (reviewed in 209).

Although DCs resident in the Peyer's patches are important mediators of immune

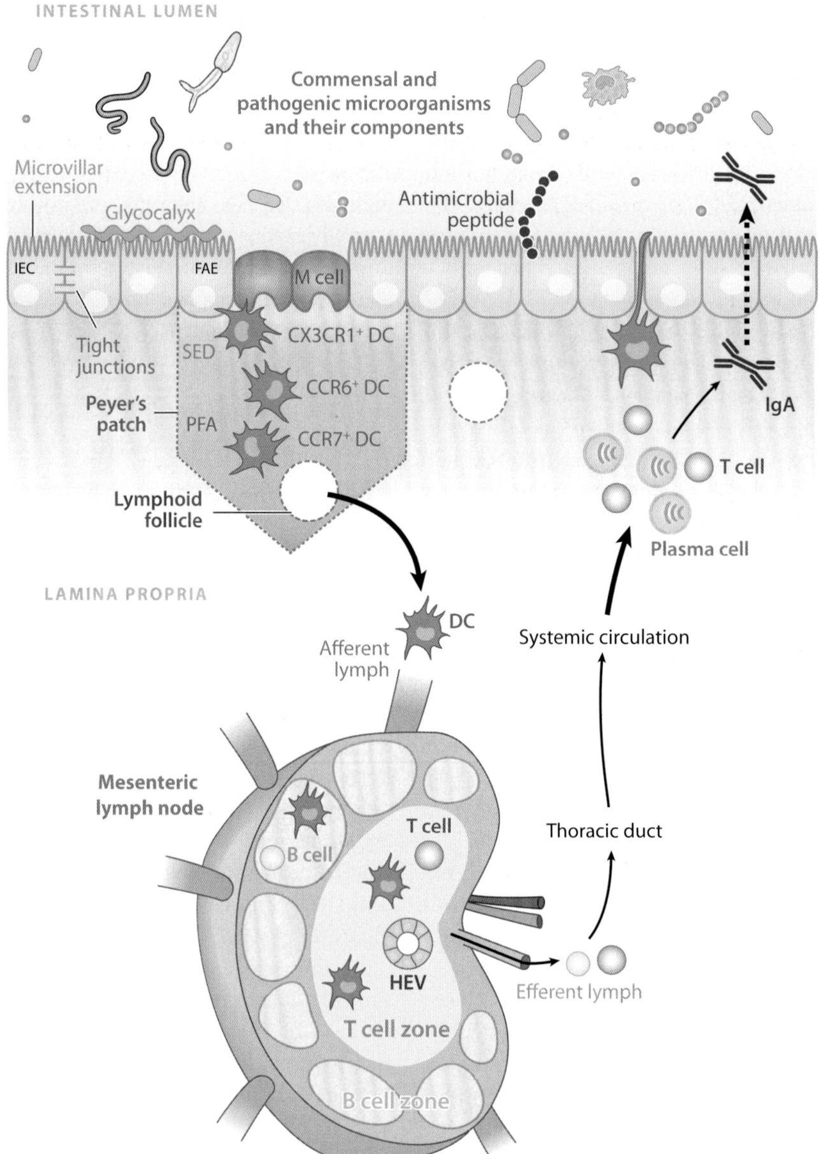

Figure 4

The mucosal immune system of the mammalian intestine. Innate recognition of signals from intestinal bacteria takes place at the intestinal epithelium, in the lamina propria, and in gut-associated lymphoid tissues such as Peyer's patches and isolated lymphoid follicles. Specialized intestinal epithelial cells known as M (microfold) cells overlie Peyer's patches and lymphoid follicles to facilitate luminal sampling and to transport microbial components to professional antigen-presenting cells present in the subepithelial dome (SED). Dendritic cells (DCs) in the SED and perifollicular area (PFA) acquire antigens and influence adaptive responses. Additionally, specialized DC subsets directly sample luminal antigens. Intestinal DCs transport antigens to mesenteric lymph nodes through the afferent lymphatic system. DCs in the mesenteric lymph node promote differentiation of regulatory and effector T lymphocytes, as well as class switching of B lymphocytes, which then exit through the efferent lymph into the systemic circulation. Some of these cells home back to the intestine, where they exert their effector functions.

function, Peyer's patches are relatively rare along the length of the intestinal tract. DCs also reside in the lamina propria of the small intestine, where they may be seeded from circulating precursors (210). LP DCs express tight-junction proteins that allow for direct luminal sampling through the extension of dendrites between IECs (211), a process that is reported to be dependent on the CX3C chemokine receptor 1 (CX3CR1) (212) and TLR ligation (213). Accordingly, CX3CR1$^{-/-}$ mice exhibit defective luminal sampling by DCs and impaired resistance to *Salmonella typhimurium* infection. As such, luminal sampling by LP DCs may play a role in the development of protective immune responses in the intestine (212). However, impaired protective immunity in this system may also be due to changes in other myeloid cells such as macrophages.

Intestinal DCs recognize bacteria through the expression of innate pattern-recognition receptors (97) that can modify luminal sampling (213), migration (105, 214), and the induction of T cell differentiation (215–217). Intestinal DCs are tolerogenic compared with systemically circulating DCs (175, 176), a phenotype that may contribute to the generation of oral tolerance (218, 219). For example, stimulation of intestinal DCs with the TLR4 ligand LPS resulted in elevated IL-10 production, whereas stimulation of systemic DCs resulted in proinflammatory activation (220, 221). The mechanisms by which intestinal DCs may be skewed toward a tolerogenic phenotype are still under investigation and include reduced TLR expression (220, 221), hyporesponsiveness to TLR stimulation (107), and/or negative regulation of the NF-κB pathway via NOD2 signaling (as discussed above) (125–129). Additionally, IECs may play an active role in regulating the functional capacity of intestinal DCs (see above).

Intestinal resident DCs regulate local T cell responses in part through the production of IL-12 and IL-23. IL-12 is a key regulatory cytokine that induces Th1 cell differentiation (222) and plays an important role in Th1-mediated experimental models of autoimmune diseases, including IBD (223–226). IL-23 is a heterodimer cytokine composed of a p40 subunit (that is shared with IL-12) and a unique p19 subunit (227). Although one study has implicated IL-23 as having a protective role in a murine model of colitis (228), others have shown that IL-23 drives inflammatory Th17 responses (229, 230; reviewed in 231) and is the causative agent in such inflammatory disorders as joint inflammation (232), intestinal inflammation (230, 233–236), and psoriasis (237, 238). The recent association of IBD with the gene that encodes the IL-23R has further increased clinical interest in an IL-23 inflammatory axis (239).

Intestinal DCs (240) transport self (241) and bacterial (80, 197) antigens to the mLNs where they can influence local immune responses. For example, LP and mLN DCs can promote conversion of naive CD4$^+$ T cells into Tregs (175, 176, 199) in a retinoic acid– and TGF-β-dependent manner. Intestinal DCs in the mLNs can also target B and T lymphocytes back to the intestine by promoting the upregulation of CCR9 and α4β7 (205, 206, 242–244). Taken together, these findings suggest that the tolerogenic phenotype of intestinal DCs may be important for maintaining mucosal homeostasis. However, the role that commensal bacteria play in maintaining or promoting the tolerogenic phenotype of mucosal DCs remains to be examined.

SIGNALS DERIVED FROM INTESTINAL BACTERIA REGULATE IMMUNE CELL DEVELOPMENT AND FUNCTION

As discussed above, signals from intestinal bacteria appear to influence human and murine models of disease by modulating innate and adaptive immune responses. One model used to study the role of microbial signals in immune cell development and regulation is the germ-free animal (245). Germ-free animals are born and live in a sterile environment and are therefore free of exposure to live microbial signals (10). Additionally, animals with altered intestinal communities, primarily achieved through the administration of antibiotics (30, 50, 103,

109, 168) or selective colonization studies, have provided a complimentary approach to germ-free studies and have identified key roles for bacterial signals in the regulation of immune cell homeostasis. In this section, we review the evidence for developmental and regulatory roles for bacterial signals in the regulation of mammalian physiology as well as innate (summarized in **Table 3**) and adaptive (summarized in **Table 4**) immune cell function.

Intestinal Morphology and Function

Germ-free animals display morphologic defects compared with conventionally reared animals. Perhaps most striking is the dramatic enlargement of the cecum (an intestinal segment located between the distal small intestine and proximal colon) observed in germ-free animals. This enlargement is due in part to the accumulation of undegraded mucus glycoproteins (246) that are produced by the intestinal epithelium and are normally degraded by glycoside hydrolases from intestinal bacteria (namely *Peptostreptococcus micros* and members of the genera Ruminococcus and Bifidobacterium) (247–249). Accordingly, cecal enlargement can be rapidly reversed through selective monoassociation with *Peptostreptococcus micros* (247). Germ-free animals also accumulate bile acids in their cecum and large intestine that may contribute to cecal distention by causing osmotic imbalances across the epithelial wall (250).

There are also histologic alterations in the architecture of the germ-free intestine. The villi of the cecum are longer and wider in germ-free compared with conventionally reared mice (50), and morphologic studies in rats suggest that colonic crypts are shorter and contain fewer cells in germ-free compared with conventionally reared animals (251). These changes in crypt architecture could be due in part to the decreased turnover of IECs in germ-free compared with conventionally reared animals (252) or could be due to anatomical changes as a result of bacterial reduction (described above).

The intestine of conventionally reared animals undergoes waves of peristalsis that help move luminal contents. Intestinal bacteria have been shown to influence enteric nerve function, as transient manipulations of intestinal communities can lead to persistent neuromuscular dysfunction and enteritis (253). Consistent with this, germ-free animals show defects in small intestinal peristalsis characterized by slower and less frequent migrating motor complexes as a result of reduced responsiveness to enteroendocrine cell products (254). Peristaltic defects can be reversed through conventionalization of germ-free animals, suggesting that bacterial signals dynamically influence the intestinal neuromuscular function (29). Conversely, intestinal motility is important for the maintenance of normal intestinal bacterial communities as the ablation of enteric neurons specifically in the jejunum and ileum results in bacterial overgrowth and jejunoileitis (255).

Gut-Associated Lymphoid Tissues

It is estimated that the intestinal mucosa of humans contains more lymphocytes, and produces more antibodies, than any other organ in the body (256). In mice, most of these cells reside in gut-associated lymphoid tissues (GALT) (257), which include the mLN, Peyer's patches (258), cecal patch, and isolated lymphoid follicles (ILF) that exist along the length of the gastrointestinal tract, with increasing frequency in the colon and rectum (258).

Germ-free mice display reduced intestinal lymphatic tissue and an underdeveloped lymphatic system compared with conventionally reared mice (259, 260). Specifically, Peyer's patch numbers and cellularity are reduced (261), as are the number of ILFs (116). Defects in lymphoid tissue genesis are not limited to the immediate intestinal compartment, as mLNs are smaller, are less cellular, and have fewer germinal centers in germ-free compared with conventionally reared animals (262). These findings suggest that microbial signals are required for lymphoid tissue development and/or maintenance in the mammalian intestine.

Several studies have begun to examine how bacterial signals influence the maintenance of

Table 3 The role of microbial signals in the development and regulation of innate immune cell function

Parameter	Evidence from germ-free compared with conventionally reared animals (reference)	Evidence from antibiotic-treated animals (reference)	Evidence from ex-germ-free animals (reference)
Secondary lymphoid tissue development	Lymphatic tissue and lymphatic system underdeveloped (259, 260, 382) Peyer's patch number and cellularity reduced (261, 382) Reduced ILFs (116) mLNs smaller and less cellular, with reduced germinal centers (262)	Subcutaneous cefmetazole decreases cellularity of Peyer's patches (263)	Recovery of lymphatic tissue and the lymphatic system upon conventionalization of germ-free animals (259) Recovery of mLN size and cellularity upon conventionalization of germ-free animals (262) Peptidoglycan from gram-negative bacteria necessary and sufficient to induce ILF genesis via NOD1 in epithelial cells (116)
Macrophage development	Decreased surface expression of macrophage activation markers in the intestine (383) Intestinal macrophages present at high levels from birth (265) Reduced monocyte/macrophage numbers in the ileum and spleen (267)		Recovery of ileum and spleen monocytes/macrophages upon monoassociation of germ-free mice with *L. acidophilus* and *L. reuteri* (267)
DC development and function	Normal expression of surface markers and ability to stimulate T cell proliferation by DCs from the spleen and mLNs (266) Reduced DCs in the intestine (264, 265)		Recruitment of DCs to the lamina propria upon monoassociation of germ-free animals with *E. coli* (264) Lamina propria APCs stimulated by ATP to produce IL-6, IL-23, and TGF-β, resulting in Th17 cell differentiation (138)
LTi/NK cell development	Reduced NK-22 cells (276)		LTi cells and NK-22 cells upregulate IL-22 production shortly after birth (276, 278)

Table 4 The role of microbial signals in the development and regulation of adaptive immune cell function

Parameter	Evidence from germ-free compared with conventionally reared animals (reference)	Evidence from antibiotic-treated animals (reference)	Evidence from ex-germ-free animals (reference)
B cell development and function	Reduced numbers of plasma cells in small intestine (262) Decreased IgA production in small intestine (288) Reduced systemic germinal centers and plasma cells (289) Low systemic immunoglobulin levels (260, 290–293) Decreased IgM and IgG response to DNP-BSA (294) Normal IgM response to sheep red blood cells or phosphorylcholine (294, 296) Normal IgM and IgG response to DNP-lys-Ficoll (294) Delayed and reduced primary antibody titers against heat-killed *E. coli* (295) Increased antibody response to ferritin and DNP-Ficoll (384, 385) Increased IgE-bearing B cells in Peyer's patches (298)	Increased IgE responses caused by antibiotic treatment (108)	Recovery of intestinal IgA upon conventionalization of germ-free animals (288, 297) Recovery of systemic germinal centers and plasma cells upon conventionalization of germ-free animals (289) Recovery of systemic immunoglobulin levels upon conventionalization of germ-free animals (290, 293)
Th17/Treg cell development and function	Reduced Th17 cells in the small intestine (307) Increased Th17 cells in the large intestine (168) Reduced Foxp3 mRNA in $CD4^+$ T cells from the mLNs (321, 322) Selective reduction in the percentage of $Foxp3^+CD4^+CD25^+$ T cells in the mLN (321) $CD4^+$ T cell proliferation not suppressed as well in vitro by Tregs from the mLN (323) Less IL-10 produced by Tregs from the mLN (322); disease not protected as well by Tregs (322) Increased frequency of $CD4^+Foxp3^+$ in the small intestine (307) Similar frequency of lamina propria $CD4^+Foxp3^+$ T cells from the colon (168)	Fewer Th17 cells in the lamina propria of the small intestine of mice treated with vancomycin (138, 307, 313) Reduced frequency of Th17 cells in the mLN of antibiotic-treated mice (50)	Monoassociation of germ-free mice with cytophaga-flavobacter-bacteroidetes rescues Th17 cell defect (307)

Th1/Th2 balance cell development and function	Decreased delayed-type hypersensitivity in response to sheep red blood cells (386) Reduced αβ TCR–bearing IELs (387) Decreased response to T cell mitogens (294, 388) Normal response to Ova but reduced oral tolerance (389–392) Reduced tolerance to Th2 antigens (393) Normal graft-versus-host reaction (394) Reduced T cell numbers in the jejunum (264)	Long-term Th2-skewed immunological memory caused by Kanamycin treatment (330) Enhanced IgE responses caused by antibiotic treatment (108)	Recovery of response to T cell mitogens upon conventionalization of germ-free animals (388) Recovery of αβ TCR-bearing IELs upon conventionalization of germ-free animals (387) Recovery of jujunal T cells upon mono-association with *E. coli* (264) Recovery of oral tolerance upon conventionalization of germ-free or antibiotic-treated animals (300, 393, 395, 396) Recovery of long-term Th2-skewed immunological memory upon Kanamycin treatment through oral inoculation with *Enterococcus faecalis* and *Lactobacillus acidophilus* (300)
$CD8^+$ T cell development and function	More diverse repertoire of $CD8^+$ IELs in germ-free rats (353), no difference in mice (397) Reduced number and cytotoxicity of $CD8^+$ IELs (262, 350, 387, 397) Delayed development of IELs (265)		Recovery of $CD8^+$ IEL diversity upon conventionalization of germ-free animals (353) Recovery of number and cytotoxicity of $CD8^+$ IELs upon conventionalization of germ-free animals (262, 350, 387, 397) Reduced numbers of naive, splenic $CD8^+$ lymphocytes in animals colonized with nonpathogenic *Clostridium* sp. compared with conventionally reared controls (355)

intestinal lymphoid tissues. Defects in intestinal lymphoid tissues observed in germ-free animals are not developmental, as selective colonization of germ-free animals with intestinal bacteria results in the recovery of intestinal lymphoid structures (259) and the recovery of mLN size and cellularity (262). Rather, bacterial signals continuously support mucosal lymphoid tissue maintenance. For example, antibiotic treatment decreases the cellularity of intestinal Peyer's patches (263). In addition, one study showed that peptidoglycan from gram-negative bacteria is both necessary and sufficient to induce ILF formation in the mammalian intestine in a NOD1-dependent manner (116). These findings support an important role for innate recognition of bacterial-derived signals in the maintenance of adaptive lymphoid tissues.

DCs/Macrophages

Signals from intestinal bacteria have developmental and regulatory influences on intestinal APCs. Intestinal DCs are present in reduced numbers in the intestine of germ-free animals (264, 265). These defects appear to be isolated to the intestinal compartment, as DCs from the spleen and mLNs of germ-free animals had normal surface marker expression of CD86 and MHCII and induced similar levels of T cell proliferation in vitro compared with those isolated from conventionally reared animals (266). Intestinal DCs were recruited to the intestinal lamina propria upon monoassociation of germ-free animals with *E. coli*, further suggesting that intestinal bacteria may play an active role in the regulation of intestinal DC populations (264). Monocyte/macrophage development may also be influenced by signals from intestinal bacteria. While monocyte/macrophage numbers in the intestine were either normal (265) or reduced (267), systemic monocyte/macrophage numbers were reduced in germ-free compared with conventionally reared animals (267). Again, systemic and intestinal defects in monocyte/macrophage populations could be recovered upon monoassociation of germ-free animals with *L. acidophilus* and *L. reuteri*, implicating signals from intestinal bacteria in the regulation of these cell types (267).

As discussed previously, some intestinal APCs have a tolerogenic phenotype that promotes tolerance to oral antigens and commensal bacteria (reviewed in 97, 199, 221). However, it is important that intestinal DCs remain responsive to potential pathogens, a characteristic that may be mediated in part through differential TLR expression. For example, TLR5 recognizes bacterial flagellin, a structural protein of flagella that promotes bacterial chemotaxis, adhesion, and invasion of host tissues (268), whereas TLR4 recognizes LPS, a component of the outer membrane of most gram-negative bacteria present in the intestinal lumen. Intestinal $CD11c^+$ lamina propria cells selectively express TLR5, but not TLR4, and produce proinflammatory cytokines in response to bacterial flagellin (216). Appropriately, these $CD11c^+$ lamina propria cells produced proinflammatory IL-6 in response to pathogenic flagellated *S. typhimurium* in a TLR5-dependent manner, but produced little IL-6 in response to the nonflagellated commensal *Enterobacter cloacae* (216). Thus, intestinal DCs may remain unresponsive to normal intestinal bacteria while mounting proinflammatory responses to potential pathogens.

The tolerogenic nature of intestinal APCs may be imparted directly or indirectly by select intestinal bacteria. For example, *Lactobacillus rhamnosus* GG decreases TNF-α production in LPS-activated macrophages in a contact-independent manner (269), a phenomenon that may be important for controlling pathogenic, proinflammatory immune responses (198). The ability of intestinal bacteria to impart a tolerogenic influence may be lost in IBD, as Crohn's disease patients have higher numbers of proinflammatory intestinal macrophages compared with healthy individuals (270). These cells express both macrophage (CD14, CD33, CD68) and DC (CD205, CD209) markers and evoke Th1 and Th17 cell differentiation (271), suggesting that intestinal APCs that lack tolerogenic properties could contribute to pathogenic states. Finally, while some intestinal DCs are thought to be specialized for induction of tolerance, evidence exists for tolerogenic DCs outside of the intestinal compartment. For example, a $CD11c^{lo}CD45RB^{hi}$ DC subset present in the spleen and lymph nodes of mice produces IL-10 and promotes suppressive functions of Tregs (272). However, whether or not signals from intestinal bacteria influence these systemic DCs remains to be tested directly.

Lymphoid-Tissue Inducer and Natural Killer Cells

Lymphoid-tissue inducer (LTi) cells are $ROR\gamma t^{+}$ IL-$7R\alpha^{+}$ innate leukocytes that induce lymph node development in the embryo through the production of lymphotoxin-β and TNF and the recruitment of circulating LTi cells, their precursors, and more mature lymphocytes (reviewed in 273). Clustering of LTi cells in the intestine is mediated by the chemokines CXCL13 and CCL21, and initial clustering seems to be dependent exclusively on CXCL13 expression by stromal organizer cells by retinoic acid and neuronal stimulation (274). In adult mice, clusters of LTi cells are found in the cryptopatches of the small intestine and in secondary lymphoid organs such as the spleen, where they participate in maintaining local lymphoid tissue anatomy (273). LTi cells are an innate source of IL-17 and IL-22 (an IL-10 family member that contributes to epithelial cell resistance and repair by inducing the production of antimicrobial proteins such as β-defensins, RegIIIγ, and S100 calcium-binding proteins) (275), although experimental evidence supporting a role for these cells in initiating or regulating immune responses is lacking at present.

The observation that lymphoid follicles are underdeveloped in germ-free mice has led some to speculate that LTi cells might be regulated by bacterial signals; however, one study to date indicated that LTi cell numbers and function were similar in the mucosa of germ-free compared with conventionally reared mice (276). Nevertheless, an intriguing connection exists between LTi cells and another cell population that is regulated by intestinal bacteria: IL-22-producing intestinal natural killer (NK)-like (NK-22) cells. Intestinal NK-22 cells are found in the cryptopatches and lamina propria of adult mice, where they are also an important innate source of IL-22 (276–279). Production of IL-22 by mucosal NK-22 cells may contribute to defense against the extracellular enteric pathogen *Citrobacter rodentium*, as the partial depletion of mucosal NK-22 cells increases the mortality of infected mice (277, 278). In addition, NK-22 cells mediate protection from experimental colitis (280), supporting the hypothesis that these cells are involved in defense against assaults to the enteric mucosa.

NK cell: natural killer cell

LTi cells differentiate into NK-like cells in vitro (281) that express both LTi and NK cell receptors (reviewed in 282). For example, human fetal LTi cells give rise to $NKp44^{+}$ cells that produce IL-17 and IL-22 in vitro (283). The dependency of NK-22 cells on RORγt expression further suggests that these cells may derive from LTi cells and has led to speculation that LTi cells and NK-22 cells may be related functionally and developmentally (273). Additionally, intestinal LTi cells and NK-22 cells upregulate IL-22 production shortly after birth, suggesting that colonization of the intestine drives IL-22 production by these cell types in humans and mice (276, 278). Finally, absolute and relative numbers of NK-22 cells are reduced in germ-free compared with conventionally reared mice (276), further implicating signals from intestinal bacteria in NK-22 cell development. These findings suggest that signals from intestinal bacteria promote mucosal homeostasis by inducing IL-22-producing innate leukocytes. However, the relationship between LTi cells and NK-22 cells in vivo remains to be investigated. For example, LTi cells are required for lymphoid tissue development, whereas lymphoid tissue development and the development of IL-22-producing intestinal NK cells are both dependent on bacterial signals. However, LTi development seems to be independent of signals from intestinal bacteria (276). As such, more investigation into the relationship between LTi cells and IL-22-producing intestinal NK cells, and the role that signals from intestinal bacteria may play in the respective development of these cell populations, is needed.

B Cells

There is an intimate relationship between intestinal communities and B lymphocytes that reside in the intestine. As discussed previously, the first immunological response to bacterial signals during colonization is IgA production and secretion into the intestinal lumen (79, 284). In fact, most B cells in the intestine are IgA-producing plasma cells that produce and secrete IgA into the intestinal lumen at an estimated rate of 0.8 g per meter of intestine per day (257, 285) (**Figure 4**). This secretory immune response, which is characterized by class switching of B cells from IgM to IgA production, is orchestrated through an intimate functional relationship between secretory epithelia and local plasma cells and is mediated by TLRs through both T cell–dependent and –independent mechanisms (82, 158). For example, intestinal bacteria trigger T cell–independent IgA class switching in B cells through IEC secretion of cytokines such as a proliferation-inducing ligand (APRIL) (158, 159). In addition, IEC-derived TSLP and IL-10, produced in response to bacterial signals, may orchestrate local B cell responses (158, 159, 286). Secretory IgA creates a first-line defense against mucosal compromise that is lost during IBD (35, 287), implicating early recognition of bacterial signals and the subsequent modulation of B cell responses as important processes that promote normal mucosal homeostasis.

Several findings in germ-free mice support a role for bacterial signals in B cell development. There are reduced numbers of plasma cells in the germ-free small intestine (262), which correlates with reduced IgA production (288). Further, there are reduced systemic numbers of germinal centers and plasma cells in germ-free mice (289), which correlates with reduced systemic immunoglobulin levels (260, 290–293). Germ-free mice also show reduced antigen-specific immunoglobulins to some antigens (DNP-BSA, *E. coli*) (294, 295) but not to others (RBC, phosphorylcholine, DNP-lys-Ficoll) (294, 296). In general, these intestinal and systemic immunoglobulin defects are corrected upon conventionalization of germ-free animals, suggesting that these defects are not purely developmental (288, 290, 293, 297).

One exception to the trend of reduced immunoglobulin levels is IgE. There are increased numbers of IgE-bearing B cells in the Peyer's patches of germ-free mice (298) and elevated serum IgE levels in germ-free and antibiotic-treated mice (108), a finding that may be linked to impaired oral tolerance to Th2 antigens in mice with reduced microbial stimulation (108, 299, 300). IgE in germ-free mice is likely composed of natural specificities and induced by a mechanism independent of MHCII cognate help (301). These findings suggest that, in general, microbial signals act as an adjuvant to immunoglobulin responses, and, with the exception of allergic IgE responses, bacterial signals may play an immunoregulatory role.

In addition, accumulating evidence suggests that B cells can play a regulatory role in many models of colitis through the production of IL-10 (reviewed in 302). For example, autoantibodies from B cells suppress colitis in mice deficient in TCRα chain (303) and intestinal inflammation induces a population of CD1d-expressing B cells in (GALT) that produces IL-10 and suppresses progression of colitis (304). Roles for B cell–derived IL-10 in controlling colitis in other animal models have also been reported (305). Although the influence of bacterial signals on regulatory B cell development and function remains to be examined, these findings suggest that B cells play an integral role in controlling inflammation in animal models of colitis.

Th17/Treg Cells

The differentiation of Th17 cells is characterized by RORγt expression, requires TGF-β

and IL-6 or IL-21, and relies on IL-23 for Th17 cell maturation and survival (reviewed in 306). In the steady state, IL-17-producing cells are present in high numbers in the lamina propria of the small intestine (307), where the Th17-related cytokines IL-22 and IL-17 play a role in host protection against extracellular pathogens (reviewed in 308, 309).

Conventionally reared animals have TLR-independent spontaneous IL-17 production in the lamina propria of the small intestine (307). Spontaneous IL-17 production was absent in the small intestine of germ-free animals, while MyD88-deficient mice had normal numbers of Th17 cells, suggesting that intestinal bacteria signal through a TLR-independent mechanism to promote Th17 cell development (307). Specific bacteria and bacterial-derived stimuli have been identified as key regulators of Th cell responses in the mammalian intestine. For example, colonization of germ-free mice with segmented filamentous bacteria induced strong Th1, Th2, Th17, and Treg responses in the lamina propria (310, 311). Another mechanism by which intestinal bacteria may regulate Th17 cell development independent of TLR signaling is through the production of other bioactive molecules (see above). Indeed, systemic or rectal administration of ATP into germ-free mice stimulates lamina propria APCs to produce IL-6, IL-23, and TGF-β, resulting in Th17 cell differentiation (138).

Although Th17 cells are reduced in the small intestine of germ-free mice, more Th17 cells have been observed in the large intestine of germ-free compared with conventionally reared mice (168). In the large intestine, bacterial signals can regulate Th17 cell development through bacterial-dependent production of the IL-17 family cytokine IL-25 (IL-17E), which downregulates IL-17 production through the inhibition of IL-23 production by lamina propria macrophages (168). These findings suggest that regulation of Th17 cell differentiation depends on anatomical location. Indeed, the small and large intestines are microbiologically and immunologically distinct sites. As discussed above, there are site-specific differences in intestinal bacterial communities along the length of the intestine (**Figure 2**). In addition, there are more IELs and LPLs per epithelial cell in the small intestine, and the lymphocyte composition and migration to the small versus large intestine is differentially regulated (307, 312). Other environmental factors, such as diet and non-live microbial signals, could also influence Th17 populations. Although more studies are required, these fundamental differences may underlie differential regulation of Th17 cells in distinct anatomical locations of the intestine.

Studies from antibiotic-treated mice mirror some of the observations made in germ-free mice and support a role for bacterial signals in influencing homeostasis of Th17 cells. For example, mice treated with vancomycin have fewer Th17 $CD4^+$ T cells in the lamina propria of the small intestine (138, 307, 313), whereas mice treated with a complex antibiotic mixture displayed reduced Th17 $CD4^+$ T cell frequencies in the mLNs (50). Additionally, Th17 cell differentiation in the lamina propria of the small intestine requires specific intestinal bacteria: cytophaga-flavobacter-bacteroidetes bacteria (307). This induction of Th17 cells is independent of TLR signaling, IL-21, or IL-23, but requires TGF-β activation, suggesting that specific intestinal bacteria may regulate the Th17/Treg balance in the mammalian intestine.

An intimate relationship exists in the intestinal mucosa between proinflammatory Th17 cells and $CD4^+$ Tregs, which play an important role in controlling Th17 cell responses (reviewed in 314, 315). Tregs are characterized as $CD4^+$ $CD25^+$ cells that express $Foxp3^+$ and suppress the proliferation of effector T cells in vitro and protect against autoimmune and other inflammatory diseases in several animal models (reviewed in 316). For example, mice carrying a loss-of-function mutation of Foxp3 completely lack Tregs and develop lethal autoimmune disease (317). Additionally, mice engineered to lack the expression of specific regulatory cytokines in T cells, including IL-10 or TGF-β, develop colitis when pathogenic bacteria are present in the intestine (318–320). These findings identify Tregs as an important regulatory cell type that contributes to intestinal and systemic immune homeostasis.

There are conflicting reports regarding the influence of bacterial signals on Treg development and function. Consistent with studies that showed reduced Foxp3 mRNA in $CD4^+$ T cells from mLNs of germ-free mice (321, 322), early studies in germ-free animals showed a selective reduction in the percentage of $Foxp3^+CD4^+CD25^+$ T cells in the mLN of germ-free mice (321). In addition to reduced frequencies, Tregs from the mLN do not suppress $CD4^+$ T cell proliferation in vitro in either germ-free animals or in conventionally reared animals (323). Furthermore, Tregs from the mLN of germ-free animals produce less IL-10 and do not protect as well against disease in a transfer model of experimental colitis, compared with Tregs from conventionally reared animals (322). Consistantly, some intestinal bacteria may help promote Treg development; for example, *Lactobacillus* and *Bifidobacterium* strains caused expansion of Tregs in the intestinal intraepithelial compartment, which correlated with protection against experimental colitis (324). These results suggest that signals from intestinal bacteria are important for normal development of Treg numbers and function in the mLNs.

However, bacterial signals seem to have different effects on other Treg populations. One study reported no change in the frequency of lamina propria $CD4^+Foxp3^+$ T cells from the colon of germ-free animals (168), whereas another reported increased percentages of $CD4^+Foxp3^+$ in the germ-free small intestine (307). These differing results could be due to sampling Treg cell subsets from different anatomical locations (mLN versus intestine). Additionally, differences in experimental methods, animal housing methods, diet, nonbacterial microbial stimulation, employed assays, or Treg identification methods could explain these conflicting results.

Th1/Th2 Cells

In humans, as in mice, several distinct patterns of cytokine secretion have been defined among $CD4^+$ helper T cell clones. Th1 cells produce IL-2, IFN-γ, and TNF-β, whereas Th2 cells produce IL-4, IL-5, IL-9, and IL-13 (reviewed in 325). These distinct immune responses are important for fighting distinct types of infection; Th1 cell responses are protective against bacterial, viral, and protozoan infections, whereas Th2 cell responses are important in mediating immunity to helminths and ectoparasites.

Inappropriate Th1 and Th2 cytokine responses result in distinct forms of human disease. For example, Crohn's disease is characterized by exaggerated IFN-γ responses, as well as IL-23 and IL-17 responses (reviewed in 231), whereas ulcerative colitis and atopic diseases are primarily associated with elevated Th2 cytokine responses (16). As discussed above, IBD patients display altered bacterial communities in their intestine (326), and tolerance to intestinal bacteria is broken in these diseases (32, 33, 35), suggesting that a dysregulated mucosal immune response to intestinal bacteria could be linked to pathogenesis (16). Consistently, animal models of IBD exhibit $CD4^+$ T cells specific for bacterial antigens (327) that induce colitis when adoptively transferred into naive SCID mice (35). The loss of regulatory mechanisms, such as mucosal T cells with regulatory properties that suppress inappropriate Th1 responses (328), may contribute to disease pathogenesis in these models (329).

The influence of intestinal bacteria on Th1 and Th2 cell development and regulation is not limited to the intestinal mucosa. For example, recent epidemiological studies indicate that antibiotic use in infancy may be associated with an increased risk of developing atopy (48). As discussed above, patients with atopic diseases such as asthma have altered intestinal bacterial communities (15), suggesting that bacterial signals influence systemic type 2 inflammatory responses. Consistent with this notion, treating animals with antibiotics during infancy promoted a shift in the Th1/Th2 balance toward a Th2-dominant immunity (330) that could be corrected by oral inoculation with *Enterococcus faecalis* or *Lactobacillus acidophilus* (300).

The balance of proinflammatory or regulatory immune responses to intestinal bacteria may be regulated by mucosal DC populations. For example, subsets of mucosal DCs have tolerogenic capacities that contribute to the induction of tolerance to intestinal bacteria and food antigens (97, 221). However, other nonhematopoietic cells may influence the balance of inflammatory or tolerogenic responses; IECs may deliver inhibitory or tolerogenic signals indirectly or directly to T cells (discussed above). In addition, T cells express pattern-recognition receptors under certain conditions and could be directly responsive to bacterial-derived signals (331), although this possibility has not been examined in detail.

Finally, granulocytes such as mast cells, basophils, and eosinophils are important effectors of protective and pathogenic type 2 inflammatory responses (332). In addition, granulocyte populations are important sources of type 2 cytokines (333), and basophils have recently be identified as an important cellular source of IL-4 that express surface MHCII and can prime antigen-specific Th2 cell differentiation (334–336), suggesting that basophils may also play a role in the initiation of type 2 responses. Several lines of evidence suggest that granulocytes are dysregulated in human inflammatory disease. For example, tissue from patients with ulcerative colitis show mast cell aggregation along the line of demarcation, dividing inflamed from healthy tissue (337), and the number of $NOD2^+$ intestinal mast cells are increased in Crohn's disease patients compared with healthy controls (338), identifying a possible role for these cells in responding to innate, bacterial-derived signals. Mast cells are of particular interest in IBD because they are thought to modify disease progress through release of histamine (339), TNF-α (340), and the T cell chemoattractants XCL-1 (341) and IL-16 (342). Indeed, in a model of experimental allergen-induced asthma, TLR4-defective mice subjected to sensitization and pulmonary challenge with a protein allergen had reductions in airway inflammation, allergen-specific IgE levels, and Th2 cytokine production (106), although rigorous investigation of potential influences that intestinal bacteria have on granulocyte development or function is lacking at present.

$CD8^+$ T Cells

The first observation that microbial signals could influence tumor immunity came in the eighteenth century when Deidier reported a correlation between patient infection and the remission of malignant disease, a finding that eventually led to the use of LPS to treat primarily inoperable sarcoma, with a cure rate of better than 10% (343). These early findings indicated that microbial signaling through TLRs is important for initiating or sustaining antitumor immune responses (reviewed in 344). This hypothesis has now been supported by several studies in animal models (345–347) and patients (102), leading to a well-accepted role for bacterial products as adjuvants that promote the recruitment and/or stimulation of $CD8^+$ cytotoxic T lymphocytes (348).

The intestinal mucosa of conventionally reared animals normally contains $CD8^+$ cytotoxic T lymphocytes. In the conventionally reared mouse intestine, $CD4^+$ T cells are found primarily in the lamina propria, whereas $CD8^+$ T cells dominate in the intraepithelial compartment. The maintenance of $CD8^+$ IELs depends on bacterial signals, as MyD88-deficient (349) and germ-free mice (350, 351) display reduced $CD8^+$ T cell numbers in the IEL compartment of the small intestine. The systemic distribution of $CD8^+$ T cells also depends on bacterial signals. The liver is a site of activated $CD8^+$ T cell sequestering and subsequent apoptosis during systemic viral immune responses, a phenomenon that is dependent on TLR4 ligands such as endotoxin from intestinal bacteria (352).

Cytotoxic activity of IELs is impaired in both germ-free (351) and antibiotic-treated mice, a phenotype that can be reversed through the administration of the TLR4 ligand LPS (345). In germ-free mice, this cytotoxic defect was isolated to $\alpha\beta$ TCR-bearing IELs, whereas the number and cytotoxicity of $\gamma\delta$ TCR-bearing IELs was comparable between germ-free and conventionally reared mice (351). These defects may be in part due to impaired clonal expansions of $CD8\alpha\beta^+$ and $CD8\alpha\alpha^+$ IELs in germ-free mice (353). This functional defect is not limited to intestinal compartments, as conventionally reared mice have a selective reduction in systemic plasmacytoid DCs as a result of enhanced cytotoxic T lymphocyte activity that is not observed in germ-free mice (354). Finally, animals colonized with nonpathogenic *Clostridium* sp. have reduced numbers of naive, splenic $CD8^+$ lymphocytes compared with conventionally reared controls (355), further suggesting that signals from intestinal bacteria play an active role in $CD8^+$ lymphocyte regulation.

Although the adjuvant effect of microbial signals on cytotoxic cells is well established, microbial stimulation can also result in tumorigenesis under some conditions. For example, MyD88-deficient mice are protected against the development of spontaneous intestinal tumors in a model of familial-associated polyposis (356), and germ-free animals have reduced intestinal tumorigenesis compared with conventionally reared animals following the same protocol of colorectal cancer induction (357). Similarly, hepatocellular carcinoma, the most common liver cancer, occurs mainly in males. This gender disparity is also seen in mice given the chemical carcinogen diethylnitrosamine and is dependent on MyD88-mediated increases in serum IL-6 (358). In humans, associations between intestinal bacteria and cancer risk have been explored (reviewed in 359), and studies were performed to identify fecal bacterial communities associated with high colorectal cancer risk (13, 66, 360), although they failed to provide conclusive results. In summary, clarifying the influence of bacterial signals in establishing normal cytotoxic immune capacities has led to exciting therapeutic possibilities, but more research is needed to fully understand the role that signals from intestinal bacteria play in tumorigenesis and control.

MANIPULATION OF INTESTINAL BACTERIAL COMMUNITIES: PROSPECTS FOR PREVENTION AND TREATMENT OF INFLAMMATORY DISEASES

The identification of the important roles that intestinal bacteria play in normal development and regulation of the mammalian immune system provides a rationale for using therapeutic agents based on bacterial-derived signals in preventative or therapeutic endeavors. Live biologics given as supplements to confer some benefit to the host are referred to as probiotics. Several studies in animal models have investigated the beneficial effects of probiotic bacteria, including *Lactobacillus* ssp. and others. In one study, administration of *Lactobacillus* ssp. protected IL-10-deficient mice from developing spontaneous colitis (361). In another, probiotic mixtures including *Lactobacillus* ssp. protected mice against chemically induced colitis (324). Probiotics are thought to mediate their beneficial effects in part through modulation of immune cell function. For example, probiotic bacteria including lactobacilli induce IL-10 production by DCs and inhibit subsequent generation of Th1 cells in vitro (148, 362), and *Lactobacillus* and *Bifidobacterium* strains prevent experimental colitis while expanding IEL $\gamma\delta$ T cells and Tregs (324).

These and other studies have led to clinical trials in human patients examining the potential role for probiotic bacteria in preventing and treating human disease. These treatments have been associated with modulation in DC function (362, 363), as well as the function of other immune cells (364), but have reported mixed successes in the treatment of intestinal inflammatory and atopic diseases (62, 365, 366). One positive study showed that *E. coli* provided an effective probiotic therapy to ulcerative colitis patients (367). In addition, delivery of probiotics seems to be effective for the prevention and treatment of pouchitis, a complication following surgical treatment of ulcerative colitis (368–371). Despite these encouraging results, how probiotics modulate intestinal communities to modify subsequent immunoregulatory signals is unknown. A better understanding of these mechanisms is necessary to realize the full potential of probiotic therapies.

In addition to interventions with unmodified bacteria, more recent work using genetically modified bacteria that act as platforms for the delivery of drugs, antimicrobial agents, vaccines, and other biologically active molecules to physiologically relevant sites has expanded the definition of probiotic therapy. For example, *Lactobacillus* strains have been engineered to produce IL-10 as a therapeutic intervention in animal models of IBD (372), while *Streptococcus gordonii*, engineered to express an antimicrobial antibody fragment, confers a therapeutic benefit to rats with vaginal *Candida albicans* infections (373). In addition, genetically modified lactobacilli that express the tetanus toxin fragment C efficiently induce local and systemic antigen protection when given orally to mice (374), while those that express CD4 molecules and secrete HIV-1 fusion inhibitors have been developed as a step toward the use of topical, genetically engineered bacteria to prevent HIV transmission (375, 376).

In the development of new therapeutics, the use of specific bacterial products with immunoregulatory characteristics, as well as their molecular derivatives, could offer new therapeutic modalities in the prevention and treatment of human disease. For example, identifying specific bacterial compounds that could be administered early in life to promote tolerance could play a role in preventing the development of atopy later in life. Similarly, bacterial products that bolster mucosal barrier function or that regulate inflammatory immune responses in the intestinal mucosa may be important in the treatment of human IBD. Finally, bacterial-derived proinflammatory molecules that modulate immune responses could play a role in vaccine development, cancer treatment, or the treatment of infection. To move such therapies into the clinics, the specific microbial products and their immunoregulatory properties must be precisely defined.

CONCLUSION

Technological and conceptual advances have ushered in an exciting time in mucosal immunology and in our understanding of how bacterial-derived signals influence the immune system. New sequencing techniques are allowing previously unattainable insights into the complex bacterial communities integral to mammalian health. Additionally, established tools such as germ-free animals are being complemented with antibiotic treatment, selective colonization, and treatment with specific microbial products to probe the molecular mechanisms that facilitate cross-talk between intestinal bacteria and their mammalian hosts. It is hoped that these insights will offer new therapeutic strategies in the prevention and treatment of human diseases.

DISCLOSURE STATEMENT

The authors are not aware of any affiliations, memberships, funding, or financial holdings that might be perceived as affecting the objectivity of this review.

ACKNOWLEDGMENTS

We thank Rick Bushman and members of the Artis laboratory for helpful discussions. Research in the Artis laboratory is supported by the NIH (AI61570 and AI74878, F32-AI72943, F31-GM082187, T32-AI060516 (DAH), T32-AI007532-08, T32-CA09140-30, T32-AI055438-06, T32-AI05528, and S10RR024525), the Burroughs Wellcome Fund (Investigator in Pathogenesis of Infectious Disease Award), the Crohn's and Colitis Foundation of America, and pilot grants from the University of Pennsylvania (CID, PGFI, and URI).

LITERATURE CITED

1. Paszkowski U. 2006. Mutualism and parasitism: the yin and yang of plant symbioses. *Curr. Opin. Plant Biol.* 9:364–70
2. Muyskens JB, Guillemin K. 2008. Bugs inside bugs: What the fruit fly can teach us about immune and microbial balance in the gut. *Cell Host Microbe* 3:117–18
3. Rae R, Riebesell M, Dinkelacker I, Wang Q, Herrmann M, et al. 2008. Isolation of naturally associated bacteria of necromenic pristionchus nematodes and fitness consequences. *J. Exp. Biol.* 211:1927–36
4. Bates JM, Akerlund J, Mittge E, Guillemin K. 2007. Intestinal alkaline phosphatase detoxifies lipopolysaccharide and prevents inflammation in zebrafish in response to the gut microbiota. *Cell Host Microbe* 2:371–82
5. Brisbin JT, Gong J, Sharif S. 2008. Interactions between commensal bacteria and the gut-associated immune system of the chicken. *Anim. Health. Res. Rev.* 9:101–10
6. Cebra JJ. 1999. Influences of microbiota on intestinal immune system development. *Am. J. Clin. Nutr.* 69:S1046–51
7. Whitman WB, Coleman DC, Wiebe WJ. 1998. Prokaryotes: the unseen majority. *Proc. Natl. Acad. Sci. USA* 95:6578–83
8. Backhed F, Ley RE, Sonnenburg JL, Peterson DA, Gordon JI. 2005. Host-bacterial mutualism in the human intestine. *Science* 307:1915–20
9. Hooper LV, Gordon JI. 2001. Commensal host-bacterial relationships in the gut. *Science* 292:1115–18
10. Macpherson AJ, Harris NL. 2004. Interactions between commensal intestinal bacteria and the immune system. *Nat. Rev. Immunol.* 4:478–85
11. Manichanh C, Rigottier-Gois L, Bonnaud E, Gloux K, Pelletier E, et al. 2006. Reduced diversity of faecal microbiota in Crohn's disease revealed by a metagenomic approach. *Gut* 55:205–11
12. Ley RE, Backhed F, Turnbaugh P, Lozupone CA, Knight RD, Gordon JI. 2005. Obesity alters gut microbial ecology. *Proc. Natl. Acad. Sci. USA* 102:11070–75
13. Moore WE, Moore LH. 1995. Intestinal floras of populations that have a high risk of colon cancer. *Appl. Environ. Microbiol.* 61:3202–7
14. Bollyky PL, Bice JB, Sweet IR, Falk BA, Gebe JA, et al. 2009. The Toll-like receptor signaling molecule Myd88 contributes to pancreatic beta-cell homeostasis in response to injury. *PLoS ONE* 4:e5063
15. Penders J, Thijs C, Van Den Brandt PA, Kummeling I, Snijders B, et al. 2007. Gut microbiota composition and development of atopic manifestations in infancy: the KOALA birth cohort study. *Gut* 56:661–67
16. Hanauer SB. 2006. Inflammatory bowel disease: epidemiology, pathogenesis, and therapeutic opportunities. *Inflamm. Bowel Dis.* 12(Suppl. 1):S3–9
17. Penders J, Stobberingh EE, Van Den Brandt PA, Thijs C. 2007. The role of the intestinal microbiota in the development of atopic disorders. *Allergy* 62:1223–36
18. Eckburg PB, Lepp PW, Relman DA. 2003. Archaea and their potential role in human disease. *Infect. Immun.* 71:591–96
19. Dubos R, Schaedler RW, Costello R, Hoet P. 1965. Indigenous, normal, and autochthonous flora of the gastrointestinal tract. *J. Exp. Med.* 122:67–76
20. Eckburg PB, Bik EM, Bernstein CN, Purdom E, Dethlefsen L, et al. 2005. Diversity of the human intestinal microbial flora. *Science* 308:1635–38
21. Hayashi H, Sakamoto M, Benno Y. 2002. Phylogenetic analysis of the human gut microbiota using 16S rDNA clone libraries and strictly anaerobic culture-based methods. *Microbiol. Immunol.* 46:535–48
22. Hold GL, Pryde SE, Russell VJ, Furrie E, Flint HJ. 2002. Assessment of microbial diversity in human colonic samples by 16S rDNA sequence analysis. *FEMS Microbiol. Ecol.* 39:33–39
23. Wang X, Heazlewood SP, Krause DO, Florin TH. 2003. Molecular characterization of the microbial species that colonize human ileal and colonic mucosa by using 16S rDNA sequence analysis. *J. Appl. Microbiol.* 95:508–20

24. Frank DN, Pace NR. 2008. Gastrointestinal microbiology enters the metagenomics era. *Curr. Opin. Gastroenterol.* 24:4–10
25. Hooper LV, Midtvedt T, Gordon JI. 2002. How host-microbial interactions shape the nutrient environment of the mammalian intestine. *Annu. Rev. Nutr.* 22:283–307
26. Artis D. 2008. Epithelial-cell recognition of commensal bacteria and maintenance of immune homeostasis in the gut. *Nat. Rev. Immunol.* 8:411–20
27. Backhed F, Ding H, Wang T, Hooper LV, Koh GY, et al. 2004. The gut microbiota as an environmental factor that regulates fat storage. *Proc. Natl. Acad. Sci. USA* 101:15718–23
28. Stappenbeck TS, Hooper LV, Gordon JI. 2002. Developmental regulation of intestinal angiogenesis by indigenous microbes via Paneth cells. *Proc. Natl. Acad. Sci. USA* 99:15451–55
29. Husebye E, Hellström PM, Midtvedt T. 1994. Intestinal microflora stimulates myoelectric activity of rat small intestine by promoting cyclic initiation and aboral propagation of migrating myoelectric complex. *Dig. Dis. Sci.* 39:946–56
30. Sekirov I, Tam NM, Jogova M, Robertson ML, Li Y, et al. 2008. Antibiotic-induced perturbations of the intestinal microbiota alter host susceptibility to enteric infection. *Infect. Immun.* 76:4726–36
31. Podolsky DK. 2002. Inflammatory bowel disease. *N. Engl. J. Med.* 347:417–29
32. Duchmann R, Kaiser I, Hermann E, Mayet W, Ewe K, Meyer zum Buschenfelde KH. 1995. Tolerance exists towards resident intestinal flora but is broken in active inflammatory bowel disease (IBD). *Clin. Exp. Immunol.* 102:448–55
33. Macpherson A, Khoo UY, Forgacs I, Philpott-Howard J, Bjarnason I. 1996. Mucosal antibodies in inflammatory bowel disease are directed against intestinal bacteria. *Gut* 38:365–75
34. Adams RJ, Heazlewood SP, Gilshenan KS, O'Brien M, McGuckin MA, Florin TH. 2008. IgG antibodies against common gut bacteria are more diagnostic for Crohn's disease than IgG against mannan or flagellin. *Am. J. Gastroenterol.* 103:386–96
35. Lodes MJ, Cong Y, Elson CO, Mohamath R, Landers CJ, et al. 2004. Bacterial flagellin is a dominant antigen in Crohn disease. *J. Clin. Investig.* 113:1296–306
36. Hugot JP, Chamaillard M, Zouali H, Lesage S, Cezard JP, et al. 2001. Association of NOD2 leucine-rich repeat variants with susceptibility to Crohn's disease. *Nature* 411:599–603
37. Ogura Y, Bonen DK, Inohara N, Nicolae DL, Chen FF, et al. 2001. A frameshift mutation in NOD2 associated with susceptibility to Crohn's disease. *Nature* 411:603–6
38. Hisamatsu T, Suzuki M, Reinecker HC, Nadeau WJ, McCormick BA, Podolsky DK. 2003. CARD15/NOD2 functions as an antibacterial factor in human intestinal epithelial cells. *Gastroenterology* 124:993–1000
39. Schultz M, Tonkonogy SL, Sellon RK, Veltkamp C, Godfrey VL, et al. 1999. IL-2-deficient mice raised under germfree conditions develop delayed mild focal intestinal inflammation. *Am. J. Physiol. Gastrointest. Liver Physiol.* 276:G1461–72
40. Sellon RK, Tonkonogy S, Schultz M, Dieleman LA, Grenther W, et al. 1998. Resident enteric bacteria are necessary for development of spontaneous colitis and immune system activation in interleukin-10-deficient mice. *Infect. Immun.* 66:5224–31
41. Dianda L, Hanby AM, Wright NA, Sebesteny A, Hayday AC, Owen MJ. 1997. T cell receptor-αβ-deficient mice fail to develop colitis in the absence of a microbial environment. *Am. J. Pathol.* 150:91–97
42. Panwala CM, Jones JC, Viney JL. 1998. A novel model of inflammatory bowel disease: mice deficient for the multiple drug resistance gene, *mdr1a*, spontaneously develop colitis. *J. Immunol.* 161:5733–44
43. Habtezion A, Toivola DM, Butcher EC, Omary MB. 2005. Keratin-8-deficient mice develop chronic spontaneous Th2 colitis amenable to antibiotic treatment. *J. Cell Sci.* 118:1971–80
44. Madsen KL, Doyle JS, Tavernini MM, Jewell LD, Rennie RP, Fedorak RN. 2000. Antibiotic therapy attenuates colitis in interleukin 10 gene-deficient mice. *Gastroenterology* 118:1094–105
45. Hoentjen F, Harmsen HJ, Braat H, Torrice CD, Mann BA, et al. 2003. Antibiotics with a selective aerobic or anaerobic spectrum have different therapeutic activities in various regions of the colon in interleukin 10 gene deficient mice. *Gut* 52:1721–27
46. Garrett WS, Lord GM, Punit S, Lugo-Villarino G, Mazmanian SK, et al. 2007. Communicable ulcerative colitis induced by T-bet deficiency in the innate immune system. *Cell* 131:33–45

47. Maddox L, Schwartz DA. 2002. The pathophysiology of asthma. *Annu. Rev. Med.* 53:477–98
48. Marra F, Marra CA, Richardson K, Lynd LD, Kozyrskyj A, et al. 2009. Antibiotic use in children is associated with increased risk of asthma. *Pediatrics* 123:1003–10
49. Vael C, Nelen V, Verhulst SL, Goossens H, Desager KN. 2008. Early intestinal *Bacteroides fragilis* colonization and development of asthma. *BMC Pulm. Med.* 8:19
50. Hill DA, Hoffmann C, Abt MC, Du Y, Kobuley D, et al. 2009. Metagenomic analyses reveal antibiotic-induced temporal and spatial changes in intestinal microbiota with associated alterations in immune cell homeostasis. *Mucosal Immunol.* In press. doi: 10.1038/mi.2009.132
51. Gore C, Munro K, Lay C, Bibiloni R, Morris J, et al. 2008. *Bifidobacterium pseudocatenulatum* is associated with atopic eczema: a nested case-control study investigating the fecal microbiota of infants. *J. Allergy Clin. Immunol.* 121:135–40
52. Penders J, Stobberingh EE, van den Brandt PA, van Ree R, Thijs C. 2008. Toxigenic and nontoxigenic clostridium difficile: determinants of intestinal colonization and role in childhood atopic manifestations. *Gut* 57:1025–26
53. Penders J, Vink C, Driessen C, London N, Thijs C, Stobberingh EE. 2005. Quantification of *Bifidobacterium* spp., *Escherichia coli* and *Clostridium difficile* in faecal samples of breast-fed and formula-fed infants by real-time PCR. *FEMS Microbiol. Lett.* 243:141–47
54. Noverr MC, Falkowski NR, McDonald RA, McKenzie AN, Huffnagle GB. 2005. Development of allergic airway disease in mice following antibiotic therapy and fungal microbiota increase: role of host genetics, antigen, and interleukin-13. *Infect. Immun.* 73:30–38
55. Amaral FA, Sachs D, Costa VV, Fagundes CT, Cisalpino D, et al. 2008. Commensal microbiota is fundamental for the development of inflammatory pain. *Proc. Natl. Acad. Sci. USA* 105:2193–97
56. Stark PL, Lee A. 1982. The microbial ecology of the large bowel of breast-fed and formula-fed infants during the first year of life. *J. Med. Microbiol.* 15:189–203
57. Adlerberth I, Wold AE. 2009. Establishment of the gut microbiota in western infants. *Acta Paediatr.* 98:229–38
58. Finegold SM, Sutter VL, Mathisen GE. 1983. Normal indigenous intestinal flora. In *Human Intestinal Microflora in Health and Disease*, ed. DJ Hentges, pp. 3–31. London: Academic
59. Suau A, Bonnet R, Sutren M, Godon JJ, Gibson GR, et al. 1999. Direct analysis of genes encoding 16S rRNA from complex communities reveals many novel molecular species within the human gut. *Appl. Environ. Microbiol.* 65:4799–807
60. Zoetendal EG, von Wright A, Vilpponen-Salmela T, Ben-Amor K, Akkermans AD, de Vos WM. 2002. Mucosa-associated bacteria in the human gastrointestinal tract are uniformly distributed along the colon and differ from the community recovered from feces. *Appl. Environ. Microbiol.* 68:3401–7
61. McKenna P, Hoffmann C, Minkah N, Aye PP, Lackner A, et al. 2008. The macaque gut microbiome in health, lentiviral infection, and chronic enterocolitis. *PLoS Pathog.* 4:e20
62. Kuitunen M, Kukkonen K, Juntunen-Backman K, Korpela R, Poussa T, et al. 2009. Probiotics prevent IgE-associated allergy until age 5 years in cesarean-delivered children but not in the total cohort. *J. Allergy Clin. Immunol.* 123:335–41
63. Diaz RL, Hoang L, Wang J, Vela JL, Jenkins S, et al. 2004. Maternal adaptive immunity influences the intestinal microflora of suckling mice. *J. Nutr.* 134:2359–64
64. Martin R, Heilig GH, Zoetendal EG, Smidt H, Rodriguez JM. 2007. Diversity of the lactobacillus group in breast milk and vagina of healthy women and potential role in the colonization of the infant gut. *J. Appl. Microbiol.* 103:2638–44
65. Palmer C, Bik EM, Digiulio DB, Relman DA, Brown PO. 2007. Development of the human infant intestinal microbiota. *PLoS Biol.* 5:e177
66. Benno Y, Suzuki K, Suzuki K, Narisawa K, Bruce WR, Mitsuoka T. 1986. Comparison of the fecal microflora in rural Japanese and urban Canadians. *Microbiol. Immunol.* 30:521–32
67. Penders J, Thijs C, Vink C, Stelma FF, Snijders B, et al. 2006. Factors influencing the composition of the intestinal microbiota in early infancy. *Pediatrics* 118:511–21
68. Stark PL, Lee A. 1982. The bacterial colonization of the large bowel of preterm low birth weight neonates. *J. Hyg.* 89:59–67

69. Blakey JL, Lubitz L, Barnes GL, Bishop RF, Campbell NT, Gillam GL. 1982. Development of gut colonization in preterm neonates. *J. Med. Microbiol.* 15:519–29
70. Gronlund MM, Lehtonen OP, Eerola E, Kero P. 1999. Fecal microflora in healthy infants born by different methods of delivery: permanent changes in intestinal flora after cesarean delivery. *J. Pediatr. Gastroenterol. Nutr.* 28:19–25
71. Hayashi H, Sakamoto M, Benno Y. 2002. Fecal microbial diversity in a strict vegetarian as determined by molecular analysis and cultivation. *Microbiol. Immunol.* 46:819–31
72. Harmsen HJ, Wildeboer-Veloo AC, Raangs GC, Wagendorp AA, Klijn N, et al. 2000. Analysis of intestinal flora development in breast-fed and formula-fed infants by using molecular identification and detection methods. *J. Pediatr. Gastroenterol. Nutr.* 30:61–67
73. Lundequist B, Nord CE, Winberg J. 1985. The composition of the faecal microflora in breastfed and bottle fed infants from birth to eight weeks. *Acta Paediatr. Scand.* 74:45–51
74. Yoshioka H, Iseki K, Fujita K. 1983. Development and differences of intestinal flora in the neonatal period in breast-fed and bottle-fed infants. *Pediatrics* 72:317–21
75. Bullen CL, Tearle PV, Willis AT. 1976. Bifidobacteria in the intestinal tract of infants: an in-vivo study. *J. Med. Microbiol.* 9:325–33
76. Renz-Polster H, David MR, Buist AS, Vollmer WM, O'Connor EA, et al. 2005. Caesarean section delivery and the risk of allergic disorders in childhood. *Clin. Exp. Allergy* 35:1466–72
77. Salam MT, Margolis HG, McConnell R, McGregor JA, Avol EL, Gilliland FD. 2006. Mode of delivery is associated with asthma and allergy occurrences in children. *Ann. Epidemiol.* 16:341–46
78. Shroff KE, Meslin K, Cebra JJ. 1995. Commensal enteric bacteria engender a self-limiting humoral mucosal immune response while permanently colonizing the gut. *Infect. Immun.* 63:3904–13
79. Macpherson AJ. 2006. IgA adaptation to the presence of commensal bacteria in the intestine. *Curr. Top. Microbiol. Immunol.* 308:117–36
80. Macpherson AJ, Uhr T. 2004. Induction of protective IgA by intestinal dendritic cells carrying commensal bacteria. *Science* 303:1662–65
81. MacPherson G, Milling S, Yrlid U, Cousins L, Turnbull E, Huang FP. 2004. Uptake of antigens from the intestine by dendritic cells. *Ann. NY Acad. Sci.* 1029:75–82
82. Macpherson AJ, Gatto D, Sainsbury E, Harriman GR, Hengartner H, Zinkernagel RM. 2000. A primitive T cell-independent mechanism of intestinal mucosal IgA responses to commensal bacteria. *Science* 288:2222–26
83. Bergqvist P, Gardby E, Stensson A, Bemark M, Lycke NY. 2006. Gut IgA class switch recombination in the absence of CD40 does not occur in the lamina propria and is independent of germinal centers. *J. Immunol.* 177:7772–83
84. Renshaw BR, Fanslow WC 3rd, Armitage RJ, Campbell KA, Liggitt D, et al. 1994. Humoral immune responses in CD40 ligand-deficient mice. *J. Exp. Med.* 180:1889–900
85. Macpherson AJ, Uhr T. 2004. Compartmentalization of the mucosal immune responses to commensal intestinal bacteria. *Ann. NY Acad. Sci.* 1029:36–43
86. Konrad A, Cong Y, Duck W, Borlaza R, Elson CO. 2006. Tight mucosal compartmentation of the murine immune response to antigens of the enteric microbiota. *Gastroenterology* 130:2050–59
87. Macpherson AJ, Hunziker L, McCoy K, Lamarre A. 2001. IgA responses in the intestinal mucosa against pathogenic and nonpathogenic microorganisms. *Microbes Infect.* 3:1021–35
88. Dann SM, Eckmann L. 2007. Innate immune defenses in the intestinal tract. *Curr. Opin. Gastroenterol.* 23:115–20
89. Vaishnava S, Behrendt CL, Ismail AS, Eckmann L, Hooper LV. 2008. Paneth cells directly sense gut commensals and maintain homeostasis at the intestinal host-microbial interface. *Proc. Natl. Acad. Sci. USA* 105:20858–63
90. Wang ML, Shin ME, Knight PA, Artis D, Silberg DG, et al. 2005. Regulation of RELM/FIZZ isoform expression by Cdx2 in response to innate and adaptive immune stimulation in the intestine. *Am. J. Physiol. Gastrointest. Liver Physiol.* 288:G1074–83
91. Brandl K, Plitas G, Schnabl B, DeMatteo RP, Pamer EG. 2007. MyD88-mediated signals induce the bactericidal lectin RegIIIγ and protect mice against intestinal *Listeria monocytogenes* infection. *J. Exp. Med.* 204:1891–900

92. Berg R. 1983. Host immune response to antigens of the indigenous intestinal flora. In *Human Intestinal Microflora in Health and Disease*, ed. D Hentges, pp. 101–26. New York: Academic
93. Hill DA, Artis D. 2009. Maintaining diplomatic relations between mammals and beneficial microbial communities. *Sci. Signal.* 2(98):pe77
94. Slack E, Hapfelmeier S, Stecher B, Velykoredko Y, Stoel M, et al. 2009. Innate and adaptive immunity cooperate flexibly to maintain host-microbiota mutualism. *Science* 325:617–20
95. Medzhitov R, Preston-Hurlburt P, Janeway CA Jr. 1997. A human homologue of the *Drosophila* Toll protein signals activation of adaptive immunity. *Nature* 388:394–97
96. West AP, Koblansky AA, Ghosh S. 2006. Recognition and signaling by Toll-like receptors. *Annu. Rev. Cell Dev. Biol.* 22:409–37
97. Medzhitov R. 2007. Recognition of microorganisms and activation of the immune response. *Nature* 449:819–26
98. Vijay-Kumar M, Aitken JD, Sanders CJ, Frias A, Sloane VM, et al. 2008. Flagellin treatment protects against chemicals, bacteria, viruses, and radiation. *J. Immunol.* 180:8280–85
99. Gewirtz AT, Vijay-Kumar M, Brant SR, Duerr RH, Nicolae DL, Cho JH. 2006. Dominant-negative TLR5 polymorphism reduces adaptive immune response to flagellin and negatively associates with Crohn's disease. *Am. J. Physiol. Gastrointest. Liver Physiol.* 290:G1157–63
100. Candia L, Marquez J, Hernandez C, Zea AH, Espinoza LR. 2007. Toll-like receptor-2 expression is upregulated in antigen-presenting cells from patients with psoriatic arthritis: a pathogenic role for innate immunity? *J. Rheumatol.* 34:374–79
101. Racila DM, Kline JN. 2005. Perspectives in asthma: molecular use of microbial products in asthma prevention and treatment. *J. Allergy Clin. Immunol.* 116:1202–5
102. Krieg AM. 2007. Development of TLR9 agonists for cancer therapy. *J. Clin. Investig.* 117:1184–94
103. Rakoff-Nahoum S, Paglino J, Eslami-Varzaneh F, Edberg S, Medzhitov R. 2004. Recognition of commensal microflora by Toll-like receptors is required for intestinal homeostasis. *Cell* 118:229–41
104. Cario E, Rosenberg IM, Brandwein SL, Beck PL, Reinecker HC, Podolsky DK. 2000. Lipopolysaccharide activates distinct signaling pathways in intestinal epithelial cell lines expressing Toll-like receptors. *J. Immunol.* 164:966–72
105. Turnbull EL, Yrlid U, Jenkins CD, MacPherson GG. 2005. Intestinal dendritic cell subsets: differential effects of systemic TLR4 stimulation on migratory fate and activation in vivo. *J. Immunol.* 174:1374–84
106. Dabbagh K, Dahl ME, Stepick-Biek P, Lewis DB. 2002. Toll-like receptor 4 is required for optimal development of Th2 immune responses: role of dendritic cells. *J. Immunol.* 168:4524–30
107. Cerovic V, Jenkins CD, Barnes AG, Milling SW, MacPherson GG, Klavinskis LS. 2009. Hyporesponsiveness of intestinal dendritic cells to TLR stimulation is limited to TLR4. *J. Immunol.* 182:2405–15
108. Bashir ME, Louie S, Shi HN, Nagler-Anderson C. 2004. Toll-like receptor 4 signaling by intestinal microbes influences susceptibility to food allergy. *J. Immunol.* 172:6978–87
109. Hall JA, Bouladoux N, Sun CM, Wohlfert EA, Blank RB, et al. 2008. Commensal DNA limits regulatory T cell conversion and is a natural adjuvant of intestinal immune responses. *Immunity* 29:637–49
110. Wang Q, McLoughlin RM, Cobb BA, Charrel-Dennis M, Zaleski KJ, et al. 2006. A bacterial carbohydrate links innate and adaptive responses through Toll-like receptor 2. *J. Exp. Med.* 203:2853–63
111. Tzianabos AO, Russell PR, Onderdonk AB, Gibson FC 3rd, Cywes C, et al. 1999. IL-2 mediates protection against abscess formation in an experimental model of sepsis. *J. Immunol.* 163:893–97
112. Mazmanian SK, Round JL, Kasper DL. 2008. A microbial symbiosis factor prevents intestinal inflammatory disease. *Nature* 453:620–25
113. Mazmanian SK, Liu CH, Tzianabos AO, Kasper DL. 2005. An immunomodulatory molecule of symbiotic bacteria directs maturation of the host immune system. *Cell* 122:107–18
114. Fritz JH, Ferrero RL, Philpott DJ, Girardin SE. 2006. Nod-like proteins in immunity, inflammation and disease. *Nat. Immunol.* 7:1250–57
115. Carneiro LA, Magalhaes JG, Tattoli I, Philpott DJ, Travassos LH. 2008. Nod-like proteins in inflammation and disease. *J. Pathol.* 214:136–48
116. Bouskra D, Brezillon C, Berard M, Werts C, Varona R, et al. 2008. Lymphoid tissue genesis induced by commensals through NOD1 regulates intestinal homeostasis. *Nature* 456:507–10

117. Magalhaes JG, Fritz JH, Le Bourhis L, Sellge G, Travassos LH, et al. 2008. Nod2-dependent Th2 polarization of antigen-specific immunity. *J. Immunol.* 181:7925–35
118. Bonen DK, Ogura Y, Nicolae DL, Inohara N, Saab L, et al. 2003. Crohn's disease-associated NOD2 variants share a signaling defect in response to lipopolysaccharide and peptidoglycan. *Gastroenterology* 124(1):140–46
119. Hisamatsu T, Suzuki M, Reinecker HC, Nadeau WJ, McCormick BA, Podolsky DK. 2003. CARD15/NOD2 functions as an antibacterial factor in human intestinal epithelial cells. *Gastroenterology* 124(4):993–1000
120. Wehkamp J, Salzman NH, Porter E, Nuding S, Weichenthal M, et al. 2005. Reduced Paneth cell alpha-defensins in ileal Crohn's disease. *Proc. Natl. Acad. Sci. USA* 102(50):18129–34
121. Kobayashi KS, Chamaillard M, Ogura Y, Henegariu O, Inohara N, et al. 2005. Nod2-dependent regulation of innate and adaptive immunity in the intestinal tract. *Science* 307:731–34
122. Pauleau AL, Murray PJ. 2003. Role of Nod2 in the response of macrophages to Toll-like receptor agonists. *Mol. Cell. Biol.* 23:7531–39
123. Maeda S, Hsu LC, Liu H, Bankston LA, Iimura M, et al. 2005. Nod2 mutation in Crohn's disease potentiates NF-κB activity and IL-1β processing. *Science* 307:734–38
124. Netea MG, Ferwerda G, de Jong DJ, Jansen T, Jacobs L, et al. 2005. Nucleotide-binding oligomerization domain-2 modulates specific TLR pathways for the induction of cytokine release. *J. Immunol.* 174:6518–23
125. Watanabe T, Kitani A, Murray PJ, Strober W. 2004. NOD2 is a negative regulator of Toll-like receptor 2-mediated T helper type 1 responses. *Nat. Immunol.* 5:800–8
126. Watanabe T, Kitani A, Murray PJ, Wakatsuki Y, Fuss IJ, Strober W. 2006. Nucleotide binding oligomerization domain 2 deficiency leads to dysregulated TLR2 signaling and induction of antigen-specific colitis. *Immunity* 25:473–85
127. Watanabe T, Asano N, Murray PJ, Ozato K, Tailor P, et al. 2008. Muramyl dipeptide activation of nucleotide-binding oligomerization domain 2 protects mice from experimental colitis. *J. Clin. Investig.* 118:545–59
128. Yang Z, Fuss IJ, Watanabe T, Asano N, Davey MP, et al. 2007. NOD2 transgenic mice exhibit enhanced MDP-mediated down-regulation of TLR2 responses and resistance to colitis induction. *Gastroenterology* 133:1510–21
129. Zeuthen LH, Fink LN, Frokiaer H. 2008. Toll-like receptor 2 and nucleotide-binding oligomerization domain-2 play divergent roles in the recognition of gut-derived lactobacilli and bifidobacteria in dendritic cells. *Immunology* 124:489–502
130. Hedl M, Li J, Cho JH, Abraham C. 2007. Chronic stimulation of Nod2 mediates tolerance to bacterial products. *Proc. Natl. Acad. Sci. USA* 104:19440–45
131. Uehara A, Yang S, Fujimoto Y, Fukase K, Kusumoto S, et al. 2005. Muramyldipeptide and diaminopimelic acid-containing desmuramylpeptides in combination with chemically synthesized Toll-like receptor agonists synergistically induced production of interleukin-8 in a NOD2- and NOD1-dependent manner, respectively, in human monocytic cells in culture. *Cell. Microbiol.* 7(1):53-61
132. Tada H, Aiba S, Shibata K, Ohteki T, Takada H. 2005. Synergistic effect of Nod1 and Nod2 agonists with Toll-like receptor agonists on human dendritic cells to generate interleukin-12 and T helper type 1 cells. *Infect. Immun.* 73:7967–76
133. Moreira LO, El Kasmi KC, Smith AM, Finkelstein D, Fillon S, et al. 2008. The TLR2-MyD88-NOD2-RIPK2 signalling axis regulates a balanced pro-inflammatory and IL-10-mediated anti-inflammatory cytokine response to Gram-positive cell walls. *Cell. Microbiol.* 10:2067–77
134. Noguchi E, Homma Y, Kang X, Netea MG, Ma X. 2009. A Crohn's disease-associated NOD2 mutation suppresses transcription of human IL10 by inhibiting activity of the nuclear ribonucleoprotein hnRNP-A1. *Nat. Immunol.* 10(5):471–79
135. Jacobson KA, Gao ZG. 2006. Adenosine receptors as therapeutic targets. *Nat. Rev. Drug Discov.* 5:247–64
136. Selmeczy Z, Csóka B, Pacher P, Vizi ES, Hasko G. 2007. The adenosine A2A receptor agonist CGS 21680 fails to ameliorate the course of dextran sulphate-induced colitis in mice. *Inflamm. Res.* 56:204–9
137. Frick JS, MacManus CF, Scully M, Glover LE, Eltzschig HK, Colgan SP. 2009. Contribution of adenosine A2B receptors to inflammatory parameters of experimental colitis. *J. Immunol.* 182:4957–64

138. Atarashi K, Nishimura J, Shima T, Umesaki Y, Yamamoto M, et al. 2008. ATP drives lamina propria T(H)17 cell differentiation. *Nature* 455:808–12
139. Pryde SE, Duncan SH, Hold GL, Stewart CS, Flint HJ. 2002. The microbiology of butyrate formation in the human colon. *FEMS Microbiol. Lett.* 217:133–39
140. Avivi-Green C, Polak-Charcon S, Madar Z, Schwartz B. 2000. Apoptosis cascade proteins are regulated in vivo by high intracolonic butyrate concentration: correlation with colon cancer inhibition. *Oncol. Res.* 12:83–95
141. Hague A, Elder DJ, Hicks DJ, Paraskeva C. 1995. Apoptosis in colorectal tumor cells: induction by the short chain fatty acids butyrate, propionate and acetate and by the bile salt deoxycholate. *Int. J. Cancer* 60:400–6
142. Thangaraju M, Cresci GA, Liu K, Ananth S, Gnanaprakasam JP, et al. 2009. GPR109A is a G-protein-coupled receptor for the bacterial fermentation product butyrate and functions as a tumor suppressor in colon. *Cancer Res.* 69:2826–32
143. Kumar A, Wu H, Collier-Hyams LS, Kwon YM, Hanson JM, Neish AS. 2009. The bacterial fermentation product butyrate influences epithelial signaling via reactive oxygen species-mediated changes in cullin-1 neddylation. *J. Immunol.* 182:538–46
144. Luhrs H, Gerke T, Muller JG, Melcher R, Schauber J, et al. 2002. Butyrate inhibits NF-κB activation in lamina propria macrophages of patients with ulcerative colitis. *Scand. J. Gastroenterol.* 37:458–66
145. Segain JP, Raingeard de la Blétière D, Bourreille A, Leray V, Gervois N, et al. 2000. Butyrate inhibits inflammatory responses through NFκB inhibition: implications for Crohn's disease. *Gut* 47:397–403
146. Maslowski KM, Vieira AT, Ng A, Kranich J, Sierro F, et al. 2009. Regulation of inflammatory responses by gut microbiota and chemoattractant receptor GPR43. *Nature* 461:1282–86
147. Rubic T, Lametschwandtner G, Jost S, Hinteregger S, Kund J, et al. 2008. Triggering the succinate receptor GPR91 on dendritic cells enhances immunity. *Nat. Immunol.* 9:1261–69
148. Konstantinov SR, Smidt H, de Vos WM, Bruijns SC, Singh SK, et al. 2008. S layer protein A of *Lactobacillus acidophilus* NCFM regulates immature dendritic cell and T cell functions. *Proc. Natl. Acad. Sci. USA* 105:19474–79
149. Sato T, Vries RG, Snippert HJ, van de Wetering M, Barker N, et al. 2009. Single Lgr5 stem cells build crypt-villus structures in vitro without a mesenchymal niche. *Nature* 459:262–65
150. Gordon JI, Hermiston ML. 1994. Differentiation and self-renewal in the mouse gastrointestinal epithelium. *Curr. Opin. Cell Biol.* 6:795–803
151. Shen L, Turner JR. 2006. Role of epithelial cells in initiation and propagation of intestinal inflammation. eliminating the static: tight junction dynamics exposed. *Am. J. Physiol. Gastrointest. Liver Physiol.* 290:G577–82
152. Neutra MR, Pringault E, Kraehenbuhl JP. 1996. Antigen sampling across epithelial barriers and induction of mucosal immune responses. *Annu. Rev. Immunol.* 14:275–300
153. Frey A, Giannasca KT, Weltzin R, Giannasca PJ, Reggio H, et al. 1996. Role of the glycocalyx in regulating access of microparticles to apical plasma membranes of intestinal epithelial cells: implications for microbial attachment and oral vaccine targeting. *J. Exp. Med.* 184:1045–59
154. Ganz T. 2003. Defensins: antimicrobial peptides of innate immunity. *Nat. Rev. Immunol.* 3:710–20
155. Cario E, Podolsky DK. 2000. Differential alteration in intestinal epithelial cell expression of Toll-like receptor 3 (TLR3) and TLR4 in inflammatory bowel disease. *Infect. Immun.* 68:7010–17
156. Gewirtz AT, Navas TA, Lyons S, Godowski PJ, Madara JL. 2001. Cutting edge: bacterial flagellin activates basolaterally expressed TLR5 to induce epithelial proinflammatory gene expression. *J. Immunol.* 167:1882–85
157. Zilbauer M, Dorrell N, Elmi A, Lindley KJ, Schuller S, et al. 2007. A major role for intestinal epithelial nucleotide oligomerization domain 1 (NOD1) in eliciting host bactericidal immune responses to *Campylobacter jejuni*. *Cell. Microbiol.* 9:2404–16
158. He B, Xu W, Santini PA, Polydorides AD, Chiu A, et al. 2007. Intestinal bacteria trigger T cell-independent immunoglobulin A(2) class switching by inducing epithelial-cell secretion of the cytokine APRIL. *Immunity* 26:812–26
159. Xu W, He B, Chiu A, Chadburn A, Shan M, et al. 2007. Epithelial cells trigger frontline immunoglobulin class switching through a pathway regulated by the inhibitor SLPI. *Nat. Immunol.* 8:294–303

160. Jung HC, Eckmann L, Yang SK, Panja A, Fierer J, et al. 1995. A distinct array of proinflammatory cytokines is expressed in human colon epithelial cells in response to bacterial invasion. *J. Clin. Investig.* 95:55–65

161. Cash HL, Whitham CV, Behrendt CL, Hooper LV. 2006. Symbiotic bacteria direct expression of an intestinal bactericidal lectin. *Science* 313:1126–30

162. Sonnenburg JL, Chen CT, Gordon JI. 2006. Genomic and metabolic studies of the impact of probiotics on a model gut symbiont and host. *PLoS Biol.* 4:e413

163. Philpott DJ, Girardin SE. 2004. The role of Toll-like receptors and Nod proteins in bacterial infection. *Mol. Immunol.* 41:1099–108

164. Uehara A, Fujimoto Y, Fukase K, Takada H. 2007. Various human epithelial cells express functional Toll-like receptors, NOD1 and NOD2 to produce antimicrobial peptides, but not proinflammatory cytokines. *Mol. Immunol.* 44:3100–11

165. Abreu MT, Vora P, Faure E, Thomas LS, Arnold ET, Arditi M. 2001. Decreased expression of Toll-like receptor-4 and MD-2 correlates with intestinal epithelial cell protection against dysregulated proinflammatory gene expression in response to bacterial lipopolysaccharide. *J. Immunol.* 167:1609–16

166. Melmed G, Thomas LS, Lee N, Tesfay SY, Lukasek K, et al. 2003. Human intestinal epithelial cells are broadly unresponsive to Toll-like receptor 2-dependent bacterial ligands: implications for host-microbial interactions in the gut. *J. Immunol.* 170:1406–15

167. Cario E, Gerken G, Podolsky DK. 2007. Toll-like receptor 2 controls mucosal inflammation by regulating epithelial barrier function. *Gastroenterology* 132:1359–74

168. Zaph C, Du Y, Saenz SA, Nair MG, Perrigoue JG, et al. 2008. Commensal-dependent expression of IL-25 regulates the IL-23-IL-17 axis in the intestine. *J. Exp. Med.* 205:2191–98

169. Brown SL, Riehl TE, Walker MR, Geske MJ, Doherty JM, et al. 2007. Myd88-dependent positioning of Ptgs2-expressing stromal cells maintains colonic epithelial proliferation during injury. *J. Clin. Investig.* 117:258–69

170. Dignass AU, Podolsky DK. 1993. Cytokine modulation of intestinal epithelial cell restitution: central role of transforming growth factor β. *Gastroenterology* 105:1323–32

171. Rimoldi M, Chieppa M, Larghi P, Vulcano M, Allavena P, Rescigno M. 2005. Monocyte-derived dendritic cells activated by bacteria or by bacteria-stimulated epithelial cells are functionally different. *Blood* 106:2818–26

172. Rimoldi M, Chieppa M, Salucci V, Avogadri F, Sonzogni A, et al. 2005. Intestinal immune homeostasis is regulated by the crosstalk between epithelial cells and dendritic cells. *Nat. Immunol.* 6:507–14

173. Taylor BC, Zaph C, Troy AE, Du Y, Guild KJ, et al. 2009. TSLP regulates intestinal immunity and inflammation in mouse models of helminth infection and colitis. *J. Exp. Med.* 206:655–67

174. Zeuthen LH, Fink LN, Frokiaer H. 2008. Epithelial cells prime the immune response to an array of gut-derived commensals towards a tolerogenic phenotype through distinct actions of thymic stromal lymphopoietin and transforming growth factor-β. *Immunology* 123:197–208

175. Sun CM, Hall JA, Blank RB, Bouladoux N, Oukka M, et al. 2007. Small intestine lamina propria dendritic cells promote de novo generation of Foxp3 T reg cells via retinoic acid. *J. Exp. Med.* 204:1775–85

176. Coombes JL, Siddiqui KR, Arancibia-Carcamo CV, Hall J, Sun CM, et al. 2007. A functionally specialized population of mucosal $CD103^+$ DCs induces $Foxp3^+$ regulatory T cells via a TGF-β and retinoic acid-dependent mechanism. *J. Exp. Med.* 204:1757–64

177. Nenci A, Becker C, Wullaert A, Gareus R, van Loo G, et al. 2007. Epithelial NEMO links innate immunity to chronic intestinal inflammation. *Nature* 446:557–61

178. Zaph C, Troy AE, Taylor BC, Berman-Booty LD, Guild KJ, et al. 2007. Epithelial-cell-intrinsic IKK-β expression regulates intestinal immune homeostasis. *Nature* 446:552–56

179. Iliev ID, Spadoni I, Mileti E, Matteoli G, Sonzogni A, et al. 2009. Human intestinal epithelial cells promote the differentiation of tolerogenic dendritic cells. *Gut* 58:1481–89

180. Iliev ID, Mileti E, Matteoli G, Chieppa M, Rescigno M. 2009. Intestinal epithelial cells promote colitis-protective regulatory T-cell differentiation through dendritic cell conditioning. *Mucosal Immunol.* 2:340–50

181. Allakhverdi Z, Comeau MR, Jessup HK, Yoon BR, Brewer A, et al. 2007. Thymic stromal lymphopoietin is released by human epithelial cells in response to microbes, trauma, or inflammation and potently activates mast cells. *J. Exp. Med.* 204:253–58
182. Bogiatzi SI, Fernandez I, Bichet JC, Marloie-Provost MA, Volpe E, et al. 2007. Cutting edge: proinflammatory and Th2 cytokines synergize to induce thymic stromal lymphopoietin production by human skin keratinocytes. *J. Immunol.* 178:3373–77
183. Kato A, Favoreto S Jr, Avila PC, Schleimer RP. 2007. TLR3- and Th2 cytokine-dependent production of thymic stromal lymphopoietin in human airway epithelial cells. *J. Immunol.* 179:1080–87
184. Li M, Hener P, Zhang Z, Kato S, Metzger D, Chambon P. 2006. Topical vitamin D3 and low-calcemic analogs induce thymic stromal lymphopoietin in mouse keratinocytes and trigger an atopic dermatitis. *Proc. Natl. Acad. Sci. USA* 103:11,736–41
185. Lee HC, Ziegler SF. 2007. Inducible expression of the proallergic cytokine thymic stromal lymphopoietin in airway epithelial cells is controlled by NFκB. *Proc. Natl. Acad. Sci. USA* 104:914–19
186. Soumelis V, Reche PA, Kanzler H, Yuan W, Edward G, et al. 2002. Human epithelial cells trigger dendritic cell mediated allergic inflammation by producing TSLP. *Nat. Immunol.* 3:673–80
187. Al-Shami A, Spolski R, Kelly J, Keane-Myers A, Leonard WJ. 2005. A role for TSLP in the development of inflammation in an asthma model. *J. Exp. Med.* 202:829–39
188. Ito T, Wang YH, Duramad O, Hori T, Delespesse GJ, et al. 2005. TSLP-activated dendritic cells induce an inflammatory T helper type 2 cell response through OX40 ligand. *J. Exp. Med.* 202:1213–23
189. Yoo J, Omori M, Gyarmati D, Zhou B, Aye T, et al. 2005. Spontaneous atopic dermatitis in mice expressing an inducible thymic stromal lymphopoietin transgene specifically in the skin. *J. Exp. Med.* 202:541–49
190. Zhou B, Comeau MR, De Smedt T, Liggitt HD, Dahl ME, et al. 2005. Thymic stromal lymphopoietin as a key initiator of allergic airway inflammation in mice. *Nat. Immunol.* 6:1047–53
191. Ziegler SF, Liu YJ. 2006. Thymic stromal lymphopoietin in normal and pathogenic T cell development and function. *Nat. Immunol.* 7:709–14
192. Massacand JC, Stettler RC, Meier R, Humphreys NE, Grencis RK, et al. 2009. Helminth products bypass the need for TSLP in Th2 immune responses by directly modulating dendritic cell function. *Proc. Natl. Acad. Sci. USA* 106:13968–73
193. Hershberg RM, Mayer LF. 2000. Antigen processing and presentation by intestinal epithelial cells—polarity and complexity. *Immunol. Today* 21:123–28
194. Buning J, Hundorfean G, Schmitz M, Zimmer KP, Strobel S, et al. 2006. Antigen targeting to MHC class II-enriched late endosomes in colonic epithelial cells: trafficking of luminal antigens studied in vivo in Crohn's colitis patients. *FASEB J.* 20:359–61
195. Telega GW, Baumgart DC, Carding SR. 2000. Uptake and presentation of antigen to T cells by primary colonic epithelial cells in normal and diseased states. *Gastroenterology* 119:1548–59
196. Sanderson IR, Ouellette AJ, Carter EA, Walker WA, Harmatz PR. 1993. Differential regulation of B7 mRNA in enterocytes and lymphoid cells. *Immunology* 79:434–38
197. Trombetta ES, Mellman I. 2005. Cell biology of antigen processing in vitro and in vivo. *Annu. Rev. Immunol.* 23:975–1028
198. Iwasaki A. 2007. Mucosal dendritic cells. *Annu. Rev. Immunol.* 25:381–418
199. Coombes JL, Powrie F. 2008. Dendritic cells in intestinal immune regulation. *Nat. Rev. Immunol.* 8:435–46
200. Tyrer P, Foxwell AR, Cripps AW, Apicella MA, Kyd JM. 2006. Microbial pattern recognition receptors mediate M-cell uptake of a gram-negative bacterium. *Infect. Immun.* 74:625–31
201. Milling SW, Cousins L, MacPherson GG. 2005. How do DCs interact with intestinal antigens? *Trends Immunol.* 26:349–52
202. Salazar-Gonzalez RM, Niess JH, Zammit DJ, Ravindran R, Srinivasan A, et al. 2006. CCR6-mediated dendritic cell activation of pathogen-specific T cells in Peyer's patches. *Immunity* 24:623–32
203. Iwasaki A, Kelsall BL. 2000. Localization of distinct Peyer's patch dendritic cell subsets and their recruitment by chemokines macrophage inflammatory protein (MIP)-3α, MIP-3β, and secondary lymphoid organ chemokine. *J. Exp. Med.* 191:1381–94

204. Iwasaki A, Kelsall BL. 1999. Freshly isolated Peyer's patch, but not spleen, dendritic cells produce interleukin 10 and induce the differentiation of T helper type 2 cells. *J. Exp. Med.* 190:229–39
205. Johansson-Lindbom B, Svensson M, Pabst O, Palmqvist C, Marquez G, et al. 2005. Functional specialization of gut CD103$^+$ dendritic cells in the regulation of tissue-selective T cell homing. *J. Exp. Med.* 202:1063–73
206. Mora JR, Bono MR, Manjunath N, Weninger W, Cavanagh LL, et al. 2003. Selective imprinting of gut-homing T cells by Peyer's patch dendritic cells. *Nature* 424:88–93
207. George A, Cebra JJ. 1991. Responses of single germinal-center B cells in T-cell-dependent microculture. *Proc. Natl. Acad. Sci. USA* 88:11–15
208. Spalding DM, Williamson SI, Koopman WJ, McGhee JR. 1984. Preferential induction of polyclonal IgA secretion by murine Peyer's patch dendritic cell-T cell mixtures. *J. Exp. Med.* 160:941–46
209. Powrie F. 2004. Immune regulation in the intestine: a balancing act between effector and regulatory T cell responses. *Ann. NY Acad. Sci.* 1029:132–41
210. Jaensson E, Uronen-Hansson H, Pabst O, Eksteen B, Tian J, et al. 2008. Small intestinal CD103$^+$ dendritic cells display unique functional properties that are conserved between mice and humans. *J. Exp. Med.* 205:2139–49
211. Rescigno M, Urbano M, Valzasina B, Francolini M, Rotta G, et al. 2001. Dendritic cells express tight junction proteins and penetrate gut epithelial monolayers to sample bacteria. *Nat. Immunol.* 2:361–67
212. Niess JH, Brand S, Gu X, Landsman L, Jung S, et al. 2005. CX3CR1-mediated dendritic cell access to the intestinal lumen and bacterial clearance. *Science* 307:254–58
213. Chieppa M, Rescigno M, Huang AY, Germain RN. 2006. Dynamic imaging of dendritic cell extension into the small bowel lumen in response to epithelial cell TLR engagement. *J. Exp. Med.* 203:2841–52
214. Yrlid U, Cerovic V, Milling S, Jenkins CD, Klavinskis LS, MacPherson GG. 2006. A distinct subset of intestinal dendritic cells responds selectively to oral TLR7/8 stimulation. *Eur. J. Immunol.* 36:2639–48
215. Minns LA, Menard LC, Foureau DM, Darche S, Ronet C, et al. 2006. TLR9 is required for the gut-associated lymphoid tissue response following oral infection of *Toxoplasma gondii*. *J. Immunol.* 176:7589–97
216. Uematsu S, Jang MH, Chevrier N, Guo Z, Kumagai Y, et al. 2006. Detection of pathogenic intestinal bacteria by Toll-like receptor 5 on intestinal CD11c$^+$ lamina propria cells. *Nat. Immunol.* 7:868–74
217. Uematsu S, Fujimoto K, Jang MH, Yang BG, Jung YJ, et al. 2008. Regulation of humoral and cellular gut immunity by lamina propria dendritic cells expressing Toll-like receptor 5. *Nat. Immunol.* 9:769–76
218. Chirdo FG, Millington OR, Beacock-Sharp H, Mowat AM. 2005. Immunomodulatory dendritic cells in intestinal lamina propria. *Eur. J. Immunol.* 35:1831–40
219. Worbs T, Bode U, Yan S, Hoffmann MW, Hintzen G, et al. 2006. Oral tolerance originates in the intestinal immune system and relies on antigen carriage by dendritic cells. *J. Exp. Med.* 203:519–27
220. Monteleone I, Platt AM, Jaensson E, Agace WW, Mowat AM. 2008. IL-10-dependent partial refractoriness to Toll-like receptor stimulation modulates gut mucosal dendritic cell function. *Eur. J. Immunol.* 38:1533–47
221. Takenaka S, Safroneeva E, Xing Z, Gauldie J. 2007. Dendritic cells derived from murine colonic mucosa have unique functional and phenotypic characteristics. *J. Immunol.* 178:7984–93
222. Trinchieri G. 2003. Interleukin-12 and the regulation of innate resistance and adaptive immunity. *Nat. Rev. Immunol.* 3:133–46
223. Davidson NJ, Hudak SA, Lesley RE, Menon S, Leach MW, Rennick DM. 1998. IL-12, but not IFN-γ, plays a major role in sustaining the chronic phase of colitis in IL-10-deficient mice. *J. Immunol.* 161:3143–49
224. Elson CO, Cong Y, McCracken VJ, Dimmitt RA, Lorenz RG, Weaver CT. 2005. Experimental models of inflammatory bowel disease reveal innate, adaptive, and regulatory mechanisms of host dialogue with the microbiota. *Immunol. Rev.* 206:260–76
225. Neurath MF, Fuss I, Kelsall BL, Stuber E, Strober W. 1995. Antibodies to interleukin 12 abrogate established experimental colitis in mice. *J. Exp. Med.* 182:1281–90
226. Simpson SJ, Shah S, Comiskey M, de Jong YP, Wang B, et al. 1998. T cell-mediated pathology in two models of experimental colitis depends predominantly on the interleukin 12/signal transducer and

activator of transcription (Stat)-4 pathway, but is not conditional on interferon γ expression by T cells. *J. Exp. Med.* 187:1225–34

227. Oppmann B, Lesley R, Blom B, Timans JC, Xu Y, et al. 2000. Novel p19 protein engages IL-12p40 to form a cytokine, IL-23, with biological activities similar as well as distinct from IL-12. *Immunity* 13:715–25
228. Becker C, Dornhoff H, Neufert C, Fantini MC, Wirtz S, et al. 2006. Cutting edge: IL-23 cross-regulates IL-12 production in T cell-dependent experimental colitis. *J. Immunol.* 177:2760–64
229. Lyakh L, Trinchieri G, Provezza L, Carra G, Gerosa F. 2008. Regulation of interleukin-12/interleukin-23 production and the T-helper 17 response in humans. *Immunol. Rev.* 226:112–31
230. Yen D, Cheung J, Scheerens H, Poulet F, McClanahan T, et al. 2006. IL-23 is essential for T cell-mediated colitis and promotes inflammation via IL-17 and IL-6. *J. Clin. Investig.* 116:1310–16
231. Ahern PP, Izcue A, Maloy KJ, Powrie F. 2008. The interleukin-23 axis in intestinal inflammation. *Immunol. Rev.* 226:147–59
232. Murphy CA, Langrish CL, Chen Y, Blumenschein W, McClanahan T, et al. 2003. Divergent pro- and antiinflammatory roles for IL-23 and IL-12 in joint autoimmune inflammation. *J. Exp. Med.* 198:1951–57
233. Hue S, Ahern P, Buonocore S, Kullberg MC, Cua DJ, et al. 2006. Interleukin-23 drives innate and T cell-mediated intestinal inflammation. *J. Exp. Med.* 203:2473–83
234. Izcue A, Hue S, Buonocore S, Arancibia-Carcamo CV, Ahern PP, et al. 2008. Interleukin-23 restrains regulatory T cell activity to drive T cell-dependent colitis. *Immunity* 28:559–70
235. Kullberg MC, Jankovic D, Feng CG, Hue S, Gorelick PL, et al. 2006. IL-23 plays a key role in helicobacter hepaticus-induced T cell-dependent colitis. *J. Exp. Med.* 203:2485–94
236. Uhlig HH, McKenzie BS, Hue S, Thompson C, Joyce-Shaikh B, et al. 2006. Differential activity of IL-12 and IL-23 in mucosal and systemic innate immune pathology. *Immunity* 25:309–18
237. Chan JR, Blumenschein W, Murphy E, Diveu C, Wiekowski M, et al. 2006. IL-23 stimulates epidermal hyperplasia via TNF and IL-20R2-dependent mechanisms with implications for psoriasis pathogenesis. *J. Exp. Med.* 203:2577–87
238. Kopp T, Lenz P, Bello-Fernandez C, Kastelein RA, Kupper TS, Stingl G. 2003. IL-23 production by cosecretion of endogenous p19 and transgenic p40 in keratin 14/p40 transgenic mice: evidence for enhanced cutaneous immunity. *J. Immunol.* 170:5438–44
239. Duerr RH, Taylor KD, Brant SR, Rioux JD, Silverberg MS, et al. 2006. A genome-wide association study identifies *IL23R* as an inflammatory bowel disease gene. *Science* 314:1461–63
240. Jang MH, Sougawa N, Tanaka T, Hirata T, Hiroi T, et al. 2006. CCR7 is critically important for migration of dendritic cells in intestinal lamina propria to mesenteric lymph nodes. *J. Immunol.* 176:803–10
241. Huang FP, Platt N, Wykes M, Major JR, Powell TJ, et al. 2000. A discrete subpopulation of dendritic cells transports apoptotic intestinal epithelial cells to T cell areas of mesenteric lymph nodes. *J. Exp. Med.* 191:435–44
242. Mora JR, Iwata M, Eksteen B, Song SY, Junt T, et al. 2006. Generation of gut-homing IgA-secreting B cells by intestinal dendritic cells. *Science* 314:1157–60
243. Stagg AJ, Kamm MA, Knight SC. 2002. Intestinal dendritic cells increase T cell expression of α4β7 integrin. *Eur. J. Immunol.* 32:1445–54
244. Svensson M, Johansson-Lindbom B, Wurbel MA, Malissen B, Marquez G, Agace W. 2004. Selective generation of gut-tropic T cells in gut-associated lymphoid tissues: requirement for GALT dendritic cells and adjuvant. *Ann. NY Acad. Sci.* 1029:405–7
245. Smith K, McCoy KD, Macpherson AJ. 2007. Use of axenic animals in studying the adaptation of mammals to their commensal intestinal microbiota. *Semin. Immunol.* 19:59–69
246. Gustafsson BE, Midtvedt T, Strandberg K. 1970. Effects of microbial contamination on the cecum enlargement of germfree rats. *Scand. J. Gastroenterol.* 5:309–14
247. Carlstedt-Duke B, Midtvedt T, Nord CE, Gustafsson BE. 1986. Isolation and characterization of a mucin-degrading strain of peptostreptococcus from rat intestinal tract. *Acta Pathol. Microbiol. Immunol. Scand. B* 94:293–300

248. Hoskins LC, Agustines M, McKee WB, Boulding ET, Kriaris M, Niedermeyer G. 1985. Mucin degradation in human colon ecosystems. isolation and properties of fecal strains that degrade ABH blood group antigens and oligosaccharides from mucin glycoproteins. *J. Clin. Investig.* 75:944–53
249. Lindstedt G, Lindstedt S, Gustafsson BE. 1965. Mucus in intestinal contents of germfree rats. *J. Exp. Med.* 121:201–13
250. Eyssen HJ, Parmentier GG, Mertens JA. 1976. Sulfate bile acids in germ-free and conventional mice. *Eur. J. Biochem.* 66:507–14
251. Alam M, Midtvedt T, Uribe A. 1994. Differential cell kinetics in the ileum and colon of germfree rats. *Scand. J. Gastroenterol.* 29:445–51
252. Abrams GD, Bauer H, Sprinz H. 1963. Influence of the normal flora on mucosal morphology and cellular renewal in the ileum. A comparison of germ-free and conventional mice. *Lab. Investig.* 12:355–64
253. Barbara G, Vallance BA, Collins SM. 1997. Persistent intestinal neuromuscular dysfunction after acute nematode infection in mice. *Gastroenterology* 113:1224–32
254. Strandberg K, Sedvall G, Midtvedt T, Gustafsson B. 1966. Effect of some biologically active amines on the cecum wall of germfree rats. *Proc. Soc. Exp. Biol. Med.* 121:699–702
255. Bush TG, Savidge TC, Freeman TC, Cox HJ, Campbell EA, et al. 1998. Fulminant jejuno-ileitis following ablation of enteric glia in adult transgenic mice. *Cell.* 93:189–201
256. Mestecky J, McGhee JR. 1987. Immunoglobulin A (IgA): molecular and cellular interactions involved in IgA biosynthesis and immune response. *Adv. Immunol.* 40:153–245
257. Brandtzaeg P, Halstensen TS, Kett K, Krajci P, Kvale D, et al. 1989. Immunobiology and immunopathology of human gut mucosa: humoral immunity and intraepithelial lymphocytes. *Gastroenterology* 97:1562–84
258. Langman JM, Rowland R. 1986. The number and distribution of lymphoid follicles in the human large intestine. *J. Anat.* 149:189–94
259. Hudson JA, Luckey TD. 1964. Bacteria induced morphologic changes. *Proc. Soc. Exp. Biol. Med.* 116:628–31
260. Hooijkaas H, Benner R, Pleasants JR, Wostmann BS. 1984. Isotypes and specificities of immunoglobulins produced by germ-free mice fed chemically defined ultrafiltered "antigen-free" diet. *Eur. J. Immunol.* 14:1127–30
261. Cebra JJ, Periwal SB, Lee G, Lee F, Shroff KE. 1998. Development and maintenance of the gut-associated lymphoid tissue (GALT): the roles of enteric bacteria and viruses. *Dev. Immunol.* 6:13–18
262. Glaister JR. 1973. Factors affecting the lymphoid cells in the small intestinal epithelium of the mouse. *Int. Arch. Allergy Appl. Immunol.* 45:719–30
263. Yaguchi Y, Fukatsu K, Moriya T, Maeshima Y, Ikezawa F, et al. 2006. Influences of long-term antibiotic administration on Peyer's patch lymphocytes and mucosal immunoglobulin A levels in a mouse model. *JPEN J. Parenter. Enter. Nutr.* 30:395–99
264. Haverson K, Rehakova Z, Sinkora J, Sver L, Bailey M. 2007. Immune development in jejunal mucosa after colonization with selected commensal gut bacteria: a study in germ-free pigs. *Vet. Immunol. Immunopathol.* 119:243–53
265. Williams AM, Probert CS, Stepankova R, Tlaskalova-Hogenova H, Phillips A, Bland PW. 2006. Effects of microflora on the neonatal development of gut mucosal T cells and myeloid cells in the mouse. *Immunology* 119:470–78
266. Walton KL, He J, Kelsall BL, Sartor RB, Fisher NC. 2006. Dendritic cells in germ-free and specific pathogen-free mice have similar phenotypes and in vitro antigen presenting function. *Immunol. Lett.* 102:16–24
267. Zhang W, Wen K, Azevedo MS, Gonzalez A, Saif LJ, et al. 2008. Lactic acid bacterial colonization and human rotavirus infection influence distribution and frequencies of monocytes/macrophages and dendritic cells in neonatal gnotobiotic pigs. *Vet. Immunol. Immunopathol.* 121:222–31
268. Macnab RM. 1992. Genetics and biogenesis of bacterial flagella. *Annu. Rev. Genet.* 26:131–58
269. Pena JA, Versalovic J. 2003. *Lactobacillus rhamnosus* GG decreases TNF-α production in lipopolysaccharide-activated murine macrophages by a contact-independent mechanism. *Cell. Microbiol.* 5:277–85

270. Kamada N, Hisamatsu T, Okamoto S, Chinen H, Kobayashi T, et al. 2008. Unique CD14 intestinal macrophages contribute to the pathogenesis of Crohn disease via IL-23/IFN-γ axis. *J. Clin. Investig.* 118:2269–80

271. Kamada N, Hisamatsu T, Honda H, Kobayashi T, Chinen H, et al. 2009. Human $CD14^+$ macrophages in intestinal lamina propria exhibit potent antigen-presenting ability. *J. Immunol.* 183:1724–31

272. Wakkach A, Fournier N, Brun V, Breittmayer JP, Cottrez F, Groux H. 2003. Characterization of dendritic cells that induce tolerance and T regulatory 1 cell differentiation in vivo. *Immunity* 18(5):605–17

273. Colonna M. 2009. Interleukin-22-producing natural killer cells and lymphoid tissue inducer-like cells in mucosal immunity. *Immunity* 31:15–23

274. van de Pavert SA, Olivier BJ, Goverse G, Vondenhoff MF, Greuter M, et al. 2009. Chemokine CXCL13 is essential for lymph node initiation and is induced by retinoic acid and neuronal stimulation. *Nat. Immunol.* 10(11):1193–99

275. Takatori H, Kanno Y, Watford WT, Tato CM, Weiss G, et al. 2009. Lymphoid tissue inducer-like cells are an innate source of IL-17 and IL-22. *J. Exp. Med.* 206:35–41

276. Sanos SL, Bui VL, Mortha A, Oberle K, Heners C, et al. 2008. RORγt and commensal microflora are required for the differentiation of mucosal interleukin 22-producing $NKp46^+$ cells. *Nat. Immunol.* 10:83–91

277. Cella M, Fuchs A, Vermi W, Facchetti F, Otero K, et al. 2008. A human natural killer cell subset provides an innate source of IL-22 for mucosal immunity. *Nature* 457:722–25

278. Satoh-Takayama N, Vosshenrich CA, Lesjean-Pottier S, Sawa S, Lochner M, et al. 2008. Microbial flora drives interleukin 22 production in intestinal $NKp46^+$ cells that provide innate mucosal immune defense. *Immunity* 29:958–70

279. Luci C, Reynders A, Ivanov II, Cognet C, Chiche L, et al. 2009. Influence of the transcription factor RORγt on the development of $NKp46^+$ cell populations in gut and skin. *Nat. Immunol.* 10:75–82

280. Zenewicz LA, Yancopoulos GD, Valenzuela DM, Murphy AJ, Stevens S, Flavell RA. 2008. Innate and adaptive interleukin-22 protects mice from inflammatory bowel disease. *Immunity* 29:947–57

281. Mebius RE, Rennert P, Weissman IL. 1997. Developing lymph nodes collect $CD4^+CD3^-$ $LT\beta^+$ cells that can differentiate to APC, NK cells, and follicular cells but not T or B cells. *Immunity* 7:493–504

282. Vivier E, Spits H, Cupedo T. 2009. Interleukin-22-producing innate immune cells: new players in mucosal immunity and tissue repair? *Nat. Rev. Immunol.* 9:229–34

283. Cupedo T, Crellin NK, Papazian N, Rombouts EJ, Weijer K, et al. 2009. Human fetal lymphoid tissue-inducer cells are interleukin 17-producing precursors to $RORC^+$ $CD127^+$ natural killer-like cells. *Nat. Immunol.* 10:66–74

284. Klaasen HL, Van der Heijden PJ, Stok W, Poelma FG, Koopman JP, et al. 1993. Apathogenic, intestinal, segmented, filamentous bacteria stimulate the mucosal immune system of mice. *Infect. Immun.* 61:303–6

285. Goldblum RM, Hannson LA, Brandtzaeg P. 1996. The mucosal defense system. In *Immunologic Disorders in Infants and Children*, ed. ER Stiehm, pp. 159–99. Philadelphia, PA: Saunders

286. Astrakhan A, Omori M, Nguyen T, Becker-Herman S, Iseki M, et al. 2007. Local increase in thymic stromal lymphopoietin induces systemic alterations in B cell development. *Nat. Immunol.* 8:522–31

287. Brandtzaeg P, Carlsen HS, Halstensen TS. 2006. The B-cell system in inflammatory bowel disease. *Adv. Exp. Med. Biol.* 579:149–67

288. Crabbe PA, Nash DR, Bazin H, Eyssen H, Heremans JF. 1970. Immunohistochemical observations on lymphoid tissues from conventional and germ-free mice. *Lab. Investig.* 22:448–57

289. Gordon HA, Bruckner-Kardoss E. 1961. Effect of the normal microbial flora on various tissue elements of the small intestine. *Acta Anat.* 44:210–25

290. Gustafsson BE, Laurell CB. 1959. Gamma globulin production in germfree rats after bacterial contamination. *J. Exp. Med.* 110:675–84

291. Ikari NS. 1964. Bactericidal antibody to *Escherichia coli* in germ-free mice. *Nature* 202:879–81

292. Sell S. 1964. Immunoglobulins of the germfree guinea pig. *J. Immunol.* 93:122–31

293. Wagner M, Wostmann BS. 1961. Serum protein fractions and antibody studies in gnotobiotic animals reared germfree or monocontaminated. *Ann. NY Acad. Sci.* 94:210–17

294. Ohwaki M, Yasutake N, Yasui H, Ogura R. 1977. A comparative study on the humoral immune responses in germ-free and conventional mice. *Immunology* 32:43–48

295. Horowitz RE, Bauer H, Paronetto F, Abrams GD, Watkins KC, Popper H. 1964. The response of the lymphatic tissue to bacterial antigen. Studies in germfree mice. *Am. J. Pathol.* 44:747–61
296. Etlinger HM, Heusser CH. 1986. T15 dominance in BALB/c mice is not controlled by environmental factors. *J. Immunol.* 136:1988–91
297. Moreau MC, Ducluzeau R, Guy-Grand D, Muller MC. 1978. Increase in the population of duodenal immunoglobulin A plasmocytes in axenic mice associated with different living or dead bacterial strains of intestinal origin. *Infect. Immun.* 21:532–39
298. Durkin HG, Bazin H, Waksman BH. 1981. Origin and fate of IgE-bearing lymphocytes. I. Peyer's patches as differentiation site of cells. Simultaneously bearing IgA and IgE. *J. Exp. Med.* 154:640–48
299. Serebrisky D, Teper AA, Huang CK, Lee SY, Zhang TF, et al. 2000. CpG oligodeoxynucleotides can reverse Th2-associated allergic airway responses and alter the B7.1/B7.2 expression in a murine model of asthma. *J. Immunol.* 165:5906–12
300. Sudo N, Yu XN, Aiba Y, Oyama N, Sonoda J, et al. 2002. An oral introduction of intestinal bacteria prevents the development of a long-term Th2-skewed immunological memory induced by neonatal antibiotic treatment in mice. *Clin. Exp. Allergy* 32:1112–16
301. McCoy KD, Harris NL, Diener P, Hatak S, Odermatt B, et al. 2006. Natural IgE production in the absence of MHC class II cognate help. *Immunity* 24:329–39
302. Bouaziz JD, Yanaba K, Tedder TF. 2008. Regulatory B cells as inhibitors of immune responses and inflammation. *Immunol. Rev.* 224:201–14
303. Mizoguchi A, Mizoguchi E, Smith RN, Preffer FI, Bhan AK. 1997. Suppressive role of B cells in chronic colitis of T cell receptor α mutant mice. *J. Exp. Med.* 186(10):1749–56
304. Mizoguchi A, Mizoguchi E, Takedatsu H, Blumberg RS, Bhan AK. 2002. Chronic intestinal inflammatory condition generates IL-10-producing regulatory B cell subset characterized by CD1d upregulation. *Immunity* 16(2):219–30
305. Ohman L, Aström RG, Hultgren Hörnquist E. 2005. Impaired B cell responses to orally administered antigens in lamina propria but not Peyer's patches of Gα2-deficient mice prior to colitis. *Immunology* 115(2):271–78
306. Korn T, Bettelli E, Oukka M, Kuchroo VK. 2009. IL-17 and Th17 cells. *Annu. Rev. Immunol.* 27:485–517
307. Ivanov II, Frutos Rde L, Manel N, Yoshinaga K, Rifkin DB, et al. 2008. Specific microbiota direct the differentiation of IL-17-producing T-helper cells in the mucosa of the small intestine. *Cell Host Microbe* 4:337–49
308. Dong C. 2008. TH17 cells in development: an updated view of their molecular identity and genetic programming. *Nat. Rev. Immunol.* 8:337–48
309. Kastelein RA, Hunter CA, Cua DJ. 2007. Discovery and biology of IL-23 and IL-27: related but functionally distinct regulators of inflammation. *Annu. Rev. Immunol.* 25:221–42
310. Gaboriau-Routhiau V, Rakotobe S, Lécuyer E, Mulder I, Lan A, et al. 2009. The key role of segmented filamentous bacteria in the coordinated maturation of gut helper T cell responses. *Immunity* 31(4):677–89
311. Ivanov II, Atarashi K, Manel N, Brodie EL, Shima T, et al. 2009. Induction of intestinal Th17 cells by segmented filamentous bacteria. *Cell* 139(3):485–98
312. Cheroutre H. 2004. Starting at the beginning: new perspectives on the biology of mucosal T cells. *Annu. Rev. Immunol.* 22:217–46
313. Niess JH, Leithauser F, Adler G, Reimann J. 2008. Commensal gut flora drives the expansion of proinflammatory CD4 T cells in the colonic lamina propria under normal and inflammatory conditions. *J. Immunol.* 180:559–68
314. Belkaid Y, Tarbell K. 2009. Regulatory T cells in the control of host-microorganism interactions. *Annu. Rev. Immunol.* 27:551–89
315. Weaver CT, Hatton RD. 2009. Interplay between the TH17 and TReg cell lineages: a (co-) evolutionary perspective. *Nat. Rev. Immunol.* 9(12):883–89
316. Barnes MJ, Powrie F. 2009. Regulatory T cells reinforce intestinal homeostasis. *Immunity* 31(3):401–11
317. Brunkow ME, Jeffery EW, Hjerrild KA, Paeper B, Clark LB, et al. 2001. Disruption of a new forkhead/winged-helix protein, scurfin, results in the fatal lymphoproliferative disorder of the scurfy mouse. *Nat. Genet.* 27:68–73

318. Li MO, Wan YY, Flavell RA. 2007. T cell-produced transforming growth factor-β1 controls T cell tolerance and regulates Th1- and Th17-cell differentiation. *Immunity* 26:579–91
319. Roers A, Siewe L, Strittmatter E, Deckert M, Schlüter D, et al. 2004. T cell-specific inactivation of the interleukin 10 gene in mice results in enhanced T cell responses but normal innate responses to lipopolysaccharide or skin irritation. *J. Exp. Med.* 200:1289–97
320. Rubtsov YP, Rasmussen JP, Chi EY, Fontenot J, Castelli L, et al. 2008. Regulatory T cell-derived interleukin-10 limits inflammation at environmental interfaces. *Immunity* 28:546–58
321. Ostman S, Rask C, Wold AE, Hultkrantz S, Telemo E. 2006. Impaired regulatory T cell function in germ-free mice. *Eur. J. Immunol.* 36:2336–46
322. Strauch UG, Obermeier F, Grunwald N, Gurster S, Dunger N, et al. 2005. Influence of intestinal bacteria on induction of regulatory T cells: lessons from a transfer model of colitis. *Gut* 54:1546–52
323. Ishikawa H, Tanaka K, Maeda Y, Aiba Y, Hata A, et al. 2008. Effect of intestinal microbiota on the induction of regulatory $CD25^+$ $CD4^+$ T cells. *Clin. Exp. Immunol.* 153:127–35
324. Roselli M, Finamore A, Nuccitelli S, Carnevali P, Brigidi P, et al. 2009. Prevention of TNBS-induced colitis by different lactobacillus and bifidobacterium strains is associated with an expansion of $\gamma\delta$ T and regulatory T cells of intestinal intraepithelial lymphocytes. *Inflamm. Bowel Dis.* 15:1526–36
325. Abbas AK, Murphy KM, Sher A. 1996. Functional diversity of helper T lymphocytes. *Nature* 383:787–93
326. Ott SJ, Musfeldt M, Wenderoth DF, Hampe J, Brant O, et al. 2004. Reduction in diversity of the colonic mucosa associated bacterial microflora in patients with active inflammatory bowel disease. *Gut* 53:685–93
327. Cong Y, Brandwein SL, McCabe RP, Lazenby A, Birkenmeier EH, et al. 1998. $CD4^+$ T cells reactive to enteric bacterial antigens in spontaneously colitic C3H/HeJBir mice: increased T helper cell type 1 response and ability to transfer disease. *J. Exp. Med.* 187:855–64
328. Cong Y, Weaver CT, Lazenby A, Elson CO. 2002. Bacterial-reactive T regulatory cells inhibit pathogenic immune responses to the enteric flora. *J. Immunol.* 169:6112–19
329. Asseman C, Read S, Powrie F. 2003. Colitogenic Th1 cells are present in the antigen-experienced T cell pool in normal mice: control by $CD4^+$ regulatory T cells and IL-10. *J. Immunol.* 171:971–78
330. Oyama N, Sudo N, Sogawa H, Kubo C. 2001. Antibiotic use during infancy promotes a shift in the T_H1/T_H2 balance toward T(H)2-dominant immunity in mice. *J. Allergy Clin. Immunol.* 107:153–59
331. Xu D, Komai-Koma M, Liew FY. 2005. Expression and function of Toll-like receptor on T cells. *Cell. Immunol.* 233:85–89
332. Schroeder JT. 2009. Basophils beyond effector cells of allergic inflammation. *Adv. Immunol.* 101:123–61
333. Gessner A, Mohrs K, Mohrs M. 2005. Mast cells, basophils, and eosinophils acquire constitutive IL-4 and IL-13 transcripts during lineage differentiation that are sufficient for rapid cytokine production. *J. Immunol.* 174:1063–72
334. Perrigoue JG, Saenz SA, Siracusa MC, Allenspach EJ, Taylor BC, et al. 2009. MHC class II-dependent basophil-$CD4^+$ T cell interactions promote T_H2 cytokine-dependent immunity. *Nat. Immunol.* 10:697–705
335. Sokol CL, Chu NQ, Yu S, Nish SA, Laufer TM, Medzhitov R. 2009. Basophils function as antigen-presenting cells for an allergen-induced T helper type 2 response. *Nat. Immunol.* 10:713–20
336. Yoshimoto T, Yasuda K, Tanaka H, Nakahira M, Imai Y, et al. 2009. Basophils contribute to T_H2-IgE responses in vivo via IL-4 production and presentation of peptide-MHC class II complexes to $CD4^+$ T cells. *Nat. Immunol.* 10:706–12
337. King T, Biddle W, Bhatia P, Moore J, Miner PB Jr. 1992. Colonic mucosal mast cell distribution at line of demarcation of active ulcerative colitis. *Dig. Dis. Sci.* 37:490–95
338. Okumura S, Yuki K, Kobayashi R, Okamura S, Ohmori K, et al. 2009. Hyperexpression of NOD2 in intestinal mast cells of Crohn's disease patients: preferential expression of inflammatory cell-recruiting molecules via NOD2 in mast cells. *Clin. Immunol.* 130:175–85
339. Raithel M, Matek M, Baenkler HW, Jorde W, Hahn EG. 1995. Mucosal histamine content and histamine secretion in Crohn's disease, ulcerative colitis and allergic enteropathy. *Int. Arch. Allergy Immunol.* 108:127–33
340. Bischoff SC, Lorentz A, Schwengberg S, Weier G, Raab R, Manns MP. 1999. Mast cells are an important cellular source of tumor necrosis factor α in human intestinal tissue. *Gut* 44:643–52

341. Middel P, Thelen P, Blaschke S, Polzien F, Reich K, et al. 2001. Expression of the T-cell chemoattractant chemokine lymphotactin in Crohn's disease. *Am. J. Pathol.* 159:1751–61
342. Middel P, Reich K, Polzien F, Blaschke V, Hemmerlein B, et al. 2001. Interleukin 16 expression and phenotype of interleukin 16 producing cells in Crohn's disease. *Gut* 49:795–803
343. Garay RP, Viens P, Bauer J, Normier G, Bardou M, et al. 2007. Cancer relapse under chemotherapy: Why TLR2/4 receptor agonists can help. *Eur. J. Pharmacol.* 563:1–17
344. Rakoff-Nahoum S, Medzhitov R. 2009. Toll-like receptors and cancer. *Nat. Rev. Cancer* 9:57–63
345. Paulos CM, Wrzesinski C, Kaiser A, Hinrichs CS, Chieppa M, et al. 2007. Microbial translocation augments the function of adoptively transferred self/tumor-specific $CD8^+$ T cells via TLR4 signaling. *J. Clin. Investig.* 117:2197–204
346. Apetoh L, Ghiringhelli F, Tesniere A, Obeid M, Ortiz C, et al. 2007. Toll-like receptor 4-dependent contribution of the immune system to anticancer chemotherapy and radiotherapy. *Nat. Med.* 13:1050–59
347. Yusuf N, Nasti TH, Long JA, Naseemuddin M, Lucas AP, et al. 2008. Protective role of Toll-like receptor 4 during the initiation stage of cutaneous chemical carcinogenesis. *Cancer Res.* 68:615–22
348. Williams MA, Bevan MJ. 2007. Effector and memory CTL differentiation. *Annu. Rev. Immunol.* 25:171–92
349. Yu Q, Tang C, Xun S, Yajima T, Takeda K, Yoshikai Y. 2006. MyD88-dependent signaling for IL-15 production plays an important role in maintenance of $CD8\alpha\alpha$ $TCR\alpha\beta$ and $TCR\gamma\delta$ intestinal intraepithelial lymphocytes. *J. Immunol.* 176:6180–85
350. Imaoka A, Matsumoto S, Setoyama H, Okada Y, Umesaki Y. 1996. Proliferative recruitment of intestinal intraepithelial lymphocytes after microbial colonization of germ-free mice. *Eur. J. Immunol.* 26:945–48
351. Kawaguchi-Miyashita M, Shimizu K, Nanno M, Shimada S, Watanabe T, et al. 1996. Development and cytolytic function of intestinal intraepithelial T lymphocytes in antigen-minimized mice. *Immunology* 89:268–73
352. John B, Crispe IN. 2005. TLR-4 regulates $CD8^+$ T cell trapping in the liver. *J. Immunol.* 175:1643–50
353. Helgeland L, Dissen E, Dai KZ, Midtvedt T, Brandtzaeg P, Vaage JT. 2004. Microbial colonization induces oligoclonal expansions of intraepithelial CD8 T cells in the gut. *Eur. J. Immunol.* 34:3389–400
354. Fujiwara D, Wei B, Presley LL, Brewer S, McPherson M, et al. 2008. Systemic control of plasmacytoid dendritic cells by $CD8^+$ T cells and commensal microbiota. *J. Immunol.* 180:5843–52
355. Huang T, Wei B, Velazquez P, Borneman J, Braun J. 2005. Commensal microbiota alter the abundance and TCR responsiveness of splenic naive $CD4^+$ T lymphocytes. *Clin. Immunol.* 117:221–30
356. Rakoff-Nahoum S, Medzhitov R. 2007. Regulation of spontaneous intestinal tumorigenesis through the adaptor protein MyD88. *Science* 317:124–27
357. Vannucci L, Stepankova R, Kozakova H, Fiserova A, Rossmann P, Tlaskalova-Hogenova H. 2008. Colorectal carcinogenesis in germ-free and conventionally reared rats: Different intestinal environments affect the systemic immunity. *Int. J. Oncol.* 32:609–17
358. Naugler WE, Sakurai T, Kim S, Maeda S, Kim K, et al. 2007. Gender disparity in liver cancer due to sex differences in MyD88-dependent IL-6 production. *Science* 317:121–24
359. Huycke MM, Gaskins HR. 2004. Commensal bacteria, redox stress, and colorectal cancer: mechanisms and models. *Exp. Biol. Med.* 229:586–97
360. Finegold SM, Flora DJ, Attebery HR, Sutter VL. 1975. Fecal bacteriology of colonic polyp patients and control patients. *Cancer Res.* 35:3407–17
361. Madsen KL, Doyle JS, Jewell LD, Tavernini MM, Fedorak RN. 1999. *Lactobacillus* species prevents colitis in interleukin 10 gene-deficient mice. *Gastroenterology* 116:1107–14
362. Hart AL, Lammers K, Brigidi P, Vitali B, Rizzello F, et al. 2004. Modulation of human dendritic cell phenotype and function by probiotic bacteria. *Gut* 53:1602–9
363. Hart AL, Al-Hassi HO, Rigby RJ, Bell SJ, Emmanuel AV, et al. 2005. Characteristics of intestinal dendritic cells in inflammatory bowel diseases. *Gastroenterology* 129:50–65
364. Ng SC, Hart AL, Kamm MA, Stagg AJ, Knight SC. 2009. Mechanisms of action of probiotics: recent advances. *Inflamm. Bowel Dis.* 15:300–10
365. Hedin C, Whelan K, Lindsay JO. 2007. Evidence for the use of probiotics and prebiotics in inflammatory bowel disease: a review of clinical trials. *Proc. Nutr. Soc.* 66:307–15

366. Kukkonen K, Savilahti E, Haahtela T, Juntunen-Backman K, Korpela R, et al. 2007. Probiotics and prebiotic galacto-oligosaccharides in the prevention of allergic diseases: a randomized, double-blind, placebo-controlled trial. *J. Allergy Clin. Immunol.* 119:192–98
367. Rembacken BJ, Snelling AM, Hawkey PM, Chalmers DM, Axon AT. 1999. Non-pathogenic *Escherichia coli* versus mesalazine for the treatment of ulcerative colitis: a randomised trial. *Lancet* 354:635–39
368. Gionchetti P, Rizzello F, Helwig U, Venturi A, Lammers KM, et al. 2003. Prophylaxis of pouchitis onset with probiotic therapy: a double-blind, placebo-controlled trial. *Gastroenterology* 124:1202–9
369. Gionchetti P, Rizzello F, Morselli C, Poggioli G, Tambasco R, et al. 2007. High-dose probiotics for the treatment of active pouchitis. *Dis. Colon Rectum* 50:2075–84
370. Gionchetti P, Rizzello F, Venturi A, Brigidi P, Matteuzzi D, et al. 2000. Oral bacteriotherapy as maintenance treatment in patients with chronic pouchitis: a double-blind, placebo-controlled trial. *Gastroenterology* 119:305–9
371. Mimura T, Rizzello F, Helwig U, Poggioli G, Schreiber S, et al. 2004. Once daily high dose probiotic therapy (VSL#3) for maintaining remission in recurrent or refractory pouchitis. *Gut* 53:108–14
372. Steidler L, Hans W, Schotte L, Neirynck S, Obermeier F, et al. 2000. Treatment of murine colitis by *Lactococcus lactis* secreting interleukin-10. *Science* 289:1352–55
373. Beninati C, Oggioni MR, Boccanera M, Spinosa MR, Maggi T, et al. 2000. Therapy of mucosal candidiasis by expression of an anti-idiotype in human commensal bacteria. *Nat. Biotechnol.* 18:1060–64
374. Shaw DM, Gaerthe B, Leer RJ, Van Der Stap JG, Smittenaar C, et al. 2000. Engineering the microflora to vaccinate the mucosa: serum immunoglobulin G responses and activated draining cervical lymph nodes following mucosal application of tetanus toxin fragment C-expressing lactobacilli. *Immunology* 100:510–18
375. Liu X, Lagenaur LA, Lee PP, Xu Q. 2008. Engineering of a human vaginal lactobacillus strain for surface expression of two-domain CD4 molecules. *Appl. Environ. Microbiol.* 74:4626–35
376. Pusch O, Kalyanaraman R, Tucker LD, Wells JM, Ramratnam B, Boden D. 2006. An anti-HIV microbicide engineered in commensal bacteria: secretion of HIV-1 fusion inhibitors by lactobacilli. *AIDS* 20:1917–22
377. Hayashi H, Sakamoto M, Kitahara M, Benno Y. 2003. Molecular analysis of fecal microbiota in elderly individuals using 16S rDNA library and T-RFLP. *Microbiol. Immunol.* 47:557–70
378. Hoffmann C, Hill DA, Minkah N, Kirn T, Troy A, et al. 2009. Community-wide response of gut microbiota to enteropathogenic citrobacter infection revealed by deep sequencing. *Infect. Immun.* 77:4668–78
379. Ryu JH, Kim SH, Lee HY, Bai JY, Nam YD, et al. 2008. Innate immune homeostasis by the homeobox gene caudal and commensal-gut mutualism in *Drosophila*. *Science* 319:777–82
380. Perrin P, Pierre F, Patry Y, Champ M, Berreur M, et al. 2001. Only fibres promoting a stable butyrate producing colonic ecosystem decrease the rate of aberrant crypt foci in rats. *Gut* 48:53–61
381. Roediger WE. 1980. Role of anaerobic bacteria in the metabolic welfare of the colonic mucosa in man. *Gut* 21:793–98
382. Gordon HA. 1959. Morphological and physiological characterization of germfree life. *Ann. NY Acad. Sci.* 78:208–20
383. Mikkelsen HB, Garbarsch C, Tranum-Jensen J, Thuneberg L. 2004. Macrophages in the small intestinal muscularis externa of embryos, newborn and adult germ-free mice. *J. Mol. Histol.* 35:377–87
384. Bakker R, Lasonder E, Bos NA. 1995. Measurement of affinity in serum samples of antigen-free, germ-free and conventional mice after hyperimmunization with 2,4-dinitrophenyl keyhole limpet hemocyanin, using surface plasmon resonance. *Eur. J. Immunol.* 25:1680–86
385. Bauer H, Paronetto F, Burns WA, Einheber A. 1966. The enhancing effect of the microbial flora on macrophage function and the immune response. A study in germfree mice. *J. Exp. Med.* 123:1013–24
386. MacDonald TT, Carter PB. 1979. Requirement for a bacterial flora before mice generate cells capable of mediating the delayed hypersensitivity reaction to sheep red blood cells. *J. Immunol.* 122:2624–29
387. Umesaki Y, Setoyama H, Matsumoto S, Okada Y. 1993. Expansion of αβ T-cell receptor-bearing intestinal intraepithelial lymphocytes after microbial colonization in germ-free mice and its independence from thymus. *Immunology* 79:32–37
388. Wells C, Balish E. 1979. The mitogenic activity of lipopolysaccharide for spleen cells from germfree, conventional, and gnotobiotic rats. *Can. J. Microbiol.* 25:1087–93

389. Walton KL, Galanko JA, Balfour Sartor R, Fisher NC. 2006. T cell-mediated oral tolerance is intact in germ-free mice. *Clin. Exp. Immunol.* 143:503–12
390. Moreau MC, Corthier G. 1988. Effect of the gastrointestinal microflora on induction and maintenance of oral tolerance to ovalbumin in C3H/HeJ mice. *Infect. Immun.* 56:2766–68
391. Moreau MC, Gaboriau-Routhiau V. 1996. The absence of gut flora, the doses of antigen ingested and aging affect the long-term peripheral tolerance induced by ovalbumin feeding in mice. *Res. Immunol.* 147:49–59
392. Maeda Y, Noda S, Tanaka K, Sawamura S, Aiba Y, et al. 2001. The failure of oral tolerance induction is functionally coupled to the absence of T cells in Peyer's patches under germfree conditions. *Immunobiology* 204:442–57
393. Sudo N, Sawamura S, Tanaka K, Aiba Y, Kubo C, Koga Y. 1997. The requirement of intestinal bacterial flora for the development of an IgE production system fully susceptible to oral tolerance induction. *J. Immunol.* 159:1739–45
394. Salomon JC. 1965. Induction of homologous disease in axenic (germ-free) newborn mice. *C. R. Acad. Sci. D* 260:4862–64
395. Gaboriau-Routhiau V, Raibaud P, Dubuquoy C, Moreau MC. 2003. Colonization of gnotobiotic mice with human gut microflora at birth protects against *Escherichia coli* heat-labile enterotoxin-mediated abrogation of oral tolerance. *Pediatr. Res.* 54:739–46
396. Gaboriau-Routhiau V, Moreau MC. 1996. Gut flora allows recovery of oral tolerance to ovalbumin in mice after transient breakdown mediated by cholera toxin or *Escherichia coli* heat-labile enterotoxin. *Pediatr. Res.* 39:625–29
397. Umesaki Y, Setoyama H, Matsumoto S, Imaoka A, Itoh K. 1999. Differential roles of segmented filamentous bacteria and clostridia in development of the intestinal immune system. *Infect. Immun.* 67:3504–11

Cumulative Indexes

Contributing Authors, Volumes 18–28

M

N

O

T

U

V

W

X

Y

Z

Chapter Titles, Volumes 18–28

Prefatory Chapters

Antigen Structure

Immunoglobulins and B Cell Receptors

T Lymphocyte and NK Cell Receptors

Major Histocompatibility Complex and Antigen Processing and Presentation

Lymphocyte Surface Antigens and Activation Mechanisms

Lymphocyte Development and Differentiation

Tolerance

Regulation of the Immune Response

Mucosal Immunity

Cytokines

Cytotoxic Cells

Complement

Phagocytosis and Inflammation

Autoimmunity

Immunodeficiency

Allergy

Immunology of Infectious Diseases and Vaccines

HIV, Aids and Other Retroviral Infections

Transplantation Immunology

Tumor Immunology

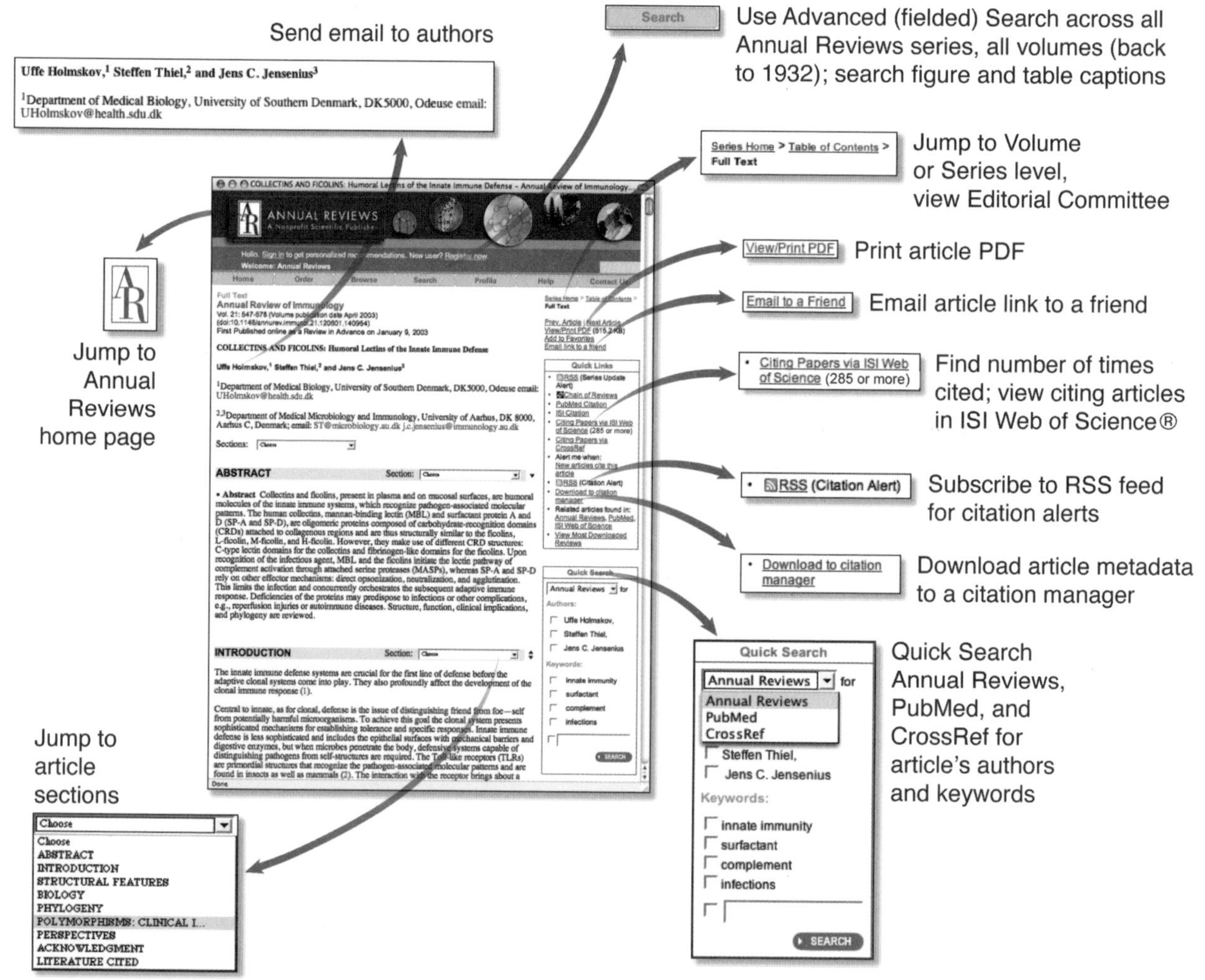